# ANATOMY & PHYSIOLOGY

## The Unity of Form and Function

Ninth Edition

KENNETH S. SALADIN
Distinguished Professor of Biology, Emeritus
*Georgia College*

**Digital Authors**

CHRISTINA A. GAN
*Highline College*

HEATHER N. CUSHMAN
*Tacoma Community College*

**BSC 2085**
**Volume 1**
Broward College

4 5 6 7 8 9 0 CD CD 25 24 23 22 21

ISBN-13: 978-1-265-95827-5
ISBN-10: 1-265-95827-0

*Solutions Program Manager: Steve Tomecek*
*Project Manager: Jennifer Bartell*
*Cover Photo Credits: Mike Kemp/Rubberball/Getty*

# BRIEF CONTENTS

# ABOUT THE AUTHORS

© Tim Vacula

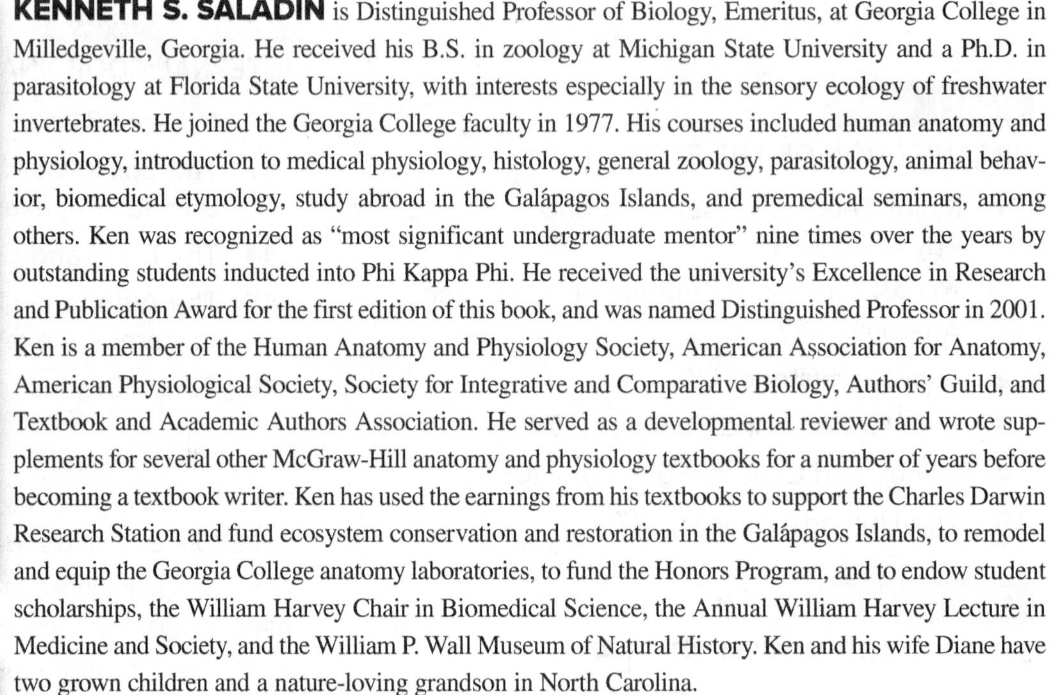

**KENNETH S. SALADIN** is Distinguished Professor of Biology, Emeritus, at Georgia College in Milledgeville, Georgia. He received his B.S. in zoology at Michigan State University and a Ph.D. in parasitology at Florida State University, with interests especially in the sensory ecology of freshwater invertebrates. He joined the Georgia College faculty in 1977. His courses included human anatomy and physiology, introduction to medical physiology, histology, general zoology, parasitology, animal behavior, biomedical etymology, study abroad in the Galápagos Islands, and premedical seminars, among others. Ken was recognized as "most significant undergraduate mentor" nine times over the years by outstanding students inducted into Phi Kappa Phi. He received the university's Excellence in Research and Publication Award for the first edition of this book, and was named Distinguished Professor in 2001. Ken is a member of the Human Anatomy and Physiology Society, American Association for Anatomy, American Physiological Society, Society for Integrative and Comparative Biology, Authors' Guild, and Textbook and Academic Authors Association. He served as a developmental reviewer and wrote supplements for several other McGraw-Hill anatomy and physiology textbooks for a number of years before becoming a textbook writer. Ken has used the earnings from his textbooks to support the Charles Darwin Research Station and fund ecosystem conservation and restoration in the Galápagos Islands, to remodel and equip the Georgia College anatomy laboratories, to fund the Honors Program, and to endow student scholarships, the William Harvey Chair in Biomedical Science, the Annual William Harvey Lecture in Medicine and Society, and the William P. Wall Museum of Natural History. Ken and his wife Diane have two grown children and a nature-loving grandson in North Carolina.

© Chris Gan/Yuen Lui Studios

**CHRISTINA A. GAN,** digital coauthor for Connect®, has been teaching anatomy and physiology, microbiology, and general biology at Highline College in Des Moines, Washington, since 2004. Before that, she taught at Rogue Community College in Medford, Oregon, for 6 years. She earned her M.A. in biology from Humboldt State University, researching the genetic variation of mitochondrial DNA in various salmonid species, and is a member of the Human Anatomy and Physiology Society. When she is not in the classroom or developing digital media, she is climbing, mountaineering, skiing, kayaking, sailing, cycling, and mountain biking throughout the Pacific Northwest.

© JC Penney Portraits/Lifetouch Portrait Studios, Inc.

**HEATHER N. CUSHMAN,** digital coauthor for Connect®, teaches anatomy and physiology at Tacoma Community College in Tacoma, Washington, and is a member of the Human Anatomy and Physiology Society. She received her Ph.D. in neuroscience from the University of Minnesota in 2002, and completed a postdoctoral fellowship at the Vollum Institute at Oregon Health & Science University in Portland, Oregon, where she studied sensory transduction and the cellular and molecular mechanisms of muscle pain. She currently resides in Tacoma, Washington, and enjoys climbing, camping, and hiking with her husband Ken and their daughter Annika.

# CONTENTS

# THE EVOLUTION OF A STORYTELLER

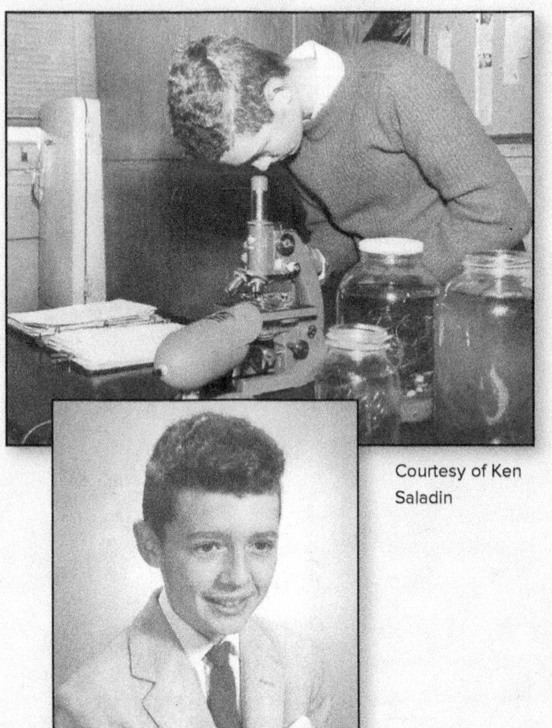

Courtesy of Ken Saladin

Ken in 1964

Ken Saladin's first step into authoring was a 318-page paper on the ecology of hydras written for his tenth-grade biology class. With his "first book," featuring 53 original India ink drawings and photomicrographs, a true storyteller was born.

*When I first became a textbook writer, I found myself bringing the same enjoyment of writing and illustrating to this book that I first discovered when I was 15.*

—Ken Saladin

Ken's "first book," *Hydra Ecology,* 1965
Courtesy of Ken Saladin

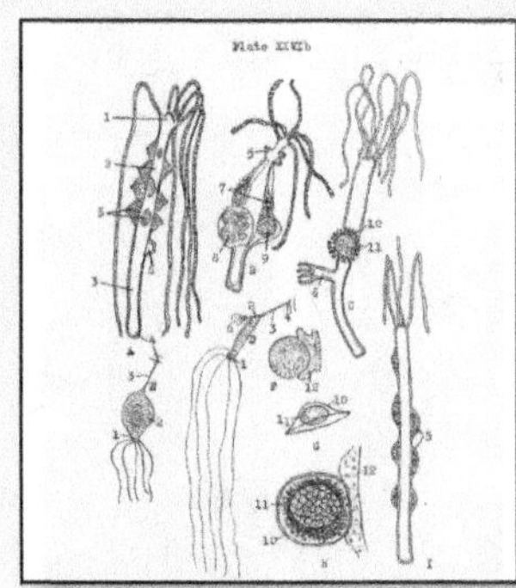

One of Ken's drawings from *Hydra Ecology*
Courtesy of Ken Saladin

Ken began working on his first book for McGraw-Hill in 1993, and in 1997 the first edition of *The Unity of Form and Function* was published. In 2020, the story continues with the ninth edition of Ken's best-selling A&P textbook.

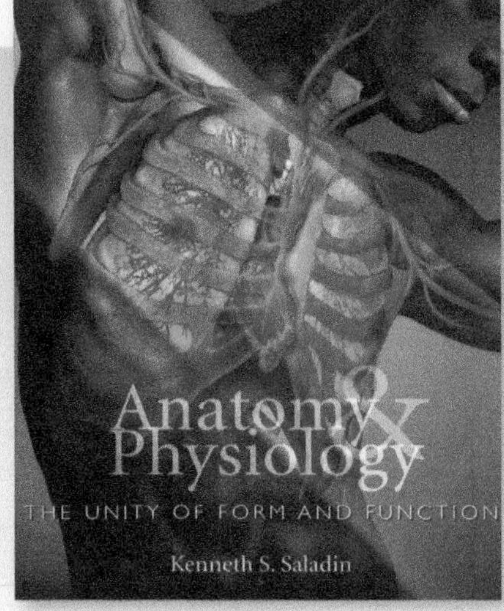


The first edition (1997)

The story continues (2020)

# PREFACE

*Anatomy & Physiology: The Unity of Form and Function* tells a story comprised of many layers, including core science, clinical applications, the history of medicine, and the evolution of the human body. Saladin combines this humanistic perspective on anatomy and physiology with vibrant photos and art to convey the beauty and excitement of the subject to beginning students.

To help students manage the tremendous amount of information in this introductory course, the narrative is broken into short segments, each framed by expected learning outcomes and self-testing review questions. This presentation strategy works as a whole to create a more efficient and effective way for students to learn A&P.

## Writing Style and Level

Saladin's text is written using plain language for A&P students who may be taking this course early in their curricula. Careful attention has been given to word selection and paragraph structure to maintain the appropriate writing level for all students.

# CHANGES TO THE NINTH EDITION

## New Science

This edition draws on recent literature and scientific conferences attended by the author to update many topics, including but not limited to molecular, vascular, and brain imaging techniques; peroxisome and mitochondrial behavior; the DNA damage response; gene regulation; epigenetics; the tissue interstitium; regenerative medicine; osteoporosis; prosthetic joints; fibromyalgia; sleep physiology; trigeminal neuralgia; pain physiology; endocrine functions of osseous and adipose tissue; diabetes mellitus; cord blood transplants; thrombopoiesis; AIDS; prostate diseases; breast cancer; aging; life expectancy; and assisted reproductive technology.

New Deeper Insight sidebar essays have been added on cardiac tamponade; biopsy; stem-cell therapy; regenerative medicine; osteomalacia and rickets; vertebral disc herniation; rotator cuff injury; carpal tunnel syndrome; shinsplints; calcaneal tendon rupture; plantar fasciitis; brain connectomics and diffusion tensor imaging; lumbar puncture; stroke; blindness; alcoholic ascites; diverticulosis and diverticulitis; colorectal cancer; and cleft lip and palate.

While new science has been added, keeping up with such growth also means pruning back topics discredited by newer literature. For this edition, these include adult cerebral neurogenesis; endorphins and runner's high; human pheromones; pineal tumors and precocial puberty; prophylactic use of low-dose aspirin; myocardial regeneration; female ejaculation; and the free-radical DNA damage theory of senescence.

In consideration of user and reviewer suggestions to reduce detail in a few areas, this edition has more concise discussions of some topics: chromatin coiling; apoptosis; skin grafting; the hair cycle; calcium and phosphate homeostasis; and spinal cord tracts.

## New Art and Photography

This edition features new drawings of epidermal histology, flat bone structure, lever mechanics, Parkinson disease, lumbar puncture, hand innervation, Bell palsy, the vagus nerve, olfactory pathways, erythropoiesis, cardiac innervation, regulation of cardiac output, air embolism, colonic histology, lipoprotein structure, cleft lip and palate, and senescent muscle atrophy.

New photos in this edition include digital subtraction angiography, molecular-scale cryo-EM imaging, diabetic gangrene, embryonic stem cells, albinism, jaundice, osteocyte SEM, rickets, muscle fiber histochemistry, diffusion tensor imaging of the brain connectome, shingles, cataracts, glaucoma, forelimb veins used for phlebotomy, kidney stones, gallstones, hepatic cirrhosis, MRI of obesity, and intracytoplasmic sperm injection.

## Organizational Changes

For improved readability, narrative descriptions of some systems are moved from tables into chapter text; selected illustrations are moved outside of the tables; and tables are distilled to more concise summaries. These include the skeletal muscles (chapter 10), spinal nerve plexuses (chapter 13), cranial nerves (chapter 14), and blood vessels (chapter 20). A detailed list of changes by chapter follows.

## Detailed List of Changes

**Chapter 1, Major Themes of Anatomy and Physiology,** now includes digital subtraction angiography among the common clinical imaging techniques.

**Atlas A, General Orientation to Human Anatomy,** has an added Deeper Insight A.1 on cardiac tamponade in relation to body cavities and membranes.

**Chapter 2, The Chemistry of Life,** has added the Nobel-winning new technique of cryo-electron microscopic imaging of biological structure at the atomic level.

**Chapter 3, Cellular Form and Function,** has enhanced discussions of limitations on cell size, the origin of peroxisomes, mitochondrial fusion and fission, and clinical mitochondrial transfer and three-parent babies.

**Chapter 4, Genes and Cellular Function,** updates protein processing by the Golgi complex, epigenetics, the DNA damage response, and the role of the nuclear lamina in gene silencing.

**Chapter 5, The Human Tissues,** has a new perspective on the tissue interstitium, updates on stem-cell therapy and regenerative medicine, and a new Deeper Insight on biopsy methods.

**Chapter 6, The Integumentary System,** has a new drawing of epidermal histology, new discussion of the evolutionary genetics of apocrine glands, an update on skin-grafting technology, and a simpler description of the hair growth cycle.

**Chapter 7, Bone Tissue,** gives a less detailed overview of calcium and phosphate homeostasis, adds a Deeper Insight on osteomalacia and rickets, and updates the pathology and treatment of osteoporosis.

**Chapter 8, The Skeletal System,** conforms the description of normal and pathological spinal curvatures to orthopedic terminology and has a new Deeper Insight on herniated discs.

**Chapter 9, Joints,** improves the discussion of joint biomechanics and updates the discussions of temporomandibular joint dysfunction and engineering of prosthetic joints.

**Chapter 10, The Muscular System,** pulls illustrations and narrative descriptions from the muscle tables, converts the narrative to easier-to-read normal text, and condenses the tables to more concise summaries. It updates inguinal hernias and adds new Deeper Insights on rotator cuff injury, shinsplints, calcaneal tendon rupture, and plantar fasciitis.

**Chapter 11, Muscular Tissue,** adds a photo of the histochemistry of fast glycolytic and slow oxidative muscle fiber types and updates the discussion of fibromyalgia.

**Chapter 12, Nervous Tissue,** includes updates on astrocyte functions, beta-endorphin and enkephalin, mutations affecting neurotransmitter reuptake and neurological disorders, and the implication of lipofuscin in some diseases. It introduces the frontier neuroscience of brain connectomics and the use of diffusion tensor imaging to visualize the connectome. There is now an illustration of the midbrain histological change and body posture characteristic of Parkinson disease.

**Chapter 13, The Spinal Cord, Spinal Nerves, and Somatic Reflexes,** adds a new Deeper Insight and illustration of lumbar puncture, reduces detail on spinal cord tracts, reformats the tables of spinal nerve plexuses, illustrates regional innervation of the hand by the major forearm nerves, and adds a photo of a shingles lesion.

**Chapter 14, The Brain and Cranial Nerves,** now adopts the concept of brainstem as excluding the diencephalon. It adds Deeper Insights on stroke and diffusion tensor imaging, and updates the Deeper Insight on trigeminal neuralgia and Bell palsy, adding an illustration of the latter. It updates sleep physiology and the functions of the midbrain colliculi and pretectal nuclei. It corrects a common misconception about the subdural space. The discussion and table of cranial nerves are reorganized.

**Chapter 16, Sense Organs,** has an updated discussion of pain physiology and includes phantom limb pain. It updates the genetics and functions of some taste sensations and flawed assumptions about human olfactory sensitivity. It deletes discredited or dubious views of endorphins and runner's high and human pheromones. It enhances the figure of olfactory projection pathways; adds the dorsal and ventral streams of visual processing pathways; adds photos of cataracts and glaucoma; adds macular degeneration and diabetic retinopathy to the Deeper Insight on blindness; and has better insights into the functions of the cornea, choroid, and vitreous body.

**Chapter 17, The Endocrine System,** updates the histology and cytology of the thyroid gland and pancreatic islets and the effects of melatonin; adds new information on hormones of osseous and adipose origin; updates the enteroendocrine system; and adds effects of lipocalin 2 on insulin action. It deletes the now-questionable idea about pineal tumors and precocial puberty. It updates the pathologies of Addison disease and myxedema, and the genetic, immunological, and treatment aspects of diabetes mellitus.

**Chapter 18, The Circulatory System: Blood,** now explains how blood is fractionated to obtain plasma and then serum, and the uses of blood serum. It has an enhanced explanation of the functional significance of the discoidal shape of erythrocytes, and includes cell proliferation in the illustration of erythropoiesis. It reports updated clinical research on the number of known blood groups and RBC antigens, cord blood transplants, other methods of bone marrow replacement, and pharmaceutical anticoagulants. It adds the surprising new discovery of abundant platelet production by megakaryocytes in the lungs and megakaryocyte migration between the lungs and bone marrow.

**Chapter 19, The Circulatory System: Heart,** is reorganized at section 19.1 to place figures closer to their references. Cardiac innervation is moved to section 19.6 on regulation of cardiac output, with a new illustration. The electrocardiogram is described with more detailed attention to interpretation of each wave, segment, and interval, with an added table. The section on cardiac arrhythmias includes a fuller explanation of atrial fibrillation.

**Chapter 20, The Circulatory System: Blood Vessels and Circulation,** has improved discussions of the vasa vasorum and metarterioles; describes the measurement of blood pressure in more depth; adds photos of edema, circulatory shock, and upper limb veins most often used for phlebotomy; and has a new drawing of air embolism. It discusses the difficulty of pancreatic surgery in light of the complex, delicate branches of the celiac trunk. The Deeper Insight on ascites is rewritten to relate it to alcoholism. The tables of blood vessels and routes of flow are now converted to normal, easier-to-read text.

**Chapter 21, The Lymphatic and Immune Systems,** updates bone marrow histology; the sources of macrophages; T cell diversity; asthma and AIDS mortality; and the obstacles to treating AIDS in pandemic countries. It adds the risk in splenectomy and the role of ATP and ADP as inflammatory chemoattractants.

**Chapter 22, The Respiratory System,** enhances descriptions of the nasal epithelium; the cricothyroid ligament in relation to emergency tracheotomy; the Deeper Insight on tracheotomy; cor pulmonale; and squamous cell carcinoma. It adds a mutational cause of Ondine's curse; discovery of pulmonary platelet production; and the potential of electronic cigarettes and legalization of recreational marijuana as emerging risk factors for lung cancer.

**Chapter 23, The Urinary System,** adds to the function of glomerular mesangial cells and has an improved Deeper Insight on kidney stones, with a new photo.

**Chapter 24, Fluid, Electrolyte, and Acid–Base Balance,** has further information on sodium and the effects of hypernatremia, and has added a new table summarizing the major electrolyte imbalances.

**Chapter 25, The Digestive System,** includes additions on the immune role of the omenta; dental proprioception; aspirin and peptic ulcer; the cell-signaling function of the intestinal mucous coat; anatomical variability of the colon and a new drawing of its histology; an updated Deeper Insight on gallstones, with a photo; a new Deeper Insight on diverticulosis and diverticulitis; a new Deeper Insight on colorectal cancer; and an improved description of intestinal lymphatic nodules.

**Chapter 26, Nutrition and Metabolism,** includes new MRI images of a morbidly obese individual compared to one of normal BMI; a new drawing of lipoprotein structure and chart of composition of the lipoprotein classes; new information on the effects of leptin on sympathetic nerve fibers and lipolysis; and a new photo of hepatic cirrhosis.

**Chapter 27, The Male Reproductive System,** has a new table and discussion of the composition of semen and function of the bulbourethral preejaculatory fluid, and updates on benign prostatic hyperplasia and prostate cancer. It adds discussion of zinc deficiency as a cause of infertility, hypothalamic maturation and GnRH in relation to the onset of puberty, and andropause in relation to declining androgen secretion.

**Chapter 28, The Female Reproductive System,** has improvements in hymen anatomy and the figure of ovarian structure; a new perspective on morning sickness as a possible factor mitigating birth defects; and updates on contraception and on breast cancer genes, risk factors, and mortality.

**Chapter 29, Human Development and Aging,** adds the role of the sperm centrosome in fertilization; chromosomal defects as a leading cause of first-trimester miscarriages; and the formation of monozygotic twins. It adds a new Deeper Insight and illustration of cleft lip and palate. It updates the telomere theory of senescence but deletes the now-doubtful theory of DNA damage by endogenous free radicals. It adds a new, MRI-based drawing of muscle atrophy in old age and a discussion of pineal gland senescence as a factor in the insomnia experienced by some older people. It updates statistics on human life expectancy and the major causes of death. The final Deeper Insight is retitled Assisted Reproductive Technology and has a new photo of intracytoplasmic sperm injection.

**Appendix D, The Genetic Code and Amino Acids,** now adds a table of the 20 amino acids and their symbols, and the structural formulae of the amino acids.

## ACKNOWLEDGMENTS

Peer review is a critical part of the scientific process, and very important to ensure the content in this book continues to meet the needs of the instructors and students who use it. We are grateful for the people who agree to participate in this process and thank them for their time, talents, and feedback. The reviewers of this text (listed here) have contributed significant comments that help us refine and update the print and digital components of this program.

Christina Gan and Heather Cushman have updated the question bank and test bank to closely correlate with the intricate changes made in this ninth edition and have greatly increased the educational value of these books through their work to create self-assessment tools and align McGraw-Hill's Connect resources with the textbook. This has contributed significantly to student and instructor satisfaction with our overall package of learning media and to the students' success as they master A&P en route to their career aspirations.

I would also like to extend appreciation to members of the Life Sciences Book Team at McGraw-Hill Education who have worked with me on this project, including Matthew Garcia, Senior Portfolio Manager; Valerie Kramer, Marketing Manager; Donna Nemmers, Senior Product Developer; Vicki Krug, Senior Content Project Manager; Lori Hancock, Lead Content Licensing Specialist; Brent dela Cruz, Senior Content Project Manager; Egzon Shaqiri, Designer; and Jeanne Patterson, freelance copy editor. Their efforts have yielded another great edition of the text and its companion media suite of Connect products.

Timothy A. Ballard
*University of North Carolina—Wilmington*

Barry N. Bates
*Atlanta Technical College*

Christopher I. Brandon Jr.
*Georgia Gwinnett College*

Nickolas A. Butkevich
*Schoolcraft College*

John W. Campbell
*Oklahoma City Community College*

Jennifer Cochran Biederman
*Winona State University*

Mary B. Colon
*Seminole State College of Florida*

Abdeslem El Idrissi
*College of Staten Island, City University of New York*

Bagie George
*Georgia Gwinnett College*

Kyle P. Harris
*Temple University*

Karen L. Kandl
*Western Carolina University*

Stephen A. Kash
*Oklahoma City Community College*

Stephanie Matlock
*Colorado Mesa University*

Deborah T. Palatinus
*Roane State Community College*

Jeffrey Alan Pence
*Excelsior College*

Carla Perry
*Community College of Philadelphia*

Franz Sainvil
*Broward College–Central Campus*

Brian Stout
*Northwest Vista College*

Andrew Van Nguyen
*The City University of New York–Queensborough Community College*

Kimberly Vietti
*Illinois Central College*

Beth L. Williams
*Wallace State Community College*

Delon Washo-Krupps
*Arizona State University*

Samia Williams
*Santa Fe College*

# THE STORY OF FORM AND FUNCTION

## INNOVATIVE CHAPTER SEQUENCING

Some chapters and topics are presented in a sequence that is more instructive than the conventional order.

### Early Presentation of Heredity

Fundamental principles of heredity are presented in the last few pages of chapter 4 rather than at the back of the book to better integrate molecular and Mendelian genetics. This organization also prepares students to learn about such genetic traits and conditions as cystic fibrosis, color blindness, blood types, hemophilia, cancer genes, and sickle-cell disease by first teaching them about dominant and recessive alleles, genotype and phenotype, and sex linkage.

### Urinary System Presented Close to Circulatory and Respiratory Systems

Most textbooks place this system near the end of the book because of its anatomical and developmental relationships with the reproductive system. However, its physiological ties to the circulatory and respiratory systems are much more important. Except for a necessary digression on lymphatics and immunity, the circulatory system is followed almost immediately with the respiratory and urinary systems, which regulate blood composition and whose functional mechanisms rely on recently covered principles of blood flow and capillary exchange.

### Muscle Anatomy and Physiology Follow Skeleton and Joints

The functional morphology of the skeleton, joints, and muscles is treated in three consecutive chapters, 8 through 10, so when students learn muscle attachments, these come only two chapters after the names of the relevant bone features. When they learn muscle actions, it is in the first chapter after learning the terms for the joint movements. This order brings another advantage: The physiology of muscle and nerve cells is treated in two consecutive chapters (11 and 12), which are thus closely integrated in their treatment of synapses, neurotransmitters, and membrane electrophysiology.

## BRIEF CONTENTS

# LEARNING TOOLS

## Engaging Chapter Layouts

- Chapters are structured around the way students learn.
- Frequent subheadings and expected learning outcomes help students plan their study time and review strategies.

**Deeper Insights** highlight areas of interest and career relevance for students.

**Chapter Outlines** provide quick previews of the content.

CHAPTER 7

BONE TISSUE

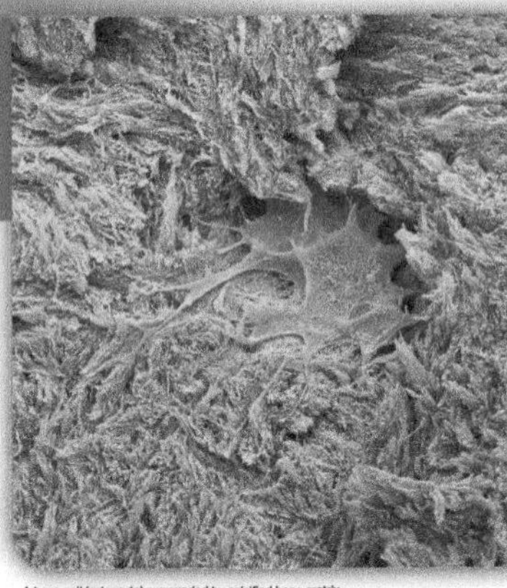

A bone cell (osteocyte) surrounded by calcified bone matrix
Eye of Science/Science Source

CHAPTER OUTLINE



DEEPER INSIGHTS

Module 5: Skeletal System

198

CHAPTER 3 Cellular Form and Function 75

BRUSHING UP

- The transport of matter through cell membranes follows the principles of flow down gradients (see section 1.6e).
- To adequately understand the structure of the cell surface, it is essential that you understand glycolipids and glycoproteins, as well as phospholipids and their amphipathic nature (see sections 2.4c and 2.4d).
- The proteins of cell membranes have a great variety of functions. To understand those depends on an acquaintance with the functions of proteins in general and how protein function depends on tertiary structure (see "Protein Structure" and "Protein Functions" in section 2.4e).

All organisms, from the simplest to the most complex, are composed of cells—whether the single cell of a bacterium or the trillions of cells that constitute the human body. These cells are responsible for all structural and functional properties of a living organism. A knowledge of cells is therefore indispensable to any true understanding of the workings of the human body, the mechanisms of disease, and the rationale of therapy. Thus, this chapter and the next one introduce the basic cell biology of the human body, and subsequent chapters expand upon this information as we examine the specialized cellular structure and function of specific organs.

3.1 Concepts of Cellular Structure

**Expected Learning Outcomes**

When you have completed this section, you should be able to

a. discuss the development and modern tenets of the cell theory;
b. describe cell shapes from their descriptive terms;
c. state the size range of human cells and discuss factors that limit their size;
d. discuss the way that developments in microscopy have changed our view of cell structure; and
e. outline the major components of a cell.

### 3.1a Development of the Cell Theory

**Cytology,**[1] the scientific study of cells, was born in 1663 when Robert Hooke observed the empty cell walls of cork and coined the word *cellulae* ("little cells") to describe them (see section 1.2). Soon he studied thin slices of fresh wood and saw living cells "filled with juices"—a fluid later named *cytoplasm*. Two centuries later, Theodor Schwann studied a wide range of animal tissues and concluded that all animals are made of cells.

Schwann and other biologists originally believed that cells came from nonliving body fluid that somehow congealed and acquired a membrane and nucleus. This idea of *spontaneous generation*—that living things arise from nonliving matter—was rooted in the scientific thought of the times. For centuries, it seemed to be simple common sense that decaying meat turned into maggots, stored grain into rodents, and mud into frogs. Schwann and his contemporaries merely extended this idea to cells. The idea of spontaneous generation wasn't discredited until some classic experiments by French microbiologist Louis Pasteur in 1859.

By the end of the nineteenth century, it was established beyond all reasonable doubt that cells arise only from other cells and every living organism is composed of cells and cell products. The cell came to be regarded, and still is, as the simplest structural and functional unit of life. There are no smaller subdivisions of a cell or organism that, in themselves, have all or most of the fundamental characteristics of life described in section 1.6a. Enzymes and organelles, for example, are not alive, although the life of a cell depends on their activity.

The development of biochemistry from the late nineteenth to the twentieth century made it further apparent that all physiological processes of the body are based on cellular activity and that the cells of all species exhibit remarkable biochemical unity. The various generalizations of these last two paragraphs now constitute the modern **cell theory.**

### 3.1b Cell Shapes and Sizes

We will shortly examine the structure of a generic cell, but the generalizations we draw shouldn't blind you to the diversity of cellular form and function in humans. There are about 200 kinds of cells in the human body, with a variety of shapes, sizes, and functions.

Descriptions of organ and tissue structure often refer to the shapes of cells by the following terms (**fig. 3.1**):

- **Squamous**[2] (SKWAY-mus)—a thin, flat, scaly shape, often with a bulge where the nucleus is, much like the shape of a fried egg "sunny side up." Squamous cells line the esophagus and form the surface layer (epidermis) of the skin.
- **Cuboidal**[3] (cue-BOY-dul)—squarish-looking in frontal sections and about equal in height and width; liver cells are a good example.
- **Columnar**—distinctly taller than wide, such as the inner lining cells of the stomach and intestines.
- **Polygonal**[4]—having irregularly angular shapes with four, five, or more sides.
- **Stellate**[5]—having multiple pointed processes projecting from the body of a cell, giving it a somewhat starlike shape. The cell bodies of many nerve cells are stellate.

[1] *cyto* = cell; *logy* = study of

[2] *squam* = scale; *ous* = characterized by
[3] *cub* = cube; *oidal* = like, resembling
[4] *poly* = many; *gon* = angles
[5] *stell* = star; *ate* = resembling, characterized by

## Tiered Assessments Based on Key Learning Outcomes

- Chapters are divided into brief sections, enabling students to set specific goals for short study periods.
- Section-ending questions allow students to check their understanding before moving on.

Each chapter begins with **Brushing Up** to emphasize the interrelatedness of concepts, which is especially useful for adult students returning to the classroom, and serves as an aid for instructors when teaching chapters out of order.

Each major section begins with **Expected Learning Outcomes** to help focus the reader's attention on the larger concepts and make the course outcome-driven. This also assists instructors in structuring their courses around expected learning outcomes.

**Questions** in figure legends and **Apply What You Know** items prompt students to think more deeply about the implications and applications of what they have learned. This helps students practice higher order thinking skills throughout the chapter.

CHAPTER 9 Joints 271

separation between the bones and length of the fibers give these joints more mobility than a suture or gomphosis has. An especially mobile syndesmosis exists between the shafts of the radius and ulna, which are joined by a broad fibrous *interosseous membrane*. This permits such movements as pronation and supination of the forearm. A less mobile syndesmosis is the one that binds the distal ends of the tibia and fibula together, side by side (see fig. 9.2c).

### 9.1c Cartilaginous Joints

A **cartilaginous joint** is also called an **amphiarthrosis**[7] (AM-fee-ar-THRO-sis). In these joints, two bones are linked by cartilage (fig. 9.4). The two types of cartilaginous joints are *synchondroses* and *symphyses*.

#### Synchondroses

A **synchondrosis**[8] (SIN-con-DRO-sis) is a joint in which the bones are bound by hyaline cartilage. An example is the temporary joint between the epiphysis and diaphysis of a long bone in a child, formed by the cartilage of the epiphysial plate. Another is the attachment of the first rib to the sternum by a hyaline costal cartilage (fig. 9.4a). (The other costal cartilages are joined to the sternum by synovial joints.)

#### Symphyses

In a **symphysis**[9] (SIM-fih-sis), two bones are joined by fibrocartilage (fig. 9.4b, c). One example is the pubic symphysis, in which the right and left pubic bones are joined anteriorly by the cartilaginous interpubic disc. Another is the joint between the bodies of two vertebrae, united by an intervertebral disc. The surface of each vertebral body is covered with hyaline cartilage. Between the vertebrae, this cartilage becomes infiltrated with collagen bundles to form fibrocartilage. Each intervertebral disc permits only slight movement between adjacent vertebrae, but the collective effect of all 23 discs gives the spine considerable flexibility.

**APPLY WHAT YOU KNOW**

*The intervertebral joints are symphyses only in the cervical through the lumbar region. How would you classify the intervertebral joints of the sacrum and coccyx in a middle-aged adult?*

[7] *amphi* = on all sides; *arthr* = joined; *osis* = condition
[8] *syn* = together; *chondr* = cartilage; *osis* = condition
[9] *sym* = together; *physis* = growth



**FIGURE 9.4 Cartilaginous Joints.** (a) A synchondrosis, represented by the costal cartilage joining rib 1 to the sternum. (b) The pubic symphysis. (c) Intervertebral discs, which join adjacent vertebrae to each other by symphyses.

*What is the difference between the pubic symphysis and the interpubic disc?*

The end-of-chapter **Study Guide** offers several methods for assessment that are useful to both students and instructors.

**Assess Your Learning Outcomes** provides students a study outline for review, and addresses the needs of instructors whose colleges require outcome-oriented syllabi and assessment of student achievement of the expected learning outcomes.

**End-of-chapter questions** build on all levels of Bloom's Taxonomy in sections to

1. test simple recall and analytical thought;
2. build medical vocabulary; and
3. apply the basic knowledge to new clinical problems and other situations.

**What's Wrong with These Statements?** questions further address Bloom's Taxonomy by asking the student to explain *why* the false statements are untrue.

**Testing Your Comprehension** questions address Bloom's Taxonomy in going beyond recall to application of ideas.

### Assess Your Learning Outcomes

*To test your knowledge, discuss the following topics with a study partner or in writing, ideally from memory.*

**9.1 Joints and Their Classification**

1. The fundamental definition of *joint (articulation)* and why it cannot be defined as a point at which one bone moves relative to an adjacent bone
3. Three essential components of a lever
4. The meaning of *mechanical advantage* (MA); how the *MA* of a lever can be determined from measurements of its effort and resistance arms; and the respective advantages of levers in which the *MA* is greater than or less than 1.0
5. Comparison of first-, second-, and third-class levers, and anatomical examples of each
12. The same for flexion, extension, hyperextension, and lateral flexion of the spine, and right and left rotation of the trunk
13. The same for elevation, depression, protraction, retraction, and lateral and medial excursion of the mandible
14. The same for dorsiflexion, plantar flexion, inversion, eversion, pronation, and supination of the foot

### Testing Your Recall

*Answers in Appendix A*

1. Internal and external rotation of the humerus is made possible by a ______ joint.
   a. pivot
   b. condylar
   c. ball-and-socket
   d. saddle
   e. hinge
2. Which of the following is the least movable?
   a. a diarthrosis
   b. a synostosis
   c. a symphysis
   d. a synovial joint
   e. a condylar joint
3. Which of the following movements are unique to the foot?
   a. dorsiflexion and inversion
   b. elevation and depression
   c. circumduction and rotation
   d. abduction and adduction
   e. opposition and reposition

### Building Your Medical Vocabulary

*Answers in Appendix A*

*State a meaning of each word element, and give a medical term from this chapter that uses it or a slight variation of it.*

1. ab-
2. arthro-
3. -ate
4. cruci-
5. cruro-
6. -duc
7. kinesio-
8. men-
9. supin-
10. -trac

### What's Wrong with These Statements?

*Answers in Appendix A*

*Briefly explain why each of the following statements is false, or reword it to make it true.*

1. More people get rheumatoid arthritis than osteoarthritis.
2. A doctor who treats arthritis is called a kinesiologist.
3. Synovial joints are also known as synarthroses.
4. Menisci occur in the elbow and knee joints.
5. Reaching behind you to take something out of your hip pocket involves flexion of the shoulder.
6. The cruciate ligaments are in the feet.
7. The femur is held tightly in the acetabulum mainly by the round ligament.
8. The knuckles are amphiarthroses.
9. Synovial fluid is secreted by the bursae.
10. Like most ligaments, the periodontal ligaments attach one bone (the tooth) to another (the mandible or maxilla).

STUDY GUIDE

### Testing Your Comprehension

1. All second-class levers produce a mechanical advantage greater than 1.0 and all third-class levers produce a mechanical advantage less than 1.0. Explain why.
2. For each of the following joint movements, state what bone the axis of rotation passes through and which of the three anatomical planes contains the axis of rotation. You may find it helpful to produce some of these actions on an articulated laboratory

the first interphalangeal joint of the index finger. (Do not bend the fingers of a wired laboratory skeletal hand, because they can break off.)

3. In order of occurrence, list the joint actions (flexion, pronation, etc.) and the joints where they would occur as you (a) sit down at a table, (b) reach out and pick up an apple, (c) take a bite, and (d) chew it. Assume that you start in anatomical

arm. Imagine a person holding a weight in the hand and abducting the arm. On a laboratory skeleton, identify the fulcrum; measure the effort arm and resistance arm; determine the mechanical advantage of this movement; and determine which of the three lever types the upper limb acts as when performing this movement.

5. List the six types of synovial joints, and for each one, if possible, identify a joint in the

## ARTWORK THAT INSPIRES LEARNING

The incredible art program in this textbook sets the standard in A&P. The stunning portfolio of art and photos was created with the aid of art focus groups and with feedback from hundreds of accuracy reviews.

### Vivid Illustrations

Rich textures and shading and bold, bright colors bring structures to life.

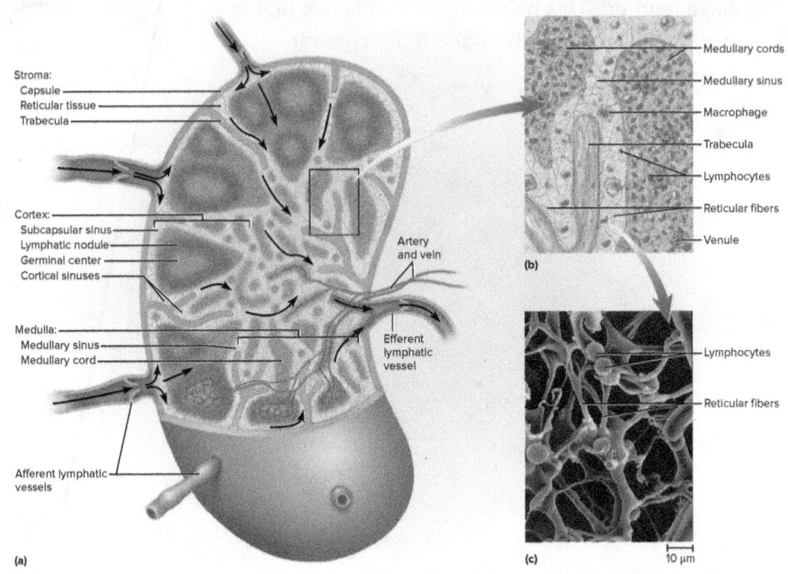


Francis Leroy, Biocosmos/Science Source

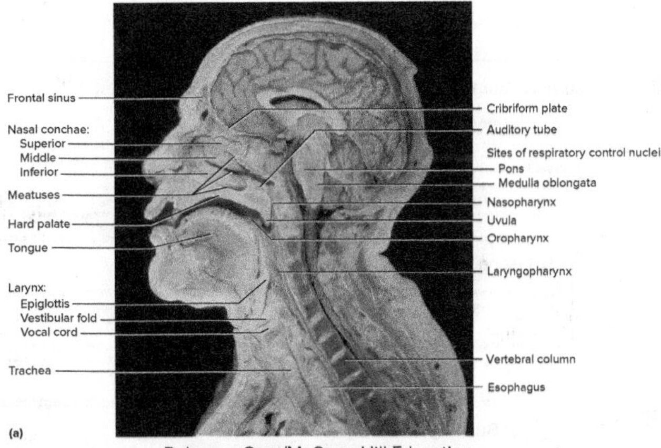


Rebecca Gray/McGraw-Hill Education

**Cadaver dissections** are paired with carefully drawn illustrations to show intricate human detail.

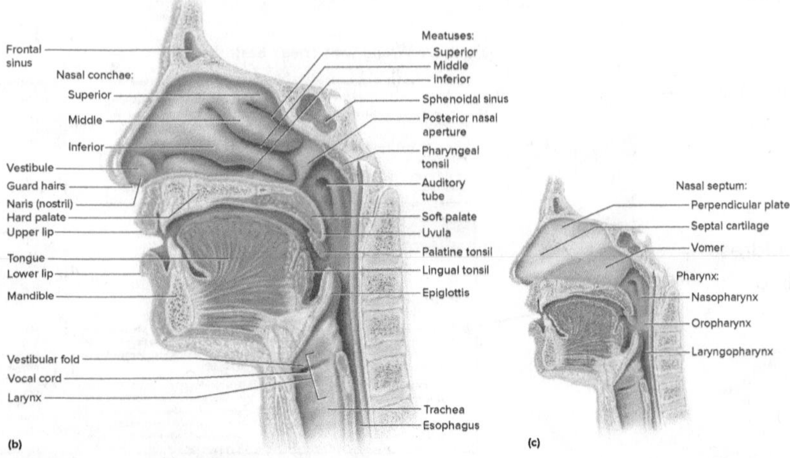

Orientation Tools

Saladin art integrates tools to help students quickly orient themselves within a figure and make connections between ideas.

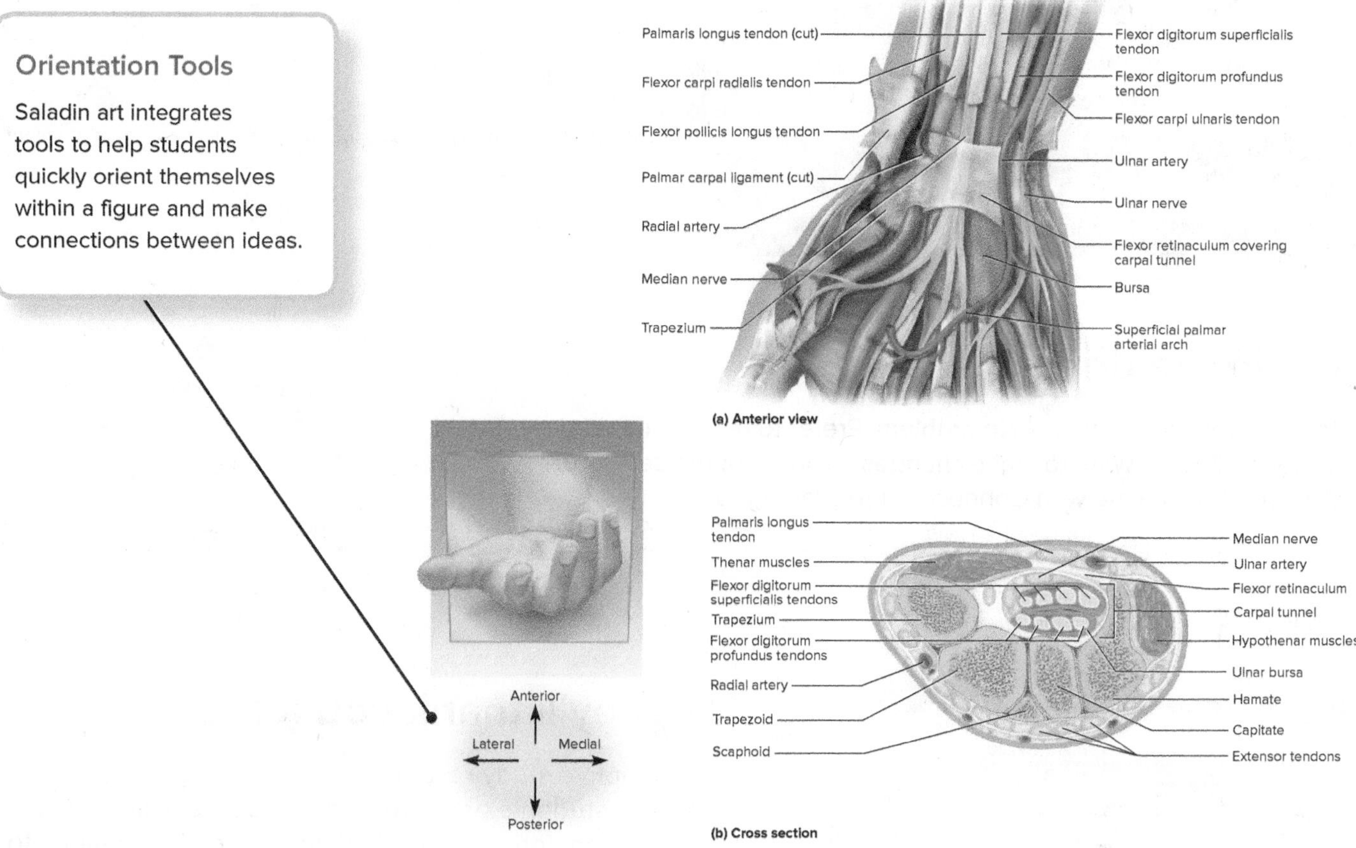


(a) Anterior view

(b) Cross section

## Conducive to Learning

- Easy-to-understand process figures
- Tools for students to easily orient themselves

Process Figures

Saladin breaks complicated physiological processes into numbered steps for a manageable introduction to difficult concepts.

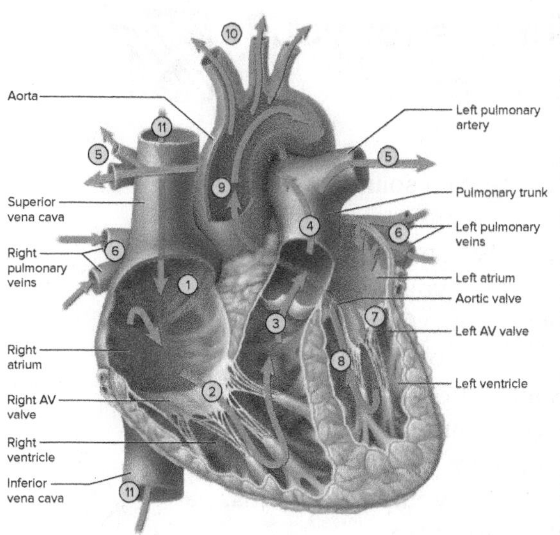


1. Blood enters right atrium from superior and inferior venae cavae.
2. Blood in right atrium flows through right AV valve into right ventricle.
3. Contraction of right ventricle forces pulmonary valve open.
4. Blood flows through pulmonary valve into pulmonary trunk.
5. Blood is distributed by right and left pulmonary arteries to the lungs, where it unloads $CO_2$ and loads $O_2$.
6. Blood returns from lungs via pulmonary veins to left atrium.
7. Blood in left atrium flows through left AV valve into left ventricle.
8. Contraction of left ventricle (simultaneous with step 3) forces aortic valve open.
9. Blood flows through aortic valve into ascending aorta.
10. Blood in aorta is distributed to every organ in the body, where it unloads $O_2$ and loads $CO_2$.
11. Blood returns to right atrium via venae cavae.

# FOR INSTRUCTORS

## You're in the driver's seat.

Want to build your own course? No problem. Prefer to use our turnkey, prebuilt course? Easy. Want to make changes throughout the semester? Sure. And you'll save time with Connect's auto-grading too.

**65%**
Less Time Grading

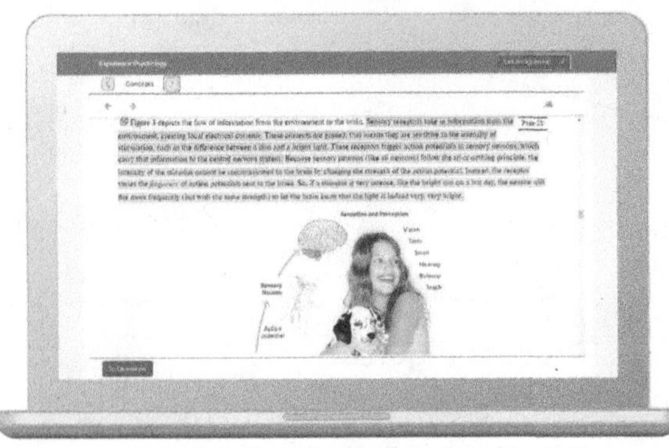

Laptop: McGraw-Hill; Woman/dog: George Doyle/Getty Images

## They'll thank you for it.

Adaptive study resources like SmartBook® 2.0 help your students be better prepared in less time. You can transform your class time from dull definitions to dynamic debates. Find out more about the powerful personalized learning experience available in SmartBook 2.0 at **www.mheducation.com/highered/connect/smartbook**

## Make it simple, make it affordable.

Connect makes it easy with seamless integration using any of the major Learning Management Systems—Blackboard®, Canvas, and D2L, among others—to let you organize your course in one convenient location. Give your students access to digital materials at a discount with our inclusive access program. Ask your McGraw-Hill representative for more information.

Padlock: Jobalou/Getty Images

## Solutions for your challenges.

A product isn't a solution. Real solutions are affordable, reliable, and come with training and ongoing support when you need it and how you want it. Our Customer Experience Group can also help you troubleshoot tech problems—although Connect's 99% uptime means you might not need to call them. See for yourself at **status.mheducation.com**

Checkmark: Jobalou/Getty Images

## FOR STUDENTS

### Effective, efficient studying.

Connect helps you be more productive with your study time and get better grades using tools like SmartBook 2.0, which highlights key concepts and creates a personalized study plan. Connect sets you up for success, so you walk into class with confidence and walk out with better grades.

### Study anytime, anywhere.

Download the free ReadAnywhere app and access your online eBook or SmartBook 2.0 assignments when it's convenient, even if you're offline. And since the app automatically syncs with your eBook and SmartBook 2.0 assignments in Connect, all of your work is available every time you open it. Find out more at **www.mheducation.com/readanywhere**

***"I really liked this app—it made it easy to study when you don't have your text-book in front of you."***

- Jordan Cunningham, Eastern Washington University

Calendar: owattaphotos/Getty Images

### No surprises.

The Connect Calendar and Reports tools keep you on track with the work you need to get done and your assignment scores. Life gets busy; Connect tools help you keep learning through it all.

### Learning for everyone.

McGraw-Hill works directly with Accessibility Services Departments and faculty to meet the learning needs of all students. Please contact your Accessibility Services office and ask them to email accessibility@mheducation.com, or visit **www.mheducation.com/about/accessibility** for more information.

Top: Jenner Images/Getty Images, Left: Hero Images/Getty Images, Right: Hero Images/Getty Images

## McGraw-Hill Connect® empowers students to learn and succeed in the Anatomy and Physiology course with user-friendly digital solutions.

### SMARTBOOK®

**SmartBook 2.0** provides personalized learning to individual student needs, continually adapting to pinpoint knowledge gaps and focus learning on concepts requiring additional study. The result? Students are highly engaged in the content and better prepared for lecture.

### LEARNSMART PREP®

**LearnSmart Prep** helps students thrive in college-level A&P by helping solidify knowledge in the key areas of cell biology, chemistry, study skills, and math. The result? Students are better prepared for the A&P course.

### Practice ATLAS

## Stop the Drop!

**50% of the country's students are unable to pass the A&P course***

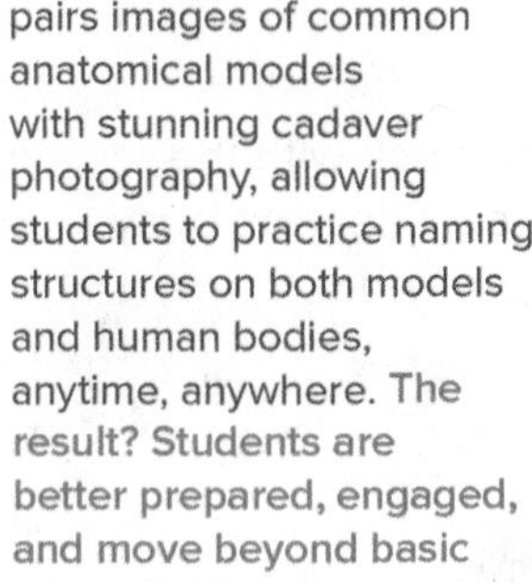

**Practice Atlas for A&P** is an interactive tool that pairs images of common anatomical models with stunning cadaver photography, allowing students to practice naming structures on both models and human bodies, anytime, anywhere. The result? Students are better prepared, engaged, and move beyond basic memorization.

**Anatomy & Physiology Revealed® (APR) 4.0** is an interactive cadaver dissection tool to enhance lecture and lab that students can use anytime, anywhere. The result? Students are prepared for lab, engaged in the material, and utilize critical thinking.

### Ph.I.L.S.

**Ph.I.L.S. 4.0 (Physiology Interactive Lab Simulations)** software is the perfect way to reinforce key physiology concepts with powerful lab experiments. The result? Students gain critical thinking skills and are better prepared for lab.

**Concept Overview Interactives** are ground-breaking interactive animations that encourage students to explore key physiological processes and difficult concepts. The result? Students are engaged and able to apply what they've learned while tackling difficult A&P concepts.

*Statistic courtesy of *The New England Journal of Higher Education*

# LETTER TO STUDENTS

When I was a young boy, I became interested in what I then called "nature study" for two reasons. One was the sheer beauty of nature. I reveled in children's books with abundant, colorful drawings and photographs of animals, plants, minerals, and gems. It was this esthetic appreciation of nature that made me want to learn more about it and made me happily surprised to discover I could make a career of it. At a slightly later age, another thing that drew me still deeper into biology was to discover writers who had a way with words—who could captivate my imagination and curiosity with their elegant prose. Once I was old enough to hold part-time jobs, I began buying zoology and anatomy books that mesmerized me with their gracefulness of writing and fascinating art and photography. I wanted to write and draw like that myself, and I began teaching myself by learning from "the masters." I spent many late nights in my room peering into my microscope and jars of pond water, typing page after page of manuscript, and trying pen and ink as an art medium. My "first book" was a 318-page paper on some little pond animals called hydras, with 53 India ink illustrations that I wrote for my tenth-grade biology class when I was 16 (see page viii).

Fast-forward about 30 years, to when I became a textbook writer, and I found myself bringing that same enjoyment of writing and illustrating to the first edition of this book you are now holding. Why? Not only for its intrinsic creative satisfaction, but because I'm guessing that you're like I was—you can appreciate a book that does more than simply give you the information you need. You appreciate, I trust, a writer who makes it enjoyable for you through his scientific, storytelling prose and his concept of the way things should be illustrated to spark interest and facilitate understanding.

I know from my own students, however, that you need more than captivating illustrations and enjoyable reading. Let's face it—A&P is a complex subject and it may seem a formidable task to acquire even a basic knowledge of the human body. It was difficult even for me to learn (and the learning never ends). So in addition to simply writing this book, I've given a lot of thought to its pedagogy—the art of teaching. I've designed my chapters to make them easier for you to study and to give you abundant opportunity to check whether you've understood what you read—to test yourself (as I advise my own students) before the instructor tests you.

Each chapter is broken down into short, digestible bits with a set of Expected Learning Outcomes at the beginning of each section, and self-testing questions (Before You Go On) just a few pages later. Even if you have just 30 minutes to read during a lunch break or a bus ride, you can easily read or review one of these brief sections. There are also numerous self-testing questions in a Study Guide at the end of each chapter, in some of the figure legends, and the occasional Apply What You Know questions dispersed throughout each chapter. The questions cover a broad range of cognitive skills, from simple recall of a term to your ability to evaluate, analyze, and apply what you've learned to new clinical situations or other problems. In this era of digital publishing, however, learning aids go far beyond what I write into the book itself. SmartBook®, available on smartphones and tablets, includes all of the book's contents plus adaptive technology that can give you personalized instruction, target the unique gaps in your knowledge, and guide you in comprehension and retention of the subject matter.

I hope you enjoy your study of this book, but I know there are always ways to make it even better. Indeed, what quality you may find in this edition owes a great deal to feedback I've received from students all over the world. If you find any typos or other errors, if you have any suggestions for improvement, if I can clarify a concept for you, or even if you just want to comment on something you really like about the book, I hope you'll feel free to write to me. I correspond quite a lot with students and would enjoy hearing from you.

Ken Saladin
Georgia College
Milledgeville, GA 31061 (USA)
ksaladin2@windstream.net

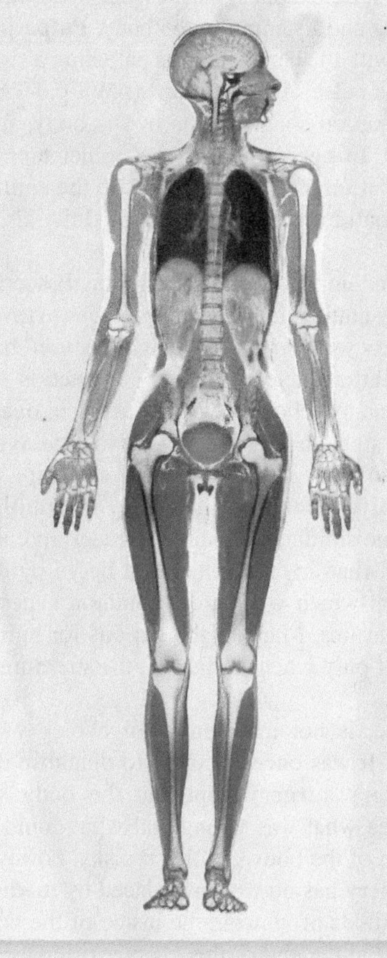

A colorized MRI scan of the human body



# CHAPTER 1

# MAJOR THEMES OF ANATOMY AND PHYSIOLOGY

## CHAPTER OUTLINE



## DEEPER INSIGHTS

**Module 1: Body Orientation**

No branch of science hits as close to home as the science of our own bodies. We're grateful for the dependability of our hearts; we're awed by the capabilities of muscles and joints displayed by Olympic athletes; and we ponder with philosophers the ancient mysteries of mind and emotion. We want to know how our body works, and when it malfunctions, we want to know what's happening and what we can do about it. Even the most ancient writings of civilization include medical documents that attest to humanity's timeless drive to know itself. You are embarking on a subject that is as old as civilization, yet one that grows by thousands of scientific publications every week.

This book is an introduction to human structure and function, the biology of the human body. It is meant primarily to give you a foundation for advanced study in health care, exercise physiology, pathology, and other fields related to health and fitness. Beyond that purpose, however, it can also provide you with a deeply satisfying sense of self-understanding.

As rewarding and engrossing as this subject is, the human body is highly complex, and understanding it requires us to comprehend a great deal of detail. The details will be more manageable if we relate them to a few broad, unifying concepts. The aim of this chapter, therefore, is to introduce such concepts and put the rest of the book into perspective. We consider the historical development of anatomy and physiology, the thought processes that led to the knowledge in this book, the meaning of human life, some central concepts of physiology, and how to better understand medical terminology.

## 1.1 The Scope of Anatomy and Physiology

**Expected Learning Outcomes**

When you have completed this section, you should be able to

a. define *anatomy* and *physiology* and relate them to each other;
b. describe several ways of studying human anatomy; and
c. define a few subdisciplines of human physiology.

**Anatomy** is the study of structure, and **physiology** is the study of function. These approaches are complementary and never entirely separable. Together, they form the bedrock of the health sciences. When we study a structure, we want to know, What does it do? Physiology thus lends meaning to anatomy; conversely, anatomy is what makes physiology possible. This *unity of form and function* is an important point to bear in mind as you study the body. Many examples of it will be apparent throughout the book—some of them pointed out for you, and others you will notice for yourself.

### 1.1a Anatomy—The Study of Form

There are several ways to examine the structure of the human body. The simplest is **inspection**—simply looking at the body's appearance, as in performing a physical examination or making a clinical diagnosis from surface appearance. Physical examinations also involve touching and listening to the body. **Palpation**[1] means feeling a structure with the hands, such as palpating a swollen lymph node or taking a pulse. **Auscultation**[2] (AWS-cul-TAY-shun) is listening to the natural sounds made by the body, such as heart and lung sounds. In **percussion,** the examiner taps on the body, feels for abnormal resistance, and listens to the emitted sound for signs of abnormalities such as pockets of fluid, air, or scar tissue.

But a deeper understanding of the body depends on **dissection** (dis-SEC-shun)—carefully cutting and separating tissues to reveal their relationships. The very words *anatomy*[3] and *dissection*[4] both mean "cutting apart"; until the nineteenth century, dissection was called "anatomizing." In many schools of health science, one of the first steps in training students is dissection of the **cadaver,**[5] a dead human body. Many insights into human structure are obtained from **comparative anatomy**—the study of multiple species in order to examine similarities and differences and analyze evolutionary trends. Anatomy students often begin by dissecting other animals with which we share a common ancestry and many structural similarities. Many of the reasons for human structure become apparent only when we look at the structure of other animals.

Dissection, of course, is not the method of choice when studying a living person! It was once common to diagnose disorders through **exploratory surgery**—opening the body and taking a look inside to see what was wrong and what could be done about it. Any breach of the body cavities is risky, however, and most exploratory surgery has now been replaced by **medical imaging** techniques—methods of viewing the inside of the body without surgery, discussed at the end of this chapter (see Deeper Insight 1.5). The branch of medicine concerned with imaging is called **radiology.** Structure that can be seen with the naked eye—whether by surface observation, radiology, or dissection—is called **gross anatomy.**

Ultimately, the functions of the body result from its individual cells. To see those, we usually take tissue specimens, thinly slice and stain them, and observe them under the microscope. This approach is called **histology**[6] **(microscopic anatomy).** **Histopathology** is the microscopic examination of tissues for signs of disease. **Cytology**[7] is the study of the structure and function of individual cells. **Ultrastructure** refers to fine detail, down to the molecular level, revealed by the electron microscope.

### 1.1b Physiology—The Study of Function

Physiology[8] uses the methods of experimental science discussed later. It has many subdisciplines such as *neurophysiology* (physiology of the nervous system), *endocrinology* (physiology of

[1]*palp* = touch, feel; *ation* = process
[2]*auscult* = listen; *ation* = process
[3]*ana* = apart; *tom* = cut
[4]*dis* = apart; *sect* = cut
[5]from *cadere* = to fall down or die
[6]*histo* = tissue; *logy* = study of
[7]*cyto* = cell; *logy* = study of
[8]*physio* = nature; *logy* = study of

hormones), and *pathophysiology* (mechanisms of disease). Partly because of limitations on experimentation with humans, much of what we know about bodily function has been gained through **comparative physiology,** the study of how different species have solved problems of life such as water balance, respiration, and reproduction. Comparative physiology is also the basis for the development of new drugs and medical procedures. For example, a cardiac surgeon may learn animal surgery before practicing on humans, and a vaccine cannot be used on human subjects until it has been demonstrated through animal research that it confers significant benefits without unacceptable risks.

**BEFORE YOU GO ON**

Answer the following questions to test your understanding of the preceding section:

1. What is the difference between anatomy and physiology? How do these two sciences support each other?
2. Name the method that would be used for each of the following: listening to a patient for a heart murmur; studying the microscopic structure of the liver; microscopically examining liver tissue for signs of hepatitis; learning the blood vessels of a cadaver; and performing a breast self-examination.

## 1.2 The Origins of Biomedical Science

**Expected Learning Outcomes**

When you have completed this section, you should be able to

a. give examples of how modern biomedical science emerged from an era of superstition and authoritarianism; and
b. describe the contributions of some key people who helped to bring about this transformation.

Any science is more enjoyable if we consider not just the current state of knowledge, but how it compares to past understandings of the subject and how our knowledge was gained. Of all sciences, medicine has one of the most fascinating histories. Medical science has progressed far more in the last 50 years than in the 2,500 years before that, but the field didn't spring up overnight. It is built upon centuries of thought and controversy, triumph and defeat. We cannot fully appreciate its present state without understanding its past—people who had the curiosity to try new things, the vision to look at human form and function in new ways, and the courage to question authority.

### 1.2a The Greek and Roman Legacy

As early as 3,000 years ago, physicians in Mesopotamia and Egypt treated patients with herbal drugs, salts, physical therapy, and faith healing. The "father of medicine," however, is usually considered to be the Greek physician **Hippocrates** (c. 460–c. 375 BCE). He and his followers established a code of ethics for physicians, the Hippocratic Oath, which is still recited in modern form by graduating physicians at some medical schools. Hippocrates urged physicians to stop attributing disease to the activities of gods and demons and to seek their natural causes, which could afford the only rational basis for therapy.

**Aristotle** (384–322 BCE) was one of the first philosophers to write about anatomy and physiology. He believed that diseases and other natural events could have either supernatural causes, which he called *theologi,* or natural ones, which he called *physici* or *physiologi*. We derive such terms as *physician* and *physiology* from the latter. Until the nineteenth century, physicians were called "doctors of physic." In his anatomy book, *On the Parts of Animals,* Aristotle tried to identify unifying themes in nature. Among other points, he argued that complex structures are built from a smaller variety of simple components—a perspective that we will find useful later in this chapter.

**▶▶▶APPLY WHAT YOU KNOW**

*When you have completed this chapter, discuss the relevance of Aristotle's philosophy to our current thinking about human structure.*

**Claudius Galen** (129–c. 200), physician to the Roman gladiators, wrote the most influential medical textbook of the ancient era—a book worshipped to excess by medical professors for centuries to follow. Cadaver dissection was banned in Galen's time because of some horrid excesses that preceded him, including public dissection of living slaves and prisoners. Aside from what he could learn by treating gladiators' wounds, Galen was therefore limited to dissecting pigs, monkeys, and other animals. Because he was not permitted to dissect cadavers, he had to guess at much of human anatomy and made some incorrect deductions from animal dissections. He described the human liver, for example, as having five fingerlike lobes, somewhat like a baseball glove, because that's what he had seen in baboons. But Galen saw science as a method of discovery, not a body of fact to be taken on faith. He warned that even his own books could be wrong and advised his followers to trust their own observations more than any book. Unfortunately, his advice was not heeded. For nearly 1,500 years, medical professors dogmatically taught what they read in Aristotle and Galen, seldom daring to question the authority of these "ancient masters."

### 1.2b The Birth of Modern Medicine

In the Middle Ages, the state of medical science varied greatly from one religious culture to another. Science was severely repressed in the Christian culture of Europe until about the sixteenth century, although some of the most famous medical schools of Europe were founded during this era. Their professors, however, taught medicine primarily as a dogmatic commentary on Galen and Aristotle, not as a field of original research. Medieval medical illustrations were crude representations of the body intended more to decorate a page than to depict the body realistically **(fig. 1.1a).** Some were astrological charts that showed which sign of the zodiac was thought to influence each organ of the body. From such pseudoscience came the word *influenza,* Italian for "influence."

Free inquiry was less inhibited in Jewish and Muslim culture during this time. Jewish physicians were the most esteemed practitioners of their art—and none more famous than *Moses ben Maimon* (1135–1204), known in Christendom as **Maimonides.** Born in Spain, he fled to Egypt at age 24 to escape antisemitic persecution. There he served the rest of his life as physician to the court of the sultan, Saladin. A highly admired rabbi, Maimonides wrote voluminously on Jewish law and theology, but also wrote 10 influential medical books and numerous treatises on specific diseases.

Among Muslims, probably the most highly regarded medical scholar was *Ibn Sina* (980–1037), known in the West as **Avicenna** or "the Galen of Islam." He studied Galen and Aristotle, combined their findings with original discoveries, and questioned authority when the evidence demanded it. Medicine in the Mideast soon became superior to European medicine. Avicenna's textbook, *The Canon of Medicine,* was the leading authority in European medical schools for over 500 years.

Chinese medicine had little influence on Western thought and practice until relatively recently; the medical arts evolved in China quite independently of European medicine. Later chapters of this book describe some of the insights of ancient China and India.

Modern Western medicine began around the sixteenth century in the innovative minds of such people as the anatomist Andreas Vesalius and the physiologist William Harvey.

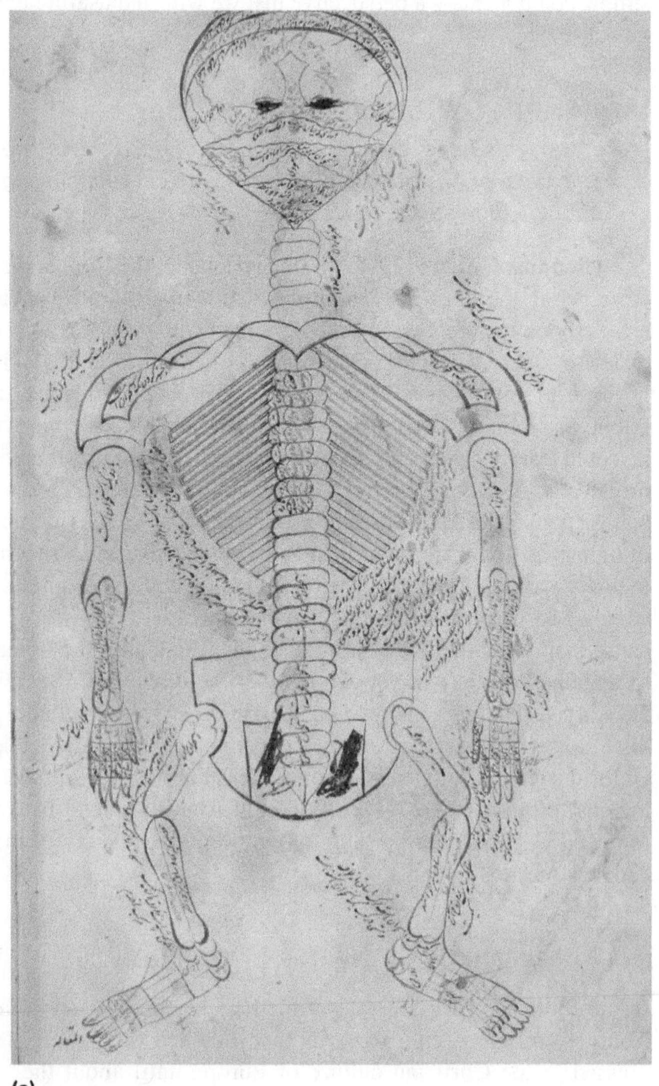

(a)

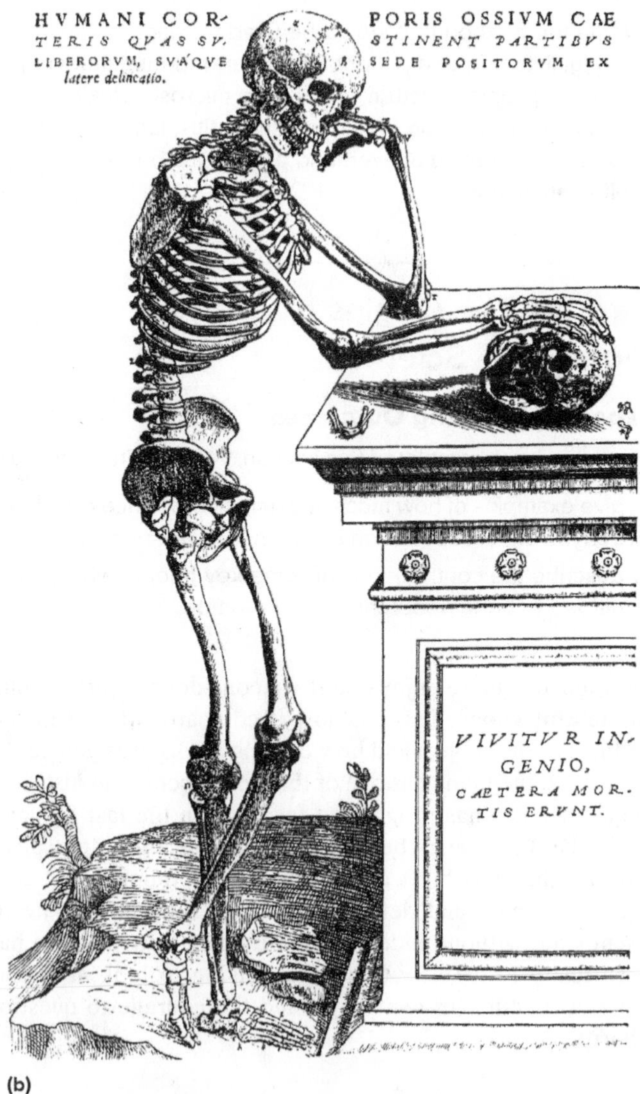


(b)

**FIGURE 1.1 The Evolution of Medical Art.** Two illustrations of the skeletal system made about 500 years apart. (a) From an eleventh-century work attributed to Persian physician Avicenna. (b) From *De Humani Corporis Fabrica* by Andreas Vesalius, 1543.

a: Source: Wellcome Library, London/CC BY 4.0; b: Suzan Oschmann/Shutterstock

**Andreas Vesalius** (1514–64) taught anatomy in Italy. In his time, the Catholic Church relaxed its prohibition against cadaver dissection, in part to allow autopsies in cases of suspicious death. Furthermore, the Italian Renaissance created an environment more friendly to innovative scholarship. Dissection gradually found its way into the training of medical students throughout Europe. It was an unpleasant business, however, and most professors considered it beneath their dignity. In those days before refrigeration or embalming, the odor from the decaying cadaver was unbearable. Dissections were a race against decay. Bleary medical students had to fight the urge to vomit, lest they incur the wrath of an overbearing professor. Professors typically sat in an elevated chair, the *cathedra,* reading dryly in Latin from Galen or Aristotle while a lower-ranking *barber–surgeon* removed putrefying organs from the cadaver and held them up for the students to see. Barbering and surgery were considered to be "kindred arts of the knife"; today's barber poles date from this era, their red and white stripes symbolizing blood and bandages.

Vesalius broke with tradition by coming down from the cathedra and doing the dissections himself. He was quick to point out that much of the anatomy in Galen's books was wrong, and he was the first to publish accurate illustrations for teaching anatomy **(fig. 1.1b).** When others began to plagiarize them, Vesalius published the first atlas of anatomy, *De Humani Corporis Fabrica (On the Structure of the Human Body),* in 1543. This book began a rich tradition of medical illustration that has been handed down to us through such milestones as *Gray's Anatomy* (1856) and the vividly illustrated atlases and textbooks of today.

Anatomy preceded physiology and was a necessary foundation for it. What Vesalius was to anatomy, the Englishman **William Harvey** (1578–1657) was to physiology. Harvey is remembered especially for his studies of blood circulation and a little book he published in 1628, known by its abbreviated title *De Motu Cordis (On the Motion of the Heart).* He and **Michael Servetus** (1511–53) were the first Western scientists to realize that blood must circulate continuously around the body, from the heart to the other organs and back to the heart again. This flew in the face of Galen's belief that the liver converted food to blood, the heart pumped blood through the veins to all other organs, and those organs consumed it. Harvey's colleagues, wedded to the ideas of Galen, ridiculed Harvey for his theory, though we now know he was correct (see chapter 20 prologue). Despite persecution and setbacks, Harvey lived to a ripe old age, served as physician to the kings of England, and later did important work in embryology. Most importantly, Harvey's contributions represent the birth of experimental physiology—the method that generated most of the information in this book.

Modern medicine also owes an enormous debt to two inventors from this era, Robert Hooke and Antony van Leeuwenhoek, who extended the vision of biologists to the cellular level. **Robert Hooke** (1635–1703), an Englishman, designed scientific instruments of various kinds, including the compound microscope. This is a tube with a lens at each end—an *objective lens* near the specimen, which produces an initial magnified image, and an *ocular lens (eyepiece)* near the observer's eye, which magnifies the first image still further. Although crude compound microscopes had existed since 1595, Hooke improved the optics and invented several of the helpful features found in microscopes today—a stage to hold the specimen, an illuminator, and coarse and fine focus controls. His microscopes magnified only about 30 times, but with them, he was the first to see and name cells. In 1663, he observed thin shavings of cork and observed that they "consisted of a great many little boxes," which he called *cellulae* (little cells) after the cubicles of a monastery **(fig. 1.2).** He later observed living cells "filled with juices." Hooke became particularly interested in microscopic examination of such material as insects, plant tissues, and animal parts. He published the first comprehensive book of microscopy, *Micrographia,* in 1665.

**Antony van Leeuwenhoek** (an-TOE-nee vahn LAY-wen-hook) (1632–1723), a Dutch textile merchant, invented a *simple* (single-lens) *microscope,* originally for the purpose of examining the weave of fabrics. His microscope was a beadlike lens mounted in a metal plate equipped with a movable specimen clip.

(a)

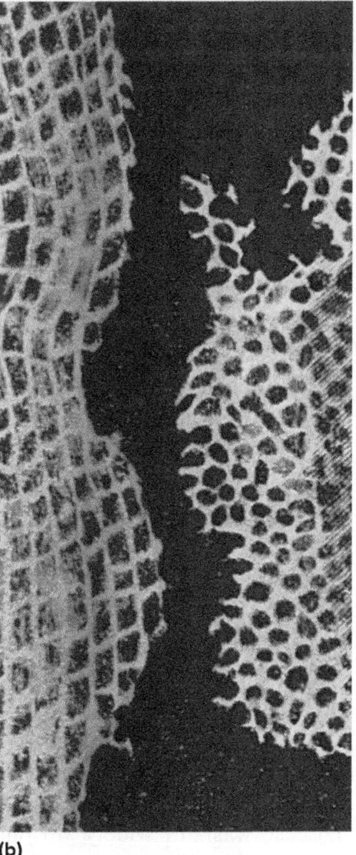
(b)

**FIGURE 1.2 Hooke's Compound Microscope.** (a) The compound microscope had a lens at each end of a tubular body. (b) Hooke's drawing of cork cells, showing the thick cell walls characteristic of plants.

a: Source: National Museum of Health and Medicine, Silver Spring, MD; b: Bettmann/Getty Images

Even though his microscopes were simpler than Hooke's, they achieved much greater useful magnification (up to 200×) owing to Leeuwenhoek's superior lens-making technique. Out of curiosity, he examined a drop of lake water and was astonished to find a variety of microorganisms—"little animalcules," he called them, "very prettily a-swimming." He went on to observe practically everything he could get his hands on, including blood cells, blood capillaries, sperm, muscular tissue, and bacteria from tooth scrapings. Leeuwenhoek began submitting his observations to the Royal Society of London in 1673. He was praised at first, and his observations were eagerly read by scientists, but enthusiasm for the microscope didn't last. By the end of the seventeenth century, it was treated as a mere toy for the upper classes, as amusing and meaningless as a kaleidoscope. Leeuwenhoek and Hooke had even become the brunt of satire. But probably no one in history had looked at nature in such a revolutionary way. By taking biology to the cellular level, the two men had laid an entirely new foundation for the modern medicine to follow centuries later.

The Hooke and Leeuwenhoek microscopes produced poor images with blurry edges *(spherical aberration)* and rainbow-like distortions *(chromatic aberration).* These problems had to be solved before the microscope could be widely used as a biological tool. In the nineteenth century, German inventors greatly improved the compound microscope, adding the condenser and developing superior optics. With improved microscopes, biologists began eagerly examining a wider variety of specimens. By 1839, botanist **Matthias Schleiden** (1804–81) and zoologist **Theodor Schwann** (1810–82) concluded that all organisms were composed of cells. Although it took another century for this idea to be generally accepted, it became the first tenet of the **cell theory,** added to by later biologists and summarized in section 3.1a. The cell theory was perhaps the most important breakthrough in biomedical history; all functions of the body are now interpreted as the effects of cellular activity.

Although the philosophical foundation for modern medicine was largely established by the time of Leeuwenhoek, Hooke, and Harvey, clinical practice was still in a dismal state. Few doctors attended medical school or received any formal education in basic science or human anatomy. Physicians tended to be ignorant, ineffective, and pompous. Their practice was heavily based on expelling imaginary toxins from the body by bleeding their patients or inducing vomiting, sweating, or diarrhea. They performed operations with filthy hands and instruments, spreading lethal infections from one patient to another and refusing, in their vanity, to believe that they themselves were the carriers of disease. Countless women died of infections acquired during childbirth from their obstetricians. Fractured limbs often became gangrenous and had to be amputated, and there was no anesthesia to lessen the pain. Disease was still widely attributed to demons and witches, and many people felt they would be interfering with God's will if they tried to treat it.

### 1.2c Living in a Revolution

This short history brings us only to the threshold of modern biomedical science; it stops short of such momentous discoveries as the germ theory of disease, the mechanisms of heredity, and the structure of DNA. In the twentieth century, basic biology and biochemistry yielded a much deeper understanding of how the body works. Advances in medical imaging enhanced our diagnostic ability and life-support strategies. We witnessed monumental developments in chemotherapy, immunization, anesthesia, surgery, organ transplants, and human genetics. By the close of the twentieth century, we had discovered the chemical "base sequence" of every human gene and begun attempting gene therapy to treat children born with diseases recently considered incurable. As future historians look back on the turn of this century, they may exult about the Genetic Revolution in which you are now living.

Several discoveries of the nineteenth and twentieth centuries, and the men and women behind them, are covered in short historical sketches in later chapters. Yet, the stories told in this chapter are different in a significant way. The people discussed here were pioneers in establishing the scientific way of thinking. They helped to replace superstition with an appreciation of natural law. They bridged the chasm between mystery and medication. Without this intellectual revolution, those who followed could not have conceived of the right questions to ask, much less a method for answering them.

**BEFORE YOU GO ON**

Answer the following questions to test your understanding of the preceding section:

3. In what way did the followers of Galen disregard his advice? How does Galen's advice apply to you and this book?
4. Describe two ways in which Vesalius improved medical education and set standards that remain relevant today.
5. How is our concept of human form and function today affected by inventors from the seventeenth to the nineteenth centuries?

## 1.3 Scientific Method

**Expected Learning Outcomes**

When you have completed this section, you should be able to

a. describe the inductive and hypothetico–deductive methods of obtaining scientific knowledge;
b. describe some aspects of experimental design that help to ensure objective and reliable results; and
c. explain what is meant by *hypothesis, fact, law,* and *theory* in science.

Prior to the seventeenth century, science was done in a haphazard way by a small number of isolated individuals. The philosophers **Francis Bacon** (1561–1626) in England and **René Descartes** (1596–1650) in France envisioned science as a far greater, systematic enterprise with enormous possibilities for human health and welfare. They detested those who endlessly debated ancient philosophy without creating anything new. Bacon argued against biased thinking and for more objectivity in science. He outlined a systematic way of seeking similarities, differences, and trends in nature and drawing useful generalizations from observable facts. You will see echoes of Bacon's philosophy in the discussion of scientific method that follows.

Though the followers of Bacon and Descartes argued bitterly with one another, both men wanted science to become a public, cooperative enterprise, supported by governments and conducted by an international community of scholars rather than a few isolated amateurs. Inspired by their vision, the French and English governments established academies of science that still flourish today. Bacon and Descartes are credited with putting science on the path to modernity, not by discovering anything new in nature or inventing any techniques—for neither man was a scientist—but by inventing new habits of scientific thought.

When we say "scientific," we mean that such thinking is based on assumptions and methods that yield reliable, objective, testable information about nature. The assumptions of science are ideas that have proven fruitful in the past—for example, the idea that natural phenomena have natural causes and nature is therefore predictable and understandable. The methods of science are highly variable. **Scientific method** refers less to observational procedures than to certain habits of disciplined creativity, careful observation, logical thinking, and honest analysis of one's observations and conclusions. It is especially important in health science to understand these habits. This field is littered with more fads and frauds than any other. We are called upon constantly to judge which claims are trustworthy and which are bogus. To make such judgments depends on an appreciation of how scientists think, how they set standards for truth, and why their claims are more reliable than others **(fig. 1.3).**

**FIGURE 1.3 Biomedical Research.** Research scientists employ habits of thought we call the scientific method to ensure the objectivity, reliability, and reproducibility of their results and conclusions.

AshTproductions/Shutterstock

### 1.3a The Inductive Method

The **inductive method,** first prescribed by Bacon, is a process of making numerous observations until one feels confident in drawing generalizations and predictions from them. What we know of anatomy is a product of the inductive method. We describe the normal structure of the body based on observations of many bodies.

This raises the issue of what is considered proof in science. We can never prove a claim beyond all possible refutation. We can, however, consider a statement as proven *beyond reasonable doubt* if it was arrived at by reliable methods of observation, tested and confirmed repeatedly, and not falsified by any credible observation. In science, all truth is tentative; there's no room for dogma. We must always be prepared to abandon yesterday's truth if tomorrow's facts disprove it.

### 1.3b The Hypothetico–Deductive Method

Most physiological knowledge was obtained by the **hypothetico–deductive method.** An investigator begins by asking a question and formulating a **hypothesis**—an educated speculation or possible answer to the question. A good hypothesis must be (1) consistent with what is already known and (2) capable of being tested and possibly falsified by evidence. **Falsifiability** means that if we claim something is scientifically true, we must be able to specify what evidence it would take to prove it wrong. If nothing could possibly prove it wrong, then it's not scientific.

**▶▶▶APPLY WHAT YOU KNOW**

*The ancients thought that gods or invisible demons caused epilepsy. Today, epileptic seizures are attributed to bursts of abnormal electrical activity in nerve cells of the brain. Explain why one of these claims is falsifiable (and thus scientific), whereas the other claim is not.*

The purpose of a hypothesis is to suggest a method for answering a question. From the hypothesis, a researcher makes a deduction, typically in the form of an "if–then" prediction: *If* my hypothesis on epilepsy is correct and I record the brain waves of patients during seizures, *then* I should observe abnormal bursts of activity. A properly conducted experiment yields observations that either support a hypothesis or require the scientist to modify or abandon it, formulate a better hypothesis, and test that one. Hypothesis testing operates in cycles of conjecture and disproof until one is found that is supported by the evidence.

### 1.3c Experimental Design

Doing an experiment properly involves several important considerations. What shall I measure and how can I measure it? What effects should I watch for and which ones should I ignore? How can I be sure my results are due to the variables that I manipulate and not due to something else? When working on human subjects, how can I prevent the subject's expectations or state of mind from influencing the results? How can I eliminate my own biases and be sure that even the most skeptical critics will have as much confidence in my conclusions as I do? Several elements of experimental design address these issues:

- **Sample size.** The number of subjects (animals or people) used in a study is the sample size. An adequate sample size controls for chance events and individual variations in response and thus enables us to place more confidence in the outcome. For example, would you rather trust your health to a drug that was tested on 5 people or one tested on 5,000? Why?
- **Controls.** Biomedical experiments require comparison between treated and untreated individuals so that we can judge whether the treatment has any effect. A **control group** consists of subjects that are as much like the **treatment group** as possible except with respect to the variable being tested. For example, there is evidence that garlic lowers blood cholesterol levels. In one study, volunteers with high cholesterol were each given 800 mg of garlic powder daily for 4 months and exhibited an average 12% reduction in cholesterol. Was this a significant reduction, and was it due to the garlic? It's impossible to say without comparison to a control group of similar people who received no treatment. In this study, the control group averaged only a 3% reduction in cholesterol, so garlic *seems* to have made a difference.
- **Psychosomatic effects.** Psychosomatic effects (effects of the subject's state of mind on his or her physiology) can have an undesirable effect on experimental results if we do not control for them. In drug research, it is therefore customary to give the control group a **placebo** (pla-SEE-bo)—a substance with no significant physiological effect on the body. If we were testing a drug, for example, we could give the treatment group the drug and the control group identical-looking sugar tablets. Neither group must know which tablets it is receiving. If the two groups showed significantly different effects, we could feel confident that it did not result from a knowledge of what they were taking.
- **Experimenter bias.** In the competitive, high-stakes world of medical research, experimenters may want certain results so much that their biases, even subconscious ones, can affect their interpretation of the data. One way to control for this is the **double-blind method.** In this procedure, neither the subject to whom a treatment is given nor the person giving it and recording the results knows whether that subject is receiving the experimental treatment or the placebo. A researcher may prepare identical-looking tablets, some with the drug and some with placebo; label them with code numbers; and distribute them to participating physicians. The physicians themselves do not know whether they are administering drug or placebo, so they cannot give the subjects even accidental hints of which substance they are taking. When the data are collected, the researcher can correlate them with the composition of the tablets and determine whether the drug had more effect than the placebo.
- **Statistical testing.** If you tossed a coin 100 times, you would expect it to come up about 50 heads and 50 tails. If it actually came up 48:52, you would probably attribute this to random error rather than bias in the coin. But what if it came up 40:60? At what point would you begin to suspect bias? This type of problem is faced routinely in research—how great a difference must there be between control and experimental groups before we feel confident that it was due to the treatment and not merely random variation? What if a treatment group exhibited a 12% reduction in cholesterol level and the placebo group a 10% reduction? Would this be enough to conclude that the treatment was effective? Scientists are well grounded in **statistical tests** that can be applied to the data—the chi-square test, the *t* test, and analysis of variance, for example. A typical outcome of a statistical test may be expressed, "We can be 99.5% sure that the difference between group A and group B was due to the experimental treatment and not to random variation." Science is grounded not in statements of absolute truth, but in statements of probability.

### 1.3d Peer Review

When a scientist applies for funds to support a research project or submits results for publication, the application or manuscript is submitted to **peer review**—a critical evaluation by other experts in that field. Even after a report is published, if the results are important or unconventional, other scientists may attempt to reproduce them to see if the author was correct. At every stage from planning to postpublication, scientists are therefore subject to intense scrutiny by their colleagues. Peer review is one mechanism for ensuring honesty, objectivity, and quality in science.

### 1.3e Facts, Laws, and Theories

The most important product of scientific research is understanding how nature works—whether it be the nature of a pond to an ecologist or the nature of a liver cell to a physiologist. We express our understanding as *facts, laws,* and *theories* of nature. It is important to appreciate the differences among these.

A scientific **fact** is information that can be independently verified by any trained person—for example, the fact that an iron deficiency leads to anemia. A **law of nature** is a generalization about the predictable ways in which matter and energy behave. It is the result of inductive reasoning based on repeated, confirmed observations. Some laws are expressed as concise verbal statements, such as the *law of complementary base pairing:* In the double helix of DNA, a chemical base called adenine always pairs with one called thymine, and a base called guanine always pairs with cytosine (see section 4.1a). Other laws are expressed as mathematical formulae, such as *Boyle's law,* used in respiratory physiology: Under specified conditions, the volume of a gas $(V)$ is inversely proportional to its pressure $(P)$—that is,

$$V \propto 1/P.$$

A **theory** is an explanatory statement or set of statements derived from facts, laws, and confirmed hypotheses. Some theories have names, such as the *cell theory,* the *fluid-mosaic theory* of cell membranes, and the *sliding filament theory* of muscle contraction. Most, however, remain unnamed. The purpose of a theory is not only to concisely summarize what we already know but, moreover, to suggest directions for further study and to help predict what the findings should be if the theory is correct.

*Law* and *theory* mean something different in science than they do to most people. In common usage, a law is a rule created and enforced by people; we must obey it or risk a penalty. A law of nature, however, is a description; laws do not *govern* the universe—they *describe* it. Laypeople tend to use the word *theory* for what a scientist would call a hypothesis—for example, "I have a theory why my car won't start." The difference in meaning causes significant confusion when it leads people to think that a scientific theory (such as the theory of evolution) is merely a guess or conjecture, instead of recognizing it as a summary of conclusions drawn from a large body of observed facts. The concepts of gravity and electrons are theories, too, but this does not mean they are merely speculations.

**▶▶▶APPLY WHAT YOU KNOW**

*Was the cell theory proposed by Schleiden and Schwann more a product of the hypothetico–deductive method or of the inductive method? Explain your answer.*

**BEFORE YOU GO ON**

Answer the following questions to test your understanding of the preceding section:

**6.** Describe the general process involved in the inductive method.

**7.** Describe some sources of potential bias in biomedical research. What are some ways of minimizing such bias?

**8.** Is there more information in an individual scientific fact or in a theory? Explain.

## 1.4 Human Origins and Adaptations

**Expected Learning Outcomes**

When you have completed this section, you should be able to

a. explain why evolution is relevant to understanding human form and function;
b. define *evolution* and *natural selection;*
c. describe some human characteristics that can be attributed to the tree-dwelling habits of earlier primates; and
d. describe some human characteristics that evolved later in connection with upright walking.

If any two theories have the broadest implications for understanding the human body, they are probably the *cell theory* and the *theory of natural selection.* No understanding of human form and function is complete without an understanding of our evolutionary history, of how natural selection adapted the body to its ancestral habitat. As an explanation of how species originate and change through time, natural selection was the brainchild of **Charles Darwin** (1809–82)—certainly the most influential biologist who ever lived. His book, *On the Origin of Species by Means of Natural Selection* (1859), has been called "the book that shook the world." In presenting the first well-supported theory of how evolution works, it not only caused the restructuring of all of biology but also profoundly changed the prevailing view of our origin, nature, and place in the universe. In *The Descent of Man* (1871), Darwin directly addressed the issue of human evolution and emphasized features of anatomy and behavior that reveal our relationship to other animals. Here we will touch just briefly on how natural selection helps explain some of the distinctive characteristics seen in *Homo sapiens* today.

### 1.4a Evolution, Selection, and Adaptation

**Evolution** simply means change in the genetic composition of a population of organisms. Examples include the evolution of bacterial resistance to antibiotics, the appearance of new strains of the AIDS virus, and the emergence of new species of organisms.

Evolution works largely through the principle of **natural selection,** which states essentially this: Some individuals within a species have hereditary advantages over their competitors—for example, better camouflage, disease resistance, or ability to attract mates—that enable them to produce more offspring. They pass these advantages on to their offspring, and such characteristics therefore become more and more common in successive generations. This brings about the genetic change in a population that constitutes evolution.

Natural forces that promote the reproductive success of some individuals more than others are called **selection pressures.** They include such things as climate, predators, disease, competition, and food. **Adaptations** are features of anatomy, physiology, and behavior that evolve in response to these selection pressures and enable an organism to cope with the challenges of its environment.

Darwin could scarcely have predicted the overwhelming mass of genetic, molecular, fossil, and other evidence of human evolution that would accumulate in the twentieth century and further substantiate his theory. A technique called DNA hybridization, for example, reveals a difference of only 1.6% in DNA structure between humans and chimpanzees. Chimpanzees and gorillas differ by 2.3%. DNA structure thus suggests that a chimpanzee's closest living relative is not the gorilla—it is us, *Homo sapiens*.

Several aspects of our anatomy make little sense without an awareness that the human body has a history (see Deeper Insight 1.1). Our evolutionary relationship to other species is also important in choosing animals for biomedical research. If there were no issues of cost, availability, or ethics, we might test drugs on our close living relatives, the chimpanzees, before approving them for human use. Their genetics, anatomy, and physiology are most similar to ours, and their reactions to drugs therefore afford the best prediction of how the human body would react. On the other hand, if we had no kinship with any other species, the selection of a test species would be arbitrary; we might as well use frogs or snails. In reality, we compromise.

## DEEPER INSIGHT 1.1
## EVOLUTIONARY MEDICINE

### *Vestiges of Human Evolution*

One of the classic lines of evidence for evolution, debated even before Darwin was born, is *vestigial organs.* These structures are the remnants of organs that apparently were better developed and more functional in the ancestors of a species. They now serve little or no purpose or, in some cases, have been converted to new functions.

Our bodies, for example, are covered with millions of hairs, each equipped with a useless little *arrector muscle.* In other mammals, these muscles fluff the hair and conserve heat. In humans, they merely produce goose bumps. Above each ear, we have three *auricularis muscles.* In other mammals, they move the ears to receive sounds better or to flick off flies and other pests, but most people cannot contract them at all. As Darwin said, it makes no sense that humans would have such structures were it not for the fact that we came from ancestors in which they were functional.

Rats and mice are used extensively for research because they are fellow mammals with a physiology similar to ours, but they present fewer of the aforementioned issues than chimpanzees or other mammals do. An animal species or strain selected for research on a particular problem is called a **model**—for example, a mouse model for leukemia.

## 1.4b Our Basic Primate Adaptations

We belong to an order of mammals called the Primates, which also includes the monkeys and apes. Some of our anatomical and physiological features can be traced to the earliest primates, which descended from certain squirrel-size, insect-eating, African mammals that took up life in the trees 55 to 60 million years ago. This **arboreal**[9] (treetop) habitat probably afforded greater safety from predators, less competition, and a rich food supply of leaves, fruit, insects, and lizards. But the forest canopy is a challenging world, with dim and dappled sunlight, swaying branches, shifting shadows, and prey darting about in the dense foliage. Any new feature that enabled arboreal animals to move about more easily in the treetops would have been strongly favored by natural selection. Thus, the shoulder became more mobile and enabled primates to reach out in any direction (even overhead, which few other mammals can do). The thumbs became fully **opposable**—they could cross the palm to touch the fingertips—and enabled primates to hold small objects and manipulate them more precisely than other mammals could. Opposable thumbs made the hands **prehensile**[10]—able to grasp objects by encircling them with the thumb and fingers **(fig. 1.4).** The thumb is so important that it receives highest priority in the repair of hand injuries. If the thumb can be saved, the hand can be reasonably functional; if it is lost, hand functions are severely diminished.

**FIGURE 1.4 Human Adaptations Shared with Other Primates.** Some major aspects of primate evolution are the opposable thumb, prehensile hand, forward-facing eyes, and stereoscopic vision. In humans, the hand became refined for increasingly sophisticated manipulation of objects.

**Chimpanzee:** Tim Davis/Science Source

The eyes of primates moved to a more forward-facing position, which allowed for **stereoscopic**[11] vision (depth perception). This adaptation provided better hand–eye coordination in catching and manipulating prey, with the added advantage of making it easier to judge distances accurately in leaping from tree to tree. Color vision, rare among mammals, is also a primate hallmark. Primates eat mainly fruit and leaves. The ability to distinguish subtle shades of orange and red enables them to distinguish ripe, sugary fruits from unripe ones. Distinguishing subtle shades of green helps them to differentiate between tender young leaves and tough, more toxic older foliage.

Various fruits ripen at different times and in widely separated places in the tropical forest. This requires a good memory of what will be available, when, and how to get there. Larger brains might have evolved in response to the challenge of efficient food finding and, in turn, laid the foundation for more sophisticated social organization.

[9] *arbor* = tree; *eal* = pertaining to
[10] *prehens* = to seize
[11] *stereo* = solid; *scop* = vision

None of this is meant to imply that humans evolved from monkeys—a common misconception about evolution that no biologist believes. Monkeys, apes, and humans do, however, share common ancestors. Our relationship is not like parent and child, but more like cousins who have the same grandparents. Observations of monkeys and apes provide insight into how primates adapt to the arboreal habitat and therefore how certain human adaptations probably originated.

### 1.4c Walking Upright

About 4 to 5 million years ago, parts of Africa became hotter and drier, and much of the forest was replaced by savanna (grassland). Some primates adapted to living on the savanna, but this was a dangerous place with more predators and less protection. Just as squirrels and monkeys stand briefly on their hind legs to look around for danger, so would these early ground dwellers. Being able to stand up not only helps an animal stay alert, but also frees the forelimbs for purposes other than walking. Chimpanzees sometimes walk upright to carry food, infants, or weapons (sticks and rocks), and it is reasonable to suppose that our early ancestors did so too.

These advantages are so great that they favored skeletal modifications that made **bipedalism**[12]—standing and walking on two legs—easier. Fossil evidence indicates that bipedalism was firmly established more than 4 million years ago. The anatomy of the human pelvis, femur, knee, great toe, foot arches, spinal column, skull, arms, and many muscles became adapted for bipedal locomotion (see Deeper Insight 8.5), as did many aspects of human family life and society. As the skeleton and muscles became adapted for bipedalism, brain volume increased dramatically, from 400 mL around 4 million years ago to an average of 1,350 mL today. It must have become increasingly difficult for a fully developed, large-brained infant to pass through the mother's pelvic outlet at birth. This may explain why humans are born in a relatively immature, helpless state compared with other mammals, before their nervous systems have matured and the bones of the skull have fused. The helplessness of human young and their extended dependence on parental care may help to explain why humans have such exceptionally strong family ties.

Most of the oldest bipedal primates are classified in the genus *Australopithecus* (aus-TRAL-oh-PITH-eh-cus). About 2.5 million years ago, hominids appeared with taller stature, greater brain volumes, simple stone tools, and probably articulate speech. These are the earliest members of the genus *Homo*. By at least 1.8 million years ago, *Homo erectus* migrated from Africa to parts of Asia. Anatomically modern *Homo sapiens*, our own species, originated in Africa about 200,000 years ago and is the sole surviving hominid species.

This brief account barely begins to explain how human anatomy, physiology, and behavior have been shaped by ancient selection pressures. Later chapters further demonstrate that the evolutionary perspective provides a meaningful understanding of why humans are the way we are. Evolution is the basis for comparative anatomy and physiology, which have been so fruitful for the understanding of human biology. If we weren't related to any other species, those sciences would be pointless.

The emerging science of **evolutionary medicine** analyzes how human disease and dysfunctions can be traced to differences between the artificial environment in which we now live, and the prehistoric environment to which *Homo sapiens* was biologically adapted. For example, we can relate sleep and mood disorders to artificial lighting and night-shift work, and the rise of asthma to our modern obsession with sanitation. Other examples in this book will relate evolution to obesity, diabetes, low-back pain, skin cancer, and other health issues.

[12]*bi* = two; *ped* = foot

**BEFORE YOU GO ON**

Answer the following questions to test your understanding of the preceding section:

9. Define *adaptation* and *selection pressure.* Why are these concepts important in understanding human anatomy and physiology?
10. Select any two human characteristics and explain how they might have originated in primate adaptations to an arboreal habitat.
11. Select two other human characteristics and explain how they might have resulted from later adaptation to a grassland habitat.

## 1.5 Human Structure

**Expected Learning Outcomes**

When you have completed this section, you should be able to

a. list the levels of human structure from the most complex to the simplest;
b. discuss the value of both reductionistic and holistic viewpoints to understanding human form and function; and
c. discuss the clinical significance of anatomical variation among humans.

Earlier in this chapter, we observed that human anatomy is studied by a variety of techniques—dissection, palpation, and so forth. In addition, anatomy is studied at several levels of detail, from the whole body down to the molecular level.

### 1.5a The Hierarchy of Complexity

Consider for the moment an analogy to human structure: The English language, like the human body, is very complex, yet an infinite variety of ideas can be conveyed with a limited number of words. All words in English are, in turn, composed of various combinations of just 26 letters. Between an essay and an alphabet are successively simpler levels of organization: paragraphs, sentences, words, and syllables. We can say that language exhibits a

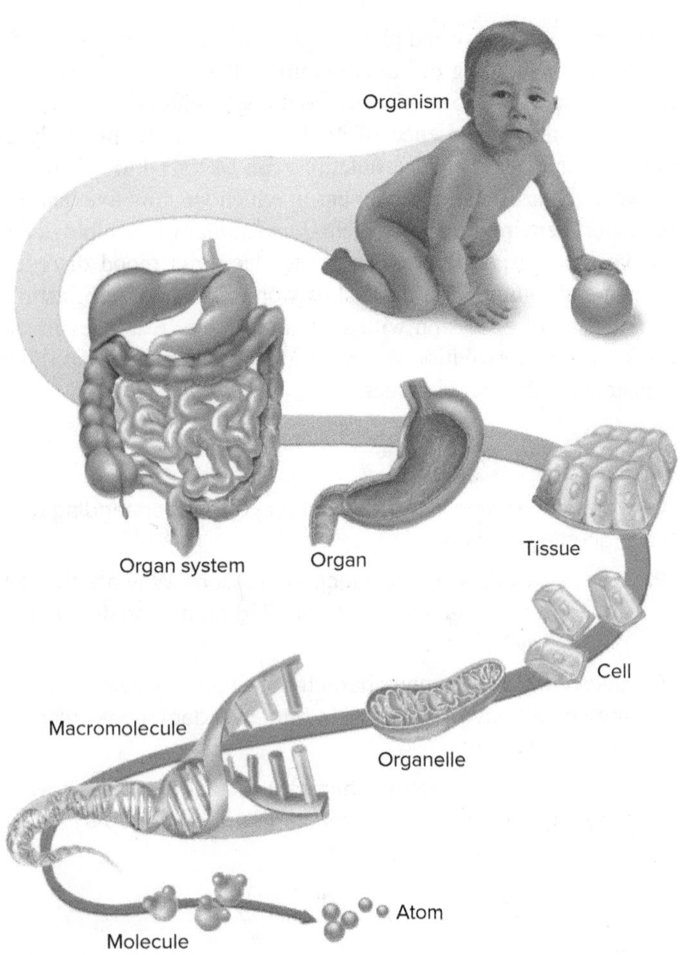


**FIGURE 1.5 The Body's Structural Hierarchy.**

hierarchy of complexity, with letters, syllables, words, and so forth being successive levels of the hierarchy. Humans have an analogous hierarchy of complexity, as follows **(fig. 1.5):**

The organism is composed of organ systems,
organ systems are composed of organs,
organs are composed of tissues,
tissues are composed of cells,
cells are composed partly of organelles,
organelles are composed of molecules, and
molecules are composed of atoms.

The **organism** is a single, complete individual.

An **organ system** is a group of organs with a unique collective function, such as circulation, respiration, or digestion. The human body has 11 organ systems, illustrated in atlas A immediately following this chapter: the integumentary, skeletal, muscular, nervous, endocrine, circulatory, lymphatic, respiratory, urinary, digestive, and reproductive systems. Usually, the organs of one system are physically interconnected, such as the kidneys, ureters, urinary bladder, and urethra, which compose the urinary system. Beginning with chapter 6, this book is organized around the organ systems.

An **organ** is a structure composed of two or more tissue types that work together to carry out a particular function. Organs have definite anatomical boundaries and are visibly distinguishable from adjacent structures. Most organs and higher levels of structure are within the domain of gross anatomy. However, there are organs within organs—the large organs visible to the naked eye often contain smaller organs visible only with the microscope. The skin, for example, is the body's largest organ. Included within it are thousands of smaller organs: Each hair, nail, gland, nerve, and blood vessel of the skin is an organ in itself. A single organ can belong to two organ systems. For example, the pancreas belongs to both the endocrine and digestive systems.

A **tissue** is a mass of similar cells and cell products that forms a discrete region of an organ and performs a specific function. The body is composed of only four primary classes of tissue: epithelial, connective, nervous, and muscular tissue. Histology, the study of tissues, is the subject of chapter 5.

**Cells** are the smallest units of an organism that carry out all the basic functions of life; nothing simpler than a cell is considered alive. A cell is enclosed in a *plasma membrane* composed of lipids and proteins. Most cells have one nucleus, an organelle that contains its DNA. *Cytology,* the study of cells and organelles, is the subject of chapters 3 and 4.

**Organelles**[13] are microscopic structures in a cell that carry out its individual functions. Examples include mitochondria, centrioles, and lysosomes.

Organelles and other cellular components are composed of **molecules.** The largest molecules, such as proteins, fats, and DNA, are called *macromolecules* (see chapter 2). A molecule is a particle composed of at least two **atoms,** the smallest particles with unique chemical identities.

The theory that a large, complex system such as the human body can be understood by studying its simpler components is called **reductionism.** First espoused by Aristotle, this has proved to be a highly productive approach; indeed, it is essential to scientific thinking. Yet the reductionistic view is not the only way of understanding human life. Just as it would be very difficult to predict the workings of an automobile transmission merely by looking at a pile of its disassembled gears and levers, one could never predict the human personality from a complete knowledge of the circuitry of the brain or the genetic sequence of DNA. **Holism**[14] is the complementary theory that there are "emergent properties" of the whole organism that cannot be predicted from the properties of its separate parts—human beings are more than the sum of their parts. To be most effective, a health-care provider treats not merely a disease or an organ system, but a whole person. A patient's perceptions, emotional responses to life, and confidence in the nurse, therapist, or physician profoundly affect the outcome of treatment. In fact, these psychological factors often play a greater role in a patient's recovery than the physical treatments administered.

[13]*elle* = little
[14]*holo* = whole, entire

### 1.5b Anatomical Variation

A quick look around any classroom is enough to show that no two humans are exactly alike; on close inspection, even identical twins exhibit differences. Yet anatomy atlases and textbooks can easily give the impression that everyone's internal anatomy is the same. This simply is not true. Books such as this one can teach you only the most common structure—the anatomy seen in about 70% or more of people. Someone who thinks that all human bodies are the same internally would make a very confused medical student or an incompetent surgeon.

Some people lack certain organs. For example, most of us have a *palmaris longus* muscle in the forearm and a *plantaris* muscle in the leg, but these are absent from others. Most of us have five lumbar vertebrae (bones of the lower spine), but some people have six and some have four. Most of us have one spleen and two kidneys, but some have two spleens or only one kidney. Most kidneys are supplied by a single *renal artery* and are drained by one *ureter,* but some have two renal arteries or ureters. **Figure 1.6** shows some common variations in human anatomy, and Deeper Insight 1.2 describes a particularly dramatic and clinically important variation.

**▶▶▶APPLY WHAT YOU KNOW**

*People who are allergic to aspirin or penicillin often wear MedicAlert bracelets or necklaces that note this fact in case they need emergency medical treatment and are unable to communicate. Why would it be important for a person with situs inversus (see Deeper Insight 1.2) to have this noted on a MedicAlert bracelet?*

**DEEPER INSIGHT 1.2**

**CLINICAL APPLICATION**

***Situs Inversus and Other Unusual Anatomy***

In most people, the spleen, pancreas, sigmoid colon, and most of the heart are on the left, while the appendix, gallbladder, and most of the liver are on the right. The normal arrangement of these and other internal organs is called *situs solitus* (SITE-us). About 1 in 8,000 people, however, is born with an abnormality called *situs inversus*—the organs of the thoracic and abdominal cavities are reversed between right and left. A selective right–left reversal of the heart is called *dextrocardia.* In *situs perversus,* a single organ occupies an atypical position—for example, a kidney located low in the pelvic cavity instead of high in the abdominal cavity.

Conditions such as dextrocardia in the absence of complete situs inversus can cause serious medical problems. Complete situs inversus, however, usually causes no functional problems because all of the viscera, though reversed, maintain their normal relationships to one another. Situs inversus is often discovered in the fetus by sonography, but many people remain unaware of their condition for decades until it is discovered by medical imaging, on physical examination, or in surgery. You can easily imagine the importance of such conditions in diagnosing appendicitis, performing gallbladder surgery, interpreting an X-ray, auscultating the heart valves, or recording an electrocardiogram.

**BEFORE YOU GO ON**

Answer the following questions to test your understanding of the preceding section:

12. In the hierarchy of human structure, what is the level between organ system and tissue? Between cell and molecule?
13. How are tissues relevant to the definition of an organ?
14. Why is reductionism a necessary but not sufficient point of view for fully understanding a patient's illness?
15. Why should medical students observe multiple cadavers and not be satisfied to dissect only one?

## 1.6 Human Function

**Expected Learning Outcomes**

When you have completed this section, you should be able to

a. state the characteristics that distinguish living organisms from nonliving objects;
b. explain the importance of physiological variation among persons;
c. define *homeostasis* and explain why this concept is central to physiology;
d. define *negative feedback,* give an example of it, and explain its importance to homeostasis;
e. define *positive feedback* and give examples of its beneficial and harmful effects; and
f. define *gradient,* describe the variety of gradients in human physiology, and identify some forms of matter and energy that flow down gradients.

### 1.6a Characteristics of Life

Why do we consider a growing child to be alive, but not a growing crystal? Is abortion the taking of a human life? If so, what about a contraceptive foam that kills only sperm? As a patient is dying, at what point does it become ethical to disconnect life-support equipment and remove organs for donation? If these organs are alive, as they must be to serve someone else, then why isn't the donor considered alive? Such questions have no easy answers, but they demand a concept of what life is—a concept that may differ with one's biological, medical, legal, or religious perspective.

From a biological viewpoint, life is not a single property. It is a collection of properties that help to distinguish living from nonliving things:

- **Organization.** Living things exhibit a far higher level of organization than the nonliving world around them. They expend a great deal of energy to maintain order, and a breakdown in this order is accompanied by disease and often death.
- **Cellular composition.** Living matter is always compartmentalized into one or more cells.

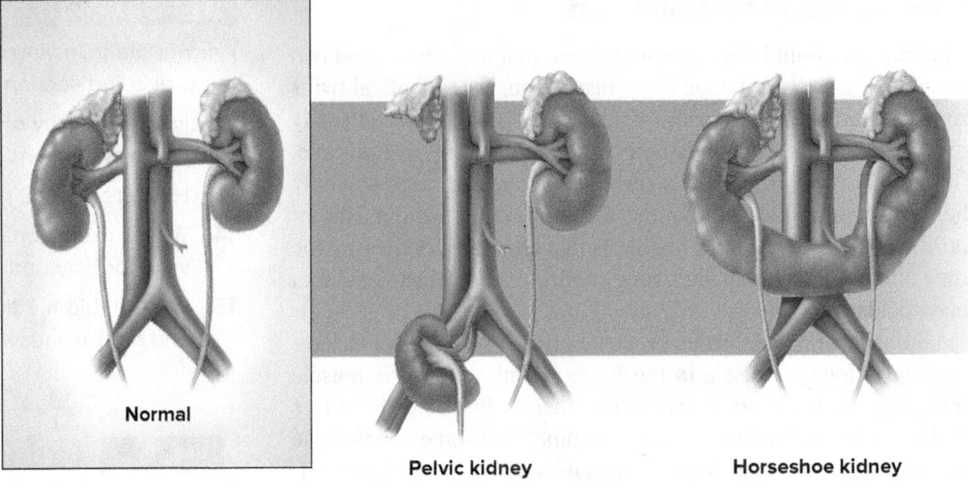


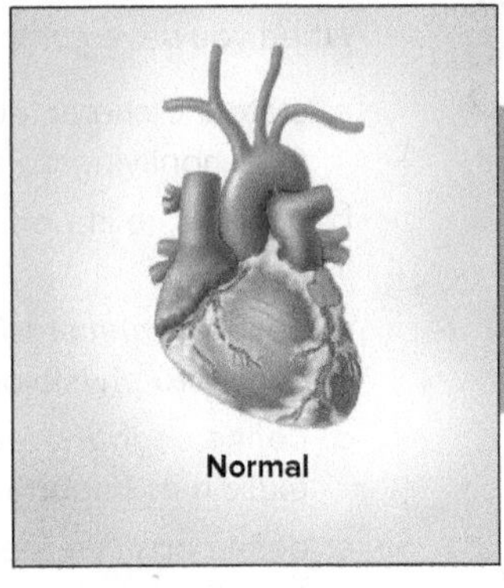


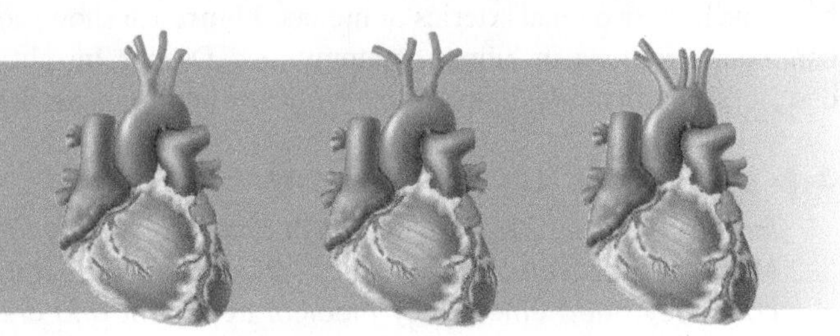


**FIGURE 1.6 Variation in Anatomy of the Kidneys and the Major Arteries Near the Heart.**

- **Metabolism.** Living things take in molecules from the environment and chemically change them into molecules that form their own structures, control their physiology, or provide them with energy. **Metabolism**[15] is the sum of all this internal chemical change. It inevitably produces chemical wastes, some of which are toxic if they accumulate. There is a constant turnover of molecules in the body. Although you sense a continuity of personality and experience from your childhood to the present, nearly every molecule of your body has been replaced within the past year.
- **Responsiveness** and **movement.** The ability to sense and react to **stimuli** (changes in the environment) is called *responsiveness* or *excitability*. It occurs at all levels from the single cell to the entire body, and it characterizes all living things from bacteria to you. Responsiveness is especially obvious in animals because of nerve and muscle cells that exhibit high sensitivity to environmental stimuli, rapid transmission of information, and quick reactions. Most living organisms are capable of self-propelled movement from place to place, and all organisms and cells are at least capable of moving substances internally, such as moving food along the digestive tract or moving molecules and organelles from place to place within a cell.
- **Homeostasis.** Although the environment around an organism changes, the organism maintains relatively stable internal conditions—for example, a stable temperature, blood pressure, and body weight. This ability to maintain internal stability, called *homeostasis,* is explored in section 1.6c.
- **Development.** Development is any change in form or function over the lifetime of the organism. In most organisms, it involves two major processes: (1) **differentiation,** the transformation of cells with no specialized function into cells that are committed to a particular task; and (2) **growth,** an increase in size. Some nonliving things grow, but not in the way your body does. If you let a saturated sugar solution evaporate, crystals will grow from it, but not through a change in the composition of the sugar. They merely add more sugar molecules from the solution to the crystal surface. The growth of the body, by contrast, occurs through chemical change (metabolism); for the most part, your body is not composed of the

[15]*metabol* = change; *ism* = process

molecules you ate but of molecules made by chemically altering your food.

- **Reproduction.** All living organisms can produce copies of themselves, thus passing their genes on to new, younger containers—their offspring.
- **Evolution.** All living species exhibit genetic change from generation to generation and therefore evolve. This occurs because *mutations* (changes in DNA structure) are inevitable and because environmental selection pressures favor the transmission of some genes more than others. Unlike the other characteristics of life, evolution is a characteristic seen only in the population as a whole. No single individual evolves over the course of its life.

Clinical and legal criteria of life differ from these biological criteria. A person who has shown no brain waves for 24 hours, and has no reflexes, respiration, or heartbeat other than what is provided by artificial life support, can be declared legally dead. At such time, however, most of the body is still biologically alive and its organs may be useful for transplant.

### 1.6b Physiological Variation

Earlier we considered the clinical importance of variations in human anatomy, but physiology is even more variable. Physiological variables differ with sex, age, weight, diet, degree of physical activity, genetics, and environment, among other things. Failure to consider such variation leads to medical mistakes such as overmedication of the elderly or medicating women on the basis of research done on young men. If a textbook states a typical human heart rate, blood pressure, red blood cell count, or body temperature, it is generally assumed, unless otherwise stated, that such values refer to a healthy 22-year-old weighing 58 kg (128 lb) for a female and 70 kg (154 lb) for a male, and a lifestyle of light physical activity and moderate caloric intake (2,000 and 2,800 kcal/day, respectively).

### 1.6c Negative Feedback and Homeostasis

The human body has a remarkable capacity for self-restoration. Hippocrates commented that it usually returns to a state of equilibrium by itself, and people recover from most illnesses even without the help of a physician. This tendency results from **homeostasis**[16] (HO-me-oh-STAY-sis), the body's ability to detect change, activate mechanisms that oppose it, and thereby maintain relatively stable internal conditions.

French physiologist **Claude Bernard** (1813–78) observed that the internal conditions of the body remain quite constant even when external conditions vary greatly. For example, whether it is freezing cold or swelteringly hot outdoors, the internal temperature of the body stays within a range of about 36° to 37°C (97°–99°F). American physiologist **Walter Cannon** (1871–1945) coined the term *homeostasis* for this tendency to maintain internal stability. This has been one of the most enlightening theories in physiology. We now see physiology as largely a group of mechanisms for maintaining homeostasis, and the loss of homeostatic control as the cause of illness and death. Pathophysiology is essentially the study of unstable conditions that result when our homeostatic controls go awry.

Do not, however, overestimate the degree of internal stability. Internal conditions aren't absolutely constant but fluctuate within a limited range, such as the range of body temperatures noted earlier. The internal state of the body is best described as a **dynamic equilibrium** (balanced change), in which there is a certain **set point** or average value for a given variable (such as 37°C for body temperature) and conditions fluctuate slightly around this point.

The fundamental mechanism that keeps a variable close to its set point is **negative feedback**—a process in which the body senses a change and activates mechanisms that negate or reverse it. By maintaining stability, negative feedback is the key mechanism for maintaining health.

These principles can be understood by comparison to a home heating system **(fig. 1.7a).** Suppose it is a cold winter day and you have set your thermostat for 20°C (68°F)—the set point. If the room becomes too cold, a temperature-sensitive switch in the thermostat turns on the furnace. The temperature rises until it is slightly above the set point, and then the switch breaks the circuit and turns off the furnace. This is a negative feedback process that reverses the falling temperature and restores it to the set point. When the furnace turns off, the temperature slowly drops again until the switch is reactivated—thus, the furnace cycles on and off all day. The room temperature doesn't stay at exactly 20°C but fluctuates slightly—the system maintains a state of dynamic equilibrium in which the temperature averages 20°C and deviates only slightly from the set point. Because feedback mechanisms alter the original changes that triggered them (temperature, for example), they are often called **feedback loops.**

Body temperature is similarly regulated by a "thermostat"—a group of nerve cells in the base of the brain that monitor the temperature of the blood. If you become overheated, the thermostat triggers heat-losing mechanisms **(fig. 1.7b).** One of these is **vasodilation** (VAY-zo-dy-LAY-shun), the widening of blood vessels. When blood vessels of the skin dilate, warm blood flows closer to the body surface and loses heat to the surrounding air. If this isn't enough to return your temperature to normal, sweating occurs; the evaporation of water from the skin has a powerful cooling effect (see Deeper Insight 1.3). Conversely, if it is cold outside and your body temperature drops much below 37°C, these nerve cells activate heat-conserving mechanisms. The first to be activated is **vasoconstriction,** a narrowing of the blood vessels in the skin, which serves to retain warm blood deeper in your body and reduce heat loss. If this isn't enough, the brain activates shivering—muscle tremors that generate heat.

Let's consider one more example—a case of homeostatic control of blood pressure. When you first rise from bed in the morning, gravity causes some of your blood to drain away from

[16]*homeo* = the same; *stas* = to place, stand, stay

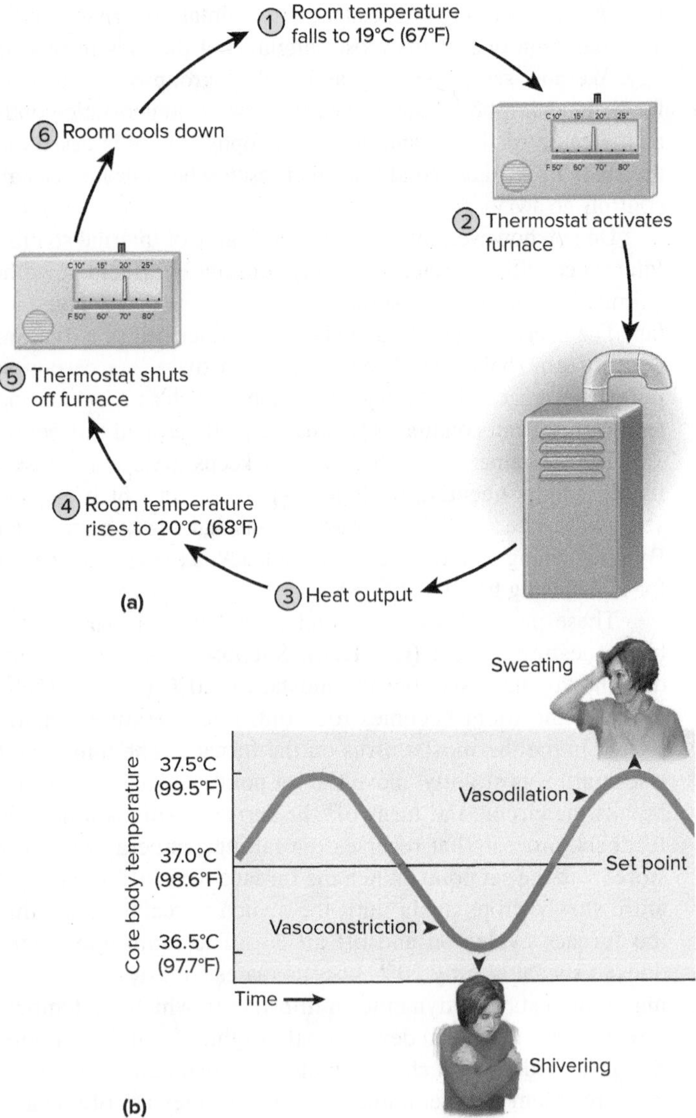


**FIGURE 1.7 Negative Feedback in Thermoregulation.**
(a) The negative feedback loop that maintains room temperature. (b) Negative feedback usually keeps the human body temperature within about 0.5°C of a 37°C set point. Cutaneous vasoconstriction and shivering set in when the body temperature falls too low, and soon raise it. Cutaneous vasodilation and sweating set in when body temperature rises too high, and soon lower it.

*How does vasodilation reduce the body temperature?*

your head and upper torso, resulting in falling blood pressure in this region—a local imbalance in your homeostasis **(fig. 1.8).** This is detected by sensory nerve endings called *baroreceptors* in large arteries near the heart. They transmit nerve signals to the brainstem, where we have a *cardiac center* that regulates the heart rate. The cardiac center responds by transmitting nerve signals to the heart, which speed it up. The faster heart rate quickly raises the blood pressure and restores normal homeostasis. In elderly people, this feedback loop is sometimes insufficiently responsive, and they may feel dizzy as they rise from a reclining

## DEEPER INSIGHT 1.3
### MEDICAL HISTORY

### *Men in the Oven*

English physician Charles Blagden (1748–1820) staged a rather theatrical demonstration of homeostasis long before Cannon coined the word. In 1775, Blagden spent 45 minutes in a chamber heated to 127°C (260°F)—along with a dog, a beefsteak, and some research associates. Being dead and unable to maintain homeostasis, the steak was cooked. But being alive and capable of evaporative cooling, the dog panted, the men sweated, and all of them survived. History does not record whether the men ate the steak in celebration or shared it with the dog.

position and their cerebral blood pressure falls. This sometimes causes fainting.

This reflexive correction of blood pressure *(baroreflex)* illustrates three common, although not universal, components of a feedback loop: a receptor, an integrating center, and an effector. The **receptor** is a structure that senses a change in the body, such as the stretch receptors that monitor blood pressure. The **integrating (control) center,** such as the cardiac center of the

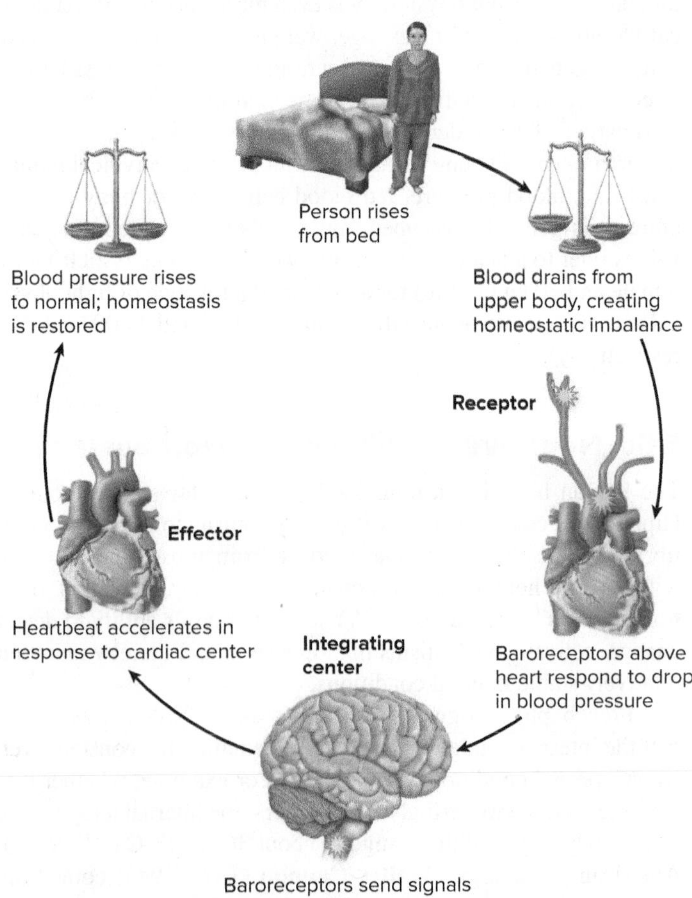


**FIGURE 1.8 Homeostatic Compensation for a Postural Change in Blood Pressure.**

brain, is a mechanism that processes this information, relates it to other available information (for example, comparing what the blood pressure is with what it should be), and makes a decision about what the appropriate response should be. The **effector** is the cell or organ that carries out the final corrective action. In the foregoing example, it is the heart. The response, such as the restoration of normal blood pressure, is then sensed by the receptor, and the feedback loop is complete.

### 1.6d Positive Feedback and Rapid Change

**Positive feedback** is a self-amplifying cycle in which a physiological change leads to even greater change in the same direction, rather than producing the corrective effects of negative feedback. Positive feedback is often a normal way of producing rapid change. When a woman is giving birth, for example, the head of the fetus pushes against her cervix (the neck of the uterus) and stimulates its nerve endings **(fig. 1.9).** Nerve signals travel to the brain, which, in turn, stimulates the pituitary gland to secrete the hormone oxytocin. Oxytocin travels in the blood and stimulates the uterus to contract. This pushes the fetus downward, stimulating the cervix still more and causing the positive feedback loop to be repeated. Labor contractions therefore become more and more intense until the fetus is expelled. Other cases of beneficial positive feedback are seen later in the book in, for example, blood clotting, protein digestion, and the generation of nerve signals.

Frequently, however, positive feedback is a harmful or even life-threatening process. This is because its self-amplifying nature can quickly change the internal state of the body to something far from its homeostatic set point. Consider a high fever, for example. A fever triggered by infection is beneficial up to a point, but if the body temperature rises much above 40°C (104°F), it may create a dangerous positive feedback loop. This high temperature raises the metabolic rate, which makes the body produce heat faster than it can get rid of it. Thus, temperature rises still further, increasing the metabolic rate and heat production still more. This "vicious circle" becomes fatal at approximately 45°C (113°F). Thus, positive feedback loops often create dangerously out-of-control situations that require emergency medical treatment.

③ Brain stimulates pituitary gland to secrete oxytocin
② Nerve impulses from cervix transmitted to brain
④ Oxytocin stimulates uterine contractions and pushes fetus toward cervix
① Head of fetus pushes against cervix

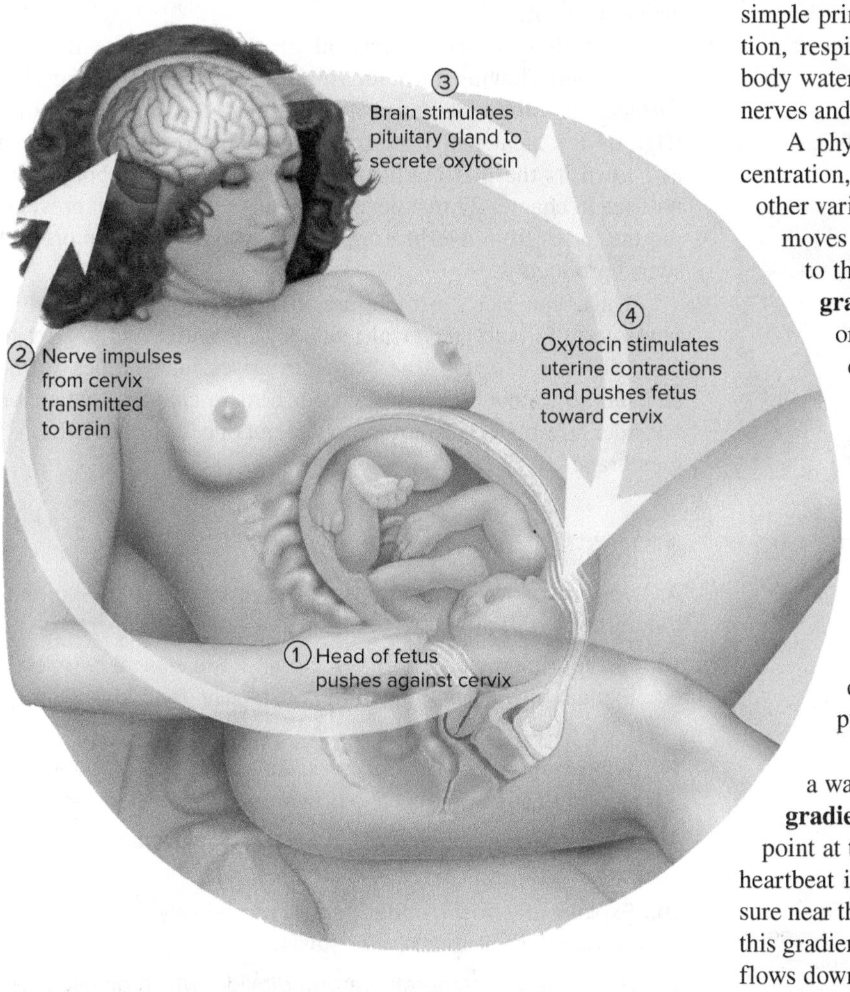

**FIGURE 1.9 Positive Feedback in Childbirth.**

*Could childbirth as a whole be considered a negative feedback event? Discuss.*

### 1.6e Gradients and Flow

Another fundamental concept that will arise repeatedly in this book is that matter and energy tend to *flow down gradients.* This simple principle underlies processes as diverse as blood circulation, respiratory airflow, urine formation, nutrient absorption, body water distribution, temperature regulation, and the action of nerves and muscles.

A physiological **gradient** is a difference in chemical concentration, electrical charge, physical pressure, temperature, or other variable between one point and another. If matter or energy moves from the point where this variable has a higher value to the point with a lower value, we say it flows **down the gradient**—for example, from a warmer to a cooler point, or a place of high chemical concentration to one of lower concentration. Movement in the opposite direction is **up the gradient.**

Outside of biology, *gradient* can mean a hill or slope, and this affords us a useful analogy to biological processes **(fig. 1.10a).** A wagon released at the top of a hill will roll down it ("flow") spontaneously, without need for anyone to exert energy to move it. Similarly, matter and energy in the body spontaneously flow down gradients, without the expenditure of metabolic energy. Movement up a gradient does require an energy expenditure, just as we would have to push or pull a wagon to move it uphill.

Consider some examples and analogies. If you open a water tap with a garden hose on it, you create a **pressure gradient;** water flows down the hose from the high-pressure point at the tap to the low-pressure point at the open end. Each heartbeat is like that, creating a gradient from high blood pressure near the heart to low pressure farther away; blood flows down this gradient away from the heart **(fig. 1.10b).** When we inhale, air flows down a pressure gradient from the surrounding atmosphere to pulmonary air passages where the pressure is lower. A pressure gradient also drives the process in which the kidneys filter water and waste products from the blood.

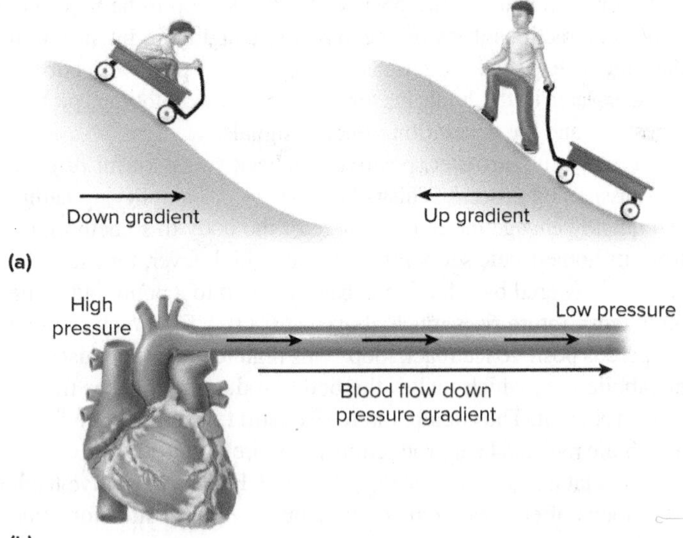


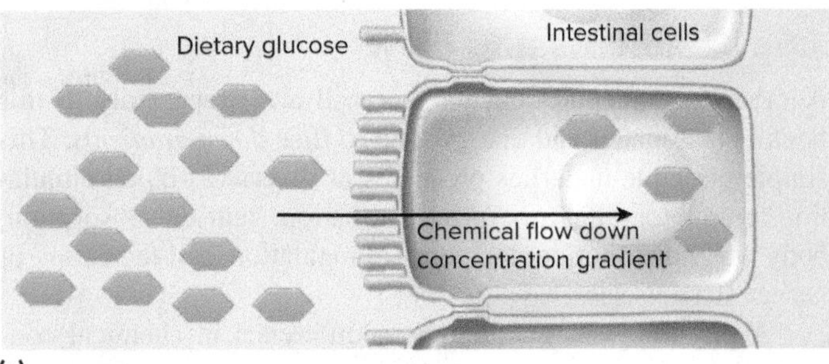


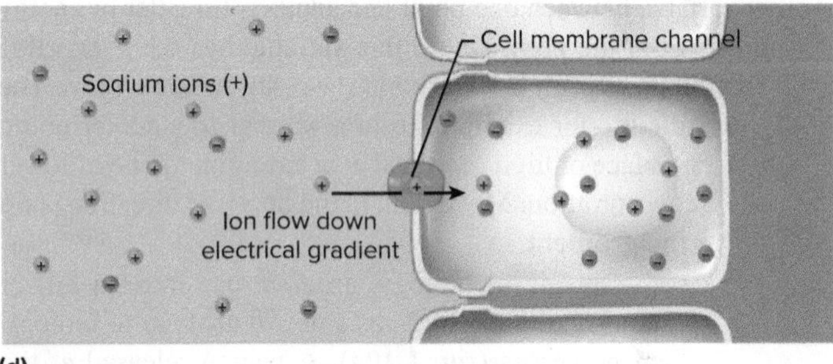


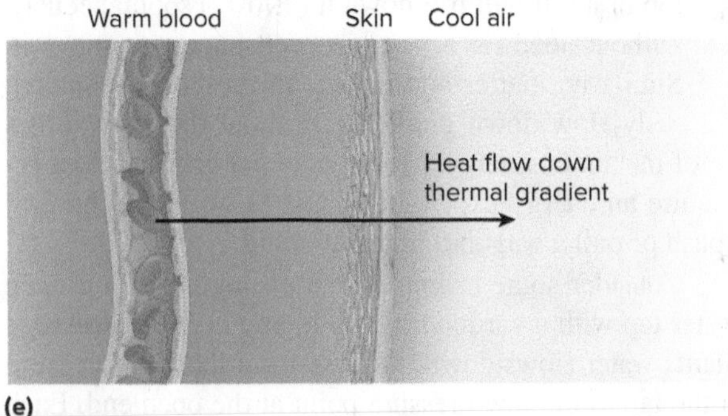


**FIGURE 1.10 Flow Down Gradients.** (a) A wagon rolling downhill (down a gradient) (left) is a useful analogy to spontaneous, gradient-driven physiological processes. Moving up a gradient (right) requires an energy input. (b) Blood flowing down a pressure gradient. (c) Dietary sugars flowing down a concentration gradient into an intestinal cell. (d) Sodium ions flowing down an electrical gradient into a cell. (e) Heat flowing down a thermal gradient to leave the body through the skin.

Chemicals flow down **concentration gradients.** When we digest starch, a high concentration of sugars accumulates in the small intestine. The cells lining the intestine contain only a low concentration of sugars, so sugars flow from the intestinal space into these cells, thus becoming absorbed into the body's tissues **(fig. 1.10c).** Water flows through cell membranes and epithelia by *osmosis,* from the side where it is more concentrated to the side where it is less so.

Charged particles flow down **electrical gradients.** Suppose there is a high concentration of sodium ions ($Na^+$) just outside a cell and much lower concentration inside, so the outer surface of the cell membrane has a relatively positive charge and the inner surface is relatively negative **(fig. 1.10d).** If we open channels in the membrane that will let sodium pass, sodium ions rush into the cell, flowing down their electrical gradient. Because each $Na^+$ carries a positive charge, this flow constitutes an electrical current through the membrane. We tap this current to make our nerves fire, our heart beat, and our muscles contract. In many cases, the flow of ions is governed by a combination of concentration and electrical charge differences between two points, and we say that ions flow down **electrochemical gradients.** These will be studied especially in connection with muscle and nerve action in chapters 11 and 12.

Heat flows down a **thermal gradient.** Suppose there is warm blood flowing through small arteries close to the skin surface, and the air temperature around the body is cooler **(fig. 1.10e).** Heat will flow from the blood to the surrounding air, down its thermal gradient, and be lost from the body. You will see in chapter 27 that heat flow is also important in preventing the testes from overheating, which would otherwise prevent sperm production.

Thus, you can see there are many applications in human physiology for this universal tendency of matter and energy to flow down gradients. This principle arises many times in the chapters to follow. We will revisit it next in chapter 3 when we consider how materials move into and out of cells through the cell membrane.

### BEFORE YOU GO ON

Answer the following questions to test your understanding of the preceding section:

16. List four biological criteria of life and one clinical criterion. Explain how a person could be clinically dead but biologically alive.
17. What is meant by *dynamic equilibrium*? Why would it be wrong to say homeostasis prevents internal change?
18. Explain why stabilizing mechanisms are called *negative feedback.*
19. Explain why positive feedback is more likely than negative feedback to disturb homeostasis.
20. Active tissues generate carbon dioxide, which diffuses out of the tissue into the bloodstream, to be carried away. Is this diffusion into the blood a case of flow up a gradient, or down? Explain.

## 1.7 The Language of Medicine

**Expected Learning Outcomes**

When you have completed this section, you should be able to

a. explain why modern anatomical terminology is so heavily based on Greek and Latin;
b. recognize eponyms when you see them;
c. describe the efforts to achieve an internationally uniform anatomical terminology;
d. break medical terms down into their basic word elements;
e. state some reasons why the literal meaning of a word may not lend insight into its definition;
f. relate singular noun forms to their plural and adjective forms; and
g. discuss why precise spelling is important in anatomy and physiology.

One of the greatest challenges faced by students of anatomy and physiology is the vocabulary. In this book, you will encounter such Latin terms as *corpus callosum* (a brain structure), *ligamentum arteriosum* (a small fibrous band near the heart), and *extensor carpi radialis longus* (a forearm muscle). You may wonder why structures aren't named in "just plain English," and how you will ever remember such formidable names. This section will give you some answers to these questions and some useful tips on mastering anatomical terminology.

### 1.7a The History of Anatomical Terminology

The major features of human gross anatomy have standard international names prescribed by a book titled the *Terminologia Anatomica (TA).* The *TA* was codified in 1998 by an international committee of anatomists and approved by professional associations of anatomists in more than 50 countries.

About 90% of today's medical terms are formed from just 1,200 Greek and Latin roots. Why those two languages? Scientific investigation began in ancient Greece and soon spread to Rome. The Greeks and Romans coined many of the words still used in human anatomy today: *duodenum, uterus, prostate, cerebellum, diaphragm, sacrum, amnion,* and others. In the Renaissance, the fast pace of discovery required a profusion of new terms to describe things. Anatomists in different countries began giving different names to the same structures. Adding to the confusion, they often named new structures and diseases in honor of their esteemed teachers and predecessors, giving us such nondescriptive terms as *fallopian tube* and *duct of Santorini.* Terms coined from the names of people, called **eponyms,**[17] afford little clue as to what a structure or condition is.

In hopes of resolving this growing confusion, anatomists began meeting as early as 1895 to devise a uniform international terminology. After several false starts, they agreed on a list of terms that rejected all eponyms and gave each structure a unique Latin name to be used worldwide. Even if you were to look at an anatomy atlas in Korean or Arabic, the illustrations may be labeled with the same Latin terms as in an English-language atlas. That list served for many decades until recently replaced by the *TA,* which prescribes both Latin names and accepted English equivalents. The terminology in this book conforms to the *TA* except where undue confusion would result from abandoning widely used, yet unofficial, terms.

### 1.7b Analyzing Medical Terms

The task of learning medical terminology seems overwhelming at first, but it is a simple skill to become more comfortable with the technical language of medicine. People who find scientific terms confusing and difficult to pronounce, spell, and remember often feel more confident once they realize the logic of how terms are composed. A term such as *hyponatremia* is less forbidding once we recognize that it is composed of three common word elements: *hypo-* (below normal), *natr-* (sodium), and *-emia* (blood condition). Thus, hyponatremia is a deficiency of sodium in the blood. Those word elements appear over and over in many other medical terms: *hypothermia, natriuretic, anemia,* and so on. Once you learn the meanings of *hypo-, natri-,* and *-emia,* you already have the tools to at least partially understand hundreds of other biomedical terms. In appendix E, you will find a lexicon of word elements commonly footnoted in this book.

Scientific terms are typically composed of one or more of the following elements:

- At least one *root (stem)* that bears the core meaning of the word. In *cardiology,* for example, the root is *cardi-* (heart). Many words have two or more roots. In *cardiomyopathy,* for example, the roots are *cardi-* (heart), *my-* (muscle), and *path-* (disease).
- *Combining vowels* that are often inserted to join roots and make the word easier to pronounce. In *cardiomyopathy,* each *o* is a combining vowel. Although *o* is the most common combining vowel, all vowels of the alphabet are used in this way, such as *a* in *ligament, e* in *vitreous, i* in *fusiform, u* in *ovulation,* and *y* in *tachycardia.* Some words, such as *intervertebral,* have no combining vowels. A combination of a root and combining vowel is called a *combining form;* for example, *chrom-* (color) + *o* (a combining vowel) make the combining form *chromo-,* as in *chromosome.*
- A *prefix* may be present to modify the core meaning of the word. For example, *gastric* (pertaining to the stomach or to the belly of a muscle) takes on a variety of new meanings when prefixes are added to it: *epigastric* (above the stomach), *hypogastric* (below the stomach), *endogastric* (within the stomach), and *digastric* (a muscle with two bellies).
- A *suffix* may be added to the end of a word to modify its core meaning. For example, *microscope, microscopy, microscopic,* and *microscopist* have different meanings because of their suffixes alone. Often two or more suffixes, or a

[17] *epo* = *epi* = upon, based upon; *nym* = name

root and suffix, occur together so often that they are treated jointly as a *compound suffix;* for example, *log* (study) + *y* (process) form the compound suffix *-logy* (the study of). Prefixes and suffixes are collectively called *affixes.*

To summarize these basic principles, consider the word *gastroenterology,* a branch of medicine dealing with the stomach and small intestine. It breaks down into *gastro/entero/logy:*

| | | |
|---|---|---|
| *gastro* | = | a combining form meaning "stomach" |
| *entero* | = | a combining form meaning "small intestine" |
| *logy* | = | a compound suffix meaning "the study of" |

"Dissecting" words in this way and paying attention to the word-origin footnotes throughout this book will help you become more comfortable with the language of anatomy. Knowing how a word breaks down and knowing the meaning of its elements make it far easier to pronounce a word, spell it, and remember its definition.

There are a few unfortunate exceptions, however. The path from original meaning to current usage has often become obscured by history (see Deeper Insight 1.4). The foregoing approach also is no help with eponyms or **acronyms**[18]—words composed of the first letter, or first few letters, of a series of words. For example, a common medical imaging method is the PET scan, an acronym for *positron emission tomography.* Note that PET is a pronounceable word, hence a true acronym. Acronyms are not to be confused with simple abbreviations such as DNA and MRI, in which each letter must be pronounced separately.

## 1.7c Plurals, Adjectives, and Possessive Forms

A point of confusion for many beginning students is how to recognize the plural forms of medical terms. Few people would fail to recognize that *ovaries* is the plural of *ovary,* but the connection is harder to make in other cases: For example, the plural of *cortex* is *cortices* (COR-ti-sees), the plural of *corpus* is *corpora,* and the plural of *ganglion* is *ganglia.* **Table 1.1** will help you make the connection between common singular and plural noun terminals.

In some cases, what appears to the beginner to be two completely different words may be only the noun and adjective forms of the same word. For example, *brachium* denotes the arm, and *brachii* (as in the muscle name *biceps brachii*) means "of the arm." *Carpus* denotes the wrist, and *carpi,* a word used in several muscle names, means "of the wrist." Adjectives can also take different forms for the singular and plural and for different degrees of comparison. The *digits* are the fingers and toes. The word *digiti* in a muscle name means "of a single finger (or toe)," whereas *digitorum* is the plural, meaning "of multiple fingers (or toes)." Thus, the *extensor digiti minimi muscle* extends only the little finger, whereas the *extensor digitorum muscle* extends all fingers except the thumb.

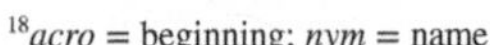

[18]*acro* = beginning; *nym* = name

### DEEPER INSIGHT 1.4
### MEDICAL HISTORY

#### *Obscure Medical Word Origins*

The literal translation of a word doesn't always provide great insight into its modern meaning. The history of language is full of twists and turns that are fascinating in their own right and say much about the history of human culture, but they can create confusion for students.

For example, the *amnion* is a transparent sac that forms around the developing fetus. The word is derived from *amnos,* from the Greek for "lamb." From this origin, *amnos* came to mean a bowl for catching the blood of sacrificial lambs, and from there the word found its way into biomedical usage for the membrane that emerges (quite bloody) as part of the afterbirth. The *acetabulum,* the socket of the hip joint, literally means "vinegar cup." Apparently the hip socket reminded an anatomist of the little cups used to serve vinegar as a condiment on dining tables in ancient Rome. The word *testicles* can be translated "little pots" or "little witnesses." The history of medical language has several amusing conjectures as to why this word was chosen to name the male gonads.

**TABLE 1.1 Singular and Plural Forms of Some Noun Terminals**

| Singular Ending | Plural Ending | Examples |
|---|---|---|
| -a | -ae | axilla, axillae |
| -en | -ina | lumen, lumina |
| -ex | -ices | cortex, cortices |
| -is | -es | diagnosis, diagnoses |
| -is | -ides | epididymis, epididymides |
| -ix | -ices | appendix, appendices |
| -ma | -mata | carcinoma, carcinomata |
| -on | -a | ganglion, ganglia |
| -um | -a | septum, septa |
| -us | -era | viscus, viscera |
| -us | -i | villus, villi |
| -us | -ora | corpus, corpora |
| -x | -ges | phalanx, phalanges |
| -y | -ies | ovary, ovaries |
| -yx | -yces | calyx, calyces |

The English words *large, larger,* and *largest* are examples of the positive, comparative, and superlative degrees of comparison. In Latin, these are *magnus, major* (from *maior*), and *maximus.* We find these in the muscle names *adductor magnus* (a *large* muscle of the thigh), the *pectoralis major* (the *larger* of two pectoral muscles of the chest), and *gluteus maximus* (the *largest* of the three gluteal muscles of the buttock).

Some noun variations indicate the possessive, such as the *rectus abdominis,* a straight *(rectus)* muscle of the abdomen (*abdominis,* "of the abdomen"), and the *erector spinae,* a muscle that straightens *(erector)* the spinal column (*spinae,* "of the spine").

Anatomical terminology also frequently follows the Greek and Latin practice of placing the adjective after the noun. Thus, we have such names as the *stratum lucidum* for a clear *(lucidum)* layer *(stratum)* of the epidermis, the *foramen magnum* for a large *(magnum)* hole *(foramen)* in the skull, and the aforementioned *pectoralis major* muscle of the chest.

This is not to say that you must be conversant in Latin or Greek grammar to proceed with your study of anatomy. These few examples, however, may alert you to some patterns to watch for in the terminology you study and, ideally, will make your encounters with anatomical terminology less confusing.

### 1.7d Pronunciation

Pronunciation is another stumbling block for many beginning anatomy and physiology students. This book gives simple pro-NUN-see-AY-shun guides for many terms when they are first introduced. Read the syllables of these guides phonetically and accent the syllables in capital letters. You can also hear pronunciations of most of the anatomical terms within Anatomy & Physiology REVEALED®.

### 1.7e The Importance of Spelling

A final word of advice for your study of anatomy and physiology: Be accurate in your spelling and use of terms. It may seem trivial if you misspell *trapezius* as *trapezium,* but in doing so, you would be changing the name of a back muscle to the name of a wrist bone. Similarly, changing *occipitalis* to *occipital* or *zygomaticus* to *zygomatic* changes other muscle names to bone names. Changing *malleus* to *malleolus* changes the name of a middle-ear bone to the name of a bony protuberance of the ankle. And there is only a one-letter difference between *ileum* (the final portion of the small intestine) and *ilium* (part of the hip bone), and between *gustation* (the sense of taste) and *gestation* (pregnancy).

The health professions demand the utmost attention to detail and accuracy—people's lives may one day be in your hands. The habit of carefulness must extend to your use of language as well. Many patients have died simply because of tragic written and oral miscommunication in the hospital. Compared to this, it is hardly tragic if your instructor deducts a point or two for an error in spelling. It should be considered a lesson learned about the importance of accuracy.

**BEFORE YOU GO ON**

Answer the following questions to test your understanding of the preceding section:

21. Explain why modern anatomical terminology is so heavily based on Greek and Latin.
22. Distinguish between an eponym and an acronym, and explain why both of these present difficulties for interpreting anatomical terms.
23. Break each of the following words down into its roots, prefixes, and suffixes, and state their meanings, following the example of *gastroenterology* analyzed earlier: *pericardium, appendectomy, subcutaneous, phonocardiogram, otorhinolaryngology*. Consult the list of word elements in appendix E for help.
24. Write the singular form of each of the following words: *pleurae, gyri, ganglia, fissures*. Write the plural form of each of the following: *villus, tibia, encephalitis, cervix, stoma*.

## 1.8 Review of Major Themes

To close this chapter, let's distill a few major points from it. These themes can provide you with a sense of perspective that will make the rest of the book more meaningful and not just a collection of disconnected facts. These are some key unifying principles behind all study of human anatomy and physiology:

- **Unity of form and function.** *Form and function complement each other; physiology cannot be divorced from anatomy.* This unity holds true even down to the molecular level. Our very molecules, such as DNA and proteins, are structured in ways that enable them to carry out their functions. Slight changes in molecular structure can destroy their activity and threaten life.
- **Cell theory.** *All structure and function result from the activity of cells.* Every physiological concept in this book ultimately must be understood from the standpoint of how cells function. Even anatomy is a result of cellular function. If cells are damaged or destroyed, we see the results in disease symptoms of the whole person.
- **Evolution.** *The human body is a product of evolution.* Like every other living species, we have been molded by millions of years of natural selection to function in a changing environment. Many aspects of human anatomy and physiology reflect our ancestors' adaptations to their environment. Human form and function cannot be fully understood except in light of our evolutionary history.
- **Hierarchy of complexity.** *Human structure can be viewed as a series of levels of complexity.* Each level is composed of a smaller number of simpler subunits than the level above it. These subunits are arranged in different ways to form diverse structures of higher complexity. Understanding the simpler components is the key to understanding higher levels of structure.
- **Homeostasis.** *The purpose of most normal physiology is to maintain stable conditions within the body.* Human physiology is essentially a group of homeostatic mechanisms that produce stable internal conditions favorable to cellular function. Any serious departure from these conditions can be harmful or fatal to cells and thus to the whole body.
- **Gradients and flow.** Matter and energy tend to flow down gradients such as differences in chemical concentration, pressure, temperature, and electrical charge. This accounts for much of their movement in human physiology.

**▶▶▶APPLY WHAT YOU KNOW**

*Architect Louis Henri Sullivan coined the phrase, "Form ever follows function." What do you think he meant by this? Discuss how this idea could be applied to the human body and cite a specific example of human anatomy to support it.*

## DEEPER INSIGHT 1.5
### CLINICAL APPLICATION

### *Medical Imaging*

The development of techniques for looking into the body without having to do exploratory surgery has greatly accelerated progress in medicine. A few of these techniques are described here.

#### Radiography

*Radiography,* first performed in 1895, is the process of photographing internal structures with X-rays **(fig. 1.11a).** Until the 1960s, this was the only widely available imaging method; even today, it accounts for more than 50% of all clinical imaging. X-rays pass through the soft tissues of the body to a photographic film or detector on the other side, where they produce relatively dark images. They are absorbed, however, by dense matter such as bones, teeth, tumors, and tuberculosis nodules, which leave the image lighter in these areas. The term *X-ray* also applies to an image *(radiograph)* made by this method. Radiography is commonly used in dentistry, mammography, diagnosis of fractures, and examination of the chest. Hollow organs can be visualized by filling them with a contrast medium that absorbs X-rays. Barium sulfate, for example, is given orally for examination of the esophagus, stomach, and small intestine or by enema for examination of the large intestine. Some disadvantages of radiography are that images of overlapping organs can be confusing and slight differences in tissue density are not easily detected. In addition, X-rays can cause mutations leading to cancer and birth defects. Radiography therefore cannot be used indiscriminately.

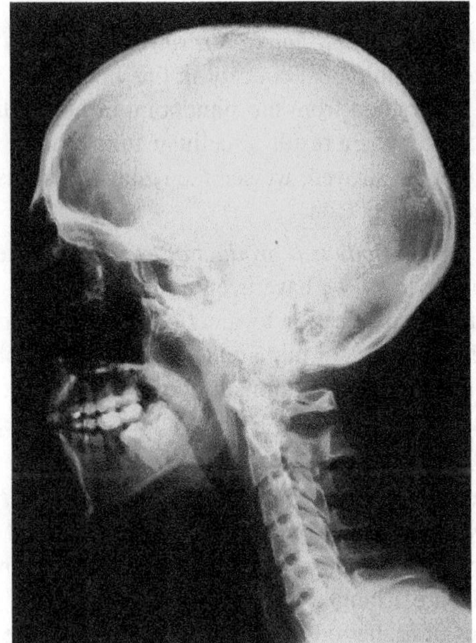

**(a) X-ray (radiograph)**

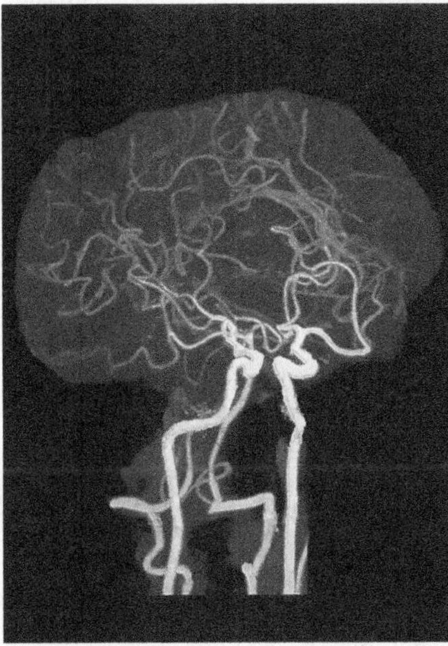

**(b) Cerebral angiogram**

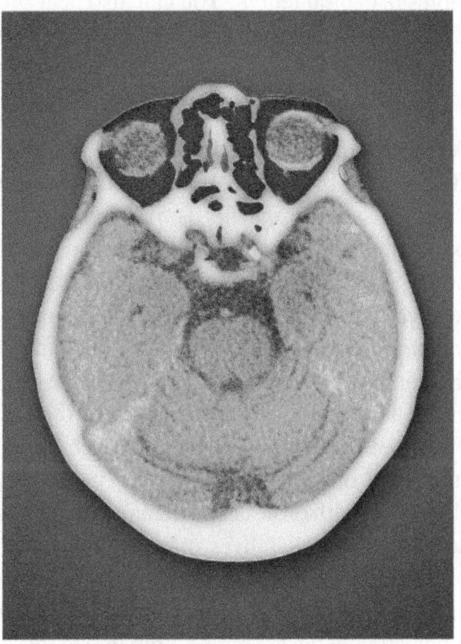

**(c) Computed tomographic (CT) scan**

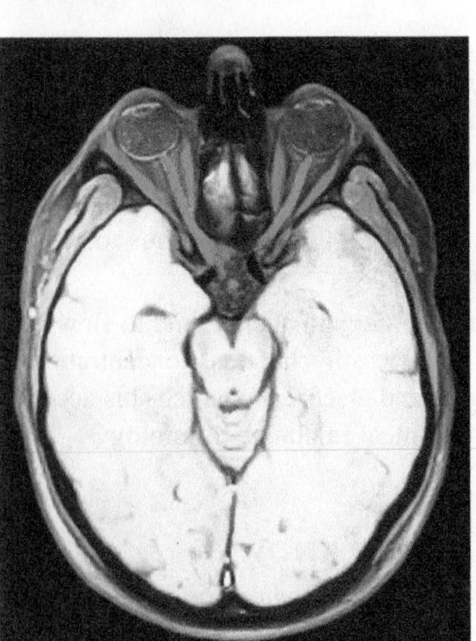

**(d) Magnetic resonance image (MRI)**

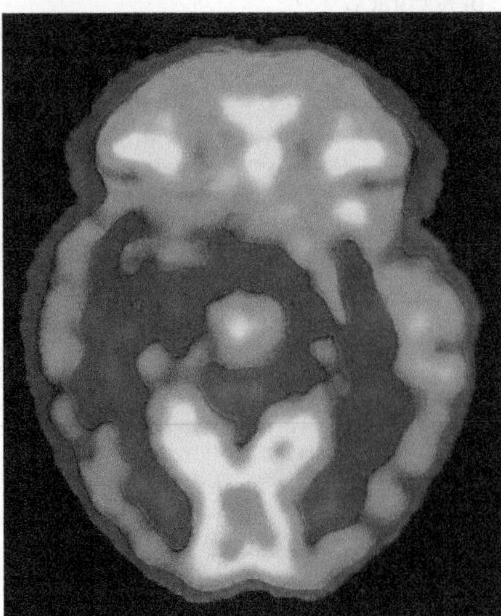

**(e) Positron emission tomographic (PET) scan**

**FIGURE 1.11 Radiologic Images of the Head.** (a) X-ray (radiograph) of the skull. (b) Digital subtraction angiogram (DSA) of the cerebral blood vessels. (c) CT scan at the level of the eyes. (d) MRI scan at the level of the eyes. The optic nerves appear in red and the muscles that move the eyes appear in green. (e) A PET scan of the brain of an unmedicated schizophrenic patient. Red areas indicate regions of high metabolic rate. In this patient, the visual center of the brain at the rear of the head (bottom of photo) was especially active during the scan.

*What structures are seen better by MRI than by X-ray? What structures are seen better by X-ray than by PET?*

a: U.H.B. Trust/The Image Bank/Getty Images; b: pang_oasis/Shutterstock; c: Miriam Maslo/Science Source; d: UHB Trust/Getty Images; e: ISM/Sovereign/Medical Images

Blood vessels can be seen especially clearly with a radiographic method called *digital subtraction angiography (DSA)* **(fig. 1.11b).** This entails taking X-rays before and after injecting a contrast medium into a vessel. A computer then "erases" the first image from the second, leaving a clear, dark image of just the injected vessels without the overlying and surrounding tissues. This is useful for showing vascular blockages and anatomical malformations, abnormalities of cerebral blood flow, and narrowing (stenosis) of renal arteries, and as an aid in threading catheters into blood vessels. DSA is already being replaced in many clinics, however, by yet newer methods that are less invasive and avoid contrast medium and radiation exposure.

### Computed Tomography

*Computed tomography*[19] (a *CT scan*) **(fig. 1.11c)** is a more sophisticated application of X-rays. The patient is moved through a ring-shaped machine that emits low-intensity X-rays on one side and receives them with a detector on the opposite side. A computer analyzes signals from the detector and produces an image of a "slice" of the body about as thin as a coin. The advantage of such thin planes of view is that there is little overlap of organs, so the image is much sharper than a conventional X-ray. It requires extensive knowledge of cross-sectional anatomy to interpret the images. CT scanning is useful for identifying tumors, aneurysms, cerebral hemorrhages, kidney stones, and other abnormalities.

### Magnetic Resonance Imaging

*Magnetic resonance imaging (MRI)* **(fig. 1.11d)** is better than CT for visualizing some soft tissues. The patient lies in either a tube or an open-sided scanner surrounded by a powerful electromagnet. Hydrogen atoms in the patient's tissues alternately align themselves with this magnetic field and with a radio-frequency field turned on and off by the technologist. These changes in hydrogen alignment generate signals that are analyzed by computer to produce an anatomical image. MRI can "see" clearly through the skull and spine to produce images of the nervous tissue within, and it is better than CT for distinguishing between soft tissues such as the white and gray matter of the brain. MRI also avoids X-ray exposure and its risks.

MRI has disadvantages, however, such as the claustrophobic feeling some patients experience in the scanner, loud noises generated by the machine, and long exposure times that prevent sharp images being made of the constantly moving stomach and intestines. It requires a patient to lie still in the enclosed space for up to 45 minutes to scan one region of the body and may entail 90 minutes to scan multiple regions such as the abdominal and pelvic cavities. Some patients find they cannot tolerate this. Open-sided MRI machines are favored by some claustrophobic or obese patients, but have weaker magnetic fields, produce poorer images, and may miss important tissue abnormalities.

*Functional MRI (fMRI)* is a variation that visualizes moment-to-moment changes in tissue function. fMRI scans of the brain, for example, show shifting patterns of activity as the brain applies itself to a specific sensory, mental, or motor task. fMRI has lately replaced the PET scan as the most important method for visualizing brain function. The use of fMRI in brain imaging is further discussed in Deeper Insight 14.5.

### Positron Emission Tomography

*Positron emission tomography* (the *PET scan*) **(fig. 1.11e)** is used to assess the metabolic state of a tissue and distinguish which tissues are most active at a given moment. The procedure begins with an injection of radioactively labeled glucose, which emits positrons (electron-like particles with a positive charge). When a positron and electron meet, they annihilate each other and give off a pair of gamma rays that can be detected by sensors and analyzed by computer. The computer displays a color image that shows which tissues were using the most glucose at the moment. PET scans are generally low-resolution, as in this photo, but nevertheless provide valuable diagnostic information. In cardiology, PET scans can show the extent of tissue death from a heart attack. Since it consumes little or no glucose, the damaged tissue appears dark. PET scans are also widely used to diagnose cancer and evaluate tumor status. The PET scan is an example of *nuclear medicine*—the use of radioactive isotopes to treat disease or to form diagnostic images of the body.

### Sonography

*Sonography*[20] **(fig. 1.12)** is the second oldest and second most widely used method of imaging. A handheld device pressed against the skin produces high-frequency ultrasound waves and receives the signals that echo back from internal organs. Sonography isn't very useful for examining bones or lungs, but it is the method of choice in obstetrics, where the image *(sonogram)* can be used to locate the placenta and evaluate fetal age, position, and development. Sonography is also used to view tissues in motion, such as fetal movements, actions of the heart wall and valves, and blood ejection from the heart and flow through arteries and veins. Sonographic imaging of the beating heart is called *echocardiography.* Sonography avoids the harmful effects of X-rays, and the equipment is inexpensive and portable. Some disadvantages are that sonography can't penetrate bone and it usually doesn't produce a very sharp image.

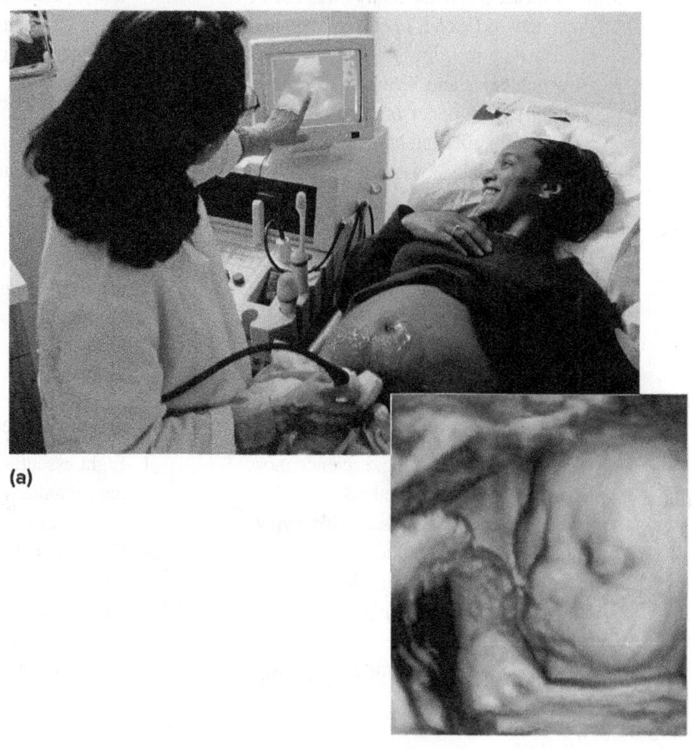


**FIGURE 1.12 Fetal Sonography.** (a) Producing a sonogram. (b) Three-dimensional fetal sonogram at 32 weeks of gestation.

a: Kevin Brofsky/Getty Images; b: Ken Saladin

[19] *tomo* = section, cut, slice; *graphy* = recording process
[20] *sono* = sound; *graphy* = recording process

# STUDY GUIDE

## Assess Your Learning Outcomes

*To test your knowledge, discuss the following topics with a study partner or in writing, ideally from memory.*

### 1.1 The Scope of Anatomy and Physiology

1. The meanings of *anatomy* and *physiology* and what it means to say these two sciences are complementary and inseparable
2. Methods of study in anatomy and clinical examination
3. Branches of anatomy that study the body at different levels of detail
4. How comparative physiology advances the understanding of human function

### 1.2 The Origins of Biomedical Science

1. Greek and Roman scholars who first gave medicine a scientific basis
2. Ways in which the work of Maimonides, Avicenna, Vesalius, and Harvey were groundbreaking in the context of their time and culture
3. Why medical science today owes such a great debt to Hooke, Leeuwenhoek, and other inventors
4. How Schleiden and Schwann revolutionized and unified the understanding of biological structure, ultimately including human anatomy and physiology

### 1.3 Scientific Method

1. How philosophers Bacon and Descartes revolutionized society's view of science, even though neither of them was a scientist
2. The essential qualities of the scientific method
3. The nature of the inductive and hypothetico–deductive methods, how they differ, and which areas of biomedical science most heavily employ each method
4. The qualities of a valid scientific hypothesis, the function of a hypothesis, and what is meant by *falsifiability* in science
5. How each of the following contributes to the reliability of a researcher's scientific conclusions and the trust that the public may place in science: sample size, control groups, the double-blind method, statistical testing, and peer review
6. The distinctions between scientific facts, laws, and theories; the purpose of a theory; and how the scientific meanings of *law* and *theory* differ from the common lay meanings

### 1.4 Human Origins and Adaptations

1. The meanings of *evolution, natural selection, selection pressure,* and *adaptation,* with examples of each
2. The historical origin of the theory of natural selection and how this theory is relevant to a complete understanding of human anatomy and physiology
3. How the kinship among all species is relevant to the choice of model animals for biomedical research
4. Ecological conditions thought to have selected for such key characteristics of *Homo sapiens* as opposable thumbs, shoulder mobility, prehensile hands, stereoscopic vision, color vision, and bipedal locomotion
5. The meaning of *evolutionary medicine*

### 1.5 Human Structure

1. Levels of human structural complexity from organism to atom
2. Reductionism and holism; how they differ and why both ideas are relevant to the study of human anatomy and physiology and to the clinical care of patients
3. Examples of why the anatomy presented in textbooks is not necessarily true of every individual

### 1.6 Human Function

1. Eight essential qualities that distinguish living organisms from nonliving things
2. The meaning of *metabolism*
3. Clinical criteria for life and death, and why clinical and biological death are not exactly equivalent
4. The clinical importance of physiological variation between people, and the assumptions that underlie typical values given in textbooks
5. The meaning of *homeostasis;* its importance for survival; and the historical origin of this concept
6. How negative feedback contributes to homeostasis; the meaning of *negative feedback loop;* how a receptor, integrating center, and effector are involved in many negative feedback loops; and at least one example of such a loop
7. How positive feedback differs from negative feedback; examples of beneficial and harmful cases of positive feedback
8. The concept of matter and energy flowing down gradients and how this applies to various areas of human physiology

### 1.7 The Language of Medicine

1. The origin and purpose of the *Terminologia Anatomica (TA)* and its relevance for anatomy students
2. How to break biomedical terms into familiar roots, prefixes, and suffixes, and why the habit of doing so aids in learning
3. Acronyms and eponyms, and why they cannot be understood by trying to analyze their roots
4. How to recognize when two or more words are singular and plural versions of one another; when one word is the possessive form of another; and when medical terms built on the same root represent different degrees of comparison (such as terms denoting *large, larger,* and *largest*)
5. Why accuracy in spelling and usage of medical terms can be a matter of life or death in a hospital or clinic, and how seemingly trivial spelling errors can radically alter meaning

### 1.8 Review of Major Themes

1. A description of six core themes of this book: unity of form and function, cell theory, evolution, hierarchy of complexity, homeostasis, and gradients and flow

# STUDY GUIDE

## Testing Your Recall

*Answers in Appendix A*

1. Structure that can be observed with the naked eye is called
   a. gross anatomy.
   b. ultrastructure.
   c. microscopic anatomy.
   d. histology.
   e. cytology.
2. The word prefix *homeo-* means
   a. tissue.
   b. metabolism.
   c. change.
   d. human.
   e. same.
3. The simplest structures considered to be alive are
   a. organisms.
   b. organs.
   c. tissues.
   d. cells.
   e. organelles.
4. Which of the following people revolutionized the teaching of gross anatomy?
   a. Vesalius
   b. Aristotle
   c. Hippocrates
   d. Leeuwenhoek
   e. Cannon
5. Which of the following embodies the greatest amount of scientific information?
   a. a fact
   b. a law of nature
   c. a theory
   d. a deduction
   e. a hypothesis
6. An informed, uncertain, but testable conjecture is
   a. a natural law.
   b. a scientific theory.
   c. a hypothesis.
   d. a deduction.
   e. a scientific fact.
7. A self-amplifying chain of physiological events is called
   a. positive feedback.
   b. negative feedback.
   c. dynamic constancy.
   d. homeostasis.
   e. metabolism.
8. Which of the following is *not* a human organ system?
   a. integumentary
   b. muscular
   c. epithelial
   d. nervous
   e. endocrine
9. ______ means studying anatomy by touch.
   a. Gross anatomy
   b. Auscultation
   c. Osculation
   d. Palpation
   e. Percussion
10. The prefix *hetero-* means
    a. same.
    b. different.
    c. both.
    d. solid.
    e. below.
11. Cutting and separating tissues to reveal structural relationships is called ______.
12. A difference in chemical concentration between one point and another is called a concentration ______.
13. By the process of ______, a medical researcher predicts what the result of a certain experiment will be if his or her hypothesis is correct.
14. Physiological effects of a person's mental state are called ______ effects.
15. The tendency of the body to maintain stable internal conditions is called ______.
16. Blood pH averages 7.4 but fluctuates from 7.35 to 7.45. A pH of 7.4 can therefore be considered the ______ for this variable.
17. Self-corrective mechanisms in physiology are called ______ loops.
18. A/an ______ is the simplest body structure to be composed of two or more types of tissue.
19. Depth perception, or the ability to form three-dimensional images, is also called ______ vision.
20. Our hands are said to be ______ because they can encircle an object such as a branch or tool. The presence of an ______ thumb is important to this ability.

## Building Your Medical Vocabulary

*Answers in Appendix A*

*State a meaning of each word element, and give a medical term from this chapter that uses it or a slight variation of it.*

1. auscult-
2. dis-
3. homeo-
4. metabolo-
5. palp-
6. physio-
7. -sect
8. -stasis
9. stereo-
10. tomo-

# STUDY GUIDE

## What's Wrong with These Statements?

*Answers in Appendix A*

*Briefly explain why each of the following statements is false, or reword it to make it true.*

1. The technique for taking a patient's pulse at the wrist is auscultation.
2. For a pregnant woman to have an MRI scan would expose her fetus to radiation that can potentially cause mutation and birth defects.
3. We usually depend on positive feedback to restore homeostatic balance and have a beneficial effect on the body.
4. There are far more cells than organelles in the body.
5. Matter doesn't generally move down a gradient in the body unless the body expends metabolic energy to move it.
6. Leeuwenhoek was a biologist who invented the simple microscope in order to examine organisms in lake water.
7. A scientific theory is just a speculation until someone finds the evidence to prove it.
8. In a typical clinical research study, volunteer patients are in the treatment group and the physicians and scientists who run the study constitute the control group.
9. Human evolution is basically a theory that humans came from monkeys.
10. Negative feedback usually has a negative (harmful) effect on the body.

## Testing Your Comprehension

1. Ellen is pregnant and tells Janet, one of her coworkers, that she is scheduled to get a fetal sonogram. Janet expresses alarm and warns Ellen about the danger of exposing a fetus to X-rays. Discuss why you think Janet's concern is warranted or unwarranted.
2. Which of the characteristics of living things are possessed by an automobile? What bearing does this have on our definition of life?
3. About 1 out of every 120 live-born infants has a structural defect in the heart such as a hole between two heart chambers. Such infants often suffer pulmonary congestion and heart failure, and about one-third of them die as a result. Which of the major themes in this chapter does this illustrate? Explain your answer.
4. How might human anatomy be different today if the forerunners of humans had never inhabited the forest canopy?
5. Suppose you have been doing heavy yard work on a hot day and sweating profusely. You become very thirsty, so you drink a tall glass of lemonade. Explain how your thirst relates to the concept of homeostasis. Which type of feedback—positive or negative—does this illustrate?

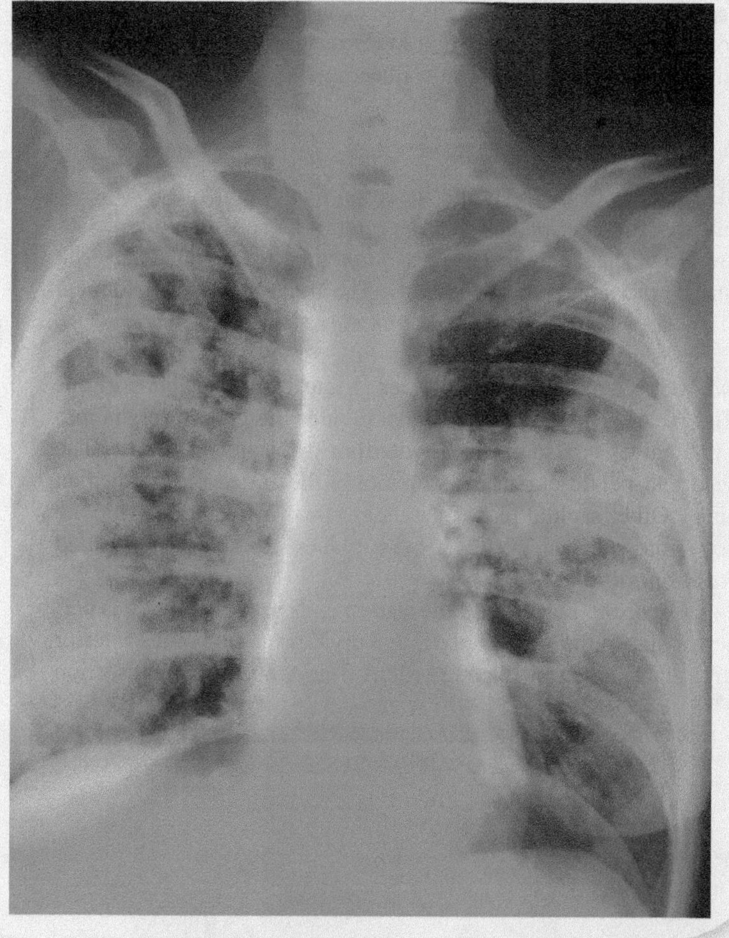

Colorized chest X-ray showing lung damage from tuberculosis
SPL/Science Source

# ATLAS A

# GENERAL ORIENTATION TO HUMAN ANATOMY

## ATLAS OUTLINE



## DEEPER INSIGHTS

**Module 1: Body Orientation**

## A.1 General Anatomical Terminology

### A.1a Anatomical Position

In describing the human body, anatomists assume that it is in **anatomical position (fig. A.1)**—that of a person standing upright with the feet flat on the floor, arms at the sides, and the palms and face directed forward. Without such a frame of reference, to say that a structure such as the sternum, thyroid gland, or aorta is "above the heart" would be vague, since it would depend on whether the subject was standing, lying face down *(prone)*, or lying face up *(supine)*. From the perspective of anatomical position, however, we can describe the thyroid as *superior* to the heart, the sternum as *anterior* to it, and the aorta as *posterior* to it. These descriptions remain valid regardless of the subject's position. Even if the body is lying down, such as a cadaver on the medical student's dissection table, to say the sternum is anterior to the heart invites the viewer to imagine the body is standing in anatomical position and not to call it "above the heart" simply because that is the way the body happens to be lying.

Unless stated otherwise, assume that all anatomical descriptions refer to anatomical position. Bear in mind that if a subject is facing you, the subject's left will be on your right and vice versa. In most anatomical illustrations, for example, the left atrium of the heart appears toward the right side of the page, and although the appendix is located in the right lower quadrant of the abdomen, it appears on the left side of most illustrations.

### A.1b Anatomical Planes

Many views of the body are based on real or imaginary "slices" called sections or planes. *Section* implies an actual cut or slice to reveal internal anatomy, whereas *plane* implies an imaginary flat surface passing through the body. The three primary anatomical planes are *sagittal, frontal,* and *transverse* (fig. A.1).

A **sagittal**[1] **plane** (SADJ-ih-tul) passes vertically through the body or an organ and divides it into right and left portions **(fig. A.2a)**. The sagittal plane that divides the body or organ into equal halves is also called the **median (midsagittal) plane.** The head and pelvic organs are commonly illustrated on the median plane. Other sagittal planes parallel to this (off center) divide the body into unequal portions. Such planes are sometimes called *parasagittal*[2] planes.

A **frontal (coronal) plane** also extends vertically, but it is perpendicular to the sagittal plane and divides the body into anterior (front) and posterior (back) portions **(fig. A.2b)**. A frontal section

[1]*sagitta* = arrow
[2]*para* = next to

Frontal plane
Transverse plane
Sagittal plane

**FIGURE A.1 Anatomical Position and the Three Primary Anatomical Planes.**

Joe DeGrandis/McGraw-Hill Education

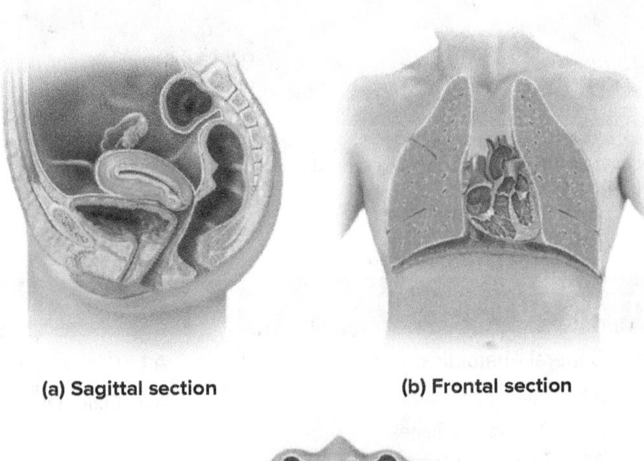

(a) Sagittal section

(b) Frontal section

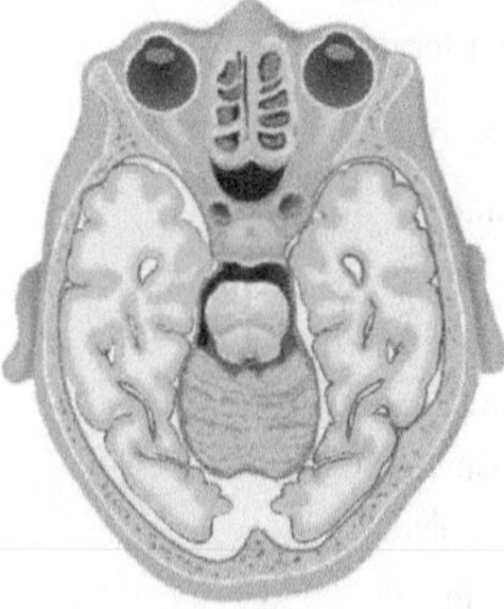

(c) Transverse section

**FIGURE A.2 Body Sections Cut Along the Three Primary Anatomical Planes.** (a) Sagittal section of the pelvic region. (b) Frontal section of the thoracic region. (c) Transverse section of the head at the level of the eyes.

**TABLE A.1 Directional Terms in Human Anatomy** APR

| Term | Meaning | Examples of Usage |
|---|---|---|
| Ventral<br>Dorsal | Toward the front* or belly<br>Toward the back or spine | The aorta is ventral to the vertebral column.<br>The vertebral column is dorsal to the aorta. |
| Anterior<br>Posterior | Toward the ventral side*<br>Toward the dorsal side* | The sternum is anterior to the heart.<br>The esophagus is posterior to the trachea. |
| Cephalic<br>Rostral<br>Caudal | Toward the head or superior end<br>Toward the forehead or nose<br>Toward the tail or inferior end | The brain develops from the cephalic end of the neural tube.<br>The forebrain is rostral to the brainstem.<br>The spinal cord is caudal to the brain. |
| Superior<br>Inferior | Above<br>Below | The heart is superior to the diaphragm.<br>The liver is inferior to the diaphragm. |
| Medial<br>Lateral | Toward the median plane<br>Away from the median plane | The heart is medial to the lungs.<br>The eyes are lateral to the nose. |
| Proximal<br>Distal | Closer to the point of attachment or origin<br>Farther from the point of attachment or origin | The elbow is proximal to the wrist.<br>The fingernails are at the distal ends of the fingers. |
| Ipsilateral<br>Contralateral | On the same side of the body (right or left)<br>On opposite sides of the body (right and left) | The liver is ipsilateral to the appendix.<br>The spleen is contralateral to the liver. |
| Superficial<br>Deep | Closer to the body surface<br>Farther from the body surface | The skin is superficial to the muscles.<br>The bones are deep to the muscles. |

*In humans only; definition differs for other animals.

of the head, for example, would divide it into one portion bearing the face and another bearing the back of the head. Contents of the thoracic and abdominal cavities are most commonly shown as frontal sections.

A **transverse (horizontal) plane** passes across the body or an organ perpendicular to its long axis; it divides the body or organ into superior (upper) and inferior (lower) portions **(fig. A.2c).** CT scans are typically transverse sections (see fig. 1.11c).

## A.1c Directional Terms

Words that describe the location of one structure relative to another are called the **directional terms** of anatomy. **Table A.1** summarizes those most frequently used. Most of these terms exist in pairs with opposite meanings: *anterior* versus *posterior, rostral* versus *caudal, superior* versus *inferior, medial* versus *lateral, proximal* versus *distal, ipsilateral* versus *contralateral,* and *superficial* versus *deep.* Intermediate directions are often indicated by combinations of these terms. For example, one's cheeks may be described as *inferolateral* to the eyes (below and to the side).

The terms *proximal* and *distal* are used especially in the anatomy of the limbs, with ***proximal*** used to denote something relatively close to the limb's point of attachment (the shoulder or hip) and ***distal*** to denote something farther away. These terms do have some applications to anatomy of the trunk, however—for example, in referring to certain aspects of the intestines and microscopic anatomy of the kidneys. But when describing the trunk and referring to a structure that lies above or below another, ***superior*** and ***inferior*** are the preferred terms. These terms are not usually used for the limbs. Although it may be technically correct, one would not generally say that the elbow is superior to the wrist, but proximal to it.

Because of the bipedal, upright stance of humans, some directional terms have different meanings for humans than they do for other animals. ***Anterior,*** for example, denotes the region of the body that leads the way in normal locomotion. For a four-legged animal such as a cat, this is the head end of the body; for a human, however, it is the front of the chest and abdomen. Thus, *anterior* has the same meaning as *ventral* for a human but not for a cat. ***Posterior*** denotes the region of the body that comes last in normal locomotion—the tail end of a cat but the dorsal side (back) of a human. In the anatomy of most other animals, *ventral* denotes the surface of the body closest to the ground and *dorsal* denotes the surface farthest away from the ground. These two words are too entrenched in human anatomy to completely ignore them, but we will minimize their use in this book to avoid confusion. You must keep such differences in mind, however, when dissecting other animals for comparison to human anatomy.

One vestige of the term *dorsal* is **dorsum,** used to denote the upper surface of the foot and the back of the hand. If you consider how a cat stands, the corresponding surfaces of its paws are uppermost, facing the same direction as the dorsal side of its trunk. Although these surfaces of the human hand and foot face entirely different directions in anatomical position, the term *dorsum* is still used.

# A.2 Major Body Regions

Knowledge of the external anatomy and landmarks of the body is important in performing a physical examination and many other clinical procedures. For purposes of study, the body is divided into two major regions called the *axial* and *appendicular* regions. Smaller areas within the major regions are described in the following paragraphs and illustrated in **figure A.3.**

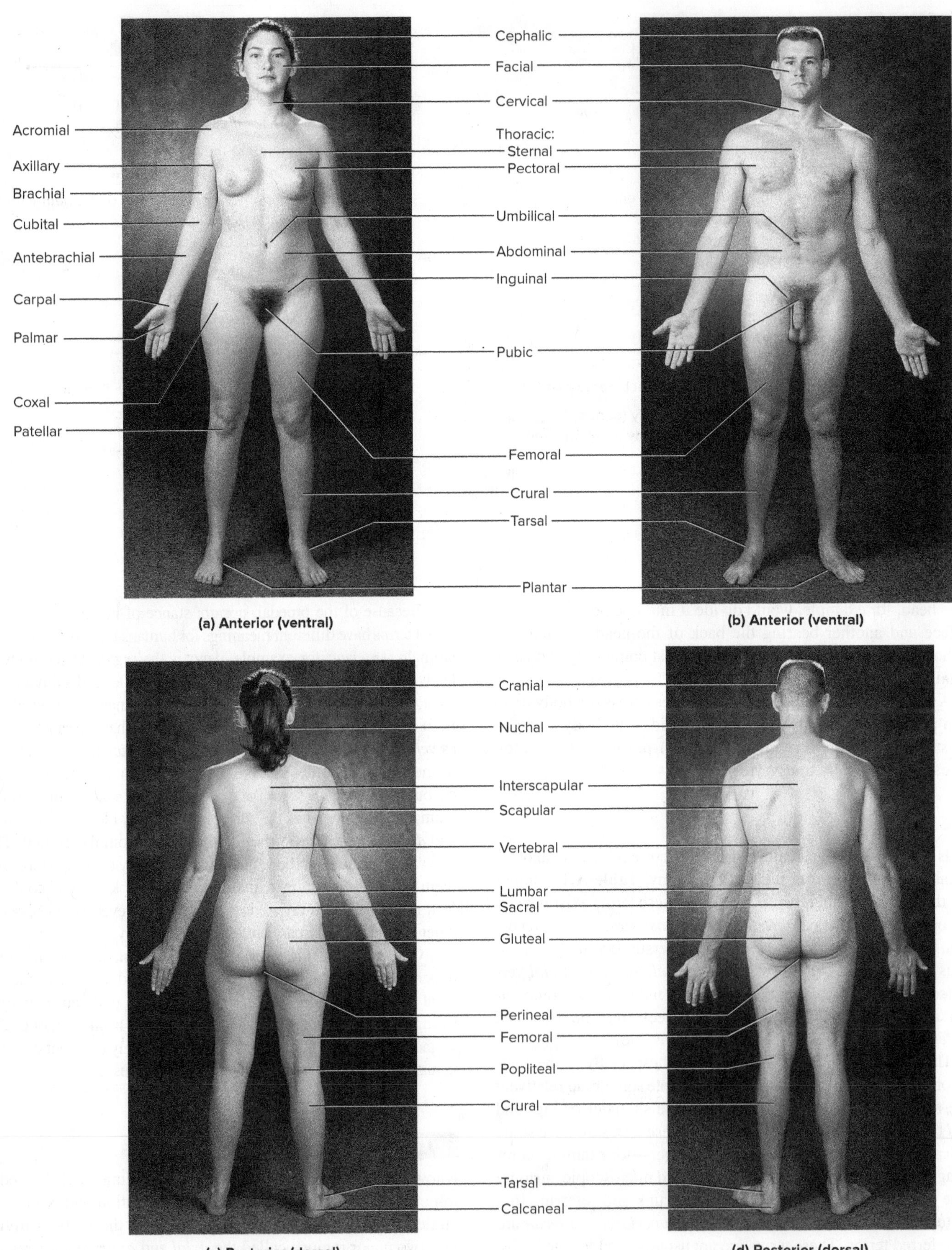


**FIGURE A.3 The Adult Female and Male Body Regions.** (a) Female, anterior. (b) Male, anterior. (c) Female, posterior. (d) Male, posterior.

**a–d:** Joe DeGrandis/McGraw-Hill Education

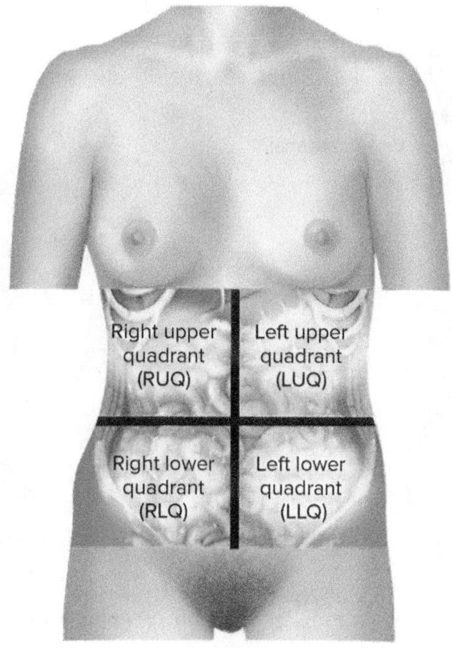


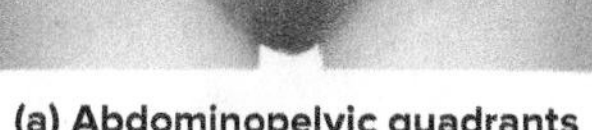


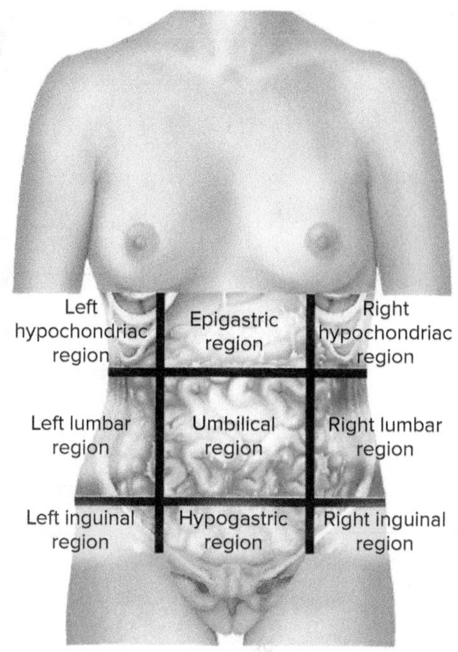

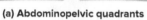

**FIGURE A.4 The Four Quadrants and Nine Regions of the Abdomen.** (a) External division into four quadrants. (b) External division into nine regions. APR

*In what quadrant would the pain of appendicitis usually be felt?*

## A.2a Axial Region

The **axial region** consists of the **head, neck (cervical[3] region),** and **trunk.** The trunk is further divided into the **thoracic region** above the diaphragm and the **abdominal region** below it.

One way of referring to the locations of abdominal structures is to divide the region into quadrants. Two perpendicular lines intersecting at the umbilicus (navel) divide the abdomen into a **right upper quadrant (RUQ), right lower quadrant (RLQ), left upper quadrant (LUQ),** and **left lower quadrant (LLQ) (fig. A.4a).** The quadrant scheme is often used to describe the site of an abdominal pain or abnormality.

The abdomen also can be divided into nine regions defined by four lines that intersect like a tic-tac-toe grid **(fig. A.4b).** Each vertical line is called a *midclavicular line* because it passes through the midpoint of the clavicle (collarbone). The superior horizontal line is called the *subcostal[4] line* because it connects the inferior borders of the lowest costal cartilages (cartilage connecting the tenth rib on each side to the inferior end of the sternum). The inferior horizontal line is called the *intertubercular[5] line* because it passes from left to right between the tubercles *(anterior superior spines)* of the pelvis—two points of bone located about where the front pockets open on most pants. The three lateral regions of this grid, from upper to lower, are the **hypochondriac,[6] lumbar,** and **inguinal[7] (iliac) regions.** The three medial regions from upper to lower are the **epigastric,[8] umbilical,** and **hypogastric (pubic)** regions.

[3]*cervic* = neck
[4]*sub* = below; *cost* = rib
[5]*inter* = between; *tubercul* = little swelling
[6]*hypo* = below; *chondr* = cartilage
[7]*inguin* = groin
[8]*epi* = above, over; *gastr* = stomach

## A.2b Appendicular Region

The **appendicular region** (AP-en-DIC-you-lur) of the body consists of the **upper** and **lower limbs** (also called *appendages* or *extremities*). The upper limb includes the **arm (brachial region)** (BRAY-kee-ul), **forearm (antebrachial[9] region)** (AN-teh-BRAY-kee-ul), **wrist (carpal region), hand,** and **fingers (digits).** The lower limb includes the **thigh (femoral region), leg (crural region)** (CROO-rul), **ankle (tarsal region), foot,** and **toes (digits).** In strict anatomical terms, *arm* refers only to that part of the upper limb between the shoulder and elbow. *Leg* refers only to that part of the lower limb between the knee and ankle.

A **segment** of a limb is a region between one joint and the next. The arm, for example, is the segment between the shoulder and elbow joints, and the forearm is the segment between the elbow and wrist joints. Flexing your fingers, you can easily see that your thumb has two segments (proximal and distal), whereas the other four digits have three segments (proximal, middle, and distal). The segment concept is especially useful in describing the locations of bones and muscles and the movements of the joints.

# A.3 Body Cavities and Membranes

The body wall encloses multiple **body cavities (fig. A.5, table A.2),** each lined with a membrane and containing internal organs called **viscera** (VISS-er-uh) (singular, *viscus[10]*). Some of these membranes are two-layered, having one layer against the organ surface (such as the heart or lung) and one layer against a surrounding structure (forming, for example, the inner lining of the rib cage); there

[9]*ante* = fore, before; *brachi* = arm
[10]*viscus* = body organ

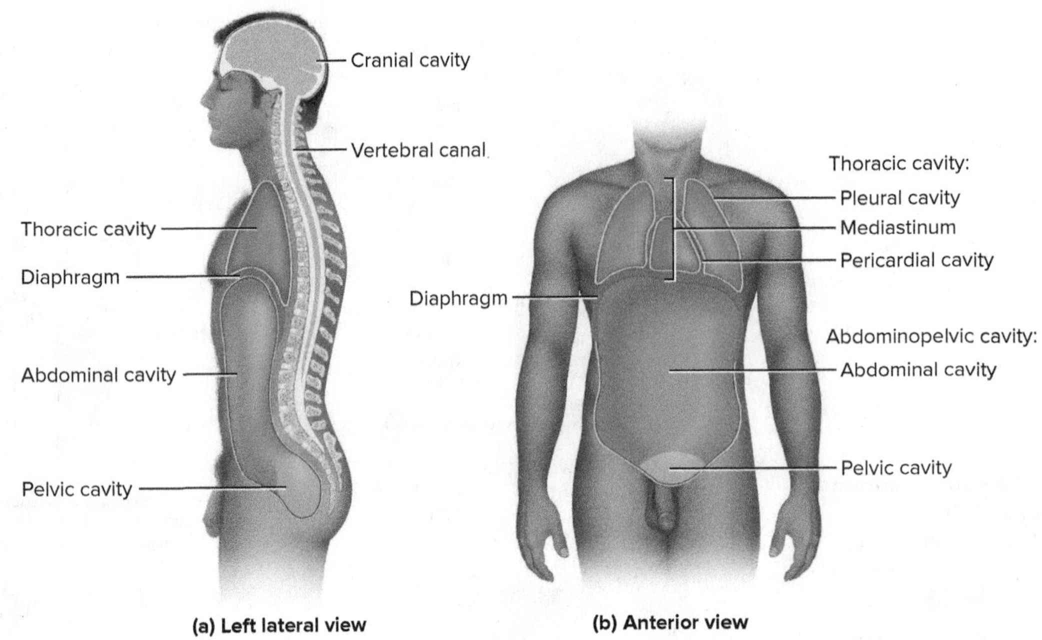


**FIGURE A.5 The Major Body Cavities.** (a) Left lateral view. (b) Anterior view.

**TABLE A.2 Body Cavities and Membranes** APR

| Name of Cavity | Associated Viscera | Membranous Lining |
|---|---|---|
| **Cranial cavity** | Brain | Meninges |
| **Vertebral canal** | Spinal cord | Meninges |
| **Thoracic cavity** | | |
| Pleural cavities (2) | Lungs | Pleurae |
| Pericardial cavity | Heart | Pericardium |
| **Abdominopelvic cavity** | | |
| Abdominal cavity | Digestive organs, spleen, kidneys | Peritoneum |
| Pelvic cavity | Bladder, rectum, reproductive organs | Peritoneum |

is only a thin film of liquid between them. In such cases, the inner layer, against the organ, is called the **visceral layer** (VISS-er-ul) of the membrane, and the more superficial or outer one, the **parietal**[11] **layer** (pa-RY-eh-tul).

## A.3a Cranial Cavity and Vertebral Canal

The **cranial cavity** is enclosed by the cranium (braincase) and contains the brain. The **vertebral canal** is enclosed by the vertebral column (spine) and contains the spinal cord. The two are continuous with each other and are lined by three membrane layers called the **meninges** (meh-NIN-jeez). Among other functions, the meninges protect the delicate nervous tissue from the hard protective bone that encloses it.

## A.3b Thoracic Cavity

The trunk of your body contains two major spaces, the thoracic cavity and abdominopelvic cavity, separated by a transverse muscular sheet, the **diaphragm.** Superior to the diaphragm, in your chest, is the **thoracic cavity,** and inferior to it, in your abdomen, is the **abdominopelvic cavity.** Both cavities are lined with thin **serous membranes,** which secrete a lubricating film of moisture similar to blood serum (hence their name).

The thoracic cavity is divided by a thick median wall called the **mediastinum**[12] (ME-dee-ah-STY-num) **(fig. A.5b).** This is the region between the lungs, extending from the base of the neck to the diaphragm. It is occupied by the heart, the major blood vessels connected to it, the esophagus, the trachea and bronchi, and a gland called the thymus.

The heart is enfolded in a two-layered membrane called the **pericardium.**[13] The inner layer of the pericardium forms the surface of the heart itself and is called the **visceral layer.** The outer layer is called the **parietal layer.** These layers are separated by a space called the **pericardial cavity (fig. A.6a),** which is lubricated by **pericardial fluid.** This space allows the heart freedom of movement during its contraction and relaxation, but can pose a life-threatening problem if it fills with serous fluid or blood (see Deeper Insight A.1).

[11]*pariet* = wall

[12]*mediastinum* = in the middle
[13]*peri* = around; *cardi* = heart

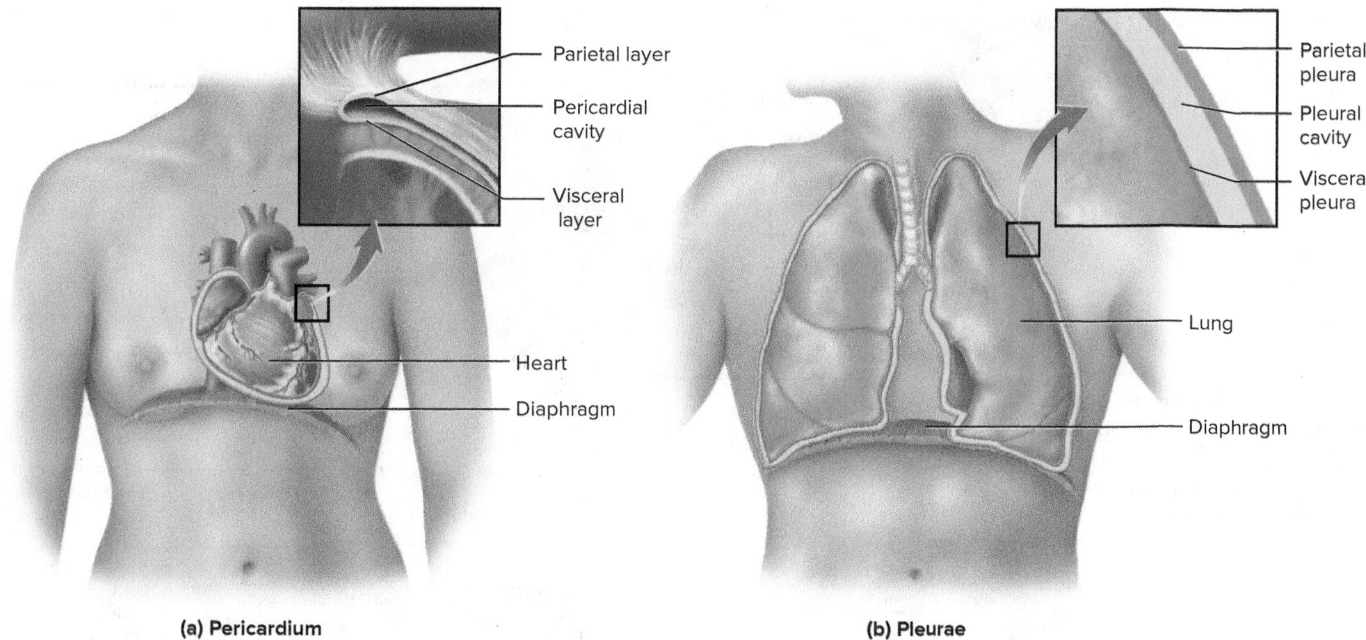


**FIGURE A.6 Parietal and Visceral Layers of Double-Walled Membranes.** (a) Relationship of the pericardium to the heart. (b) Relationship of the pleurae to the lungs.

### Cardiac Tamponade

Being confined by the pericardium can cause a problem for the heart under some circumstances. If a heart wall weakened by disease should rupture, or if it suffers a penetrating injury such as a knife or gunshot wound, blood spurts from the heart into the pericardial cavity, filling the cavity more and more with each heartbeat. Diseased hearts also sometimes seep serous fluid into the pericardial sac. Either way, the effect is the same: The pericardial sac has little room to expand, so the accumulating fluid puts pressure on the heart, squeezing it and preventing it from refilling between beats. This condition is called *cardiac tamponade*. If the heart chambers cannot refill, then cardiac output declines and a person may die of catastrophic circulatory failure. A similar situation occurs if serous fluid or air accumulates in the pleural cavity, causing collapse of a lung.

The right and left sides of the thoracic cavity contain the lungs. Each lung is enfolded by a serous membrane called the **pleura**[14] (PLOOR-uh) **(fig. A.6b).** Like the pericardium, the pleura has visceral (inner) and parietal (outer) layers. The **visceral pleura** forms the external surface of the lung, and the **parietal pleura** lines the inside of the rib cage. The narrow space between them is called the **pleural cavity** (see fig. B.11 in atlas B, following chapter 10). It is lubricated by slippery **pleural fluid.**

Note that in both the pericardium and the pleura, the visceral layer of the membrane *covers* an organ surface and the parietal layer *lines* the inside of a body cavity. We will see this pattern elsewhere, including the abdominopelvic cavity.

[14]*pleur* = rib, side

## A.3c Abdominopelvic Cavity

The abdominopelvic cavity consists of the **abdominal cavity** superiorly and the **pelvic cavity** inferiorly. The abdominal cavity contains most of the digestive organs as well as the spleen, kidneys, and ureters. It extends inferiorly to the level of a bony landmark called the *brim* of the pelvis (see figs. B.7 and 8.36). The pelvic cavity, below the brim, is continuous with the abdominal cavity (no wall separates them), but it is markedly narrower and tilts posteriorly (see fig. A.5a). It contains the rectum, urinary bladder, urethra, and reproductive organs.

The abdominopelvic cavity contains a two-layered serous membrane called the **peritoneum**[15] (PERR-ih-toe-NEE-um). Its outer layer, the **parietal peritoneum,** lines the cavity wall. Along the posterior midline, it turns inward and becomes another layer, the **visceral peritoneum,** suspending certain abdominal viscera from the body wall, covering their outer surfaces, and holding them in place. The **peritoneal cavity** is the space between the parietal and visceral layers. It is lubricated by **peritoneal fluid.**

Some organs of the abdominal cavity lie against the posterior body wall and are covered by peritoneum only on the side facing the peritoneal cavity. They are said to have a **retroperitoneal**[16] position **(fig. A.7).** These include the kidneys, ureters, adrenal glands, most of the pancreas, and abdominal portions of two major blood vessels—the aorta and inferior vena cava (see fig. B.6). Organs that are encircled by peritoneum and connected to the posterior body wall by peritoneal sheets are described as **intraperitoneal.**[17]

The visceral peritoneum is also called a **mesentery**[18] (MESS-en-tare-ee) at points where it forms a translucent, membranous

[15]*peri* = around; *tone* = stretched
[16]*retro* = behind
[17]*intra* = within
[18]*mes* = in the middle; *enter* = intestine

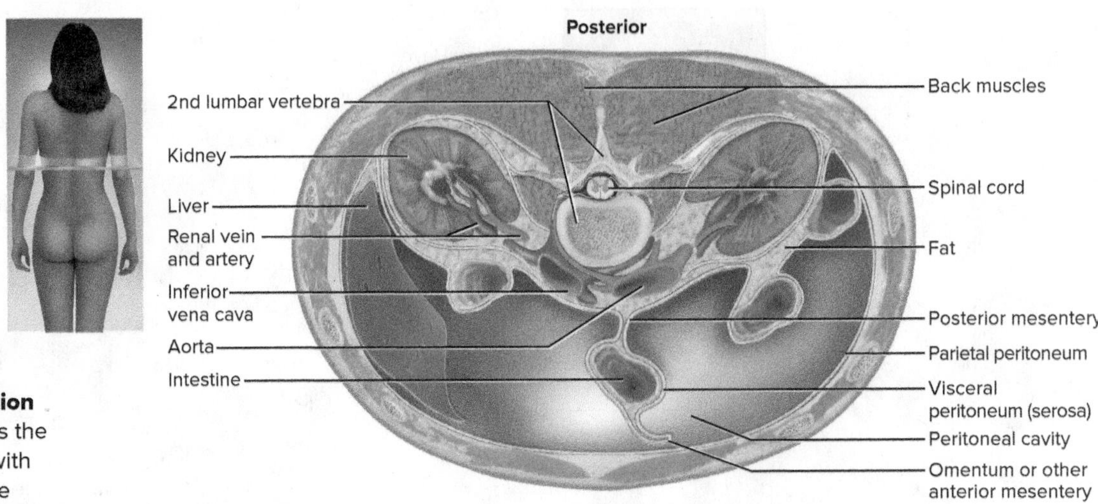


**FIGURE A.7 Transverse Section Through the Abdomen.** Shows the peritoneum, peritoneal cavity (with most viscera omitted), and some retroperitoneal organs.

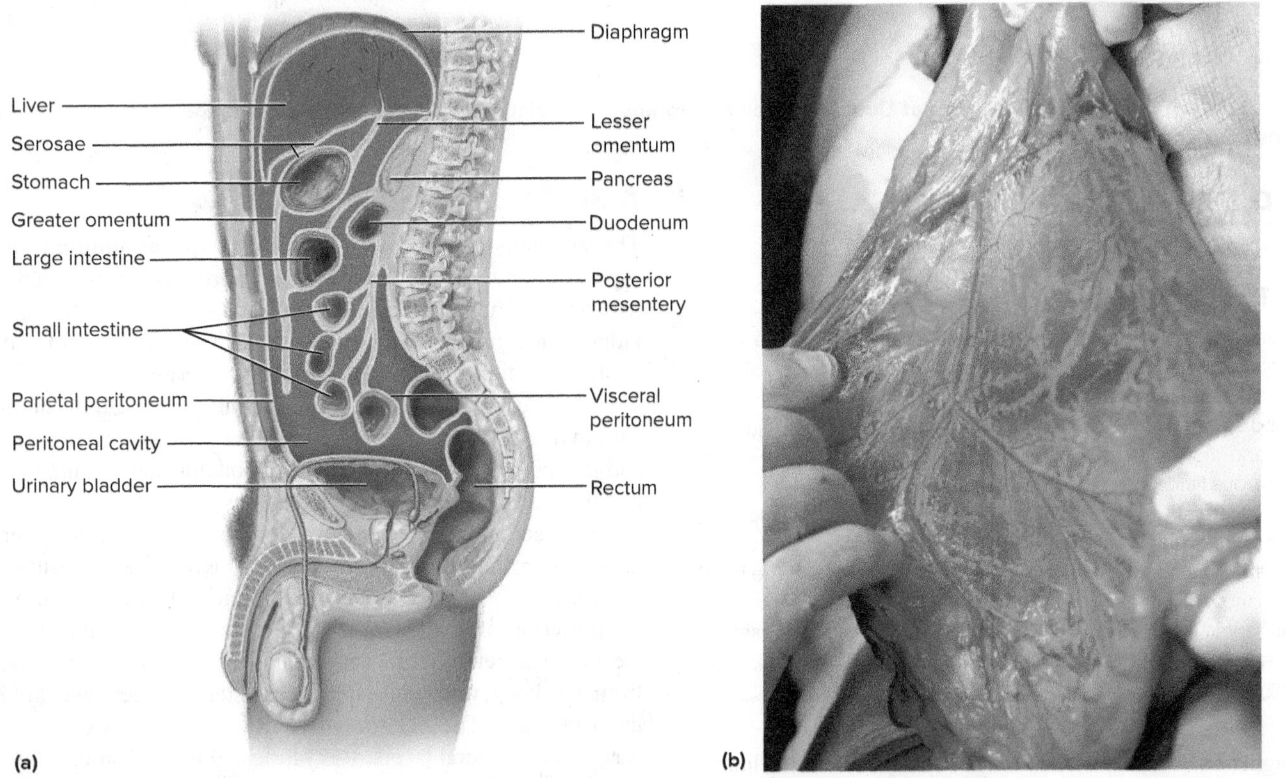


**FIGURE A.8 Serous Membranes of the Abdominal Cavity.** (a) Sagittal section, left lateral view. (b) Photo of the mesentery of the small intestine. Mesenteries contain blood vessels, lymphatic vessels, and nerves supplying the viscera. APR

*Is the urinary bladder in the peritoneal cavity?*

b: MedicImage/Universal Images Group/Getty Images

curtain suspending and anchoring the viscera **(fig. A.8),** and a **serosa** (seer-OH-sa) at points where it enfolds and covers the outer surfaces of organs such as the stomach and small intestine. The intestines are suspended from the posterior (dorsal) abdominal wall by the **posterior mesentery.** The posterior mesentery of the large intestine is called the **mesocolon.** In some places, after wrapping around the intestines or other viscera, the mesentery continues toward the anterior body wall as the **anterior mesentery.** The most significant example of this is a fatty membrane called the **greater omentum,**[19] which hangs like an apron from the inferolateral margin of the stomach and overlies the intestines (figs. A.8a and B.4). The greater omentum is unattached at its inferior border and can be lifted to reveal the intestines. A smaller **lesser omentum** extends from the superomedial margin of the stomach to the liver.

[19]*omentum* = covering

## DEEPER INSIGHT A.2
### CLINICAL APPLICATION

#### *Peritonitis*

Peritonitis is inflammation of the peritoneum. It is a critical, life-threatening condition necessitating prompt treatment. The most serious cause of peritonitis is a perforation in the digestive tract, such as a ruptured appendix or a gunshot wound. Digestive juices cause immediate chemical inflammation of the peritoneum, followed by microbial inflammation as intestinal bacteria invade the body cavity. Anything that perforates the abdominal wall can also lead to peritonitis, such as abdominal trauma or surgery. So, too, can free blood in the abdominal cavity, as from a ruptured aneurysm (a weak point in a blood vessel) or ectopic pregnancy (implantation of an embryo anywhere other than the uterus); blood itself is a chemical irritant to the peritoneum. Peritonitis tends to shift fluid from the circulation into the abdominal cavity. Death can follow within a few days from severe electrolyte imbalance, respiratory distress, kidney failure, and widespread blood clotting called *disseminated intravascular coagulation.*

### A.3d Potential Spaces

Some of the spaces between body membranes are considered to be **potential spaces,** so named because under normal conditions, the membranes are pressed firmly together and there is no actual space between them. The membranes are not physically attached, however, and under unusual conditions, they may separate and create a space filled with fluid or other matter. Thus there is normally no actual space, but only a potential for membranes to separate and create one.

The pleural cavity is one example. Normally the parietal and visceral pleurae are pressed together without a gap between them, but under pathological conditions, air or serous fluid can accumulate between the membranes and open up a space. The internal cavity **(lumen)** of the uterus is another. In a nonpregnant uterus, the mucous membranes of opposite walls are pressed together so that there is no open space in the organ. In pregnancy, of course, a growing fetus occupies this space and pushes the mucous membranes apart.

## A.4 Organ Systems

The human body has 11 **organ systems (fig. A.9)** and an immune system, which is better described as a population of cells that inhabit multiple organs rather than as an organ system. The organ systems are classified in the following list by their principal functions, but this is an unavoidably flawed classification. Some organs belong to two or more systems—for example, the male urethra is part of both the urinary and reproductive systems; the pharynx is part of the respiratory and digestive systems; and the mammary glands can be considered part of the integumentary and female reproductive systems. The organ systems are as follows:

**Systems of protection, support, and movement**
Integumentary system
Skeletal system
Muscular system

**Systems of internal communication and control**
Nervous system
Endocrine system

**Systems of fluid transport**
Circulatory system
Lymphatic system

**Systems of intake and output**
Respiratory system
Urinary system
Digestive system

**Systems of reproduction**
Male reproductive system
Female reproductive system

Some medical terms combine the names of two systems—for example, the *musculoskeletal system, cardiopulmonary system,* and *urogenital (genitourinary) system.* These terms serve to call attention to the close anatomical or physiological relationships between two systems, but these are not literally individual organ systems.

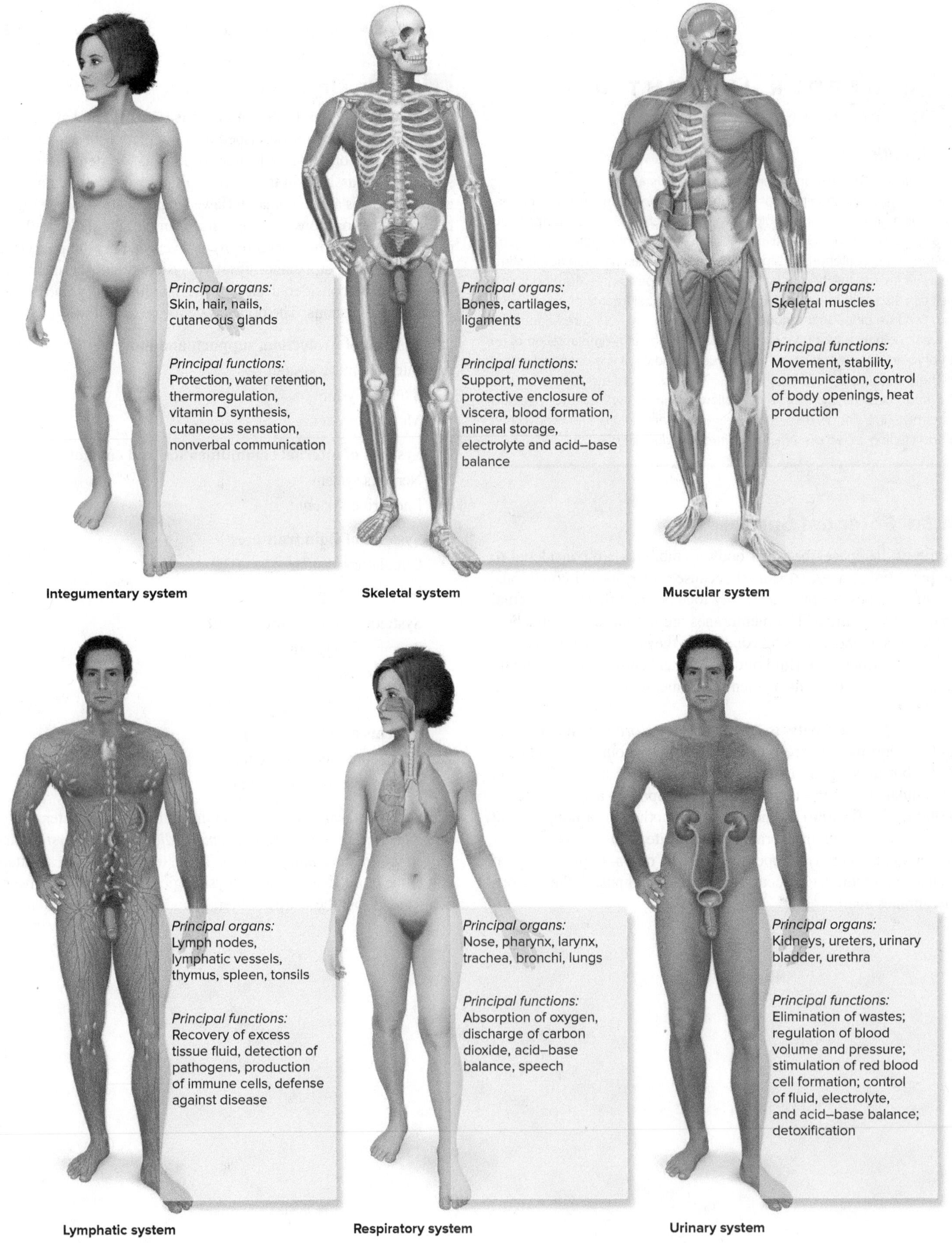

*Principal organs:*
Skin, hair, nails, cutaneous glands

*Principal functions:*
Protection, water retention, thermoregulation, vitamin D synthesis, cutaneous sensation, nonverbal communication

**Integumentary system**

*Principal organs:*
Bones, cartilages, ligaments

*Principal functions:*
Support, movement, protective enclosure of viscera, blood formation, mineral storage, electrolyte and acid–base balance

**Skeletal system**

*Principal organs:*
Skeletal muscles

*Principal functions:*
Movement, stability, communication, control of body openings, heat production

**Muscular system**

*Principal organs:*
Lymph nodes, lymphatic vessels, thymus, spleen, tonsils

*Principal functions:*
Recovery of excess tissue fluid, detection of pathogens, production of immune cells, defense against disease

**Lymphatic system**

*Principal organs:*
Nose, pharynx, larynx, trachea, bronchi, lungs

*Principal functions:*
Absorption of oxygen, discharge of carbon dioxide, acid–base balance, speech

**Respiratory system**

*Principal organs:*
Kidneys, ureters, urinary bladder, urethra

*Principal functions:*
Elimination of wastes; regulation of blood volume and pressure; stimulation of red blood cell formation; control of fluid, electrolyte, and acid–base balance; detoxification

**Urinary system**

**FIGURE A.9 The Human Organ Systems.**

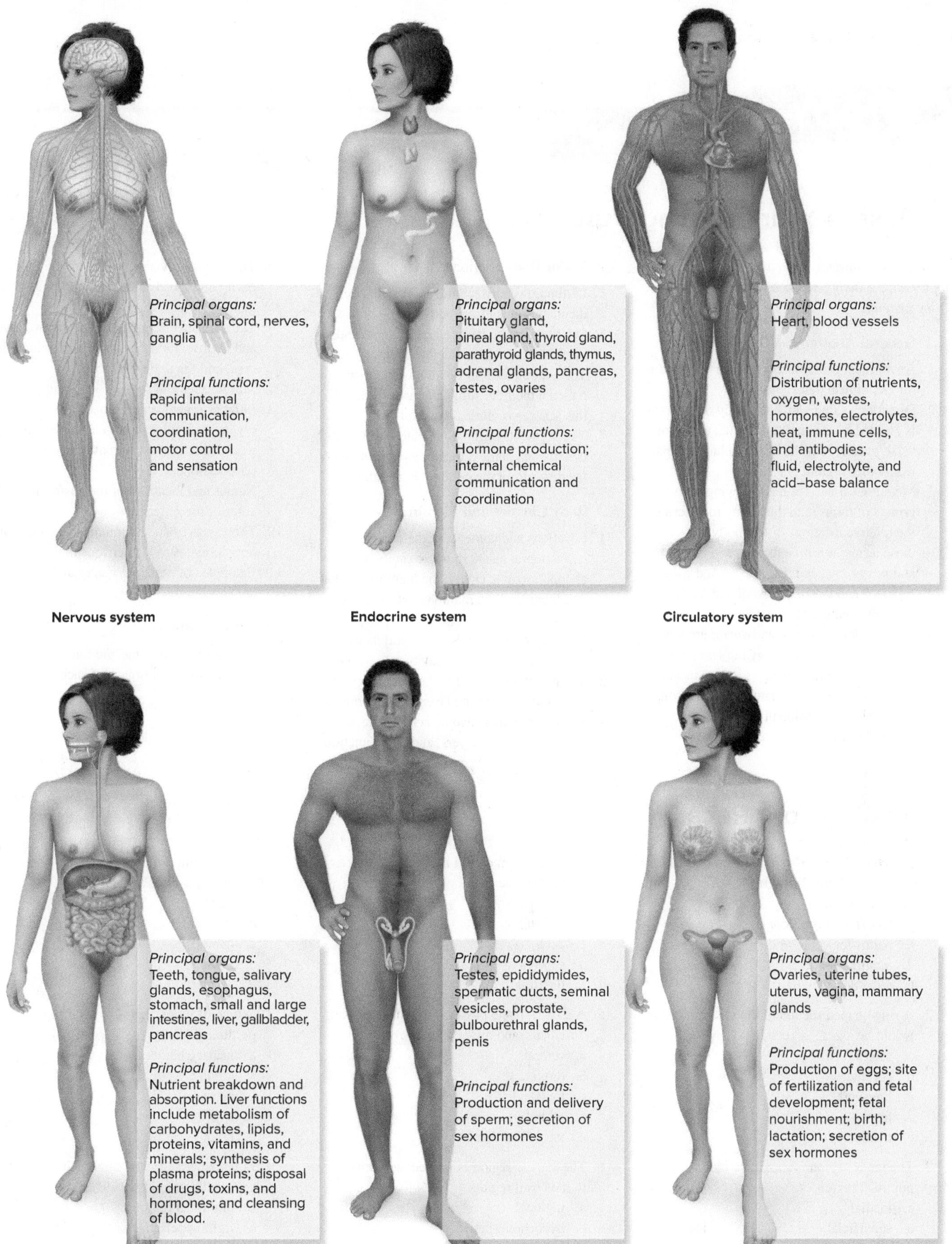

*Principal organs:*
Brain, spinal cord, nerves, ganglia
*Principal functions:*
Rapid internal communication, coordination, motor control and sensation
Nervous system
*Principal organs:*
Pituitary gland, pineal gland, thyroid gland, parathyroid glands, thymus, adrenal glands, pancreas, testes, ovaries
*Principal functions:*
Hormone production; internal chemical communication and coordination
Endocrine system
*Principal organs:*
Heart, blood vessels
*Principal functions:*
Distribution of nutrients, oxygen, wastes, hormones, electrolytes, heat, immune cells, and antibodies; fluid, electrolyte, and acid–base balance
Circulatory system
*Principal organs:*
Teeth, tongue, salivary glands, esophagus, stomach, small and large intestines, liver, gallbladder, pancreas
*Principal functions:*
Nutrient breakdown and absorption. Liver functions include metabolism of carbohydrates, lipids, proteins, vitamins, and minerals; synthesis of plasma proteins; disposal of drugs, toxins, and hormones; and cleansing of blood.
Digestive system
*Principal organs:*
Testes, epididymides, spermatic ducts, seminal vesicles, prostate, bulbourethral glands, penis
*Principal functions:*
Production and delivery of sperm; secretion of sex hormones
Male reproductive system
*Principal organs:*
Ovaries, uterine tubes, uterus, vagina, mammary glands
*Principal functions:*
Production of eggs; site of fertilization and fetal development; fetal nourishment; birth; lactation; secretion of sex hormones
Female reproductive system


**FIGURE A.9 The Human Organ Systems (continued).**

# STUDY GUIDE

## Assess Your Learning Outcomes

*To test your knowledge, discuss the following topics with a study partner or in writing, ideally from memory.*

### A.1 General Anatomical Terminology

1. Anatomical position and why it is important for anatomical description
2. Directions along which the body or an organ is divided by the sagittal, frontal, and transverse planes; how the median plane differs from other sagittal planes
3. Meanings of each of the following pairs or groups of terms, and the ability to describe the relative locations of two body parts using these terms: *ventral* and *dorsal; anterior* and *posterior; cephalic, rostral,* and *caudal; superior* and *inferior; medial* and *lateral; proximal* and *distal; superficial* and *deep*
4. Why the terms *ventral* and *dorsal* are ambiguous in human anatomy but less so in most other animals; what terms are used in their place in human anatomy; and reasons why they are occasionally appropriate or unavoidable in human anatomy

### A.2 Major Body Regions

1. Distinctions between the axial and appendicular regions of the body
2. Subdivisions of the axial region and landmarks that divide and define them
3. The abdomen's four quadrants and nine regions; their defining landmarks; and why this scheme is clinically useful
4. The segments of the upper and lower limbs; how the anatomical meanings of *arm* and *leg* differ from the colloquial meanings

### A.3 Body Cavities and Membranes

1. Locations and contents of the cranial cavity, vertebral canal, thoracic cavity, and abdominopelvic cavity; the membranes that line them; and the main viscera contained in each
2. Contents of the mediastinum and its relationship to the thoracic cavity as a whole
3. The pericardium, its two layers, the space and fluid between the layers, and its function
4. The pleurae, their two layers, the space and fluid between the layers, and their function
5. The two subdivisions of the abdominopelvic cavity and the skeletal landmark that divides them
6. The peritoneum; its functions; its two layers and their relationship to the abdominal viscera; and the peritoneal fluid
7. Mesenteries and serosae
8. Intraperitoneal versus retroperitoneal organs, examples of both, and how one would identify an organ as being intra- or retroperitoneal
9. Names and locations of the posterior and anterior mesenteries
10. The serosa of an abdominopelvic organ and how it relates to the peritoneum
11. Examples of potential spaces and why they are so named

### A.4 Organ Systems

1. The 11 organ systems, the functions of each, and the principal organs of each system

## Testing Your Recall

*Answers in Appendix A*

1. Which of the following is *not* an essential part of anatomical position?
   a. feet together
   b. feet flat on the floor
   c. palms forward
   d. mouth closed
   e. arms down to the sides
2. A ring-shaped section of the small intestine would be a ______ section.
   a. sagittal
   b. coronal
   c. transverse
   d. frontal
   e. median
3. The tarsal region is ______ to the popliteal region.
   a. medial
   b. superficial
   c. superior
   d. dorsal
   e. distal
4. The greater omentum is ______ to the small intestine.
   a. posterior
   b. parietal
   c. deep
   d. superficial
   e. proximal
5. A ______ plane passes through the sternum, umbilicus, and mons pubis.
   a. central
   b. proximal
   c. midclavicular
   d. midsagittal
   e. intertubercular
6. The ______ region is immediately medial to the coxal region.
   a. inguinal
   b. hypochondriac
   c. umbilical
   d. popliteal
   e. cubital
7. Which of the following regions is not part of the upper limb?
   a. plantar
   b. carpal
   c. cubital
   d. brachial
   e. palmar
8. Which of these organs is within the peritoneal cavity?
   a. urinary bladder
   b. kidneys
   c. heart
   d. liver
   e. brain
9. In which area do you think pain from the gallbladder would be felt?
   a. umbilical region
   b. right upper quadrant
   c. hypogastric region
   d. left hypochondriac region
   e. left lower quadrant

# STUDY GUIDE

10. Which organ system regulates blood volume, controls acid–base balance, and stimulates red blood cell production?
    a. digestive system
    b. lymphatic system
    c. nervous system
    d. urinary system
    e. circulatory system
11. The translucent membranes that suspend the intestines and hold them in place are called ______.
12. The superficial layer of the pleura is called the ______ pleura.
13. The right and left pleural cavities are separated by a thick wall called the ______.
14. The back of the neck is the ______ region.
15. The manual region is more commonly known as the ______ and the pedal region is more commonly known as the ______.
16. The cranial cavity is lined by membranes called the ______.
17. Organs that lie within the abdominal cavity but not within the peritoneal cavity are said to have a ______ position.
18. The sternal region is ______ to the pectoral region.
19. The pelvic cavity can be described as ______ to the abdominal cavity in position.
20. The anterior pit of the elbow is the ______ region, and the corresponding (but posterior) pit of the knee is the ______ region.

## Building Your Medical Vocabulary

*Answers in Appendix A*

*State a meaning of each word element, and give a medical term from this atlas that uses it or a slight variation of it.*

1. ante-
2. cervico-
3. epi-
4. hypo-
5. inguino-
6. intra-
7. parieto-
8. peri-
9. retro-
10. sagitto-

## What's Wrong with These Statements?

*Answers in Appendix A*

*Briefly explain why each of the following statements is false, or reword it to make it true.*

1. Both lungs could be shown in one sagittal section of the body.
2. A single frontal section of the head cannot include both eyes.
3. The knee is distal to the tarsal region.
4. The diaphragm is posterior to the lungs.
5. The esophagus is inferior to the stomach.
6. The liver is in the lumbar region.
7. The heart is in the space between the parietal and visceral pericardium, called the pericardial cavity.
8. The kidneys are in the peritoneal cavity of the abdomen.
9. The peritoneum lines the inside of the stomach and intestines.
10. The sigmoid colon is in the lower right quadrant of the abdomen.

## Testing Your Comprehension

1. Identify which anatomical plane—sagittal, frontal, or transverse—is the only one that could *not* show (a) both the brain and tongue, (b) both eyes, (c) both the hypogastric and gluteal regions, (d) both kidneys, (e) both the sternum and vertebral column, and (f) both the heart and uterus.
2. Laypeople often misunderstand anatomical terminology. What do you think people really mean when they say they have "planter's warts"?
3. Name one structure or anatomical feature that could be found in each of the following locations relative to the ribs: medial, lateral, superior, inferior, deep, superficial, posterior, and anterior. Try not to use the same example twice.
4. Based on the illustrations in this atlas, identify an internal organ that is (a) in the upper left quadrant and retroperitoneal, (b) in the lower right quadrant of the peritoneal cavity, (c) in the hypogastric region, (d) in the right hypochondriac region, and (e) in the pectoral region.
5. Why do you think people with imaginary illnesses came to be called hypochondriacs?

CHAPTER 2

# THE CHEMISTRY OF LIFE

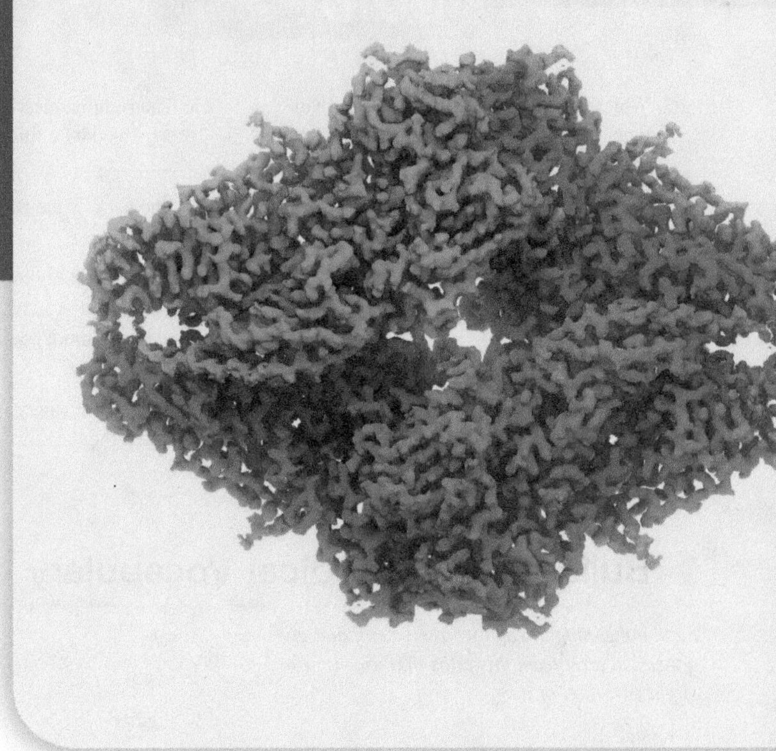

**Coronavirus protein seen by cryo-electron microscopy (cryo-EM), using the electron microscope and a supercomputer to image supercooled proteins and reveal structure even to the level of individual atoms**

NCI/Science Source

## CHAPTER OUTLINE



## DEEPER INSIGHTS

**Module 2: Cells and Chemistry**

## BRUSHING UP

Beginning here, each chapter builds on information presented in earlier ones. If you do not clearly remember these concepts, you may find that brushing up on them before you proceed will enable you to get more out of each new chapter.

- "Characteristics of Life" in section 1.6a introduces metabolism as one of the most fundamental human functions. Here we will delve more deeply into metabolism and its two subdivisions, anabolism and catabolism.

Why is too much sodium or cholesterol harmful? Why does an iron deficiency cause anemia and an iodine deficiency cause a goiter? Why does a pH imbalance make some drugs less effective? Why do some pregnant women suffer convulsions after several days of vomiting? How can radiation cause cancer as well as cure it?

None of these questions can be answered, nor would the rest of this book be intelligible, without understanding the chemistry of life. A little knowledge of chemistry can help you choose a healthy diet, use medications more wisely, avoid worthless health fads and frauds, and explain treatments and procedures to your patients or clients. Thus, we begin our study of the human body with basic chemistry, the simplest level of the body's structural organization.

We will progress from general chemistry to **biochemistry,** study of the molecules that compose living organisms—especially molecules unique to living things, such as carbohydrates, fats, proteins, and nucleic acids. Most people have at least heard of these; it's common knowledge that we need proteins, fats, carbohydrates, vitamins, and minerals in our diet, and that we should avoid consuming too much saturated fat and cholesterol. But most people have only a vague concept of what these molecules are, much less how they function in the body. Such knowledge is very helpful in matters of personal fitness and patient education and is essential to the comprehension of the rest of this book.

## 2.1 Atoms, Ions, and Molecules

### Expected Learning Outcomes

When you have completed this section, you should be able to

a. identify the elements of the body from their symbols;
b. distinguish between elements and compounds;
c. state the functions of minerals in the body;
d. explain the basis for radioactivity and the types and hazards of ionizing radiation;
e. distinguish between ions, electrolytes, and free radicals; and
f. define the types of chemical bonds.

### 2.1a The Chemical Elements

A chemical **element** is the simplest form of matter to have unique chemical properties. Water, for example, has unique properties, but it can be broken down into two elements, hydrogen and oxygen, that have unique chemical properties of their own. If we carry this process any further, however, we find that hydrogen and oxygen are made of protons, neutrons, and electrons—and none of these are unique. A proton of gold is identical to a proton of oxygen. Hydrogen and oxygen are the simplest chemically unique components of water and are thus elements.

Each element is identified by an *atomic number,* the number of protons in its nucleus. The atomic number of carbon is 6 and that of oxygen is 8, for example. The periodic table of the elements (see appendix C) arranges the elements in order by their atomic numbers. The elements are represented by one- or two-letter symbols, usually based on their English names: C for carbon, Mg for magnesium, Cl for chlorine, and so forth. A few symbols are based on Latin names, such as K for potassium *(kalium),* Na for sodium *(natrium),* and Fe for iron *(ferrum).*

There are 91 naturally occurring elements on earth, 24 of which play normal physiological roles in humans. **Table 2.1** groups these 24 according to their abundance in the body. Six of them account for 98.5% of the body's weight: oxygen, carbon, hydrogen, nitrogen, calcium, and phosphorus. The next 0.8% consists of another 6 elements: sulfur, potassium, sodium, chlorine, magnesium, and iron. The remaining 12 elements account for 0.7% of body weight, and no one of them accounts for more than 0.02%; thus, they are

**TABLE 2.1 Elements of the Human Body**

| Name and Symbol | Percentage of Body Weight | Name and Symbol | Percentage of Body Weight |
|---|---|---|---|
| **Major Elements (Total 98.5%)** | | | |
| Oxygen (O) | 65.0 | Nitrogen (N) | 3.0 |
| Carbon (C) | 18.0 | Calcium (Ca) | 1.5 |
| Hydrogen (H) | 10.0 | Phosphorus (P) | 1.0 |
| **Lesser Elements (Total 0.8%)** | | | |
| Sulfur (S) | 0.25 | Chlorine (Cl) | 0.15 |
| Potassium (K) | 0.20 | Magnesium (Mg) | 0.05 |
| Sodium (Na) | 0.15 | Iron (Fe) | 0.006 |
| **Trace Elements (Total 0.7%) (Names and symbols only)** | | | |
| Chromium (Cr) | Fluorine (F) | Molybdenum (Mo) | Tin (Sn) |
| Cobalt (Co) | Iodine (I) | Selenium (Se) | Vanadium (V) |
| Copper (Cu) | Manganese (Mn) | Silicon (Si) | Zinc (Zn) |

known as **trace elements.** Despite their minute quantities, trace elements play vital roles in physiology. Other elements without natural physiological roles can contaminate the body and severely disrupt its functions, as in heavy-metal poisoning with lead or mercury.

Several of these elements are classified as **minerals**—inorganic elements extracted from the soil by plants and passed up the food chain to humans and other organisms. Minerals constitute about 4% of the human body by weight. Nearly three-quarters of this is Ca and P; the rest is mainly Cl, Mg, K, Na, and S. Minerals contribute significantly to body structure. The bones and teeth consist partly of crystals of calcium, phosphate, magnesium, fluoride, and sulfate ions. Many proteins include sulfur, and phosphorus is a major component of nucleic acids, ATP, and cell membranes. Minerals also enable enzymes and other organic molecules to function. Iodine is a component of thyroid hormone; iron is a component of hemoglobin; and some enzymes function only when manganese, zinc, copper, or other minerals are bound to them. The electrolytes needed for nerve and muscle function are mineral salts. The biological roles of minerals are discussed in more detail in chapters 24 and 26.

## 2.1b Atomic Structure

In the fifth century BCE, the Greek philosopher Democritus reasoned that we can cut matter such as a gold nugget into smaller and smaller pieces, but there must ultimately be particles so small that nothing could cut them. He called these imaginary particles **atoms**[1] ("indivisible"). Atoms were only a philosophical concept until 1803, when English chemist John Dalton began to develop an atomic theory based on experimental evidence. In 1913, Danish physicist Niels Bohr proposed a model of atomic structure similar to planets orbiting the sun **(fig. 2.1).** Although this *planetary model* is too simple to account for many of the properties of atoms, it remains useful for elementary purposes.

At the center of an atom is the *nucleus,* composed of protons and neutrons. **Protons ($p^+$)** have a single positive charge and **neutrons ($n^0$)** have no charge. Each proton or neutron weighs approximately 1 *atomic mass unit (amu).* The *atomic mass* of an element is approximately equal to its total number of protons and neutrons.

Around the nucleus are one or more clouds of **electrons ($e^-$),** tiny particles with a single negative charge and very low mass. It takes 1,836 electrons to equal the mass of one proton, so for most purposes we can disregard their mass. A person who weighs 64 kg (140 lb) contains less than 24 g (1 oz) of electrons. This hardly means that we can ignore electrons, however. They determine the chemical properties of an atom, thereby governing what molecules can exist and what chemical reactions can occur. The number of electrons equals the number of protons, so their charges cancel each other and an atom is electrically neutral.

Electrons swarm about the nucleus in concentric regions called *electron shells (energy levels).* The more energy an electron has, the farther away from the nucleus its orbit lies. Each shell holds a limited number of electrons. The elements known to date have up to seven electron shells, but those ordinarily involved in human physiology do not exceed four. Electrons of the outermost shell, called **valence electrons,** determine the chemical bonding properties of an atom. Illustrations of atoms greatly understate the distances between their nuclei and electrons in order to fit the page. If you imagine the nucleus of an atom to be the size of a basketball, its nearest electron would be about 48 km (30 mi.) away. In other words, atoms (and your body) consist mostly of empty space!

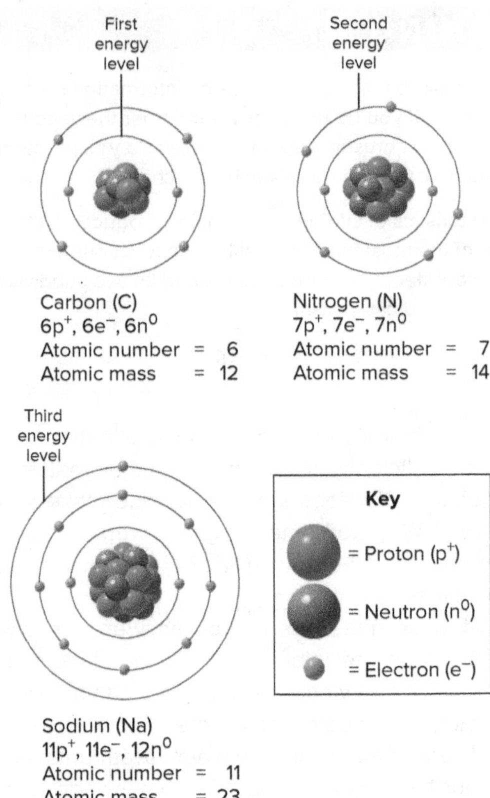


**FIGURE 2.1 Bohr Planetary Models of Three Representative Elements.** Note the filling of electron shells as atomic number increases.

## 2.1c Isotopes and Radioactivity

Dalton believed that every atom of an element was identical. We now know, however, that all elements have varieties called **isotopes,**[2] which differ from one another only in number of neutrons and therefore in atomic mass. Hydrogen atoms, for example, have only one proton. In the most common isotope, symbolized $^1H$, that is all there is to the nucleus. Hydrogen has two other isotopes, however: *deuterium* ($^2H$) with one proton and one neutron, and *tritium* ($^3H$) with one proton and two neutrons **(fig. 2.3).** Over 99% of carbon atoms have an atomic mass of 12 ($6p^+, 6n^0$)

[1] *a* = not; *tom* = cut

[2] *iso* = same; *top* = place (same position in the periodic table)

## DEEPER INSIGHT 2.1
### MEDICAL HISTORY

### Radiation and Madame Curie

In 1896, French scientist Henri Becquerel (1852–1908) discovered that uranium darkened photographic plates through several thick layers of paper. Marie Curie (1867–1934) and her husband Pierre Curie (1859–1906) discovered that polonium and radium did likewise. Marie Curie coined the term *radioactivity* for the emission of energy by these elements. Becquerel and the Curies shared a Nobel Prize in 1903 for this discovery.

Marie Curie **(fig. 2.2)** was not only the first woman in the world to receive a Nobel Prize but also the first woman in France to receive a Ph.D. She received a second Nobel Prize in 1911 for further work in radiation. Curie crusaded to train women for careers in science, and in World War I, she and her daughter, Irène Joliot-Curie (1897–1956), trained physicians in the use of X-ray machines. Marie pioneered radiation therapy for breast and uterine cancer.

In the wake of such discoveries, radium was regarded as a wonder drug. Unaware of its danger, people drank radium tonics and flocked to health spas to bathe in radium-enriched waters. Marie herself suffered extensive damage to her hands from handling radioactive minerals and died of radiation poisoning at age 67. The following year, Irène and her husband, Frédéric Joliot (1900–1958), were awarded a Nobel Prize for work in artificial radioactivity and synthetic radioisotopes. Apparently also a martyr to her science, Irène died of leukemia, possibly induced by radiation exposure.

**FIGURE 2.2 Marie Curie (1867–1934).** This portrait was made in 1911, when Curie received her second Nobel Prize.
Source: Library of Congress Prints and Photographs Division

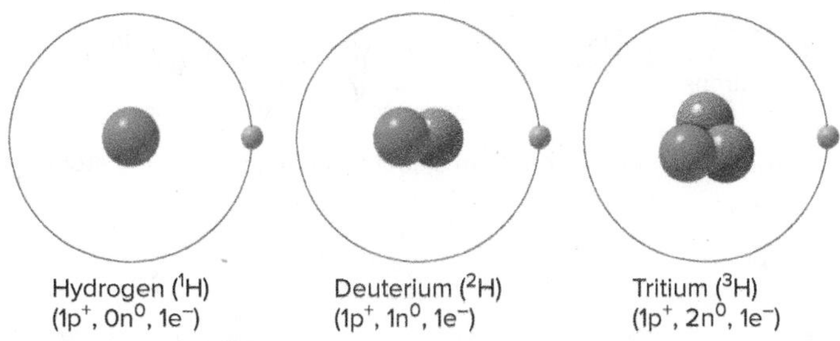


**FIGURE 2.3 Isotopes of Hydrogen.** The three isotopes differ only in the number of neutrons present.

and are called carbon-12 ($^{12}$C), but a small percentage of carbon atoms are $^{13}$C, with seven neutrons, and $^{14}$C, with eight. All isotopes of a given element behave the same chemically. Deuterium ($^2$H), for example, reacts with oxygen the same way $^1$H does to produce water.

The *atomic weight (relative atomic mass)* of an element accounts for the fact that an element is a mixture of isotopes. If all carbon were $^{12}$C, the atomic weight of carbon would be the same as its atomic mass, 12.000. But since a sample of carbon also contains small amounts of the heavier isotopes $^{13}$C and $^{14}$C, the atomic weight is slightly higher, 12.011.

Although different isotopes of an element exhibit identical chemical behavior, they differ in physical behavior. Many of them are unstable and *decay* (break down) to more stable isotopes by giving off radiation. Unstable isotopes are therefore called **radioisotopes,** and the process of decay is called **radioactivity** (see Deeper Insight 2.1). Every element has at least one radioisotope. Oxygen, for example, has three stable isotopes and five radioisotopes. All of us contain radioisotopes such as $^{14}$C and $^{40}$K—that is, we are all mildly radioactive!

High-energy radiation, such as that emitted by radioisotopes, ejects electrons from atoms, converting atoms to ions; thus, it is called **ionizing radiation.** It destroys molecules and produces dangerous free radicals and ions in human tissues. In high doses, ionizing radiation is quickly fatal. In lower doses, it can be *mutagenic* (causing mutations in DNA) and *carcinogenic* (triggering cancer as a result of mutation).

Examples of ionizing radiation include ultraviolet rays, X-rays, and three kinds of radiation produced by nuclear decay: *alpha ($\alpha$) particles, beta ($\beta$) particles,* and *gamma ($\gamma$) rays.* An alpha particle consists of two protons and two neutrons (equivalent to a helium nucleus), and a beta particle is a free electron. Alpha particles are too large to penetrate the skin, and beta particles penetrate only a few millimeters. They're relatively harmless when emitted by sources outside the body, but very dangerous when emitted by radioisotopes that have gotten into the body. Strontium-90 ($^{90}$Sr), for example, has been released by nuclear accidents and the atmospheric testing of nuclear weapons. It settles onto pastures and contaminates cow's milk. In the body, it behaves chemically like calcium, becoming incorporated into the bones, where it emits beta particles for years. Uranium and plutonium emit gamma rays. Because of their high penetrating power, these are very dangerous even when emitted by sources outside the body.

Each radioisotope has a characteristic **physical half-life,** the time required for 50% of its atoms to decay to a more stable isotope. One gram of $^{90}Sr$, for example, would be half gone in 28 years. In 56 years, there would still be 0.25 g left, in 84 years 0.125 g, and so forth. Many radioisotopes are much longer-lived. The half-life of $^{40}K$, for example, is 1.3 billion years. Nuclear power plants produce hundreds of radioisotopes that will be intensely radioactive for at least 10,000 years—longer than the life of any disposal container yet conceived.

The **biological half-life** of a radioisotope is the time required for half of it to disappear from the body. Some is lost by radioactive decay and even more by excretion from the body. Cesium-137, for example, has a physical half-life of 30 years but a biological half-life of only 17 days. Chemically, it behaves like potassium; it is quite mobile and rapidly excreted by the kidneys.

There are several ways to measure the intensity of ionizing radiation, the amount absorbed by the body, and its biological effects. To understand the units of measurement requires a grounding in physics beyond the scope of this book, but the standard international (SI) unit of radiation dosage is the *sievert*[3] *(Sv),* which takes into account the type and intensity of radiation and its biological effect. Doses of 5 Sv or more are usually fatal. The average person worldwide receives about 2.4 millisieverts (mSv) per year in *background radiation* from natural sources and another 0.6 mSv from artificial sources. The most significant natural source is *radon,* a gas produced by the decay of uranium in the earth; it can accumulate in buildings to unhealthy levels. Artificial sources of radiation exposure include medical X-rays, CT and PET scans, radiation therapy, and consumer products such as color televisions, smoke detectors, and luminous watch dials. A CT scan averages about 10 to 30 mSv for a full-body scan and 10 mSv for an abdominopelvic scan only; a typical mammogram is 0.4 to 0.6 mSv; a chest X-ray is about 0.1 mSv; and a hand or foot X-ray is about 0.001 mSv. Such voluntary exposure must be considered from the standpoint of its risk-to-benefit ratio. The benefits of a smoke detector or mammogram far outweigh the risk from the low levels of radiation involved. Radiation therapists and radiologists face a greater risk than their patients, however, and astronauts and airline flight crews receive more than average exposure. U.S. federal standards set a limit of 50 mSv/year as acceptable occupational exposure to ionizing radiation.

## 2.1d Ions, Electrolytes, and Free Radicals

**Ions** are charged particles with unequal numbers of protons and electrons. An ion can consist of a single atom with a positive or negative charge (such as $Na^+$ or $Cl^-$); a group of atoms such as phosphate ($PO_4^{3-}$) and bicarbonate ($HCO_3^-$) ions; or a molecule as large as a protein with many charges on it.

Ions form because elements with one to three valence electrons tend to give them up, and those with four to seven electrons tend to gain more. If an atom of the first kind is exposed to an atom of the second, electrons may transfer from one to the other and turn both of them into ions. This process is called *ionization.* The particle that gains electrons acquires a negative charge and is called an **anion** (AN-eye-on). The one that loses electrons acquires a positive charge (because it then has a surplus of protons) and is called a **cation** (CAT-eye-on).

This happens, for example, when sodium and chlorine meet **(fig. 2.4).** One electron transfers from sodium to chlorine, producing a sodium ion with a unit positive charge ($Na^+$) and a chloride ion with a unit negative charge ($Cl^-$).

Some elements exist in two or more ionized forms. Iron, for example, has ferrous ($Fe^{2+}$) and ferric ($Fe^{3+}$) ions. Note that some ions have a single positive or negative charge, whereas others have

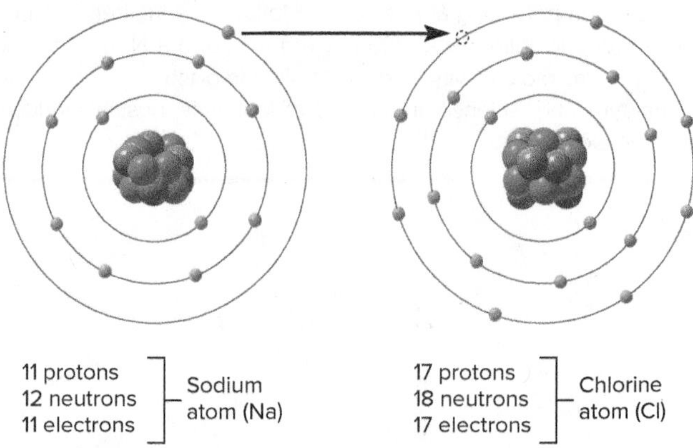


(1) Transfer of an electron from a sodium atom to a chlorine atom

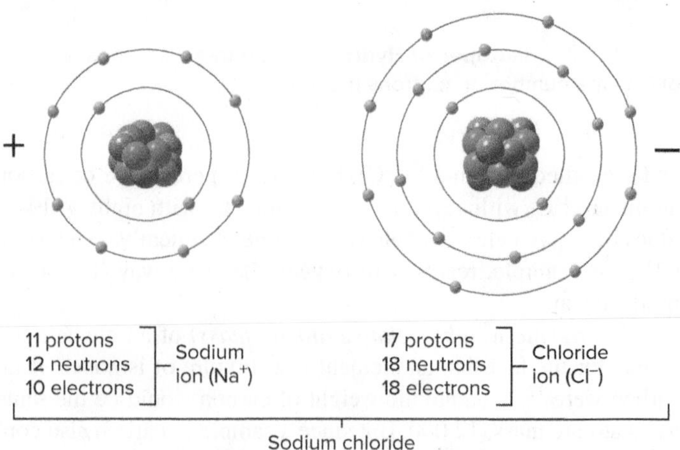


(2) The charged sodium ion ($Na^+$) and chloride ion ($Cl^-$) that result

**FIGURE 2.4 Ionization.**

[3]Rolf Maximillian Sievert (1896–1966), Swedish radiologist

**TABLE 2.2 Major Electrolytes and the Ions Released by their Dissociation**

| Electrolyte | | Cations and Anions |
|---|---|---|
| Calcium chloride ($CaCl_2$) | ⟶ | $Ca^{2+} + 2\ Cl^-$ |
| Disodium phosphate ($Na_2HPO_4$) | ⟶ | $2\ Na^+ + HPO_4^{2-}$ |
| Magnesium chloride ($MgCl_2$) | ⟶ | $Mg^{2+} + 2\ Cl^-$ |
| Potassium chloride (KCl) | ⟶ | $K^+ + Cl^-$ |
| Sodium bicarbonate ($NaHCO_3$) | ⟶ | $Na^+ + HCO_3^-$ |
| Sodium chloride (NaCl) | ⟶ | $Na^+ + Cl^-$ |

charges of ±2 or ±3 because they gain or lose more than one electron. The charge on an ion is called its *valence*.

Ions with opposite charges are attracted to each other and tend to follow each other through the body. Thus, when $Na^+$ is excreted in the urine, $Cl^-$ tends to follow it. The attraction of cations and anions to each other is especially important in the excitation of muscle and nerve cells, as we shall see in chapters 11 and 12.

**Electrolytes** are substances that ionize in water (acids, bases, or salts) and form solutions capable of conducting electricity **(table 2.2).** We can detect electrical activity of the muscles, heart, and brain with electrodes on the skin because electrolytes in the body fluids conduct electrical currents from these organs to the skin surface. Electrolytes are important for their chemical reactivity (as when calcium phosphate becomes incorporated into bone), osmotic effects (influence on water content and distribution in the body), and electrical effects (which are essential to nerve and muscle function). Electrolyte balance is one of the most important considerations in patient care (see section 24.2). Electrolyte imbalances have effects ranging from muscle cramps and brittle bones to coma and cardiac arrest.

**Free radicals** are unstable, highly reactive chemical particles with an odd number of electrons. For example, oxygen normally exists as a stable molecule composed of two oxygen atoms, $O_2$; but if an additional electron is added, it becomes a free radical called the *superoxide anion,* $O_2^{-}\bullet$. Free radicals are represented with a dot to symbolize the odd electron.

Free radicals are produced by some normal metabolic reactions of the body (such as the ATP-producing oxidation reactions in mitochondria, and a reaction that some white blood cells use to kill bacteria); by radiation (such as ultraviolet radiation and X-rays); and by chemicals (such as nitrites, used as preservatives in some wine, meat, and other foods). They are short-lived and combine quickly with molecules such as fats, proteins, and DNA, converting them into free radicals and triggering chain reactions that destroy still more molecules. Among the damages caused by free radicals are some forms of cancer and myocardial infarction, the death of heart tissue. One theory of aging is that it results in part from lifelong cellular damage by free radicals.

Because free radicals are so common and destructive, we have mechanisms for neutralizing them. An **antioxidant** is a chemical that neutralizes free radicals. For example, the body produces an enzyme called *superoxide dismutase (SOD)* that converts superoxide into oxygen and hydrogen peroxide. Selenium, vitamin E (α-tocopherol), vitamin C (ascorbic acid), and carotenoids (such as β-carotene) are some antioxidants obtained from the diet. Dietary deficiencies of antioxidants have been associated with increased risk of heart attacks, sterility, muscular dystrophy, and other disorders.

## 2.1e Molecules and Chemical Bonds

**Molecules** are chemical particles composed of two or more atoms united by a chemical bond. The atoms may be identical, as in nitrogen ($N_2$), or different, as in glucose ($C_6H_{12}O_6$). Molecules composed of two or more elements are called **compounds.** Oxygen ($O_2$) and carbon dioxide ($CO_2$) are both molecules, because they consist of at least two atoms; but only $CO_2$ is a compound, because it has atoms of two different elements.

Molecules are represented by *molecular formulae* that identify their elements and show how many atoms of each are present. Molecules with identical molecular formulae but different arrangements of their atoms are called **isomers**[4] of each other. For example, both ethanol and ethyl ether have the molecular formula $C_2H_6O$, but they are certainly not interchangeable! To show the difference between them, we use *structural formulae* that show the location of each atom **(fig. 2.5).**

The **molecular weight (MW)** of a compound is the sum of the atomic weights of its atoms. Rounding to whole numbers, we can calculate the approximate MW of glucose ($C_6H_{12}O_6$), for example:

| | | | | |
|---|---|---|---|---|
| 6 C atoms | × | 12 amu each | = | 72 amu |
| 12 H atoms | × | 1 amu each | = | 12 amu |
| 6 O atoms | × | 16 amu each | = | 96 amu |
| Molecular weight (MW) | | | = | 180 amu |

Molecular weight is needed to compute some measures of concentration discussed later (see section 2.2d and appendix B).

[4] *iso* = same; *mer* = part

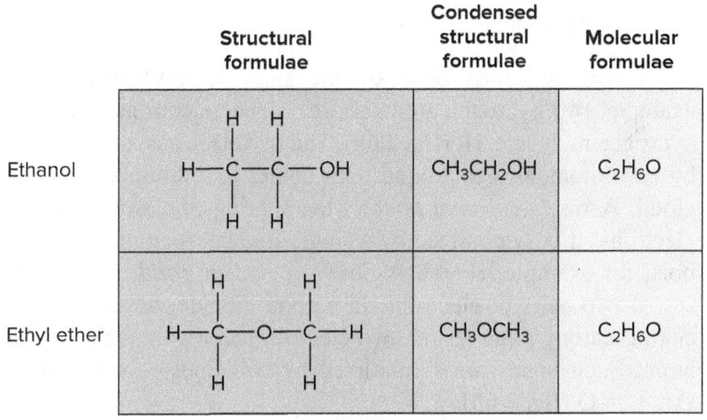

| | Structural formulae | Condensed structural formulae | Molecular formulae |
|---|---|---|---|
| Ethanol | H—C(H)(H)—C(H)(H)—OH | $CH_3CH_2OH$ | $C_2H_6O$ |
| Ethyl ether | H—C(H)(H)—O—C(H)(H)—H | $CH_3OCH_3$ | $C_2H_6O$ |

**FIGURE 2.5 Two Structural Isomers—Ethanol and Ethyl Ether.** The molecular formulae are identical, but their structures, chemical properties, and physiological effects are different.

**TABLE 2.3 Types of Chemical Bonds**

| Bond Type | Definition and Remarks |
|---|---|
| **Ionic Bond** | Relatively weak attraction between an anion and a cation. Easily disrupted in water, as when salt dissolves. |
| **Covalent Bond** | Sharing of one or more pairs of electrons between nuclei. |
| Single covalent | Sharing of one electron pair. |
| Double covalent | Sharing of two electron pairs. Often occurs between carbon atoms, between carbon and oxygen, and between carbon and nitrogen. |
| Nonpolar covalent | Covalent bond in which electrons are equally attracted to both nuclei. May be single or double. Strongest type of chemical bond. |
| Polar covalent | Covalent bond in which electrons are more attracted to one nucleus than to the other, resulting in slightly positive and negative regions in one molecule. May be single or double. |
| **Hydrogen Bond** | Weak attraction between polarized molecules or between polarized regions of the same molecule. Important in the three-dimensional folding and coiling of large molecules. Easily disrupted by temperature and pH changes. |
| **Van der Waals Force** | Weak, brief attraction due to random disturbances in the electron clouds of adjacent atoms. Weakest of all bonds individually, but can have strong effects collectively. |

A molecule is held together, and molecules are attracted to one another, by forces called **chemical bonds.** The bonds of greatest physiological interest are *ionic bonds, covalent bonds, hydrogen bonds,* and *van der Waals forces* **(table 2.3).**

An **ionic bond** is the attraction of a cation to an anion. Sodium ($Na^+$) and chloride ($Cl^-$) ions, for example, are attracted to each other and form the compound sodium chloride (NaCl), common table salt. Ionic compounds can be composed of more than two ions, such as calcium chloride, $CaCl_2$. Ionic bonds are weak and easily dissociate (break up) in the presence of something more attractive, such as water. The ionic bonds of NaCl break down easily as salt dissolves in water, because both $Na^+$ and $Cl^-$ are more attracted to water molecules than they are to each other.

**▶▶▶APPLY WHAT YOU KNOW**

*Do you think ionic bonds are common in the human body? Explain your answer.*

**Covalent bonds** form by the sharing of electrons. For example, two hydrogen atoms share valence electrons to form a hydrogen molecule, $H_2$ **(fig. 2.6a).** The two electrons, one donated by each atom, swarm around both nuclei in a dumbbell-shaped cloud. A *single covalent bond* is the sharing of a single pair of electrons. It is symbolized by a single line between atomic symbols, for example, H—H. A *double covalent bond* is the sharing of two pairs of electrons. In carbon dioxide, for example, a central carbon atom shares two electron pairs with each oxygen atom. Such bonds are symbolized by two lines—for example, O=C=O **(fig. 2.6b).**

When shared electrons spend approximately equal time around each nucleus, they form a *nonpolar covalent bond* **(fig. 2.7a),** the strongest of all chemical bonds. Carbon atoms bond to each other with nonpolar covalent bonds. If shared electrons spend significantly more time orbiting one nucleus than they do the other, they lend their negative charge to the region where they spend the most time, and they form a *polar covalent bond* **(fig. 2.7b).** When hydrogen bonds with oxygen, for example, the electrons are more attracted to the oxygen nucleus and orbit it more than they do the hydrogen. This makes the oxygen region

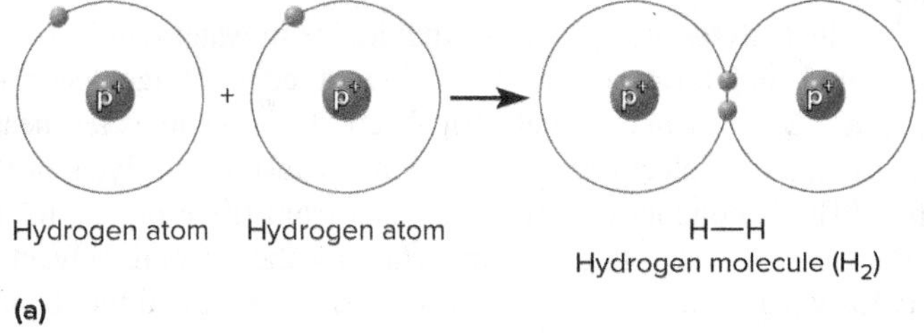


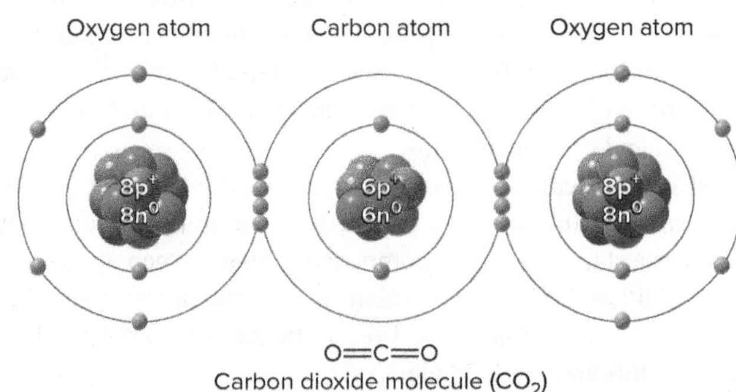


**FIGURE 2.6 Covalent Bonding.** (a) Two hydrogen atoms share a single pair of electrons to form a hydrogen molecule. (b) A carbon dioxide molecule, in which a carbon atom shares two pairs of electrons with each oxygen atom, forming double covalent bonds.

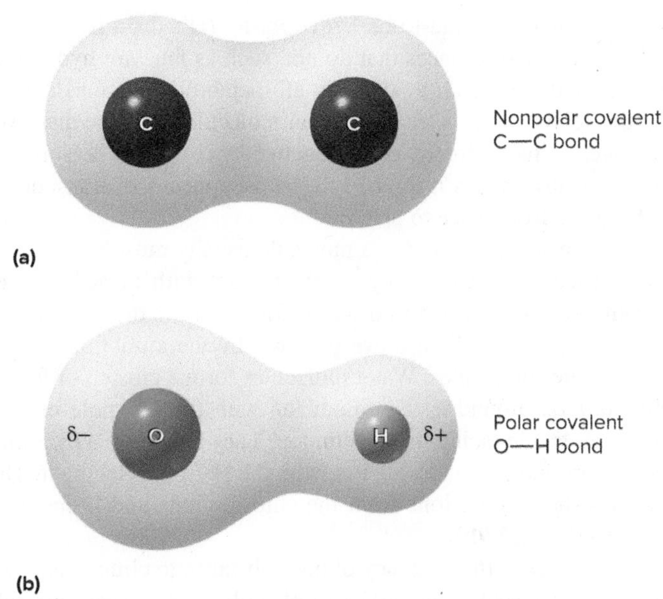


**FIGURE 2.7 Nonpolar and Polar Covalent Bonds.** (a) A nonpolar covalent bond between two carbon atoms, formed by electrons that spend an equal amount of time around each nucleus, as represented by the symmetric blue cloud. (b) A polar covalent bond, in which electrons orbit one nucleus significantly more than the other, as represented by the asymmetric cloud. This results in a slight negative charge (δ–) in the region where the electrons spend most of their time, and a slight positive charge (δ+) at the other pole.

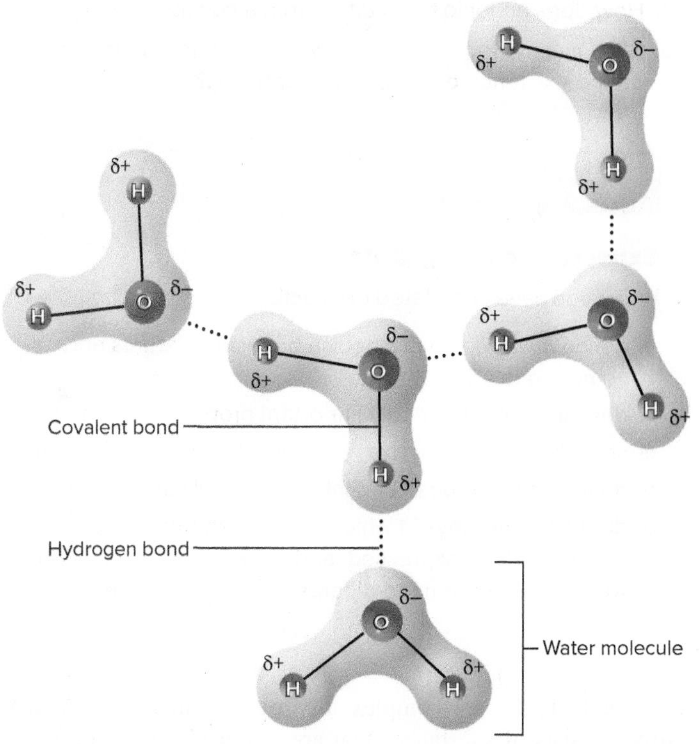

**FIGURE 2.8 Hydrogen Bonding of Water.** The polar covalent bonds of water molecules enable each oxygen to form a hydrogen bond with a hydrogen of a neighboring molecule. Thus, the water molecules are weakly attracted to each other.

? *Why would this behavior raise the boiling point of water above that of a nonpolar liquid?*

of the molecule slightly negative and the hydrogen region slightly positive. The Greek delta (δ) is used to symbolize a charge less than that of one electron or proton. A slightly negative region of a molecule is represented δ– and a slightly positive region is represented δ+.

A **hydrogen bond** is a weak attraction between a slightly positive hydrogen atom in one molecule and a slightly negative oxygen or nitrogen atom in another. Water molecules, for example, are weakly attracted to each other by hydrogen bonds **(fig. 2.8).** Hydrogen bonds also form between different regions of the same molecule, especially in very large molecules such as proteins and DNA. They cause such molecules to fold or coil into precise three-dimensional shapes. Hydrogen bonds are represented by dotted or broken lines between atoms: —C=O···H—N—. Hydrogen bonds are relatively weak, but they are enormously important to physiology.

**Van der Waals[5] forces** are important in protein folding, the binding of proteins to each other and to other molecules such as hormones, and the association of lipid molecules with each other in cell membranes. They are weak, brief attractions between neutral atoms. When electrons orbit a nucleus, they don't maintain a uniform distribution but show random fluctuations in density. If the electrons briefly crowd toward one side of an atom, they render that side slightly negative and the other side slightly positive for a moment. If another atom is close enough to this one, the second atom responds with disturbances in its own electron cloud. Oppositely charged regions of the two atoms then attract each other for a very brief moment.

A single van der Waals force is only about 1% as strong as a covalent bond, but when two surfaces or large molecules meet, the van der Waals forces between large numbers of atoms can create a very strong attraction. This is how plastic wrap clings to food and dishes; flies and spiders walk across a ceiling; and even a heavy lizard or tree frog can walk up a windowpane.

## BEFORE YOU GO ON

Answer the following questions to test your understanding of the preceding section:

1. Consider iron (Fe), hydrogen gas ($H_2$), and ammonia ($NH_3$). Which of them is or are atoms? Which of them is or are molecules? Which of them is or are compounds? Explain each answer.
2. Why is the biological half-life of a radioisotope shorter than its physical half-life?
3. Where do free radicals come from? What harm do they do? How is the body protected from free radicals?

[5]Johannes Diderik van der Waals (1837–1923), Dutch physicist

4. How does an ionic bond differ from a covalent bond?
5. What is a hydrogen bond? Why do hydrogen bonds depend on the existence of polar covalent bonds?

## 2.2 Water and Mixtures

### Expected Learning Outcomes

When you have completed this section, you should be able to

a. define *mixture* and distinguish between mixtures and compounds;
b. describe the biologically important properties of water;
c. show how three kinds of mixtures differ from each other;
d. define *acid* and *base* and interpret the pH scale; and
e. discuss some ways in which the concentration of a solution can be expressed, and the kinds of information we can derive from the different units of measure.

Our body fluids are complex mixtures of chemicals. A **mixture** consists of substances that are physically blended but not chemically combined. Each substance retains its own chemical properties. To contrast a mixture with a compound, consider sodium chloride again. Sodium is a lightweight metal that bursts into flame if exposed to water, and chlorine is a yellow-green poisonous gas that was once used in chemical warfare. When these elements chemically react, they form common table salt. Clearly, the compound has properties much different from the properties of its elements. But if you were to put a little salt on your watermelon, the watermelon would taste salty and sweet because the sugar of the melon and the salt you added would merely form a mixture in which each compound retained its individual properties.

### 2.2a Water

Most mixtures in our bodies consist of chemicals dissolved or suspended in water. Water constitutes 50% to 75% of your body weight, depending on age, sex, fat content, and other factors. Its structure, simple as it is, has profound biological effects. Two aspects of its structure are particularly important: (1) Its atoms are joined by polar covalent bonds, and (2) the molecule is V-shaped, with a 105° bond angle **(fig. 2.9a).** This makes the molecule as a whole polar, because there is a slight negative charge ($\delta-$) on the oxygen at the apex of the V and a slight positive charge ($\delta+$) on each hydrogen. Like little magnets, water molecules are attracted to one another by hydrogen bonds (fig. 2.8). This gives water a set of properties that account for its ability to support life: *solvency, cohesion, adhesion, chemical reactivity,* and *thermal stability.*

*Solvency* is the ability to dissolve other chemicals. Water is called the *universal solvent* because it dissolves a broader range of substances than any other liquid. Substances that dissolve in water, such as sugar, are said to be **hydrophilic**[6] (HY-dro-FILL-ic); the relatively few substances that do not, such as fats, are **hydrophobic**[7] (HY-dro-FOE-bic). Virtually all metabolic reactions depend on the solvency of water. Biological molecules must be dissolved in water to move freely, come together, and react. The solvency of water also makes it the body's primary means of transporting substances from place to place.

To be soluble in water, a molecule usually must be polarized or charged so that its charges can interact with those of water. When NaCl is dropped into water, for example, the ionic bonds between $Na^+$ and $Cl^-$ are overpowered by the attraction of each ion to water molecules. Water molecules form a cluster, or *hydration sphere,* around each sodium ion with the $O^{\delta-}$ pole of each water molecule facing the sodium ion. They also form a hydration sphere around each chloride ion, with the $H^{\delta+}$ poles facing it. This isolates the sodium ions from the chloride ions and keeps them dissolved **(fig. 2.9b).**

*Adhesion* is the tendency of one substance to cling to another, whereas *cohesion* is the tendency of molecules of the same substance to cling to each other. Water adheres to the body's tissues and forms a lubricating film on membranes such as the pleura and pericardium. This reduces friction as the lungs and heart contract and expand and rub against these membranes. Water also is a very cohesive liquid because of its hydrogen bonds. This is why, when you spill water on the floor, it forms a puddle and evaporates slowly. By contrast, if you spill a nonpolar substance such as liquid nitrogen, it dances about and evaporates in seconds, like a drop of water in a hot dry skillet. This is because nitrogen molecules have no attraction for each other, so the little bit of heat provided by the floor is enough to disperse them into the air. The cohesion of water is especially evident at its surface, where it forms an elastic layer called the *surface film* held together by a force called *surface tension.* This force causes water to hang in drops from a leaky faucet and travel in rivulets down a window.

The *chemical reactivity* of water is its ability to participate in chemical reactions. Not only does water ionize many other chemicals such as acids and salts, but water itself ionizes into $H^+$ and $OH^-$. These ions can be incorporated into other molecules, or released from them, in the course of chemical reactions such as *hydrolysis* and *dehydration synthesis,* described later in this chapter.

The *thermal stability* of water helps to stabilize the internal temperature of the body. It results from the high *heat capacity* of water—the amount of heat required to raise the temperature of 1 g of a substance by 1°C. The base unit of heat is the **calorie**[8] **(cal)**—1 cal is the amount of heat that raises the temperature of 1 g of water 1°C. The same amount of heat would raise the temperature of a nonpolar substance such as nitrogen about four times as much. The difference stems from the presence or absence of hydrogen bonding. To increase in temperature, the molecules of a substance must move around more actively. The hydrogen bonds of water molecules inhibit their movement, so water can absorb

[6]*hydro* = water; *philic* = loving, attracted to
[7]*hydro* = water; *phobic* = fearing, avoiding
[8]*calor* = heat

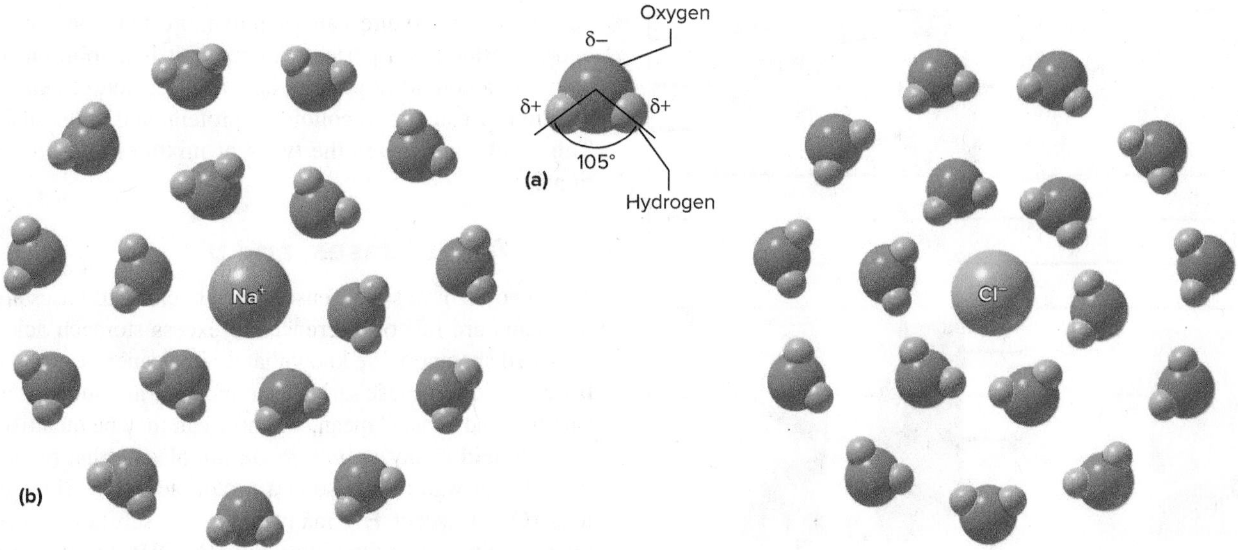


**FIGURE 2.9 Water and Hydration Spheres.** (a) A water molecule showing its bond angle and polarity. (b) Water molecules aggregate around a sodium ion with their negatively charged oxygen poles facing the $Na^+$ and aggregate around a chloride ion with their positively charged hydrogen poles facing the $Cl^-$.

a given amount of heat without changing temperature (molecular motion) as much.

The high heat capacity of water also makes it a very effective coolant. When it changes from a liquid to a vapor, water carries a large amount of heat with it. One milliliter of perspiration evaporating from the skin removes about 500 cal of heat from the body. This effect is very apparent when you are sweaty and stand in front of a fan.

**▶▶▶APPLY WHAT YOU KNOW**

*Why are heat and temperature not the same thing?*

### 2.2b Solutions, Colloids, and Suspensions

Mixtures of other substances in water can be classified as *solutions, colloids,* and *suspensions.*

A **solution** consists of particles of matter called the **solute** mixed with a more abundant substance (usually water) called the **solvent.** The solute can be a gas, solid, or liquid—as in a solution of oxygen, sodium chloride, or alcohol in water, respectively. Solutions are defined by the following properties:

- The solute particles are under 1 nanometer (nm) in size. The solute and solvent therefore cannot be visually distinguished from each other, even with a microscope.
- Such small particles don't scatter light noticeably, so solutions are usually transparent **(fig. 2.10a).**
- The solute particles can pass through most selectively permeable membranes, such as dialysis tubing and cell membranes.
- The solute doesn't separate from the solvent when the solution is allowed to stand.

The most common **colloids**[9] in the body are mixtures of protein and water, such as the albumin in blood plasma. Many colloids can change from liquid to gel states—gelatin desserts, agar culture media, and the fluids within and between our cells, for example. Colloids are defined by the following physical properties:

- The colloidal particles range from 1 to 100 nm in size.
- Particles this large scatter light, so colloids are usually cloudy **(fig. 2.10b).**
- The particles are too large to pass through most selectively permeable membranes.
- The particles are still small enough, however, to remain permanently mixed with the solvent when the mixture stands.

The blood cells in our blood plasma exemplify a **suspension.** Suspensions are defined by the following properties:

- The suspended particles exceed 100 nm in size.
- Such large particles render suspensions cloudy or opaque.
- The particles are too large to penetrate selectively permeable membranes.
- The particles are too heavy to remain permanently suspended, so suspensions separate on standing. Blood cells, for example, form a suspension in the blood plasma and settle to the bottom of a tube when blood is allowed to stand without mixing **(fig. 2.10c, d).**

An **emulsion** is a suspension of one liquid in another, such as oil-and-vinegar salad dressing. The fat in breast milk is an emulsion, as are medications such as Kaopectate and milk of magnesia.

[9] *collo* = glue; *oid* = like, resembling

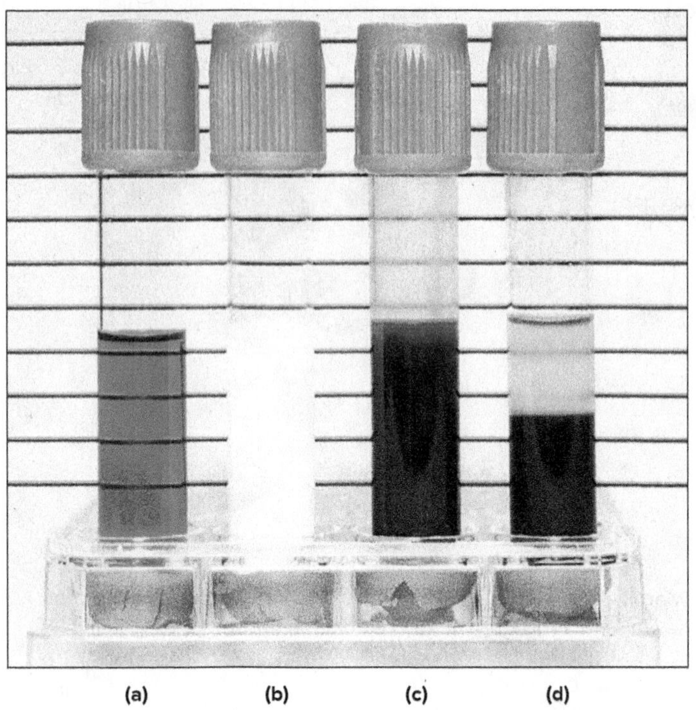


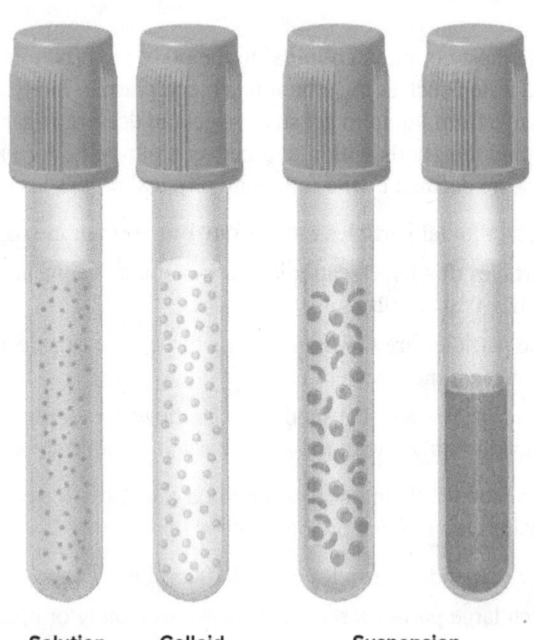


**FIGURE 2.10 A Solution, a Colloid, and a Suspension.** Top row: Photographs of a representative solution, colloid, and suspension. Bottom row: Symbolic representation of the particle sizes in each mixture. (a) In a copper sulfate solution, the solute particles are so small they remain permanently mixed and the solution is transparent. (b) In milk, the protein molecules are small enough to remain permanently mixed, but large enough to scatter light, so the mixture is opaque. (c) In blood, the red blood cells scatter light and make the mixture opaque. (d) Red blood cells are too large to remain evenly mixed, so they settle to the bottom as in this blood specimen that stood overnight.

Top: Ken Saladin

A single mixture can fit into more than one of these categories. Blood is a perfect example—it is a solution of sodium chloride, a colloid of protein, and a suspension of cells. Milk is a solution of calcium, a colloid of protein, and an emulsion of fat. **Table 2.4** summarizes the types of mixtures and provides additional examples.

## 2.2c Acids, Bases, and pH

Most people have some sense of what acids and bases are. Advertisements are full of references to excess stomach acid and pH-balanced shampoo. We know that drain cleaner (a strong base) and battery acid can cause serious chemical burns. But what exactly do "acidic" and "basic" mean, and how can they be quantified?

An **acid** is any *proton donor,* a molecule that releases a proton ($H^+$) in water. A **base** is a proton acceptor. Since hydroxide ions ($OH^-$) accept $H^+$, many bases are substances that release hydroxide ions—sodium hydroxide (NaOH), for example. A base doesn't have to be a hydroxide donor, however. Ammonia ($NH_3$) is also a base. It doesn't release hydroxide ions, but it readily accepts hydrogen ions to become the ammonium ion ($NH_4^+$).

Acidity is expressed in terms of **pH,** a measure derived from the molarity of $H^+$. Molarity (explained in the next section) is represented by square brackets, so $H^+$ molarity is symbolized $[H^+]$. pH is the negative logarithm of hydrogen ion molarity—that is, pH = $-\log [H^+]$. In pure water, 1 in 10 million molecules ionizes into hydrogen and hydroxide ions: $H_2O \rightleftharpoons H^+ + OH^-$. (The symbol $\rightleftharpoons$ denotes a reversible chemical reaction.) Pure water has a neutral pH because it contains equal amounts of $H^+$ and $OH^-$. Since 1 in 10 million molecules ionize, the molarity of $H^+$ and the pH of water are

$$[H^+] = 0.0000001 \text{ molar} = 10^{-7}\text{M};$$
$$\log[H^+] = -7; \text{ and}$$
$$\text{pH} = -\log[H^+] = 7.$$

The pH scale **(fig. 2.11)** was invented in 1909 by Danish biochemist and brewer Sören Sörensen to measure the acidity of beer. The scale extends from 0.0 to 14.0. A solution with a pH of 7.0 is **neutral;** solutions with pH below 7 are **acidic;** and solutions with pH above 7 are **basic (alkaline).** The lower the pH value, the more hydrogen ions a solution has and the more acidic it is. Since the pH scale is logarithmic, a change of one whole number on the scale represents a 10-fold change in $H^+$ concentration. In other words, a solution with pH 4 is 10 times as acidic as one with pH 5 and 100 times as acidic as one with pH 6.

Slight disturbances of pH can seriously disrupt physiological functions and alter drug actions (see Deeper Insight 2.2), so it is important that the body carefully control its pH. Blood, for example, normally has a pH ranging from 7.35 to 7.45. Deviations from this range cause tremors, fainting, paralysis, or even death. Chemical solutions that resist changes in pH are called **buffers.** Buffers and acid–base balance are considered in detail in section 24.3.

**▶▶▶APPLY WHAT YOU KNOW**

*A pH of 7.20 is slightly alkaline, yet a blood pH of 7.20 is called* acidosis. *Why do you think it is called this?*

**TABLE 2.4 Types of Mixtures**

| | Solution | Colloid | Suspension |
|---|---|---|---|
| Particle size | <1 nm | 1–100 nm | >100 nm |
| Appearance | Clear | Often cloudy | Cloudy-opaque |
| Will particles settle out? | No | No | Yes |
| Will particles pass through a selectively permeable membrane? | Yes | No | No |
| Examples | Glucose in blood<br>$O_2$ in water<br>Saline solutions<br>Sugar in coffee | Proteins in blood<br>Intracellular fluid<br>Milk protein<br>Gelatin | Blood cells<br>Cornstarch in water<br>Fats in blood<br>Kaopectate |

## 2.2d Other Measures of Concentration

Solutions are often described in terms of their concentration—how much solute is present in a given volume of solution. Concentration is expressed in different ways for different purposes, briefly itemized here and more fully explained in appendix B.

- **Weight per volume.** This is the weight of solute (such as grams, g, or milligrams, mg) in a given volume of solution (such as liters, L, or deciliters, dL). For example, a typical serum cholesterol concentration is 200 mg/dL.
- **Percentage.** This is the weight of solute as a percentage of solution volume (weight per volume, w/v) or volume of a liquid as a percentage of total solution volume (volume per volume, v/v). For example, a common intravenous fluid is D5W, which means 5% w/v dextrose in distilled water. Ethanol is often used as a 70% v/v solution.
- **Molarity.** One mole of a chemical is the number of grams equal to its molecular weight, and molarity (M) is a measure of the number of moles of solute per liter of solution. This reflects not merely the weight of solute in the solution, but the number of molecules per volume. It is the number of molecules, not their total weight, that determines the physiological effect of a solution, so molarity is often the most meaningful measure of concentration. Body fluids are usually quantified in millimolar (mM) concentrations, since they are much less than 1 molar.
- **Milliequivalents per liter.** This unit of measure (expressed mEq/L) is used to express electrolyte concentrations; it takes into account not only the millimolar concentration of a solute but the electrical charge on its particles. This is important to processes such as nerve firing, the heartbeat, and muscle contractions, which are driven by electrical phenomena. The mEq/L concentration of electrolytes is critically important in giving intravenous fluids.

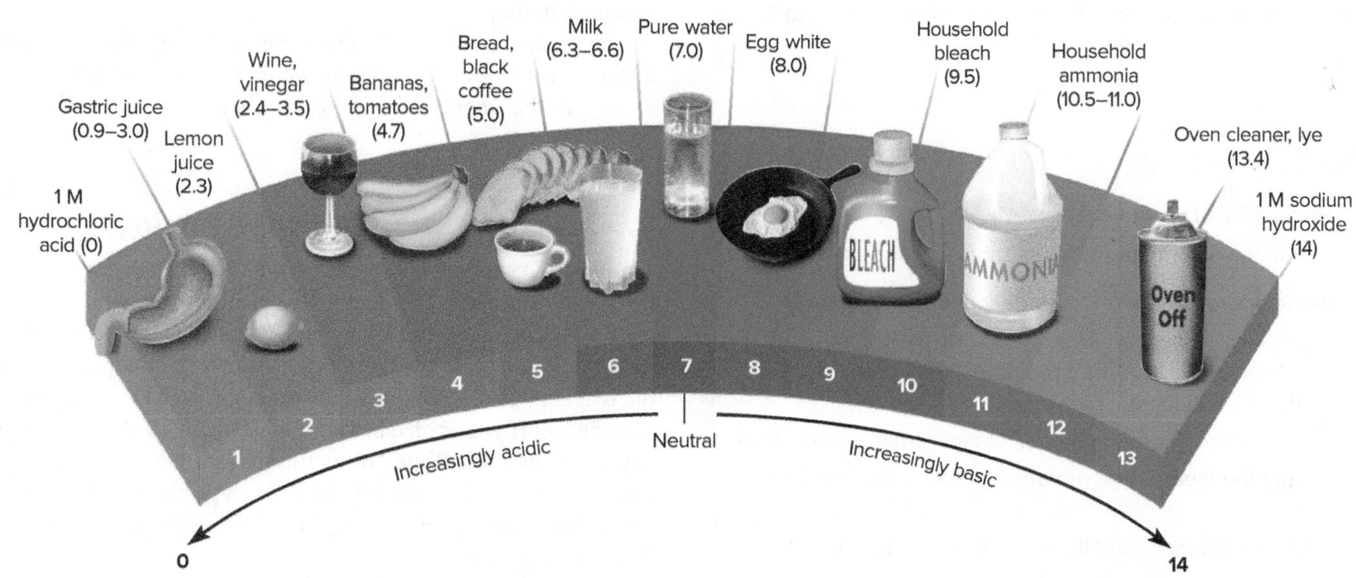


**FIGURE 2.11 The pH Scale and Approximate pH of Some Familiar Household Substances.** The pH is shown within the colored bar. $H^+$ molarity increases 10-fold for every step down the scale.

## DEEPER INSIGHT 2.2

### CLINICAL APPLICATION

### *pH and Drug Action*

The pH of our body fluids has a direct bearing on how we react to drugs. Depending on pH, drugs such as aspirin, phenobarbital, and penicillin can exist in charged (ionized) or uncharged forms. Whether a drug is charged or not can determine whether it will pass through cell membranes. When aspirin is in the acidic environment of the stomach, for example, it is uncharged and passes easily through the stomach lining into the bloodstream. Here it encounters a basic pH, whereupon it ionizes. In this state, it is unable to pass back through the membrane, so it accumulates in the blood. This effect, called *ion trapping (pH partitioning)*, can be controlled to help clear poisons from the body. The pH of the urine, for example, can be manipulated so that poisons become trapped there and are more rapidly excreted from the body.

**BEFORE YOU GO ON**

Answer the following questions to test your understanding of the preceding section:

6. What is the difference between a mixture and a compound?
7. What are hydrophilic and hydrophobic substances? Give an example of each.
8. Why would the cohesion and thermal stability of water be less if water did not have polar covalent bonds?
9. How do solutions, colloids, and suspensions differ from each other? Give an example of each in the human body.
10. If solution A had a $H^+$ concentration of $10^{-8}$ M, what would be its pH? If solution B had 1,000 times this $H^+$ concentration, what would be its pH? Would solution A be acidic or basic? What about solution B?
11. What information can we get from the molarity of a solution that we cannot know from its percentage concentration? What do we know from a concentration in mEq/L that we could not know from molarity alone?

## 2.3 Energy and Chemical Reactions

**Expected Learning Outcomes**

When you have completed this section, you should be able to

a. define *energy* and *work*, and describe some types of energy;
b. understand how chemical reactions are symbolized by chemical equations;
c. list and define the fundamental types of chemical reactions;
d. identify the factors that govern the speed and direction of a reaction;
e. define *metabolism* and its two subdivisions; and
f. define *oxidation* and *reduction*, and relate these to changes in the energy content of a molecule.

### 2.3a Energy and Work

**Energy** is the capacity to do work. To do **work** means to move something, whether it is a muscle or a molecule. Some examples of physiological work are breaking chemical bonds, building molecules, pumping blood, and contracting skeletal muscles. All of the body's activities are forms of work.

Energy is broadly classified as *potential* or *kinetic energy*. *Potential energy* is energy contained in an object because of its position or internal state but that is not doing work at the time. *Kinetic energy* is energy of motion, energy that is doing work. It is observed in musculoskeletal movements, the flow of ions into a cell, and vibration of the eardrum, for example. The water behind a dam has potential energy because of its position. Let the water flow through, and it exhibits kinetic energy that can be tapped for generating electricity. Like water behind a dam, ions concentrated on one side of a cell membrane have potential energy that can be released by opening gates in the membrane. As the ions flow through the gates, their kinetic energy can be tapped to create a nerve signal or make the heart beat.

Within the two broad categories of potential and kinetic energy, several forms of energy are relevant to human physiology. *Chemical energy* is potential energy stored in the bonds of molecules. Chemical reactions release this energy and make it available for physiological work. *Heat* is the kinetic energy of molecular motion. The temperature of a substance is a measure of rate of this motion, and adding heat to a substance increases molecular motion. *Electromagnetic energy* is the kinetic energy of moving "packets" of radiation called *photons*. The most familiar form of electromagnetic energy is light. *Electrical energy* has both potential and kinetic forms. It is potential energy when charged particles have accumulated at a point such as a battery terminal or on one side of a cell membrane; it becomes kinetic energy when these particles begin to move and create an electrical current—for example, when electrons move through your household wiring or sodium ions move through a cell membrane.

**Free energy** is the potential energy available in a system to do useful work. In human physiology, the most relevant free energy is the energy stored in the chemical bonds of organic molecules.

### 2.3b Classes of Chemical Reactions

A **chemical reaction** is a process in which a covalent or ionic bond is formed or broken. The course of a chemical reaction is symbolized by a **chemical equation** that typically shows the *reactants* on the left, the *products* on the right, and an arrow pointing from the reactants to the products. For example, consider this common occurrence: If you open a bottle of wine and let it stand for several days, it turns sour. Wine "turns to vinegar" because oxygen gets into the bottle and reacts with ethanol to produce acetic acid and water. Acetic acid gives the tart flavor to vinegar and spoiled wine. The equation for this reaction is

$$\underset{\text{Ethanol}}{CH_3CH_2OH} + \underset{\text{Oxygen}}{O_2} \longrightarrow \underset{\text{Acetic acid}}{CH_3COOH} + \underset{\text{Water}}{H_2O}$$

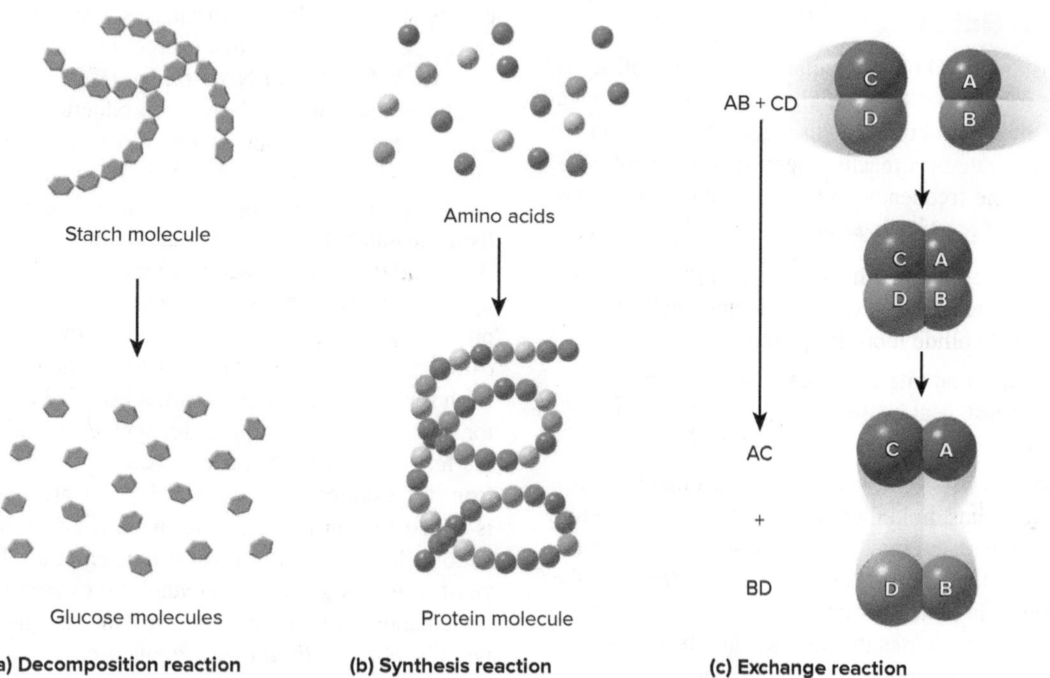


(a) Decomposition reaction (b) Synthesis reaction (c) Exchange reaction

**FIGURE 2.12 Decomposition, Synthesis, and Exchange Reactions.** (a) In a decomposition reaction, large molecules are broken down into simpler ones. (b) In a synthesis reaction, smaller molecules are joined to form larger ones. (c) In an exchange reaction, two molecules exchange atoms.

*To which of these categories does the digestion of food belong?*

Ethanol and oxygen are the reactants, and acetic acid and water are the products of this reaction. Not all reactions are shown with the arrow pointing from left to right. In complex biochemical equations, reaction chains are often written vertically or even in circles.

Chemical reactions can be classified as *decomposition, synthesis,* or *exchange reactions*. In **decomposition reactions,** a large molecule breaks down into two or more smaller ones **(fig. 2.12a);** symbolically, $AB \longrightarrow A + B$. When you eat a potato, for example, digestive enzymes decompose its starch into thousands of glucose molecules, and most cells further decompose glucose to water and carbon dioxide. Starch, a very large molecule, ultimately yields about 36,000 molecules of $H_2O$ and $CO_2$.

**Synthesis reactions** are just the opposite—two or more small molecules combine to form a larger one; symbolically, $A + B \longrightarrow AB$ **(fig. 2.12b).** When the body synthesizes proteins, for example, it combines 50 or more amino acids into one protein molecule.

In **exchange reactions,** two molecules exchange atoms or groups of atoms; $AB + CD \longrightarrow AC + BD$ **(fig. 2.12c).** For example, when stomach acid (HCl) enters the small intestine, the pancreas secretes sodium bicarbonate ($NaHCO_3$) to neutralize it. The reaction between the two is

$$NaHCO_3 + HCl \longrightarrow NaCl + H_2CO_3.$$

We could say the sodium atom has exchanged its bicarbonate group ($-HCO_3$) for a chlorine atom.

**Reversible reactions** can go in either direction under different circumstances. For example, carbon dioxide combines with water to produce carbonic acid, which in turn decomposes into bicarbonate ions and hydrogen ions:

$$\underset{\text{Carbon dioxide}}{CO_2} + \underset{\text{Water}}{H_2O} \rightleftharpoons \underset{\text{Carbonic acid}}{H_2CO_3} \rightleftharpoons \underset{\text{Bicarbonate ion}}{HCO_3^-} + \underset{\text{Hydrogen ion}}{H^+}$$

This reaction appears in this book more often than any other, especially as we discuss respiratory, urinary, and digestive physiology.

The direction in which a reversible reaction goes is determined by the relative abundance of substances on each side of the equation. If there is a surplus of $CO_2$, this reaction proceeds left to right and produces bicarbonate and hydrogen ions. If bicarbonate and hydrogen ions are present in excess, the reaction proceeds right to left and generates $CO_2$ and $H_2O$. Reversible reactions follow the **law of mass action:** They proceed from the reactants in greater quantity to the substances with the lesser quantity. This law will help to explain processes discussed in later chapters, such as why hemoglobin binds oxygen in the lungs yet releases it to muscle tissue.

In the absence of upsetting influences, reversible reactions exist in a state of **equilibrium,** in which the ratio of products to reactants is stable. The carbonic acid reaction, for example, normally maintains a 20:1 ratio of bicarbonate ions to carbonic acid molecules. This equilibrium can be upset, however, by a surplus of hydrogen ions, which drives the reaction to the left, or adding carbon dioxide and driving it to the right.

### 2.3c Reaction Rates

Chemical reactions are based on molecular motion and collisions. All molecules are in constant motion, and reactions occur when mutually reactive molecules collide with sufficient force and the right orientation. The rate of a reaction depends on the nature of the reactants and on the frequency and force of these collisions. Some factors that affect reaction rates are

- **Concentration.** Reaction rate increases when the reactants are more concentrated. This is because the molecules are more crowded and collide more frequently.
- **Temperature.** Reaction rate increases as the temperature rises. This is because heat causes molecules to move more rapidly and collide with greater force and frequency.
- **Catalysts** (CAT-uh-lists). These are substances that temporarily bind to reactants, hold them in a favorable position to react with each other, and may change the shapes of reactants in ways that make them more likely to react. By reducing the element of chance in molecular collisions, a catalyst speeds up a reaction. It then releases the products and is available to repeat the process with more reactants. The catalyst itself is not consumed or changed by the reaction. The most important biological catalysts are enzymes, discussed later in this chapter.

### 2.3d Metabolism, Oxidation, and Reduction

All the chemical reactions in the body are collectively called **metabolism.** Metabolism has two divisions: *catabolism* and *anabolism*. **Catabolism**[10] (ca-TAB-oh-lizm) consists of energy-releasing decomposition reactions. Such reactions break covalent bonds, produce smaller molecules from larger ones, and release energy that can be used for other physiological work. Energy-releasing reactions are called *exergonic*[11] reactions. If you hold a beaker of water in your hand and pour sulfuric acid into it, for example, the beaker will get so hot you may have to put it down. If you break down energy-storage molecules to run a race, you too will get hot. In both cases, the heat signifies that exergonic reactions are occurring.

**Anabolism**[12] (ah-NAB-oh-lizm) consists of energy-storing synthesis reactions, such as the production of protein or fat. Reactions that require an energy input, such as these, are called *endergonic*[13] reactions. Anabolism is driven by the energy that catabolism releases, so endergonic and exergonic processes, anabolism and catabolism, are inseparably linked.

**Oxidation** is any chemical reaction in which a molecule gives up electrons and releases energy. A molecule is *oxidized* by this process, and whatever molecule takes the electrons from it is an *oxidizing agent (electron acceptor).* The term *oxidation* stems from the fact that oxygen is often involved as the electron acceptor. Thus, we can sometimes recognize an oxidation reaction from the fact that oxygen has been added to a molecule. The rusting of iron, for example, is a slow oxidation process in which oxygen is added to iron to form iron oxide ($Fe_2O_3$). Many oxidation reactions, however, don't involve oxygen at all. For example, when yeast ferments glucose to ethanol, no oxygen is required; indeed, the ethanol *contains less oxygen* than the glucose originally did, but it is *more oxidized* than the glucose:

$$\underset{\text{Glucose}}{C_6H_{12}O_6} \longrightarrow \underset{\text{Ethanol}}{2\,CH_3CH_2OH} + \underset{\text{Carbon dioxide}}{2\,CO_2}$$

**Reduction** is a chemical reaction in which a molecule gains electrons and energy. When a molecule accepts electrons, it is said to be *reduced;* a molecule that donates electrons to another is therefore called a *reducing agent (electron donor).* The oxidation of one molecule is always accompanied by the reduction of another, so these electron transfers are known as *oxidation–reduction (redox) reactions.*

It isn't necessary that *only* electrons be transferred in a redox reaction. Often, the electrons are transferred in the form of hydrogen atoms. The fact that a proton (the hydrogen nucleus) is also transferred is immaterial to whether we consider a reaction oxidation or reduction.

**Table 2.5** summarizes these energy-transfer reactions. We can symbolize oxidation and reduction as follows, letting A and B

[10] *cato* = down, to break down
[11] *ex, exo* = out; *erg* = work
[12] *ana* = up, to build up
[13] *end, endo* = in; *erg* = work

**TABLE 2.5 Energy-Transfer Reactions in the Human Body**

| | |
|---|---|
| **Exergonic Reactions** | Reactions in which there is a net release of energy. The products have less total free energy than the reactants did. |
| Oxidation | An exergonic reaction in which electrons are removed from a reactant. Electrons may be removed one or two at a time and may be removed in the form of hydrogen atoms (H or $H_2$). The product is then said to be oxidized. |
| Decomposition | A reaction such as digestion and cell respiration, in which larger molecules are broken down into smaller ones. |
| Catabolism | The sum of all decomposition reactions in the body. |
| **Endergonic Reactions** | Reactions in which there is a net input of energy. The products have more total free energy than the reactants did. |
| Reduction | An endergonic reaction in which electrons are donated to a reactant. The product is then said to be reduced. |
| Synthesis | A reaction such as protein and glycogen synthesis, in which two or more smaller molecules are combined into a larger one. |
| Anabolism | The sum of all synthesis reactions in the body. |

symbolize arbitrary molecules and letting $e^-$ represent one or more electrons that transfer from molecule A to molecule B:

| $Ae^-$ | + | B | $\longrightarrow$ | A | + | $Be^-$ |
|---|---|---|---|---|---|---|
| High-energy reduced state | | Low-energy oxidized state | | Low-energy oxidized state | | High-energy reduced state |

$Ae^-$ is a reducing agent because it reduces B, and B is an oxidizing agent because it oxidizes $Ae^-$.

**BEFORE YOU GO ON**

Answer the following questions to test your understanding of the preceding section:

**12.** Define *energy.* Distinguish potential energy from kinetic energy.

**13.** Define *metabolism, catabolism,* and *anabolism.*

**14.** What does *oxidation* mean? What does *reduction* mean? Which of them is endergonic and which is exergonic?

**15.** When sodium chloride forms, which element—sodium or chlorine—is oxidized? Which one is reduced?

## 2.4 Organic Compounds

### Expected Learning Outcomes

When you have completed this section, you should be able to

a. explain why carbon is especially well suited to serve as the structural foundation of many biological molecules;
b. identify some common functional groups of organic molecules from their formulae;
c. discuss the relevance of polymers to biology and explain how they are formed and broken by dehydration synthesis and hydrolysis;
d. discuss the types and functions of carbohydrates;
e. discuss the types and functions of lipids;
f. discuss protein structure and function;
g. explain how enzymes function;
h. describe the structure, production, and function of ATP;
i. identify other nucleotide types and their functions; and
j. identify the principal types of nucleic acids.

### 2.4a Carbon Compounds and Functional Groups

*Organic chemistry* is the study of compounds of carbon. By 1900, biochemists had classified the large organic molecules of life into four primary categories: *carbohydrates, lipids, proteins,* and *nucleic acids.* We examine the first three in this chapter but describe the details of nucleic acids, which are concerned with genetics, in section 4.1.

Carbon is an especially versatile atom that serves as the basis of a wide variety of structures. It has four valence electrons, so it bonds with other atoms that can provide it with four more to complete its valence shell. Carbon atoms readily bond with each other and can form long chains, branched molecules, and rings—an enormous variety of **carbon backbones** for organic molecules. Carbon also commonly forms covalent bonds with hydrogen, oxygen, nitrogen, and sulfur.

Carbon backbones carry a variety of **functional groups**—small clusters of atoms that determine many of the properties of an organic molecule. For example, organic acids bear a **carboxyl group** (car-BOC-sil), and ATP is named for its three **phosphate groups.** Other common functional groups include **hydroxyl, methyl,** and **amino groups (fig. 2.13).**

### 2.4b Monomers and Polymers

Since carbon can form long chains, some organic molecules are gigantic *macromolecules* with molecular weights that range

| Name and Symbol | Structure | Occurs in |
|---|---|---|
| Hydroxyl (—OH) | 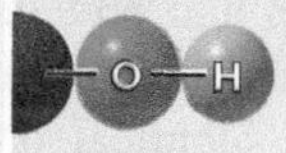 O, H | Sugars, alcohols |
| Methyl (—$CH_3$) | 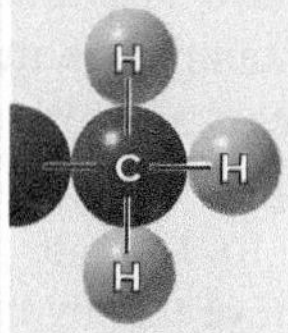 H, C, H, H | Fats, oils, steroids, amino acids |
| Carboxyl (—COOH) | 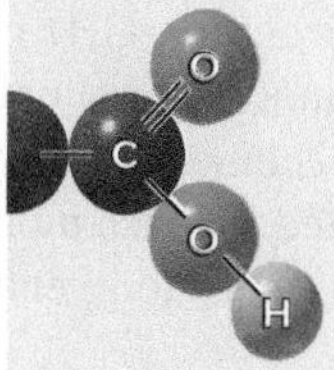 O, C, O, H | Amino acids, sugars, proteins |
| Amino (—$NH_2$) | 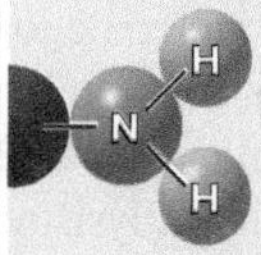 H, N, H | Amino acids, proteins |
| Phosphate (—$H_2PO_4$) | 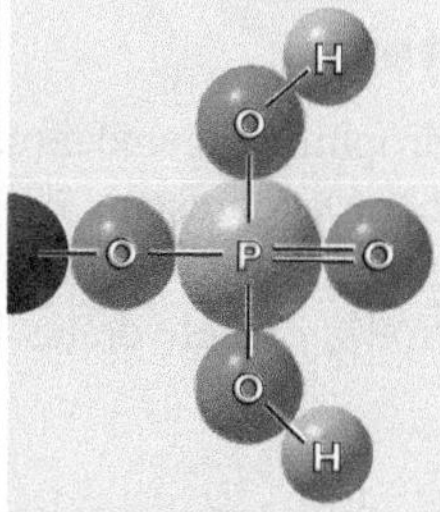 H, O, O, P, O, O, H | Nucleic acids, ATP |

**FIGURE 2.13 Functional Groups of Organic Molecules.**

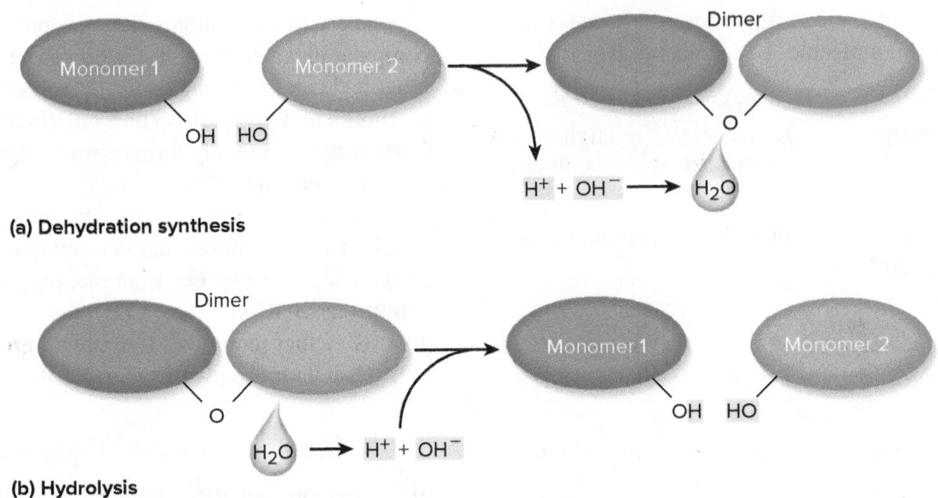


**FIGURE 2.14 Dehydration Synthesis and Hydrolysis Reactions.** (a) Dehydration synthesis, creating a new covalent bond between two monomers and producing water as a by-product. (b) Hydrolysis, consuming a water molecule to break a covalent bond.

from the thousands (as in starch and proteins) to the millions (as in DNA). Most macromolecules are **polymers**[14]—molecules made of a repetitive series of identical or similar subunits called **monomers.** Starch, for example, is a polymer of about 3,000 glucose monomers. In starch, the monomers are identical, whereas in other polymers they have a basic structural similarity but differ in detail. DNA, for example, is made of 4 different kinds of monomers (nucleotides), and proteins are made of 20 kinds (amino acids).

The joining of monomers to form a polymer is called *polymerization.* Living cells achieve this by means of a reaction called **dehydration synthesis (condensation) (fig. 2.14a).** An enzyme removes a hydroxyl group (—OH) from one monomer and a hydrogen (—H) from another, producing water as a by-product. The two monomers become joined by a covalent bond, forming a *dimer.* This is repeated for each monomer added to the chain, potentially leading to a chain long enough to be considered a polymer.

The opposite of dehydration synthesis is **hydrolysis**[15] (fig. 2.14b). In hydrolysis, a water molecule ionizes into $OH^-$ and $H^+$. An enzyme breaks the covalent bond linking one monomer to another, and adds $OH^-$ to one monomer and $H^+$ to the other one. All chemical digestion consists of hydrolysis reactions.

## 2.4c Carbohydrates

A **carbohydrate**[16] is a hydrophilic organic molecule with the general formula $(CH_2O)n$, where $n$ represents the number of carbon atoms. In glucose, for example, $n = 6$ and the formula is $C_6H_{12}O_6$. As the generic formula shows, carbohydrates have a 2:1 ratio of hydrogen to oxygen.

[14]*poly* = many; *mer* = part
[15]*hydro* = water; *lysis* = splitting apart
[16]*carbo* = carbon; *hydr* = water

**APPLY WHAT YOU KNOW**

*Why is carbohydrate an appropriate name for this class of compounds? Relate this name to the general formula of carbohydrates.*

The names of individual carbohydrates are often built on the word root *sacchar-* or the suffix *-ose,* both of which mean "sugar" or "sweet." The most familiar carbohydrates are sugars and starches.

The simplest carbohydrates are monomers called **monosaccharides**[17] (MON-oh-SAC-uh-rides), or simple sugars. The three of primary importance are **glucose, galactose,** and **fructose,** all with the molecular formula $C_6H_{12}O_6$; they are isomers of each other **(fig. 2.15).** We obtain these sugars mainly by the digestion of more complex carbohydrates. Glucose is the "blood sugar" that provides energy to most of our cells. Two other monosaccharides, ribose and deoxyribose, are important components of RNA and DNA, respectively.

**Disaccharides** are sugars composed of two monosaccharides. The three disaccharides of greatest importance are **sucrose** (made of glucose + fructose), **lactose** (glucose + galactose), and **maltose** (glucose + glucose) **(fig. 2.16).** Sucrose is produced by sugarcane and sugar beets and used as common table sugar. Lactose is milk sugar. Maltose is a product of starch digestion and is present in a few foods such as malt beverages and germinating grains.

Short chains of three or more monosaccharides are called **oligosaccharides,** and long chains (up to thousands of monosaccharides long) are called **polysaccharides.** There is no exact criterion for when a chain is long enough to be called a polysaccharide, but a chain of 10 or 20 monosaccharides would generally be considered an oligosaccharide, whereas a chain of 50 or more would generally be considered a polysaccharide. Polysaccharides

[17]*mono* = one; *sacchar* = sugar

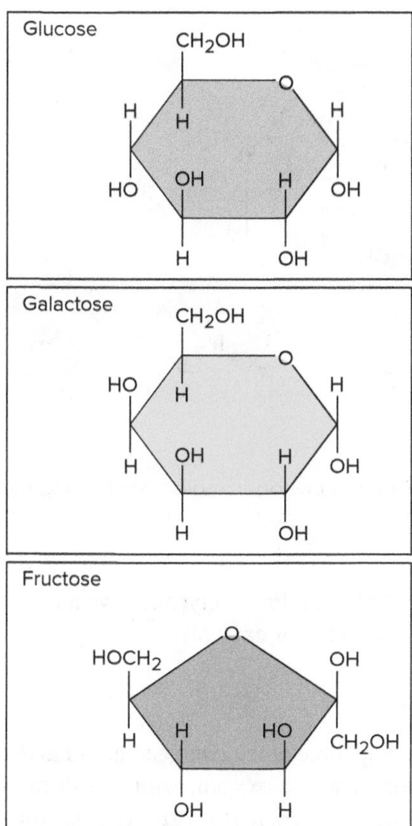

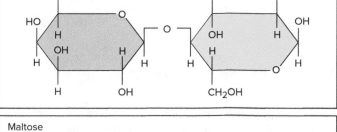

**FIGURE 2.15 The Three Major Monosaccharides.** Glucose, galactose, and fructose all have the molecular formula $C_6H_{12}O_6$, but with the atoms arranged differently as shown. Each angle in the rings represents a carbon atom except the one where oxygen is shown. This is a conventional way of representing carbon in the structural formulae of organic compounds.

Sucrose

Lactose

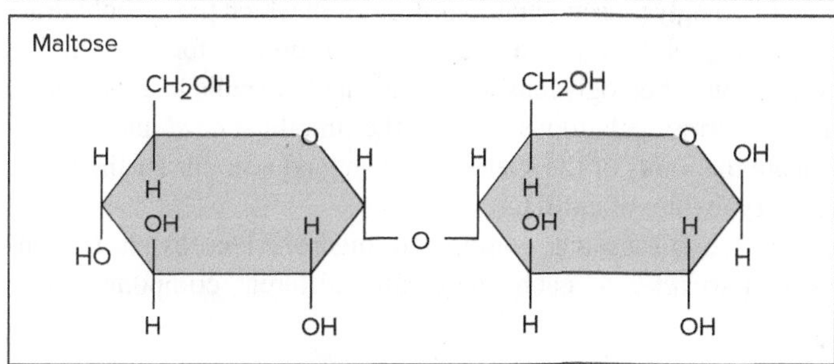


**FIGURE 2.16 The Three Major Disaccharides.** Sucrose, lactose, and maltose all consist of two monosaccharides joined through an oxygen atom.

can be thousands of sugars long and may have molecular weights of 500,000 or more (compared with 180 for a single glucose). Three polysaccharides of interest to human physiology are glycogen, starch, and cellulose—all composed solely of glucose. Animals, including ourselves, make glycogen, whereas starch and cellulose are plant products.

**Glycogen**[18] is an energy-storage polysaccharide made by cells of the liver, muscles, brain, uterus, and vagina. It is a long, branched, glucose polymer **(fig. 2.17).** The liver produces glycogen after a meal, when the blood glucose level is high, and then breaks it down between meals to maintain blood glucose levels when there is no food intake. Muscle stores glycogen for its own energy needs, and the uterus uses it in early pregnancy to nourish the embryo.

**Starch** is the corresponding energy-storage polysaccharide of plants. They store it when sunlight and nutrients are available and draw from it when photosynthesis is not possible (for example, at night and in winter, when a plant has shed its leaves). Starch is the only significant digestible polysaccharide in the human diet.

**Cellulose** is a structural polysaccharide that gives strength to the cell walls of plants. It is the principal component of wood, cotton, and paper. It is composed of a chain of a few thousand glucose monomers. Cellulose is the most abundant organic compound on earth and it is a common component of the diets of humans and other animals—yet we have no enzymes to digest it and thus derive no energy or nutrition from it. Nevertheless, it is important as dietary fiber ("bulk" or "roughage"). It swells with water in the digestive tract and helps move other materials through the intestine.

Carbohydrates are, above all, a source of energy that can be quickly mobilized. All digested carbohydrate is ultimately converted to glucose, and glucose is oxidized to make ATP, a high-energy compound discussed later. But carbohydrates have other functions as well **(table 2.6).** They are often **conjugated**[19] with (covalently bound to) proteins and lipids. Many lipid and protein molecules at the external surface of the cell membrane have chains of up to 12 sugars attached to them, thus forming **glycolipids** and **glycoproteins,** respectively. Among other functions, glycoproteins are a major component of mucus, which traps particles in the respiratory system, resists infection, and protects the digestive tract from its own acid and enzymes.

[18] *glyco* = sugar; *gen* = producing

[19] *con* = together; *jug* = join

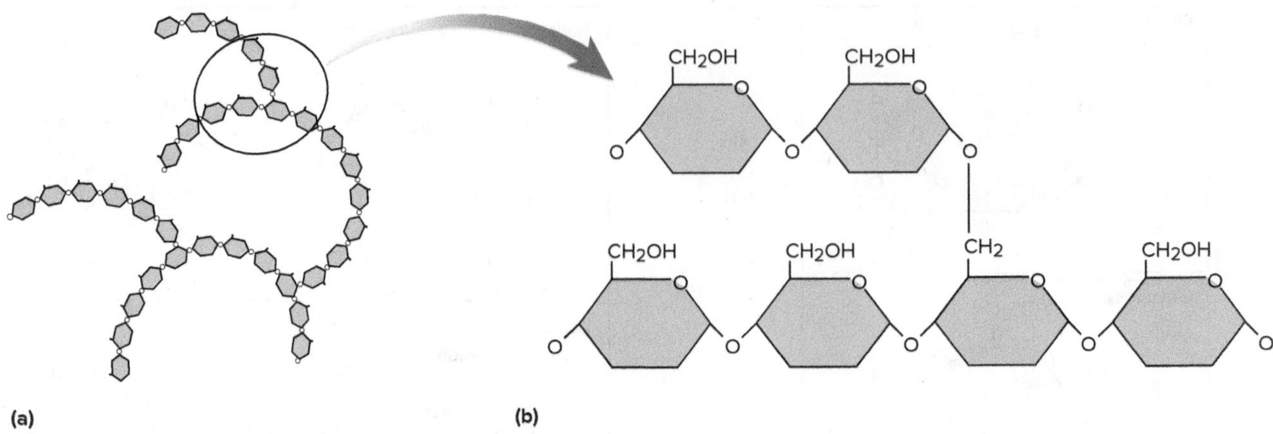


**FIGURE 2.17 Glycogen.** This is the only polysaccharide found in human tissues. (a) Part of a glycogen molecule showing the chain of glucose monomers and branching pattern. (b) Detail of the molecule at a branch point.

**Proteoglycans** are macromolecules in which the carbohydrate component is dominant and a peptide or protein forms a smaller component. Proteoglycans form gels that hold cells and tissues together, form a gelatinous filler in the umbilical cord and eye, lubricate the joints of the skeletal system, and account for the tough rubbery texture of cartilage.

When discussing conjugated macromolecules, it is convenient to refer to each chemically different component as a **moiety**[20] (MOY-eh-tee). Proteoglycans have a protein moiety and a carbohydrate moiety, for example.

**TABLE 2.6 Carbohydrate Functions**

| Type | Function |
|---|---|
| **Monosaccharides** | |
| Glucose | Blood sugar—energy source for most cells |
| Galactose | Converted to glucose and metabolized |
| Fructose | Fruit sugar—converted to glucose and metabolized |
| **Disaccharides** | |
| Sucrose | Cane sugar—digested to glucose and fructose |
| Lactose | Milk sugar—digested to glucose and galactose; important in infant nutrition |
| Maltose | Malt sugar—product of starch digestion, further digested to glucose |
| **Polysaccharides** | |
| Cellulose | Structural polysaccharide of plants; dietary fiber |
| Starch | Energy storage in plant cells; energy source in human diet |
| Glycogen | Energy storage in animal cells (liver, muscle, brain, uterus, vagina) |
| **Conjugated Carbohydrates** | |
| Glycoprotein | Component of the cell surface coat and mucus, among other roles |
| Glycolipid | Component of the cell surface coat |
| Proteoglycan | Cell adhesion; lubrication; supportive filler of some tissues and organs |

## 2.4d Lipids

A **lipid** is a hydrophobic organic molecule, usually composed only of carbon, hydrogen, and oxygen, with a high ratio of hydrogen to oxygen. A fat called *tristearin* (tri-STEE-uh-rin), for example, has the molecular formula $C_{57}H_{110}O_6$—more than 18 hydrogens for every oxygen. Lipids are less oxidized than carbohydrates, and thus have more calories per gram. Beyond these criteria, it is difficult to generalize about lipids; they are much more variable in structure than the other macromolecules we are considering. We consider here the five primary types of lipids in humans—*fatty acids, triglycerides, phospholipids, eicosanoids,* and *steroids* **(table 2.7).**

[20]*moiet* = half

**TABLE 2.7 Lipid Functions**

| Type | Function |
|---|---|
| Bile acids | Steroids that aid in fat digestion and nutrient absorption |
| Cholesterol | Component of cell membranes; precursor of other steroids |
| Eicosanoids | Chemical messengers between cells |
| Fat-soluble vitamins (A, D, E, and K) | Involved in a variety of functions including blood clotting, wound healing, vision, and calcium absorption |
| Fatty acids | Precursor of triglycerides; source of energy |
| Phospholipids | Major component of cell membranes; aid in fat digestion |
| Steroid hormones | Chemical messengers between cells |
| Triglycerides | Energy storage; thermal insulation; filling space; binding organs together; cushioning organs |

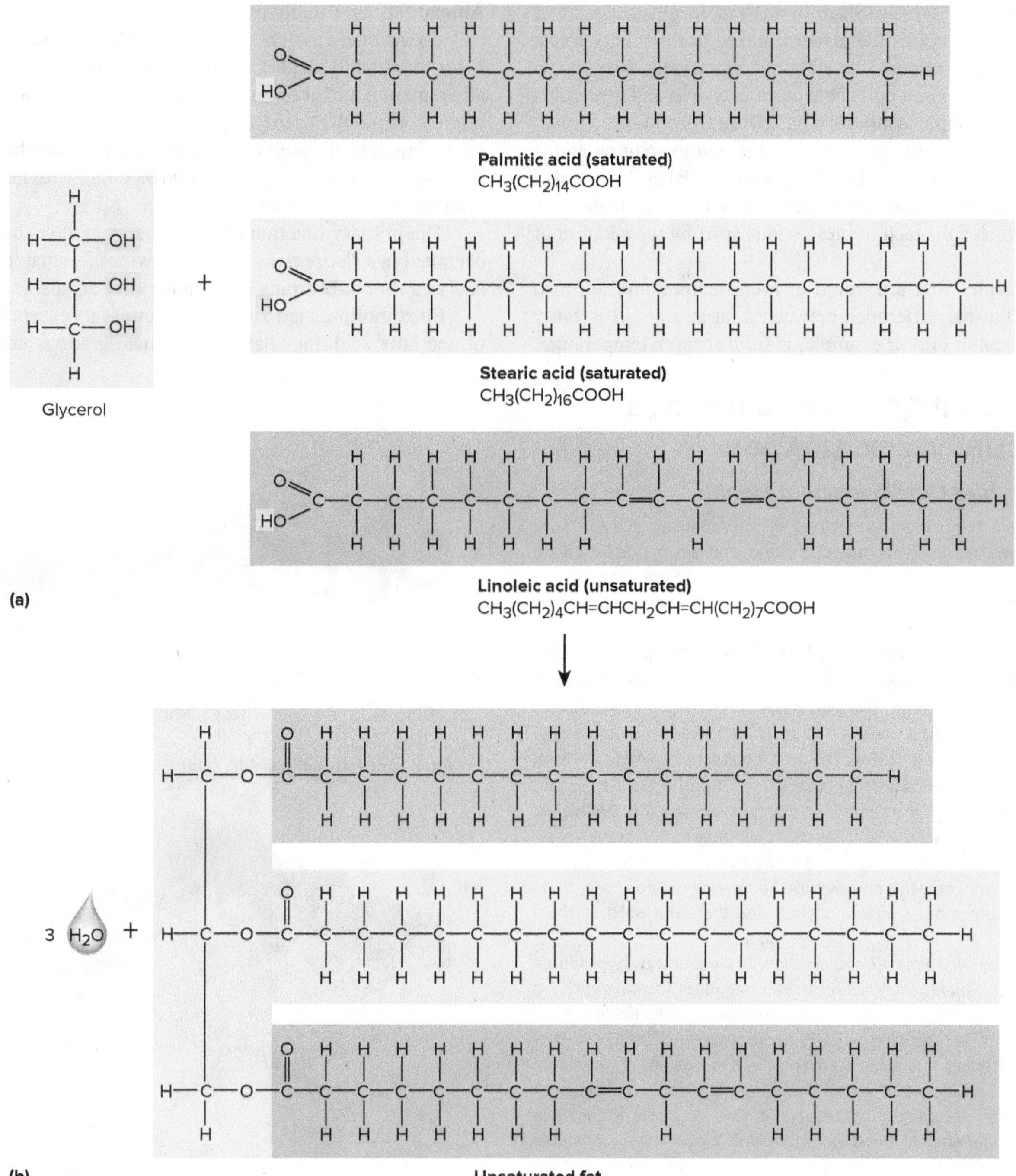


**FIGURE 2.18 Triglyceride (Fat) Synthesis.** The three fatty acids above the arrow (a) combine with glycerol (left) to produce the triglyceride (fat) below the arrow (b). Note the difference between saturated and unsaturated fatty acids and the production of 3 $H_2O$ as a by-product of this dehydration synthesis reaction.

A **fatty acid** is a chain of usually 4 to 24 carbon atoms with a carboxyl group at one end and a methyl group at the other. Fatty acids and the fats made from them are classified as *saturated* or *unsaturated.* A **saturated fatty acid** such as palmitic acid has as much hydrogen as it can carry. No more could be added without exceeding four covalent bonds per carbon; thus, it is "saturated" with hydrogen. In **unsaturated fatty acids** such as linoleic acid, however, some carbon atoms are joined by double covalent bonds **(fig. 2.18a).** Each of these could potentially share one pair of electrons with another hydrogen atom instead of the adjacent carbon, so hydrogen could be added to this molecule. **Polyunsaturated fatty acids** are those with multiple C=C bonds. Most fatty acids can be synthesized by the human body, but a few, called **essential fatty acids,** must be obtained from the diet because we cannot synthesize them.

A **triglyceride** (try-GLISS-ur-ide) is a molecule consisting of a three-carbon alcohol called **glycerol** linked to three fatty acids; triglycerides are more correctly, although less widely, also known as *triacylglycerols.* Each bond between a fatty acid and glycerol is formed by dehydration synthesis **(fig. 2.18b).** Once joined to glycerol, a fatty acid can no longer donate a proton to solution and is therefore no longer an acid. For this reason, triglycerides are also called **neutral fats.** Triglycerides are broken down by hydrolysis reactions, which split each of these bonds apart by the addition of water.

Triglycerides that are liquid at room temperature are also called *oils,* but the difference between a fat and an oil is fairly arbitrary. Coconut oil, for example, is solid at room temperature. Animal fats are usually made of saturated fatty acids, so they are called *saturated fats.* They are solid at room or body temperature. Most plant triglycerides are *polyunsaturated fats,* which generally remain liquid at room temperature. Examples include peanut, olive, corn, and linseed oils. Saturated fats contribute more to cardiovascular disease than unsaturated fats, and for this reason it's healthier to cook with vegetable oils than with lard, bacon fat, or butter (but see Deeper Insight 2.3).

The primary function of fat is energy storage, but when concentrated in *adipose tissue,* it also provides thermal insulation and acts as a shock-absorbing cushion for vital organs.

**Phospholipids** are similar to neutral fats except that in place of one fatty acid, they have a phosphate group which, in turn, is

## DEEPER INSIGHT 2.3

### CLINICAL APPLICATION

### Trans *Fats and Cardiovascular Health*

*Trans* fats have been a significant part of the American diet for more than a century. Yet in 2015, the U.S. Food and Drug Administration (FDA) ordered food manufacturers to discontinue their use. So what are *trans* fats, why were they so popular for so long, and why are they now almost entirely banished?

A *trans* fat is a triglyceride containing one or more *trans*-fatty acids. In such fatty acids, there is at least one unsaturated C═C double bond. On each side of that bond, the single covalent C—C bonds angle in opposite directions (*trans* means "across from") like a pair of bicycle pedals (see arrows in **fig. 2.19a**). This is in contrast to *cis*-fatty acids, in which the two C—C bonds adjacent to the C═C bond angle in the same direction (*cis* means "on the same side"). As you can see **(fig. 2.19b),** the *cis* configuration creates a kink in the chain, whereas the *trans* configuration results in a relatively straight chain. The kink prevents triglycerides with *cis* bonds from packing closely together; hence they are oils. *Trans* fats, however, are more densely packed and therefore solid at room temperature.

Small amounts of *trans* fat occur naturally in meat and dairy products, but in 1911, a food manufacturer invented a method for forcing hydrogen through liquid vegetable oils and converting liquid *cis*-fatty acids to solid *trans*-fatty acids. The resulting *partially hydrogenated oil (PHO),* sold as vegetable shortening, had several advantages and was heavily marketed for household and industrial use. It was easier to use in making such baked goods as pie crusts and biscuits; it gave products a desirable texture and longer shelf life; and to vegetarians, it was more acceptable than animal fat such as lard. *Trans* fats came to be abundantly used not only by home cooks but also in snack foods, baked goods, frosting, coffee creamer, margarine, and fast foods such as french fries and take-out fried chicken.

But *trans* fats resist enzymatic breakdown in the human body, remain in circulation longer, and have more tendency to deposit in the arteries than saturated and *cis* fats do. Therefore, they raise the risk of coronary heart disease (CHD). A study of more than 80,000 nurses who tracked their diets from 1980 to 1994 showed, among other things, that for every 2% increase in calories from *trans* fats as compared to carbohydrates, the women had a 93% elevated incidence of CHD. As the dangers of *trans* fats became widely known, their consumption in the United States declined greatly after 2003 and they were banned in some cities and states, until the FDA concluded in 2015 that they are "not safe for human consumption" and must be eliminated from processed and restaurant foods.

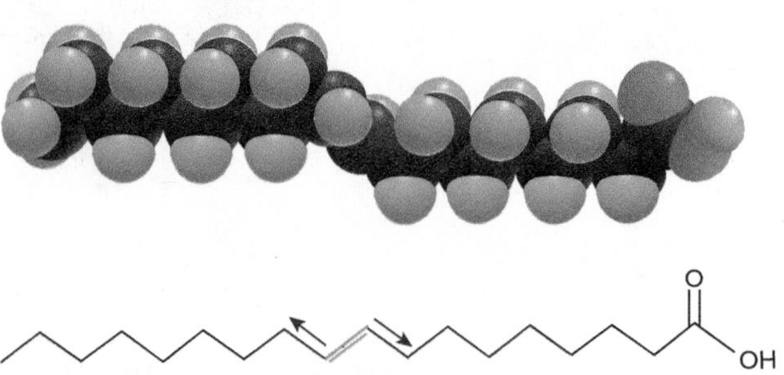


**(a) A *trans*-fatty acid (elaidic acid)**

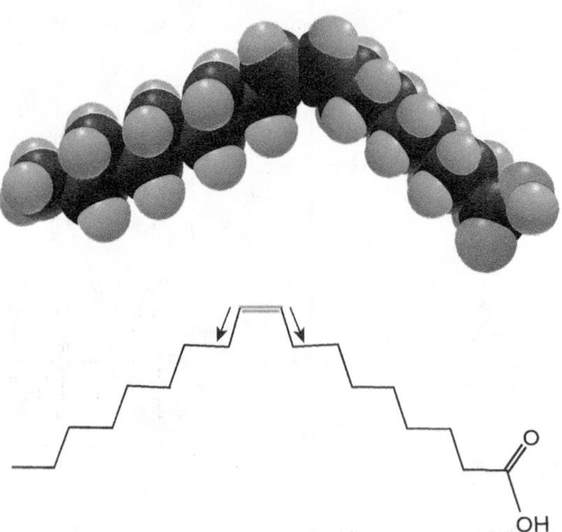


**(b) A *cis*-fatty acid (oleic acid)**

**FIGURE 2.19** ***Trans*- and *Cis*-Fatty Acids.** Each example is unsaturated at the C═C double bond in red. (a) In a *trans*-fatty acid, the bonds on opposite sides of the C═C bond angle in opposite directions (arrows). (b) In a *cis*-fatty acid, the bonds on opposite sides of the C═C bond angle in the same direction. The straight-chain *trans*-fatty acids pack more tightly together, thus remain solid (greasy) at room temperature. Oleic acid melts at 13.5°C (56.3°F), whereas elaidic acid melts at 46.5°C (115.7°F) and therefore would not liquify in the human body.

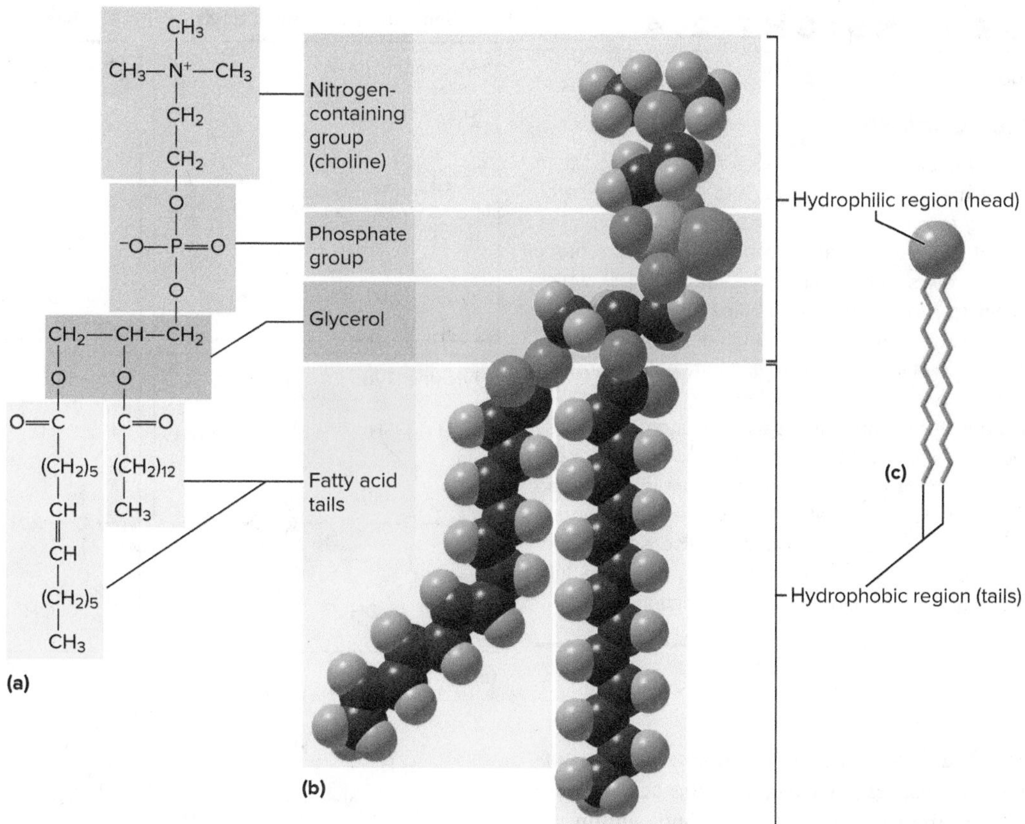


**FIGURE 2.20 Lecithin, a Representative Phospholipid.** (a) Structural formula. (b) A space-filling model that gives some idea of the actual shape of the molecule. (c) A simplified representation of the phospholipid molecule used in diagrams of cell membranes.

linked to other functional groups. Lecithin is a common phospholipid in which the phosphate is bonded to a nitrogenous group called *choline* (CO-leen) **(fig. 2.20).** Phospholipids have a dual nature. The two fatty acid "tails" of the molecule are hydrophobic, but the phosphate "head" is hydrophilic. Thus, phospholipids are said to be **amphipathic**[21] (AM-fih-PATH-ic). Together, the head and the two tails of a phospholipid give it a shape like a clothespin. The most important function of phospholipids is to serve as the structural foundation of cell membranes (see section 3.2a).

**Eicosanoids**[22] (eye-CO-sah-noyds) are 20-carbon compounds derived from a fatty acid called *arachidonic acid* (ah-RACK-ih-DON-ic). They function primarily as hormonelike chemical signals between cells. The most functionally diverse eicosanoids are **prostaglandins,** in which five of the carbon atoms are arranged in a ring **(fig. 2.21).** These were originally found in the secretions of bovine prostate glands—hence their name—but they are now known to be produced in almost all tissues. They play a variety of signaling roles in inflammation, blood clotting, hormone action, labor contractions, control of blood vessel diameter, and other processes.

A **steroid** is a lipid with 17 of its carbon atoms arranged in four rings **(fig. 2.22). Cholesterol** is the "parent" steroid from

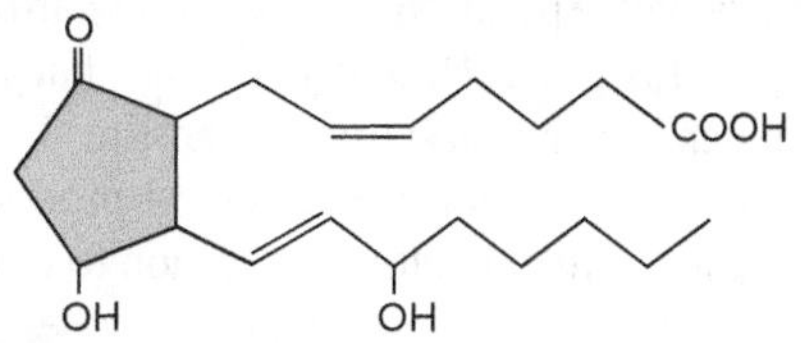

**FIGURE 2.21 Prostaglandin.** This is a modified fatty acid with five of its carbon atoms arranged in a ring.

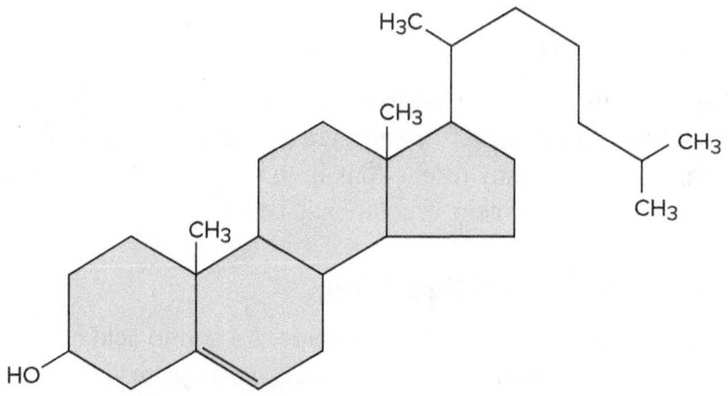

**FIGURE 2.22 Cholesterol.** All steroids have this basic four-ringed structure, with variations in the functional groups and locations of double bonds within the rings.

[21] *amphi* = both; *pathic* = feeling
[22] *eicosa* = 20

## DEEPER INSIGHT 2.4

### CLINICAL APPLICATION

#### *"Good" and "Bad" Cholesterol*

There is only one kind of cholesterol, and it does far more good than harm. When the popular media refer to "good" and "bad" cholesterol, they are actually referring to droplets in the blood called *lipoproteins,* which are a complex of cholesterol, fat, phospholipids, and protein. So-called bad cholesterol refers to low-density lipoprotein (LDL), which has a high ratio of lipid to protein and contributes to cardiovascular disease. So-called good cholesterol refers to high-density lipoprotein (HDL), which has a lower ratio of lipid to protein and may help to prevent cardiovascular disease.

Even when food products are advertised as cholesterol-free, they may be high in saturated fat, which stimulates the body to produce more cholesterol. Palmitic acid seems to be the greatest culprit in stimulating elevated cholesterol levels, while linoleic acid has a cholesterol-lowering effect. Both are shown in figure 2.18. Cardiovascular disease is further discussed in Deeper Insight 19.4, and LDLs and HDLs are more fully explained at "Cholesterol and Serum Lipoproteins" in section 26.1g.

which the other steroids are synthesized. The others include cortisol, progesterone, estrogens, testosterone, and bile acids. These differ from each other in the location of C=C bonds within the rings and in the functional groups attached to the rings.

We obtain dietary cholesterol only from foods of animal origin; plants make only trace amounts of no dietary importance. The average adult contains over 200 g (half a pound) of cholesterol. Cholesterol has a bad reputation as a factor in cardiovascular disease (see Deeper Insight 2.4), and it is true that hereditary and dietary factors can elevate blood cholesterol to dangerously high levels. Nevertheless, cholesterol is a natural product of the body and is necessary for human health. In addition to being the precursor of other steroids, it is an important component of cell membranes and is required for proper nervous system function. Only about 15% of our cholesterol comes from the diet; the other 85% is internally synthesized, primarily by the liver.

The principal lipids and their functions are summarized in table 2.7.

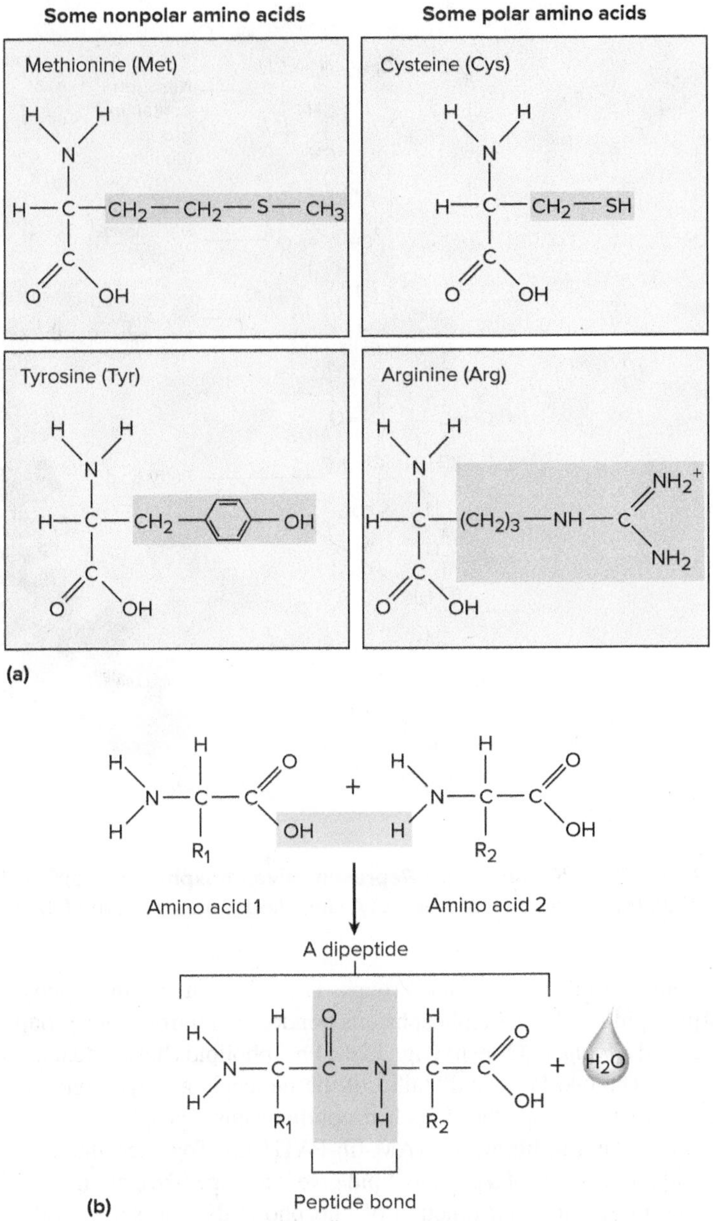

## 2.4e Proteins

The word *protein* is derived from the Greek word *proteios,* meaning "of first importance." Proteins are the most versatile molecules in the body, and many discussions in this book will draw on your understanding of protein structure and behavior.

### Amino Acids and Peptides

A **protein** is a polymer of **amino acids.** An amino acid has a central carbon atom with an amino (—$NH_2$) and a carboxyl (—COOH) group bound to it **(fig. 2.23a).** The 20 amino acids used to make proteins are identical except for a third functional group called the *radical* (R group) attached to the central carbon. In the simplest amino acid, glycine, R is merely a hydrogen atom, whereas in the



**FIGURE 2.23 Amino Acids and Peptides.** (a) Four representative amino acids and their symbols. Note that they differ only in the R group, shaded in pink. For structures of all 20 amino acids, see appendix D. (b) The joining of two amino acids by a peptide bond, forming a dipeptide. Side groups $R_1$ and $R_2$ could be the groups indicated in pink in part (a), among other possibilities.

largest amino acids it includes rings of carbon. Some radicals are hydrophilic and some are hydrophobic. Being composed of many amino acids, proteins as a whole are therefore often amphipathic. The 20 amino acids involved in proteins are shown in appendix D along with their standard abbreviations.

A **peptide** is any molecule composed of two or more amino acids joined by **peptide bonds.** A peptide bond, formed by dehydration synthesis, joins the amino group of one amino acid to the carboxyl group of the next **(fig. 2.23b).** Peptides are named for the number of amino acids they have—for example, dipeptides have two and tripeptides have three. Chains of fewer than 10 or 15 amino acids are called **oligopeptides,**[23] and chains larger than that are called **polypeptides.** An example of an oligopeptide is the childbirth-inducing hormone oxytocin, composed of 9 amino acids. A representative polypeptide is adrenocorticotropic hormone (ACTH), which is 39 amino acids long. A protein is a polypeptide of 50 amino acids or more. A typical amino acid has a molecular weight of about 80 amu, and the molecular weights of the smallest proteins are around 4,000 to 8,000 amu. The average protein weighs in at about 30,000 amu, and some of them have molecular weights in the hundreds of thousands.

## Protein Structure

Proteins have complex coiled and folded structures that are critically important to the roles they play. Even slight changes in their **conformation** (three-dimensional shape) can destroy protein function. Protein structure is now visible even to the level of individual atoms by the newly invented technique of cryo-electron microscopy (cryo-EM), pairing a transmission electron microscope with a supercomputer to image supercooled protein molecules (see this chapter's opening photo). This invention won the 2017 Nobel Prize in Chemistry for its inventors Joachim Frank, Richard Henderson, and Jacques Dubochet.

Protein molecules have three to four levels of complexity, from primary through quaternary structure **(fig. 2.24).**

**Primary structure** is the protein's sequence of amino acids, which is encoded in the genes (**fig. 2.25;** see also section 4.2b).

**Secondary structure** is a coiled or folded shape held together by hydrogen bonds between the slightly negative $—C{=}O$ group of one peptide bond and the slightly positive —NH group of another one some distance away. The most common secondary structures are a springlike shape called the **alpha (α) helix** and a pleated, ribbonlike shape, the **beta (β) sheet (β-pleated sheet).** Many proteins have multiple α-helical and β-pleated regions joined by short segments with less orderly geometry. A single protein molecule may fold back on itself and have two or more β-pleated regions linked to one another by hydrogen bonds. Separate, parallel protein chains also may be hydrogen-bonded to each other through their β-pleated regions.

**Tertiary**[24] **structure** (TUR-she-air-ee) is formed by the further bending and folding of proteins into various globular and fibrous shapes. It results from hydrophobic radicals associating with each other and avoiding water while hydrophilic radicals are attracted to the surrounding water. Van der Waals forces play a significant role in stabilizing tertiary structure. *Globular proteins,* somewhat resembling a wadded ball of yarn, have a compact tertiary structure well suited for proteins embedded in cell membranes and proteins that must move around freely in the body fluids, such as enzymes and antibodies. *Fibrous proteins* such as myosin, keratin, and collagen are slender filaments better suited for such roles as muscle contraction and providing strength to skin, hair, and tendons.

The amino acid cysteine (Cys), whose radical is $—CH_2—SH$ (see fig. 2.23a), often stabilizes a protein's tertiary structure by forming covalent **disulfide bridges.** When two cysteines align with each other, each can release a hydrogen atom, leaving the sulfur atoms to form a disulfide (—S—S—) bridge. Disulfide bridges hold separate polypeptide chains together in such molecules as antibodies and insulin (fig. 2.25).

**Quaternary**[25] **structure** (QUA-tur-nare-ee) is the association of two or more polypeptide chains by noncovalent forces such as ionic bonds and hydrophilic–hydrophobic interactions. It occurs in only some proteins. Hemoglobin, for example, consists of four polypeptides: two identical alpha chains and two identical, slightly longer beta chains (fig. 2.24d).

One of the most important properties of proteins is their ability to change conformation, especially tertiary structure. This can be triggered by such influences as voltage changes on a cell membrane during the action of nerve cells, the binding of a hormone to a protein, or the dissociation of a molecule from a protein. Subtle, reversible changes in conformation are important to processes such as enzyme function, muscle contraction, and the opening and closing of pores in cell membranes. **Denaturation** is a more drastic conformational change in response to conditions such as extreme heat or pH. It is seen, for example, when you cook an egg and the egg white (albumen) turns from clear and runny to opaque and stiff. Denaturation makes a protein unable to perform its normal function. It is sometimes reversible, but usually it permanently destroys protein function.

*Conjugated proteins* have a non–amino acid moiety called a **prosthetic**[26] **group** covalently bound to them. Hemoglobin, for example, not only has the four polypeptide chains described earlier, but each chain also has a complex iron-containing ring called a *heme* moiety attached to it (fig. 2.24d). Hemoglobin cannot transport oxygen unless this group is present. In glycoproteins, as described earlier, the carbohydrate moiety is a prosthetic group.

## Protein Functions

Proteins have more diverse functions than other macromolecules. These include

- **Structure.** *Keratin,* a tough structural protein, gives strength to the nails, hair, and skin surface. Deeper layers of the skin, as well as bones, cartilage, and teeth, contain an abundance of the durable protein *collagen.*
- **Communication.** Some hormones and other cell-to-cell signals are proteins, as are the receptors to which the signal molecules bind in the receiving cell. Any hormone or other molecule that reversibly binds to a protein is called a **ligand**[27] (LIG-and).

[23]*oligo* = a few
[24]*tert* = third
[25]*quater* = fourth
[26]*prosthe* = appendage, addition
[27]*lig* = to bind

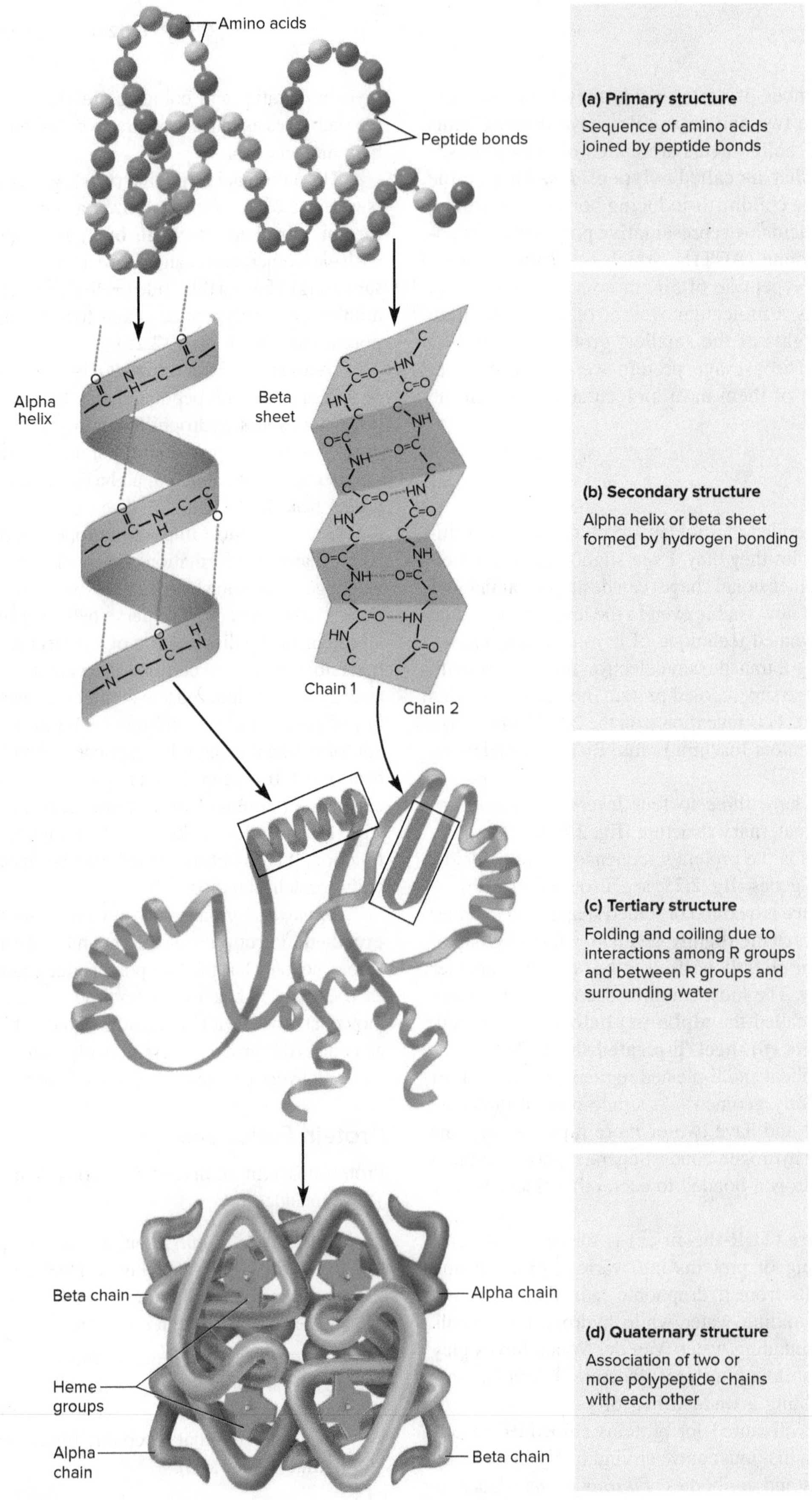


**FIGURE 2.24 Four Levels of Protein Structure.** (a) Primary structure, the amino acid sequence. (b) Secondary structure, the alpha helix or beta sheet. (c) Tertiary structure, folding and coiling of the chain. (d) Quaternary structure, the association of two or more chains with each other. This example of quaternary structure is hemoglobin, composed of four polypeptide chains. The heme groups are iron-containing nonprotein moieties.

**FIGURE 2.25 Primary Structure of Insulin.** Insulin is composed of two polypeptide chains joined by three disulfide bridges (heavy bars). See appendix D to interpret the three-letter amino acid symbols.

- **Membrane transport.** Some proteins form channels in cell membranes that govern what passes through the membranes and when. Others act as carriers that briefly bind to solute particles and transport them to the other side of the membrane. Among their other roles, such proteins turn nerve and muscle activity on and off.
- **Catalysis.** Most metabolic pathways of the body are controlled by enzymes, which are globular proteins that function as catalysts.
- **Recognition and protection.** The role of glycoproteins in immune recognition was mentioned earlier. Antibodies and other proteins attack and neutralize organisms that invade the body. Clotting proteins protect the body against blood loss.
- **Movement.** Movement is fundamental to all life, from the intracellular transport of molecules to the galloping of a racehorse. Proteins, with their special ability to change shape repeatedly, are the basis for all such movement. Some proteins are called *molecular motors (motor proteins)* for this reason.
- **Cell adhesion.** Proteins bind cells to each other, which enables sperm to fertilize eggs, enables immune cells to bind to enemy cancer cells, and keeps tissues from falling apart.

## 2.4f Enzymes and Metabolism

Most **enzymes** are proteins that function as biological catalysts. (Some RNAs also play enzymatic roles.) They enable biochemical reactions to occur rapidly at normal body temperatures. Enzymes were initially given somewhat arbitrary names, some of which are still with us, such as *pepsin* and *trypsin.* The modern system of naming enzymes, however, is more uniform and informative. It identifies the substance the enzyme acts upon, called its **substrate;** sometimes refers to the enzyme's action; and adds the suffix *-ase.* Thus, *amylase* digests starch *(amyl-* = starch) and *carbonic anhydrase* removes water *(anhydr-)* from carbonic acid. Enzyme names may be further modified to distinguish different forms of the same enzyme found in different tissues (see Deeper Insight 2.5).

## DEEPER INSIGHT 2.5
### CLINICAL APPLICATION

### *Blood Enzymes as Disease Markers*

A given enzyme may exist in slightly different forms, called *isoenzymes,* in different cells. Isoenzymes catalyze the same chemical reactions but have enough structural differences that they can be distinguished by standard laboratory techniques. This is useful in the diagnosis of disease. When organs are diseased, some cells break down and release specific isoenzymes that can be detected in the blood. Normally, these isoenzymes would not be present in the blood or would have very low concentrations. An elevation in blood levels can help pinpoint what cells in the body have been damaged.

For example, creatine kinase (CK) occurs in different forms in different cells. An elevated serum level of CK-1 indicates a breakdown of skeletal muscle and is one of the signs of muscular dystrophy. An elevated CK-2 level indicates heart disease, because this isoenzyme comes only from cardiac muscle. There are five isoenzymes of lactate dehydrogenase (LDH). High serum levels of LDH-1 may indicate a tumor of the ovaries or testes, whereas LDH-5 may indicate liver disease or muscular dystrophy. Different isoenzymes of phosphatase in the blood may indicate bone or prostate disease.

To appreciate the effect of an enzyme, think of what happens when paper burns. Paper is composed mainly of glucose (in the form of cellulose). The burning of glucose can be represented by the equation

$$C_6H_{12}O_6 + 6\ O_2 \longrightarrow 6\ CO_2 + 6\ H_2O.$$

Paper doesn't spontaneously burst into flame because few of its molecules have enough kinetic energy to react. Lighting the paper with a match, however, raises the kinetic energy enough to initiate combustion (rapid oxidation). The energy needed to get the reaction started, supplied by the match, is called the **activation energy (fig. 2.26a).**

In the body, we carry out the same reaction and oxidize glucose to water and carbon dioxide to extract its energy. We can't tolerate the heat of combustion in our bodies, however, so we must oxidize glucose in a more controlled way at a biologically feasible and safe temperature. Enzymes make this happen by lowering the activation energy—that is, by reducing the barrier to glucose oxidation **(fig. 2.26b)**—and by releasing the energy in small steps rather than a single burst of heat.

### Enzyme Structure and Action

**Figure 2.27** illustrates the action of an enzyme, using the example of *sucrase,* an enzyme that breaks sucrose down to glucose and fructose. The process occurs in three principal steps:

(1) A substrate molecule (such as sucrose) approaches a pocket on the enzyme surface called the **active site.** Amino acid side groups in this region of the enzyme are arranged so as to bind functional groups on the substrate molecule. Many enzymes have two active sites, enabling them to bind two different substrates and bring them together in a way that makes them react more readily with each other.

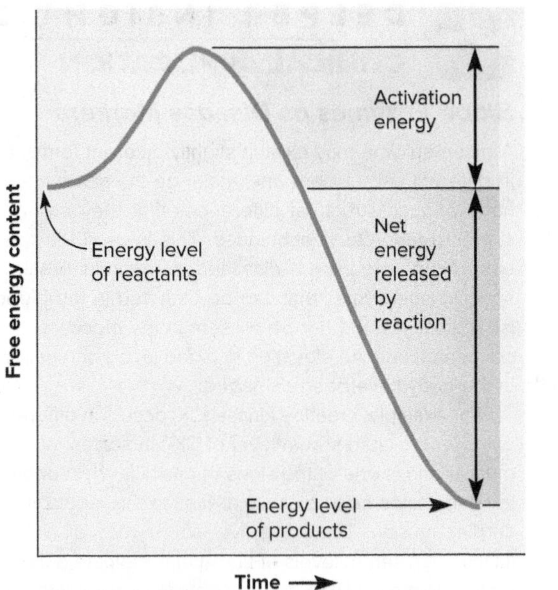

(a) Reaction occurring slowly without a catalyst

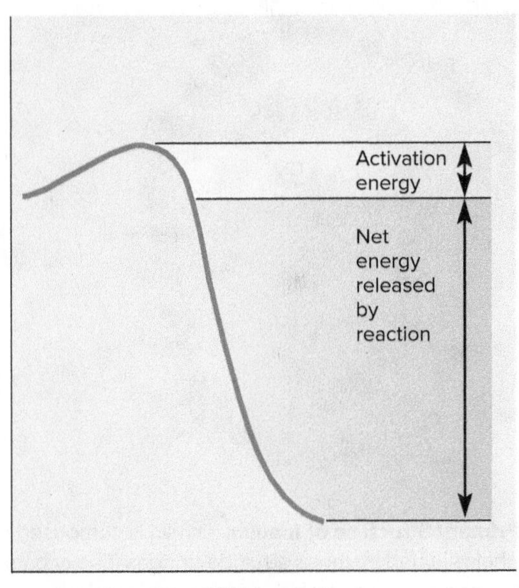

(b) Reaction occuring quickly with a catalyst

**FIGURE 2.26 Effect of an Enzyme on Activation Energy.** (a) Without catalysts, some chemical reactions proceed slowly because of the high activation energy needed to get molecules to react. (b) A catalyst facilitates molecular interaction, thus lowering the activation energy and making the reaction proceed more rapidly.

*Does an enzyme release more energy from its substrate than an uncatalyzed reaction would release?*

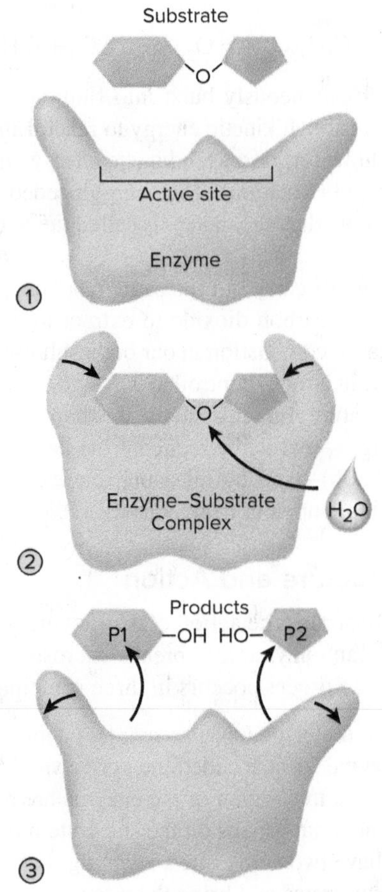

**FIGURE 2.27 The Three Steps of an Enzymatic Reaction.**

(2) The substrate binds to the enzyme, forming an **enzyme–substrate complex.** The fit between a particular enzyme and its substrate is often compared to a lock and key. Just as only one key fits a particular lock, sucrose is the only substrate that fits the active site of sucrase. Sucrase cannot digest other disaccharides such as maltose or lactose. This selectivity is called **enzyme–substrate specificity.** Unlike a simple lock and key, however, the substrate slightly changes the shape of the enzyme to create a better fit between the two, as shown by the arrows in the figure.

(3) Sucrase breaks the bond between the two sugars of sucrose, adding $—H^+$ and $—OH^-$ groups from water. This hydrolyzes sucrose to two monosaccharides, glucose and fructose, which are then released by the enzyme as its **reaction products.** The enzyme remains unchanged and is ready to repeat the process if another sucrose is available.

Since an enzyme is not consumed by the reaction it catalyzes, one enzyme molecule can consume millions of substrate molecules, and at astonishing speed. A single molecule of carbonic anhydrase, for example, breaks carbonic acid ($H_2CO_3$) down to $H_2O$ and $CO_2$ at a rate of 36 million molecules per minute.

Factors that change the shape of an enzyme—notably temperature and pH—tend to alter or destroy the ability of the enzyme to bind its substrate. They disrupt the hydrogen bonds and other weak forces that hold the enzyme in its proper conformation, essentially changing the shape of the "lock" so that the "key" no longer fits. Enzymes vary in optimum pH according to where in the body they normally function. Thus, salivary amylase, which digests starch in the mouth, functions best at pH 7 and is inactivated when it is exposed to stomach acid; pepsin, which works in the acidic environment of the stomach, functions best around pH 2; and trypsin, a digestive enzyme that works in the alkaline environment of the small intestine, has an optimum pH of 9.5. Our internal body temperature is nearly the same everywhere, however, and all human enzymes have a temperature optimum near 37°C at which they produce their fastest reaction rates.

**▶▶▶APPLY WHAT YOU KNOW**

*Why does enzyme function depend on homeostasis?*

### Cofactors

About two-thirds of human enzymes require a nonprotein partner called a **cofactor.** Inorganic cofactors include iron, copper, zinc, magnesium, and calcium ions. Some of these work by binding to the enzyme and inducing it to fold into a shape that activates its active site. **Coenzymes** are organic cofactors usually derived from niacin, riboflavin, and other water-soluble vitamins. They accept electrons from an enzyme in one metabolic pathway and transfer them to an enzyme in another. For example, cells partially oxidize glucose through a pathway called *glycolysis.* A coenzyme called $NAD^+$,[28] derived from niacin, shuttles electrons from this pathway to another one called *aerobic respiration,* which uses energy from the electrons to make ATP **(fig. 2.28).** If $NAD^+$ is unavailable, the glycolysis pathway shuts down.

### Metabolic Pathways

A **metabolic pathway** is a chain of reactions with each step usually catalyzed by a different enzyme. A simple metabolic pathway can be symbolized

$$A \xrightarrow{\alpha} B \xrightarrow{\beta} C \xrightarrow{\gamma} D$$

[28]nicotinamide adenine dinucleotide

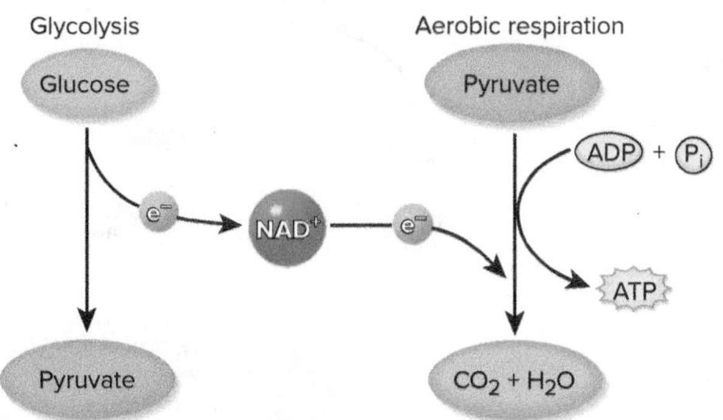


**FIGURE 2.28 The Action of a Coenzyme.** A coenzyme such as $NAD^+$ acts as a shuttle that picks up electrons from one metabolic pathway (in this case, glycolysis) and delivers them to another (in this case, aerobic respiration).

where A is the initial *reactant,* B and C are *intermediates,* and D is the *end product.* The Greek letters above the reaction arrows represent enzymes that catalyze each step of the reaction. A is the substrate for enzyme α, B is the substrate for enzyme β, and C for enzyme γ. Such a pathway can be turned on or off by altering the conformation of any of these enzymes, thereby activating or deactivating them. This can be done by such means as the binding or dissociation of a cofactor, or by an end product of the pathway binding to an enzyme at an earlier step (product D binding to enzyme α and shutting off the reaction chain at that step, for example). In these and other ways, cells are able to turn on metabolic pathways when their end products are needed and shut them down when the end products are not needed.

## 2.4g ATP, Other Nucleotides, and Nucleic Acids

**Nucleotides** are organic compounds with three principal components: a single or double carbon–nitrogen ring called a *nitrogenous base,* a monosaccharide, and one or more phosphate groups. One of the best-known nucleotides is ATP **(fig. 2.29a),** in which the nitrogenous base is a double ring called *adenine,* the sugar is *ribose,* and there are three phosphate groups.

### Adenosine Triphosphate

**Adenosine triphosphate (ATP)** is the body's most important energy-transfer molecule. It briefly gains energy from exergonic reactions such as glucose oxidation and releases it within seconds for physiological work such as polymerization reactions, muscle contraction, and pumping ions through cell membranes. The second and third phosphate groups of ATP are attached to the rest of the molecule by high-energy covalent bonds traditionally indicated by a wavy line (~) in the structural formula. Since phosphate groups are negatively charged, they repel each other. It requires a high-energy bond to overcome that repellent force and hold them together—especially to add the third phosphate group to a chain that already has two negatively charged phosphates. Most energy transfers to and from ATP involve adding or removing that third phosphate.

Enzymes called **adenosine triphosphatases (ATPases)** are specialized to hydrolyze the third phosphate bond, producing **adenosine diphosphate (ADP)** and an inorganic phosphate group ($P_i$). This reaction releases 7.3 kilocalories (kcal) of energy for every mole (505 g) of ATP. Most of this energy escapes as heat, but we live on the portion of it that does useful work. We can summarize this as follows:

$$ATP + H_2O \xrightarrow{\text{ATPase}} ADP + P_i + \text{Energy} \begin{cases} \nearrow \text{Heat} \\ \searrow \text{Work} \end{cases}$$

The free phosphate groups released by ATP hydrolysis are often added to enzymes or other molecules to activate them. This addition of $P_i$, called **phosphorylation,** is carried out by enzymes called **kinases.** The phosphorylation of an enzyme is sometimes the "switch" that turns a metabolic pathway on or off.

ATP is a short-lived molecule, usually consumed within 60 seconds of its formation. The entire amount in the body would

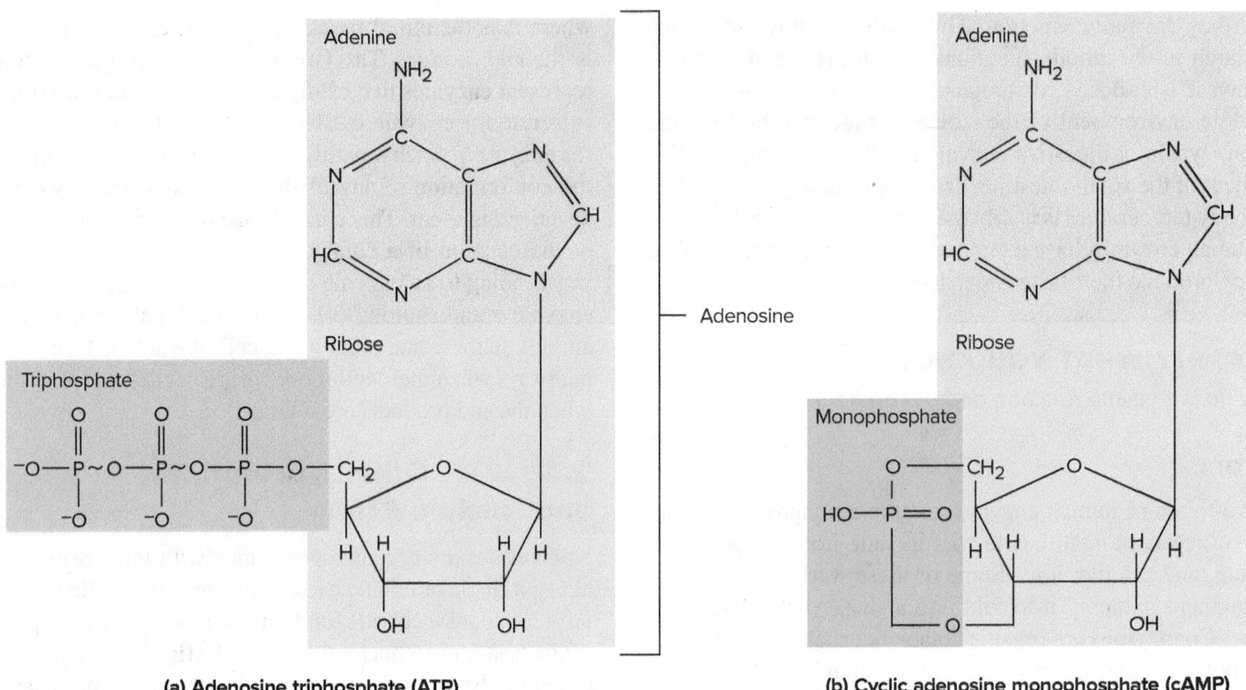

(a) Adenosine triphosphate (ATP)

(b) Cyclic adenosine monophosphate (cAMP)

**FIGURE 2.29 Two Major Nucleotides.** (a) Adenosine triphosphate (ATP). (b) Cyclic adenosine monophosphate (cAMP). The last two P~O bonds in ATP, indicated by wavy lines, are high-energy bonds.

support life for less than 1 minute if it weren't continually replenished. At a moderate rate of physical activity, a full day's supply of ATP would weigh twice as much as you do. Even if you never got out of bed, you would need about 45 kg (99 lb) of ATP to stay alive for a day. The reason cyanide is so lethal is that it halts ATP synthesis.

ATP synthesis is explained in detail in chapter 26, but you will find it necessary to become familiar with the general idea of it before you reach that chapter—especially in understanding muscle physiology (chapter 11). Much of the energy for ATP synthesis comes from glucose oxidation **(fig. 2.30).** The first stage in glucose oxidation **(fig. 2.31)** is the reaction pathway known as **glycolysis** (gly-COLL-ih-sis). This literally means "sugar splitting," and indeed its major effect is to split the six-carbon glucose molecule into two three-carbon molecules of *pyruvate.* A little ATP is produced in this stage (a net yield of 2 ATP per glucose), but most of the chemical energy of the glucose is still in the pyruvate.

What happens to pyruvate depends on how much oxygen is available relative to ATP demand. When the demand for ATP outpaces the oxygen supply, excess pyruvate is converted to lactate by a pathway called **anaerobic**[29] **fermentation** (AN-err-OH-bic). This pathway has two noteworthy disadvantages: First, it doesn't extract any more energy from pyruvate; second, the lactate it produces is toxic, so most cells can use anaerobic fermentation only as a temporary measure. The only advantage to this pathway is that it enables glycolysis to continue (for reasons explained in chapter 26) and thus enables a cell to continue producing a small amount of ATP.

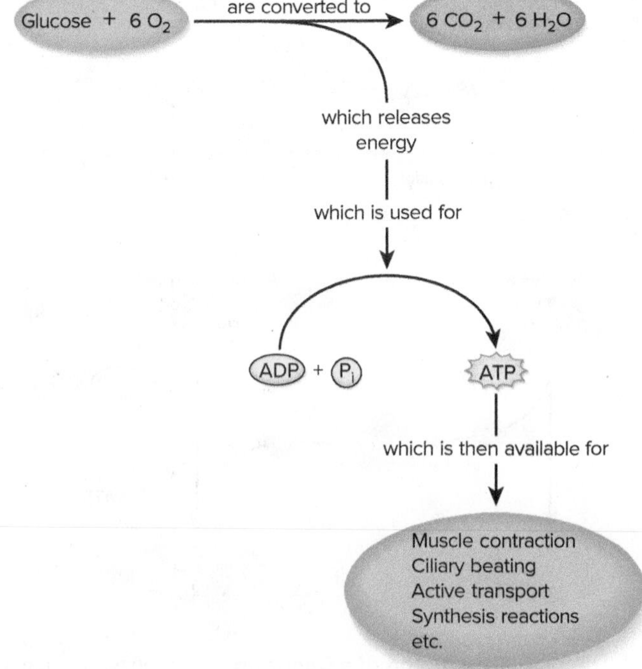


**FIGURE 2.30 The Source and Uses of ATP.**

[29]*an* = without; *aer* = air, oxygen; *obic* = pertaining to life

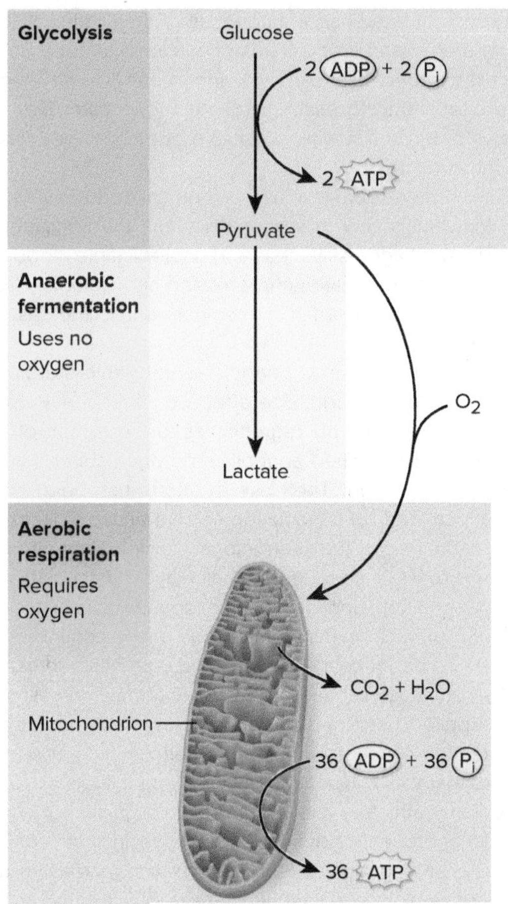


**FIGURE 2.31 ATP Production.** Glycolysis produces pyruvate and a net gain of two ATPs. Anaerobic fermentation converts pyruvate to lactate and permits glycolysis to continue producing ATP in the absence of oxygen. Aerobic respiration produces a much greater ATP yield but requires oxygen.

If enough oxygen is available, a more efficient pathway called **aerobic respiration** occurs. This breaks pyruvate down to carbon dioxide and water and generates up to 36 more molecules of ATP for each of the original glucose molecules. The reactions of aerobic respiration are carried out in the cell's *mitochondria*, described in chapter 3 (section 3.4b), so mitochondria are regarded as a cell's principal "ATP factories."

## Other Nucleotides

**Guanosine triphosphate (GTP)** (GWAH-no-seen) is another nucleotide involved in energy transfers. In some reactions, it donates phosphate groups to other molecules. For example, it can donate its third phosphate group to ADP to regenerate ATP.

**Cyclic adenosine monophosphate (cAMP) (fig. 2.29b)** is a nucleotide formed by the removal of both the second and third phosphate groups from ATP. In many cases, when a hormone or other chemical signal ("first messenger") binds to a cell surface, it triggers an internal reaction that converts ATP to cAMP. The cAMP then acts as a "second messenger" to activate metabolic effects within the cell.

## Nucleic Acids

**Nucleic acids** (new-CLAY-ic) are polymers of nucleotides. The largest of them, **deoxyribonucleic acid (DNA),** is typically 100 million to 1 billion nucleotides long. It constitutes our genes, gives instructions for synthesizing all of the body's proteins, and transfers hereditary information from cell to cell when cells divide and from generation to generation when organisms reproduce. Three forms of **ribonucleic acid (RNA),** which range from 70 to 10,000 nucleotides long, carry out those instructions and synthesize the proteins, assembling amino acids in the right order to produce each protein "described" by the DNA. The detailed structure of DNA and RNA and the mechanisms of protein synthesis and heredity are described in chapter 4.

## DEEPER INSIGHT 2.6
## CLINICAL APPLICATION

### *Anabolic–Androgenic Steroids*

It is routine news to hear of sports celebrities suspended or stripped of their honors for the use of anabolic steroids. Magazines of physical culture carry many tragic reports of the deaths of amateur athletes, or violent crimes committed by them, attributed to steroid abuse.

Anabolic steroids, as they are known on the street, are more properly called anabolic–androgenic[30] steroids. They are hormones derived from testosterone that stimulate muscle growth (the anabolic effect) and masculinize the body (the androgenic effect). Perhaps the earliest notion to put them to use arose in Nazi Germany, where testosterone was given to SS troops in an effort to make them more aggressive—but with no proven success. In the 1950s, however, when Soviet weight-lifting teams were routinely defeating American teams, it came to light that the Soviets were using testosterone as a performance enhancer. American team physician John Ziegler began experimenting with this back in the United States. He disliked the androgenic side effects and approached the Ciba Pharmaceutical Company to develop a testosterone analog (a molecule of slightly altered structure) that would enhance the anabolic effect and weaken the androgenic effect. Ciba soon developed Dianabol. It produced spectacular effects in weight lifters and by the 1960s, several testosterone analogs were freely and legally available, designed to enhance anabolic potency, reduce androgenic effects, and prolong the half-life of the drug in the body. Some are taken orally and others by intramuscular (I.M.) injection.

In limited doses, these steroids have legitimate medical uses such as the treatment of anemia, breast cancer, osteoporosis, and some muscle diseases and to prevent the atrophy of muscles in immobilized patients. Some amateur and professional athletes, however, use them in doses 10 to 1,000 times stronger than therapeutic doses. While such doses bulk up the muscles **(fig. 2.32),** they have hidden, devastating effects on the body. They raise cholesterol levels, which promotes fatty degeneration of the arteries *(atherosclerosis)*. This can lead to coronary artery disease, heart and kidney failure, and stroke. Deteriorating circulation

[30] *andro* = male; *genic* = producing

**FIGURE 2.32 The Effect of Heavy Use of Anabolic–Androgenic Steroids.**

Master1305/Shutterstock

also sometimes results in gangrene, and many users have suffered amputation of the lower limbs as a result. As the liver attempts to dispose of the high concentration of steroids, liver cancer and other liver diseases may ensue. In addition, steroids suppress the immune system, so the user is more subject to infection and cancer. They cause a premature end to bone elongation, so people who use anabolic steroids in adolescence may never attain normal adult height.

Paradoxically, anabolic–androgenic steroids can have masculinizing effects on women and feminizing effects on men. In women, who are especially sensitive to the androgenic effect, the steroids commonly produce growth of facial hair, enlargement of the clitoris, atrophy of the breasts and uterus, and irregularities of ovulation and menstruation. An enzyme called *aromatase* converts androgens to estrogens, and in men these often induce breast enlargement *(gynecomastia)*, atrophy of the testes, impotence (inability to achieve or maintain an erection), low sperm count, and infertility.

Especially in men, steroid abuse can be linked to severe emotional disorders. Individuals vary in susceptibility, but the androgenic effects include heightened aggressiveness and unpredictable mood swings, so some abusers vacillate between depression and violence ("roid rage"), including physical abuse of family members and crimes as serious as homicide.

As the recreational use of anabolic–androgenic steroids became widespread, so did the tragic side effects of such heavy use—an outcome that Dr. Ziegler deeply regretted as the low point of his career. The U.S. Congress classified anabolic–androgenic steroids as a controlled substance in 1991. Their use in sports has been condemned by the American Medical Association and American College of Sports Medicine and banned by the International Olympic Committee, National Football League, Major League Baseball Players' Association, National Basketball Association, and National Collegiate Athletic Association.

Yet in spite of such warnings and bans, many continue to use steroids and related performance-enhancing drugs, which remain available through unscrupulous coaches, physicians, Internet sources, and foreign mail-order suppliers under a cloud of confusing trade names (Durabolin, Anadrol, Oxandrin, Dianabol, Winstrol, Primobolan, and others). By some estimates, as many as 80% of competitive weight lifters, 30% of college and professional athletes, and 20% of male high-school athletes now use anabolic–androgenic steroids. The National Institutes of Health find increasing use among high-school students and increasing denial that the steroids present a significant health hazard.

---

**BEFORE YOU GO ON**

Answer the following questions to test your understanding of the preceding section:

**16.** Which reaction—dehydration synthesis or hydrolysis—converts a polymer to its monomers? Which one converts monomers to a polymer? Explain your answer.

**17.** What is the chemical name of blood sugar? What carbohydrate is polymerized to form starch and glycogen?

**18.** What is the main chemical similarity between carbohydrates and lipids? What are the main differences between them?

**19.** Explain the statement, All proteins are polypeptides but not all polypeptides are proteins.

**20.** Which is more likely to be changed by heating a protein, its primary structure or its tertiary structure? Explain.

**21.** Use the lock-and-key analogy to explain why excessively acidic body fluids (acidosis) could destroy enzyme function.

**22.** How does ATP change structure in the process of releasing energy?

**23.** What advantage and disadvantage does anaerobic fermentation have compared with aerobic respiration?

**24.** How is DNA related to nucleotides?

# STUDY GUIDE

## Assess Your Learning Outcomes

*To test your knowledge, discuss the following topics with a study partner or in writing, ideally from memory.*

### 2.1 Atoms, Ions, and Molecules

1. The definition of *chemical element;* the six most abundant elements in the human body; and trace elements important in human physiology
2. The structure of an atom and the special functional relevance of its valence electrons
3. How isotopes of the same element differ from each other, and how radioisotopes differ from other isotopes
4. The clinical relevance of ionizing radiation; its three forms; the difference between the physical and biological half-life of a radioisotope; and the clinical relevance of that difference
5. The difference between an ion and an atom; how ions form; and the two types of ions and examples of each
6. How an electrolyte differs from an atom and from an ion; the most common ions that constitute electrolytes; and the functions and medical relevance of electrolytes
7. The definition of *free radical;* the medical relevance of free radicals; and how the body is partially protected against them
8. The definitions of *molecule* and *compound*
9. How isomers resemble and differ from each other
10. How a molecule's molecular weight is determined
11. The nature and distinguishing characteristics of ionic bonds, covalent bonds, hydrogen bonds, and van der Waals forces; how polar and nonpolar covalent bonds differ from each other; and how polar covalent bonds can give rise to hydrogen bonds

### 2.2 Water and Mixtures

1. How the biologically important properties of water arise from the polarity and bond angle of its molecules
2. The difference between a mixture and a compound
3. The differences between solutions, colloids, and suspensions, and examples of body fluids in each category
4. How pH is mathematically defined; the pH scale; and the meanings of *acid* and *base*
5. The action and physiological function of buffers
6. How various measures of chemical concentration differ from each other—weight per volume, percentage, molarity, and milliequivalents per liter—and how each unit of measure provides different kinds of information about the concentration of a solution

### 2.3 Energy and Chemical Reactions

1. The definition of *energy,* and the two basic forms of energy
2. The differences between decomposition, synthesis, and exchange reactions
3. What determines the direction of a reversible chemical reaction; the nature of a chemical equilibrium
4. Factors that determine the rate of a chemical reaction
5. The definition of *metabolism* and its two subdivisions
6. The difference between oxidation and reduction

### 2.4 Organic Compounds

1. The criterion for considering a compound to be organic
2. The difference between the carbon backbone and the functional group(s) of an organic molecule; the physiological relevance of functional groups
3. The structures of hydroxyl, methyl, carboxyl, amino, and phosphate functional groups
4. The difference between monomers and polymers; how dehydration synthesis and hydrolysis reactions convert one to the other; and the role of water in both types of reactions
5. The defining characteristics of carbohydrates and their principal roles in the body
6. The names of and basic structural differences between the three monosaccharides, three disaccharides, and three polysaccharides that are most abundant in the diet and most relevant in human physiology
7. The defining characteristics of lipids and their principal roles in the body
8. The major categories of lipids in human physiology, and the roles of each
9. How fatty acids and triglycerides are related through dehydration synthesis and hydrolysis reactions
10. The defining characteristics of amino acids and how the 20 amino acids involved in protein structure differ from each other
11. How amino acids are polymerized, and the structure of peptide bonds
12. Differences between a dipeptide, oligopeptide, polypeptide, and protein
13. The nature of the primary through quaternary levels of protein structure, and how an alpha helix differs from a beta sheet
14. Why protein function depends so strongly on the shape (conformation) of the molecule; how and why functionality is affected by denaturation; and the most common causes of protein denaturation
15. What defines a *conjugated* protein; the general term for the nonprotein component of such a molecule; and examples of conjugated proteins
16. The functions of proteins in human anatomy and physiology
17. How enzymes differ from other proteins, and the general role played by all enzymes
18. The general term for substances acted upon by enzymes; the relevance of active sites to enzyme action; why the active sites limit the range of substances on which an enzyme can act; and the name for this principle of selective enzyme action
19. The nature of cofactors and coenzymes, with examples
20. The term for a chain of linked enzymatic reactions; for its input and output; and for the intermediate steps between the input and output molecules
21. The basic structural components of adenosine triphosphate (ATP) and their organization in the molecule; the function of ATP and why life instantly ceases without it; and where in its molecular structure ATP carries the energy that is transferred to other chemicals
22. Differences between the aerobic and anaerobic mechanisms of producing ATP
23. How guanosine triphosphate (GTP) and cyclic adenosine monophosphate (cAMP) are related to ATP, and their functions
24. The basic chemical nature of the nucleic acids, DNA and RNA; their fundamental function; and how they are structurally related to ATP

# STUDY GUIDE

## Testing Your Recall

*Answers in Appendix A*

1. A substance that _____ is considered to be a chemical compound.
   a. contains at least two different elements
   b. contains at least two atoms
   c. has a chemical bond
   d. has a stable valence shell
   e. has covalent bonds

2. An ionic bond is formed when
   a. two anions meet.
   b. two cations meet.
   c. an anion meets a cation.
   d. electrons are unequally shared between nuclei.
   e. electrons transfer completely from one atom to another.

3. The ionization of a sodium atom to produce $Na^+$ is an example of
   a. oxidation.
   b. reduction.
   c. catabolism.
   d. anabolism.
   e. decomposition.

4. The weakest and most temporary of the following chemical bonds are
   a. polar covalent bonds.
   b. nonpolar covalent bonds.
   c. hydrogen bonds.
   d. ionic bonds.
   e. double covalent bonds.

5. A substance capable of dissolving freely in water is
   a. hydrophilic.
   b. hydrophobic.
   c. hydrolyzed.
   d. hydrated.
   e. amphipathic.

6. A carboxyl group is symbolized
   a. —OH.
   b. $—NH_2$.
   c. $—CH_3$.
   d. $—CH_2OH$.
   e. —COOH.

7. The only polysaccharide synthesized in the human body is
   a. cellulose.
   b. glycogen.
   c. cholesterol.
   d. starch.
   e. prostaglandin.

8. The arrangement of a polypeptide into a fibrous or globular shape is called its
   a. primary structure.
   b. secondary structure.
   c. tertiary structure.
   d. quaternary structure.
   e. conjugated structure.

9. Which of the following functions is more characteristic of carbohydrates than of proteins?
   a. contraction
   b. energy storage
   c. catalyzing reactions
   d. immune defense
   e. intercellular communication

10. The feature that most distinguishes a lipid from a carbohydrate is that a lipid has
    a. more phosphate.
    b. more sulfur.
    c. a lower ratio of carbon to oxygen.
    d. a lower ratio of oxygen to hydrogen.
    e. a greater molecular weight.

11. When an atom gives up an electron and acquires a positive charge, it is called a/an _____.

12. Dietary antioxidants are important because they neutralize _____.

13. Any substance that increases the rate of a reaction without being consumed by it is a/an _____. In the human body, _____ serve this function.

14. All the synthesis reactions in the body form a division of metabolism called _____.

15. A chemical reaction that joins two organic molecules into a larger one and produces water as a by-product is called _____.

16. The suffix _____ denotes a sugar, whereas the suffix _____ denotes an enzyme.

17. The amphipathic lipids of cell membranes are called _____.

18. A chemical named _____ is derived from ATP and widely employed as a "second messenger" in cellular signaling.

19. When oxygen is too limited to meet a cell's ATP demand, a cell can employ a metabolic pathway called _____ to produce ATP.

20. A substance acted upon and changed by an enzyme is called the enzyme's _____.

## Building Your Medical Vocabulary

*Answers in Appendix A*

*State a meaning of each word element, and give a medical term from this chapter that uses it or a slight variation of it.*

1. a-
2. aero-
3. amphi-
4. caloro-
5. collo-
6. hydro-
7. -mer
8. mono-
9. oligo-
10. -philic

# STUDY GUIDE

## What's Wrong with These Statements?

Answers in Appendix A

*Briefly explain why each of the following statements is false, or reword it to make it true.*

1. The monomers of a polysaccharide are called amino acids.
2. Most of the body's reserve energy is stored in the form of ATP.
3. Two molecules with the same atoms arranged in a different order are called isotopes.
4. The products of catabolism contain more chemical energy than the reactants did.
5. A polysaccharide is a chain of simple sugars joined by peptide bonds.
6. A saturated fat is defined as a fat to which no more carbon can be added.
7. Enzymes are often consumed by the reactions they catalyze.
8. The higher the temperature is, the faster an enzyme works.
9. Two percent sucrose and 2% sodium bicarbonate have the same number of molecules per liter of solution.
10. A solution of pH 8 has 10 times the hydrogen ion concentration of a solution with pH 7.

## Testing Your Comprehension

1. Suppose a pregnant woman with severe morning sickness has been vomiting steadily for several days. How will her loss of stomach acid affect the pH of her body fluids? Explain.
2. Suppose a person with a severe anxiety attack hyperventilates and exhales $CO_2$ faster than his body produces it. Consider the carbonic acid reaction in section 2.3b, and explain what effect this hyperventilation will have on his blood pH. (*Hint:* Remember the law of mass action.)
3. In one form of nuclear decay, a neutron breaks down into a proton and electron and emits a gamma ray. Is this an endergonic or exergonic reaction, or neither? Is it an anabolic or catabolic reaction, or neither? Explain both answers.
4. How would the body's metabolic rate be affected if there were no such thing as enzymes? Explain.
5. Some metabolic conditions such as diabetes mellitus cause disturbances in the acid–base balance of the body, which gives the body fluids an abnormally low pH. Explain how this could affect enzyme–substrate reactions and metabolic pathways in the body.

CHAPTER

# 3

# CELLULAR FORM AND FUNCTION

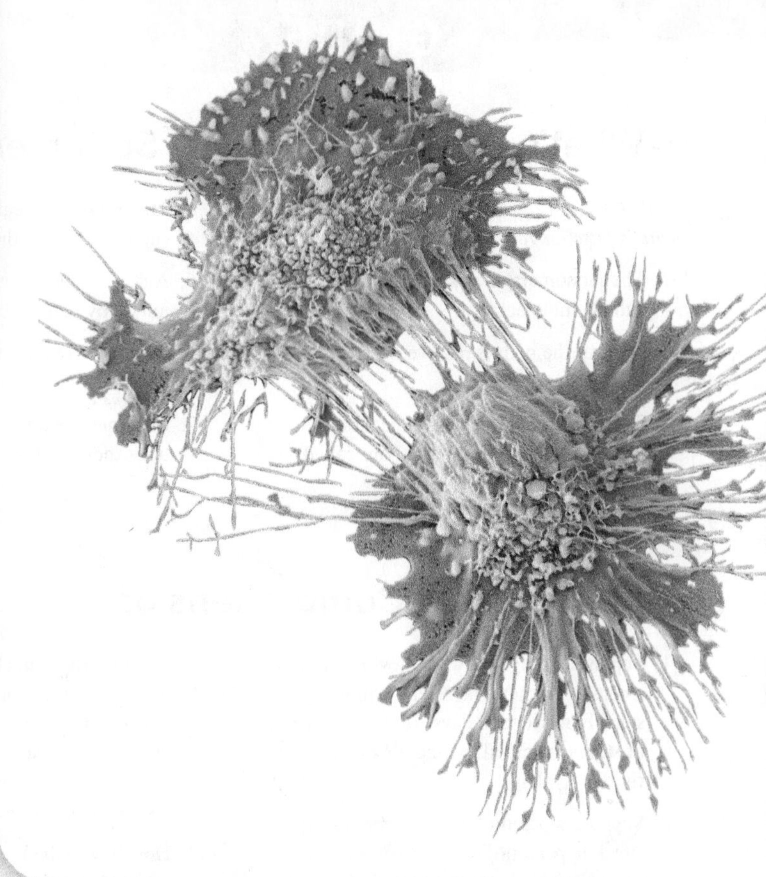

**Dividing cancer cells from an adenocarcinoma. Adenocarcinoma is a tumor arising from glands in the mucous membrane of an organ such as the lung.**
Eye of Science/Science Source

## CHAPTER OUTLINE



## DEEPER INSIGHTS

**Module 2: Cells and Chemistry**

## BRUSHING UP

- The transport of matter through cell membranes follows the principles of flow down gradients (see section 1.6e).
- To adequately understand the structure of the cell surface, it is essential that you understand glycolipids and glycoproteins, as well as phospholipids and their amphipathic nature (see sections 2.4c and 2.4d).
- The proteins of cell membranes have a great variety of functions. To understand those depends on an acquaintance with the functions of proteins in general and how protein function depends on tertiary structure (see "Protein Structure" and "Protein Functions" in section 2.4e).

All organisms, from the simplest to the most complex, are composed of cells—whether the single cell of a bacterium or the trillions of cells that constitute the human body. These cells are responsible for all structural and functional properties of a living organism. A knowledge of cells is therefore indispensable to any true understanding of the workings of the human body, the mechanisms of disease, and the rationale of therapy. Thus, this chapter and the next one introduce the basic cell biology of the human body, and subsequent chapters expand upon this information as we examine the specialized cellular structure and function of specific organs.

## 3.1 Concepts of Cellular Structure

**Expected Learning Outcomes**

When you have completed this section, you should be able to

a. discuss the development and modern tenets of the cell theory;
b. describe cell shapes from their descriptive terms;
c. state the size range of human cells and discuss factors that limit their size;
d. discuss the way that developments in microscopy have changed our view of cell structure; and
e. outline the major components of a cell.

### 3.1a Development of the Cell Theory

**Cytology,**[1] the scientific study of cells, was born in 1663 when Robert Hooke observed the empty cell walls of cork and coined the word *cellulae* ("little cells") to describe them (see section 1.2). Soon he studied thin slices of fresh wood and saw living cells "filled with juices"—a fluid later named *cytoplasm.* Two centuries later, Theodor Schwann studied a wide range of animal tissues and concluded that all animals are made of cells.

Schwann and other biologists originally believed that cells came from nonliving body fluid that somehow congealed and acquired a membrane and nucleus. This idea of *spontaneous generation*—that living things arise from nonliving matter—was rooted in the scientific thought of the times. For centuries, it seemed to be simple common sense that decaying meat turned into maggots, stored grain into rodents, and mud into frogs. Schwann and his contemporaries merely extended this idea to cells. The idea of spontaneous generation wasn't discredited until some classic experiments by French microbiologist Louis Pasteur in 1859.

By the end of the nineteenth century, it was established beyond all reasonable doubt that cells arise only from other cells and every living organism is composed of cells and cell products. The cell came to be regarded, and still is, as the simplest structural and functional unit of life. There are no smaller subdivisions of a cell or organism that, in themselves, have all or most of the fundamental characteristics of life described in section 1.6a. Enzymes and organelles, for example, are not alive, although the life of a cell depends on their activity.

The development of biochemistry from the late nineteenth to the twentieth century made it further apparent that all physiological processes of the body are based on cellular activity and that the cells of all species exhibit remarkable biochemical unity. The various generalizations of these last two paragraphs now constitute the modern **cell theory.**

### 3.1b Cell Shapes and Sizes

We will shortly examine the structure of a generic cell, but the generalizations we draw shouldn't blind you to the diversity of cellular form and function in humans. There are about 200 kinds of cells in the human body, with a variety of shapes, sizes, and functions.

Descriptions of organ and tissue structure often refer to the shapes of cells by the following terms **(fig. 3.1):**

- **Squamous**[2] (SKWAY-mus)—a thin, flat, scaly shape, often with a bulge where the nucleus is, much like the shape of a fried egg "sunny side up." Squamous cells line the esophagus and form the surface layer (epidermis) of the skin.
- **Cuboidal**[3] (cue-BOY-dul)—squarish-looking in frontal sections and about equal in height and width; liver cells are a good example.
- **Columnar**—distinctly taller than wide, such as the inner lining cells of the stomach and intestines.
- **Polygonal**[4]—having irregularly angular shapes with four, five, or more sides.
- **Stellate**[5]—having multiple pointed processes projecting from the body of a cell, giving it a somewhat starlike shape. The cell bodies of many nerve cells are stellate.

[1]*cyto* = cell; *logy* = study of

[2]*squam* = scale; *ous* = characterized by
[3]*cub* = cube; *oidal* = like, resembling
[4]*poly* = many; *gon* = angles
[5]*stell* = star; *ate* = resembling, characterized by

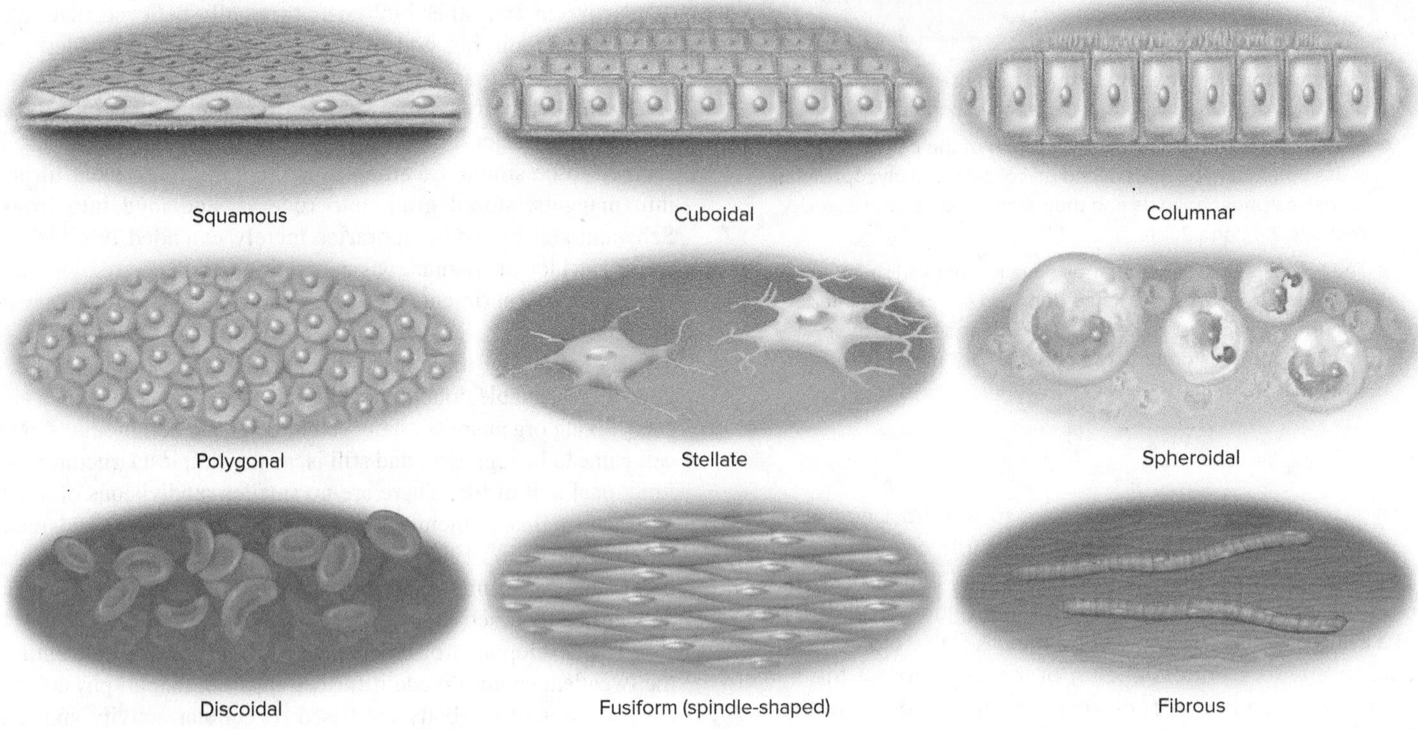


**FIGURE 3.1 Common Cell Shapes.** APR

- **Spheroidal** to **ovoid**—round to oval, as in egg cells and white blood cells.
- **Discoidal**—disc-shaped, as in red blood cells.
- **Fusiform**[6] (FEW-zih-form)—spindle-shaped; elongated, with a thick middle and tapered ends, as in smooth muscle cells.
- **Fibrous**—long, slender, and threadlike, as in skeletal muscle cells and the axons (nerve fibers) of nerve cells.

Some of these shapes refer to the way a cell looks in typical tissue sections, not to the complete three-dimensional shape of the cell. A cell that looks squamous, cuboidal, or columnar in a tissue section, for example, usually looks polygonal if viewed from its upper surface.

The most useful unit of measure for designating cell sizes is the **micrometer (μm),** formerly called the micron—one-millionth ($10^{-6}$) of a meter, one-thousandth ($10^{-3}$) of a millimeter. (See appendix B for units of measurement.) The smallest objects most people can see with the naked eye are about 100 μm, which is about one-quarter the size of the period at the end of a typical sentence of print. A few human cells fall within this range, such as the egg cell and some fat cells, but most human cells are about 10 to 15 μm wide. The longest human cells are nerve cells (sometimes over a meter long) and muscle cells (up to 30 cm long), but both are usually too slender to be seen with the naked eye.

There are several factors that limit the size of cells. If a cell swelled to excessive size, it could rupture like an overfilled water balloon. In addition, cell size is limited by the relationship between its volume and surface area. The surface area of a cell is proportional to the square of its diameter, while volume is proportional to the cube of its diameter. Thus, for a given increase in diameter, volume increases much more than surface area. Picture a cuboidal cell 10 μm on each side **(fig. 3.2).** It would have a surface area of 600 $\mu m^2$ (10 μm × 10 μm × 6 sides) and a volume of 1,000 $\mu m^3$ (10 × 10 × 10 μm). Now, suppose it grew by another 10 μm on each side. Its new surface area would be 2,400 $\mu m^2$ (20 μm × 20 μm × 6) and its volume would be 8,000 $\mu m^3$ (20 × 20 × 20 μm). The 20 μm cell has eight times as much cytoplasm needing nourishment and waste removal, but only four times as much membrane surface through which wastes and nutrients can be exchanged. A cell that is too big cannot support itself.

Further, if a cell were too large, molecules couldn't diffuse from place to place fast enough to support its metabolism. The time required for diffusion is proportional to the square of distance, so if a cell diameter doubled, the travel time for molecules within the cell would increase fourfold. For example, if it took 10 seconds for a molecule to diffuse from the surface to the center of a cell with a 10 μm radius, then we increased the cell radius to 1 mm, it would take 278 hours to reach the center—far too slow to support the cell's life activities.

[6]*fusi* = spindle; *form* = shape

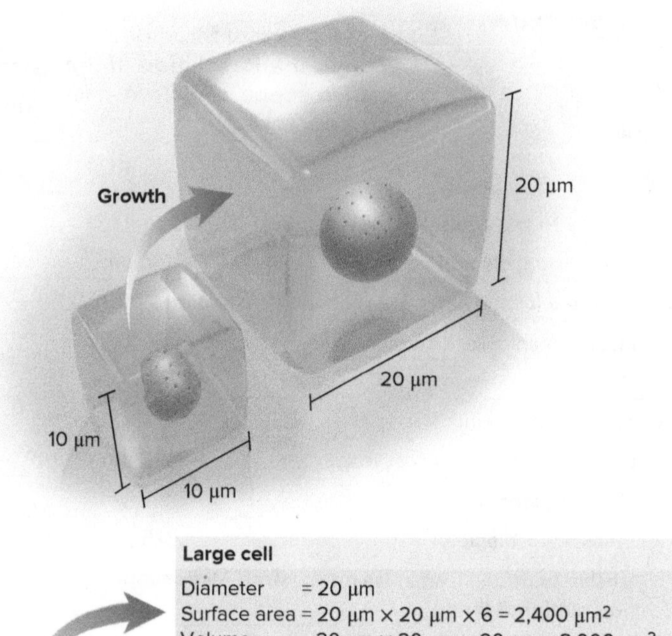


**Large cell**
Diameter = 20 µm
Surface area = 20 µm × 20 µm × 6 = 2,400 µm²
Volume = 20 µm × 20 µm × 20 µm = 8,000 µm³

**Small cell**
Diameter = 10 µm
Surface area = 10 µm × 10 µm × 6 = 600 µm²
Volume = 10 µm × 10 µm × 10 µm = 1,000 µm³

**Effect of cell growth:**
Diameter ($D$) increased by a factor of 2
Surface area increased by a factor of 4 (= $D^2$)
Volume increased by a factor of 8 (= $D^3$)

FIGURE 3.2 **The Relationship Between Cell Surface Area and Volume.** As a cell doubles in diameter, its volume increases eightfold, but its surface area increases only fourfold. A cell that is too large may have too little plasma membrane to serve the metabolic needs of the increased volume of cytoplasm.

Having organs composed of many small cells instead of fewer large ones has another advantage. The death of one or a few cells has less effect on the structure and function of the whole organ.

## 3.1c Basic Components of a Cell

In Schwann's time, little was known about cells except that they were enclosed in a membrane and contained a nucleus. The fluid between the nucleus and surface membrane, its **cytoplasm,**[7] was thought to be little more than a gelatinous mixture of chemicals and vaguely defined particles. The **transmission electron microscope (TEM),** invented in the mid-twentieth century, radically changed this concept. Using a beam of electrons in place of light, the TEM enabled biologists to see a cell's *ultrastructure,* a fine degree of detail extending even to the molecular level. The most important thing about a good microscope is not magnification but **resolution**—the ability to reveal detail. Any image can be photographed and enlarged as much as we wish, but if enlargement fails to reveal any more useful detail, it is *empty magnification.* A big blurry image is not nearly as informative as one that is small and sharp. The TEM reveals far more detail than the light microscope (LM) **(fig. 3.3).** A later invention, the **scanning electron microscope (SEM),** produces dramatic three-dimensional images at high magnification and resolution (see fig. 3.10a), but can view only surface features.

A stunning application of SEM, often seen in this book, is the *vascular corrosion cast* technique for visualizing the blood vessels of an organ. The vessels are drained and flushed with saline, then carefully filled with a resin. After the resin solidifies, the actual tissue is dissolved with a corrosive agent such as potassium hydroxide. This leaves only a resin cast of the vessels, which is then photographed with the SEM. The resulting images are not only strikingly beautiful, but also give great insights into the blood supply to an organ from macro- to microscopic levels (see figs. 19.10c, 23.10a, and the opening page of chapter 17).

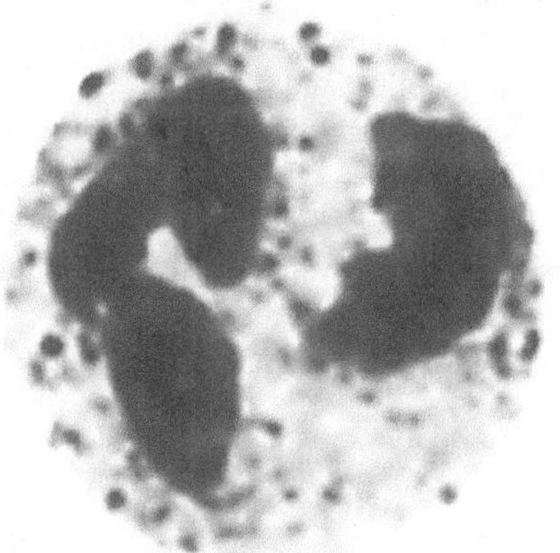

(a) Light microscope (LM)

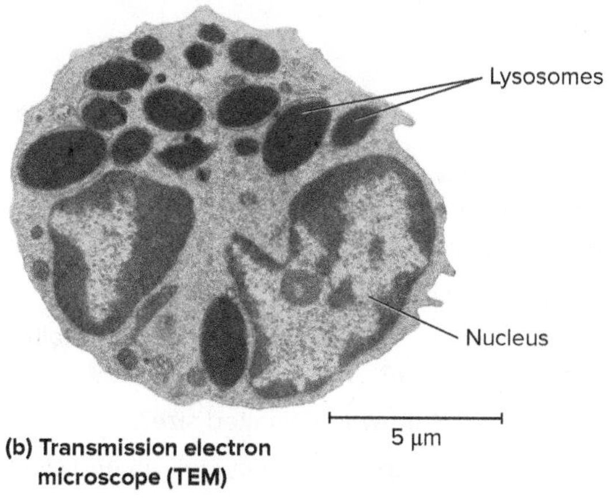


(b) Transmission electron microscope (TEM)

FIGURE 3.3 **Magnification Versus Resolution.** Two white blood cells (neutrophils) shown at the same magnification. (a) Photographed with the light microscope (LM). (b) Photographed with the transmission electron microscope (TEM). Note the finer detail (resolution) obtained with the TEM.

a: Alvin Telser/McGraw-Hill Education; b: Biophoto Associates/Science Source

[7]*cyto* = cell; *plasm* = formed, molded

**Table 3.1** gives the sizes of some cells and subcellular objects relative to the resolution of the naked eye, light microscope, and TEM. You can see why the very existence of cells was unsuspected until the light microscope was invented, and why little was known about their internal components until the TEM became available.

**Figure 3.4** shows some major constituents of a typical cell. The cell is surrounded by a **plasma (cell) membrane** made of proteins and lipids. The composition and functions of this membrane can differ significantly from one region of a cell to another, especially between the basal, lateral, and apical (upper) surfaces of cells like the one pictured.

The cytoplasm is crowded with fibers, tubules, passages, and compartments. It contains the *cytoskeleton,* a supportive framework of protein filaments and tubules; an abundance of *organelles,* diverse structures that perform various metabolic tasks for the cell; and *inclusions,* which are foreign matter or stored cell products. A cell may have 10 billion protein molecules, including potent enzymes with the potential to destroy the cell if they're not contained and isolated from other cellular components. You can imagine the enormous problem of keeping track of all this material, directing molecules to the correct destinations, and maintaining order against nature's incessant trend toward disorder. Cells maintain order partly by compartmentalizing their contents in the organelles.

The cytoskeleton, organelles, and inclusions are embedded in a clear gel called the **cytosol**[8] or **intracellular fluid (ICF).** All body fluids not contained in the cells are collectively called the **extracellular fluid (ECF).** The ECF located amid the cells is also called **tissue (interstitial) fluid.** Some other extracellular fluids include blood plasma, lymph, and cerebrospinal fluid.

In summary, we regard cells as having the following major components:

- Plasma membrane
- Cytoplasm
  - Cytoskeleton
  - Organelles (including nucleus)
  - Inclusions
  - Cytosol

**BEFORE YOU GO ON**

Answer the following questions to test your understanding of the preceding section:

1. What are the basic principles of the cell theory?
2. What does it mean to say a cell is squamous, stellate, columnar, or fusiform?
3. Why can cells not grow to unlimited size?
4. What is the difference between cytoplasm and cytosol?
5. Define *intracellular fluid (ICF)* and *extracellular fluid (ECF).*

[8]*cyto* = cell; *sol* = dissolved matter

**TABLE 3.1 Sizes of Biological Structures in Relation to the Resolution of the Eye, Light Microscope, and Transmission Electron Microscope**

| Object | Size |
|---|---|
| **Visible to the Naked Eye (Resolution 70–100 µm)** | |
| Human egg, diameter | 100 µm |
| **Visible with the Light Microscope (Resolution 200 nm)** | |
| Most human cells, diameter | 10–15 µm |
| Cilia, length | 7–10 µm |
| Mitochondria, width × length | 0.2 × 4 µm |
| Bacteria *(Escherichia coli),* length | 1–3 µm |
| Microvilli, length | 1–2 µm |
| Lysosomes, diameter | 0.5 µm = 500 nm |
| **Visible with the Transmission Electron Microscope (Resolution 0.5 nm)** | |
| Nuclear pores, diameter | 30–100 nm |
| Centriole, diameter × length | 20 × 50 nm |
| Poliovirus, diameter | 30 nm |
| Ribosomes, diameter | 15 nm |
| Globular proteins, diameter | 5–10 nm |
| Plasma membrane, thickness | 7.5 nm |
| DNA molecule, diameter | 2.0 nm |
| Plasma membrane channels, diameter | 0.8 nm |

## 3.2 The Cell Surface

### Expected Learning Outcomes

When you have completed this section, you should be able to

a. describe the structure of the plasma membrane;
b. explain the functions of the lipid, protein, and carbohydrate components of the plasma membrane;
c. describe a second-messenger system and discuss its importance in human physiology;
d. explain the composition and functions of the glycocalyx that coats cell surfaces; and
e. describe the structure and functions of microvilli, cilia, flagella, and pseudopods.

Many physiologically important processes occur at the surface of a cell—immune responses, the binding of egg and sperm, cell-to-cell signaling by hormones, and the detection of tastes and smells, for example. A substantial part of this chapter is therefore

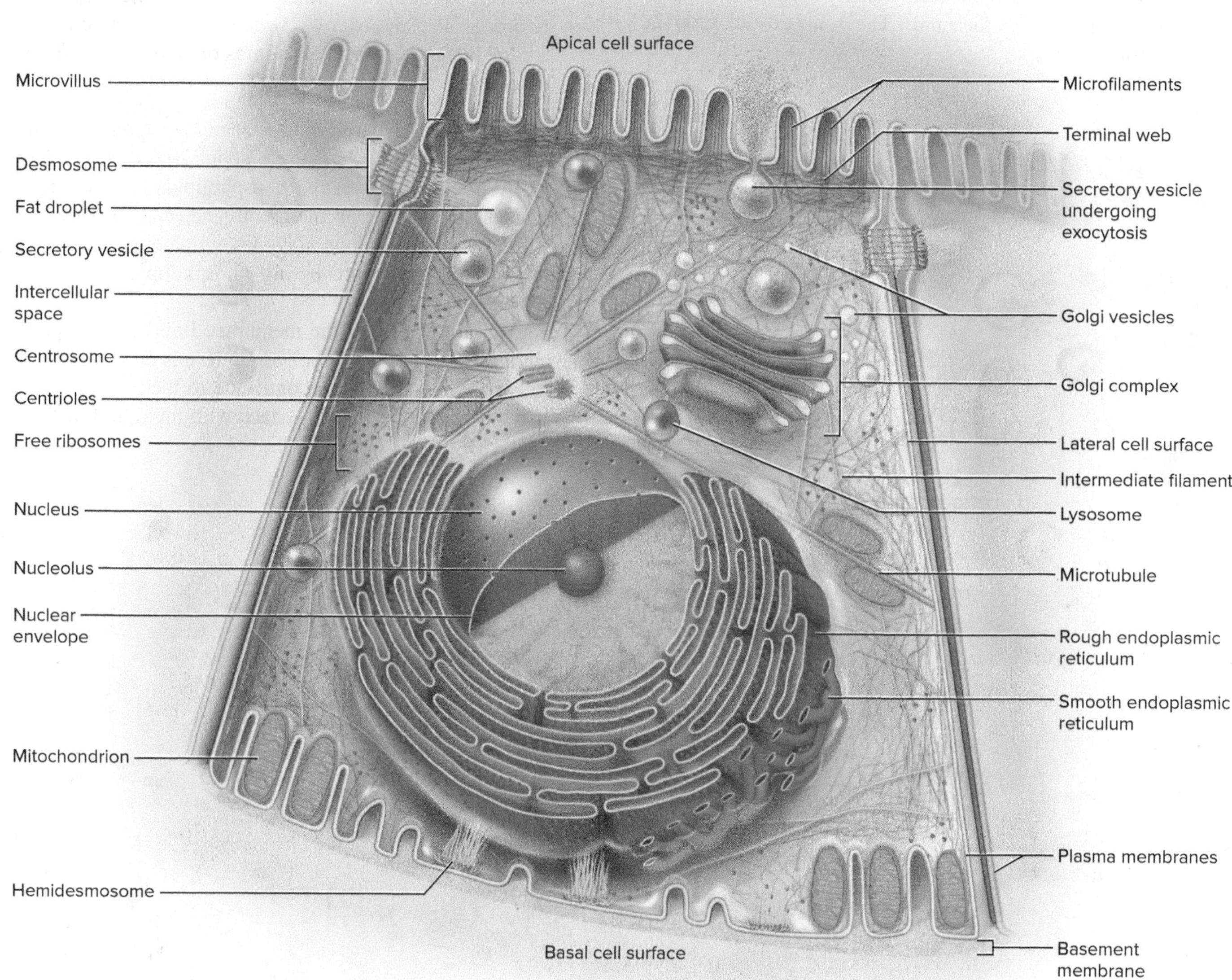


**FIGURE 3.4 Structure of a Representative Cell.**

concerned with the cell surface. Like explorers of a new continent, we will examine the interior only after we've investigated its coastline. In this section, we examine the structure of the plasma membrane, surface features such as cilia and microvilli, and methods of transport through the membrane.

## 3.2a The Plasma Membrane

The plasma membrane defines the boundaries of the cell, governs its interactions with other cells, and controls the passage of materials into and out of the cell. It appears to the electron microscope as a pair of dark parallel lines with a total thickness of about 7.5 nm **(fig. 3.5a).** The side that faces the cytoplasm is the *intracellular face* of the membrane, and the side that faces outward is the *extracellular face.* Similar membranes enclose most of a cell's organelles and control their uptake and release of chemicals.

### Membrane Lipids

**Figure 3.5b** shows our current concept of the molecular structure of the plasma membrane—an oily film of lipids with proteins embedded in it. Typically about 98% of the membrane molecules are lipids, and about 75% of those are phospholipids. These amphipathic molecules arrange themselves into a bilayer, with their hydrophilic phosphate-containing heads facing the water on each side and their hydrophobic tails directed toward the center, avoiding the water. The phospholipids drift laterally from place to place, spin on their axes, and flex their tails. These movements keep the membrane fluid.

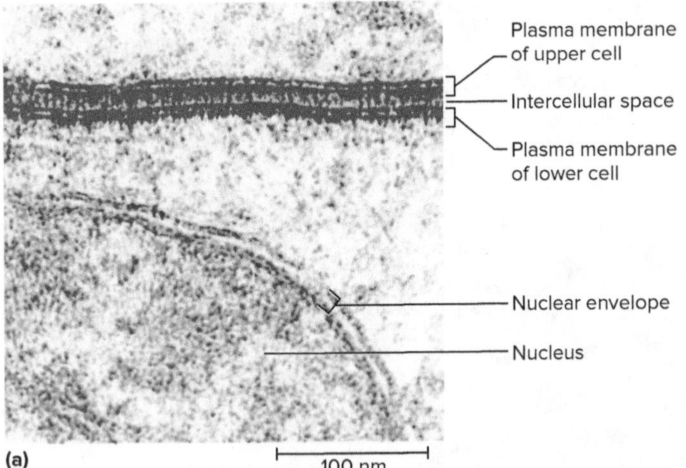


### ▶▶▶APPLY WHAT YOU KNOW

*What would happen if the plasma membrane were made primarily of a hydrophilic substance such as carbohydrate? Which of the major themes at the end of chapter 1 does this point best exemplify?*

Cholesterol molecules, found near the membrane surfaces amid the phospholipids, constitute about 20% of the membrane lipids. By interacting with the phospholipids and holding them still, cholesterol can stiffen the membrane (make it less fluid) in spots. Higher concentrations of cholesterol, however, can increase membrane fluidity by preventing phospholipids from packing closely together.

The remaining 5% of the membrane lipids are glycolipids—phospholipids with short carbohydrate chains on the extracellular face of the membrane. They contribute to the *glycocalyx,* a carbohydrate coating on the cell surface with multiple functions described shortly.

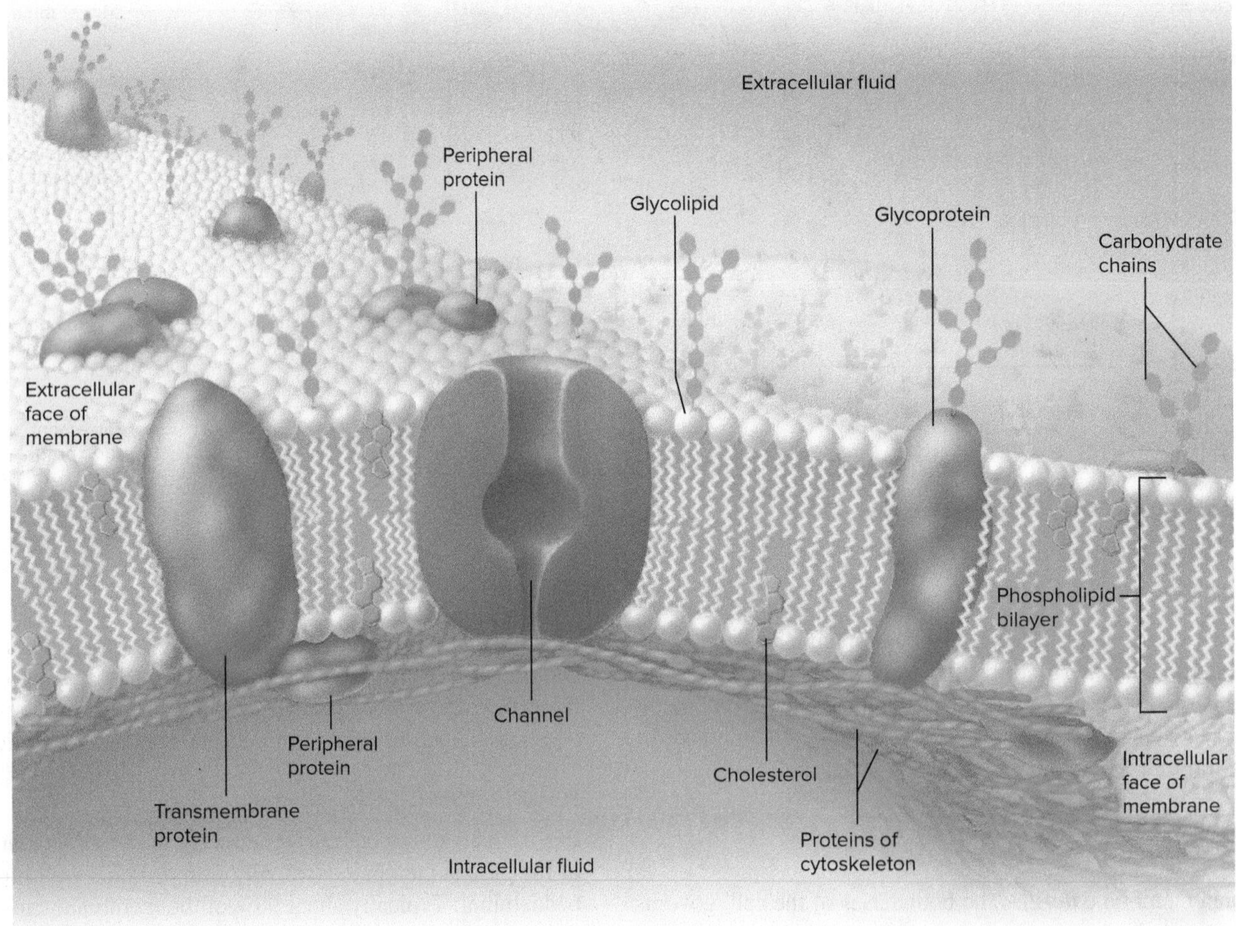


**FIGURE 3.5 The Plasma Membrane.** (a) Plasma membranes of two adjacent cells (TEM). (b) Molecular structure of the plasma membrane.

a: Dr. Donald Fawcett/Science Source

## Membrane Proteins

Although proteins are only about 2% of the molecules of the plasma membrane, they are larger than lipids and average about 50% of the membrane weight. There are two broad classes of membrane proteins: transmembrane and peripheral. **Transmembrane proteins** pass completely through the phospholipid bilayer. They have hydrophilic regions in contact with the water on both sides of the membrane, and hydrophobic regions that pass back and forth through the lipid **(fig. 3.6).** Most transmembrane proteins are glycoproteins, bound to oligosaccharides on the extracellular side of the membrane. Many of these proteins drift about freely in the phospholipid film, like ice cubes floating in a bowl of water. Others are anchored to the *cytoskeleton*—an intracellular system of tubules and filaments discussed later. **Peripheral proteins** do not protrude into the phospholipid layer but adhere to either the inner or outer face of the membrane. Those on the inner face are typically anchored to a transmembrane protein as well as to the cytoskeleton.

The functions of membrane proteins include:

- **Receptors (fig. 3.7a).** Many of the chemical signals by which cells communicate (epinephrine, for example) cannot enter the target cell but bind to surface proteins called receptors. Receptors are usually specific for one particular messenger, much like an enzyme that is specific for one substrate. Plasma membranes also have receptor proteins that bind chemicals and transport them into the cell, as discussed later in this chapter.
- **Second-messenger systems.** When a messenger binds to a surface receptor, it may trigger changes within the cell that produce a second messenger in the cytoplasm. This process involves both transmembrane proteins (the receptors) and peripheral proteins. Second-messenger systems are also discussed later in more detail.
- **Enzymes (fig. 3.7b).** Enzymes in the plasma membrane carry out the final stages of starch and protein digestion in the small intestine, help produce second messengers, and break down hormones and other signaling molecules whose job is done, thus stopping them from excessively stimulating a cell.
- **Channel proteins (fig. 3.7c).** Channels are passages that allow water and hydrophilic solutes to move through the membrane. A channel is a tunnel that passes through a complex of multiple proteins or between subunits of an individual protein. Some of them, called **leak channels,** are always open and allow materials to pass through continually. Others, called **gates (gated channels),** open and close under different circumstances and allow solutes through at some times, but not others **(fig. 3.7d).** These gates respond to three types of stimuli: **ligand-gated channels** respond to chemical messengers, **voltage-gated channels** to changes in electrical potential (voltage) across the plasma membrane, and **mechanically gated channels** to physical stress on a cell, such as stretch and pressure. By controlling the movement of electrolytes through the plasma membrane, gated channels play an important role in the timing of nerve signals and muscle contraction (see Deeper Insight 3.1). Some receptors double in function as gated channels. When a nerve stimulates a muscle, for example, a chemical from the nerve fiber binds to a receptor on the muscle fiber and the receptor opens to allow sodium and potassium ions to flow through and excite the muscle. Defects in channel proteins are responsible for a family of diseases called *channelopathies.*

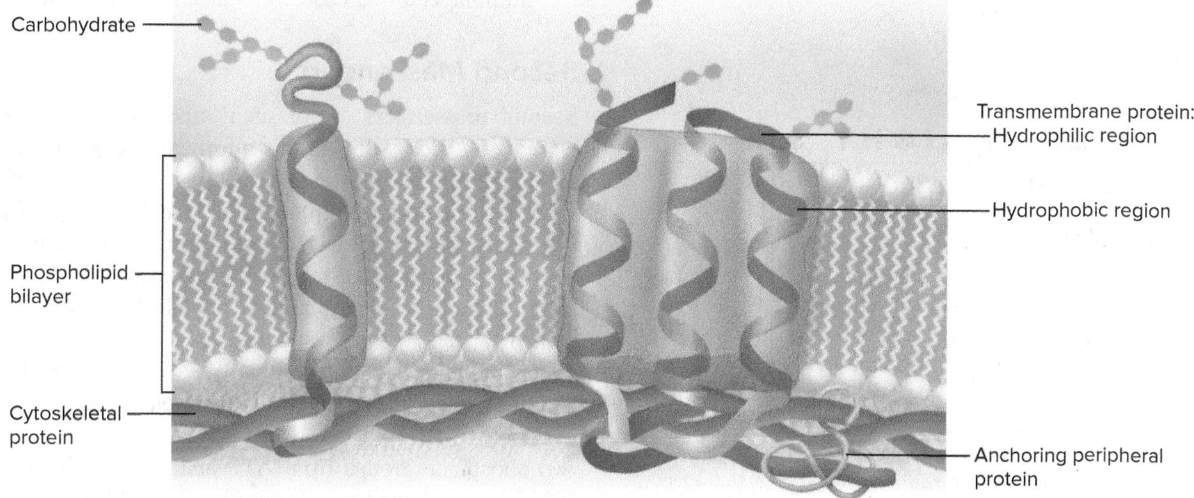


FIGURE 3.6 **Transmembrane Proteins.** A transmembrane protein has hydrophobic regions embedded in the phospholipid bilayer and hydrophilic regions projecting into the intracellular and extracellular fluids. The protein may cross the membrane once (left) or multiple times (right). The intracellular regions are often anchored to the cytoskeleton by peripheral proteins.

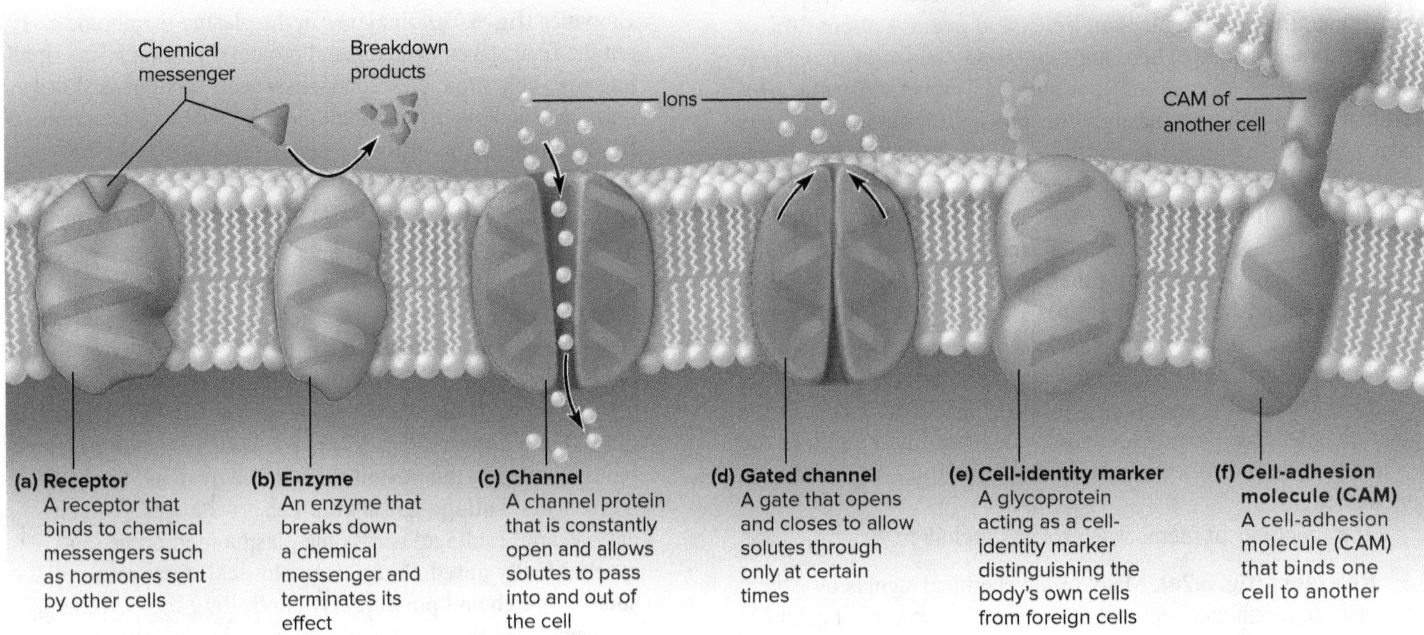
Chemical messenger
Breakdown products
Ions
CAM of another cell
(a) Receptor
A receptor that binds to chemical messengers such as hormones sent by other cells
(b) Enzyme
An enzyme that breaks down a chemical messenger and terminates its effect
(c) Channel
A channel protein that is constantly open and allows solutes to pass into and out of the cell
(d) Gated channel
A gate that opens and closes to allow solutes through only at certain times
(e) Cell-identity marker
A glycoprotein acting as a cell-identity marker distinguishing the body's own cells from foreign cells
(f) Cell-adhesion molecule (CAM)
A cell-adhesion molecule (CAM) that binds one cell to another

**FIGURE 3.7 Some Functions of Membrane Proteins.**

- **Carriers** (see fig. 3.17). Carriers are transmembrane proteins that bind to glucose, electrolytes, and other solutes and transfer them to the other side of the membrane. Some carriers, called **pumps,** consume ATP in the process.
- **Cell-identity markers (fig. 3.7e).** Glycoproteins contribute to the glycocalyx, which acts like an "identification tag" that enables our bodies to tell which cells belong to it and which are foreign invaders.
- **Cell-adhesion molecules (fig. 3.7f).** Cells adhere to one another and to extracellular material through membrane proteins called cell-adhesion molecules (CAMs). With few exceptions (such as blood cells and metastasizing cancer cells), cells don't grow or survive normally unless they're mechanically linked to the extracellular material. Special events such as sperm–egg binding and the binding of an immune cell to a cancer cell also require CAMs.

## DEEPER INSIGHT 3.1

### CLINICAL APPLICATION

### *Calcium Channel Blockers*

*Calcium channel blockers* are a class of drugs that show the therapeutic relevance of understanding gated membrane channels. The walls of the arteries contain smooth muscle that contracts or relaxes to change their diameter. These changes modify the blood flow and strongly influence blood pressure. Blood pressure rises when the arteries constrict and falls when they relax and dilate. Excessive, widespread vasoconstriction can cause hypertension (high blood pressure), and vasoconstriction in the coronary blood vessels of the heart can cause pain (angina) due to inadequate blood flow to the cardiac muscle. In order to contract, a smooth muscle cell must open calcium channels in its plasma membrane and allow calcium to enter from the extracellular fluid. Calcium channel blockers prevent these channels from opening and thereby relax the arteries, increase blood flow, relieve angina, and lower the blood pressure.

## Second Messengers

**Second messengers** are of such importance that they require a closer look. You will find this information essential for your later understanding of hormone and neurotransmitter action. Let's consider how the hormone epinephrine stimulates a cell. Epinephrine, the "first messenger," cannot pass through the plasma membrane, so it binds to a surface receptor. The receptor is linked on the intracellular side to a peripheral **G protein (fig. 3.8).** G proteins are named for the ATP-like chemical, guanosine triphosphate (GTP), from which they get their energy. When activated by the receptor, a G protein relays the signal to another membrane protein, **adenylate cyclase** (ah-DEN-ih-late SY-clase). Adenylate cyclase removes two phosphate groups from ATP and converts it to **cyclic AMP (cAMP),** the second messenger (see fig. 2.29b). Cyclic AMP then activates cytoplasmic enzymes called **kinases** (KY-nace-es), which add phosphate groups to other cellular enzymes. This activates some enzymes and deactivates others, but either way, it triggers a great variety of physiological changes within the cell. Up to 60% of drugs work by altering the activity of G proteins.

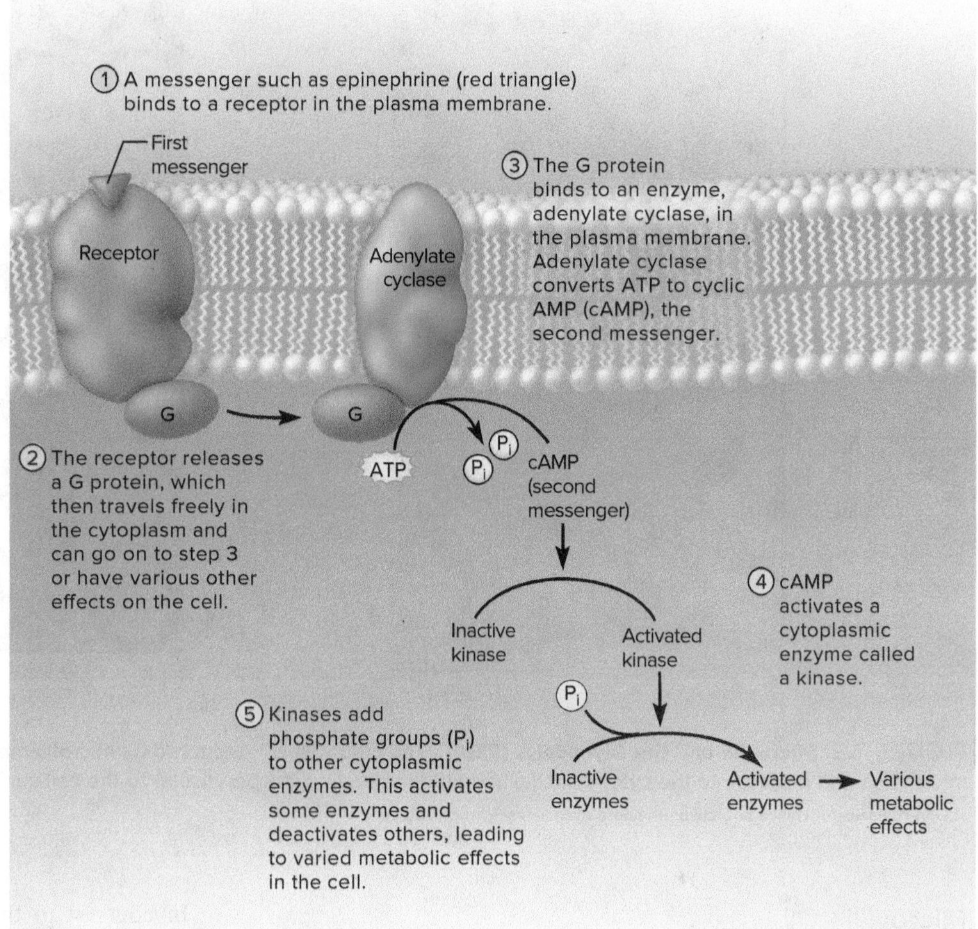

① A messenger such as epinephrine (red triangle) binds to a receptor in the plasma membrane.
First messenger
Receptor
Adenylate cyclase
③ The G protein binds to an enzyme, adenylate cyclase, in the plasma membrane. Adenylate cyclase converts ATP to cyclic AMP (cAMP), the second messenger.
G
G
② The receptor releases a G protein, which then travels freely in the cytoplasm and can go on to step 3 or have various other effects on the cell.
ATP
$P_i$
$P_i$
cAMP (second messenger)
④ cAMP activates a cytoplasmic enzyme called a kinase.
Inactive kinase
Activated kinase
$P_i$
⑤ Kinases add phosphate groups ($P_i$) to other cytoplasmic enzymes. This activates some enzymes and deactivates others, leading to varied metabolic effects in the cell.
Inactive enzymes
Activated enzymes
Various metabolic effects

**FIGURE 3.8 A Second-Messenger System.**

*Is adenylate cyclase a transmembrane protein or a peripheral protein? What about the G protein?*

## 3.2b The Glycocalyx

External to the plasma membrane, all animal cells have a fuzzy coat called the **glycocalyx**[9] (GLY-co-CAY-licks) **(fig. 3.9),** composed of the carbohydrate moieties of membrane glycolipids and glycoproteins. It is chemically unique in everyone but identical twins, and acts like an identification tag that enables the body to distinguish its own healthy cells from transplanted tissues, invading organisms, and diseased cells. Human blood types and transfusion compatibility are determined by glycolipids. Functions of the glycocalyx are summarized in **table 3.2.**

## 3.2c Extensions of the Cell Surface

Many cells have surface extensions called *microvilli, cilia, flagella,* and *pseudopods.* These aid in absorption, movement, and sensory processes.

| TABLE 3.2 | Functions of the Glycocalyx |
|---|---|
| Protection | Cushions the plasma membrane and protects it from physical and chemical injury |
| Immunity to infection | Enables the immune system to recognize and selectively attack foreign organisms |
| Defense against cancer | Changes in the glycocalyx of cancerous cells enable the immune system to recognize and destroy them |
| Transplant compatibility | Forms the basis for compatibility of blood transfusions, tissue grafts, and organ transplants |
| Cell adhesion | Binds cells together so tissues do not fall apart |
| Fertilization | Enables sperm to recognize and bind to eggs |
| Embryonic development | Guides embryonic cells to their destinations in the body |

[9] *glyco* = sugar; *calyx* = cup, vessel

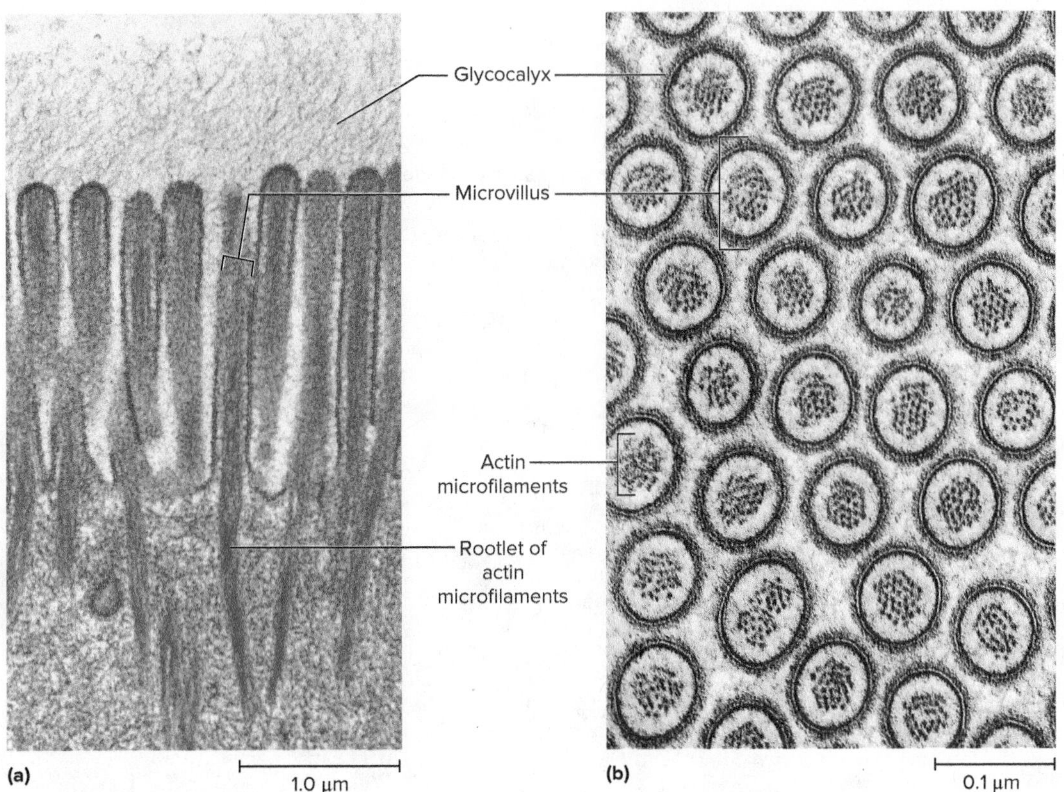


**FIGURE 3.9 Microvilli and the Glycocalyx (TEM).** The microvilli are anchored by microfilaments of actin, which occupy the core of each microvillus and project into the cytoplasm. (a) Longitudinal section, perpendicular to the cell surface. (b) Cross section.

a: Don W. Fawcett/Science Source; b: Biophoto Associates/Science Source

## Microvilli

**Microvilli**[10] (MY-cro-VIL-eye; singular, *microvillus*) are extensions of the plasma membrane that serve primarily to increase a cell's surface area (figs. 3.9 and 3.10a, c). They are best developed in cells specialized for absorption, such as the epithelial cells of the intestines and kidneys. They give such cells 15 to 40 times as much absorptive surface area as they would have if their apical surfaces were flat.

Individual microvilli cannot be distinguished very well with the light microscope because they are only 1 to 2 µm long. On some cells, they are very dense and appear as a fringe called the **brush border** at the apical cell surface. With the scanning electron microscope, they resemble a deep-pile carpet. With the transmission electron microscope, microvilli typically look like finger-shaped projections of the cell surface. They show little internal structure, but some have a bundle of stiff filaments of a protein called *actin.* Actin filaments attach to the inside of the plasma membrane at the tip of the microvillus, and at its base they extend a little way into the cell and anchor the microvillus to a protein mesh called the *terminal web.* When tugged by another protein in the cytoplasm, actin can shorten a microvillus to milk its absorbed contents downward into the cell.

In contrast to the long, shaggy microvilli of absorptive cells, those on many other cells are little more than tiny bumps on the surface. On cells of the taste buds and inner ear, they are well developed but serve sensory rather than absorptive functions.

## Cilia and Flagella

**Cilia** (SIL-ee-uh; singular, *cilium*[11]) **(fig. 3.10)** are hairlike processes about 7 to 10 µm long. Nearly every human cell has a single, nonmotile *primary cilium* a few micrometers long. Its function in some cases is still a mystery, but many of them are sensory, serving as the cell's "antenna" for monitoring nearby conditions. In the inner ear, they play a role in the sense of balance; in the retina of the eye, they are highly elaborate and form the light-absorbing part of the receptor cells; and in the kidney, they're thought to monitor the flow of fluid as it is processed into urine. In some cases, they open calcium gates in the plasma membrane, activating an informative signal in the cell. Sensory cells in the nose have multiple nonmotile cilia that bind odor molecules. Defects in the development, structure, or function of cilia—especially these nonmotile primary cilia—are sometimes responsible for birth defects and hereditary diseases called

[10] *micro* = small; *villi* = hairs

[11] *cilium* = eyelash

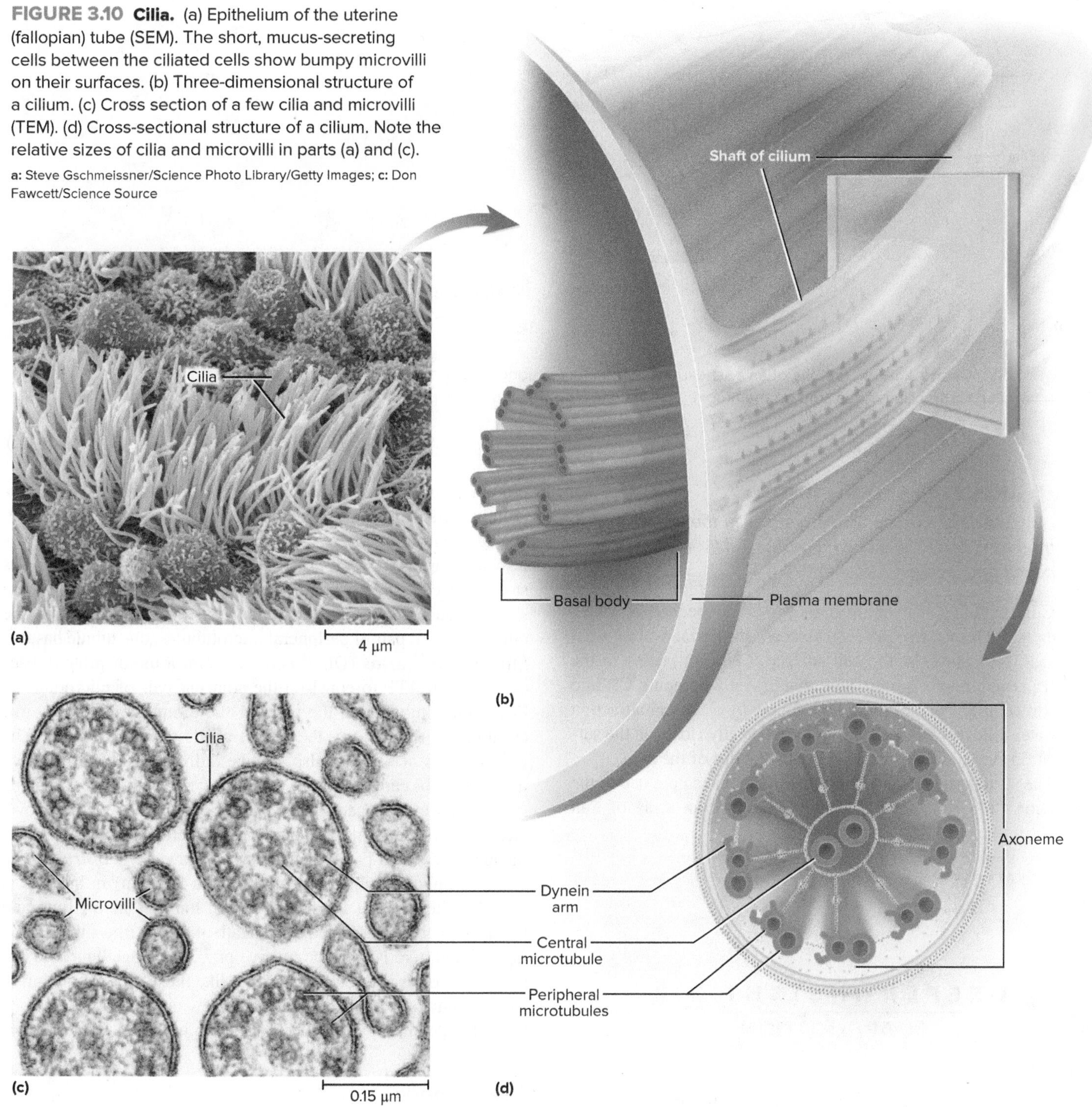


**FIGURE 3.10 Cilia.** (a) Epithelium of the uterine (fallopian) tube (SEM). The short, mucus-secreting cells between the ciliated cells show bumpy microvilli on their surfaces. (b) Three-dimensional structure of a cilium. (c) Cross section of a few cilia and microvilli (TEM). (d) Cross-sectional structure of a cilium. Note the relative sizes of cilia and microvilli in parts (a) and (c).

a: Steve Gschmeissner/Science Photo Library/Getty Images; c: Don Fawcett/Science Source

*ciliopathies.* (See Testing Your Comprehension question 5 at the end of this chapter.)

Motile cilia are less widespread, but more numerous on the cells that do have them. They occur in the respiratory tract, uterine (fallopian) tubes, internal cavities *(ventricles)* of the brain, and short ducts *(efferent ductules)* associated with the testes. There may be 50 to 200 cilia on the surface of one cell. They beat in waves that sweep across the surface of an epithelium, always in the same direction **(fig. 3.11),** propelling such materials as mucus, an egg cell, or cerebrospinal fluid. Each cilium bends stiffly forward and produces a *power stroke* that pushes along the mucus or other matter. Shortly after a cilium begins its power stroke, the one just ahead of it begins, and the next and the next—collectively producing a wavelike motion. After a cilium completes its power stroke, it is pulled limply back by a *recovery stroke* that restores it to the upright position, ready to flex again.

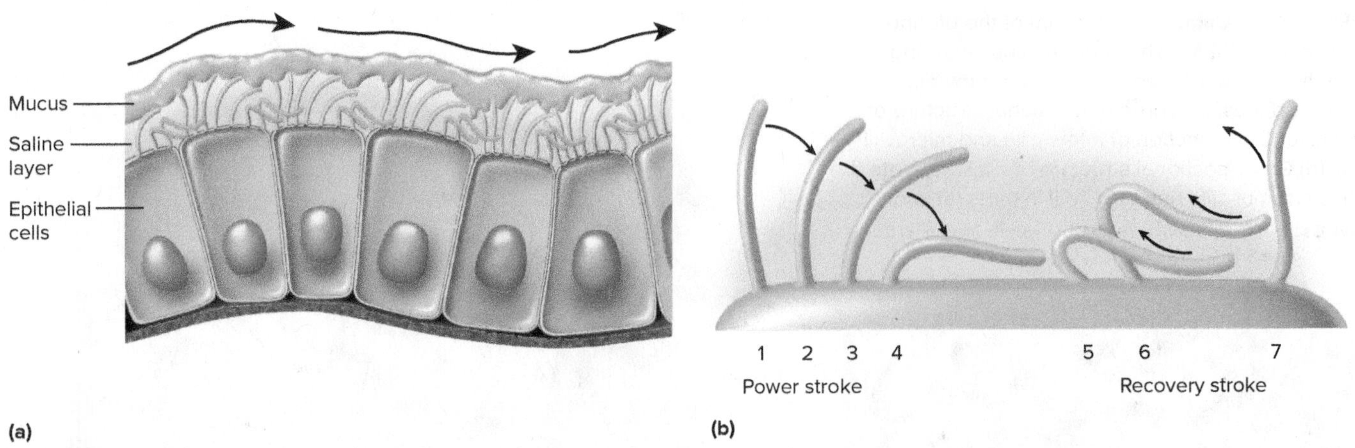


**FIGURE 3.11 Ciliary Action.** (a) Cilia of an epithelium moving mucus along a surface layer of saline. (b) Power and recovery strokes of an individual cilium. The cilium goes limp on the recovery stroke to return to its original position without touching the mucus above.

**APPLY WHAT YOU KNOW**

*How would the movement of mucus in the respiratory tract be affected if cilia were equally stiff on both their power and recovery strokes?*

Cilia couldn't beat freely if they were embedded in sticky mucus (see Deeper Insight 3.2). Instead, they beat within a saline (saltwater) layer at the cell surface. *Chloride pumps* in the apical plasma membrane produce this layer by pumping $Cl^-$ into the extracellular fluid. Sodium ions follow by electrical attraction and water follows by osmosis. Mucus essentially floats on the surface of this layer and is pushed along by the tips of the cilia.

The structural basis for ciliary movement is a core called the **axoneme**[12] (ACK-so-neem), which consists of an array of thin protein cylinders called *microtubules.* There are two central microtubules surrounded by a ring of nine microtubule pairs—an arrangement called the *9 + 2 structure.* In cross section, it is reminiscent of a Ferris wheel (fig. 3.10d). The central microtubules stop at the cell surface, but the peripheral microtubules continue a short distance into the cell as part of a **basal body** that anchors the cilium. In each pair of peripheral microtubules, one tubule has two little **dynein**[13] **arms** (DINE-een). Dynein, a motor protein, uses energy from ATP to crawl up the adjacent pair of microtubules. When microtubules on the front of the cilium crawl up the microtubules behind them, the cilium bends toward the front. The microtubules of a cilium also act like railroad tracks along which motor proteins carry materials up and down the cilium for use in its growth and maintenance. The primary cilia, which cannot move, lack the two central microtubules and dynein arms, but still have the nine peripheral pairs; they are said to have a *9 + 0 structure.*

The only functional **flagellum**[14] (fla-JEL-um) in humans is the whiplike tail of a sperm. It is much longer than a cilium and has an axoneme surrounded by a sheath of coarse fibers that stiffen the tail and give it more propulsive power. A flagellum does not beat with power and recovery strokes like those of a cilium, but in a more undulating, snakelike or corkscrew fashion. It is described in further detail as part of sperm structure in section 27.4c.

### Pseudopods

**Pseudopods**[15] (SOO-do-pods) are cytoplasm-filled extensions of the cell varying in shape from fine, filamentous processes to blunt fingerlike ones **(fig. 3.12).** Unlike the other three kinds of surface extensions, they change continually. Some form anew as the cell surface bubbles outward and cytoplasm flows into a lengthening

## DEEPER INSIGHT 3.2
## CLINICAL APPLICATION

### *Cystic Fibrosis*

The significance of chloride pumps becomes especially evident in *cystic fibrosis (CF),* a hereditary disease affecting primarily white children of European descent. CF is usually caused by a defect in which cells make chloride pumps but fail to install them in the plasma membrane. Consequently, there is an inadequate saline layer on the cell surface and the mucus is dehydrated and overly sticky. This thick mucus plugs the ducts of the pancreas and prevents it from secreting digestive enzymes into the small intestine, so digestion and nutrition are compromised. In the respiratory tract, the mucus clogs the cilia and prevents them from beating freely. The respiratory tract becomes congested with thick mucus, often leading to chronic infection and pulmonary collapse. The mean life expectancy of people with CF is about 30 years.

[12] *axo* = axis; *neme* = thread

[13] *dyn* = power, energy; *in* = protein

[14] *flagellum* = whip

[15] *pseudo* = false; *pod* = foot

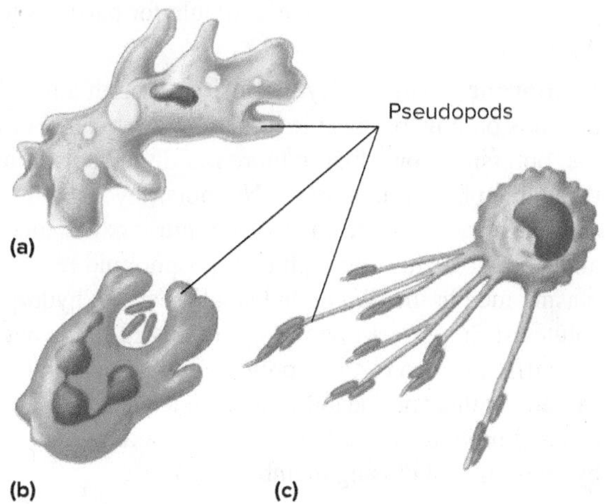


**FIGURE 3.12 Pseudopods.** (a) *Amoeba*, a freshwater organism that crawls and captures food by means of pseudopods. (b) A neutrophil (white blood cell) that similarly uses pseudopods for locomotion and capturing bacteria. (c) A macrophage extending filamentous pseudopods to snare and "reel in" bacteria (the red rods).

pseudopod, while others are retracted into the cell by disassembling protein filaments that supported them like a scaffold.

The freshwater organism *Amoeba* furnishes a familiar example of pseudopods, which it uses for locomotion and food capture. White blood cells called *neutrophils* crawl about like amebae by means of fingerlike pseudopods, and when they encounter a bacterium or other foreign particle, they reach out with their pseudopods to surround and engulf it. *Macrophages*—tissue cells derived from certain white blood cells—reach out with thin filamentous pseudopods to snare bacteria and cell debris and "reel them in" to be digested by the cell. Like little janitors, macrophages thereby keep our tissues cleaned up. Blood platelets reach out with thin pseudopods to adhere to each other and to the walls of damaged blood vessels, forming plugs that temporarily halt bleeding (see fig. 18.20).

**BEFORE YOU GO ON**

Answer the following questions to test your understanding of the preceding section:

6. How does the structure of a plasma membrane depend on the amphipathic nature of phospholipids?
7. Define *peripheral* versus transmembrane *proteins*.
8. Explain the differences between a receptor, pump, and cell-adhesion molecule.
9. How does a gate differ from other channel proteins? What three factors open and close membrane gates?
10. What related roles do cAMP, adenylate cyclase, and kinases play in cellular function?
11. Identify several reasons why the glycocalyx is important to human survival.
12. How do microvilli and cilia differ in structure and function?

## 3.3 Membrane Transport

**Expected Learning Outcomes**

When you have completed this section, you should be able to

a. explain what is meant by a *selectively permeable membrane;*
b. describe the various mechanisms for transporting material through cellular membranes; and
c. define *osmolarity* and *tonicity* and explain their importance.

One of the most important functions of cellular membranes is to control the passage of materials into and out of the organelles and the cell as a whole. The plasma membrane is both a barrier and gateway between the cytoplasm and ECF. It is **selectively permeable**—it allows some things through, such as nutrients and wastes, but usually prevents other things, such as proteins and phosphates, from entering or leaving the cell.

The methods of moving substances through the membrane can be classified in two overlapping ways: as passive or active mechanisms and as carrier-mediated or not. *Passive* mechanisms require no energy (ATP) expenditure by the cell. In most cases, the random molecular motion of the particles themselves provides the necessary energy. Passive mechanisms include filtration, diffusion, and osmosis. *Active* mechanisms, however, consume ATP. These include active transport and vesicular transport. *Carrier-mediated* mechanisms use a membrane protein to transport substances from one side of the membrane to the other, but some transport processes, such as osmosis, do not involve carriers.

### 3.3a Filtration

Filtration is a process in which a physical pressure forces fluid through a selectively permeable membrane. A coffee filter is an everyday example. The weight of the water drives water and dissolved matter through the filter, while the filter holds back larger particles (the coffee grounds). In physiology, the most important case of filtration is seen in the blood capillaries, where blood pressure forces fluid through gaps in the capillary wall **(fig. 3.13).** This is how water, salts, nutrients, and other solutes are transferred from the bloodstream to the tissue fluid and how the kidneys filter wastes from the blood. Capillaries hold back larger particles such as blood cells and proteins. In most cases, water and solutes filter through narrow gaps between the capillary cells. In some capillaries, however, the cells have large *filtration pores* through them, like the holes in a slice of Swiss cheese, allowing for more rapid filtration of large solutes such as protein hormones.

### 3.3b Simple Diffusion

**Simple diffusion** is the net movement of particles from a place of high concentration to a place of lower concentration as a result of their constant, spontaneous motion. In other words, substances diffuse *down their concentration gradients* (see "Gradients and Flow," section 1.6e). Molecules move at astonishing speeds.

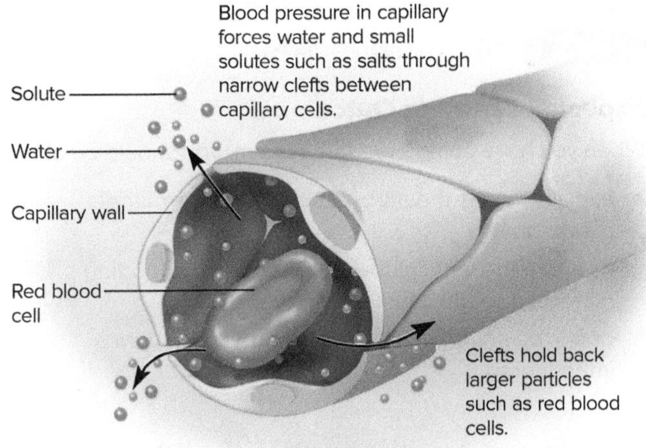
Blood pressure in capillary forces water and small solutes such as salts through narrow clefts between capillary cells.
Solute
Water
Capillary wall
Red blood cell
Clefts hold back larger particles such as red blood cells.

**FIGURE 3.13 Filtration Through the Wall of a Blood Capillary.** Water and small solutes pass through gaps between cells, while blood cells and other large particles are held back.

At body temperature, the average water molecule moves about 2,500 km/h (1,500 mi./h)! However, a molecule can travel only a short distance before colliding with another and careening off in a new direction, like colliding billiard balls. The rate of diffusion, therefore, is much slower than the speed of molecular motion.

Diffusion occurs readily in air or water and doesn't necessarily need a membrane—for example, when an odor spreads from its source to your nose. However, if there is a membrane in the path of the diffusing molecules, and if it is permeable to that substance, the molecules will pass from one side of the membrane to the other. This is how oxygen passes from the air we inhale into the bloodstream. Dialysis treatment for kidney patients is based on diffusion of solutes through artificial *dialysis membranes.*

Diffusion rates are important to cell survival because they determine how quickly a cell can acquire nutrients or rid itself of wastes. Some factors that affect the rate of diffusion through a membrane are as follows:

- **Temperature.** Diffusion is driven by the kinetic energy of the particles, and temperature is a measure of that kinetic energy. The warmer a substance is, the more rapidly its particles diffuse. This is why sugar diffuses more quickly through hot tea than through iced tea.
- **Molecular weight.** Heavy molecules such as proteins move more sluggishly and diffuse more slowly than light particles such as electrolytes and gases. Small molecules also pass through membrane pores more easily than large ones.
- **"Steepness" of the concentration gradient.** The steepness of a gradient refers to the concentration difference between two points. Particles diffuse more rapidly if there is a greater concentration difference.
- **Membrane surface area.** As noted earlier, the apical surface of cells specialized for absorption (for example, in the small intestine) is often extensively folded into microvilli. This makes more membrane available for particles to diffuse through.
- **Membrane permeability.** Diffusion through a membrane depends on how permeable it is to the particles. For example, potassium ions diffuse more rapidly than sodium ions through a plasma membrane. Nonpolar, hydrophobic, lipid-soluble substances such as oxygen, nitric oxide, alcohol, and steroids diffuse through the phospholipid regions of a plasma membrane. Water and small charged, hydrophilic solutes such as electrolytes don't mix with lipids but diffuse primarily through channel proteins in the membrane. Cells can adjust their permeability to such a substance by adding channel proteins to the membrane, by taking them away, or by opening and closing membrane gates.

### 3.3c Osmosis

**Osmosis**[16] is the net flow of water from one side of a selectively permeable membrane to the other. It is crucial to the body's water distribution (fluid balance). Imbalances in osmosis underlie such problems as diarrhea, constipation, hypertension, and edema (tissue swelling); osmosis also is a vital consideration in intravenous (I.V.) fluid therapy.

Osmosis occurs through nonliving membranes, such as cellophane and dialysis membranes, and through the plasma membranes of cells. The usual direction of net movement is from the more watery side, with a lower concentration of dissolved matter, to the less watery side, with a greater concentration of solute. The reason for the accumulation of water on the high-solute side is that when water molecules encounter a solute particle, they tend to associate with it to form a *hydration sphere* (see fig. 2.9). Even though this is a loose, reversible attraction, it does make those water molecules less available to diffuse back across the membrane to the side from which they came. In essence, solute particles on one side of the membrane draw water away from the other side. Thus, water accumulates on the side with the most solute. All of this assumes that the solute molecules in question can't pass through the membrane, but stay on one side. The rate and direction of osmosis depend on the relative concentration of these nonpermeating solutes on the two sides of the membrane.

Significant amounts of water pass even through the hydrophobic, phospholipid regions of a plasma membrane, but water passes more easily through channel proteins called **aquaporins,** specialized for water. Cells can increase the rate of osmosis by installing more aquaporins in the membrane or decrease the rate by removing them. Certain cells of the kidney, for example, regulate the rate of urinary water loss by adding or removing aquaporins.

A cell can exchange a tremendous amount of water by osmosis. In red blood cells, for example, the amount of water passing through the plasma membrane every second is 100 times the volume of the cell.

[16]*osm* = push, thrust; *osis* = condition, process

**Figure 3.14** is a conceptual model of osmosis. Imagine a chamber divided by a selectively permeable membrane. Side A contains distilled water and side B contains large particles of a *nonpermeating* solute—that is, a solute such as protein that cannot pass through the membrane pores because of its size or other properties. Water passes from side A to B (fig. 3.14a) and associates with the solute molecules on side B, hindering water movement back to side A.

Under such conditions, the water level in side A would fall and the level in side B would rise. It may seem as if this would continue indefinitely until side A dried up. This would not happen, however, because as water accumulated in side B, it would become heavier and exert more force, called **hydrostatic pressure,** on that side of the membrane. This would cause some filtration of water from B back to A. At some point, the rate of filtration would equal the rate of "forward" osmosis, water would pass through the membrane equally in both directions, and net osmosis would slow down and stop. At this point, an equilibrium (balance between opposing forces) would exist. The hydrostatic pressure required on side B to halt osmosis is called **osmotic pressure.** The more nonpermeating solute there is in B, the greater the osmotic pressure.

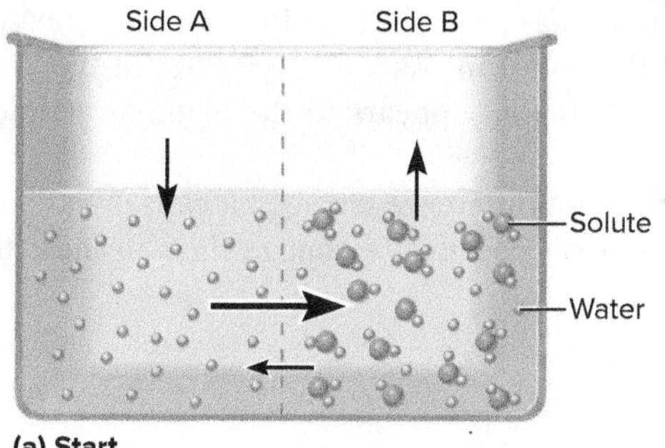


(a) Start

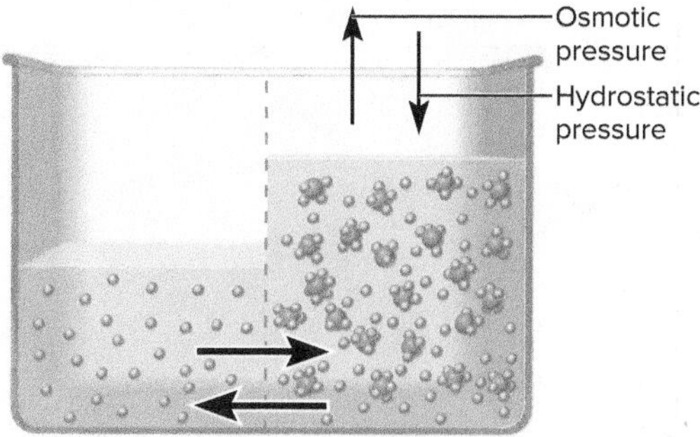


(b) 30 minutes later

**FIGURE 3.14 Osmosis.** The dashed line represents a selectively permeable membrane dividing the chamber in half. (a) Initial net flow of water from side A to side B. (b) Equilibrium between osmotic and hydrostatic pressure, hence between osmosis and filtration, with no net flow. Water molecules aggregate around solute molecules and thus accumulate on side B.

**▶▶▶APPLY WHAT YOU KNOW**

*If the solute concentration on side B was half what it was in the original experiment, would the fluid on that side reach a higher or lower level than before? Explain.*

**Reverse osmosis** is a process in which a mechanical pressure applied to one side of the system can override osmotic pressure and drive water through a membrane against its concentration gradient. This principle is used to create highly purified water for laboratory use and to desalinate seawater, converting it to drinkable freshwater—handy for arid countries and ships at sea. The body's principal pump, the heart, drives water out of the smallest blood vessels (the capillaries) by reverse osmosis—a process called *capillary filtration.* The equilibrium between osmosis and filtration will be an important consideration when we study fluid exchange by the capillaries in section 20.3. Blood plasma also contains albumin. In the preceding discussion, side B is analogous to the high-protein bloodstream and side A to the low-protein tissue fluid surrounding the capillaries. Water leaves the capillaries by filtration, but this is approximately balanced by water reentering the capillaries by osmosis.

## 3.3d Osmolarity and Tonicity

The **osmolarity,** or osmotic concentration, of body fluids has such a great effect on cellular function that it is important to understand the units in which it is measured. Physiologists and clinicians usually express this in terms of **milliosmoles per liter (mOsm/L),** a unit of measure that expresses the quantity of nonpermeating particles per liter of solution. The basis of this unit of concentration is explained in appendix B. Blood plasma, tissue fluid, and intracellular fluids measure about 300 mOsm/L.

**Tonicity** is the ability of a solution to affect the fluid volume and pressure in a cell. If a solute cannot pass through a plasma membrane but remains more concentrated on one side of the membrane than on the other, it causes osmosis. A **hypotonic**[17] solution has a lower concentration of nonpermeating solutes than the intracellular fluid (ICF). Cells in a hypotonic solution absorb water, swell, and may burst *(lyse)* **(fig. 3.15a).** Distilled water is the extreme example; a sufficient quantity given to a person intravenously would lyse the blood cells, with dire consequences. A **hypertonic**[18] solution is one with a higher concentration of nonpermeating solutes than the ICF. It causes cells to lose water and shrivel *(crenate)* **(fig. 3.15c).** Such cells may die of torn membranes and cytoplasmic loss. In **isotonic**[19] solutions, the total concentration of nonpermeating solutes is the same as in the ICF—hence, isotonic solutions cause no change in cell volume or shape **(fig. 3.15b).**

It is essential for cells to be in a state of osmotic equilibrium with the fluid around them, and this requires that the ECF have the same concentration of nonpermeating solutes as the ICF. Intravenous fluids given to patients are usually isotonic solutions, but

[17]*hypo* = less; *ton* = tension
[18]*hyper* = more; *ton* = tension
[19]*iso* = equal; *ton* = tension

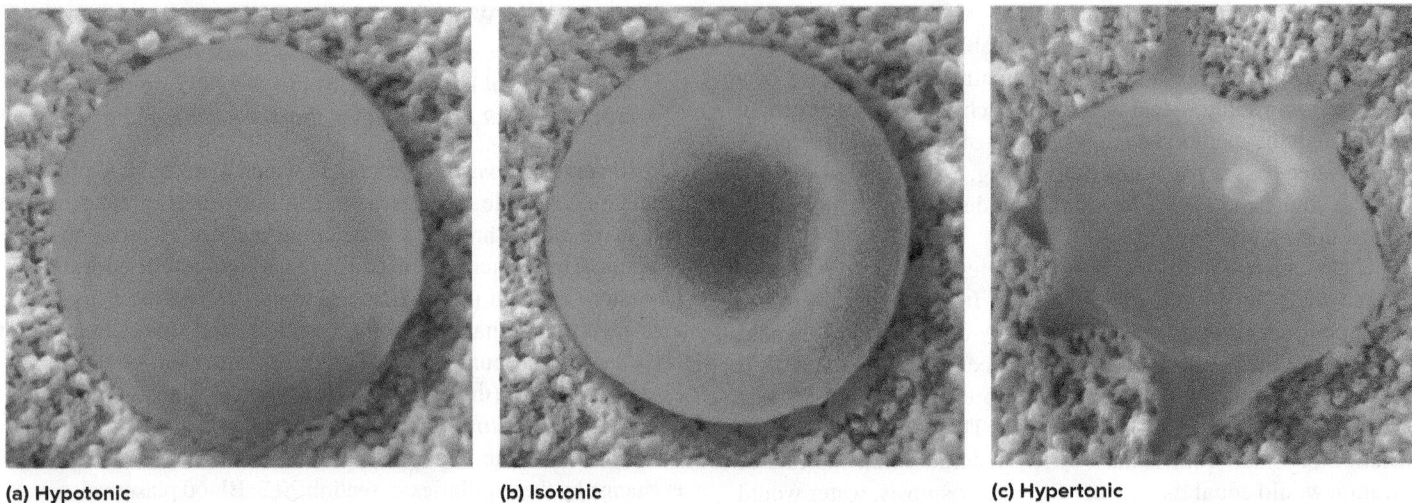


**FIGURE 3.15 Effects of Tonicity on Red Blood Cells (RBCs).** (a) RBC swelling in a hypotonic medium such as distilled water. (b) Normal RBC size and shape in an isotonic medium such as 0.9% NaCl. (c) RBC shriveling in a hypertonic medium such as 2% NaCl.

a–c: David M. Phillips/Science Source

hypertonic or hypotonic fluids are given for special purposes. A 0.9% solution of NaCl, called *normal saline,* is isotonic to human blood cells.

It is important to note that osmolarity and tonicity are not the same. Urea, for example, is a small organic molecule that easily penetrates plasma membranes. If cells are placed in 300 mOsm/L urea, urea diffuses into them (down its concentration gradient), water follows by osmosis, and the cells swell and burst. Thus, 300 mOsm/L urea is not isotonic to the cells. Sodium chloride, by contrast, penetrates plasma membranes poorly. In 300 mOsm/L NaCl, there is little change in cell volume; this solution is isotonic to cells.

### 3.3e Carrier-Mediated Transport

The processes of membrane transport described up to this point don't necessarily require a cell membrane; they can occur as well through artificial membranes. Now, however, we come to processes for which a cell membrane is necessary, because they employ transport proteins, or carriers. Thus, the next three processes are classified as **carrier-mediated transport.** In these cases, a solute binds to a carrier in the plasma membrane, which then changes shape and releases the solute to the other side. Carriers can move substances into or out of a cell, and into or out of organelles within the cell. The process is very rapid; for example, one carrier can transport 1,000 glucose molecules per second across the membrane.

Carriers act like enzymes in some ways: The solute is a ligand that binds to a specific receptor site on the carrier, like a substrate binding to the active site of an enzyme. The carrier exhibits **specificity** for its ligand, just as an enzyme does for its substrate. A glucose carrier, for example, cannot transport fructose. Carriers also exhibit **saturation;** as the solute concentration rises, its rate of transport increases, but only up to a point. When every carrier is occupied, adding more solute can't make the process go any faster. The carriers are saturated—no more are available to handle the increased demand, and transport levels off at a rate called the **transport maximum ($T_m$) (fig. 3.16).** You could think of carriers as analogous to buses. If all the buses on a given line are full ("saturated"), they can't carry any more passengers, regardless of how many people are waiting at the bus stop. As we'll see later in the book, the $T_m$ explains why glucose appears in the urine of people with diabetes mellitus.

An important difference between a carrier and an enzyme is that carriers don't chemically change their ligands; they simply

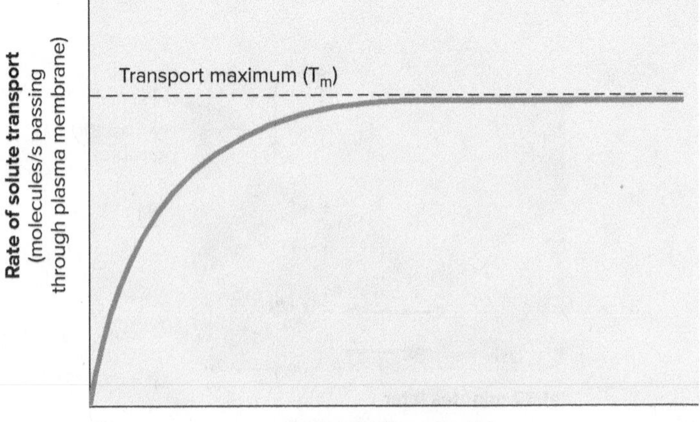


**FIGURE 3.16 Carrier Saturation and Transport Maximum.** Up to a point, increasing the solute concentration increases the rate of transport through a membrane. At the transport maximum ($T_m$), however, all carrier proteins are busy and cannot transport the solute any faster, even if more solute is added.

pick them up on one side of the membrane and release them, unchanged, on the other.

There are three kinds of carriers: uniports, symports, and antiports. A **uniport**[20] carries only one type of solute. For example, most cells pump out calcium by means of a uniport, maintaining a low intracellular concentration so calcium salts don't crystallize in the cytoplasm. Some carriers move two or more solutes through a membrane simultaneously in the same direction; this process is called **cotransport**[21] and the carrier protein that performs it is called a **symport.**[22] For example, absorptive cells of the small intestine and kidneys have a symport that takes up sodium and glucose simultaneously. Other carriers move two or more solutes in opposite directions; this process is called **countertransport** and the carrier protein is called an **antiport.**[23] For example, nearly all cells have an antiport called the *sodium–potassium pump* that continually removes $Na^+$ from the cell and brings in $K^+$.

There are three mechanisms of carrier-mediated transport: facilitated diffusion, primary active transport, and secondary active transport. **Facilitated**[24] **diffusion (fig. 3.17)** is the carrier-mediated transport of a solute through a membrane *down its concentration gradient.* It requires no expenditure of metabolic energy (ATP) by the cell. It transports solutes such as glucose that cannot pass through the membrane unaided. The solute attaches to a binding site on the carrier, then the carrier changes conformation and releases the solute on the other side of the membrane.

**Primary active transport** is a process in which a carrier moves a substance through a cell membrane *up its concentration gradient* using energy provided by ATP. Just as rolling a ball up a ramp would require you to push it (an energy input), this mechanism requires energy to move material up its concentration gradient. ATP supplies this energy by transferring a phosphate group to the transport protein. The calcium pump mentioned previously uses this mechanism. Even though $Ca^{2+}$ is already more concentrated in the ECF than within the cell, this carrier pumps still more of it out. Active transport also enables cells to absorb amino acids that are already more concentrated in the cytoplasm than in the ECF.

**Secondary active transport** also requires an energy input, but depends only indirectly on ATP. For example, certain kidney tubules have proteins called *sodium–glucose transporters (SGLTs)* that simultaneously bind sodium ions ($Na^+$) and glucose molecules and transport them into the tubule cells, saving glucose from being lost in the urine **(fig. 3.18).** An SGLT itself doesn't use ATP. However, it depends on the fact that the cell actively maintains a low internal $Na^+$ concentration, so $Na^+$ will diffuse down its gradient into the cell. Glucose "hitches a ride" with the incoming $Na^+$. But what keeps the intracellular $Na^+$ concentration low is that the basal membrane of the cell has an ATP-driven sodium–potassium pump that constantly removes $Na^+$ from the cell. If not for this, the $Na^+$ and glucose inflow via the SGLT would soon cease. Therefore, the SGLT doesn't use ATP directly, but depends on ATP to drive the

[20] *uni* = one; *port* = carry
[21] *co* = together; *trans* = across; *port* = carry
[22] *sym* = together; *port* = carry
[23] *anti* = opposite; *port* = carry
[24] *facil* = easy

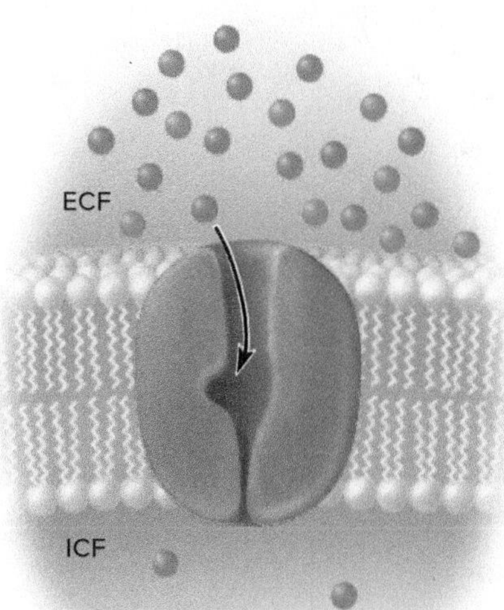


(1) A solute particle enters the channel of a membrane protein (carrier).

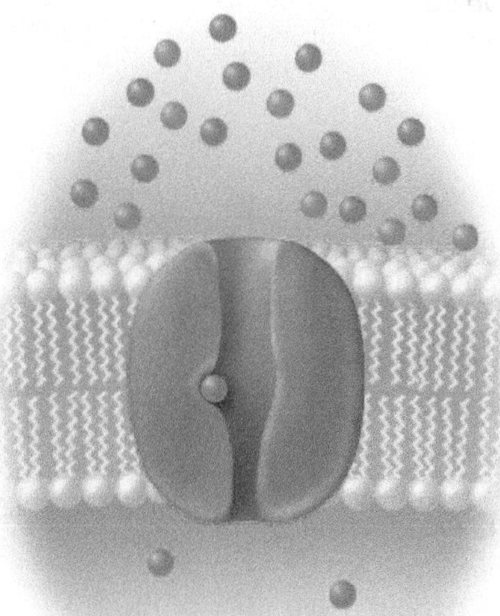

(2) The solute binds to a receptor site on the carrier and the carrier changes conformation.

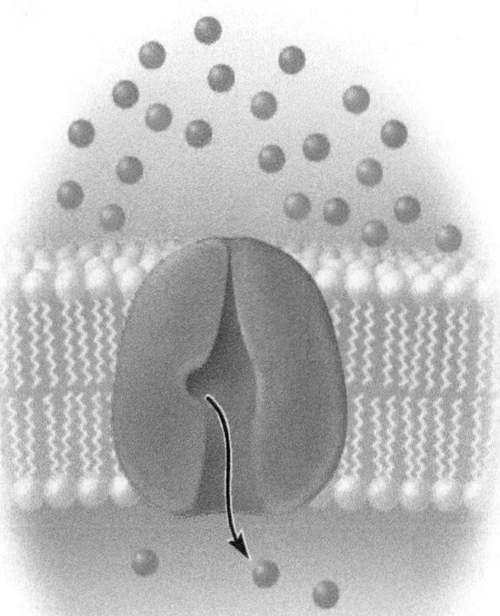

(3) The carrier releases the solute on the other side of the membrane.

**FIGURE 3.17 Facilitated Diffusion.** Note that the solute moves down its concentration gradient.

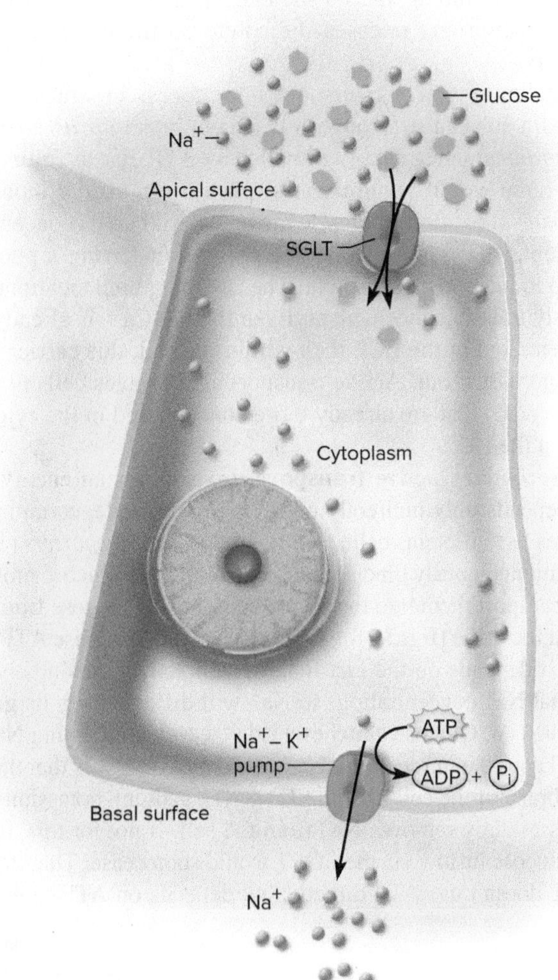


**FIGURE 3.18 Secondary Active Transport.** In this example, the sodium–glucose transporter (SGLT) at the apical cell surface carries out facilitated diffusion, but depends on active transport by the $Na^+$–$K^+$ pump at the base of the cell to keep it running.

$Na^+$–$K^+$ pump; it is therefore a secondary active transport protein. (*Secondary active transport* is an unfortunate name for this, as the SGLT is actually carrying out facilitated diffusion, but its dependence on a primary active transport pump has led to this name.)

The **sodium–potassium ($Na^+$–$K^+$) pump** itself **(fig. 3.19)** is a good example of primary active transport. It is also known as *$Na^+$–$K^+$ ATPase* because it is an enzyme that hydrolyzes ATP. The $Na^+$–$K^+$ pump binds three $Na^+$ simultaneously on the cytoplasmic side of the membrane, releases these to the ECF, binds two $K^+$ simultaneously from the ECF, and releases these into the cell. Each cycle of the pump consumes one ATP and exchanges three $Na^+$ for two $K^+$. This keeps the $K^+$ concentration higher and the $Na^+$ concentration lower within the cell than they are in the ECF. These ions continually leak through the membrane, and the $Na^+$–$K^+$ pump compensates like bailing out a leaky boat.

Lest you question the importance of the $Na^+$–$K^+$ pump, consider that half of the calories you use each day go to this purpose alone. The pump typically operates at about 10 cycles/s, but under certain conditions it can achieve 100 cycles/s. Various types of cells have from just a few hundred $Na^+$–$K^+$ pumps (red blood cells) to millions of them (nerve cells), so an average cell may exchange 30 million $Na^+$ ions and 20 million $K^+$ ions and consume 10 million ATPs per second. Beyond compensating for a leaky plasma membrane, the $Na^+$–$K^+$ pump has at least four functions:

1. **Secondary active transport.** It maintains a steep $Na^+$ concentration gradient across the membrane. Like water behind a dam, this gradient is a source of potential energy that can be tapped to do other work. The secondary active transport described previously is an example of this.
2. **Regulation of cell volume.** Certain anions are confined to the cell and cannot penetrate the plasma membrane. These "fixed anions," such as proteins and phosphates, attract and retain cations. If there were nothing to correct for it, the retention of these ions would cause osmotic swelling and possibly lysis of the cell. Cellular swelling, however, elevates activity of the $Na^+$–$K^+$ pumps. Since each cycle of the pump removes one ion more than it brings in, the pumps are part of a negative feedback loop that reduces intracellular ion concentration, controls osmolarity, and prevents cellular swelling.

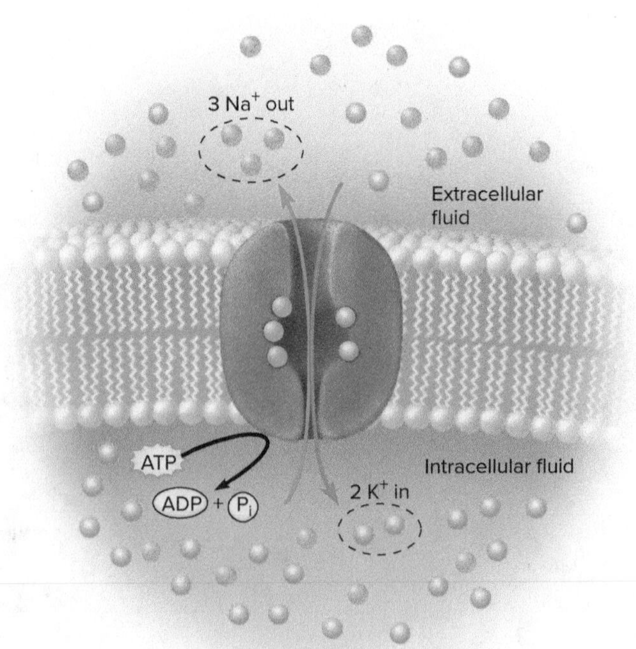


**FIGURE 3.19 The Sodium–Potassium Pump ($Na^+$–$K^+$ ATPase).**

? *Why would the $Na^+$–$K^+$ pump, but not osmosis, cease to function after a cell dies?*

3. **Maintenance of a membrane potential.** All living cells have an electrical charge difference called the *resting membrane potential* across the plasma membrane. Like the two poles of a battery, the inside of the membrane is negatively charged and the outside is positively charged. This difference stems from the unequal distribution of ions on the two sides of the membrane, maintained by the $Na^+$–$K^+$ pump. The membrane potential is essential to the excitability of nerve and muscle cells.
4. **Heat production.** When the weather turns chilly, we turn up not only the furnace in our home but also the "furnace" in our body. Thyroid hormone stimulates cells to produce more $Na^+$–$K^+$ pumps. As these pumps consume ATP, they release heat from it, compensating for the body heat we lose to the cold air around us.

**▶▶▶APPLY WHAT YOU KNOW**

*An important characteristic of proteins is their ability to change conformation in response to the binding or dissociation of a ligand (see "Protein Structure" in section 2.4e). Explain how this characteristic is essential to carrier-mediated transport.*

In summary, carrier-mediated transport is any process in which solute particles move through a membrane by means of a transport protein. The protein is a uniport if it transports only one solute, a symport if it carries two types of solutes at once in the same direction, and an antiport if it carries two or more solutes in opposite directions. If the carrier doesn't depend on ATP at all and it moves solutes down their concentration gradient, the process is called facilitated diffusion. If the carrier itself consumes ATP and moves solutes up their concentration gradient, the process is called primary active transport. If the carrier doesn't directly use ATP, but depends on a concentration gradient produced by ATP-consuming $Na^+$–$K^+$ pumps elsewhere in the plasma membrane, the process is called secondary active transport.

## 3.3f Vesicular Transport

So far, we have considered processes that move one or a few ions or molecules at a time through the plasma membrane. **Vesicular transport** processes, by contrast, move large particles, droplets of fluid, or numerous molecules at once through the membrane, contained in bubblelike **vesicles** of membrane. Vesicular processes that bring matter into a cell are called **endocytosis**[25] (EN-doe-sy-TOE-sis) and those that release material from a cell are called **exocytosis**[26] (EC-so-sy-TOE-sis). These processes employ motor proteins whose movements are energized by ATP.

There are three forms of endocytosis: phagocytosis, pinocytosis, and receptor-mediated endocytosis. **Phagocytosis**[27] (FAG-oh-sy-TOE-sis), or "cell eating," is the process of engulfing particles such as bacteria, dust, and cellular debris—particles large enough to be seen with a microscope. For example, neutrophils (a class of white blood cells) protect the body from infection by phagocytizing and killing bacteria. A neutrophil spends most of its life crawling about in the connective tissues by means of its pseudopods. When a neutrophil encounters a bacterium, it surrounds it with pseudopods and traps it in a vesicle called a **phagosome**[28]—a vesicle in the cytoplasm surrounded by a unit membrane **(fig. 3.20).** A lysosome merges with the phagosome, converting it to a *phagolysosome,* and contributes enzymes that destroy the invader. Some other kinds of phagocytic cells are described in section 21.1b. In general, phagocytosis is a way of keeping the tissues free of debris and infectious microbes. Some cells called *macrophages* (literally, "big eaters") phagocytize the equivalent of 25% of their own volume per hour.

**Pinocytosis**[29] (PIN-oh-sy-TOE-sis), or "cell drinking," is the process of taking in droplets of ECF containing molecules of some use to the cell. While phagocytosis occurs in only a few specialized cells, pinocytosis occurs in all human cells. The process begins as the plasma membrane becomes dimpled, or caved in, at points. These pits soon separate from the surface membrane and form small membrane-bounded **pinocytotic vesicles** in the cytoplasm. The vesicles contain droplets of the ECF with whatever molecules happen to be there.

**Receptor-mediated endocytosis (fig. 3.21)** is a more selective form of either phagocytosis or pinocytosis. It enables a cell to take in specific molecules from the ECF with a minimum of unnecessary matter. Particles in the ECF bind to specific receptors on the plasma membrane. The receptors then cluster together and the membrane sinks in at this point, creating a pit coated with a peripheral membrane protein called *clathrin.*[30] The pit soon pinches off to form a *clathrin-coated vesicle* in the cytoplasm. Clathrin may serve as an "address label" on the coated vesicle that directs it to an appropriate destination in the cell, or it may inform other structures in the cell what to do with the vesicle.

One example of receptor-mediated endocytosis is the uptake of *low-density lipoproteins (LDLs)*—protein-coated droplets of cholesterol and other lipids in the blood (described in section 26.1g). The thin endothelial cells that line our blood vessels have LDL receptors on their surfaces and absorb LDLs in clathrin-coated vesicles. Inside the cell, the LDL is freed from the vesicle and metabolized, and the membrane with its receptors is recycled to the cell surface.

Endothelial cells also imbibe insulin by receptor-mediated endocytosis. Insulin is too large to pass through channels in the plasma membrane, yet it must somehow get out of the blood and

[25]*endo* = into; *cyt* = cell; osis = process
[26]*exo* = out of; *cyt* = cell; osis = process

[27]*phago* = eating; *cyt* = cell; *osis* = process
[28]*phago* = eaten; *some* = body
[29]*pino* = drinking; *cyt* = cell; *osis* = process
[30]*clathr* = lattice; *in* = protein

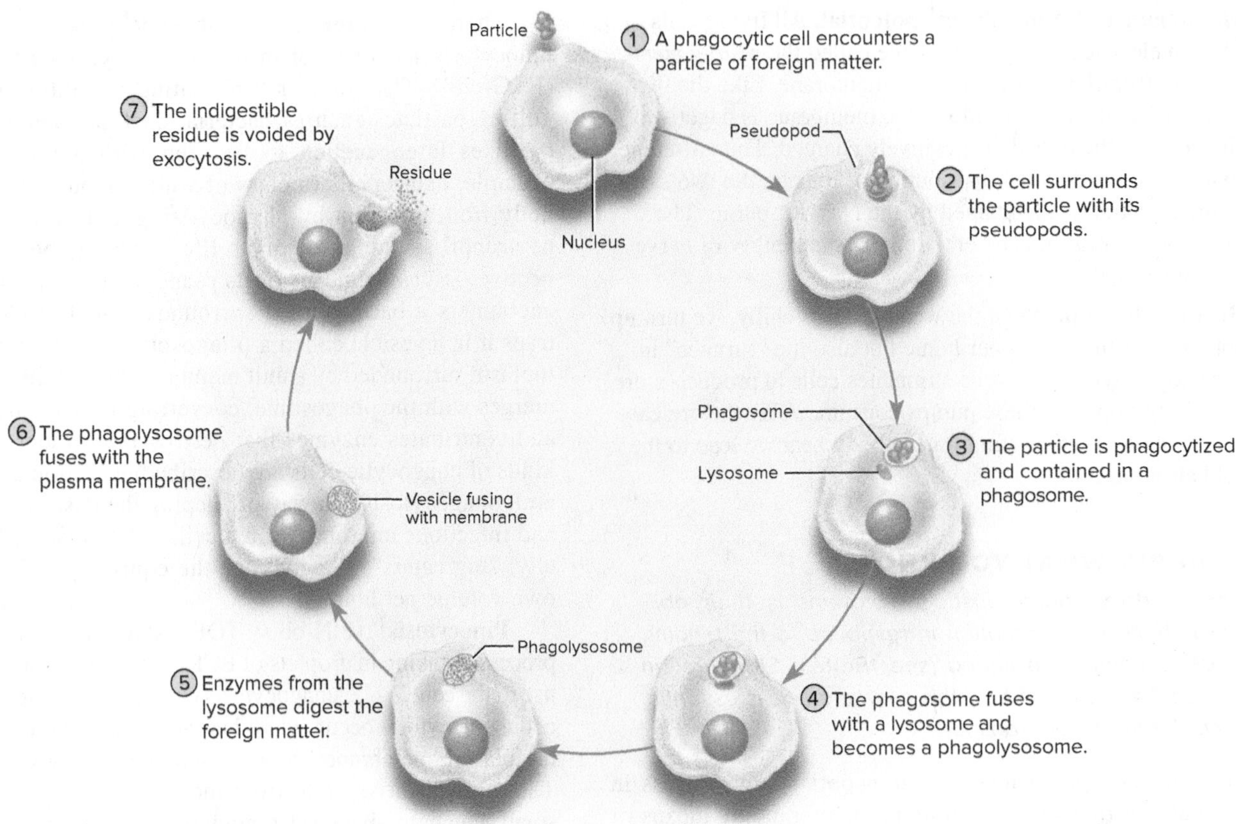

Particle
① A phagocytic cell encounters a particle of foreign matter.
Pseudopod
② The cell surrounds the particle with its pseudopods.
Nucleus
Phagosome
Lysosome
③ The particle is phagocytized and contained in a phagosome.
④ The phagosome fuses with a lysosome and becomes a phagolysosome.
Phagolysosome
⑤ Enzymes from the lysosome digest the foreign matter.
⑥ The phagolysosome fuses with the plasma membrane.
Vesicle fusing with membrane
⑦ The indigestible residue is voided by exocytosis.
Residue

**FIGURE 3.20 Phagocytosis, Intracellular Digestion, and Exocytosis.**

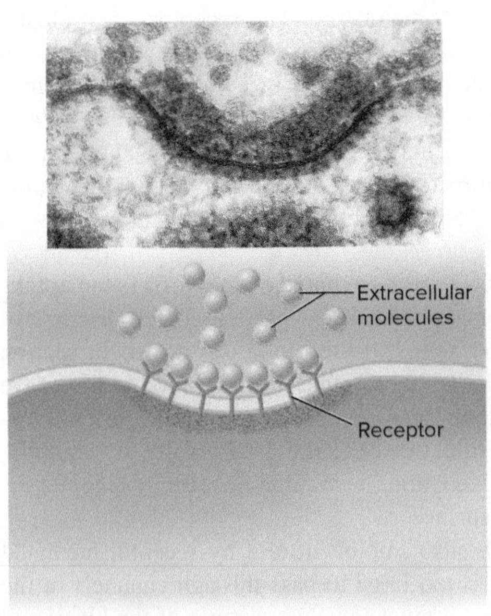

Extracellular molecules
Receptor
① Extracellular molecules bind to receptors on plasma membrane; receptors cluster together.

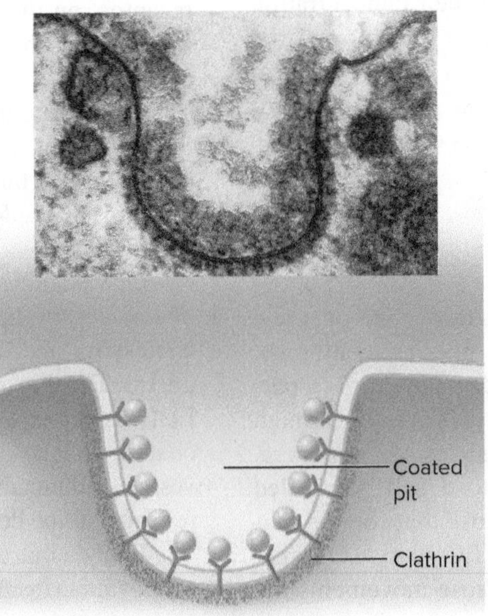

Coated pit
Clathrin
② Plasma membrane sinks inward, forms clathrin-coated pit.

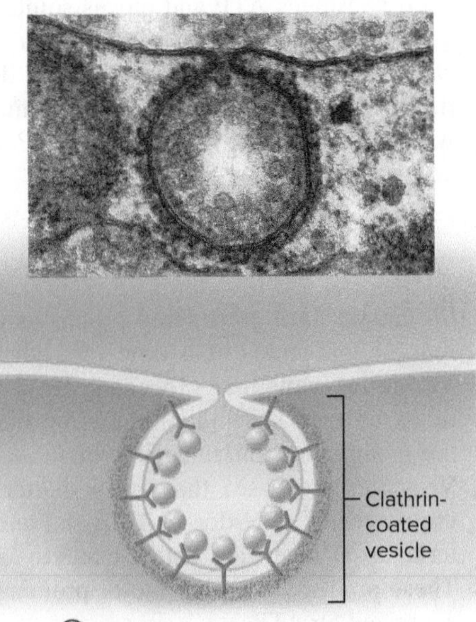

Clathrin-coated vesicle
③ Pit separates from plasma membrane, forms clathrin-coated vesicle containing concentrated molecules from ECF.

**FIGURE 3.21 Receptor-Mediated Endocytosis.**

1–3: Courtesy of The Company of Biologists, Ltd.

reach the surrounding cells if it is to have any effect. Endothelial cells take up insulin by receptor-mediated endocytosis, transport the vesicles across the cell, and release the insulin on the other side, where tissue cells await it. Such transport of material across a cell (capture on one side and release on the other) is called **transcytosis**[31] **(fig. 3.22).** This process is especially active in muscle capillaries and transfers a significant amount of blood albumin into the tissue fluid.

Receptor-mediated endocytosis isn't always to our benefit; hepatitis, polio, and AIDS viruses trick our cells into engulfing them by receptor-mediated endocytosis, thus exploiting this mechanism to establish infection.

**Exocytosis (fig. 3.23)** is a process of discharging material from a cell. It occurs, for example, when endothelial cells release insulin to the tissue fluid, sperm cells release enzymes for penetrating an egg, mammary gland cells secrete milk sugar, and other gland cells release hormones. It bears a superficial resemblance to endocytosis in reverse. A secretory vesicle in the cell migrates to the surface and "docks" on peripheral proteins of the plasma membrane. These proteins pull the membrane inward and create a dimple that eventually fuses with the vesicle and allows it to release its contents.

The question might occur to you, If endocytosis continually takes away bits of plasma membrane to form intracellular vesicles, why doesn't the membrane grow smaller and smaller? Another purpose of exocytosis, however, is to replace plasma membrane that has been removed by endocytosis or that has become damaged or worn out. Plasma membrane is continually recycled from the cell surface into the cytoplasm and back to the surface.

**Table 3.3** summarizes these mechanisms of transport.

[31]*trans* = across; *cyt* = cell; *osis* = process

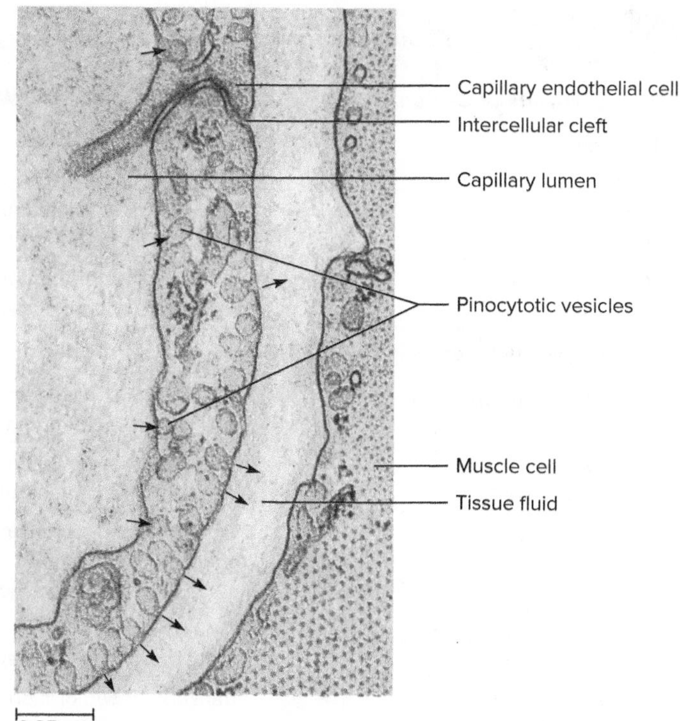
Capillary endothelial cell
Intercellular cleft
Capillary lumen
Pinocytotic vesicles
Muscle cell
Tissue fluid
0.25 μm

**FIGURE 3.22 Transcytosis.** An endothelial cell of a capillary imbibes droplets of blood plasma at sites indicated by arrows along the left. This forms pinocytotic vesicles, which the cell transports to the other side. Here, it releases the contents by exocytosis at sites indicated by arrows along the right side of the cell.

Don Fawcett/Science Source

? *Why isn't transcytosis listed as a separate means of membrane transport, in addition to pinocytosis and the others?*

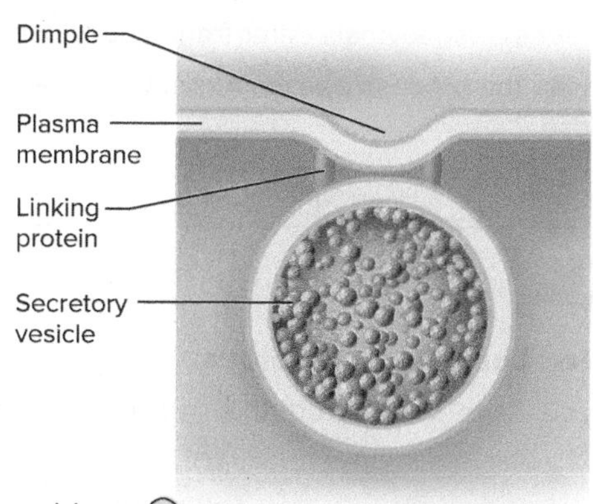
Dimple
Plasma membrane
Linking protein
Secretory vesicle
(a)
① A secretory vesicle approaches the plasma membrane and docks on it by means of linking proteins. The plasma membrane caves in at that point to meet the vesicle.

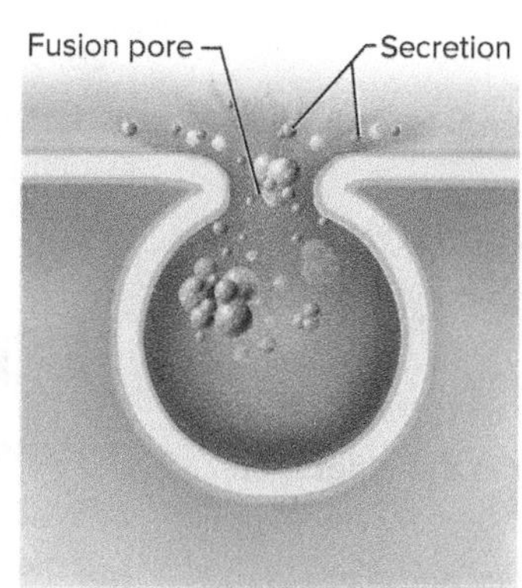
Fusion pore
Secretion
② The plasma membrane and vesicle unite to form a fusion pore through which the vesicle contents are released.

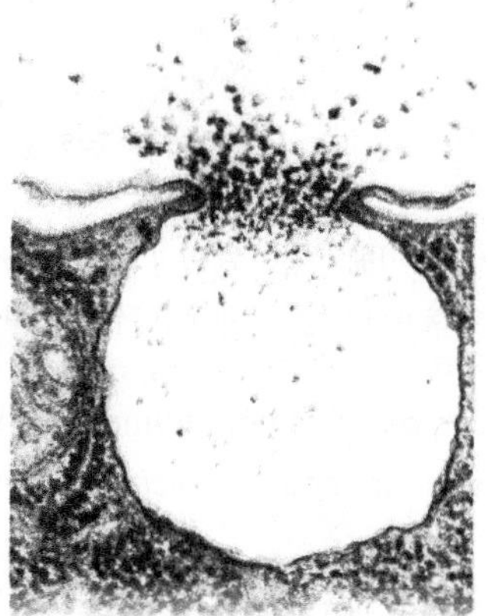
(b)

**FIGURE 3.23 Exocytosis.** (a) Stages of exocytosis. (b) Electron micrograph of exocytosis.

b: Courtesy Dr. Birgit Satir, Albert Einstein College of Medicine

**TABLE 3.3 Methods of Membrane Transport**

| Transport Without Carriers | Movement of Material Without the Aid of Carrier Proteins |
|---|---|
| Filtration | Movement of water and solutes through a selectively permeable membrane as a result of hydrostatic pressure |
| Simple diffusion | Diffusion of particles through water or air or through a living or artificial membrane, down their concentration gradient, without the aid of membrane carriers |
| Osmosis | Net flow of water through a selectively permeable membrane, driven by either a difference in solute concentration or a mechanical force |
| **Carrier-Mediated Transport** | **Movement of Material Through a Cell Membrane by Carrier Proteins** |
| Facilitated diffusion | Transport of particles through a selectively permeable membrane, down their concentration gradient, by a carrier that does not directly consume ATP |
| Primary active transport | Transport of solute particles through a selectively permeable membrane, up their concentration gradient, by a carrier that consumes ATP |
| Secondary active transport | Transport of solute particles through a selectively permeable membrane, up their concentration gradient, by a carrier that doesn't use ATP itself but depends on concentration gradients produced by primary active transport elsewhere in the membrane |
| Cotransport | Simultaneous transport of two or more solutes in the same direction through a membrane by a carrier protein called a *symport,* using either facilitated diffusion or active transport |
| Countertransport | Transport of two or more solutes in opposite directions through a membrane by a carrier protein called an *antiport,* using either facilitated diffusion or active transport |
| **Vesicular (Bulk) Transport** | **Movement of Fluid and Particles Through a Plasma Membrane by Way of Membrane Vesicles; Consumes ATP** |
| Endocytosis | Vesicular transport of particles into a cell |
| Phagocytosis | Process of engulfing large particles by means of pseudopods; "cell eating" |
| Pinocytosis | Process of imbibing extracellular fluid in which the plasma membrane sinks in and pinches off small vesicles containing droplets of fluid; "cell drinking" |
| Receptor-mediated endocytosis | Phagocytosis or pinocytosis in which specific solute particles bind to receptors on the plasma membrane, and are then taken into the cell in clathrin-coated vesicles with a minimal amount of extraneous matter |
| Exocytosis | Process of eliminating material from a cell by means of a vesicle approaching the cell surface, fusing with the plasma membrane, and expelling its contents; used to release cell secretions, replace worn-out plasma membrane, and replace membrane that has been internalized by endocytosis |

**BEFORE YOU GO ON**

Answer the following questions to test your understanding of the preceding section:

**13.** What is the importance of filtration to human physiology?

**14.** What does it mean to say a solute moves down its concentration gradient?

**15.** How does osmosis help to maintain blood volume?

**16.** Define *osmolarity* and *tonicity,* and explain the difference between them.

**17.** Define *hypotonic, isotonic,* and *hypertonic,* and explain why these concepts are important in clinical practice.

**18.** What do facilitated diffusion and active transport have in common? How are they different?

**19.** How does the $Na^+$–$K^+$ pump exchange sodium ions for potassium ions across the plasma membrane? What are some purposes served by this pump?

**20.** How does phagocytosis differ from pinocytosis?

**21.** Describe the process of exocytosis. What are some of its purposes?

## 3.4 The Cell Interior

### Expected Learning Outcomes

When you have completed this section, you should be able to

a. describe the cytoskeleton and its functions;

b. list the main organelles of a cell, describe their structure, and explain their functions; and

c. give some examples of cell inclusions and explain how inclusions differ from organelles.

We now probe more deeply into the cell to study its internal structures. These are classified into three groups—*cytoskeleton, organelles,* and *inclusions*—all embedded in the clear, gelatinous cytosol.

## 3.4a The Cytoskeleton

The **cytoskeleton** is a network of protein filaments and cylinders that structurally support a cell, determine its shape, organize its contents, direct the movement of materials within the cell, and contribute to movements of the cell as a whole. It forms a dense supportive scaffold in the cytoplasm **(fig. 3.24).** It is connected to transmembrane proteins of the plasma membrane, and they in turn are connected to protein fibers external to the cell, creating a strong structural continuity from extracellular material to the cytoplasm. Cytoskeletal elements may even connect to chromosomes in the nucleus, enabling physical tension on a cell to move nuclear contents and mechanically stimulate genetic function.

The cytoskeleton is composed of *microfilaments, intermediate filaments,* and *microtubules.* If you think of intermediate filaments as being like the stiff rods of uncooked spaghetti, you could, by comparison, think of microfilaments as being like fine angel-hair pasta and microtubules as being like tubular penne pasta.

**Microfilaments (thin filaments)** are about 6 nm thick and are made of the protein *actin.* They are widespread throughout the cell but especially concentrated in a fibrous mat called the **terminal web (membrane skeleton)** on the cytoplasmic side of the plasma membrane. The phospholipids of the plasma membrane spread out over the terminal web like butter on a slice of bread. The web, like the bread, provides physical support, whereas the lipids, like butter, provide a permeability barrier. It is thought that without the support of the terminal web, the phospholipids would break up into little droplets and the plasma membrane would not hold together. As described earlier, actin microfilaments also form the supportive cores of the microvilli and play a role in cell movement. Through its role in cell motility, actin plays a crucial role in embryonic development, muscle contraction, immune function, wound healing, cancer metastasis, and other processes that involve cell migration.

**Intermediate filaments** (8–10 nm thick) are thicker and stiffer than microfilaments. They give the cell its shape, resist stress, and participate in junctions that attach cells to their neighbors. In epidermal cells, they are made of the tough protein *keratin* and occupy most of the cytoplasm. They are responsible for the strength of hair and fingernails.

**Microtubules** (25 nm in diameter) are cylinders made of 13 parallel strands called *protofilaments.* Each protofilament is a long chain of globular proteins called *tubulin* **(fig. 3.25).** Microtubules radiate from an area of the cell called the *centrosome.* They hold organelles in place, form bundles that maintain cell shape and rigidity, and act somewhat like monorail tracks. Motor proteins walk along these tracks carrying organelles and macromolecules to specific destinations in the cell. Microtubules form the axonemes of cilia and flagella and are responsible for their beating movements, and form the mitotic spindle that guides chromosome movement during cell division. Microtubules are not permanent structures. They come and go moment by moment as tubulin molecules assemble into a tubule and then suddenly break apart again to be used somewhere else in the cell. The microtubules in cilia, flagella, basal bodies, and centrioles, however, are more stable.

## 3.4b Organelles

**Organelles** are internal structures of a cell that carry out specialized metabolic tasks. Some are surrounded by membranes and are therefore referred to as *membranous organelles.* These are the nucleus, mitochondria, lysosomes, peroxisomes, endoplasmic reticulum, and Golgi complex. Organelles without membranes include ribosomes, proteasomes, centrosomes, centrioles, and basal bodies.

### The Nucleus

The **nucleus (fig. 3.26)** is usually the largest organelle and the only one clearly visible with the light microscope. It contains the cell's chromosomes and is therefore the genetic control center of cellular activity. It is typically spheroidal to elliptical in shape and about 5 µm in diameter. Most cells have a single nucleus, but there are exceptions. Mature red blood cells have none; they are **anuclear.** A few cell types are **multinuclear,** having 2 to 50 nuclei. Examples include skeletal muscle cells, some liver cells, and certain bone-dissolving cells.

**Figure 3.27** shows the details of nuclear structure. The nucleus is enclosed in a double membrane, the **nuclear envelope.** The envelope is perforated with **nuclear pores** formed by a ring of proteins called the *nuclear pore complex.* These proteins regulate molecular traffic through the envelope and act like a rivet to hold the two membrane layers together. Hundreds of molecules pass through the nuclear pores every minute. Coming into the nucleus are raw materials for DNA and RNA synthesis, enzymes that are made in the cytoplasm but function in the nucleus, and hormones and other chemical messengers that activate certain genes. Going the other way, RNA is made in the nucleus but leaves to perform its job in the cytoplasm.

Immediately inside the nuclear envelope is a narrow but densely fibrous zone called the **nuclear lamina,** composed of a web of intermediate filaments. It supports the nuclear envelope and pores, provides points of attachment and organization for the chromosomes inside the nucleus, and plays a role in regulating DNA replication and the cell life cycle. Abnormalities of its structure or function are associated with certain genetic diseases and premature cell death.

The material in the nucleus is called **nucleoplasm.** This includes **chromatin**[32] (CRO-muh-tin)—fine threadlike matter composed of DNA and protein—and one or more dark-staining

[32]*chromat* = colored; *in* = substance

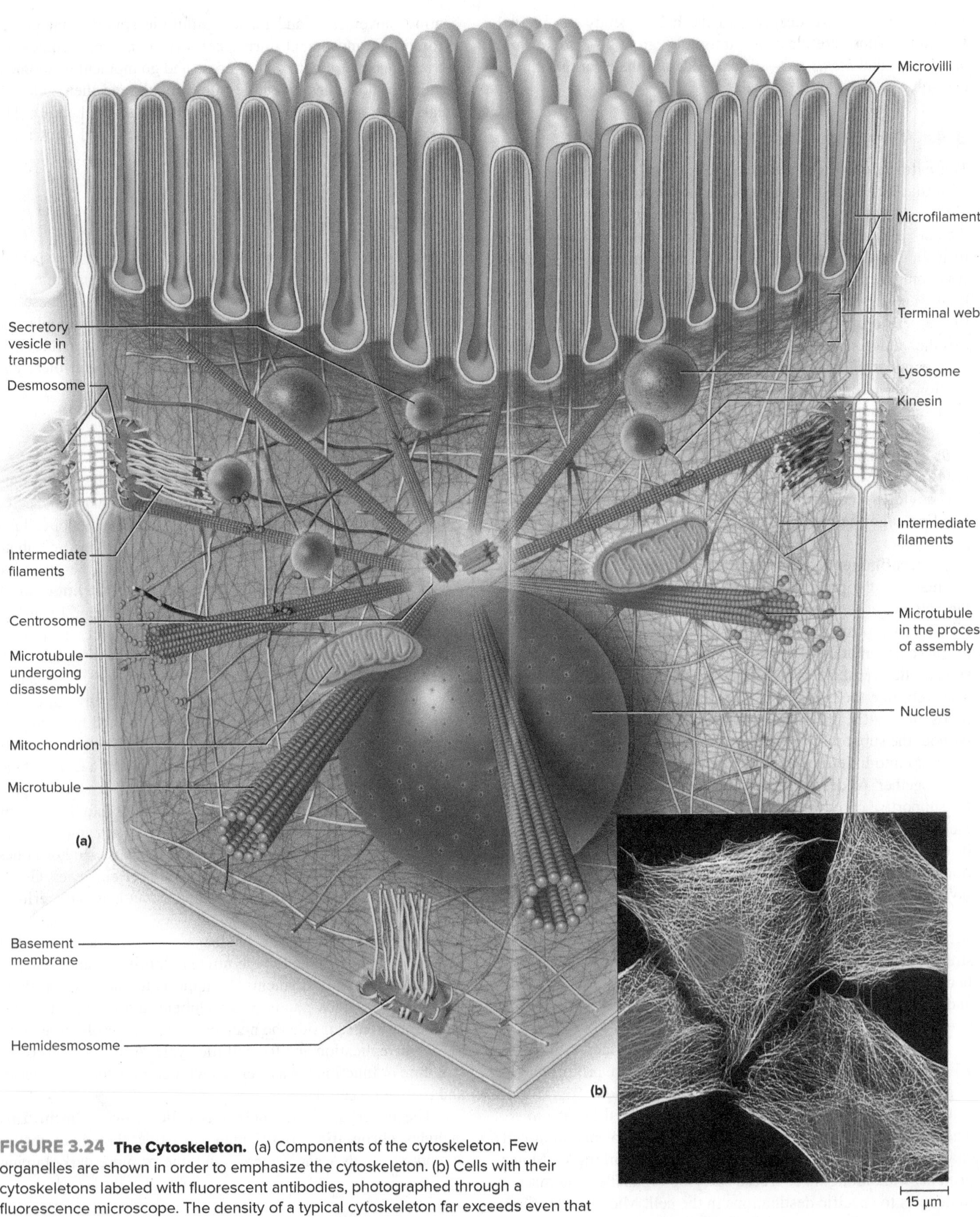


**FIGURE 3.24 The Cytoskeleton.** (a) Components of the cytoskeleton. Few organelles are shown in order to emphasize the cytoskeleton. (b) Cells with their cytoskeletons labeled with fluorescent antibodies, photographed through a fluorescence microscope. The density of a typical cytoskeleton far exceeds even that shown in part (a). The pink bodies are the cell nuclei.

b: Dr. Torsten Wittmann/Science Source

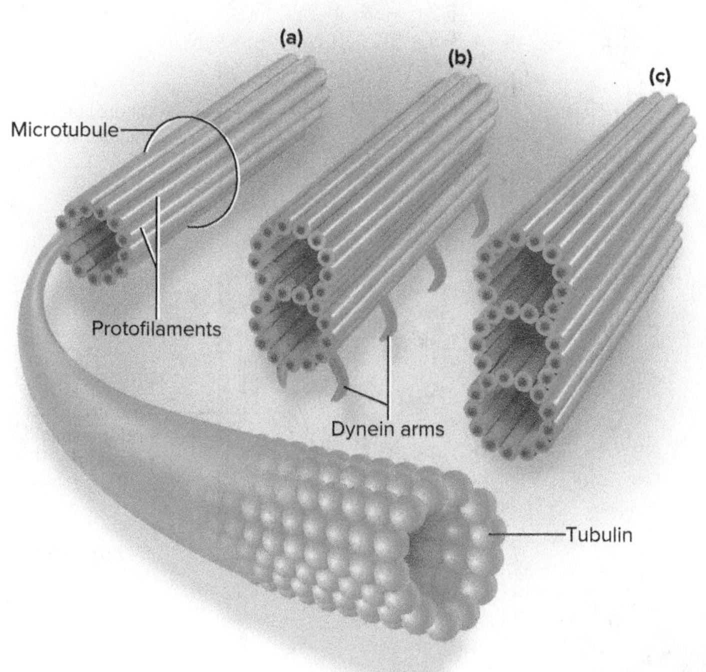


**FIGURE 3.25 Microtubules.** (a) A microtubule is composed of 13 protofilaments. Each protofilament is a helical array of globular proteins called tubulin. (b) One of the nine microtubule pairs that form the axonemes of cilia and flagella, with the motor protein dynein attached. (c) One of the nine microtubule triplets that form a centriole.

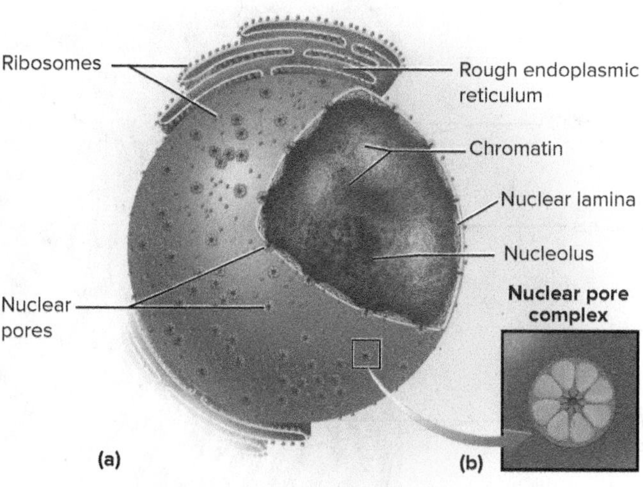


**FIGURE 3.27 Structure of the Nucleus.** (a) Cutaway view showing the nuclear surface and contents of the nucleoplasm. (b) Detail of a nuclear pore complex.

*Why do these nuclear pores have to be larger in diameter than the channels in the cell's plasma membrane? (See table 3.1.)*

masses called **nucleoli** (singular, *nucleolus*), where ribosomes are produced. The genetic function of the nucleus is described in section 4.2.

## Endoplasmic Reticulum

**Endoplasmic reticulum (ER)** literally means "little network within the cytoplasm." It is a system of interconnected channels

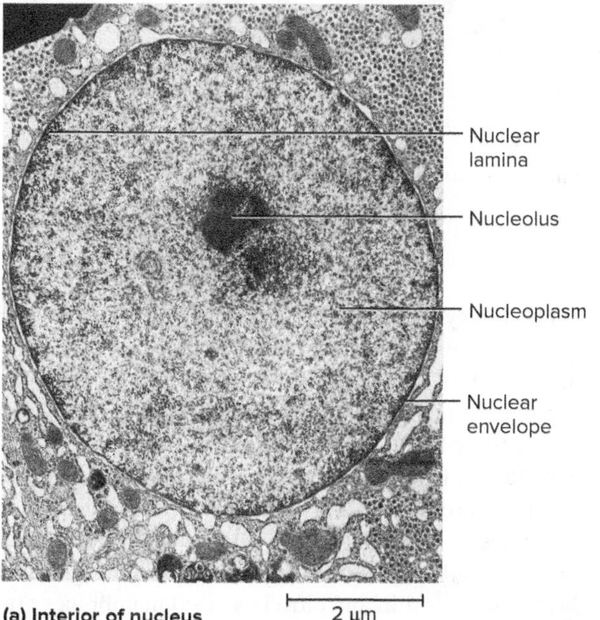


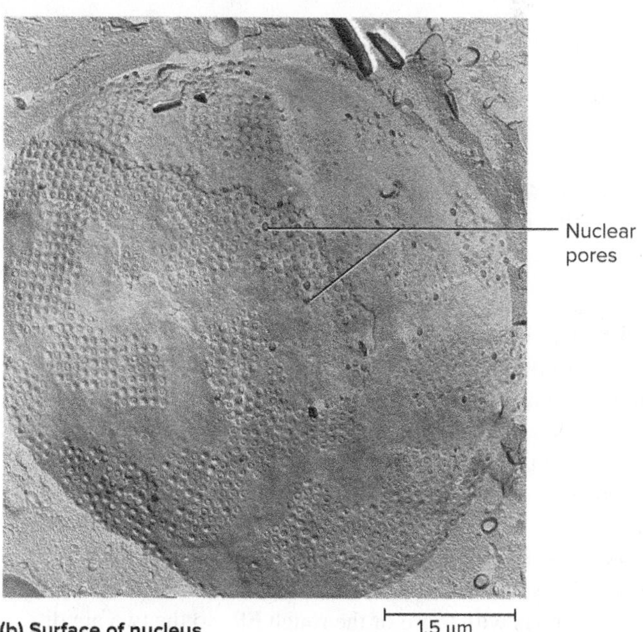


**FIGURE 3.26 The Nucleus as Seen by Electron Microscopy.** These photomicrographs were made by different TEM methods to show the internal structure of the nucleus and surface of the nuclear envelope. (a) Interior of the nucleus. (b) Surface of the nucleus, showing clusters of nuclear pores.

a: Richard Chao; b: ©E.G. Pollock

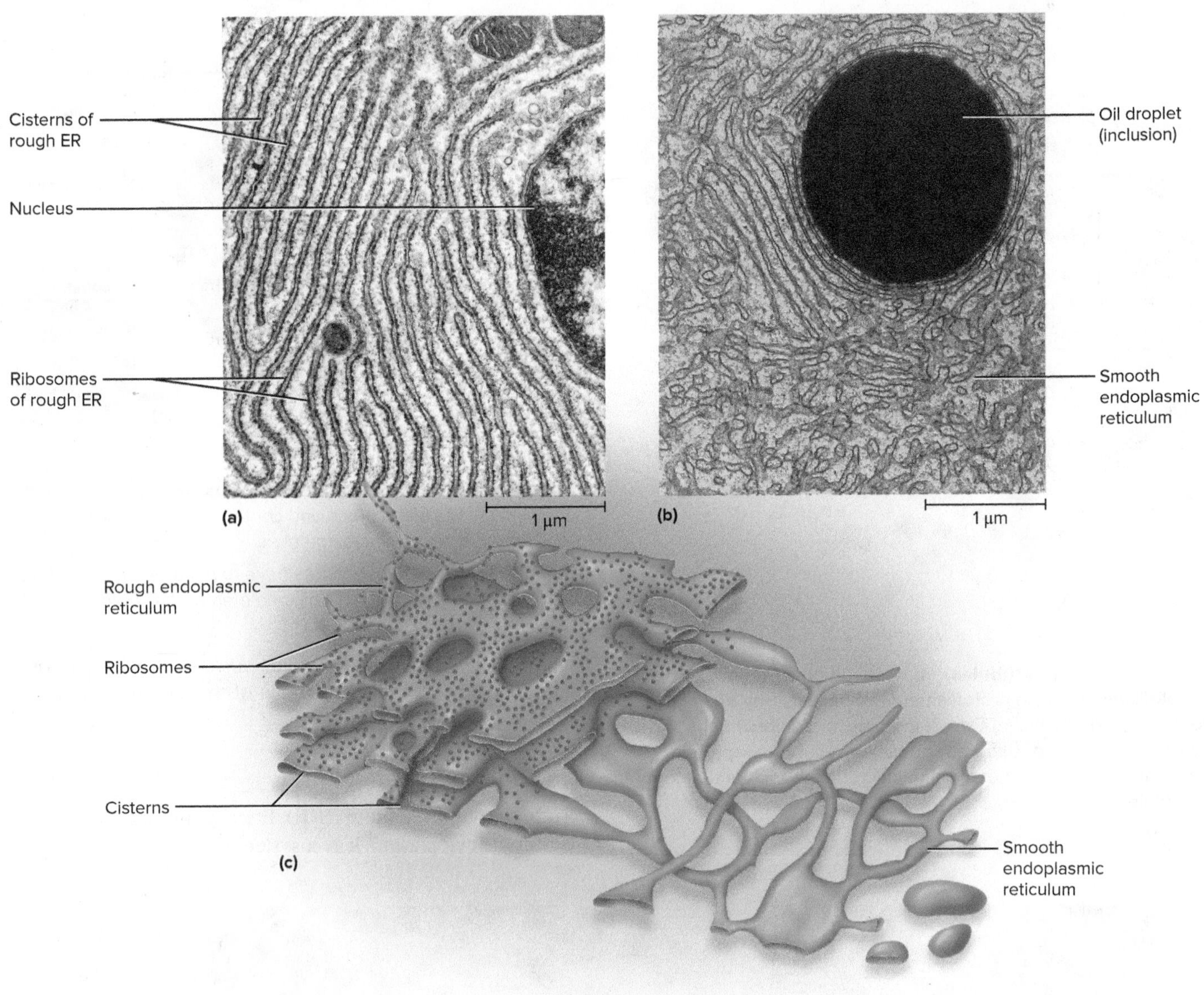


**FIGURE 3.28 Endoplasmic Reticulum (ER).** (a) Rough ER. (b) Smooth ER and an inclusion (oil droplet). (c) Structure of the endoplasmic reticulum, with rough and smooth regions.

a-b: Don Fawcett/Science Source

called **cisterns**[33] enclosed by a unit membrane **(fig. 3.28).** In areas called **rough endoplasmic reticulum,** the cisterns are parallel, flattened sacs covered with granules called *ribosomes.* Adjacent cisterns are connected by bridges to create one continuous internal space. The rough ER is continuous with the outer membrane of the nuclear envelope, and some authorities regard the nuclear envelope as simply a modified extension of it. In areas called **smooth endoplasmic reticulum,** the cisterns are more tubular, branch more extensively, and lack ribosomes. The cisterns of the smooth ER are continuous with those of the rough ER, so the two are different parts of the same network.

The ER synthesizes steroids and other lipids, detoxifies alcohol and other drugs, and manufactures nearly all membranes of the cell. Rough ER produces the phospholipids and proteins of the plasma membrane and synthesizes proteins that are either secreted from the cell or packaged in organelles such as lysosomes. Rough ER is most abundant in cells that synthesize large amounts of protein, such as antibody-producing cells and cells of the digestive glands. In such cells, the ER is often the largest organelle of all, although it isn't visible to the light microscope (LM) because its thin and closely spaced membranes are beyond the LM's limit of resolution.

Most cells have only a scanty smooth ER, but it is relatively abundant in cells that engage extensively in detoxification, such as liver and kidney cells. Long-term abuse of alcohol, barbiturates, and other drugs leads to tolerance partly because the smooth ER

[33]*cistern* = reservoir

proliferates and detoxifies the drugs more quickly. Smooth ER is also abundant in cells of the testes and ovaries that synthesize steroid hormones. Skeletal and cardiac muscle contain extensive networks of smooth ER that store calcium and release it to trigger muscle contraction.

## Ribosomes

**Ribosomes** are small granules of protein and RNA found in the nucleoli, in the cytosol, in mitochondria, and on the outer surfaces of the rough ER and nuclear envelope. They "read" coded genetic messages (messenger RNA) and assemble amino acids into proteins specified by the code. The unattached ribosomes scattered throughout the cytoplasm make enzymes and other proteins for use within the cell. Free ribosomes within the nucleus and mitochondria make proteins for use in those organelles. Ribosomes attach to the rough ER when they make proteins destined to be packaged in lysosomes or to be secreted from the cell, such as digestive enzymes, antibodies, and some hormones.

## Golgi Complex

The **Golgi**[34] **complex** (GOAL-jee) is a small system of cisterns that synthesize carbohydrates and put the finishing touches on protein and glycoprotein synthesis. The complex resembles a stack of pita bread. It consists of only a few cisterns, slightly separated from each other; each cistern is a flattened, often curved sac with swollen edges **(fig. 3.29).** The Golgi complex receives newly synthesized proteins from the rough ER. It sorts them, cuts and splices some of them, and adds carbohydrate moieties to some. Finally, the most mature cistern with the finished cell product breaks up into membrane-bounded **Golgi vesicles,** which are abundant in the neighborhood of the Golgi complex. Some vesicles become *lysosomes,* the organelle discussed next; some migrate to the plasma membrane and fuse with it, contributing fresh protein and phospholipid to the membrane; and some become **secretory vesicles** that store a cell product, such as breast milk or digestive enzymes, for later release. The roles of the endoplasmic reticulum, ribosomes, and Golgi complex in protein synthesis and secretion are detailed in sections 4.2c and 4.2d.

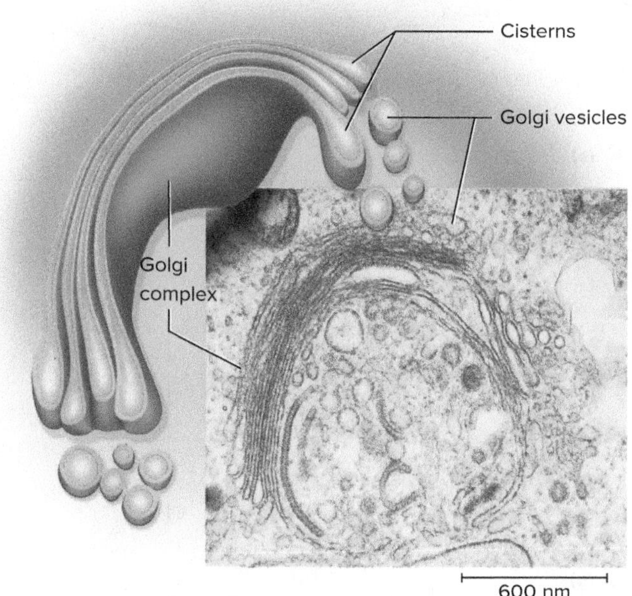


**FIGURE 3.29 The Golgi Complex.**

David M. Phillips/Science Source

## Lysosomes

A **lysosome**[35] (LY-so-some) **(fig. 3.30a)** is a package of enzymes bounded by a membrane. Although often round or oval, lysosomes are extremely variable in shape. When viewed with the TEM, they often exhibit dark gray contents devoid of structure, but sometimes show crystals or parallel layers of protein. At least 50 lysosomal enzymes have been identified. They hydrolyze proteins, nucleic acids, complex carbohydrates, phospholipids, and other substrates. In the liver, lysosomes break down glycogen to release glucose into the bloodstream. White blood cells use lysosomes to digest phagocytized bacteria. Lysosomes also digest and dispose of surplus or nonvital organelles and other cell components in order to recycle their nutrients to more important cell needs; this process is called **autophagy**[36] (aw-TOFF-uh-jee). Lysosomes also aid in a process of "cell suicide." Some cells are meant to do a certain job and then destroy themselves. The uterus, for example, weighs about 900 g at full-term pregnancy and shrinks to 60 g within 5 or 6 weeks after birth. This shrinkage is due to **autolysis,**[37] the digestion of surplus cells by their own lysosomal enzymes.

## Peroxisomes

**Peroxisomes (fig. 3.30b)** resemble lysosomes but contain different enzymes. They are produced by collaboration between the endoplasmic reticulum and mitochondria and by fission of preexisting peroxisomes. Their general function is to use molecular oxygen ($O_2$) to oxidize organic molecules. These reactions produce hydrogen peroxide ($H_2O_2$)—hence, the name of the organelle. $H_2O_2$ is then used to oxidize other molecules, and the excess is broken down to water and oxygen by an enzyme called *catalase.*

Peroxisomes occur in nearly all cells but are especially abundant in liver and kidney cells. They neutralize free radicals and detoxify alcohol, other drugs, and a variety of blood-borne toxins. Peroxisomes also decompose fatty acids into two-carbon fragments that the mitochondria use as an energy source for ATP synthesis.

[34]Camillo Golgi (1843–1926), Italian histologist

[35]*lyso* = loosen, dissolve; *some* = body
[36]*auto* = self; *phagy* = eating
[37]*auto* = self; *lysis* = dissolving

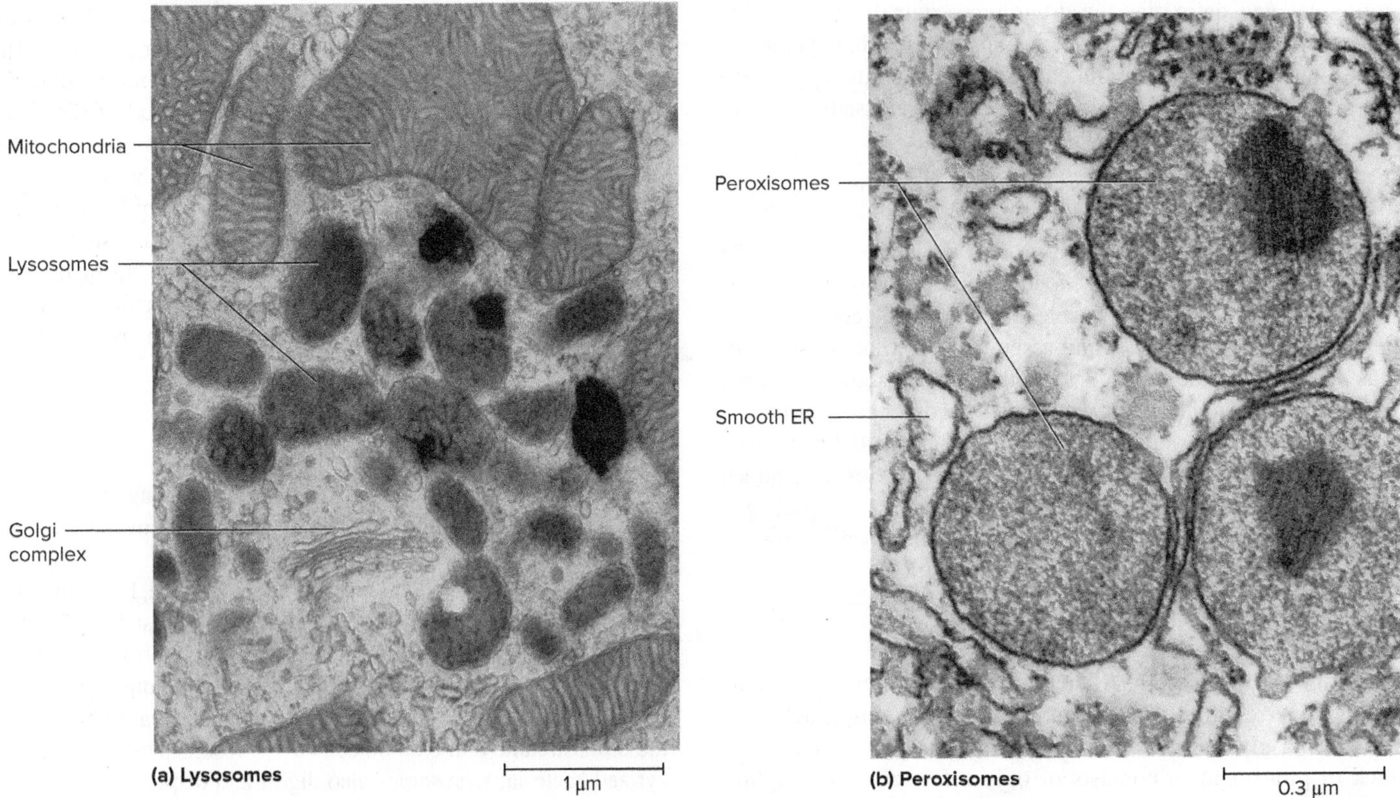


**FIGURE 3.30 Lysosomes and Peroxisomes.** (a) Lysosomes, produced from Golgi vesicles. (b) Peroxisomes, which look similar but are produced by mitochondria working with the endoplasmic reticulum, and by division of other peroxisomes.

a–b: Don Fawcett/Science Source

## Proteasomes

Cells must tightly control the concentration of proteins in their cytoplasm. Therefore, they must not only synthesize new proteins, but also dispose of those that are no longer needed. Cells also need to rid themselves of damaged and nonfunctional proteins and foreign proteins introduced by such events as viral infection. Protein synthesis, we have seen, is the domain of the ribosomes; protein disposal is the function of another structurally simple organelle called a **proteasome.**

Proteasomes are hollow, cylindrical complexes of proteins located in both the cytoplasm and nucleus **(fig. 3.31).** A cell tags undesirable proteins for destruction and transports them to a proteasome. As the undesirable protein passes through the core of this organelle, the proteasome's enzymes unfold it and break it down into short peptides and free amino acids. These can be used to synthesize new proteins or be presented to the immune system for further degradation. Proteasomes degrade more than 80% of a cell's proteins.

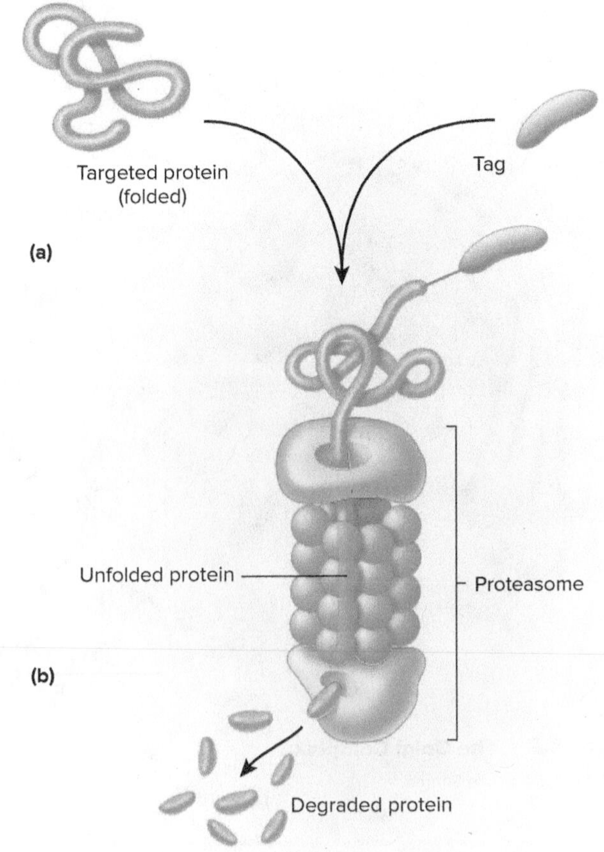


**FIGURE 3.31 Protein Degradation by a Proteasome.** (a) The unwanted protein targeted for destruction is tagged and transported to a proteasome. (b) As the protein passes down the core of the proteasome, it is unfolded and cleaved into small peptides and free amino acids. (c) The degraded protein fragments are released from the other end of the proteasome.

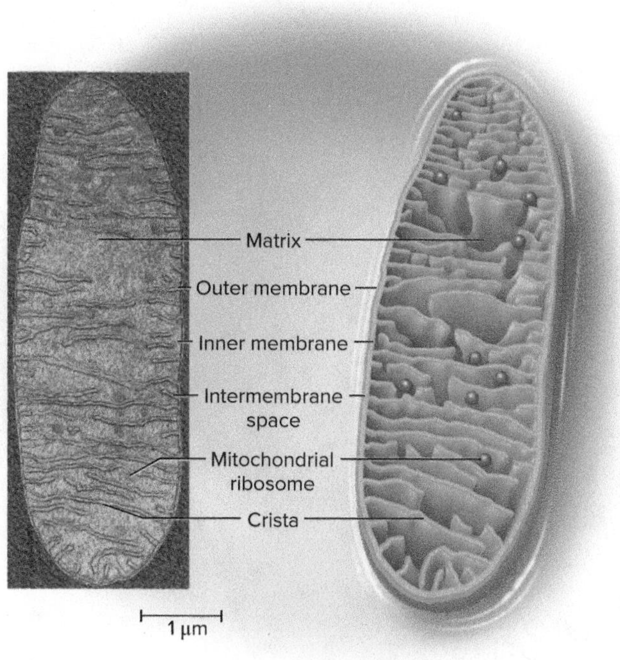


**FIGURE 3.32 A Mitochondrion.**

Keith R. Porter/Science Source

## Mitochondria

**Mitochondria**[38] (MY-toe-CON-dree-uh) (singular, *mitochondrion*) are organelles specialized for synthesizing ATP. They have a variety of shapes—spheroidal, rod-shaped, kidney-shaped, or threadlike **(fig. 3.32).** They are quite mobile, squirming and changing shape continually. They sometimes undergo fusion (two mitochondria joining to become one) and fission (one mitochondrion dividing in two). Like the nucleus, a mitochondrion is surrounded by a double membrane. The inner membrane usually has folds called **cristae**[39] (CRIS-tee), which project like shelves across the organelle. The space between the cristae, called the **matrix,** contains ribosomes; enzymes used in ATP synthesis; and many small, circular DNA molecules called *mitochondrial DNA (mtDNA).* Mitochondria are the "powerhouses" of the cell. Energy is not *made* here, but it is extracted from organic compounds and transferred to ATP, primarily by enzymes located on the cristae. The role of mitochondria in ATP synthesis is explained in detail in section 26.2d, and some evolutionary and clinical aspects of mitochondria are discussed in Deeper Insight 3.3.

[38]*mito* = thread; *chondr* = grain
[39]*crista* = crest

## DEEPER INSIGHT 3.3
### EVOLUTIONARY MEDICINE

### *Mitochondria—Evolution and Clinical Significance*

It is virtually certain that mitochondria evolved from bacteria that invaded another primitive cell, survived in its cytoplasm, and became permanent residents. The double membranes around the mitochondrion suggest that the original bacterium provided the inner membrane, and the host cell's phagosome provided the outer membrane when the bacterium was phagocytized.

Several comparisons show the apparent relationship of mitochondria to bacteria. Their ribosomes are more like bacterial ribosomes than those of eukaryotic (nucleated) cells. Mitochondrial DNA (mtDNA) is a small, circular molecule that resembles the circular DNA of bacteria, not the linear DNA of the cell nucleus. It replicates independently of nuclear DNA. Mitochondrial DNA codes for some of the enzymes employed in ATP synthesis. It consists of 16,569 *base pairs* (explained in section 4.1), comprising 37 genes, compared with over 3 billion base pairs and about 20,000 genes in nuclear DNA.

When a sperm fertilizes an egg, any mitochondria introduced by the sperm are destroyed and only those provided by the egg are passed on to the developing embryo. Therefore, mtDNA is inherited exclusively through the mother. While nuclear DNA is reshuffled in every generation by sexual reproduction, mtDNA remains unchanged except by random mutation. Because of the known pace of such mutations, biologists and anthropologists can use mtDNA as a "molecular clock" to trace evolutionary lineages in humans and other species. The amount of difference between the mtDNAs of related species affords a record of how much time has passed since they diverged from their last common ancestor. Anthropologists have gained evidence from mtDNA that of all the women who lived in Africa 200,000 years ago, only one has any descendants still living today. This "mitochondrial Eve" is ancestor to us all. Mitochondrial DNA has also been used as evidence in criminal law and to identify the remains of soldiers killed in combat. It was used in 2001 to identify the remains of the famed bandit Jesse James, who was killed in 1882.

Mutations in mtDNA are responsible for various rare hereditary diseases and death in early childhood. Tissues and organs with the highest energy demands are the most vulnerable to mitochondrial dysfunctions—nervous tissue, the heart, the kidneys, and skeletal muscles, for example. *Mitochondrial myopathy* is a degenerative muscle disease in which the muscle displays "ragged red fibers," cells with abnormal mitochondria that stain red with a particular histological stain. Another mtDNA disease is *Leber hereditary optic neuropathy (LHON),* a form of blindness that usually appears in young adulthood as a result of damage to the optic nerve. *Kearns–Sayre syndrome (KSS)* involves paralysis of the eye muscles, degeneration of the retina, heart disease, hearing loss, diabetes, and kidney failure. Damage to mtDNA has also been implicated as a possible factor in Alzheimer disease, Huntington disease, and other degenerative diseases of old age.

Some women known to carry mtDNA mutations can now avoid passing such diseases to their children through in vitro fertilization (IVF) with mitochondrial replacement therapy (MRT). The techniques of MRT are complex and diverse, but the essence of it is to provide an egg of the patient with healthy mitochondria from another woman, an egg donor; fertilize the recipient egg with the father's sperm; and implant this in the patient's uterus. The successful result is a "three-parent baby" who has the father's nuclear DNA, the birth mother's nuclear DNA, and the mitochondria donor's mtDNA.

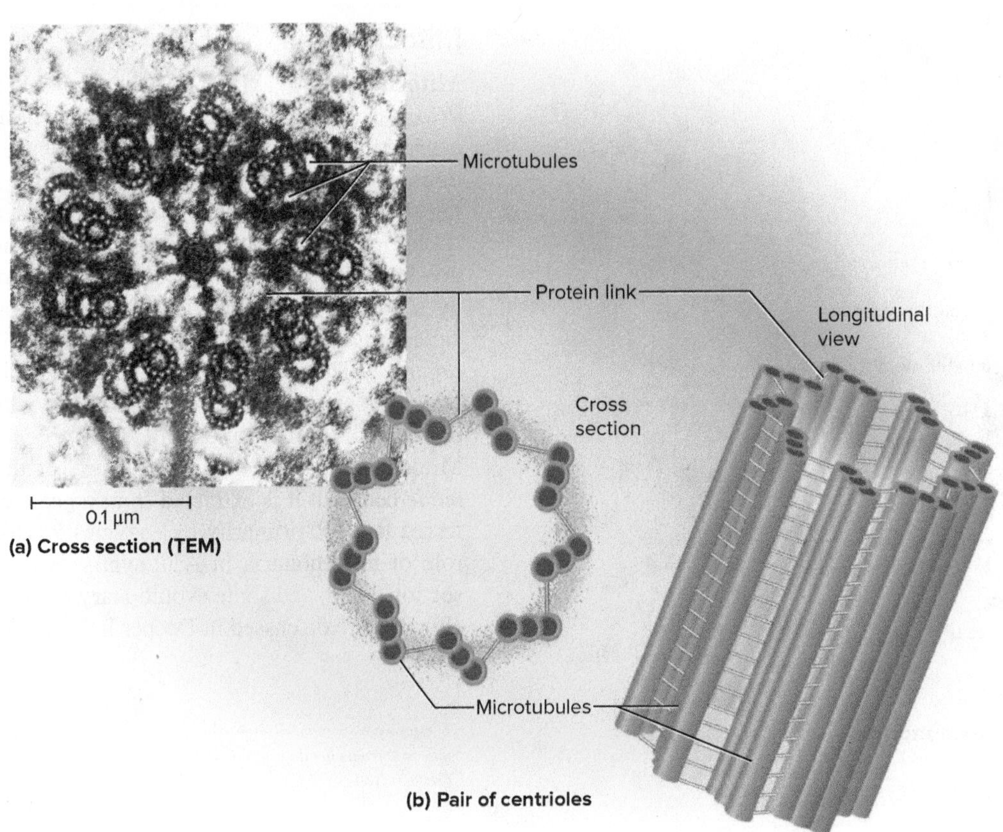


**FIGURE 3.33 Centrioles.** (a) Electron micrograph of a centriole as seen in cross section. (b) A pair of perpendicular centrioles.

a: Don W Fawcett/Getty Images

*How does a centriole resemble the axoneme of a cilium? How does it differ?*

### Centrioles

A **centriole** (SEN-tree-ole) is a short cylindrical assembly of microtubules, arranged in nine groups of three microtubules each **(fig. 3.33).** Near the nucleus, most cells have a small, clear patch of cytoplasm called the **centrosome**[40] containing a pair of mutually perpendicular centrioles **(see fig. 3.24).** Centrioles play a role in cell division described in section 4.3d. Each basal body of a flagellum or cilium is a single centriole oriented perpendicular to the plasma membrane. Basal bodies originate in a *centriolar organizing center* and migrate to the plasma membrane. Two microtubules of each triplet then elongate to form the nine pairs of peripheral microtubules of the axoneme. A cilium can grow to its full length in less than an hour.

## 3.4c Inclusions

**Inclusions** are of two kinds: accumulated cell products such as glycogen granules, pigments, and oil droplets (see fig. 3.28b); and foreign bodies such as viruses, bacteria, and dust particles and other debris phagocytized by a cell. Inclusions are never enclosed in a membrane, and unlike the organelles and cytoskeleton, they are not essential to cell survival.

The major features of a cell are summarized in **table 3.4.**

**BEFORE YOU GO ON**

Answer the following questions to test your understanding of the preceding section:

22. Distinguish between organelles and inclusions. State two examples of each.
23. Briefly state how each of the following cell components can be recognized in electron micrographs: the nucleus, a mitochondrion, a lysosome, and a centriole. What is the primary function of each?
24. What three organelles are involved in protein synthesis?
25. In what ways do rough and smooth endoplasmic reticulum differ?
26. Define *centriole, microtubule, cytoskeleton,* and *axoneme.* How are these structures related to one another?

[40]*centro* = central; *some* = body

**TABLE 3.4 Summary of Organelles and Other Cellular Structures**

| Structure | Appearance to TEM | Function |
|---|---|---|
| Plasma membrane (fig. 3.5) | Two dark lines at cell surface, separated by a narrow light space | Prevents escape of cell contents; regulates exchange of materials between cytoplasm and extracellular fluid; involved in intercellular communication |
| Microvilli (fig. 3.9) | Short, densely spaced, hairlike processes or scattered bumps on cell surface; interior featureless or with bundle of microfilaments | Increase absorptive surface area; widespread sensory roles (hearing, equilibrium, taste) |
| Cilia (fig. 3.10) | Long hairlike projections of apical cell surface; axoneme with usually a 9 + 2 array of microtubules | Move substances along cell surface; widespread sensory roles (equilibrium, smell, vision) |
| Flagellum | Long, single, whiplike process with axoneme | Sperm motility |
| Microfilaments (figs. 3.9 and 3.24) | Thin protein filaments (6 nm diameter), often in parallel bundles or dense networks in cytoplasm | Support microvilli and plasma membrane; involved in muscle contraction and other cell motility, endocytosis, and cell division |
| Intermediate filaments (fig. 3.24) | Thicker protein filaments (8–10 nm diameter) extending throughout cytoplasm or concentrated at cell-to-cell junctions | Give shape and physical support to cell; anchor cells to each other and to extracellular material; compartmentalize cell contents |
| Microtubules (figs. 3.24 and 3.25) | Hollow protein cylinders (25 nm diameter) radiating from centrosome | Form axonemes of cilia and flagella, centrioles, basal bodies, and mitotic spindles; enable motility of cell parts; form trackways that direct organelles and macromolecules to their destinations within a cell |
| Nucleus (figs. 3.4, 3.26, and 3.27) | Largest organelle in most cells, surrounded by double membrane with nuclear pores | Genetic control center of cell; directs protein synthesis; shelters the DNA |
| Rough ER (fig. 3.28a) | Extensive sheets of parallel membranes with ribosomes on outer surface | Protein synthesis and manufacture of cellular membranes |
| Smooth ER (fig. 3.28b) | Branching network of tubules with smooth surface (no ribosomes); usually broken into numerous small segments in TEM photos | Lipid synthesis, detoxification, calcium storage |
| Ribosomes (fig. 3.28c) | Small dark granules free in cytosol, on surface of rough ER and nuclear envelope, and inside nucleus and mitochondria | Interpret the genetic code and synthesize polypeptides |
| Golgi complex (fig. 3.29) | Several closely spaced, parallel cisterns with thick edges, usually near nucleus, often with many Golgi vesicles nearby | Receives and modifies newly synthesized polypeptides; synthesizes carbohydrates; adds carbohydrates to glycoproteins; packages cell products into Golgi vesicles |
| Golgi vesicles (fig. 3.29) | Round to irregular sacs near Golgi complex, usually with light, featureless contents | Become secretory vesicles and carry cell products to apical surface for exocytosis, or become lysosomes |
| Lysosomes (fig. 3.30a) | Round to oval sacs with single enclosing membrane, often a dark featureless interior but sometimes with protein layers or crystals | Contain enzymes for intracellular digestion, autophagy, programmed cell death, and glucose mobilization |
| Peroxisomes (fig. 3.30b) | Similar to lysosomes; often lighter in color | Contain enzymes for detoxification of free radicals, alcohol, and other drugs; oxidize fatty acids |
| Proteasomes (fig. 3.31) | Small cytoplasmic granules composed of a cylindrical array of proteins | Degrade proteins that are undesirable or no longer needed by a cell |
| Mitochondria (fig. 3.32) | Round, rod-shaped, bean-shaped, or threadlike structures with double enclosing membrane and shelflike infoldings called cristae | ATP synthesis |
| Centrioles (fig. 3.33) | Short cylindrical bodies, each composed of a circle of nine triplets of microtubules | Form mitotic spindle during cell division; unpaired centrioles form basal bodies of cilia and flagella |
| Centrosome (fig. 3.24) | Clear area near nucleus containing a pair of centrioles | Organizing center for formation of microtubules of cytoskeleton and mitotic spindle |
| Basal body (fig. 3.10b) | Unpaired centriole at the base of a cilium or flagellum | Point of origin, growth, and anchorage of a cilium or flagellum; produces axoneme |
| Inclusions (fig. 3.28b) | Highly variable—fat droplets, glycogen granules, protein crystals, dust, bacteria, viruses; never enclosed in membranes | Storage products or other products of cellular metabolism, or foreign matter retained in cytoplasm |

# STUDY GUIDE

## Assess Your Learning Outcomes

*To test your knowledge, discuss the following topics with a study partner or in writing, ideally from memory.*

### 3.1 Concepts of Cellular Structure

1. The scope of cytology
2. Basic tenets of the cell theory
3. The nine common cell shapes
4. The size range of most human cells; some extremes outside this range; and some factors that limit cells from growing indefinitely large
5. The two kinds of electron microscopes; why they have enhanced the modern understanding of cells; and the distinction between magnification and resolution in microscopy
6. Basic structural components of a cell
7. The distinction between intracellular fluid (ICF) and extracellular fluid (ECF)

### 3.2 The Cell Surface

1. The molecules of the plasma membrane and how they are organized
2. The distinctive roles of phospholipids, glycolipids, cholesterol, integral proteins, peripheral proteins, and glycoproteins in membrane structure
3. Seven roles played by membrane proteins
4. Distinctions between leak channels and gated channels, and between ligand-gated, voltage-gated, and mechanically gated channels
5. The function of second-messenger systems associated with the plasma membrane; the specific roles of membrane receptors, G proteins, adenylate cyclase, cyclic adenosine monophosphate, and kinases in the cAMP second-messenger system
6. Composition and functions of the glycocalyx
7. Structure and functions of microvilli, and where they are found
8. Structure and functions of cilia, and where they are found
9. Structure and function of the only human flagellum
10. Structure and function of pseudopods

### 3.3 Membrane Transport

1. What it means to say that a plasma membrane is selectively permeable, and why this property is important for human survival
2. Filtration, where it occurs in the body, and why it depends on hydrostatic pressure
3. Simple diffusion, factors that determine its speed, and examples of its physiological and clinical relevance
4. Osmosis, examples of its physiological and clinical relevance, factors that determine its speed and direction, and the role of aquaporins
5. Reverse osmosis, where it occurs in the body, and the purpose it serves
6. In relation to osmosis, the meaning of *osmotic pressure, osmolarity, tonicity,* and *milliosmoles per liter (mOsm/L)*
7. Distinctions between hypotonic, hypertonic, and isotonic solutions; their effects on cells; and how this relates to intravenous fluid therapy
8. How carrier-mediated transport differs from other types of transport, and the relevance of specificity to this process
9. How carrier-mediated transport is limited by carrier saturation and the transport maximum ($T_m$)
10. Distinctions between a uniport, symport, and antiport; the meanings of *cotransport* and *countertransport*; and examples of where each is relevant in human physiology
11. Similarities and differences between facilitated diffusion and active transport
12. The distinction between primary and secondary active transport
13. The mechanism and roles of the sodium–potassium ($Na^+$–$K^+$) pump
14. How vesicular transport differs from other modes of membrane transport; the difference between endocytosis and exocytosis; different forms of endocytosis; and examples of the physiological relevance of each kind of vesicular transport
15. Of the preceding mechanisms of transport, which ones require a membrane; which ones require a plasma membrane and which ones can also occur through artificial membranes; which ones require ATP and cease if ATP is unavailable, as upon death

### 3.4 The Cell Interior

1. Distinctions between cytoplasm, cytosol, cytoskeleton, organelles, and inclusions; and the respective, general roles of each in the internal organization of a cell
2. Overall functions of the cytoskeleton and the differences between microfilaments, intermediate filaments, and microtubules
3. Which organelles are considered membranous and why, and which of these are enclosed in single or double membranes
4. Structure and function of the nucleus, especially the nuclear envelope and nuclear lamina
5. General structure of the endoplasmic reticulum (ER); the two types of ER and the structural and functional differences between them
6. The composition, location, and function of ribosomes
7. The structure and functions of the Golgi complex; the origin and destiny of Golgi vesicles
8. The structures and functions of lysosomes and peroxisomes, and the similarities and differences between them
9. Structure and function of proteasomes
10. Structure and function of mitochondria
11. Structures and functions of centrioles, the centrosome, and basal bodies; and how these relate to each other
12. How inclusions differ from organelles; the origins and types of inclusions

## Testing Your Recall

Answers in Appendix A

1. The clear, structureless gel in a cell is its
   a. nucleoplasm.
   b. protoplasm.
   c. cytoplasm.
   d. neoplasm.
   e. cytosol.

2. The $Na^+$–$K^+$ pump is
   a. a peripheral protein.
   b. a transmembrane protein.
   c. a G protein.
   d. a glycolipid.
   e. a phospholipid.

3. Which of the following processes could occur *only* in the plasma membrane of a living cell?
   a. facilitated diffusion
   b. simple diffusion
   c. filtration
   d. active transport
   e. osmosis

# STUDY GUIDE

4. Cells specialized for absorption of matter from the ECF are likely to show an abundance of
   a. lysosomes.
   b. microvilli.
   c. mitochondria.
   d. secretory vesicles.
   e. ribosomes.

5. Aquaporins are transmembrane proteins that promote
   a. pinocytosis.
   b. carrier-mediated transport.
   c. active transport.
   d. facilitated diffusion.
   e. osmosis.

6. Membrane carriers resemble enzymes except for the fact that carriers
   a. are not proteins.
   b. do not have binding sites.
   c. are not selective for particular ligands.
   d. change conformation when they bind a ligand.
   e. do not chemically change their ligands.

7. The cotransport of glucose derives energy from
   a. a $Na^+$ concentration gradient.
   b. the glucose being transported.
   c. a $Ca^{2+}$ gradient.
   d. the membrane voltage.
   e. body heat.

8. The function of cAMP in a cell is
   a. to activate a G protein.
   b. to remove phosphate groups from ATP.
   c. to activate kinases.
   d. to bind to the first messenger.
   e. to add phosphate groups to enzymes.

9. Most cellular membranes are made by
   a. the nucleus.
   b. the cytoskeleton.
   c. enzymes in the peroxisomes.
   d. the endoplasmic reticulum.
   e. replication of existing membranes.

10. Matter can leave a cell by any of the following means *except*
    a. active transport.
    b. pinocytosis.
    c. an antiport.
    d. simple diffusion.
    e. exocytosis.

11. Most human cells are 10 to 15 ______ in diameter.

12. When a hormone cannot enter a cell, it activates the formation of a/an ______ inside the cell.

13. ______ channels in the plasma membrane open or close in response to changes in the electrical charge difference across the membrane.

14. The force exerted on a membrane by water is called ______.

15. A concentrated solution that causes a cell to shrink is ______ to the cell.

16. Fusion of a secretory vesicle with the plasma membrane and release of the vesicle's contents is a process called ______.

17. ______ and ______ are two granular organelles (enzyme complexes) that, respectively, synthesize and degrade proteins.

18. Liver cells can detoxify alcohol with two organelles, the ______ and ______.

19. An ion gate in the plasma membrane that opens or closes when a chemical binds to it is called a/an ______.

20. The space enclosed by the membranes of the Golgi complex and endoplasmic reticulum is called the ______.

## Building Your Medical Vocabulary

*Answers in Appendix A*

*State a meaning of each word element, and give a medical term from this chapter that uses it or a slight variation of it.*

1. anti-
2. chromato-
3. co-
4. cyto-
5. endo-
6. facil-
7. fusi-
8. -logy
9. -osis
10. phago-

## What's Wrong with These Statements?

*Answers in Appendix A*

*Briefly explain why each of the following statements is false, or reword it to make it true.*

1. If a cell were poisoned so it could not make ATP, osmosis through its membrane would cease.
2. Each cell of the human body has a single nucleus.
3. A cell's second messengers serve mainly to transport solutes through the membrane.
4. The Golgi complex makes all of a cell's lysosomes and peroxisomes.
5. Some membrane channels are peripheral proteins.
6. The plasma membrane consists primarily of protein molecules.
7. The brush border of a cell is composed of cilia.
8. Human cells placed in hypertonic saline will swell and burst.
9. The transport maximum ($T_m$) sets an upper limit on the rate of osmosis.
10. All of a cell's ribosomes are found on the nuclear envelope and the rough endoplasmic reticulum.

# STUDY GUIDE

## Testing Your Comprehension

1. If someone bought a saltwater fish in a pet shop and put it in a freshwater aquarium at home, what would happen to the fish's cells? What would happen if someone put a freshwater fish in a saltwater aquarium? Explain.

2. A farmer's hand and forearm are badly crushed in a hay baler. When examined at the hospital, his blood potassium level is found to be abnormal. Would you expect it to be higher or lower than normal? Explain.

3. Many children worldwide suffer from a severe deficiency of dietary protein. As a result, they have very low levels of blood albumin. How do you think this affects the water content and volume of their blood? Explain.

4. It is often said, even in some textbooks, that mitochondria make energy for a cell. Why is this statement false?

5. Kartagener syndrome is a hereditary disease in which dynein arms are lacking from the axonemes of cilia and flagella. Predict the effect of Kartagener syndrome on a man's ability to father a child. Predict its effect on his respiratory health. Explain both answers.

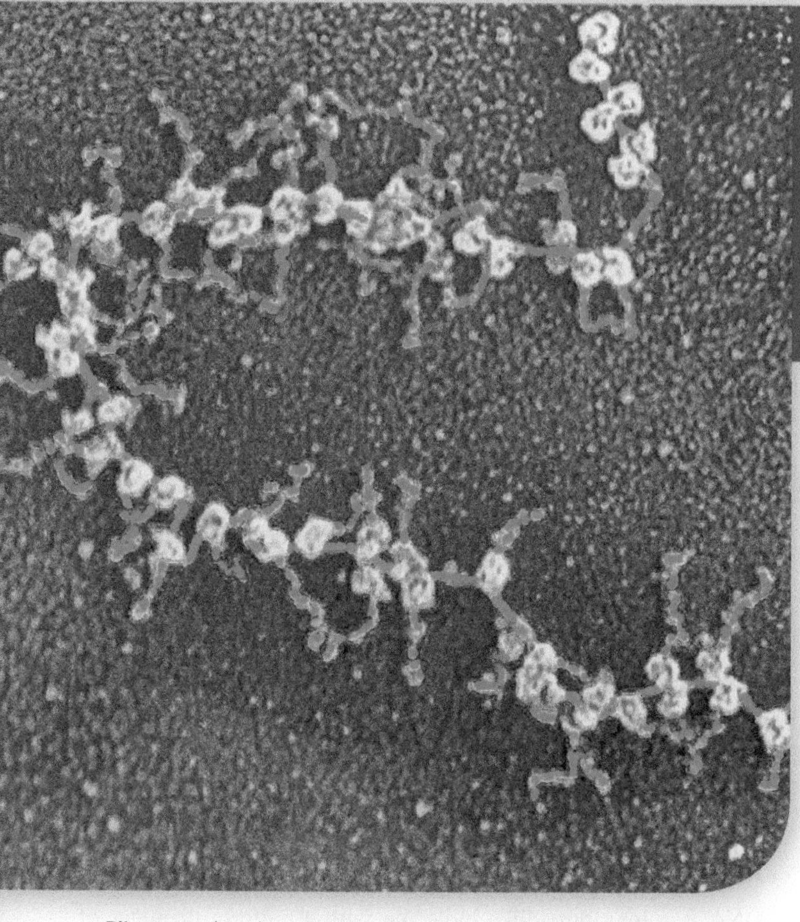

Ribosomes (gray) reading the genetic instructions on a messenger RNA strand (red), generating proteins (green) with an amino acid sequence determined by the genetic code (TEM)

Dr. Elena Kiseleva/Science Source

CHAPTER

# 4

# GENES AND CELLULAR FUNCTION

## CHAPTER OUTLINE



## DEEPER INSIGHTS

Module 2: Cells and Chemistry

**BRUSHING UP**

- To understand how genes direct the synthesis of proteins, you must be familiar with protein structure (see section 2.4e).
- Understanding the processing and packaging of proteins depends on familiarity with the organelles that carry out these processes (see section 3.4b).
- Brush up on exocytosis (see section 3.3f) to understand how a cell secretes newly synthesized proteins made for use outside the cell.
- Be sure you are familiar with microtubules and centrioles, both in section 3.4a, as a basis for understanding cell division by mitosis.

Several chapters in this book discuss hereditary traits such as blood types and hair color and genetic disorders such as color blindness, cystic fibrosis, diabetes mellitus, and hemophilia. To understand such conditions, it is necessary to have some familiarity with DNA and genes. This chapter is intended to provide such preparation.

Heredity has been a matter of human interest dating even to biblical writings, but a scientific understanding of how traits pass from parents to offspring began with the Austrian monk Gregor Mendel (1822–84) and his famous experiments on garden peas. By the late nineteenth century, biologists had observed chromosomes and their behavior during cell division. In the early twentieth century, they rediscovered Mendel's work and realized the correlation between chromosome behavior and his laws of heredity. From that simple but insightful beginning, genetics has grown into a highly diverse science with several subdisciplines and is arguably the most dynamic of all natural sciences in these early decades of the twenty-first century.

*Mendelian genetics* deals with parent–offspring and larger family relationships to discern and predict patterns of inheritance within a family line. *Cytogenetics* uses the techniques of cytology and microscopy to study chromosomes and their relationship to hereditary traits. *Molecular genetics* uses the techniques of biochemistry to study the structure and function of DNA. *Genomic medicine* comprehensively studies the entire DNA endowment of an individual (the *genome*), how it influences health and disease, and how this knowledge can be used to prevent, treat, or cure diseases. We will examine these perspectives in this chapter.

## 4.1 DNA and RNA—The Nucleic Acids

**Expected Learning Outcomes**

When you have completed this section, you should be able to

a. describe the structure of DNA and relate this to its function;
b. explain how DNA and proteins are organized to form the chromosomes; and
c. describe the types of RNA, their structural and functional differences, and how they compare with DNA.

With improvements in the microscope, biologists of the late nineteenth century saw that cell division is immediately preceded by nuclear division, and during nuclear division, the chromosomes split neatly in two and distribute their halves to the two daughter cells. They came to suspect that the nucleus was the center of heredity and cellular control, and they began probing it for the biochemical secrets of heredity. Swiss biochemist Johann Friedrich Miescher (1844–95) studied the nuclei of white blood cells extracted from pus in hospital bandages, and later the nuclei of salmon sperm, since both cell types offered large nuclei with minimal amounts of contaminating cytoplasm. In 1869, he discovered an acidic, phosphorus-rich substance he named *nuclein.* He correctly believed this to be the cell's hereditary matter, although he was never able to convince other scientists of this. We now call this substance **deoxyribonucleic acid (DNA)** and know it to be the repository of our genes.

By 1900, biochemists knew the basic components of DNA—sugar, phosphate groups, and organic rings called nitrogenous bases—but they didn't have the technology to determine how these were put together. That understanding didn't come until 1953, in one of the twentieth century's most dramatic and important stories of scientific discovery (see Deeper Insight 4.1). The following description of DNA is largely the outcome of that work.

### 4.1a DNA Structure and Function

DNA is a long threadlike molecule with a uniform diameter of 2 nm, although its length varies greatly from the smallest to the largest chromosomes. Most human cells have 46 molecules of DNA totaling 2 m in length. This makes the average DNA molecule about 43 mm (almost 2 in.) long. To put this in perspective, imagine that an average DNA molecule was scaled up to the diameter of a utility pole (about 20 cm, or 8 in.). At this diameter, a pole proportionate to DNA would rise about 4,400 km (2,700 mi.) into space—far higher than the orbits of space shuttles (320–390 km) and the Hubble Space Telescope (600 km).

At the molecular level, DNA and other nucleic acids are polymers of **nucleotides.** A nucleotide consists of a sugar, a phosphate group, and a single- or double-ringed **nitrogenous base (fig. 4.1a).** Two of the bases in DNA—**cytosine (C)** and **thymine (T)**—have a single carbon–nitrogen ring and are classified as *pyrimidines* (py-RIM-ih-deens). The other two bases—**adenine (A)** and **guanine (G)**—have double rings and are classified as *purines* **(fig. 4.1b).**

The structure of DNA, commonly described as a *double helix,* resembles a spiral staircase **(fig. 4.2).** Each sidepiece is a backbone composed of phosphate groups alternating with the sugar *deoxyribose.* The steplike connections between the backbones are pairs of nitrogenous bases. The bases face the inside of the helix and hold the two backbones together with hydrogen bonds. Across from a purine on one backbone, there is a pyrimidine on the other. The pairing of each small, single-ringed pyrimidine with a large, double-ringed purine gives the DNA molecule its uniform 2 nm width.

A given purine cannot arbitrarily bind to just any pyrimidine. Adenine and thymine form two hydrogen bonds with each other, and guanine and cytosine form three, as shown in figure 4.2c. Therefore, where there is an A on one backbone, there is normally a T across from it, and every C is normally paired with a G. A—T and C—G are called the **base pairs.** The fact that one strand governs the base sequence of the other is called the **law of complementary base pairing.** It enables us to predict the base sequence of one strand if we know the sequence of the complementary strand.

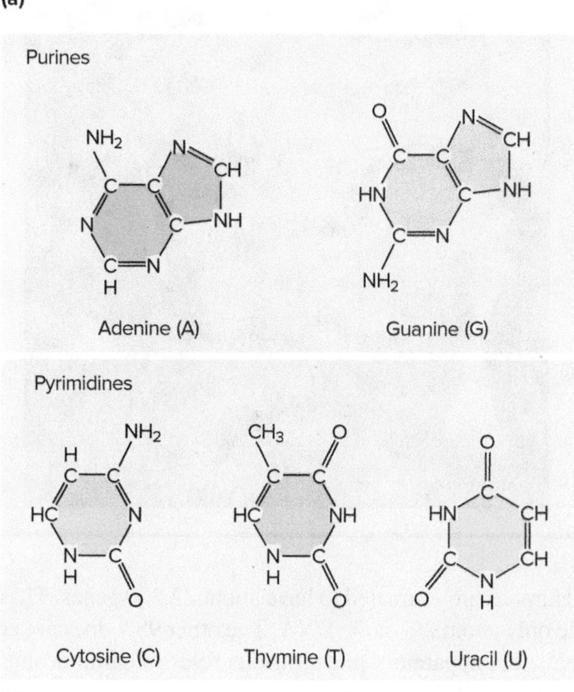


**FIGURE 4.1 Nucleotides and Nitrogenous Bases.** (a) The structure of a nucleotide, one of the monomers of DNA and RNA. In RNA, the sugar is ribose. (b) The five nitrogenous bases found in DNA and RNA.

*How would the uniform 2 nm diameter of DNA be affected if two purines or two pyrimidines could pair with each other?*

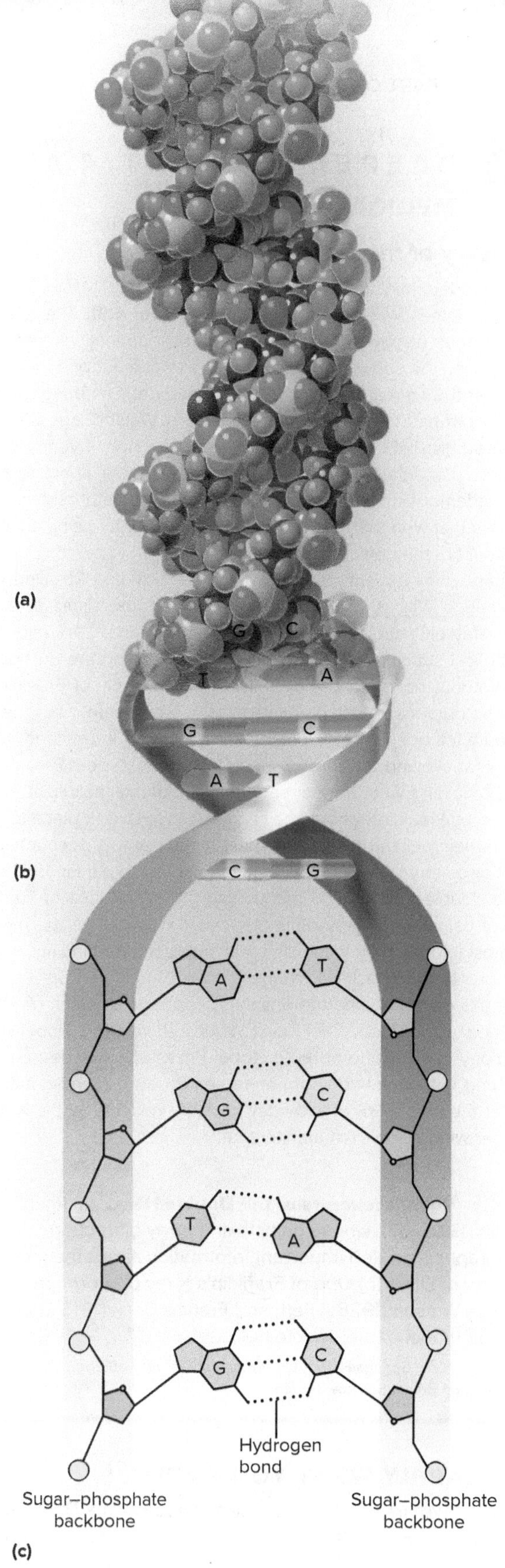


**FIGURE 4.2 DNA Structure.** (a) A molecular space-filling model of DNA giving some impression of its molecular geometry. (b) The "spiral staircase" structure. The two sugar–phosphate backbones twine around each other while complementary bases (colored bars) face each other on the inside of the double helix. (c) A small segment of DNA showing the composition of the backbone and complementary pairing of the nitrogenous bases.

## DEEPER INSIGHT 4.1
## MEDICAL HISTORY

### *Discovery of the Double Helix*

Credit for determining the double-helical structure of DNA has gone mainly to James Watson and Francis Crick **(fig. 4.3).** The events surrounding their discovery form one of the most dramatic stories of modern science—the subject of many books and at least one movie. When Watson and Crick came to share a laboratory at Cambridge University in 1951, both had barely begun their careers. Watson, age 23, had just completed his Ph.D. in the United States, and Crick, 11 years older, was a doctoral candidate in England. Yet the two were about to become the most famous molecular biologists of the twentieth century, and the discovery that won them such acclaim came without a single laboratory experiment of their own.

Others were fervently at work on DNA, including Rosalind Franklin and Maurice Wilkins at King's College in London. Using a technique called X-ray diffraction, Franklin had determined that DNA had a repetitious helical structure with sugar and phosphate on the outside of the helix. Without her permission, Wilkins showed one of Franklin's best X-ray photographs to Watson. Watson said, "The instant I saw the picture my mouth fell open and my pulse began to race." It provided a flash of insight that allowed the Watson and Crick team to beat Franklin to the goal. Combining what they already knew with the molecular geometry revealed by Franklin's photo, they were quickly able to piece together a scale model from cardboard and sheet metal that fully accounted for the known geometry of DNA. They rushed a paper into print in 1953 describing the double helix, barely mentioning the importance of Franklin's 2 years of painstaking X-ray diffraction work in unlocking the mystery of life's most important molecule. Franklin published her findings in a separate paper back to back with theirs.

For this discovery and the ensuing decade of research on DNA that it opened up, Watson, Crick, and Wilkins shared the Nobel Prize for Physiology or Medicine in 1962. Nobel Prizes are awarded only to the living, and in the final irony of her career, Rosalind Franklin had died in 1958, at the age of 37, of a cancer possibly induced by the X-rays that were her window on DNA architecture.

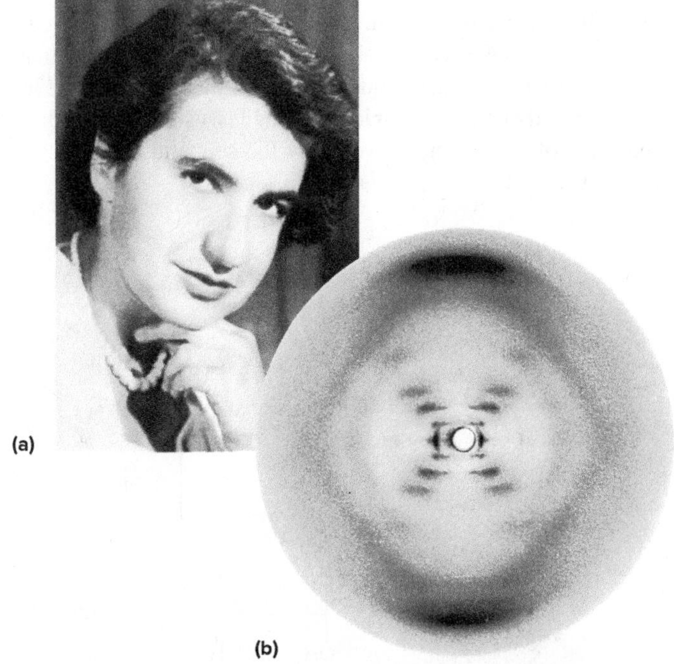

**FIGURE 4.3 Discoverers of the Double Helix.** (a) Rosalind Franklin (1920–58), whose painstaking X-ray diffraction photographs revealed important information about the molecular geometry of DNA. (b) One of Franklin's X-ray photographs. (c) James Watson (1928–) (left) and Francis Crick (1916–2004) with their model of the double helix.

**a:** Courtesy of Cold Springs Harbor Laboratory; **b:** Courtesy of King's College, London; **c:** A. Barrington Brown/Science Source

#### ▶▶▶ APPLY WHAT YOU KNOW

*What would be the base sequence of the DNA strand across from ATTGACTCG? If a DNA molecule was known to be 20% adenine, predict its percentage of cytosine and explain your answer.*

The essential function of DNA is to carry instructions, called *genes,* for the synthesis of proteins. At this point in the chapter, we will provisionally regard a gene as a segment of DNA that codes for a protein. Later, we shall have to confront the fact that this is an inadequate definition, and we'll examine the meaning of the word more deeply.

Humans are estimated to have about 22,300 genes. These constitute only about 2% of the DNA. The other 98% does not code for proteins, but apparently plays various roles in chromosome structure and regulation of gene activity.

### 4.1b Chromatin and Chromosomes

DNA doesn't exist as a naked double helix in the nucleus of a cell, but is complexed with proteins to form a fine filamentous material called **chromatin.** In most cells, the chromatin occurs as 46 long filaments called **chromosomes.** There is a stupendous amount of DNA in one nucleus—about 2 m (6 ft) of it in the first half of a cell's life cycle and twice as much when a cell has replicated its DNA in preparation for cell division. It is a prodigious feat to pack this much DNA into a nucleus only about 5 μm in diameter—and in such an orderly fashion that it doesn't become tangled, broken, and damaged beyond use.

In order to achieve such packing, DNA is extensively coiled and supercoiled. **Figure 4.4** shows the successive levels of this organization. The DNA first winds around spools of proteins called *histones* to form the little granules *(core particles)* visible in figure 4.4a. The chromatin then folds into successive zigzags, loops, and coils, getting thicker and shorter as it does so (fig. 4.4b). Ultimately the DNA, itself 2 nm in diameter, is consolidated into chromatin strands 150 times thicker and 1,000 times shorter than the naked DNA. Finally, each chromosome is packed into its own spheroidal region of the nucleus, called a *chromosome territory.* A chromosome territory is permeated with channels that allow regulatory chemicals to have access to the genes.

This is the state of the DNA in a nondividing cell. It's not a static structure, but changes from moment to moment according to the genetic activity of the cell as individual genes are turned on and off. Whole chromosomes migrate to new territories as a cell develops—for example, moving from the edge to the core of a nucleus as its genes are activated for a certain developmental task, or back to the nuclear lamina to silence some genes. This allows genes on different chromosomes to partner with each other in bringing about developmental changes in the cell.

When a cell is preparing to divide, it makes an exact copy of all its nuclear DNA by a process described later, increasing its allotment to about 4 m of DNA. Each chromosome then consists of two parallel filaments called **sister chromatids.** In the early stage of cell division *(prophase),* these chromatids coil some more until each one becomes, at its most compact, 10,000 times shorter but 350 times thicker than the DNA double helix. Only now are the chromosomes thick enough to be seen with a light microscope. This compaction not only allows the 4 m of DNA to

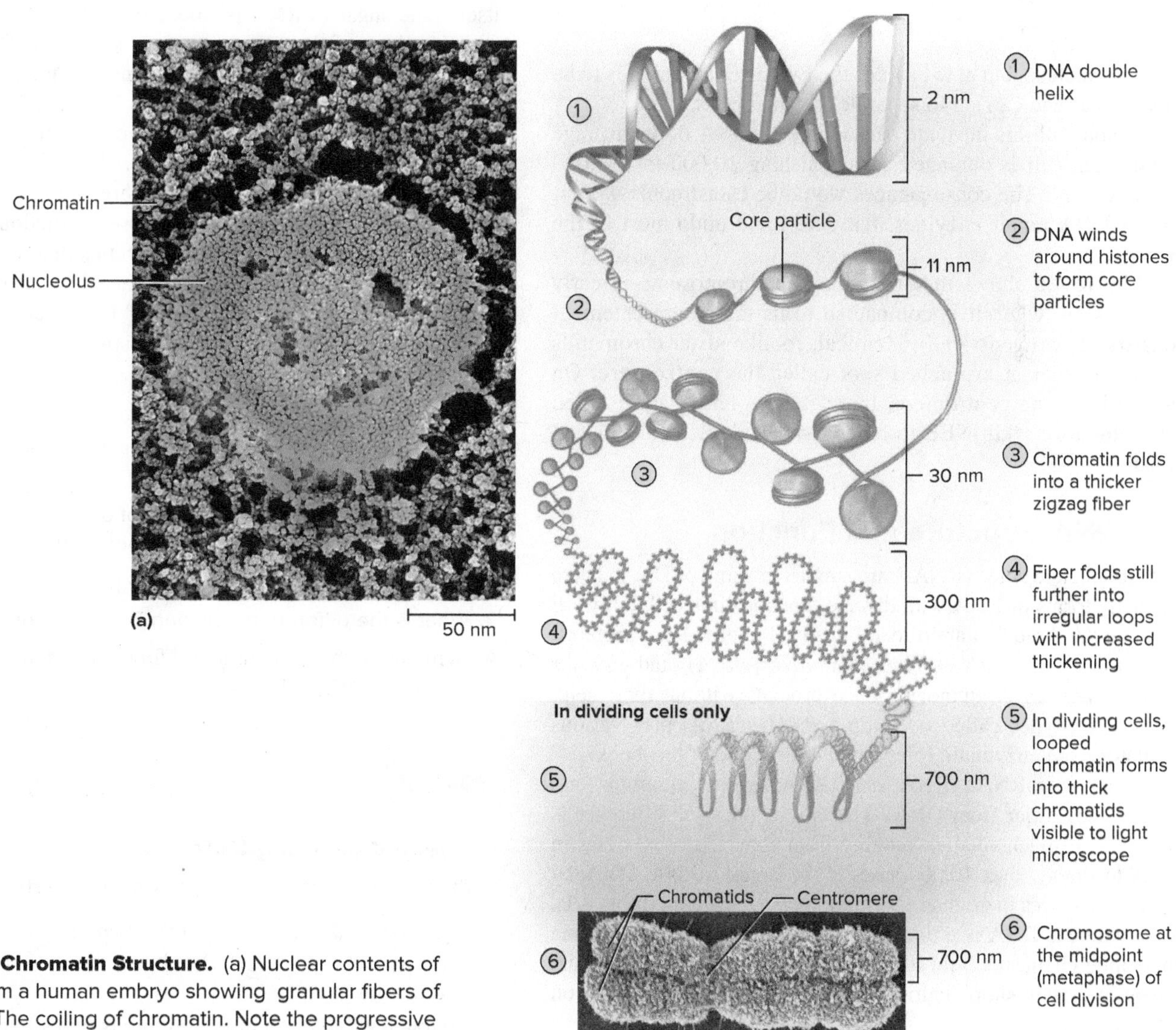
Chromatin
Nucleolus
(a)
50 nm
① DNA double helix
2 nm
Core particle
② DNA winds around histones to form core particles
11 nm
③ Chromatin folds into a thicker zigzag fiber
30 nm
④ Fiber folds still further into irregular loops with increased thickening
300 nm
In dividing cells only
⑤ In dividing cells, looped chromatin forms into thick chromatids visible to light microscope
700 nm
Chromatids
Centromere
⑥ Chromosome at the midpoint (metaphase) of cell division
700 nm
(b)

**FIGURE 4.4 Chromatin Structure.** (a) Nuclear contents of a germ cell from a human embryo showing granular fibers of chromatin. (b) The coiling of chromatin. Note the progressive thickening of the fiber from top to bottom.

a: P. Motta & T. Naguro/SPL/Science Source; b: Biophoto Associates/Science Source

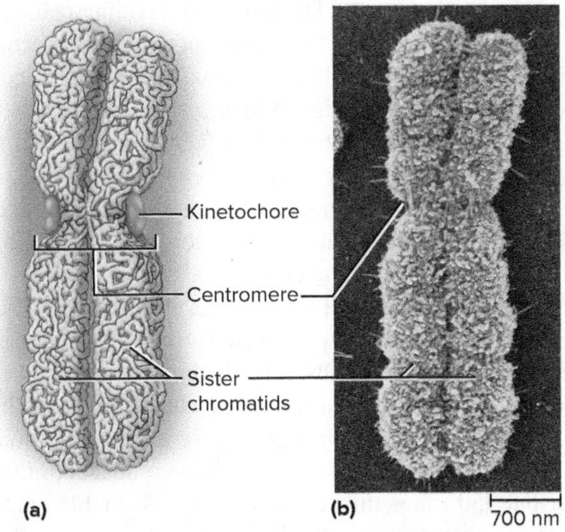


**FIGURE 4.5 Chromosome Structure at Metaphase.** (a) Drawing of a metaphase chromosome. (b) Scanning electron micrograph.

b: Biophoto Associates/Science Source

| TABLE 4.1 | Comparison of DNA and RNA | |
|---|---|---|
| **Feature** | **DNA** | **RNA** |
| Sugar | Deoxyribose | Ribose |
| Types of nitrogenous bases | A, T, C, G | A, U, C, G |
| Number of nitrogenous bases | Averages $10^8$ base pairs | 70–10,000 bases, mostly unpaired |
| Number of nucleotide chains | Two (double helix) | One |
| Site of action | Functions in nucleus; cannot leave | Leaves nucleus; functions mainly in cytoplasm |
| Function | Codes for synthesis of RNA and protein | Carries out the instructions in DNA; assembles proteins |

fit in the nucleus, but also enables the two sister chromatids to be pulled apart and carried to separate daughter cells.

Despite all this intricate packaging, the DNA of the average mammalian cell is damaged an astonishing 10,000 to 100,000 times per day! The consequences would be catastrophic were it not for DNA repair enzymes that detect and undo most of the damage.

**Figure 4.5** shows the structure of a chromosome in early cell division, when it is compacted to its maximum extent. It consists of two genetically identical, rodlike sister chromatids joined together at a pinched spot called the **centromere.** On each side of the centromere, there is a protein plaque called a **kinetochore**[1] (kih-NEE-to-core), which plays a role in cell division.

## 4.1c RNA Structure and Function

The ribonucleic acids (RNAs) are smaller cousins of DNA. There are many forms of RNA with diverse functions in a cell, but we'll focus on the three that are directly involved in producing proteins: *messenger RNA (mRNA), ribosomal RNA (rRNA),* and *transfer RNA (tRNA).* DNA cannot produce proteins without their help. Other RNA types called *noncoding RNA (ncRNA)* play various regulatory and enzymatic roles beyond the scope of this book.

What do mRNA, rRNA, and tRNA have in common, and how do they differ from DNA? The most significant difference is that RNA is much smaller, ranging from about 70 to 90 bases in tRNA to slightly over 10,000 bases in the largest mRNA. DNA, by contrast, averages more than 100 million base pairs long **(table 4.1).** Also, whereas DNA is a double helix, RNA consists of only one nucleotide chain, not held together by complementary base pairs except in certain short regions where the molecule folds back on itself. The sugar in RNA is ribose instead of deoxyribose. RNA contains three of the same nitrogenous bases as DNA—adenine, cytosine, and guanine—but it has no thymine; a base called **uracil (U)** takes its place (see fig. 4.1b). Transfer RNA has more than 50 different nitrogenous bases, but for our purposes, we don't need to consider any except A, U, C, and G.

The essential function of the three principal RNAs is to interpret the code in DNA and use those instructions to synthesize proteins. RNA is a disposable molecule that works mainly in the cytoplasm, while DNA is irreplaceable and remains safely behind in the nucleus, "giving orders" from there. This process is described in the next section of the chapter.

[1]*kineto* = motion; *chore* = place

**BEFORE YOU GO ON**

Answer the following questions to test your understanding of the preceding section:

1. What are the three components of a nucleotide? Which component varies from one nucleotide to another in DNA?
2. What governs the pattern of base pairing in DNA?
3. What is the difference between DNA and chromatin?
4. Summarize the structural and functional differences between DNA and RNA.

## 4.2 Genes and Their Action

### Expected Learning Outcomes

When you have completed this section, you should be able to

a. give a working definition of the *gene* and explain why new discoveries in genetics have changed our concept of what a gene is;
b. explain what the human genome is and what relationship it has to the health sciences;

c. define *genetic code* and describe how DNA codes for protein structure;
d. describe the process of assembling amino acids to form a protein;
e. explain what happens to a protein after its amino acid sequence has been synthesized;
f. describe some ways that a gene can be turned on or off; and
g. explain how DNA indirectly regulates the synthesis of nonprotein molecules.

## 4.2a What Is a Gene?

As much as biologists talk about genes, the term is devilishly difficult to define. The classical concept of the gene, rooted in Mendel's studies of heredity in peas, was that it is an abstract "unit of heredity" by which a trait passes from parent to offspring. Following discovery of the double helix, molecular biologists worked out the *genetic code* contained in the four bases of DNA and considered a gene to be a segment of the DNA that carries the code for a particular protein. Now, however, we know that the human body has millions of different proteins but only 22,300 protein-coding genes; obviously there isn't a separate gene for every protein. In addition, we know now that several human genes produce only ncRNA molecules that never go on to direct the synthesis of a protein; RNA is their final product. Other recent discoveries have complicated our concept of the gene still more—genes overlapping each other, so some segments of DNA belong to two different genes; short genes embedded within longer ones; multiple related proteins encoded by a single gene; and other unexpected arrangements. As molecular biologists have learned more and more about DNA, the definition of the gene has become more and more frayed around the edges.

For the purposes of this introductory book, however, we can settle for an approximate meaning. We will define ***gene*** as an information-containing segment of DNA that codes for the production of a molecule of RNA, which in most cases goes on to play a role in the synthesis of one or more proteins. The amino acid sequence of a protein is determined by a nucleotide sequence in the DNA.

The 46 human chromosomes come in two sets of 23 each, one set from each parent. Some of these are gene-rich, such as chromosomes 17, 19, and 22, whereas others are gene-poor, such as 4, 8, 13, 18, 21, and the Y chromosome (see fig. 4.16). All the DNA, both coding and noncoding, in one 23-chromosome set is called the **genome.** The total genome consists of about 3.1 billion nucleotide pairs. Individual genes average about 3,000 nucleotides long, but range up to 2.4 million. Most genes are identical in every human being. All humans, worldwide, are at least 99.99% genetically identical, but even the 0.01% variation means that we can differ from one another in more than 3 million base pairs. Various combinations of these **single-nucleotide polymorphisms**[2] account for all human genetic variation.

**Genomics** is a relatively young science concerned with the comprehensive study of the genome and how its genes and noncoding DNA affect the structure and function of the organism. Among the other fruits of this research, we now know the chromosomal locations of more than 1,400 disease-producing mutations. This information has opened the door to a branch of medical diagnosis and therapy called **genomic medicine** (see Deeper Insight 4.2).

[2]*poly* = multiple; *morph* = form

### DEEPER INSIGHT 4.2
### CLINICAL APPLICATION

#### *Genomic Medicine*

*Genomic medicine* is the application of our knowledge of the genome to the prediction, diagnosis, and treatment of disease. It is relevant to disorders as diverse as cancer, Alzheimer disease, schizophrenia, obesity, and even a person's susceptibility to nonhereditary diseases such as AIDS and tuberculosis.

Genomic technology has advanced to the point that for less than $1,000, one can have one's entire genome scanned for markers of disease risk. Why would anyone want to? Because knowing one's genome could dramatically change clinical care. It may allow clinicians to forecast a person's risk of disease and to predict its course; mutations in a single gene can affect the severity of such diseases as hemophilia, muscular dystrophy, cancer, and cystic fibrosis. Genomics should also allow for earlier detection of diseases and for earlier, more effective clinical intervention. Drugs that are safe for most people can have serious side effects in others, owing to genetic variations in drug metabolism. Genomics has begun providing a basis for choosing the safest or most effective drugs and for adjusting dosages for different patients on the basis of their genetic makeup.

Knowing the sites of disease-producing mutations expands the potential for *gene-substitution therapy.* This is a procedure in which cells are removed from a patient with a genetic disorder, supplied with a normal gene in place of the defective one, and reintroduced to the body. The hope is that these genetically modified cells will proliferate and provide the patient with a gene product that he or she was lacking—perhaps insulin for a patient with diabetes or a blood-clotting factor for a patient with hemophilia. Researchers are currently exploring a new gene-editing technology called *CRISPR-Cas9* that enables one to locate a specific gene in the DNA and remove or replace it. Clinical applicability and safety were still under investigation and in early clinical trials as this textbook edition was written.

Genomics is introducing new problems in medical ethics and law. Should your genome be a private matter between you and your physician? Should an insurance company be entitled to know your genome before issuing health or life insurance to you so it can know your risk of contracting a catastrophic illness, adjust the cost of your coverage, or even deny coverage? Should a prospective employer have the right to know your genome before offering employment? These are areas in which biology, politics, and law converge to shape public policy.

### 4.2b The Genetic Code

It seems remarkable that the body can make millions of different proteins (called the **proteome**), all from the same 20 amino acids and all encoded by genes made of just 4 nucleotides (A, T, C, G). This is a striking illustration of how a great variety of complex structures can be made from a small variety of simpler components. The **genetic code** is a system that enables these 4 nucleotides to code for the amino acid sequences of all proteins.

It's not unusual for simple codes to represent complex information. Computers store and transmit complex information, including pictures and sounds, in a binary code with only the symbols 1 and 0. Thus, it should not be surprising that a mere 20 amino acids can be represented by a code of 4 nucleotides; all this requires is to combine these symbols in varied ways. It requires more than 2 nucleotides to code for each amino acid, because the A, U, C, and G of mRNA can combine in only 16 different pairs (AA, AU, AC, AG, UA, UU, and so on). The minimum code to symbolize 20 amino acids is 3 nucleotides per amino acid, and indeed, this is the case in DNA. A sequence of 3 DNA nucleotides that stands for 1 amino acid is called a **base triplet.** When messenger RNA is produced, it carries a coded message based on these DNA triplets. A 3-base sequence in mRNA is called a **codon.** The genetic code is expressed in terms of codons.

**Table 4.2** shows a few illuminating examples of how the DNA triplets relate to the mRNA codons and how those, in turn, relate to the amino acids of a protein (see appendix D for the entire genetic code). You can see from the table that sometimes two or more codons represent the same amino acid. The reason for this is easy to explain mathematically. Four symbols *(N)* taken three at a time *(x)* can be combined in $N^x$ different ways; that is, there are $4^3 = 64$ possible codons available to represent the 20 amino acids.

Only 61 of these, however, code for amino acids. The other 3 —UAG, UGA, and UAA—are called **stop codons;** they signal "end of message," like the period at the end of a sentence. A stop codon enables the cell's protein-synthesizing machinery to sense that it has reached the end of the instruction for a particular protein. The codon AUG plays two roles: It serves as a code for methionine and as a **start codon.** This dual function is explained shortly.

**TABLE 4.2 Examples of the Genetic Code***

| Base Triplet of DNA | Codon of mRNA | Name of Amino Acid | Abbreviation for Amino Acid |
|---|---|---|---|
| CCT | GGA | Glycine | Gly |
| CCA | GGU | Glycine | Gly |
| CCC | GGG | Glycine | Gly |
| CGA | GCU | Alanine | Ala |
| CGT | GCA | Alanine | Ala |
| TGG | ACC | Threonine | Thr |
| TGC | ACG | Threonine | Thr |
| GTA | CAU | Histidine | His |
| TAC | AUG | Methionine | Met |

*For the complete genetic code, see appendix D.

### 4.2c Protein Synthesis

We can now move on to an understanding of how DNA and RNA collaborate to produce proteins. Before studying the details, however, it will be helpful to consider the big picture. In brief, the genetic code in DNA specifies which proteins a cell can make. All the body's cells except the sex cells and some immune cells contain identical genes. However, different genes are activated in different cells; for example, genes for digestive enzymes are active in stomach cells but not in muscle cells. Any given cell uses only one-third to two-thirds of its genes; the rest remain dormant in that cell, but may be functional in other types of cells.

When a gene is activated, a **messenger RNA (mRNA)** is made—a mirror image of the gene, more or less. Most mRNA migrates from the nucleus to the cytoplasm, where it serves as a code for assembling amino acids in the right order to make a particular protein. In summary, you can think of the process of protein synthesis as DNA ⟶ mRNA ⟶ protein, with each arrow reading as "codes for the production of." The step from DNA to mRNA is called *transcription,* and the step from mRNA to protein is called *translation.* Transcription occurs in the nucleus, where the DNA is. Most translation occurs in the cytoplasm, but 10% to 15% of proteins may be synthesized in the nucleus, with both steps occurring there.

#### Transcription

DNA is too large to leave the nucleus and participate directly in cytoplasmic protein synthesis. It is necessary, therefore, to make a small mRNA copy that can migrate through a nuclear pore into the cytoplasm. Just as we might transcribe (copy) a document, **transcription** in genetics means the process of copying genetic instructions from DNA to RNA. An enzyme called **RNA polymerase** (po-LIM-ur-ase) binds to the DNA and assembles the RNA. It opens up the DNA helix about 17 base pairs at a time, reading the bases from one strand of the DNA and making a corresponding RNA. Where it finds a C on the DNA, it adds G to the RNA; where it finds an A, it adds U; and so forth. The enzyme then rewinds the DNA helix behind it. Another RNA polymerase may follow closely behind the first one; thus, a gene may be transcribed by several polymerase molecules at once, and numerous copies of the same RNA are made. At the end of the gene is a base sequence that serves as a terminator, which signals the polymerase to stop.

The RNA produced by transcription is an "immature" form called *pre-mRNA.* This molecule contains segments called *exons* that will be translated into a protein, and segments called *introns* that are removed before translation. Enzymes cut out the introns and splice the exons together into a functional mRNA molecule, which then usually leaves the nucleus. It may help you in remembering these if you think of *in*trons being removed while still *in* the nucleus and the *ex*ons being *ex*ported from the nucleus to

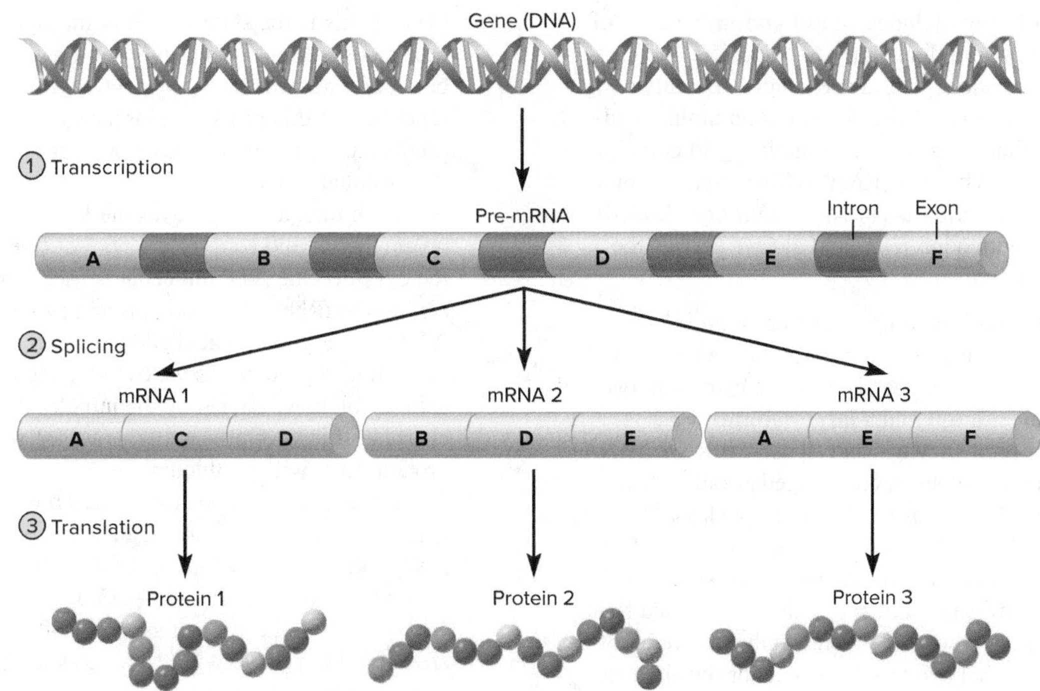


**FIGURE 4.6 Alternative Splicing of mRNA.** By splicing together different combinations of exons from a single pre-mRNA, a cell can generate multiple proteins from a single gene.

undergo translation in the cytoplasm. The introns are not entirely useless, but code for a variety of regulatory RNAs.

Through a mechanism called *alternative splicing,* one gene can code for more than one protein. Suppose a gene produced a pre-mRNA containing six exons separated by noncoding introns. As shown in **figure 4.6,** these exons can be spliced together in various combinations to yield codes for two or more proteins. This is a partial explanation of how the body can produce millions of different proteins with little more than 22,000 genes.

## Translation

Just as we might translate a work from Spanish into English, genetic **translation** converts the language of nucleotides into the language of amino acids. This job is carried out by the following participants:

1. **Messenger RNA (mRNA),** which carries the genetic code from the nucleus to the cytoplasm. During its synthesis in the nucleus, mRNA acquires a protein cap that acts like a passport, permitting it to pass through a nuclear pore into the cytosol. The cap also acts as a recognition site that tells a ribosome where to begin translation.
2. **Transfer RNA (tRNA),** a relatively small RNA whose job is to bind a free amino acid in the cytosol and deliver it to the ribosome to be added to a growing protein chain. tRNA is a single-stranded molecule that turns back and coils on itself to form an angular L shape **(fig. 4.7).** One

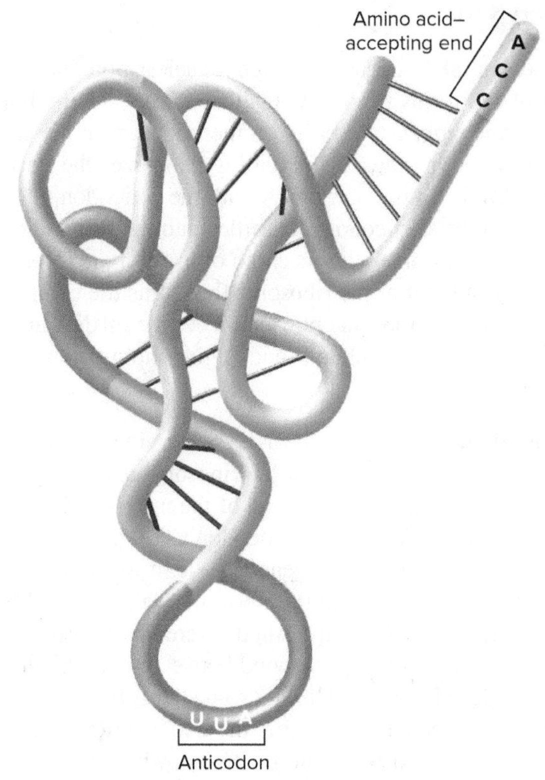


**FIGURE 4.7 Transfer RNA (tRNA).**

loop of the molecule includes an **anticodon,** a series of three nucleotides complementary to a specific codon of mRNA. For the codon AUG, for example, the anticodon is UAC. The other end of the tRNA has an amino acid–accepting end that binds a specific amino acid corresponding to that codon. The first tRNA to bind to a ribosome at the start of translation is called the *initiator tRNA.* It always has the anticodon UAC and always carries the amino acid methionine.

3. **Ribosomes,** the little "reading machines" found in the cytosol and on the outside of the rough ER and nuclear envelope. Inactive ribosomes occur in the cytosol in two pieces—a **small subunit** and a **large subunit.** Each is composed of several enzymes and ribosomal RNA (rRNA) molecules. The two subunits come together only when translating mRNA. A ribosome has three pockets that serve as binding sites for tRNA. In the course of translation, a tRNA usually binds first to the *A site* on one side of the ribosome, then shifts to the *P site* in the middle, and finally to the *E site* on the other side. To remember the order of these sites, it may help you to think of *A* for the site that *accepts* a new amino acid; *P* for the site that carries the growing *protein;* and *E* for *exit.* (*A* and *P* actually stand for *aminoacyl* and *peptidyl* sites.)

Translation occurs in three steps called *initiation, elongation,* and *termination.* These are shown in **figure 4.8,** panels 1 through 3; panel 4 illustrates a further aspect of the production of proteins destined to be packaged into lysosomes or secretory vesicles.

(1) **Initiation.** mRNA passes through a nuclear pore into the cytosol and forms a loop. A small ribosomal subunit binds to a *leader sequence* of bases on the mRNA near the cap, then slides along the mRNA until it recognizes the start codon AUG. An initiator tRNA with the anticodon UAC pairs with the start codon and settles into the P (middle) site of the ribosome with its cargo of methionine (Met). The large subunit of the ribosome then joins the complex. The assembled ribosome now embraces the mRNA in a groove between the subunits and begins sliding along it, reading its bases.

(2) **Elongation.** The next tRNA arrives, carrying another amino acid; it binds to the A site of the ribosome and its anticodon pairs with the second codon of the mRNA—GCU, for example. A tRNA with the anticodon CGA would bind here, and according to the genetic code, it would carry alanine (Ala). An enzyme in the ribosome transfers the Met of the initiator tRNA to the Ala delivered by the second tRNA and creates a peptide bond between them, giving us a dipeptide, Met—Ala. The ribosome then slides down to read the next codon. This shifts the initiator tRNA (now carrying no amino acid) into the E site, where it leaves the ribosome. The second tRNA (now carrying Met—Ala) shifts into the P site. The now-vacant A site binds a third tRNA. Suppose the next codon is ACG. A tRNA with anticodon UGC would bind here, and would carry threonine (Thr). (This is the state shown in the figure.) The ribosome transfers the Met—Ala to the Thr, creates another peptide bond, and we now have a tripeptide, Met—Ala—Thr. By repetition of this process, a larger and larger protein is produced. As the protein elongates, it folds into its three-dimensional shape.

Each time a tRNA leaves the E site, it goes off to pick up another amino acid from a pool of free amino acids in the cytosol. One ATP molecule is used in binding the amino acid to the tRNA; therefore, protein synthesis consumes one ATP for every amino acid added to the chain.

All new proteins, as we can see, begin with the amino acid methionine, carried by the initiator tRNA. This is often cleaved off in later processing, however, so not every finished protein starts with methionine.

Codon–anticodon pairing is less precise than just depicted; it tolerates some mismatches, especially at the third base of the codon. Therefore, UGC isn't necessarily the only anticodon that can pair with ACG. Due to this imprecision or "wobble" in the system, as few as 48 different tRNAs are needed to pair up with the 61 codons that represent the amino acids.

(3) **Termination.** When the ribosome reaches a stop codon, its A site binds a protein called a *release factor* instead of a tRNA. The release factor causes the finished protein to break away from the ribosome. The ribosome then dissociates into its two subunits, but since these are now so close to the mRNA's leader sequence, they often reassemble on the same mRNA and repeat the process, making another copy of the same protein.

(4) **Making proteins for packaging or export.** If a protein is to be packaged into a lysosome or secreted from the cell (such as a digestive enzyme), the ribosome docks on the rough endoplasmic reticulum and the new protein spools off into the cistern of the ER instead of into the cytosol. The ER modifies this protein and packages it into *transport vesicles* whose destiny we will examine later.

One ribosome can work very rapidly, adding about two to six amino acids per second. Most proteins take from 20 seconds to several minutes to make. But a ribosome doesn't work at the task alone. After one ribosome moves away from the leader sequence, another one often binds there and begins the process, following along behind the first—and then another and another, so that a single mRNA is commonly translated by 10 or 20 ribosomes at once. This cluster of ribosomes, all translating the same mRNA, is called a **polyribosome** (see the photo on the opening page of this chapter). The farther along the mRNA each ribosome is, the longer is the protein spooling from it. Not only is each mRNA translated by all these ribosomes at once, but a cell may have 300,000 identical mRNA molecules, each being simultaneously translated by some 20 ribosomes. With so many "factory workers" doing the same task, a cell may produce over 100,000 protein molecules per second—a remarkably productive factory! As much as 25% of the dry weight of liver cells, which are highly active in protein synthesis, consists of ribosomes.

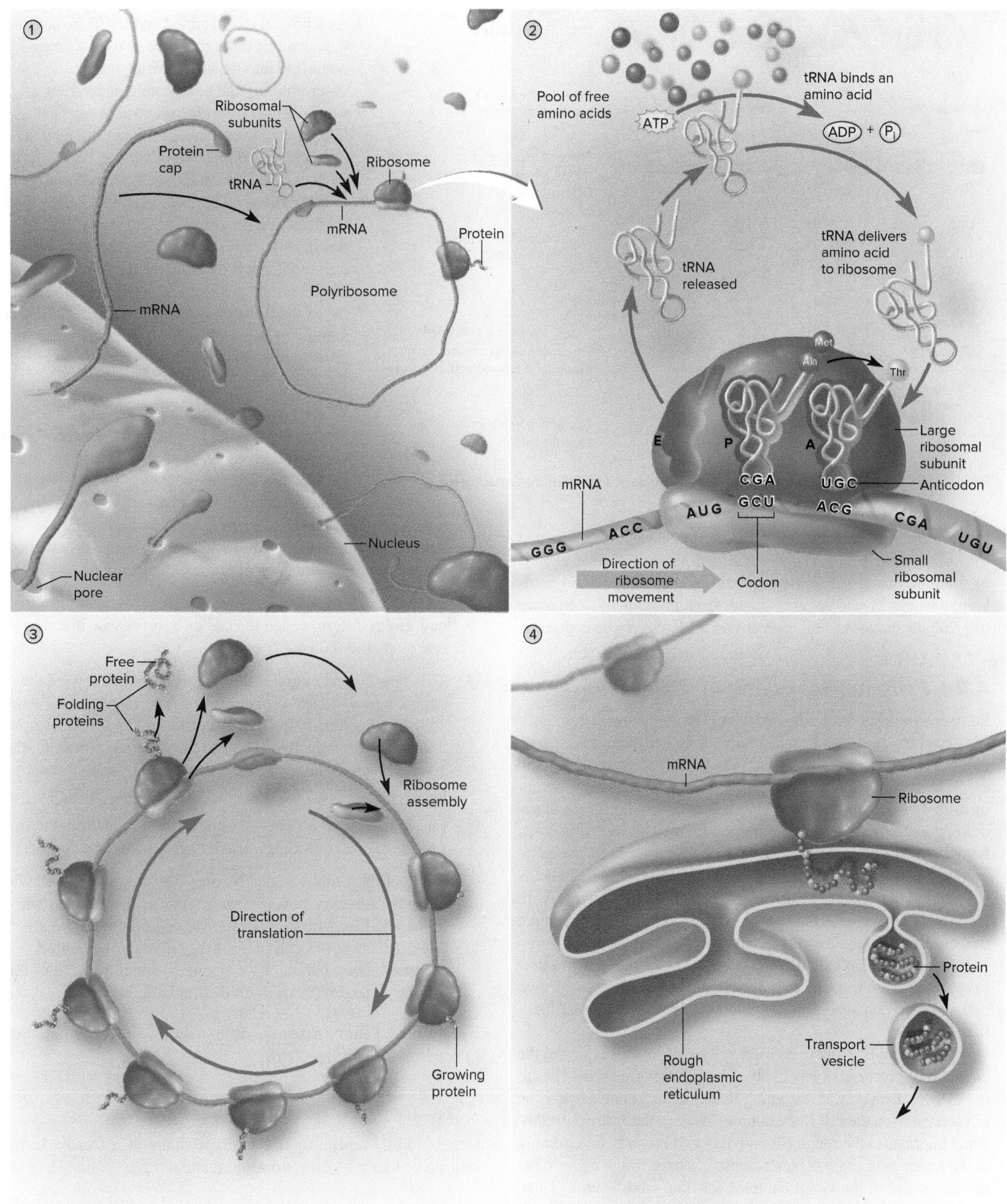


**FIGURE 4.8 Translation of mRNA.** See the text for explanation of the processes occurring at each step.

? *Why would translation not work if ribosomes could bind only one tRNA at a time?*

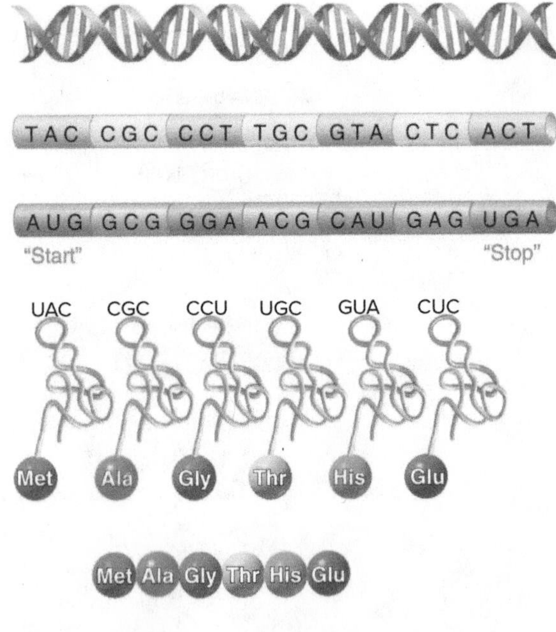


FIGURE 4.9 **Relationship of a DNA Base Sequence to Peptide Structure.**

**Figure 4.9** summarizes transcription and translation and shows how a nucleotide sequence translates to a hypothetical peptide of 6 amino acids. An average protein is about 400 amino acids long; it would have to be represented, at a minimum, by a sequence of 1,203 nucleotides (3 for each amino acid, plus a stop codon).

## 4.2d Protein Processing and Secretion

Protein synthesis isn't finished when its amino acid sequence (primary structure) has been assembled. To be functional, it must coil or fold into precise secondary and tertiary structures; in some cases, it associates with other protein chains (quaternary structure) or binds with a nonprotein such as a vitamin or carbohydrate. As a new protein is assembled by a ribosome, it is often bound by an older protein called a **chaperone.** The chaperone guides the new protein in folding into the proper shape and helps to prevent improper associations between different proteins. As in the colloquial sense of the word, a chaperone is an older protein that escorts and regulates the behavior of the "youngsters." Some chaperones are also called *stress proteins* or *heat shock proteins* because they're produced in response to heat or other stress on a cell and help damaged proteins fold back into their correct functional shapes.

If a protein is going to be used in the cytosol (for example, the enzymes of glycolysis), it is likely to be made by free ribosomes in the cytosol. However, if it is going to be packaged into a lysosome or secreted from the cell (for example, insulin), the entire polyribosome migrates to the rough ER and docks on its surface. Assembly of the amino acid chain is then completed on the rough ER, and the protein is sent to the Golgi complex for final modification. Thus, we turn to the functions of the ER and Golgi in the processing and secretion of a protein. Compare the following description to **figure 4.10.**

1. As a protein is assembled on the ER surface, it threads itself through a pore in the ER membrane and into the cistern. Enzymes in the cistern modify the new protein in a variety of ways—removing some amino acid segments, folding the protein and stabilizing it with disulfide bridges, adding carbohydrates, and so forth. Such changes are called **posttranslational modification.** Insulin, for example, is first synthesized as a protein 86 amino acids long. In posttranslational modification, the chain folds back on itself, 3 disulfide bridges are formed, and 35 amino acids are removed from the middle of the protein. The final insulin molecule is therefore made of 2 chains of 21 and 30 amino acids held together by disulfide bridges (see fig. 2.25).
2. When the rough ER is finished with a protein, it pinches off bubblelike **transport vesicles** coated with a protein called *clathrin.* Clathrin apparently helps to select the proteins to be transported in the vesicles, and as a basketlike cage, it helps to mold the forming vesicles. Soon after the vesicles detach from the ER, they fuse into irregularly shaped clusters that carry their cargo to the Golgi complex.
3. As they reach the complex, these clusters fuse and form a new Golgi cistern, called the *cis*[3] cistern because it is the one closest to the ER.
4. This new cistern migrates through the complex toward the opposite *(trans)* face. It matures as it travels, producing new enzymes that modify the cargo in different ways. For example, it may add carbohydrate chains to the proteins, producing the *glycoproteins* mentioned in section 2.4c. Thyroid-stimulating hormone is one such glycoprotein made in this way.
5. Finally, the *trans*[4] cistern—the one farthest away from the ER—breaks up into Golgi vesicles laden with the cell product.
6. Some of the Golgi vesicles become lysosomes, while others become **secretory vesicles** that migrate to the plasma membrane and fuse with it, releasing the cell product by exocytosis. This is how a cell of a salivary gland, for example, secretes mucus and digestive enzymes, and how a cell of the pituitary gland releases thyroid-stimulating hormone.

**Table 4.3** summarizes the diverse destinations and functions of newly synthesized proteins.

## 4.2e Gene Regulation

Genes don't simply produce their products at a steady, incessant pace, like a 24-hour nonstop manufacturing plant. They are

[3]*cis* = on the same side
[4]*trans* = across from

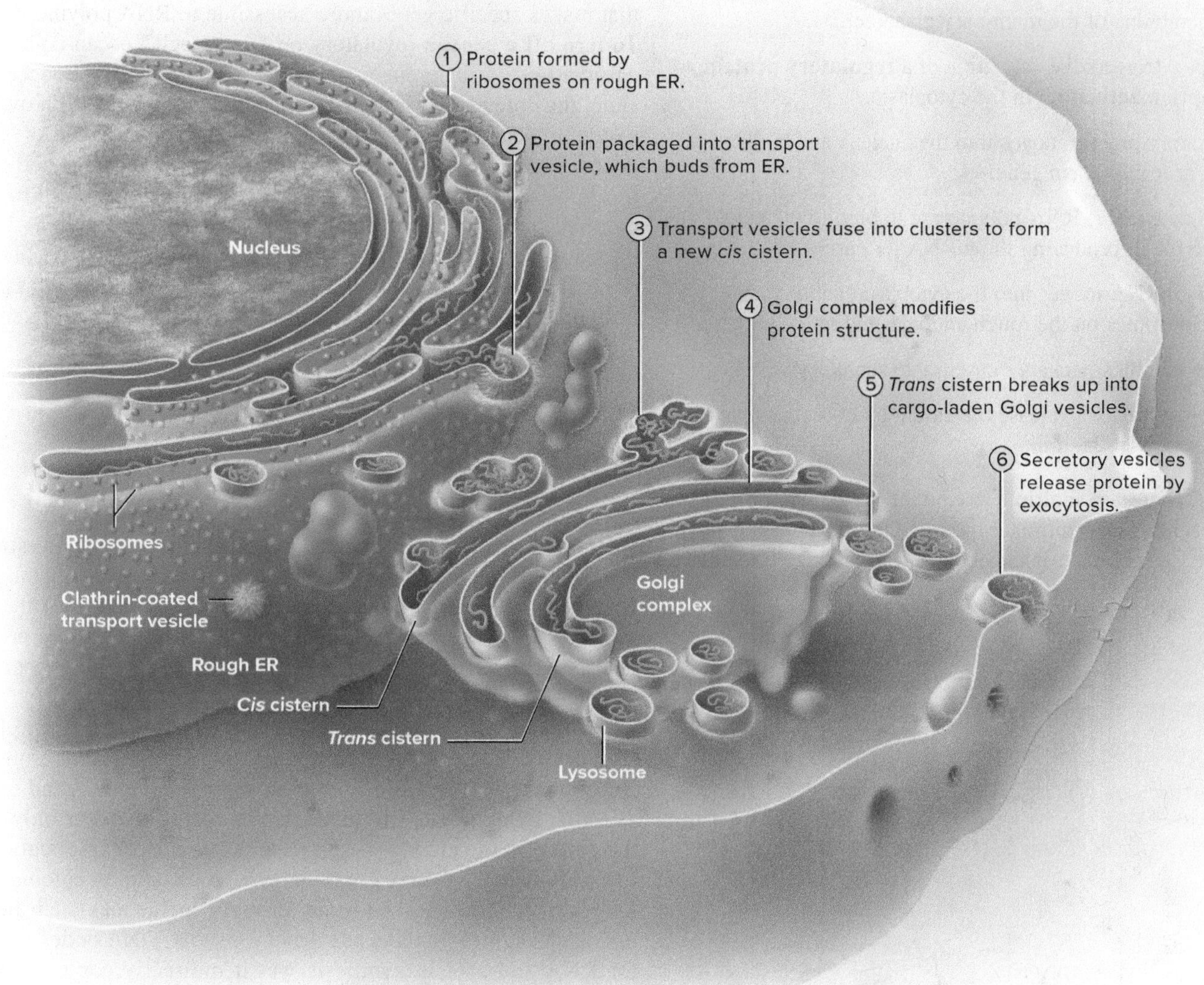

① Protein formed by ribosomes on rough ER.
② Protein packaged into transport vesicle, which buds from ER.
③ Transport vesicles fuse into clusters to form a new cis cistern.
④ Golgi complex modifies protein structure.
⑤ Trans cistern breaks up into cargo-laden Golgi vesicles.
⑥ Secretory vesicles release protein by exocytosis.
Nucleus
Ribosomes
Clathrin-coated transport vesicle
Rough ER
Cis cistern
Trans cistern
Golgi complex
Lysosome

**FIGURE 4.10 Protein Processing and Secretion.** See the text for further explanation of the numbered steps.

turned on and off from day to day, even hour to hour, as their products are needed or not, and many genes are permanently turned off in any given cell. The genes for hemoglobin and digestive enzymes, for example, are present but inactive in liver cells and skin cells.

There are several ways to turn genes on or off. We cannot consider all of them here, but an example can convey the general principle. Consider a woman who has just given birth to her first baby. In the ensuing days, the hormone *prolactin* stimulates cells of her mammary glands to synthesize the various components of breast milk, including the protein *casein*—something her body has never synthesized before. How is the gene for casein turned on at this point in her life? **Figure 4.11** shows the steps leading from prolactin stimulation to casein secretion.

**TABLE 4.3 Some Destinations and Functions of Newly Synthesized Proteins**

| Destination or Function | Proteins (Examples) |
|---|---|
| Deposited as a structural protein within cells | Actin of cytoskeleton; keratin of epidermis |
| Used in the cytosol as a metabolic enzyme | ATPase; kinases |
| Returned to the nucleus for use in nuclear metabolism | Histones of chromatin; RNA polymerase |
| Packaged in lysosomes for autophagy, intracellular digestion, and other functions | Numerous lysosomal enzymes |
| Delivered to other organelles for intracellular use | Catalase of peroxisomes; mitochondrial enzymes |
| Delivered to plasma membrane to serve transport and other functions | Hormone receptors; sodium–potassium pumps |
| Secreted by exocytosis for extracellular functions | Digestive enzymes; casein of breast milk |

1. Prolactin binds to its receptor, a pair of proteins in the plasma membrane of the mammary gland cell.
2. The receptor triggers the activation of a **regulatory protein (transcription activator)** in the cytoplasm.
3. The regulatory protein moves into the nucleus and binds to the DNA near the casein gene.
4. This binding enables RNA polymerase to bind to the gene and transcribe it, producing the mRNA for casein.
5. The casein mRNA moves into the cytoplasm and is translated by ribosomes on the rough endoplasmic reticulum.
6. The Golgi complex packages casein into secretory vesicles.
7. The secretory vesicles release the casein by exocytosis, and it becomes part of the milk.

At step 4, there are multiple ways that regulatory proteins can activate gene transcription. Some of them attract and position RNA polymerase so it can begin transcribing the gene. Others modify the coiling of DNA in a nucleosome in a way that makes specific genes more accessible to RNA polymerase. To turn off a gene, a regulatory protein or ncRNA can coil the chromatin in a different way that makes the gene less accessible, thus preventing transcription. Moving the chromatin over to the nuclear lamina is another way of silencing some of its genes. There are several additional ways, beyond the scope of this book, for inducing or halting the production of a gene product, but the casein example shows how a certain gene may lie dormant in a person until, only a few times in one's life (and only if one bears children), it is activated by a stimulus such as a hormonal signal. Section 4.4h describes a further aspect of gene regulation called *epigenetics*.

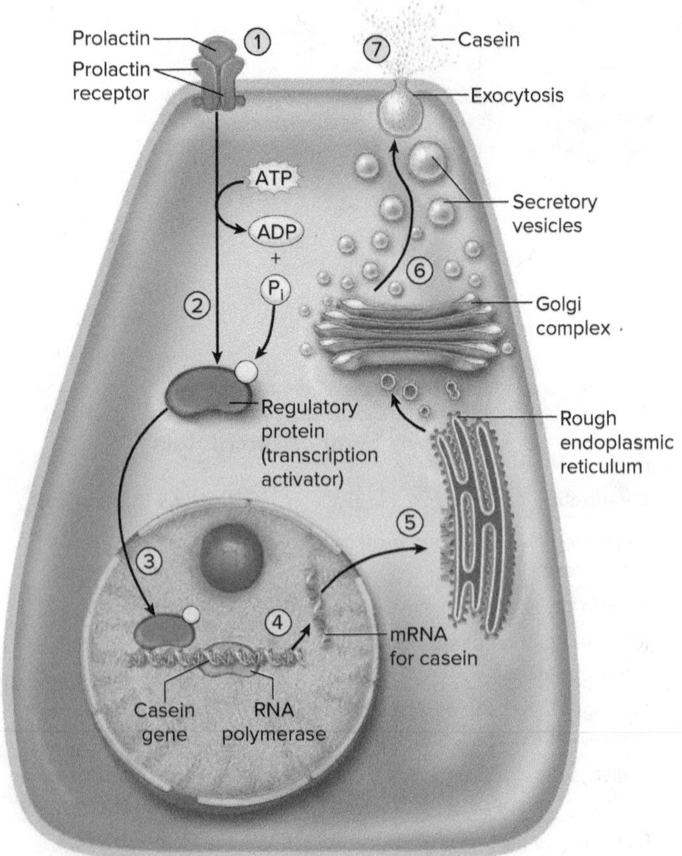


**FIGURE 4.11 A Mechanism of Gene Activation.** The hormone prolactin triggers intracellular reactions that activate a regulatory protein and lead ultimately to the secretion of casein. See the text for further explanation of the numbered steps.

## 4.2f Synthesizing Compounds Other Than Proteins

Cells, of course, make more than proteins—they also synthesize glycogen, fat, steroids, phospholipids, pigments, and many other compounds. There are no genes for these cell products, yet their synthesis is under indirect genetic control. How? They are produced by enzymatic reactions, and enzymes are proteins encoded by genes.

Consider the production of testosterone, for example (**fig. 4.12**). This is a steroid; there is no gene for testosterone. But to make it, a cell of the testis takes in cholesterol and enzymatically converts it to testosterone. This can occur only if the genes for the enzymes are active. Yet a further implication of this is that genes may greatly affect such complex outcomes as behavior, since testosterone strongly influences such behaviors as aggression and sex drive. In short, DNA codes only for RNA and protein synthesis, yet it indirectly controls the synthesis of a much wider range of substances concerned with all aspects of anatomy, physiology, and behavior.

**BEFORE YOU GO ON**

Answer the following questions to test your understanding of the preceding section:

5. Define *gene, genetic code, codon,* and *anticodon*.
6. Describe the roles of RNA polymerase, ribosomes, and tRNA in producing a protein.
7. What is the difference between genetic transcription and translation?
8. Summarize the processing of a protein from the time a ribosome finishes its work to the time a protein is secreted from the cell. What roles do the endoplasmic reticulum and Golgi complex play in this?
9. Describe some ways a gene can be turned on or off at different times in a person's life.
10. Considering that genes can code only for RNA or proteins, how can the synthesis of nonprotein substances such as carbohydrates or steroids be under genetic control?

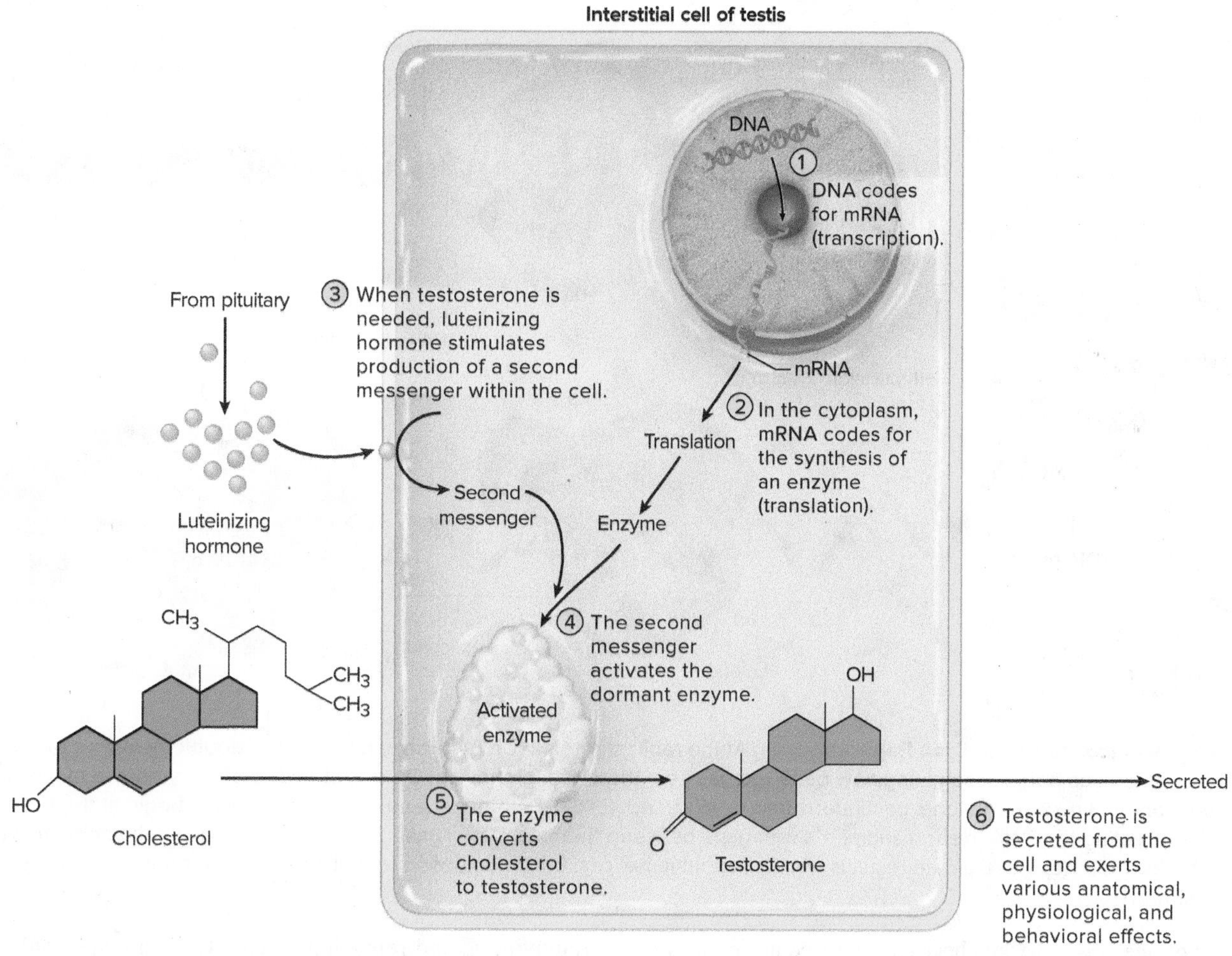


**FIGURE 4.12 Indirect Control of Testosterone Synthesis by DNA.** There is no gene for testosterone, but DNA regulates its production by coding for enzymes that convert cholesterol to testosterone.

## 4.3 DNA Replication and the Cell Cycle

### Expected Learning Outcomes

When you have completed this section, you should be able to

a. describe how DNA is replicated;
b. discuss the consequences of replication errors;
c. describe the life history of a cell, including the events of mitosis; and
d. explain how the timing of cell division is regulated.

Before a cell divides, it must duplicate its DNA so it can give complete and identical copies of all of its genes to each daughter cell. Since DNA controls all cellular function, this replication process must be very exact. We now examine how it is accomplished and consider the consequences of mistakes.

### 4.3a DNA Replication

The law of complementary base pairing shows that we can predict the base sequence of one DNA strand if we know the sequence of the other. More importantly, it enables a cell to reproduce one strand based on information in the other. The fundamental steps of the replication process are as follows **(fig. 4.13):**

1. The double helix unwinds from the histones.
2. Like a zipper, an enzyme called **DNA helicase** opens up one short segment of the helix at a time, exposing its nitrogenous bases. The point where the DNA is opened up, like the two halves of a zipper separating, is called the **replication fork.**
3. Molecules of the enzyme **DNA polymerase** move along each strand, read the exposed bases, and like a matchmaker, arrange "marriages" with complementary free nucleotides. If the polymerase finds the sequence TCG, for example, it assembles AGC across from it. The two separated strands of DNA are copied by separate polymerase molecules, proceeding in opposite directions. On one strand (top of figure 4.13), the polymerase moves toward the replication fork and makes a long, continuous, new strand of DNA to complement the old one. On the other strand (bottom of the figure), another polymerase moves away from the replication fork and copies only a short segment of DNA at a time. The segments are then joined together by another enzyme called **DNA ligase.** Ultimately, from the old *parental DNA* molecule, two new *daughter DNA* molecules are made. Each daughter DNA

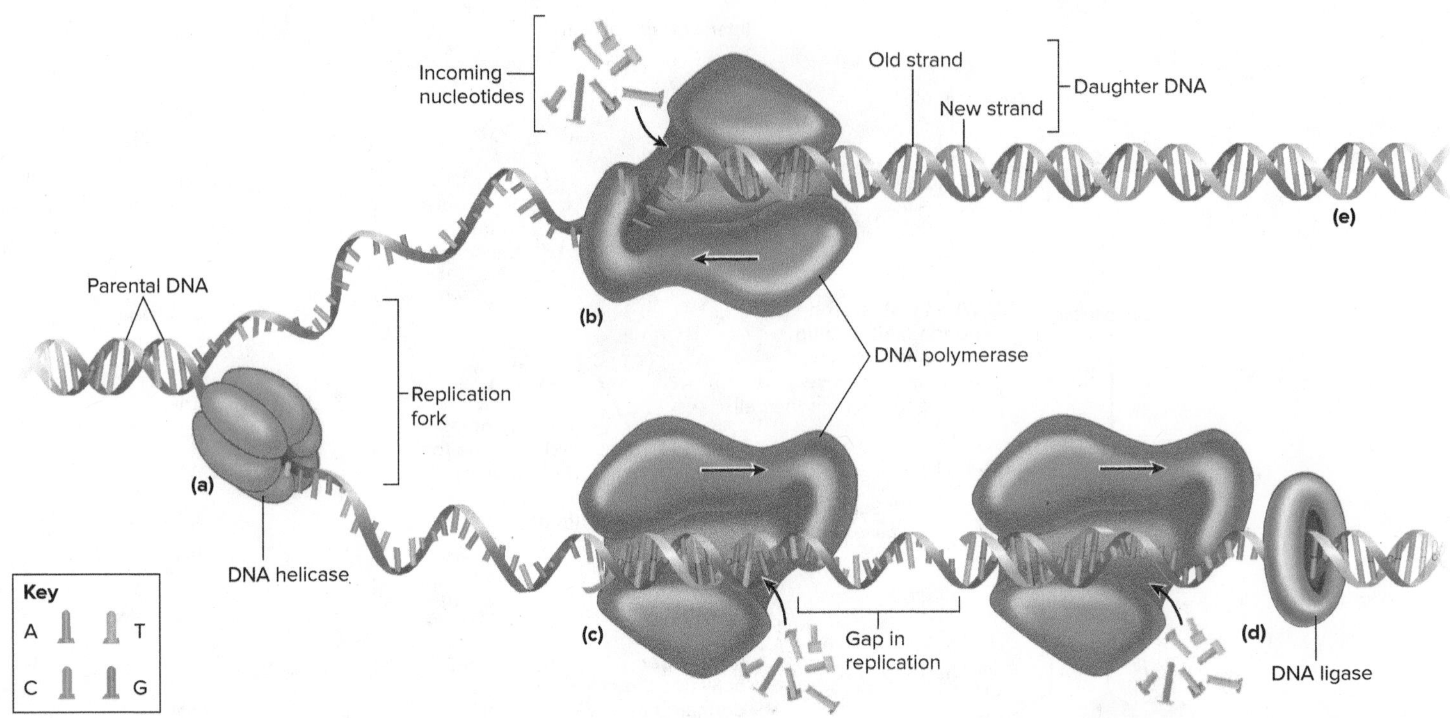


**FIGURE 4.13 Semiconservative DNA Replication.** (a) At the replication fork, DNA helicase unwinds the double helix and exposes the bases. DNA polymerases begin assembling new bases across from the existing ones. (b) On one strand, DNA polymerase moves toward the replication fork and makes one long, continuous new DNA strand. (c) On the other strand, DNA polymerases begin at the fork and move away from it, replicating the DNA in short segments with gaps between them. (d) DNA ligase closes the gaps to join the segments into a continuous double helix. (e) The ultimate result is two DNA double helices, each composed of one strand of the original DNA and one newly synthesized strand.

consists of one new helix synthesized from free nucleotides and one old helix conserved from the parental DNA. The process is therefore called **semiconservative replication.**

4. While DNA is synthesized in the nucleus, new histones are synthesized in the cytoplasm. Millions of histones are transported into the nucleus within a few minutes after DNA replication, and each new DNA helix wraps around them to make new nucleosomes.

Despite the complexity of this process, each DNA polymerase works at an impressive rate of about 100 base pairs per second. Even at this rate, however, it would take weeks for one polymerase molecule to replicate even one chromosome. But in reality, thousands of polymerase molecules work simultaneously on each DNA molecule, and all 46 chromosomes are replicated in a mere 6 to 8 hours.

### 4.3b Errors and Mutations

DNA polymerase is fast and accurate, but it makes mistakes. For example, it might read A and place a C across from it where it should have placed a T. If nothing were done to correct such errors, each generation of cells could have thousands of faulty proteins, coded for by DNA that had been miscopied. To prevent such catastrophic damage to the cell, there are multiple modes of correcting replication errors, collectively called the *DNA damage response (DDR).* DNA polymerase itself double-checks the new base pair and tends to replace incorrect, biochemically unstable pairs with more stable, correct pairs—for example, removing C and replacing it with T. As a result, only one mistake remains for every billion base pairs replicated—a very high degree of replication accuracy, if not completely flawless.

Changes in DNA structure, called **mutations,**[5] can result from replication errors or from environmental factors such as radiation, chemicals, and viruses. Uncorrected mutations can be passed on to the descendants of that cell, but many of them have no adverse effect. One reason is that a new base sequence sometimes codes for the same thing as the old one. For example, TGG and TGC both code for threonine (see table 4.2), so a mutation from G to C in the third place wouldn't necessarily change protein structure. Another reason is that a change in protein structure isn't always critical to its function. For example, the beta chain of hemoglobin is 146 amino acids long in both humans and horses, but 25 of these amino acids differ between the two species. Nevertheless, the hemoglobin is fully functional in both species. Furthermore, since 98% of the DNA doesn't code for any proteins, the great majority of mutations don't affect protein structure at all. Other mutations, however, may kill a cell, turn it cancerous, or cause genetic defects in future generations. When a mutation changes the sixth amino acid of β-hemoglobin from glutamic acid to valine, for example, the result is a crippling disorder called sickle-cell disease. Clearly some amino acid substitutions are more critical than others, and this affects the severity of a mutation. More than 30 diseases are known to result from defects in the DNA damage response, including some forms of anemia, cancer, immune deficiency, and brain defects.

[5]*muta* = change; *ation* = process

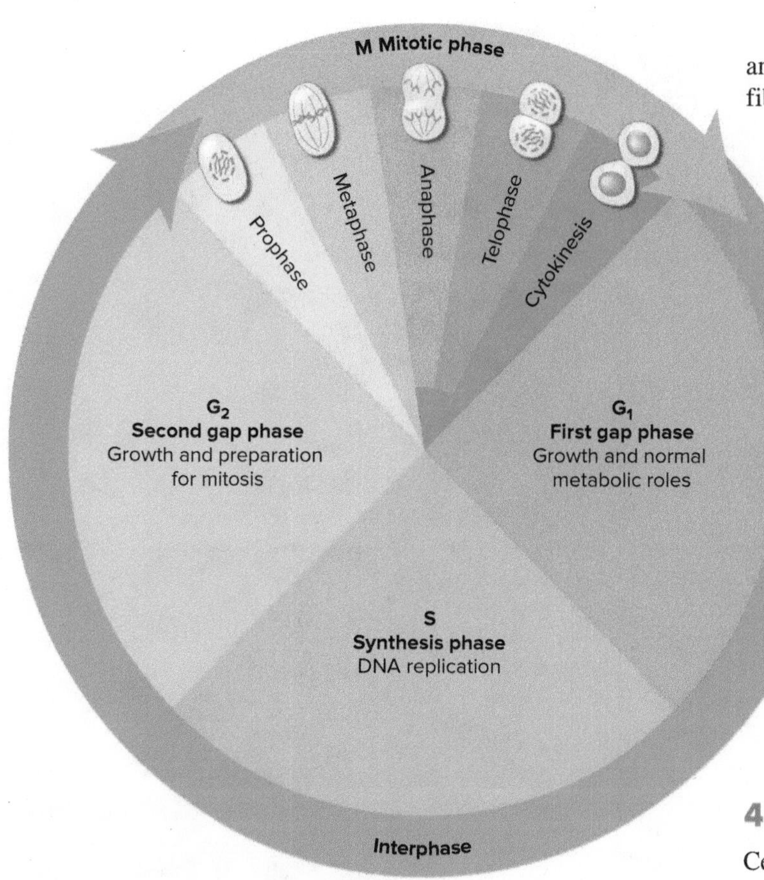


FIGURE 4.14 **The Cell Cycle.**

## 4.3c The Cell Cycle

Most cells periodically divide into two daughter cells, so a cell has a life cycle extending from one division to the next. This **cell cycle** is divided into four main phases: $G_1$, $S$, $G_2$, and $M$ **(fig. 4.14).**

**$G_1$** is the **first gap phase,** an interval between cell division and DNA replication. During this time, a cell synthesizes proteins, grows, and carries out its preordained tasks for the body. Almost all of the discussion in this book relates to what cells do in the $G_1$ phase. Cells in $G_1$ also accumulate the materials needed to replicate their DNA in the next phase. In cultured cells called fibroblasts, which divide every 18 to 24 hours, $G_1$ lasts 8 to 10 hours.

**S** is the **synthesis phase,** in which a cell makes a duplicate copy of its centrioles and nuclear DNA. This is the point at which the cell carries out the semiconservative replication described earlier. The two identical sets of DNA molecules are then available to be divided up between daughter cells at the next cell division. This phase takes 6 to 8 hours in cultured fibroblasts.

**$G_2$,** the **second gap phase,** is the interval (4–6 hours in fibroblasts) between DNA replication and cell division. In $G_2$, a cell exhibits further growth, makes more organelles, finishes replicating its centrioles, and synthesizes enzymes that control cell division. It also checks the fidelity of DNA replication and usually repairs any errors that are detected.

**M** is the **mitotic phase,** in which a cell replicates its nucleus and then pinches in two to form new daughter cells. In cultured fibroblasts, the M phase takes 1 to 2 hours. The details of this phase are considered in the next section. Phases $G_1$, S, and $G_2$ are collectively called **interphase**—the time between M phases.

The length of the cell cycle varies greatly from one cell type to another. Stomach and skin cells divide rapidly, whereas bone and cartilage cells divide slowly. Some cells leave the cell cycle for a "rest" and cease to divide for days, years, or the rest of one's life—mature neurons, skeletal muscle cells, and adipocytes, for example. Such cells are said to be in the **$G_0$ (G-zero) phase.** The balance between cells that are actively cycling and those standing by in $G_0$ is an important factor in determining the number of cells in the body. An inability to stop cycling and enter $G_0$ is characteristic of cancer cells (see Deeper Insight 4.3).

**▶▶▶ APPLY WHAT YOU KNOW**

*What is the maximum number of DNA molecules ever contained in a cell over the course of its life cycle? (Assume the cell has only one nucleus, and disregard mitochondrial DNA.)*

## 4.3d Mitosis

Cells divide by two mechanisms called mitosis and meiosis. Meiosis, however, is restricted to one purpose, the production of eggs and sperm, and is therefore treated in section 27.4a on reproduction. **Mitosis** serves all the other functions of cell division:

- development of an individual, composed of some 50 trillion cells, from a one-celled fertilized egg;
- growth of all tissues and organs after birth;
- replacement of cells that die; and
- repair of damaged tissues.

Four phases of mitosis are recognizable: *prophase, metaphase, anaphase,* and *telophase* **(fig. 4.15).**

(1) **Prophase.**[6] At the outset of mitosis, the chromosomes shorten and thicken, eventually coiling into compact rods that are easier to distribute to daughter cells than the long, delicate chromatin of interphase. There are 46 chromosomes, each with two chromatids and one molecule of DNA per chromatid. The nuclear envelope disintegrates during prophase and releases the chromosomes into the cytosol. The centrioles begin to sprout elongated microtubules called **spindle fibers,** which push the centrioles apart as they grow. Eventually, a pair of centrioles comes to lie at each pole of the cell. Some spindle fibers grow toward the chromosomes and become attached to the kinetochore on each side of the centromere (see fig. 4.5). The spindle fibers then tug the chromosomes back and forth until they line up along the midline of the cell.

[6]*pro* = first

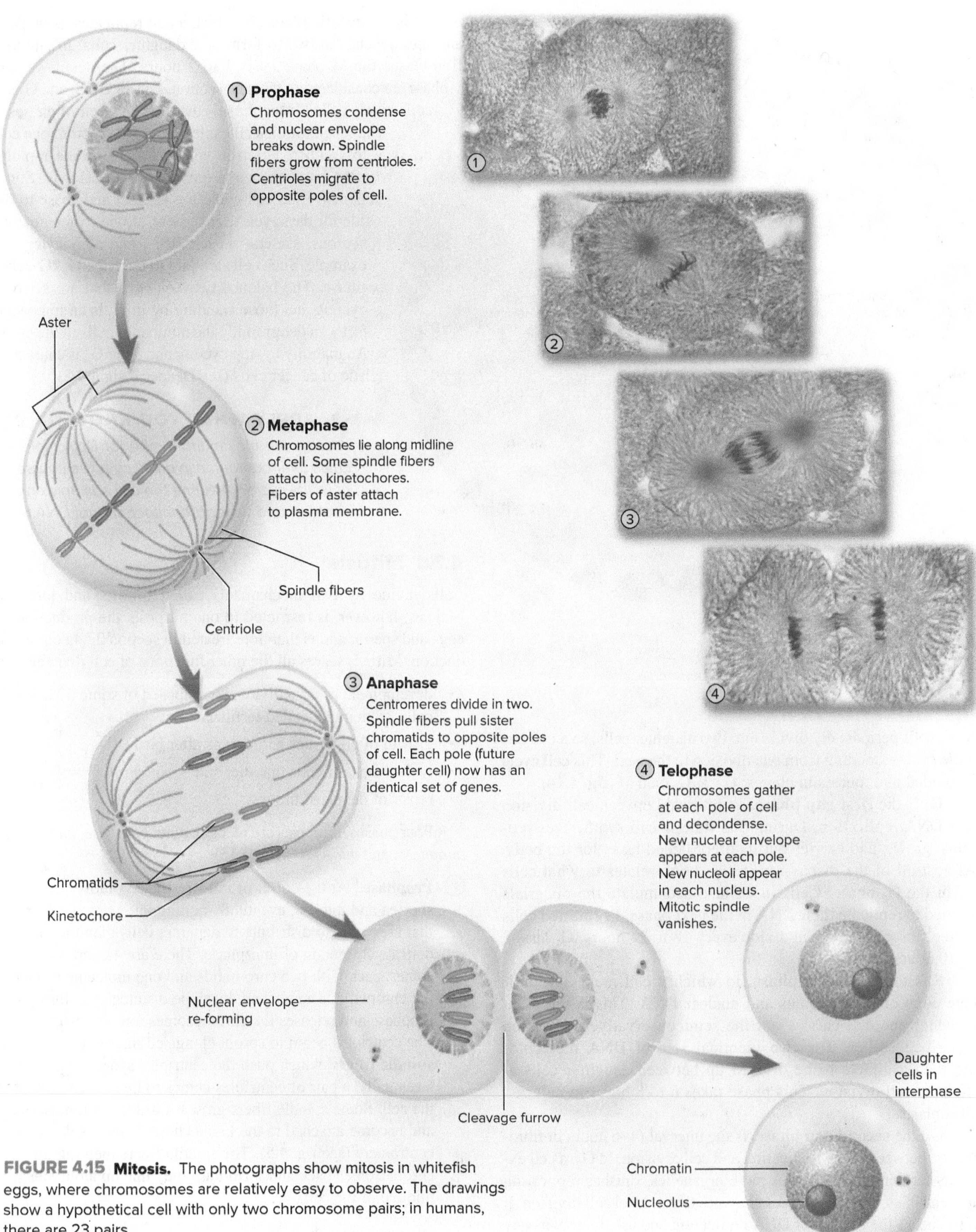

① Prophase
Chromosomes condense and nuclear envelope breaks down. Spindle fibers grow from centrioles. Centrioles migrate to opposite poles of cell.
Aster
② Metaphase
Chromosomes lie along midline of cell. Some spindle fibers attach to kinetochores. Fibers of aster attach to plasma membrane.
Spindle fibers
Centriole
③ Anaphase
Centromeres divide in two. Spindle fibers pull sister chromatids to opposite poles of cell. Each pole (future daughter cell) now has an identical set of genes.
Chromatids
Kinetochore
④ Telophase
Chromosomes gather at each pole of cell and decondense. New nuclear envelope appears at each pole. New nucleoli appear in each nucleus. Mitotic spindle vanishes.
Nuclear envelope re-forming
Cleavage furrow
Daughter cells in interphase
Chromatin
Nucleolus
1
2
3
4

**FIGURE 4.15 Mitosis.** The photographs show mitosis in whitefish eggs, where chromosomes are relatively easy to observe. The drawings show a hypothetical cell with only two chromosome pairs; in humans, there are 23 pairs.

**1–4:** ©Ed Reschke

② **Metaphase.**[7] The chromosomes are aligned on the cell equator, oscillating slightly and awaiting a signal that stimulates each of them to split in two at the centromere. The spindle fibers now form a lemon-shaped array called the **mitotic spindle.** Long microtubules reach out from each centriole to the chromosomes, and shorter microtubules form a starlike *aster,*[8] which anchors the assembly to the inside of the plasma membrane at each end of the cell.

③ **Anaphase.**[9] This phase begins with activation of an enzyme that cleaves the two sister chromatids from each other at the centromere. Each chromatid is now regarded as a separate, single-stranded *daughter chromosome.* One daughter chromosome migrates to each pole of the cell, with its centromere leading the way and the arms trailing behind. Migration is achieved by means of motor proteins in the kinetochore crawling along the spindle fiber as the fiber itself is "chewed up" and disassembled at the chromosomal end. Since sister chromatids are genetically identical, and since each daughter cell receives one chromatid from each chromosome, the daughter cells of mitosis are genetically identical.

④ **Telophase.**[10] The daughter chromosomes cluster on each side of the cell. The rough ER produces a new nuclear envelope around each cluster, and the chromosomes begin to uncoil and return to the thinly dispersed chromatin form. The mitotic spindle breaks up and vanishes. Each new nucleus forms nucleoli, indicating it has already begun making RNA and is preparing for protein synthesis.

Telophase is the end of nuclear division but overlaps with **cytokinesis**[11] (SY-toe-kih-NEE-sis), division of the cytoplasm into two cells. Early traces of cytokinesis are visible even at anaphase. It is achieved by the motor protein myosin pulling on microfilaments of actin in the terminal web of the cytoskeleton. This creates a crease called the *cleavage furrow* around the equator of the cell, and the cell eventually pinches in two. Interphase has now begun for these new cells. Be aware, however, that mitosis (nuclear division) can occur without cytokinesis (cellular division). This is why some cells acquire two or more nuclei or multiple identical sets of chromosomes.

## 4.3e Regulation of Cell Division

One of the most important questions in biology is what signals cells when to divide and when to stop. The activation and inhibition of cell division are subjects of intense research for obvious reasons such as management of cancer and tissue repair. Cells divide when (1) they grow large enough to have enough cytoplasm to distribute to their two daughter cells; (2) they have replicated their DNA, so they can give each daughter cell a duplicate set of genes; (3) they receive an adequate supply of nutrients; (4) they are stimulated by **growth factors,** chemical signals secreted by blood platelets, kidney cells, and other sources; or (5) neighboring cells die, opening up space in a tissue to be occupied by new cells. Growth factors and their receptors are a central issue in understanding the uncontrolled growth of cancer (see Deeper Insight 4.3). Cells stop dividing when they snugly contact neighboring cells or when nutrients or growth factors are withdrawn. The cessation of cell division in response to contact with other cells is called **contact inhibition.** An absence of contact inhibition, leading to uncontrolled cell division, is one of the characteristics of cancer.

The cell cycle is regulated by a molecular timer and certain checkpoints at which the cell checks its own status before moving on to the next phase. Two key elements of the timer are families of proteins called **cyclins** and **cyclin-dependent kinases (Cdks).** Remember from section 2.4g that a kinase is an enzyme that phosphorylates (adds phosphate to) other proteins, thereby activating or suppressing their function. Cdks exist at fairly stable levels in cells, but without cyclins, they lie dormant and perform no function. Cyclin levels rise and fall through the cell cycle. In early interphase, cyclin genes are transcribed and cyclin levels rise. As they bind to Cdks, those enzymes phosphorylate proteins with various effects described shortly. At the end of mitosis, proteasomes degrade the cyclins, their levels fall, and the Cdks become dormant again until the next cycle.

Among other functions of cyclin–Cdk complexes, they control (1) the replication of DNA and centrioles in the S phase; (2) the condensation of chromosomes, breakdown of the nuclear envelope, formation of the mitotic spindle, and attachment of chromosomes to the spindle in prophase; and (3) splitting of the centromere and separation of the sister chromatids at anaphase.

At specific **checkpoints** during the cell cycle, a cyclin binds to a Cdk and activates a cascade of biochemical reactions that prepare a cell to move on to the next phase of the cycle. One of these, called the *Start* or *$G_1$ checkpoint,* either allows the cell to proceed toward the S phase or, if it doesn't, the cell goes into the noncycling $G_0$ phase. A *$G_2$/M checkpoint* late in the $G_2$ phase determines whether the cell is able to proceed to mitosis. A third checkpoint at the transition from metaphase to anaphase determines whether the cell can proceed to anaphase, leading to separation of its sister chromatids.

Malfunctions of this process can be disastrous to the cell and even to the life of the whole person. If it fails to allow a cell to progress through the cell cycle, the result can be a failure of tissue maintenance and repair. On the other hand, if the cell cycle progresses too readily, out of control, the result can be uncontrolled tissue growth (neoplasia) and cancer.

**BEFORE YOU GO ON**

Answer the following questions to test your understanding of the preceding section:

11. Describe the genetic roles of DNA helicase and DNA polymerase. Contrast the function of DNA polymerase with that of RNA polymerase.
12. Explain why DNA replication is called *semiconservative.*

[7] *meta* = next in a series
[8] *aster* = star
[9] *ana* = apart
[10] *telo* = end, final
[11] *cyto* = cell; *kinesis* = action, motion

13. Define *mutation.* Explain why some mutations are harmless and others can be lethal.
14. List the stages of the cell cycle and summarize what occurs in each one.
15. List the stages of mitosis and the main processes that occur in each one.
16. Concisely explain how cyclins, Cdks, and checkpoints control the cell cycle.

## 4.4 Chromosomes and Heredity

### Expected Learning Outcomes

When you have completed this section, you should be able to

a. describe the paired arrangement of chromosomes in the human karyotype;
b. define *allele* and discuss how alleles affect the traits of an individual; and
c. discuss the interaction of heredity and environment in producing individual traits.

**Heredity** is the transmission of genetic characteristics from parent to offspring. In the following discussion, we will examine a few basic principles of normal heredity, thus establishing a basis for understanding hereditary traits in later chapters. Hereditary defects are described in section 29.3c along with nonhereditary birth defects.

### 4.4a The Karyotype

As we have seen, the agents of heredity are the genes, and the genes are carried on the chromosomes. When we lay the 46 chromosomes out in order by size and other physical features, we get a chart called a **karyotype**[12] **(fig. 4.16).** The chromosomes occur in 23 pairs; the two members of each pair are called **homologous**[13] **chromosomes** (ho-MOLL-uh-gus). One member of each pair is inherited from the individual's mother and one from the father. Except for the X and Y chromosomes, two homologous chromosomes look alike and carry the same genes, although they may have different varieties of those genes. Chromosomes X and Y are called the **sex chromosomes** because they determine the individual's sex; all the others are called **autosomes.** A female normally has a homologous pair of X chromosomes, whereas a male has one X and a much smaller Y.

**APPLY WHAT YOU KNOW**

*Why would a cell in metaphase be more useful than a cell in interphase for producing a karyotype?*

Any cell with 23 pairs of chromosomes is said to be **diploid (2*n*).**[14] Sperm and egg cells, however, are **haploid (*n*),**[15] meaning

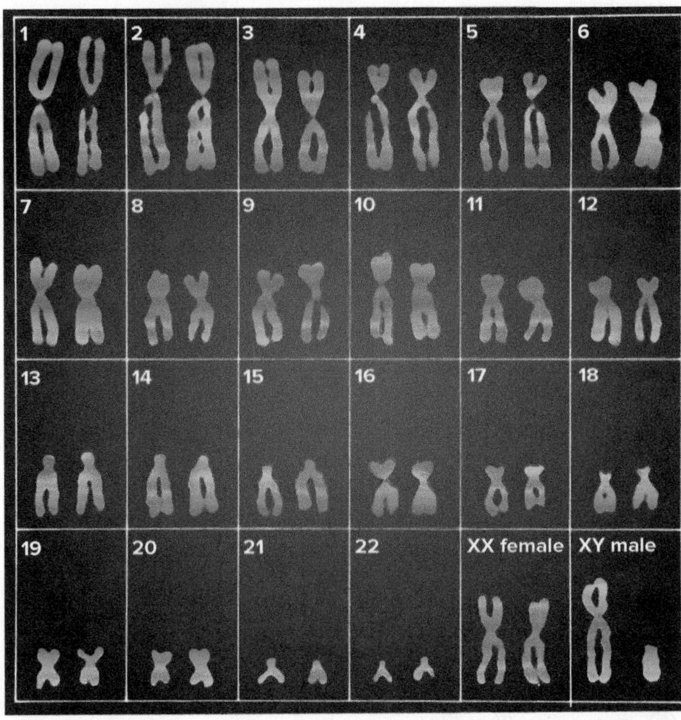


**FIGURE 4.16 The Normal Human Karyotype.** This is a micrograph of chromosomes stained to accentuate their banding patterns. The two chromosomes of each homologous pair exhibit similar size, shape, and banding. Each chromosome at this stage has two chromatids.

Omikron/Science Source

they contain only 23 unpaired chromosomes. Sperm and eggs, and cells on their way to becoming sperm and eggs, are called **germ cells.** All other cells of the body are called **somatic cells.** In meiosis (see section 27.4a), the two homologous chromosomes of each pair become *segregated* into separate daughter cells leading to the haploid germ cells. At fertilization, one set of *paternal* (sperm) chromosomes unites with a set of *maternal* (egg) chromosomes, restoring the diploid number to the fertilized egg and the somatic cells that arise from it.

### 4.4b Genes and Alleles

The location of a particular gene on a chromosome is called its **locus.** Homologous chromosomes have the same gene at the same locus, although they may carry different forms of that gene, called **alleles**[16] (ah-LEELS), which produce alternative forms of a particular trait. Frequently, one allele is **dominant** and the other one **recessive.** If at least one chromosome carries the dominant allele, the corresponding trait is usually detectable in the individual. A dominant allele masks the effect of any recessive allele that may be present. Typically, but not always, dominant alleles code for a normal, functional protein and recessive alleles for a nonfunctional variant of the protein.

[12]*karyo* = nucleus
[13]*homo* = same; *log* = relation
[14]*diplo* = double
[15]*haplo* = half

[16]*allo* = different

A feature of the chin presents an example of dominant and recessive genetic effects. Some people have a *cleft chin,* with a deep dimple in the middle, whereas most people do not **(fig. 4.17a).** The allele for cleft chin is dominant; we will represent it with a capital *C*. Those who inherit this from one or both parents normally have a cleft chin. The allele for an uncleft chin is recessive, here represented with a lowercase *c*. (It is customary to represent a dominant allele with a capital letter and a recessive allele with its lowercase equivalent.) One must inherit the recessive allele from both parents to have an uncleft chin.

Individuals with two identical alleles, such as *CC* or *cc,* are said to be **homozygous**[17] (HO-mo-ZY-gus) for that trait. If the homologous chromosomes have different alleles for that gene *(Cc),* the individual is **heterozygous**[18] (HET-er-oh-ZY-gus). The paired alleles that an individual possesses for a particular trait constitute the **genotype** (JEE-no-type). An observable trait such as cleft or uncleft chin is called the **phenotype**[19] (FEE-no-type).

We say that an allele is **expressed** if it shows in the phenotype of an individual. Chin allele *c* is expressed only when it is present in a homozygous state *(cc);* allele *C* is expressed whether it is homozygous *(CC)* or heterozygous *(Cc)*. The only way most recessive alleles can be expressed is for an individual to inherit them from both parents.

Recessive traits can "skip" one or more generations. A diagram called a *Punnett square* **(fig. 4.17b)** shows how two heterozygous parents with cleft chins can produce a child with an uncleft chin. Across the top are the two genetically possible types of eggs the mother could produce, and on the left side are the possible types of sperm from the father. The four cells of the square show the genotypes and phenotypes that would result from each possible combination of sperm and egg. You can see that three of the possible combinations would produce a child with a cleft chin (genotypes *CC* and *Cc*), but one combination *(cc)* would produce a child with an uncleft chin. Therefore, the uncleft chin trait skipped the parental generation in this case but could be expressed in their child.

This phenomenon becomes more significant when parents are heterozygous **carriers** of hereditary diseases such as cystic fibrosis—individuals who carry a recessive allele and may pass it on, but do not phenotypically express it in themselves. For some hereditary diseases, tests are available to detect carriers and allow couples to weigh their risk of having children with genetic disorders. *Genetic counselors* perform genetic testing or refer clients for tests, advise couples on the probability of transmitting genetic diseases, and assist people in coping with genetic disease.

**APPLY WHAT YOU KNOW**

*Would it be possible for a woman with an uncleft chin to have children with cleft chins? Use a Punnett square and one or more hypothetical genotypes for the father to demonstrate your point.*

[17]*homo* = same; *zygo* = union, joined
[18]*hetero* = different; *zygo* = union, joined
[19]*pheno* = showing, evident

(a)

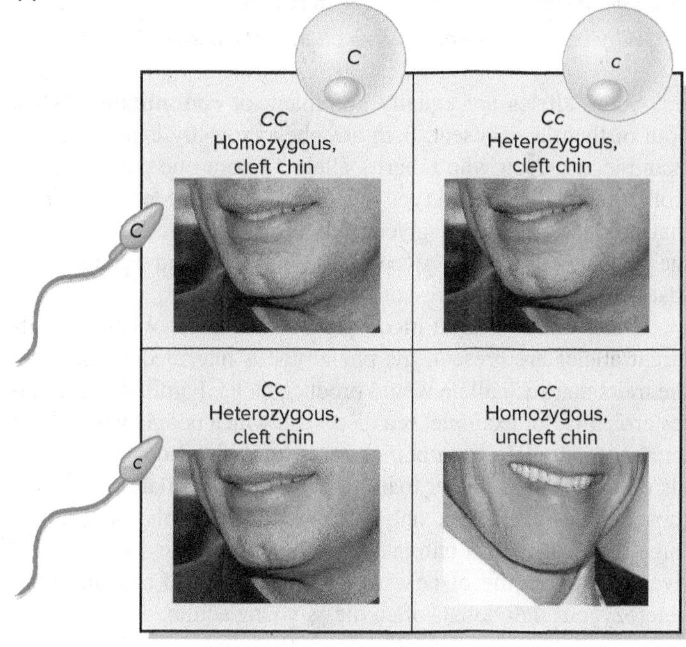


(b)

**FIGURE 4.17 Genetics of Cleft Chin.** (a) A cleft chin occurs if even one allele of the pair is dominant *(C)*. The more common uncleft chin occurs only when both alleles are recessive *(c)*. (b) A Punnett square shows why such a trait can "skip a generation." Both parents in this case have heterozygous genotypes *(Cc)* and cleft chins. An egg from the mother can carry either allele *C* or *c* (top), as can a sperm from the father (left). This gives their offspring a one-in-four chance of having an uncleft chin *(cc)*.

**a (left):** Brad Barket/Getty Images; **a (right):** Kurt Krieger/Corbis Entertainment/Getty Images; **b (top left, top right, bottom left):** Brad Barket/Getty Images; **b (bottom right):** Kurt Krieger/Corbis Entertainment/Getty Images

## 4.4c Multiple Alleles, Codominance, and Incomplete Dominance

Some genes exist in more than two allelic forms—that is, there are **multiple alleles** within the collective genetic makeup, or **gene pool,** of the population as a whole. For example, there are over 100 alleles responsible for cystic fibrosis, and there are 3 alleles for

ABO blood types. Two of the ABO blood type alleles are dominant and symbolized with a capital *I* (for *immunoglobulin*) and a superscript: $I^A$ and $I^B$. There is one recessive allele, symbolized with a lowercase *i*. Which two alleles one inherits determine the blood type, as follows:

| Genotype | Phenotype |
|---|---|
| $I^AI^A$ | Type A |
| $I^Ai$ | Type A |
| $I^BI^B$ | Type B |
| $I^Bi$ | Type B |
| $I^AI^B$ | Type AB |
| $ii$ | Type O |

**APPLY WHAT YOU KNOW**

*Why can't one person have all three of the ABO alleles?*

Some alleles are equally dominant, or **codominant.** When both of them are present, both are phenotypically expressed. For example, a person who inherits allele $I^A$ from one parent and $I^B$ from the other has blood type AB. These alleles code for enzymes that produce the surface glycolipids of red blood cells. Type AB means that both A and B glycolipids are present, and type O means that neither of them is present.

Other alleles exhibit **incomplete dominance.** When two different alleles are present, the phenotype is intermediate between the traits that each allele would produce alone. Familial hypercholesterolemia, for example, is a disease in which people who inherit an abnormal allele from both parents have blood cholesterol levels up to six times higher than in the general population, whereas those who inherit it from only one parent have levels about two or three times normal. If untreated, those homozygous for the defective allele often die of heart attacks in childhood and untreated heterozygous individuals often die as young adults.

## 4.4d Polygenic Inheritance and Pleiotropy

**Polygenic (multiple-gene) inheritance (fig. 4.18)** is a phenomenon in which genes at two or more loci, or even on different chromosomes, contribute to a single phenotypic trait. Human eye and skin colors are normal polygenic traits, for example. They result from the combined expression of all the genes for each trait. Several diseases are also thought to stem from polygenic inheritance, including some forms of alcoholism, mental illness, cancer, and heart disease.

**Pleiotropy**[20] (ply-OT-roe-pee) is a phenomenon in which one gene produces multiple phenotypic effects. For example, about 1 in 200,000 people has a genetic disorder called *alkaptonuria,* caused by a mutation on chromosome 3. The mutation blocks the normal breakdown of the amino acid tyrosine, resulting in the accumulation of an intermediate breakdown product, homogentisic acid, in the body fluids and connective tissues. When homogentisic acid oxidizes, it binds to collagen and turns the tissues gray to bluish black, and for unknown reasons, it causes degeneration of cartilages and other connective tissues. Among the multiple phenotypic effects of this disorder **(fig. 4.19)** are darkening of the skin; darkening and degeneration of the cartilages in

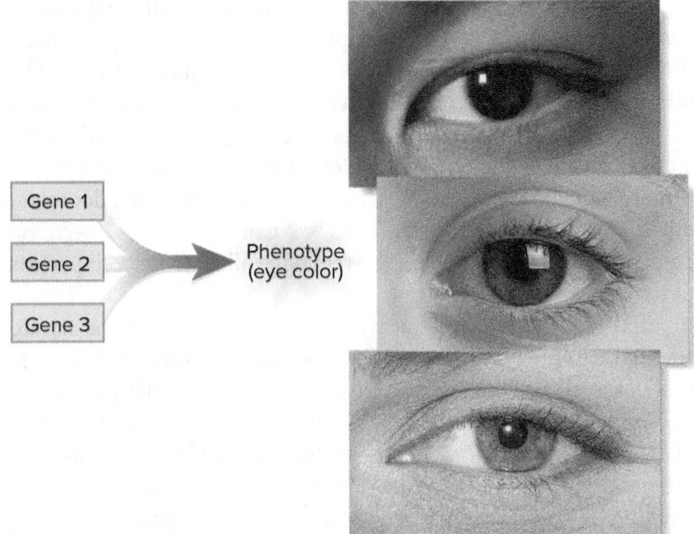


**FIGURE 4.18 Polygenic Inheritance of Eye Color.** A polygenic trait such as eye color is determined by the contributions of genes at multiple loci.

(top): Monica Lau/Getty Images; (middle): Anthony Saint James/Getty Images; (bottom): JupiterImages/Comstock/Getty Images

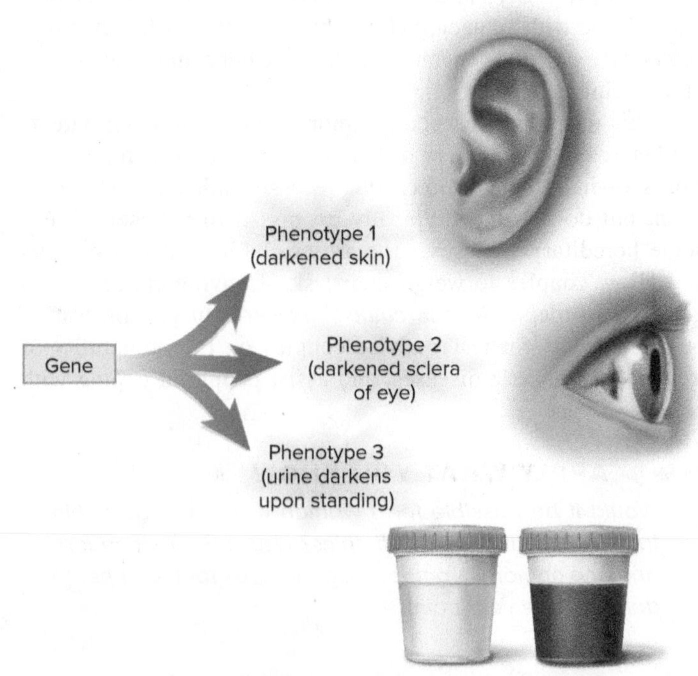


**FIGURE 4.19 Pleiotropy in Alkaptonuria.** Multiple phenotypic effects can result from a single gene mutation.

[20]*pleio* = more; *trop* = changes

places such as the ears, knees, and intervertebral discs; darkening of the urine when it stands long enough for the homogentisic acid to oxidize; discoloration of the teeth and the whites of the eyes; arthritis of the shoulders, hips, and knees; and damage to the heart valves, prostate gland, and other internal organs. Another well-known example of pleiotropy is sickle-cell disease, detailed in section 18.2.

## 4.4e Sex Linkage

**Sex-linked traits** are carried on the X or Y chromosome and therefore tend to be inherited by one sex more than the other. Men are more likely than women to have red–green color blindness or hemophilia, for example, because the allele for each is recessive and located on the X chromosome *(X-linked).* Women have two X chromosomes. If a woman inherits the recessive color-blindness allele *(c)* on one of her X chromosomes, there is still a good chance that her other X chromosome will carry a dominant allele *(C)* for normal color vision. Men, on the other hand, have only one X chromosome and normally express any allele found there **(fig. 4.20).** Ironically, even though color blindness is far more common among men than women, a man can inherit it only from his mother. Why? Because only his mother contributes an X chromosome to him. If he inherits *c* on his mother's X chromosome, he will be color-blind. He has no "second chance" to inherit a normal allele on a second X chromosome. A woman, however, gets an X chromosome from both parents. Even if one parent transmits the recessive allele to her, the chances are high that she will inherit a normal allele from her other parent. She would have to inherit it from both parents in order for her to have a trait such as red–green color blindness.

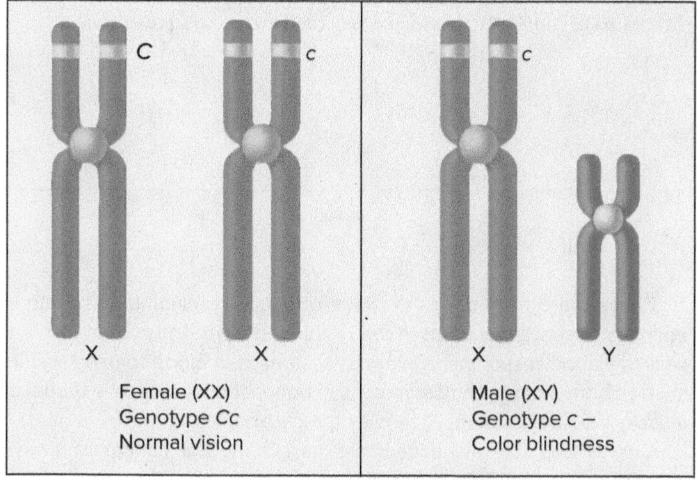


**FIGURE 4.20 Sex-Linked Inheritance of Red–Green Color Blindness.** Left: A female who inherits a recessive allele *(c)* for color blindness from one parent but a dominant allele *(C)* for normal vision from her other parent will have normal color vision. Right: A male who inherits *c* from his mother will exhibit red–green color blindness; the Y chromosome from his father has no corresponding gene to mask the effect of *c*.

The X chromosome carries about 260 genes, most of which have nothing to do with determining an individual's sex. There are so few functional genes on the Y chromosome—concerned mainly with development of the testes—that all proven sex-linked traits are associated with the X chromosome.

## 4.4f Dominant and Recessive Alleles at the Population Level

It is a common misconception that dominant alleles must be more common in the gene pool than recessive alleles. The truth is that dominance and recessiveness have little to do with how common an allele is. For example, type O is the most common ABO blood type in North America, but it is caused by the recessive allele *i.* Blood type AB, caused by the two dominant ABO alleles, is the rarest. *Polydactyly,*[21] the presence of extra fingers or toes, is a dominant trait, yet rare in the population. We also saw earlier that people with cleft chins are in a minority, even though the allele for that is dominant as well.

## 4.4g Environmental Effects and Gene Expression

It's one thing for any given cell to have all the usual genes in its nucleus, but it's a different matter whether those genes are turned on or off—whether the cell shows any detectable effects from them. For a gene to be turned on and have an effect on the individual is called **gene expression.** Even if an allele is dominant, it won't always be expressed in the phenotype. If a dominant allele is silenced and has no effect on some people who carry it, it is said to show **incomplete penetrance** in that population—that is, the genotype does not "penetrate to" and affect everyone who has it.

One reason the connection between genotype and phenotype is not inevitable is that environmental factors play an important role in the expression of all genes. At the very least, all gene expression depends on nutrition. Brown eyes, for example, require not only genes for the enzymes that synthesize the pigment melanin, but also the dietary raw material, phenylalanine, from which the melanin is made **(fig. 4.21).**

No gene can produce a phenotypic effect without nutritional and other environmental input, and no nutrients can produce a body or specific phenotype without genetic instructions that tell cells what to do with them. Just as you need both a recipe and ingredients to make a cake, it takes both heredity and environment to make a phenotype.

## 4.4h Epigenetics

It is often superficially believed that the only way gene expression can change is for the DNA base sequence to change—that is, through mutation. It is clear, however, that other mechanisms called **epigenetic**[22] **effects** can alter gene expression—reversibly

[21] *poly* = many; *dactyl* = fingers, toes

[22] *epi* = after, beyond, above the level of; *genet* = the gene or genome

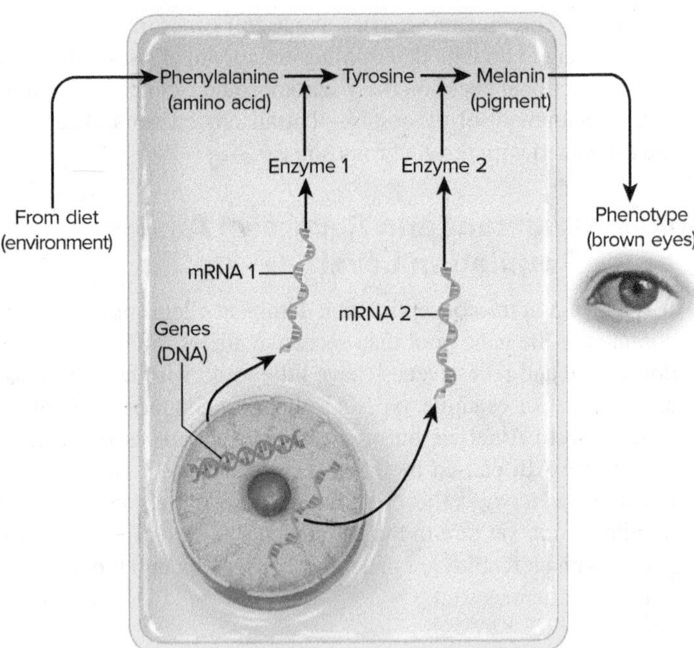


**FIGURE 4.21 The Roles of Environment and Heredity in Producing a Phenotype.** Brown eye color requires phenylalanine from the diet (environment) and two genetically coded (hereditary) enzymes to convert phenylalanine to melanin, the eye pigment.

activating or silencing genes without changes in base sequence. Among these are variations in the higher-order packaging of chromatin, modification of the histones, gene silencing by noncoding RNA (ncRNA), and *DNA methylation*—adding methyl ($-CH_3$) groups to DNA bases, especially cytosine, with usually a gene-silencing effect.

Many epigenetic changes occur normally and affect such things as how stem cells end up as liver, nerve, or skin cells. Different kinds of body cells are genetically identical, yet very different in structure and function because of epigenetic effects. Some epigenetic changes, however, may trigger such diseases and disorders as cancer, obesity, diabetes mellitus, or heart disease. Epigenetics is thought to be a possible culprit, for example, in the hereditary disorder *Prader–Willi syndrome,*[23] in which gene silencing leads to diverse effects including poor muscle tone, short stature, overeating, and childhood behavioral problems.

Particularly striking is the fact of **epigenetic inheritance;** we can pass on changes in gene expression to the next generation without changes in the structure of the genes themselves. Our habits and experiences today may affect gene expression in our children and perhaps even grandchildren. Anything from diet, smoking, or the use of recreational drugs to pollution, stress, epidemics, or famines can have epigenetic effects lasting for another generation or two. In light of epigenetics, we must now view heredity as entailing not only the genes passed from one generation to the next, but also whether other factors have abnormally activated or silenced those genes.

**BEFORE YOU GO ON**

Answer the following questions to test your understanding of the preceding section:

17. Why must the carrier of a genetic disease be heterozygous?
18. State at least three reasons why a person's phenotype can't always be determined from the genotype.
19. A man can inherit color blindness only from his mother, whereas a woman must inherit it from both her father and mother to show the trait. Explain this apparent paradox.

[23]Andrea Prader (1919–2001) and Heinrich Willi (1900–1971), Swiss pediatricians

## DEEPER INSIGHT 4.3

### CLINICAL APPLICATION

### *Cancer*

Anyone awaiting the results of a tumor biopsy hopes for the good news: benign! This means the tumor is slow-growing and contained in a fibrous capsule so it will not metastasize, and in most cases it is relatively easy to treat. The dreaded news is that it's malignant, meaning that it tends to grow rapidly and to *metastasize*—to give off cells that seed the growth of multiple tumors elsewhere, such as colon cancer metastasizing to the lungs and brain **(fig. 4.22).**

*Oncology* is a medical specialty that deals with both benign and malignant tumors, but only malignancies are called *cancer.* The word *cancer* literally means "crab." Hippocrates was the first to use the word this way, upon seeing a breast tumor with a tangle of blood vessels that reminded him of a crab's outstretched legs. Energy-hungry tumors often stimulate such ingrowth of blood vessels—a phenomenon called *tumor angiogenesis.*

Cancers are named for the tissue of origin: *carcinomas* originate in epithelial tissue; *lymphomas* in the lymph nodes; *melanomas* in pigment cells (melanocytes) of the epidermis; *leukemias* in blood-forming tissues such as bone marrow; and *sarcomas* in bone, other connective tissue, or muscle. About 90% of malignancies are carcinomas.

Only 5% to 10% of cancers are hereditary, but cancer is always a genetic disease. This is not as contradictory as it may seem. Most cases are due to mutations arising anew in the affected individual, not to genes inherited from a parent. Mutations can arise through errors in DNA replication or from exposure to carcinogens—radiation such as ultraviolet rays and X-rays; chemicals such as cigarette tar; and viruses such as human papillomavirus (HPV), hepatitis C, and type 2 herpes simplex.

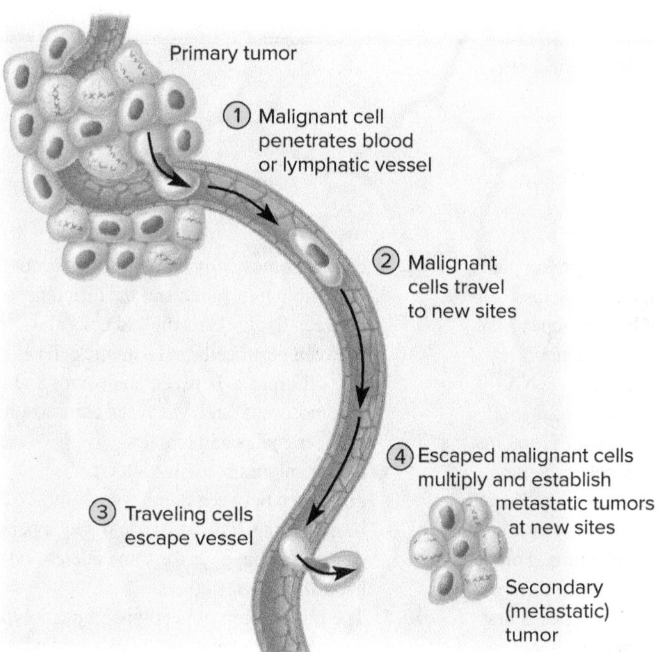
Primary tumor
① Malignant cell penetrates blood or lymphatic vessel
② Malignant cells travel to new sites
③ Traveling cells escape vessel
④ Escaped malignant cells multiply and establish metastatic tumors at new sites
Secondary (metastatic) tumor

**FIGURE 4.22 Metastasis.** The process by which malignant cells escape from a primary tumor, travel in the blood or lymph, and seed the growth of new (metastatic) tumors in other localities. Colon cancer, for example, can metastasize to the liver or brain by this method.

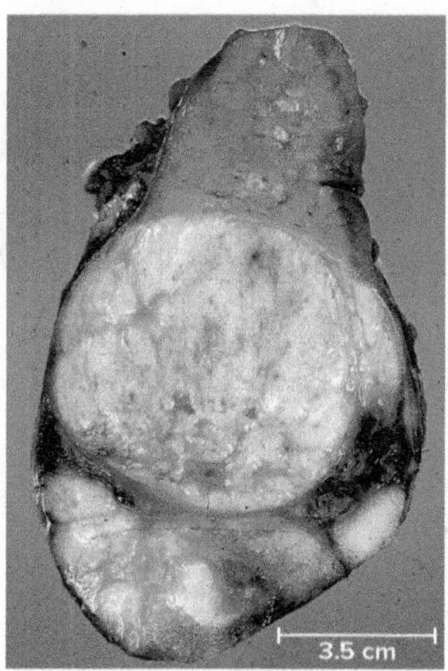
3.5 cm

**FIGURE 4.23 Wilms Tumor.** A malignant tumor of the kidney occurring especially in children.

Source: From the University of Alabama at Birmingham, Department of Pathology PEIR Digital Library © http://peir.net

Oncologists are especially interested in two families of cancer genes called oncogenes and tumor suppressor genes. An *oncogene* is analogous to a stuck accelerator on a car—it causes cell division to accelerate out of control, sometimes by inducing the excessive secretion of growth factors that stimulate mitosis, or the production of excessive growth-factor receptors. An oncogene called *ras* underlies about one-quarter of human cancers, and *erbB2* is a common factor in breast and ovarian cancer. *Tumor suppressor (TS) genes* inhibit cancer by opposing oncogene action, coding for DNA-repair enzymes, and other means. Consequently, mutations that destroy their protective "braking" function can lead to cancer. Mutation of a TS gene called *p53,* for example, is involved in about 50% of cases of leukemia and colon, lung, breast, liver, brain, and esophageal tumors. Many human cancers are associated, however, not with mutation but with aberrant DNA methylation, which can, for example, silence one's TS genes and thus turn off their protective function.

Cancer seldom results from just one mutation. It usually requires 5 to 10 mutations at different gene loci. It takes time for so many mutations to accumulate, which is why cancer is more common in the elderly than in the young. In addition, as we age, we accrue more lifetime exposure to carcinogens, our DNA- and tissue-repair mechanisms become less efficient, and our immune system grows weaker and less able to detect and destroy malignant cells.

About one in every five of us in America will die of cancer. Cancer is almost always fatal if not treated. Malignant tumors replace functional tissue in vital organs **(fig. 4.23);** they steal nutrients from the rest of the body, sometimes causing a severe wasting away called *cachexia* (ka-KEX-ee-ah); they weaken one's immunity, opening the door to *opportunistic infections* that a healthier person could ward off; and they often invade blood vessels, lung tissue, or brain tissue, with such consequences as hemorrhage, pulmonary collapse, seizures, or coma. Mortality usually results not from the original (primary) tumor, but from metastasis.

Cancer is usually treated with surgery, chemotherapy, or radiation therapy. Two lively areas of cancer research today are the development of drugs to starve tumors by blocking tumor angiogenesis, and *cancer immunotherapy,* programming one's own immune cells (T cells) to selectively recognize and attack tumor cells.

# STUDY GUIDE

## Assess Your Learning Outcomes

*To test your knowledge, discuss the following topics with a study partner or in writing, ideally from memory.*

### 4.1 DNA and RNA—The Nucleic Acids

1. The general name of the monomers that compose DNA and RNA; the three universal structural components of each monomer; the purines and pyrimidines involved in DNA and RNA structure; and how a purine differs from a pyrimidine
2. Structure of the double helix of DNA; what holds the two strands of the helix together; why DNA normally has only A—T and C—G base pairs (not A—C or G—T); and the law of complementary base pairing
3. The approximate number of genes in the human genome; what percentage of the DNA consists of genes; and to what extent, and in what ways, the remaining DNA may serve a purpose
4. How DNA and protein are combined to form chromatin; how the chromatin is coiled and supercoiled to fit into the compact cell nucleus and minimize damage; and the role of histones and nucleosomes in the organization of chromatin
5. The structure of a metaphase chromosome and how many chromosomes are in a typical cell
6. How RNA differs from DNA in structure and function, and the three types of RNA involved in protein synthesis

### 4.2 Genes and Their Action

1. The definition of *gene;* how genes relate to the amino acid sequence of proteins; why it cannot be said that every gene codes for protein structure; and why not every protein is encoded by its own unique gene
2. Definitions of *genome, genomics,* and *genomic medicine*
3. The organization of nucleotides into DNA triplets; how these relate to but differ from the codons of mRNA; the number of codons; and stop codons and their function
4. How the genetic code relates mRNA codons to protein structure
5. The process and outcome of genetic transcription; the enzyme that carries it out; the difference between pre-mRNA and mRNA; and the significance of introns and exons
6. How alternative splicing partially explains why the diversity of human proteins vastly exceeds the number of human genes
7. The process and outcome of genetic translation; the roles of mRNA, tRNA, and ribosomes in translation
8. Posttranslational modification of proteins, where it occurs, and how new proteins destined for extracellular use are packaged and released from a cell
9. How gene expression can be turned on or off according to the functions of different kinds of cells or physiological needs that change over time, such as a temporary need for breast milk
10. How the synthesis of nonproteins such as carbohydrates and steroids is regulated by the genes, even though genes code only for RNA or protein

### 4.3 DNA Replication and the Cell Cycle

1. Why every generation of cells must synthesize new DNA even though the chromosome number remains constant from generation to generation
2. Semiconservative replication, the enzymes that carry it out, and why it results in two DNA molecules that each contain one old and one new nucleotide polymer
3. What a mutation is and how a cell detects and corrects most mutations that arise during DNA replication; the varied consequences of uncorrected mutations
4. The four stages of the cell cycle, what occurs in each stage, and which stages occur during interphase
5. The functions of mitosis; its four stages; what occurs in each stage; and why the amount of DNA in a cell is halved by mitosis, yet the number of chromosomes remains the same
6. Cytokinesis and how it overlaps but differs from telophase
7. How mitosis can be either stimulated or inhibited according to the need for tissue maintenance or growth
8. How cyclins and cyclin-dependent kinases regulate the cell cycle

### 4.4 Chromosomes and Heredity

1. The definition of *heredity*
2. Organization of the karyotype; the number of homologous pairs of human chromosomes; why chromosomes occur in homologous pairs; and the differences between haploid and diploid cells and between germ cells and somatic cells
3. The differences between autosomes and sex chromosomes, and which sex chromosomes occur in males and females
4. Dominant and recessive alleles, the difference between homozygous and heterozygous individuals, and why a person can be homozygous for some alleles and heterozygous for others
5. The relationship of genotype to phenotype, the difference between the two, and why phenotype is not determined solely by genotype
6. Why a recessive trait can skip a generation, with examples; what is meant by a *carrier*
7. The differences between the genotype, genome, and gene pool; why a genotype can never be composed of more than two alleles of the same gene, but the gene pool can contain three or more alleles of one gene
8. How codominance and incomplete dominance differ from simple dominance of an allele
9. What polygenic inheritance and pleiotropy imply about the relationship between a certain phenotype and its associated genes; examples of both
10. Why some traits occur more in males than in females, the name of this phenomenon, and examples
11. Why some individuals may not exhibit the phenotype that one would predict from their genotype; the name for this incomplete expression of certain genotypes
12. Why it cannot be said that any human trait is exclusively the result of the genes or of the environment; an example that demonstrates this
13. Why it cannot be said that dominant alleles are the most common ones in a population and recessive alleles are less common; examples that support this point
14. The meaning of *gene expression* and the variety of factors that affect it
15. How heredity and health are affected not only by genetic changes (mutations) but also epigenetic ones

# STUDY GUIDE

## ▶ Testing Your Recall

*Answers in Appendix A*

1. Production of more than one phenotypic trait by a single gene is called
   a. pleiotropy.
   b. genetic determinism.
   c. codominance.
   d. penetrance.
   e. genetic recombination.

2. When a ribosome reads a codon on mRNA, it must bind to the ______ of a corresponding tRNA.
   a. start codon
   b. stop codon
   c. intron
   d. exon
   e. anticodon

3. The normal functions of a liver cell—synthesizing proteins, detoxifying wastes, storing glycogen, and so forth—are done during its
   a. anaphase.
   b. telophase.
   c. $G_1$ phase.
   d. $G_2$ phase.
   e. synthesis phase.

4. Two genetically identical strands of a metaphase chromosome, joined at the centromere, are its
   a. kinetochores.
   b. centrioles.
   c. sister chromatids.
   d. homologous chromatids.
   e. nucleosomes.

5. Which of the following is *not* found in DNA?
   a. thymine
   b. phosphate
   c. cytosine
   d. deoxyribose
   e. uracil

6. Genetic transcription is performed by
   a. ribosomes.
   b. RNA polymerase.
   c. DNA polymerase.
   d. helicase.
   e. chaperones.

7. A chaperone comes into play in
   a. the folding of a new protein into its tertiary structure.
   b. keeping DNA organized within the nucleus.
   c. escorting sister chromatids to opposite daughter cells during mitosis.
   d. repairing DNA that has been damaged by mutagens.
   e. preventing malignant cells from metastasizing.

8. An allele that is not phenotypically expressed in the presence of an alternative allele of the same gene is said to be
   a. codominant.
   b. lacking penetrance.
   c. heterozygous.
   d. recessive.
   e. subordinate.

9. Semiconservative replication occurs during
   a. transcription.
   b. translation.
   c. posttranslational modification.
   d. the S phase of the cell cycle.
   e. mitosis.

10. Mutagens sometimes cause no harm to cells for all of the following reasons *except*
    a. some mutagens are natural, harmless products of the cell itself.
    b. most of the human DNA does not code for any proteins.
    c. the body's DNA repair mechanisms detect and correct genetic damage.
    d. change in a codon does not always change the amino acid encoded by it.
    e. some mutations change protein structure in ways that are not critical to normal function.

11. The cytoplasmic division at the end of mitosis is called ______.

12. At the checkpoints of the cell cycle, proteins called cyclins bind to ______ and activate reactions that enable the cell to proceed to the next stage of the cycle.

13. The pattern of nitrogenous bases that represents the 20 amino acids of a protein is called the ______.

14. Several ribosomes attached to one mRNA, which they are all transcribing, form a cluster called a/an ______.

15. The enzyme that produces pre-mRNA from the instructions in DNA is ______.

16. All the DNA in a haploid set of chromosomes is called a person's ______.

17. At prophase, a cell has ______ chromosomes, ______ chromatids, and ______ molecules of DNA.

18. The cytoplasmic granule of RNA and protein that reads the message in mRNA is a/an ______.

19. Cells are stimulated to divide by chemical signals called ______.

20. All chromosomes except the sex chromosomes are called ______.

## ▶ Building Your Medical Vocabulary

*Answers in Appendix A*

*State a meaning of each word element, and give a medical term from this chapter that uses it or a slight variation of it.*

1. allo-
2. dactylo-
3. diplo-
4. haplo-
5. hetero-
6. karyo-
7. meta-
8. morpho-
9. muta-
10. poly-

# STUDY GUIDE

## What's Wrong with These Statements?

Answers in Appendix A

*Briefly explain why each of the following statements is false, or reword it to make it true.*

1. Proteins destined to be exported from a cell are made by ribosomes on the surface of the Golgi complex.
2. Steroids, carbohydrates, and phospholipids are encoded by different types of genes than are proteins.
3. Since uracil and thymine are very similar, a molecule of RNA would have about the same molecular weight as a stretch of DNA of the same length.
4. Each amino acid of a protein is represented by its own unique base pair in DNA.
5. Each gene codes for just one protein.
6. The law of complementary base pairing describes the way the bases in an mRNA codon pair up with the bases of a tRNA anticodon during translation.
7. All human DNA codes for the synthesis of proteins.
8. All mutations result in the production of defective proteins and are therefore harmful.
9. Males have only one sex chromosome whereas females have two.
10. A gene can be transcribed by only one RNA polymerase at a time.

## Testing Your Comprehension

1. Why would the supercoiled, condensed form of chromosomes seen in metaphase not be suitable for the $G_1$ phase of the cell cycle? Why would the finely dispersed chromatin of the $G_1$ phase not be suitable for mitosis?
2. Suppose a woman was heterozygous for blood type A and her husband had blood type AB. With the aid of a Punnett square, explain what blood type(s) their children could possibly have.
3. Given the information in this chapter, present an argument that evolution is not merely possible but inevitable. (*Hint:* Review the definition of *evolution* in chapter 1.)
4. What would be the minimum length (approximate number of bases) of an mRNA that coded for a protein 300 amino acids long?
5. Biology textbooks once taught the concept of "one gene, one protein"—that a gene is a segment of DNA that codes for just one protein, and every protein is represented by a separate, unique gene. Discuss the evidence that shows that this can no longer be regarded as true.

CHAPTER 5

# THE HUMAN TISSUES

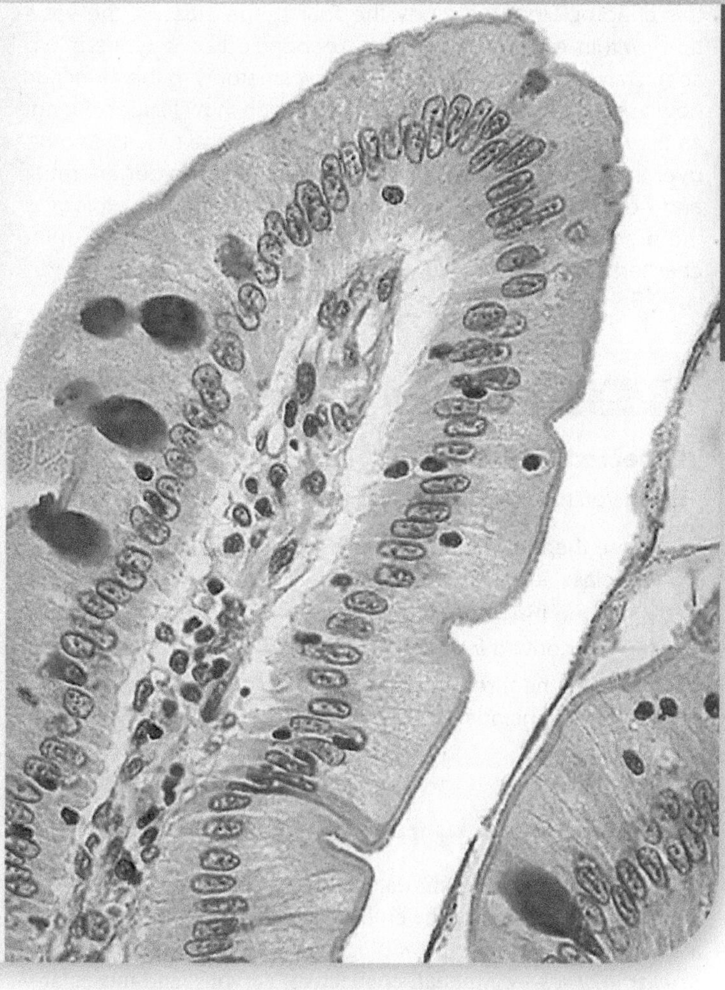

**The lining of the small intestine, showing simple columnar epithelium with mucus-secreting goblet cells (magenta) (LM)**
Victor P. Eroschenko

## CHAPTER OUTLINE



## DEEPER INSIGHTS

**Module 3: Tissues**

## BRUSHING UP

- This chapter details the structure of the body's serous and mucous membranes; refresh your memory of where such membranes are found in atlas A, section A.3.
- Connective tissues are characterized by a large amount of ground substance, two of the chief components of which are the glycoproteins and proteoglycans introduced in section 2.4c.
- The terminology of cell shapes introduced in figure 3.1 is used in the naming of epithelial tissue in this chapter.
- Secretory vesicles and exocytosis (see section 3.3f) are central to understanding the gland types to be introduced in this chapter.

With its 50 trillion cells and thousands of organs, the human body may seem to be a structure of forbidding complexity. Fortunately for our health, longevity, and self-understanding, biologists of the past were not discouraged by this complexity, but discovered patterns that made it more understandable. One such pattern is the fact that these trillions of cells belong to only 200 types or so, and they are organized into tissues that fall into just four primary categories—*epithelial, connective, nervous,* and *muscular tissue*—although there are at least 23 subtypes of these four.

Organs derive their function not from their cells alone but from how the cells are organized into tissues. Cells are specialized for certain tasks: muscle contraction, defense, enzyme secretion, and so forth. No one cell type can carry out all of the body's vital functions. Cells therefore work together at certain tasks and form tissues that carry out a particular function, such as nerve signaling or nutrient digestion. An organ is a structure with discrete boundaries that is composed of two or more tissue types.

The study of tissues and how they are arranged into organs is called **histology,**[1] or **microscopic anatomy**—the subject of this chapter. Here we study the four tissue classes; the variations within each class; how to recognize tissue types microscopically and relate their microscopic anatomy to their function; how tissues are arranged to form an organ; how tissues change as they grow, shrink, or change from one tissue type to another over the life of the individual; and modes of tissue degeneration and death. Histology bridges the gap between the cytology of the preceding chapters and the organ system approach of the chapters that follow.

[1]*histo* = tissue; *logy* = study of

## 5.1 The Study of Tissues

**Expected Learning Outcomes**

When you have completed this section, you should be able to

a. name the four primary classes into which all adult tissues are classified;
b. name the three embryonic germ layers and some adult tissues derived from each; and
c. visualize the three-dimensional shape of a structure from a two-dimensional tissue section.

### 5.1a The Primary Tissue Classes

A **tissue** is a group of similar cells and cell products that arise from the same region of the embryo and work together to perform a specific structural or physiological role in an organ. The four *primary tissues*—epithelial, connective, nervous, and muscular—are summarized in **table 5.1.** They differ in the types and functions of their cells, the characteristics of the **matrix (extracellular material)** that surrounds the cells, and the relative amount of space occupied by the cells and matrix. In muscle and epithelium, the cells are so close together that the matrix is scarcely visible, but in most connective tissues, the matrix occupies much more space than the cells do.

**TABLE 5.1 The Four Primary Tissue Classes**

| Type | Definition | Representative Locations |
|---|---|---|
| Epithelial | Tissue composed of layers of closely spaced cells that cover organ surfaces, form glands, and serve for protection, secretion, and absorption | Epidermis<br>Inner lining of digestive tract<br>Liver and other glands |
| Connective | Tissue with usually more matrix than cell volume, often specialized to support and protect organs and to bind other tissues and organs to each other | Tendons and ligaments<br>Cartilage and bone<br>Blood |
| Nervous | Tissue containing excitable cells specialized for rapid transmission of coded information to other cells | Brain<br>Spinal cord<br>Nerves |
| Muscular | Tissue composed of elongated, excitable muscle cells specialized for contraction | Skeletal muscles<br>Heart (cardiac muscle)<br>Walls of viscera (smooth muscle) |

Photos (Epithelial): ©Ed Reschke/Getty Images; (Connective): Dennis Strete/McGraw-Hill Education; (Nervous, Muscular): Ed Reschke

The matrix is composed of fibrous proteins and, usually, a clear gel variously known as **ground substance, tissue fluid, extracellular fluid (ECF),** or **interstitial[2] fluid.** In cartilage and bone, it can be rubbery or stony in consistency. The ground substance contains water, gases, minerals, nutrients, wastes, hormones, and other chemicals. This is the medium from which all cells obtain their oxygen, nutrients, and other needs, and into which cells release metabolic wastes, hormones, and other products.

In summary, a tissue is composed of cells and matrix, and the matrix is composed of fibers and ground substance.

## 5.1b Embryonic Tissues

Human development begins with a single cell, the fertilized egg, which soon divides to produce scores of identical, smaller cells. The first tissues appear when these cells start to organize themselves into layers—first two, and soon three strata called the **primary germ layers,** which give rise to all of the body's mature tissues. The three primary germ layers are called *ectoderm, mesoderm,* and *endoderm.* The **ectoderm**[3] is an outer layer that gives rise to the epidermis and nervous system. The innermost layer, the **endoderm,**[4] gives rise to the mucous membranes of the digestive and respiratory tracts and to the digestive glands, among other things. Between these two is the **mesoderm,**[5] a layer of more loosely organized cells. Mesoderm eventually turns to a gelatinous tissue called **mesenchyme,** composed of fine, wispy collagen (protein) fibers and branching *mesenchymal cells* embedded in a gelatinous ground substance. Mesenchyme gives rise to cardiac muscle, bone, and blood, among other tissues. (The development of the three primary tissues in the embryo is detailed at "Embryogenesis" in section 29.1f.) Most organs are composed of tissues derived from two or more primary germ layers. The rest of this chapter concerns the "mature" tissues that exist from infancy through adulthood.

## 5.1c Interpreting Tissue Sections

In your study of histology, you may be presented with various tissue preparations mounted on microscope slides. Most such preparations are thin slices called **histological sections.** The best anatomical insight depends on an ability to deduce the three-dimensional structure of an organ from these two-dimensional sections **(fig. 5.1).** This ability, in turn, depends on an awareness of how tissues are prepared for study.

[2]*inter* = between; *stit* = to stand
[3]*ecto* = outer; *derm* = skin
[4]*endo* = inner; *derm* = skin
[5]*meso* = middle; *derm* = skin

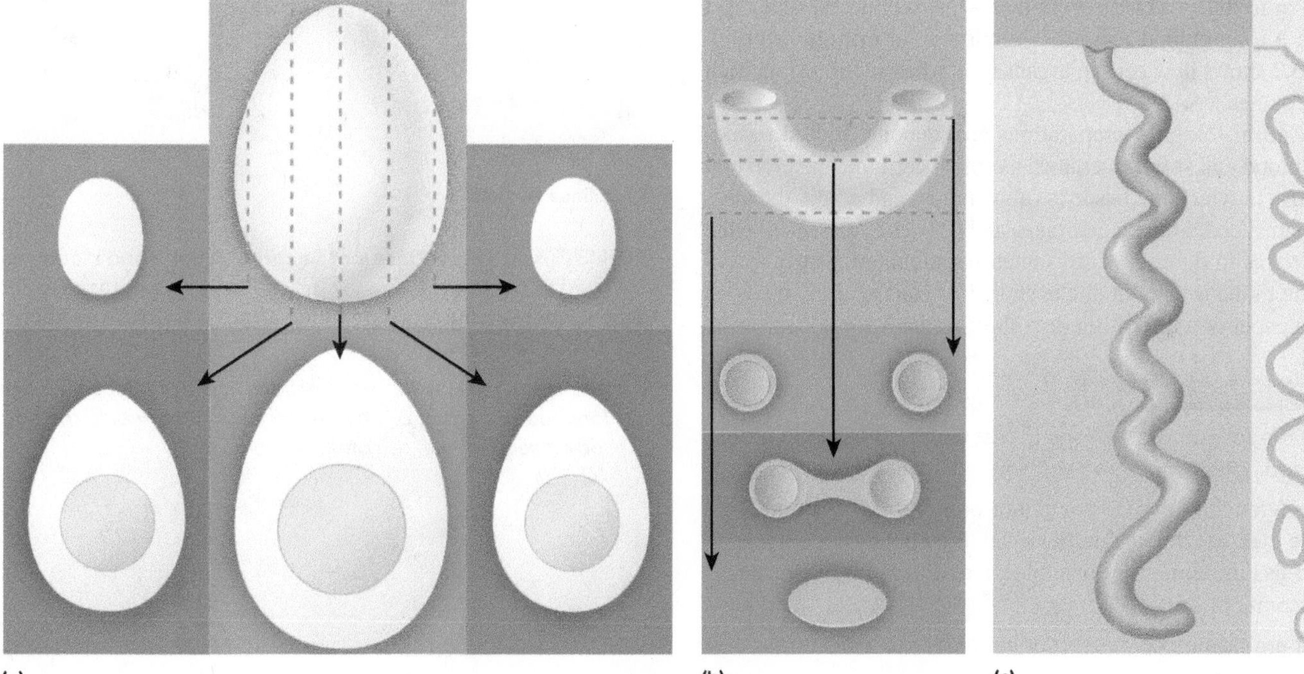


**FIGURE 5.1 Three-Dimensional Interpretation of Two-Dimensional Images.** (a) A boiled egg. Grazing sections (top left and right) would miss the yolk, just as a tissue section may miss a nucleus or other structure. (b) Elbow macaroni, which resembles many curved ducts and tubules. A section far from the bend would give the impression of two separate tubules; a section near the bend would show two interconnected lumina (cavities); and a section still farther down could miss the lumen completely. (c) A coiled gland in three dimensions and as it would look in a vertical tissue section of a tissue such as the lining of the uterus.

Histologists use a variety of techniques for preserving, sectioning (slicing), and staining tissues to show their structural details as clearly as possible. Tissue specimens are preserved in a **fixative**—a chemical such as formalin that prevents decay. After fixation, most tissues are cut into sections typically only one or two cells thick. Sectioning is necessary to allow the light of a microscope to pass through and so the image is not confused by too many layers of overlapping cells. The sections are then mounted on slides and artificially colored with histological **stains** to enhance detail. If they were not stained, most tissue sections would appear pale gray. With stains that bind to different components of a tissue, however, you may see pink cytoplasm; violet nuclei; and blue, green, or golden-brown protein fibers, depending on the stain used.

Sectioning a tissue reduces a three-dimensional structure to a series of two-dimensional slices. You must keep this in mind and try to translate the microscopic image into a mental image of the whole structure. Like the boiled egg and elbow macaroni in figure 5.1, an object may look quite different when it is cut at various levels, or *planes of section.* A coiled tube, such as a gland of the uterus (fig. 5.1c), is often broken up into multiple portions since it meanders in and out of the plane of section. An experienced viewer, however, recognizes that the separated pieces are parts of a single tube winding its way to the organ surface. Note that a grazing slice through a boiled egg might miss the yolk, just as a tissue section might miss the nucleus of a cell even though it was present.

Many anatomical structures are longer on one axis than another—the humerus and esophagus, for example. A tissue cut on its long axis is called a **longitudinal section (l.s.),** and one cut perpendicular to this is a **cross section (c.s.).** A section cut on a slant between a longitudinal and cross section is an **oblique section. Figure 5.2** shows how certain organs look when sectioned on each of these planes.

Not all histological preparations are sections. Liquid tissues such as blood and soft tissues such as spinal cord may be prepared as **smears,** in which the tissue is rubbed or spread across the slide rather than sliced. Some membranes and cobwebby tissues like the *areolar tissue* in figure 5.14 are sometimes mounted as **spreads,** in which the tissue is laid out on the slide, like placing a small square of tissue paper or a tuft of lint on a sheet of glass.

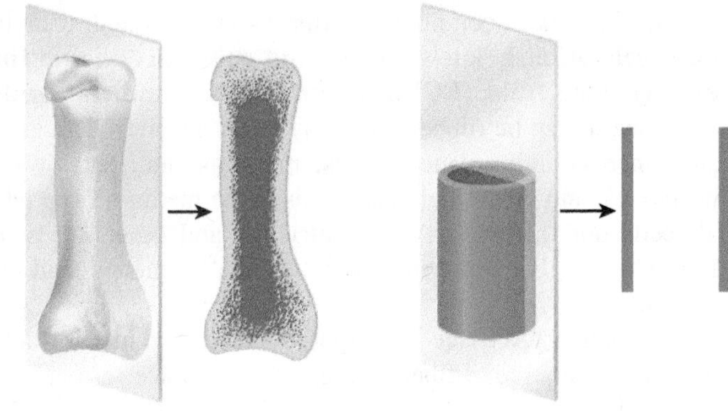

**(a) Longitudinal sections**

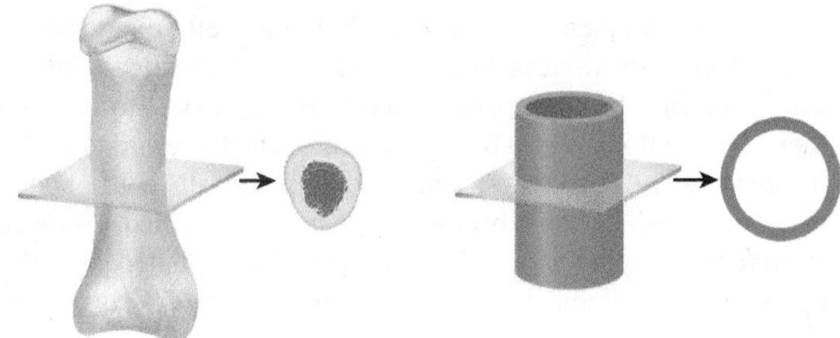

**(b) Cross sections**

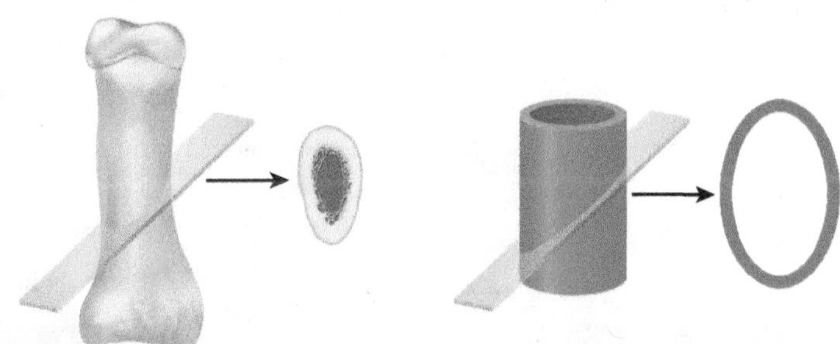

**(c) Oblique sections**

FIGURE 5.2 **Three Planes of Section.** A bone and blood vessel are used to relate two-dimensional sectioned appearance to three-dimensional structure. (a) Longitudinal sections. (b) Cross sections. (c) Oblique sections.

? *Would you classify the egg sections in the previous figure as longitudinal, cross, or oblique sections? How would the egg look if sectioned in the other two planes?*

## BEFORE YOU GO ON

Answer the following questions to test your understanding of the preceding section:

1. Classify each of the following into one of the four primary tissue classes: the skin surface, fat, the spinal cord, most heart tissue, bone, tendons, blood, and the inner lining of the stomach.
2. What are tissues composed of in addition to cells?
3. What embryonic germ layer gives rise to nervous tissue? To the liver? To muscle?
4. What is the term for a thin, stained slice of tissue mounted on a microscope slide?

## 5.2 Epithelial Tissue

**Expected Learning Outcomes**

When you have completed this section, you should be able to

a. describe the properties that distinguish epithelium from other tissue classes;
b. list and classify eight types of epithelium, distinguish them from each other, and state where each type can be found in the body;
c. explain how the structural differences between epithelia relate to their functional differences; and
d. visually recognize each epithelial type from specimens or photographs.

**Epithelial**[6] **tissue** consists of a sheet of closely adhering cells, one or more cells thick, with the upper surface usually exposed to the environment or to an internal space in the body. Epithelium covers the body surface, lines body cavities, forms the external and internal linings of many organs, and constitutes most gland tissue. The functions of epithelial tissue include

- **Protection.** Epithelia protect deeper tissues from invasion and injury. The epidermis of the skin, for example, is a barrier to infection, and the inner lining of the stomach protects its deeper tissues from stomach acid and enzymes.
- **Secretion.** Epithelia produce mucus, sweat, enzymes, hormones, and most of the body's other secretions; glands are composed largely of epithelial tissue.
- **Excretion.** Epithelia void wastes from the tissues, such as $CO_2$ across the pulmonary epithelium and bile from the epithelium of the liver.
- **Absorption.** Epithelia absorb chemicals from the adjacent medium; nutrients, for example, are absorbed through the epithelium of the small intestine.
- **Filtration.** All substances leaving the blood are selectively filtered through the epithelium that lines the blood vessels; all urinary waste is filtered through epithelia of the kidneys.
- **Sensation.** Epithelia are provided with nerve endings that sense stimulation ranging from a touch on the skin to irritation of the stomach.

The cells and extracellular material of an epithelium can be loosely compared to the bricks and mortar of a wall. The extracellular material ("mortar") is so thin, however, that it is barely visible with a light microscope, and the cells appear pressed very close together. Epithelia are *avascular*[7] (without blood vessels)—there is no room for them between the cells. Epithelia, however, usually lie on a vessel-rich layer of connective tissue, which furnishes them with nutrients and waste removal. Epithelial cells closest to the connective tissue typically exhibit a high rate of mitosis. This allows epithelia to repair themselves quickly—an ability of special importance in protective epithelia that are highly vulnerable to such injuries as skin abrasions and erosion by stomach acid.

Between an epithelium and the underlying connective tissue is a layer called the **basement membrane.** It contains collagen, glycoproteins, and other protein–carbohydrate complexes, and blends into other proteins of the connective tissue. The basement membrane serves to anchor an epithelium to the connective tissue; it controls the exchange of materials between the epithelium and the underlying tissues; and it binds growth factors from below that regulate epithelial development. The surface of an epithelial cell that faces the basement membrane is its **basal surface,** the one that faces away from it toward the body surface or the internal cavity (lumen) of an organ is the **apical surface,** and between these two, the "sidewall" of a cell is called the **lateral surface.**

Epithelia are classified into two broad categories—*simple* and *stratified*—with four types in each category. In a simple epithelium, every cell is anchored to the basement membrane, whereas in a stratified epithelium, some cells rest on top of other cells and do not contact the basement membrane **(fig. 5.3).**

**Table 5.2** (containing **figs. 5.4** to **5.7**) summarizes the structural and functional differences between the four simple epithelia. In this and subsequent tables, each photograph is accompanied by a labeled drawing of the same specimen. The drawings clarify cell boundaries and other relevant features that may otherwise be difficult to see or identify in photographs or through the microscope. Each figure indicates the approximate magnification at which the original photograph was made. Each is enlarged much more than this when printed in the book, but selecting the closest magnification on a microscope should enable you to see a comparable level of detail (resolution).

### 5.2a Simple Epithelia

Generally, a **simple epithelium** has only one layer of cells, although this is a somewhat debatable point in the *pseudostratified columnar* type. Three types of simple epithelia are named for the shapes of their cells: **simple squamous**[8] (thin scaly cells), **simple cuboidal** (squarish or round cells), and **simple columnar** (tall narrow cells). In the fourth type, **pseudostratified columnar,** not all cells reach the surface; the shorter cells are covered by the taller ones. This epithelium looks stratified in most tissue sections, but careful examination, especially with the electron microscope, shows that every cell reaches the basement membrane—like trees in a forest, where some grow taller than others but all are anchored in the soil below.

Simple columnar and pseudostratified columnar epithelia often have wineglass-shaped **goblet cells** that produce protective

[6] *epi* = upon; *theli* = nipple, female
[7] *a* = without; *vas* = blood vessels
[8] *squam* = scale

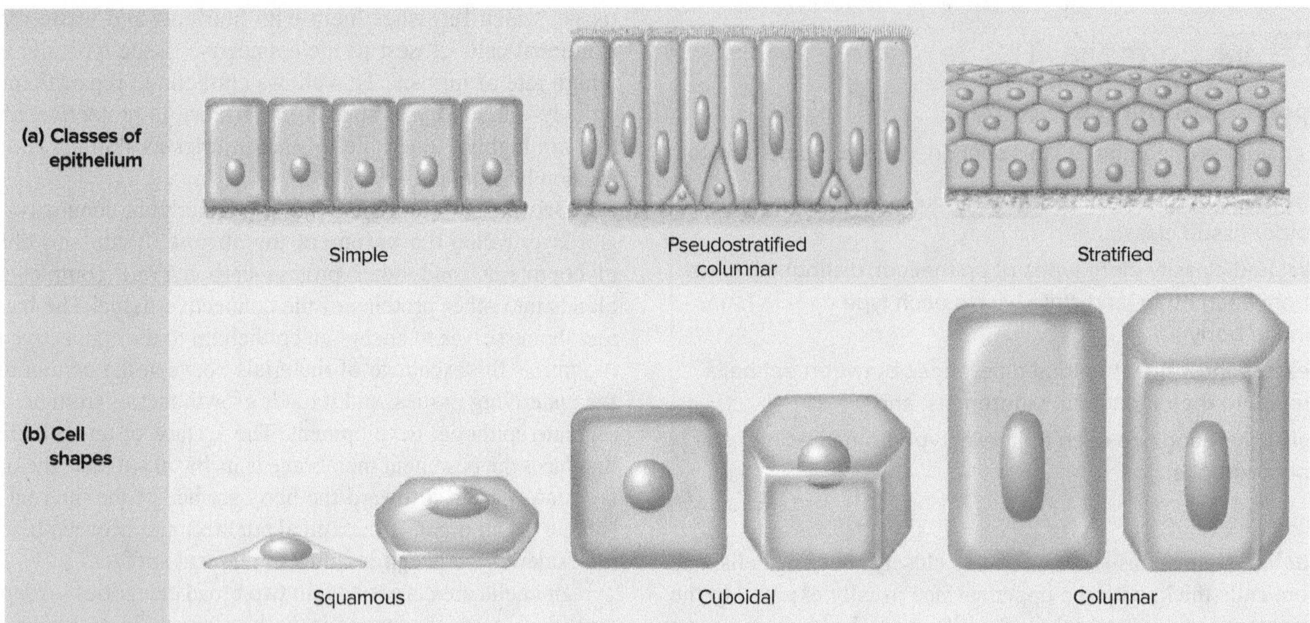


**FIGURE 5.3 Cell Shapes and Epithelial Types.** (a) Frontal sections of three classes of epithelium. Pseudostratified columnar epithelium is a special type of simple epithelium that gives a false appearance of multiple cell layers. (b) Frontal and oblique views of three cell shapes—squamous, cuboidal, and columnar. Note that these traditional terms describe the frontal appearance, but all three are polygonal when viewed from above.

mucous coatings over the mucous membranes. These cells have an expanded apical end filled with secretory vesicles; their product becomes mucus when it is secreted and absorbs water. The basal part of the cell is a narrow stem, like that of a wineglass, that reaches to the basement membrane.

### 5.2b Stratified Epithelia

**Stratified epithelia** range from 2 to 20 or more layers of cells, with some cells resting directly on others and only the deepest layer attached to the basement membrane **(table 5.3,** containing **figs. 5.8** to **5.11).** Three of the stratified epithelia are named for the shapes of their surface cells: **stratified squamous, stratified cuboidal,** and **stratified columnar epithelia.** The deeper cells, however, may be of a different shape than the surface cells. The fourth type, **urothelium,** is named for the fact that it's unique to the urinary tract. It is sometimes called by an older name, *transitional epithelium,* that arose from a misunderstanding that it represented a transitional stage between stratified squamous and stratified columnar epithelium.

Stratified columnar epithelium is rare and of relatively minor importance—seen only in places where two other epithelial types meet, as in limited regions of the pharynx, larynx, anal canal, and male urethra. We will not consider this type any further.

The most widespread epithelium in the body is stratified squamous epithelium, which deserves further discussion. Its deepest layer of cells are cuboidal to columnar, and include mitotically active stem cells. Their daughter cells push toward the surface and become flatter (more scaly) as they migrate farther upward, until they finally die and flake off. Their loss is called **exfoliation (desquamation) (fig. 5.12);** the study of exfoliated cells is called *exfoliate cytology.* You can easily study exfoliated cells by scraping your gums with a toothpick, smearing this material on a slide, and staining it with iodine for microscopic examination. A similar procedure is used in the *Pap smear,* an examination of exfoliated cells from the cervix for signs of uterine cancer (see fig. 28.5).

Stratified squamous epithelia are of two kinds—keratinized and nonkeratinized. A **keratinized (cornified)** epithelium, found in the epidermis, is covered with a layer of dead compressed cells. These cells, called **keratinocytes,** are packed with the durable protein *keratin* and coated with a water-repellent glycolipid. The skin surface is therefore relatively dry; it retards water loss from the body; and it resists penetration by disease organisms. (Keratin is also the protein of which animal horns are made, hence its name.[9]) The tongue, esophagus, vagina, and a few other internal membranes are covered with the **nonkeratinized** type, which lacks the surface layer of dead cells. This type provides a surface that is, again, abrasion-resistant, but also moist and slippery. These characteristics are well suited to resist stress produced by chewing and swallowing food and by sexual intercourse and childbirth.

Urothelium is another particularly interesting type of stratified epithelium. Why is it limited to the urinary tract? The answer relates to the fact that urine is usually acidic and hypertonic to the intracellular fluid. It would tend to draw water out of the cells by osmosis and kill them if there were nothing to protect them. The

*(text continued after table 5.3)*

[9] *kerat* = horn

## TABLE 5.2 Simple Epithelia

### Simple Squamous Epithelium

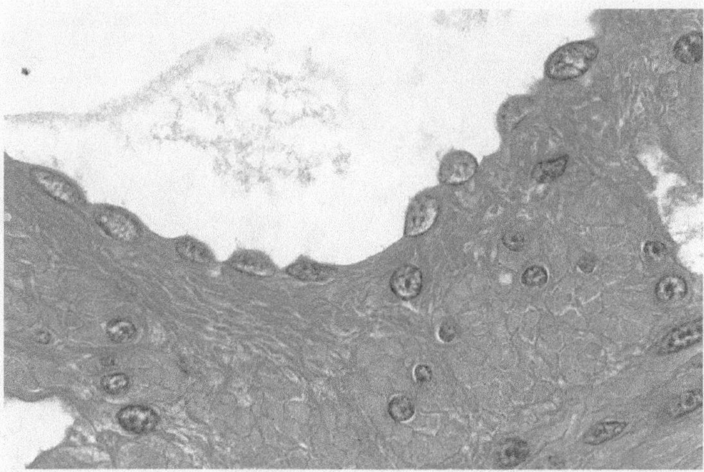

(a)

Squamous epithelial cells
Nuclei of smooth muscle
Basement membrane

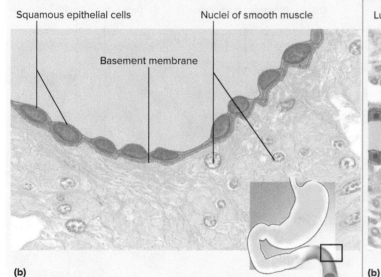

(b)

**FIGURE 5.4 Simple Squamous Epithelium.** Serosa of the small intestine (×400). (a) Light micrograph. (b) Labeled drawing. APR

a: Dennis Strete/McGraw-Hill Education

**Microscopic appearance:** Single layer of thin cells, shaped like fried eggs with bulge where nucleus is located; nucleus flattened in the plane of the cell, like an egg yolk; cytoplasm may be so thin it is hard to see in tissue sections; in surface view, cells have angular contours and nuclei appear round

**Representative locations:** Air sacs (alveoli) of lungs; glomerular capsules of kidneys; some kidney tubules; inner lining (endothelium) of heart and blood vessels; serous membranes of stomach, intestines, and some other viscera; surface mesothelium of pleura, pericardium, peritoneum, and mesenteries

**Functions:** Allows rapid diffusion or transport of substances through membrane; secretes lubricating serous fluid

### Simple Cuboidal Epithelium

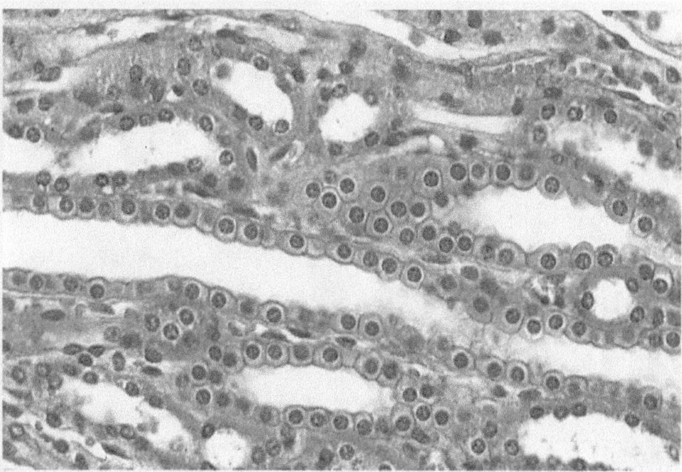

(a)

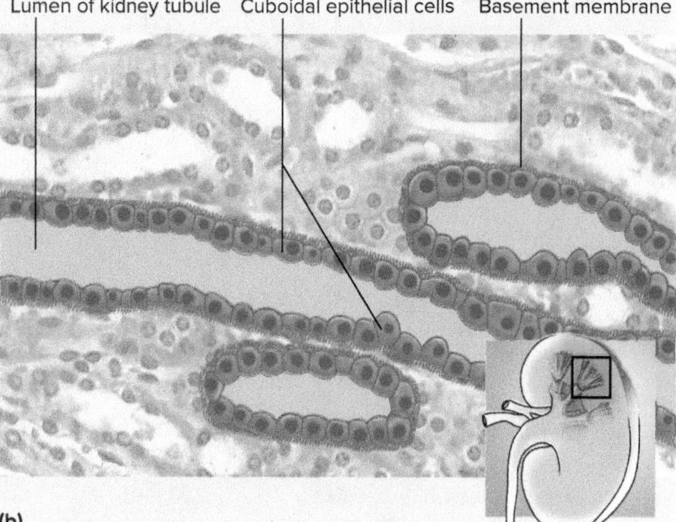


(b)

**FIGURE 5.5 Simple Cuboidal Epithelium.** Kidney tubules (×400). (a) Light micrograph. (b) Labeled drawing. APR

a: Dennis Strete/McGraw-Hill Education

**Microscopic appearance:** Single layer of square or round cells; in glands, cells often pyramidal and arranged like segments of an orange around a central space; spherical, centrally placed nuclei; with a brush border of microvilli in some kidney tubules; ciliated in bronchioles of lung

**Representative locations:** Liver, thyroid, mammary, salivary, and other glands; most kidney tubules; bronchioles

**Functions:** Absorption and secretion; production of protective mucous coat; movement of respiratory mucus

**TABLE 5.2** **Simple Epithelia *(continued)***

**Simple Columnar Epithelium**

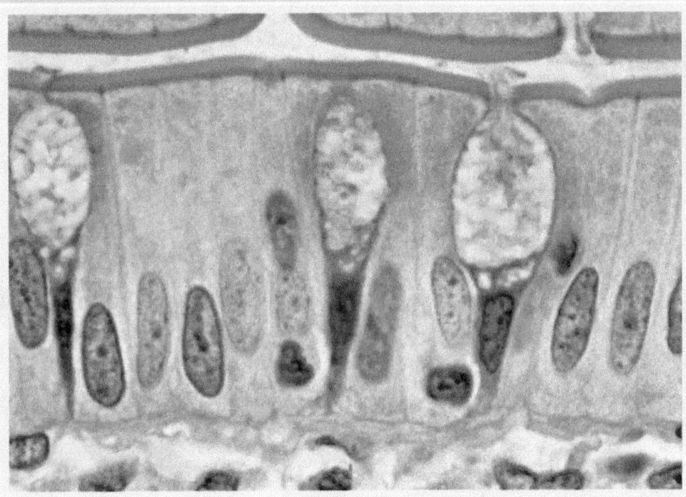

(a)

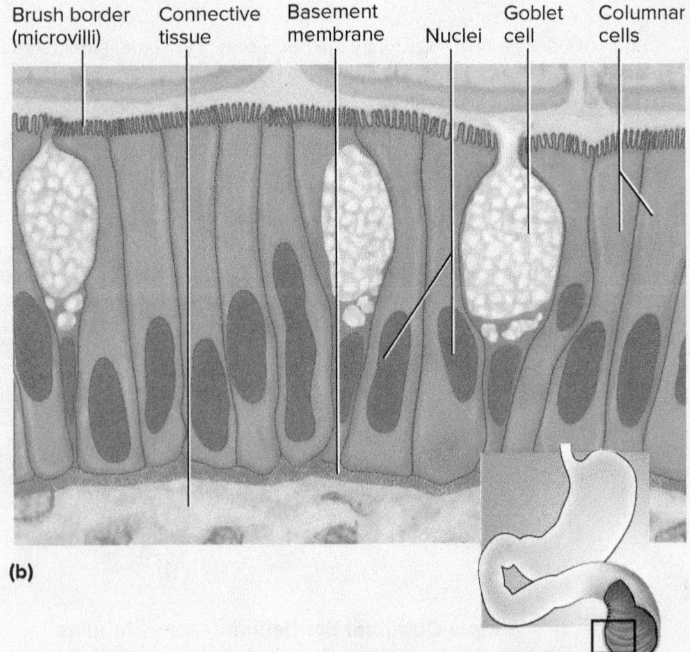


(b)

**FIGURE 5.6 Simple Columnar Epithelium.** Mucosa of the small intestine (×400). (a) Light micrograph. (b) Labeled drawing. APR

a: Ed Reschke/Getty Images

**Microscopic appearance:** Single layer of tall, narrow cells; oval or sausage-shaped nuclei, vertically oriented, usually in basal half of cell; apical portion of cell often shows secretory vesicles visible with TEM; often shows a brush border of microvilli; ciliated in some organs; may possess goblet cells

**Representative locations:** Inner lining of stomach, intestines, gallbladder, uterus, and uterine tubes; some kidney tubules

**Functions:** Absorption; secretion of mucus and other products; movement of egg and embryo in uterine tube

**Pseudostratified Columnar Epithelium**

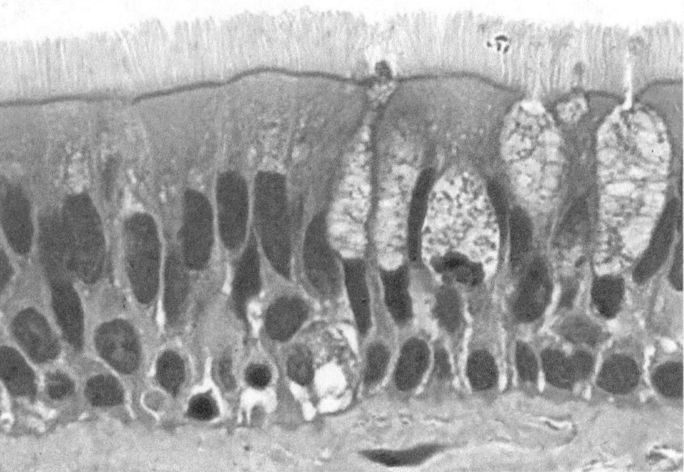

(a)

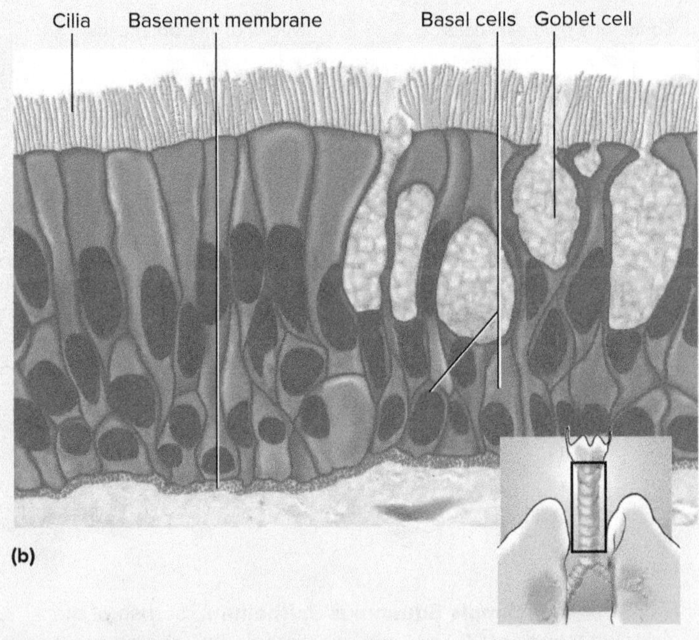


(b)

**FIGURE 5.7 Ciliated Pseudostratified Columnar Epithelium.** Mucosa of the trachea (×400). (a) Light micrograph. (b) Labeled drawing. APR

a: Dennis Strete/McGraw-Hill Education

**Microscopic appearance:** Looks multilayered; some cells do not reach free surface, but all cells reach basement membrane; nuclei at several levels in deeper half of epithelium; often with goblet cells; often ciliated

**Representative locations:** Respiratory tract from nasal cavity to bronchi; portions of male urethra

**Functions:** Secretes and propels mucus

## TABLE 5.3 Stratified Epithelia

### Stratified Squamous Epithelium—Keratinized

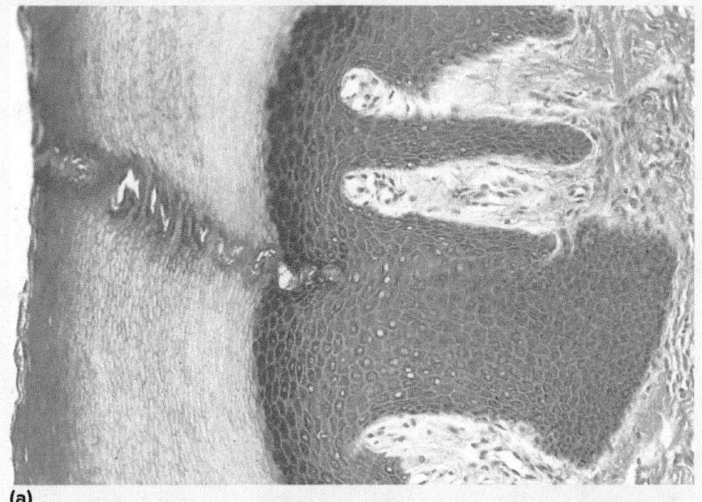
(a)

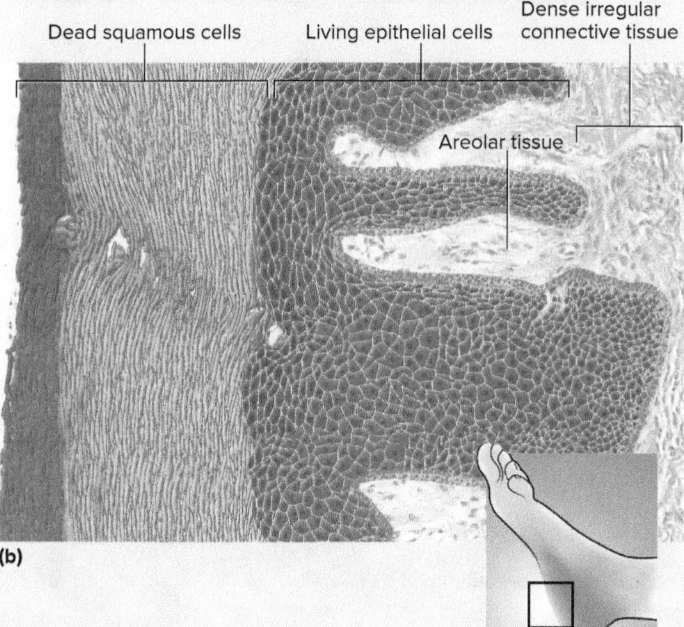


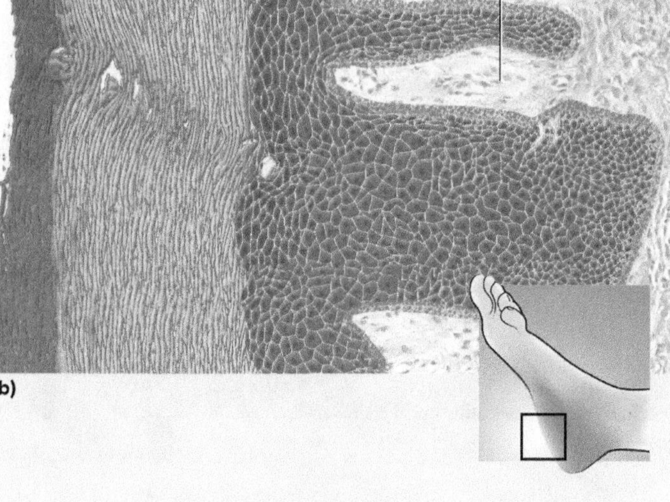
(b)

**FIGURE 5.8 Keratinized Stratified Squamous Epithelium.** Epidermis of the sole of the foot (×400). (a) Light micrograph. (b) Labeled drawing. APR

a: ©Ed Reschke

**Microscopic appearance:** Multiple cell layers with cells becoming increasingly flat and scaly toward surface; surface covered with a layer of compact dead cells without nuclei; basal cells may be cuboidal to columnar

**Representative locations:** Epidermis; palms and soles are especially heavily keratinized

**Functions:** Resists abrasion and penetration by pathogenic organisms; retards water loss through skin

### Stratified Squamous Epithelium—Nonkeratinized

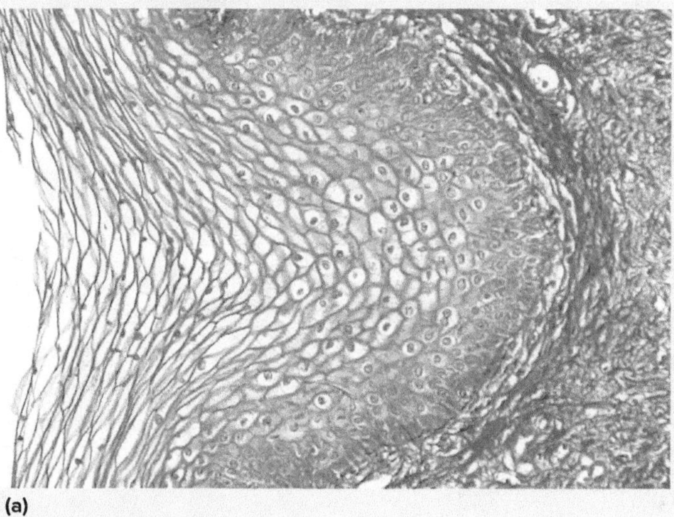
(a)

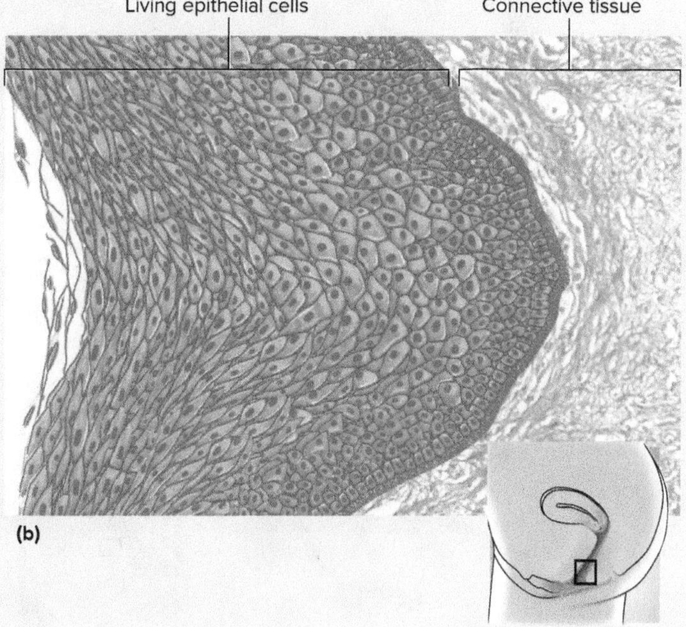

(b)

**FIGURE 5.9 Nonkeratinized Stratified Squamous Epithelium.** Mucosa of the vagina (×400). (a) Light micrograph. (b) Labeled drawing. APR

a: ©Ed Reschke

**Microscopic appearance:** Same as keratinized epithelium but without the surface layer of dead cells

**Representative locations:** Tongue, oral mucosa, esophagus, anal canal, vagina

**Functions:** Resists abrasion and penetration by pathogenic organisms

## TABLE 5.3 Stratified Epithelia *(continued)*

### Stratified Cuboidal Epithelium

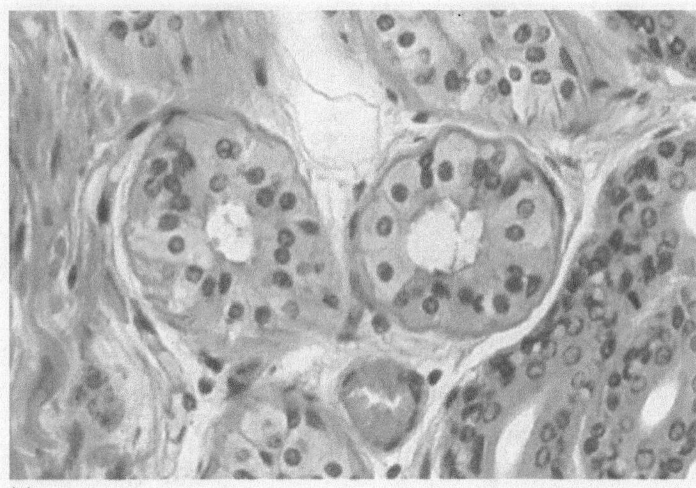

(a)

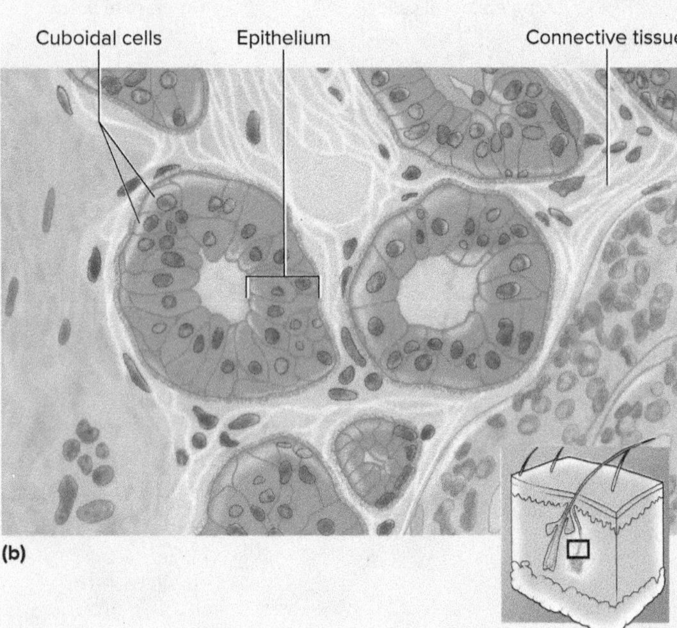


(b)

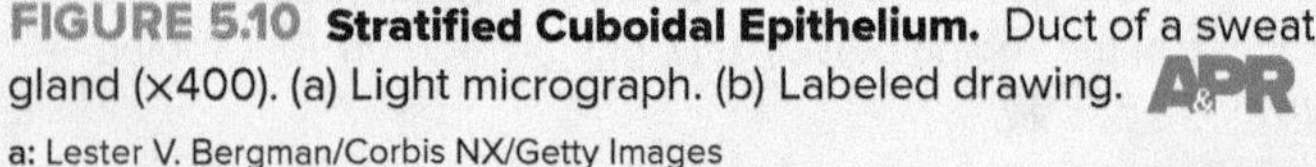

**FIGURE 5.10 Stratified Cuboidal Epithelium.** Duct of a sweat gland (×400). (a) Light micrograph. (b) Labeled drawing. APR

a: Lester V. Bergman/Corbis NX/Getty Images

**Microscopic appearance:** Two or more layers of cells; surface cells square or round

**Representative locations:** Sweat gland ducts; egg-producing vesicles (follicles) of ovaries; sperm-producing ducts (seminiferous tubules) of testis

**Functions:** Contributes to sweat secretion; secretes ovarian hormones; produces sperm

### Urothelium

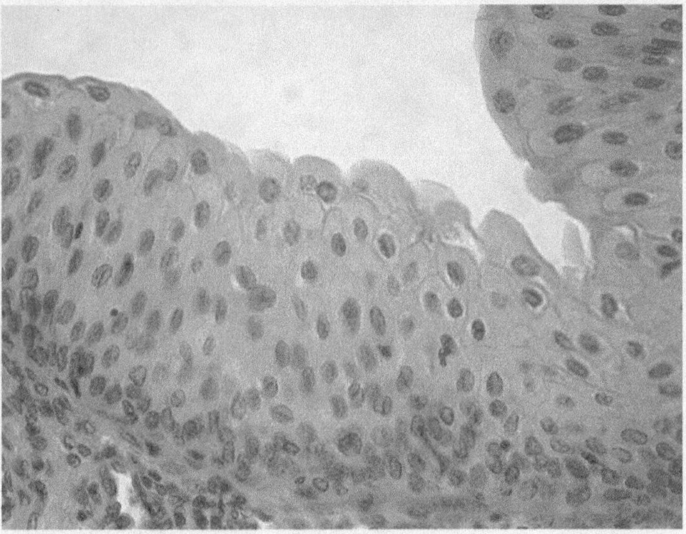

(a)

Basement membrane
Connective tissue
Binucleate epithelial cell

(b)

**FIGURE 5.11 Urothelium.** Kidney (×400). (a) Light micrograph. (b) Labeled drawing. APR

a: Johnny R. Howze

**Microscopic appearance:** Somewhat resembles stratified squamous epithelium, but surface cells are rounded, not flattened, and often bulge at surface; typically five or six cells thick when relaxed and two or three cells thick when stretched; cells may be flatter and thinner when urothelium is stretched (as in a distended bladder); some cells have two nuclei

**Representative locations:** Urinary tract—part of kidney, ureter, bladder, part of urethra

**Functions:** Stretches to allow filling of urinary tract; protects underlying tissues from osmotic damage by urine

**FIGURE 5.12 Exfoliation of Squamous Cells from the Mucosa of the Vagina.**

David M. Phillips/Science Source

? *Aside from the gums and vagina, name another epithelium in the body that would look like this to the scanning electron microscope.*

domed surface cells of urothelium, however, have a unique protective property. They are called **umbrella cells.** On the upper surface of an umbrella cell, the outer phospholipid layer of the plasma membrane is thicker than usual and has dense patches called *lipid rafts* with embedded proteins called *uroplakins.* Uroplakins are impermeable to urine and protect the urothelium, including the cytoplasm of the umbrella cell itself. Lipid rafts are connected to each other by hinges of ordinary plasma membrane. When the bladder is empty and relaxed, these plaques fold at the hinges (like folding a laptop computer) and drop into the cell interior for storage, and the cell bulges upward as seen in figure 5.11. As the bladder fills with urine, the hinges open (like opening the computer), the plaques spread out over the surface to protect the cell, and the umbrella cells become thinner and flatter. Not surprisingly, this type of epithelium is best developed in the bladder, where it is subject to prolonged contact with stored urine.

**BEFORE YOU GO ON**

Answer the following questions to test your understanding of the preceding section:

5. Distinguish between simple and stratified epithelia, and explain why pseudostratified columnar epithelium belongs in the former category despite its superficial appearance.
6. Explain how to distinguish a stratified squamous epithelium from a urothelium.
7. What function do keratinized and nonkeratinized stratified squamous epithelia have in common? What is the structural difference between these two? How is this structural difference related to a functional difference between them?
8. How do the epithelia of the esophagus and stomach differ? How does this relate to their respective functions?

## DEEPER INSIGHT 5.1
### CLINICAL APPLICATION

### Biopsy

*Biopsy*[10] means the removal and microscopic examination of a sample of living tissue. One purpose of a biopsy is diagnosis of diseases that can be identified only from the microscopic appearance of cells or tissues—for example, a malignancy such as colon cancer, an infection such as tuberculosis, or an inflammatory disease such as lupus. Diagnosis may include the *staging* of a cancer to express how advanced it is. (See Deeper Insight 28.1, Pap Smears and Cervical Cancer.) Another purpose is treatment planning. The appropriate drug for cancer chemotherapy, for example, may depend on the type of cancer revealed by the biopsy, and for cervical or breast cancer, it depends on the stage of the cancer. A third purpose is surgical guidance. A specimen from a patient undergoing lumpectomy for breast cancer, for example, may be examined for *clear margins* so the surgeon can know if all the malignant tissue has been removed or it is necessary to cut more widely.

Cutting out and examining an entire suspicious mass, such as a breast lump or lymph node, is called *excisional biopsy*. An *incisional (core) biopsy* is removal of just a portion of the mass, such as a suspected skin melanoma, for diagnostic examination. A *needle biopsy* may be done to obtain a sample of cells when it isn't necessary to maintain the exact structure of the tissue, such as a sample of bone marrow for the diagnosis of leukemia. Sucking out such a specimen with a needle is called *needle aspiration biopsy*. Some needle biopsies employ an instrument with jaws, inserted through a needle, to take a "bite" of the suspicious tissue or remove an entire mass such as a colon polyp. In some procedures called *CT guided needle biopsy*, exact placement of the needle is guided by watching it on a CT monitor.

In some cases, the biopsy specimen will be examined by an in-house pathologist while the patient is still under anesthesia and the surgeon awaits the lab report in order to know how to proceed. In outpatient cases, a specimen such as a lymph node may be sent to a medical diagnostics laboratory elsewhere, which will report the result back to the physician.

[10] *bio* = living; *opsy* = *viewing*

## 5.3 Connective Tissue

**Expected Learning Outcomes**

When you have completed this section, you should be able to

a. describe the properties that most connective tissues have in common;
b. discuss the types of cells found in connective tissue;
c. explain what the matrix of a connective tissue is and describe its components;
d. name and classify 10 types of connective tissue, describe their cellular components and matrix, and explain what distinguishes them from each other; and
e. visually recognize each connective tissue type from specimens or photographs.

### 5.3a Overview

**Connective tissues** are the most abundant, widely distributed, and histologically variable of the primary tissues. They include fibrous tissue, adipose tissue, cartilage, bone, and blood. Such diverse tissues may seem to have little in common, but as a rule, their cells occupy less space than the extracellular matrix. Usually their cells are not in direct contact with each other, but are separated by expanses of matrix. Connective tissues vary greatly in vascularity, from rich networks of blood vessels in the loose connective tissues to few or no blood vessels in cartilage.

The functions of connective tissue include

- **Binding of organs.** Tendons bind muscle to bone, ligaments bind one bone to another, fat holds the kidneys and eyes in place, and fibrous tissue binds the skin to underlying muscle.
- **Support.** Bones support the body; cartilage supports the ears, nose, larynx, and trachea; fibrous tissues form the framework of organs such as the spleen.
- **Physical protection.** The cranium, ribs, and sternum protect delicate organs such as the brain, lungs, and heart; fatty cushions protect the kidneys and eyes.
- **Immune protection.** Connective tissue cells attack foreign invaders, and connective tissue fiber forms a "battlefield" under the skin and mucous membranes where immune cells can be quickly mobilized against disease agents.
- **Movement.** Bones provide the lever system for body movement, cartilages are involved in movement of the vocal cords, and cartilages on bone surfaces ease joint movements.
- **Storage.** Fat is the body's major energy reserve; bone is a reservoir of calcium and phosphorus that can be drawn upon when needed.
- **Heat production.** Metabolism of brown fat generates heat in infants and children.
- **Transport.** Blood transports gases, nutrients, wastes, hormones, and blood cells.

The mesenchyme described earlier in this chapter is a form of embryonic connective tissue. The mature connective tissues fall into four broad categories: fibrous connective tissue, adipose tissue, supportive connective tissues (cartilage and bone), and fluid connective tissue (blood).

### 5.3b Fibrous Connective Tissue

Fibrous connective tissue is the most diverse type. Nearly all connective tissues contain fibers, but the tissues considered here are classified together because the fibers are so conspicuous. Fibers are, of course, just one component of the tissue, which also includes cells and ground substance. Before examining specific types of fibrous connective tissue, let's examine these components.

#### Components of Fibrous Connective Tissue

***Cells*** The cells of fibrous connective tissue include the following types:

- **Fibroblasts.**[11] These are large, fusiform or stellate cells that often show slender, wispy branches. They produce the fibers and ground substance that form the matrix of the tissue.
- **Macrophages.**[12] These are large phagocytic cells that wander through the connective tissues, where they engulf and destroy bacteria, other foreign particles, and dead or dying cells of our own body. They also activate the immune system when they sense foreign matter called *antigens.* They arise from white blood cells called *monocytes* or from the same stem cells as monocytes.
- **Leukocytes,**[13] or **white blood cells (WBCs).** WBCs travel briefly in the bloodstream, then crawl out through the walls of small blood vessels and spend most of their time in the connective tissues. The two most common types are *neutrophils,* which wander about attacking bacteria, and *lymphocytes,* which react against bacteria, toxins, and other foreign agents. Lymphocytes often form dense patches in the mucous membranes.
- **Plasma cells.** Certain lymphocytes turn into plasma cells when they detect foreign agents. The plasma cells then synthesize disease-fighting proteins called *antibodies.* Plasma cells are rarely seen except in the wall of the intestines and in inflamed tissue.
- **Mast cells.** These cells, found especially alongside blood vessels, secrete a chemical called *heparin* that inhibits blood clotting, and one called *histamine* that increases blood flow by dilating blood vessels.
- **Adipocytes** (AD-ih-po-sites), or **fat cells.** These appear in small clusters in some fibrous connective tissues. When they dominate an area, the tissue is called *adipose tissue.*

[11]*fibro* = fiber; *blast* = producing
[12]*macro* = big; *phage* = eater
[13]*leuko* = white; *cyte* = cell

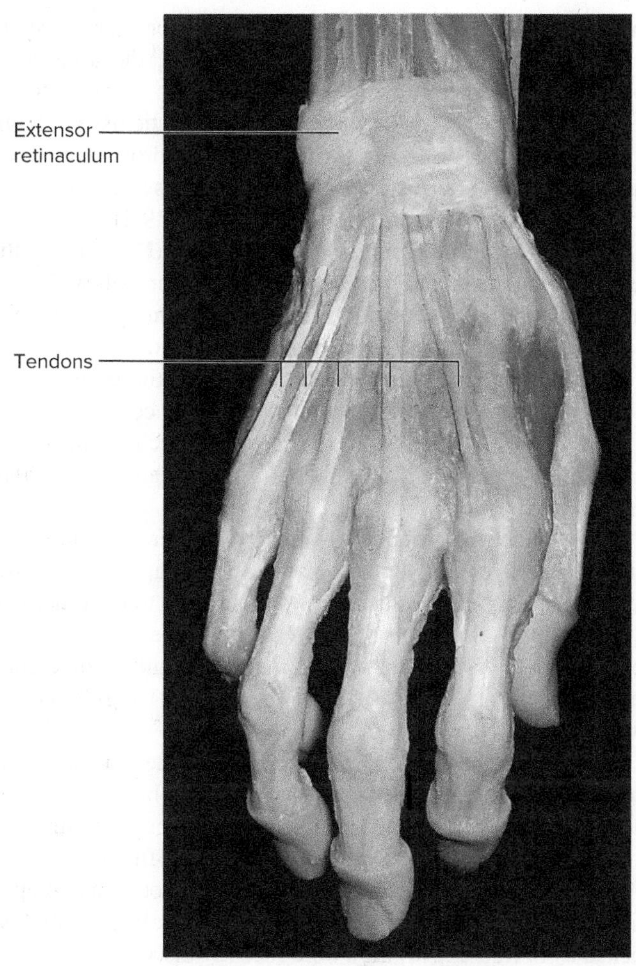


FIGURE 5.13 **Tendons and Ligament.** The tendons of the hand and the ligamentous band (extensor retinaculum) of the wrist are composed of collagen, which has a white glistening appearance.
Rebecca Gray/McGraw-Hill Education

***Fibers*** Three types of protein fibers are found in fibrous connective tissues:

- **Collagenous fibers** (col-LADJ-eh-nus). These fibers, made of collagen, are tough and flexible and resist stretching. Collagen is the body's most abundant protein, constituting about 25% of the total. It is the base of such animal products as gelatin, leather, and glue.[14] In fresh tissue, collagenous fibers have a glistening white appearance, as seen in tendons and some cuts of meat **(fig. 5.13);** thus, they are often called *white fibers.* In tissue sections, collagen forms coarse, wavy bundles, often dyed pink, blue, or green by the most common histological stains. Tendons, ligaments, and the dermis of the skin are made mainly of collagen. Less visibly, collagen pervades the matrix of cartilage and bone.
- **Reticular[15] fibers.** These are thin collagen fibers coated with glycoprotein. They form a spongelike framework for such organs as the spleen and lymph nodes and constitute part of the basement membranes underlying epithelia.
- **Elastic fibers.** These are thinner than collagenous fibers, and they branch and rejoin each other along their course. They are made of a protein called **elastin** coated with a glycoprotein *(fibrillin).* The coiled structure of elastin allows it to stretch and recoil like a rubber band. Elastic fibers account for the ability of the skin, lungs, and arteries to spring back after they are stretched. (Elasticity is not the ability to stretch, but the tendency to recoil when tension is released.)

***Ground Substance*** Amid the cells and fibers in some tissue sections, there appears to be a lot of empty space. In life, this space is occupied by the featureless **ground substance.** Ground substance usually has a gelatinous to rubbery consistency resulting from three classes of large molecules: glycosaminoglycans, proteoglycans, and adhesive glycoproteins. It absorbs compressive forces and, like the styrofoam packing in a shipping carton, protects the more delicate cells from mechanical injury.

A **glycosaminoglycan (GAG)** (GLY-co-seh-ME-no-GLY-can) is a long polysaccharide composed of unusual disaccharides called *amino sugars* and *uronic acid.* GAGs are negatively charged and thus tend to attract sodium and potassium ions, which in turn cause them to absorb and retain water. Thus, GAGs play an important role in regulating the water and electrolyte balance of tissues. The most common GAG is **chondroitin sulfate** (con-DRO-ih-tin). It is abundant in blood vessels and bones and gives cartilage its relative stiffness. Other GAGs that you will read of in this book are *heparin* (an anticoagulant) and *hyaluronic acid* (HY-uh-loo-RON-ic). The latter is a gigantic molecule up to 20 μm long, as large as most cells. It is a viscous, slippery substance that forms a lubricant in the joints and constitutes much of the jellylike *vitreous body* of the eyeball.

A **proteoglycan** is another gigantic molecule. It is shaped somewhat like a bottle brush, with a central core of protein and bristlelike outgrowths composed of GAGs. The entire proteoglycan may be attached to hyaluronic acid, thus forming an enormous molecular complex. Proteoglycans form thick colloids similar to those of gravy, gelatin, and glue. This gel slows the spread of pathogenic organisms through the tissues. Some proteoglycans are embedded in the plasma membranes of cells, attached to the cytoskeleton on the inside and to other extracellular molecules in the matrix. They create a strong structural bond between cells and extracellular macromolecules and help to hold tissues together.

**Adhesive glycoproteins** are protein–carbohydrate complexes that bind plasma membrane proteins to extracellular collagen and proteoglycans. They bind the components of a tissue together and mark paths that guide migrating embryonic cells to their destinations in a tissue.

## Types of Fibrous Connective Tissue

Fibrous connective tissue is divided into two broad categories according to the relative abundance of fiber: *loose* and *dense connective tissue.* In loose connective tissue, much of the space is

[14]*colla* = glue; *gen* = producing
[15]*ret* = network; *icul* = little

occupied by ground substance, which dissolves out of the tissue during histological fixation and leaves empty space in prepared tissue sections. The loose connective tissues we will discuss are *areolar* and *reticular tissue* **(table 5.4).** In **dense connective tissue,** fiber occupies more space than the cells and ground substance, and appears closely packed in tissue sections. We will discuss two types: *dense regular* and *dense irregular connective tissue* **(table 5.5).**

**Areolar**[16] **tissue** (AIR-ee-OH-lur) exhibits loosely organized fibers, abundant blood vessels, and a lot of seemingly empty space. It possesses all six of the aforementioned cell types. Its fibers run in random directions and are mostly collagenous, but elastic and reticular fibers are also present. Areolar tissue is highly variable in appearance. In many serous membranes, it looks like **figure 5.14,** but in the skin and mucous membranes, it is more compact (see fig. 5.8) and sometimes difficult to distinguish from dense irregular connective tissue. Some advice on how to tell them apart is given after the discussion of dense irregular connective tissue.

Areolar tissue is found in tissue sections from almost every part of the body. It surrounds blood vessels and nerves and penetrates with them even into the small spaces of muscle, tendon, and other tissues. Nearly every epithelium rests on a layer of areolar tissue, whose blood vessels provide the epithelium with nutrition, waste removal, and a ready supply of infection-fighting leukocytes in times of need. Because of the abundance of open, fluid-filled space, leukocytes can move about freely in areolar tissue and can easily find and destroy pathogens.

**Reticular tissue (fig. 5.15)** is a mesh of reticular fibers and fibroblasts. It forms the framework (stroma) of such organs as the lymph nodes, spleen, thymus, and bone marrow. The space amid the fibers is filled with blood cells. If you imagine a sponge soaked with blood, the sponge fibers are analogous to the reticular tissue stroma.

**Dense regular connective tissue (fig. 5.16)** is named for two properties: (1) The collagen fibers are closely packed (dense) and leave relatively little open space, and (2) the fibers are parallel to each other (regular). It is found especially in tendons and ligaments. The parallel arrangement of fibers is an adaptation to the fact that musculoskeletal stresses pull tendons and ligaments in predictable directions. With minor exceptions such as blood vessels and sensory nerve fibers, the only cells in this tissue are fibroblasts, visible by their slender, violet-staining nuclei squeezed between bundles of collagen. This type of tissue has few blood vessels, so injured tendons and ligaments are slow to heal.

The vocal cords and some spinal ligaments are made of a dense regular connective tissue called **elastic tissue.** In addition to the densely packed collagen fibers, it exhibits branching elastic fibers and more fibroblasts. The fibroblasts have larger, more conspicuous nuclei than seen in most dense regular connective tissue. Elastic tissue also forms wavy sheets in large and medium arteries. When the heart pumps blood into the arteries, these sheets enable them to expand and relieve some of the pressure on smaller vessels downstream. When the heart relaxes, the arterial wall springs back and keeps the blood pressure from dropping too low between heartbeats. The importance of this elastic tissue becomes especially clear in diseases such as Marfan syndrome (see Deeper Insight 5.2) and arteriosclerosis, where the tissue is stiffened by lipid and calcium deposits (see Deeper Insight 19.4).

**Dense irregular connective tissue (fig. 5.17)** also has thick bundles of collagen and relatively little room for cells and ground substance, but the collagen bundles run in seemingly random directions. This arrangement enables the tissue to resist unpredictable stresses. This tissue constitutes most of the dermis, where it binds the skin to the underlying muscle and connective tissue. It forms a protective capsule around organs such as the kidneys, testes, and spleen and a tough fibrous sheath around the bones, nerves, and most cartilages.

It is sometimes difficult to judge whether a tissue is areolar or dense irregular. In the dermis, for example, these tissues occur side by side, and the transition from one to the other is not at all obvious (see fig. 5.8). A relatively large amount of clear space suggests areolar tissue, and thicker bundles of collagen and relatively little clear space suggest dense irregular connective tissue.

Fibrous connective tissue often forms a filler, or *interstitium,* around and between other structures such as blood vessels and gland ducts and within the walls of some organs. In some places, this interstitium is like a honeycomb of fluid-filled spaces supported by thick bundles of collagen. These are not seen in prepared slides, where the spaces are empty and the collagen is densely packed as in figure 5.17; they were recently discovered in surgical

## DEEPER INSIGHT 5.2
### CLINICAL APPLICATION

### *Marfan Syndrome—A Connective Tissue Disease*

*Marfan*[17] *syndrome* is a hereditary defect in elastic fibers, usually resulting from a mutation in the gene for *fibrillin,* a glycoprotein that forms the structural scaffold for elastin. Clinical signs of Marfan syndrome include hyperextensible joints, hernias of the groin, and visual problems resulting from abnormally elongated eyes and deformed lenses. People with Marfan syndrome typically show unusually tall stature, long limbs, spidery fingers, abnormal spinal curvature, and a protruding "pigeon breast." More serious problems are weakened heart valves and arterial walls. The aorta, where blood pressure is highest, is sometimes enormously dilated close to the heart and may rupture. Marfan syndrome is present in about 1 out of 20,000 live births, and most victims die by their mid-30s. Abraham Lincoln's tall, gangly physique and spindly fingers led some authorities to suspect that he had Marfan syndrome, but the evidence is inconclusive. Some star athletes have died at a young age of Marfan syndrome, including Olympic volleyball champion Flo Hyman (1954–86), who died at the age of 31 of a ruptured aorta during a game in Japan.

[16]*areola* = little space

[17]Antoine Bernard-Jean Marfan (1858–1942), French physician

## TABLE 5.4 Loose Connective Tissues

| Areolar Tissue | Reticular Tissue |
|---|---|
| 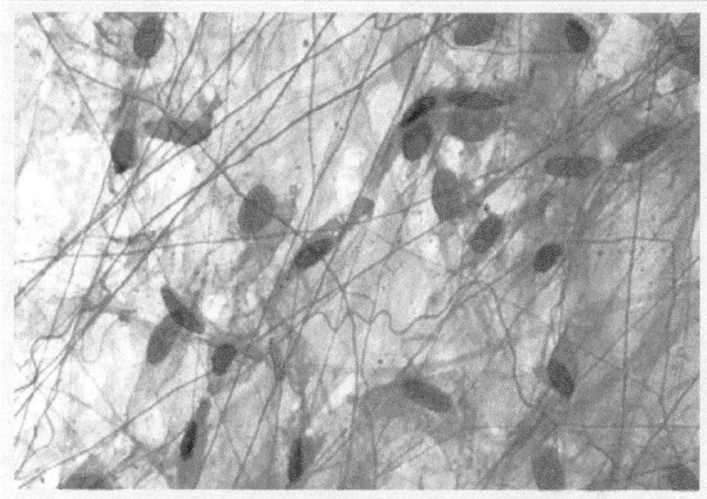 (a) 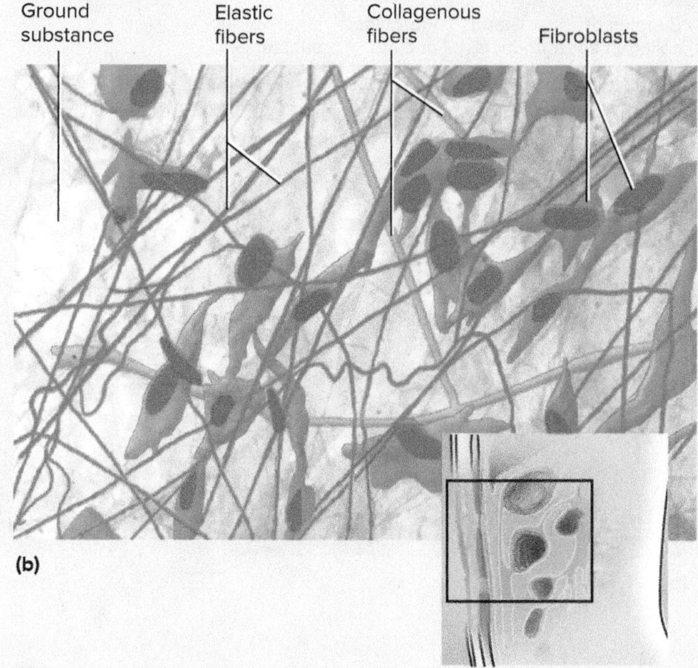  (b) | 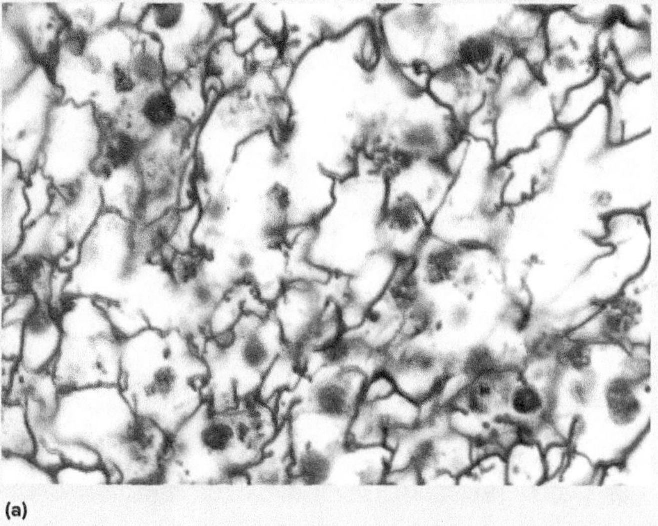 (a) 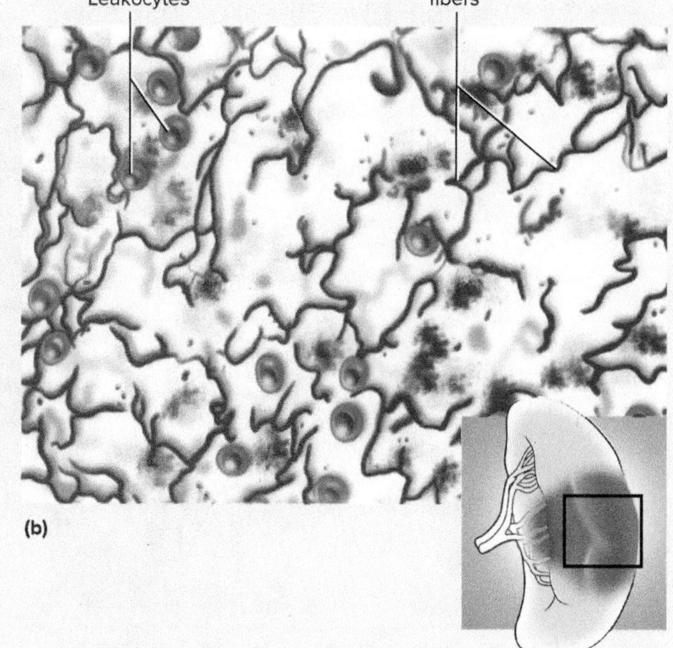  (b) |
| **FIGURE 5.14 Areolar Tissue.** Spread of the mesentery (×400). (a) Light micrograph. (b) Labeled drawing. APR<br>a: Dennis Strete/McGraw-Hill Education | **FIGURE 5.15 Reticular Tissue.** Spleen (×400). (a) Light micrograph. (b) Labeled drawing. APR<br>a: McGraw-Hill Education/Al Telser, photographer |
| **Microscopic appearance:** Loose arrangement of collagenous and elastic fibers; scattered cells of various types; abundant ground substance; numerous blood vessels<br>**Representative locations:** Underlying nearly all epithelia; surrounding blood vessels, nerves, esophagus, and trachea; fascia between muscles; mesenteries; visceral layers of pericardium and pleura<br>**Functions:** Loosely binds epithelia to deeper tissues; allows passage of nerves and blood vessels through other tissues; provides an arena for immune defense; blood vessels provide nutrients and waste removal for overlying epithelia | **Microscopic appearance:** Loose network of reticular fibers and cells, infiltrated with numerous leukocytes, especially lymphocytes<br>**Representative locations:** Lymph nodes, spleen, thymus, bone marrow<br>**Function:** Forms supportive stroma (framework) for lymphatic organs |

## TABLE 5.5 Dense Connective Tissues

| Dense Regular Connective Tissue | Dense Irregular Connective Tissue |
|---|---|
| 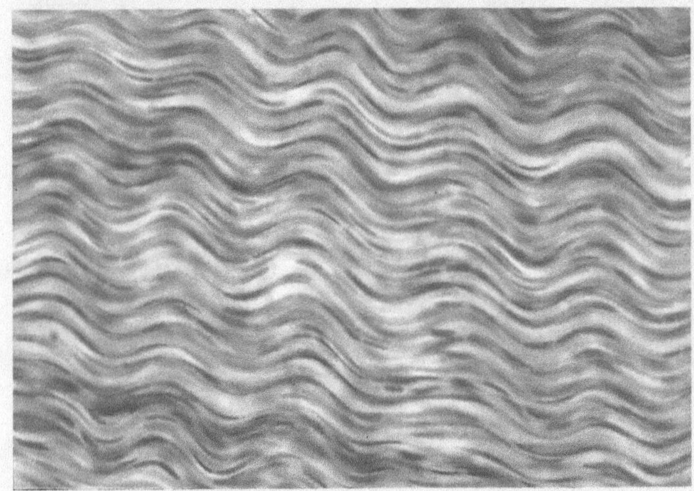 (a) 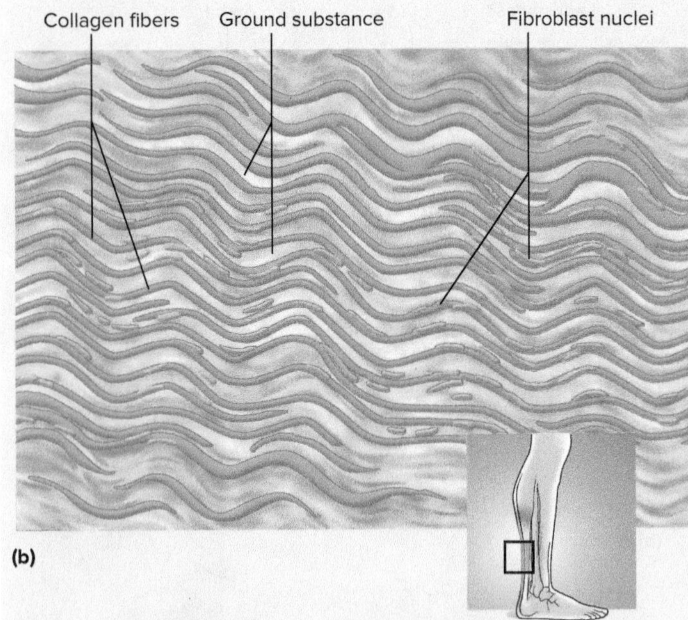  (b) | 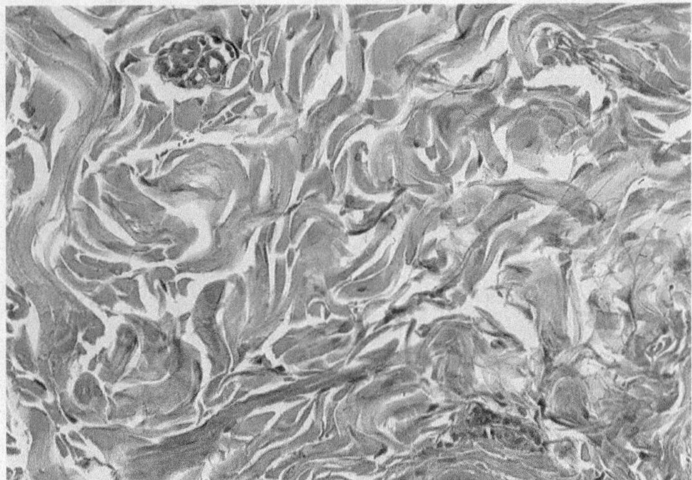 (a) 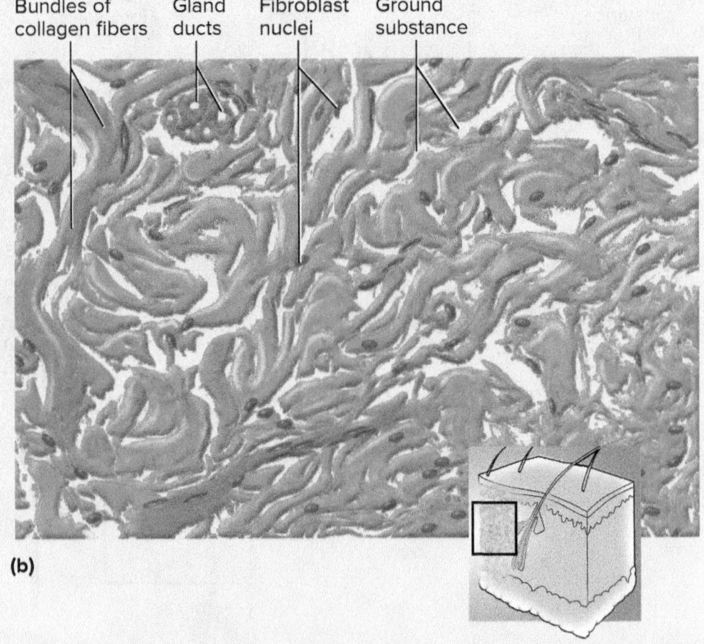  (b) |
| **FIGURE 5.16 Dense Regular Connective Tissue.** Tendon (×400). (a) Light micrograph. (b) Labeled drawing. APR<br>a: Dennis Strete/McGraw-Hill Education | **FIGURE 5.17 Dense Irregular Connective Tissue.** Dermis of the skin (×400). (a) Light micrograph. (b) Labeled drawing. APR<br>a: McGraw-Hill Education/Dennis Strete, photographer |
| **Microscopic appearance:** Densely packed, parallel, often wavy collagen fibers; slender fibroblast nuclei compressed between collagen bundles; scanty open space (ground substance); scarcity of blood vessels<br>**Representative locations:** Tendons and ligaments<br>**Functions:** Ligaments tightly bind bones together and resist stress; tendons attach muscle to bone and transfer muscular tension to bones | **Microscopic appearance:** Densely packed collagen fibers running in random directions; scanty open space (ground substance); few visible cells; scarcity of blood vessels<br>**Representative locations:** Deeper portion of dermis of skin; capsules around viscera such as liver, kidney, spleen; fibrous sheaths around cartilages and bones<br>**Functions:** Withstands stresses applied in unpredictable directions; imparts durability to tissues |

patients by a new microscopic imaging technique. They are found especially in areas subject to frequent compression, such as the dermis of the skin, the bile duct, and walls of the digestive tract and urinary bladder. They drain into the lymph nodes and may be important as a route of cancer metastasis.

## 5.3c Adipose Tissue

**Adipose tissue,** or **fat,** is tissue in which adipocytes are the dominant cell type **(table 5.6** and **fig. 5.18).** Adipocytes may also occur singly or in small clusters in areolar tissue. The space between adipocytes is occupied by areolar tissue, reticular tissue, and blood capillaries.

Fat is the body's primary energy reservoir. The quantity of stored triglyceride and the number of adipocytes are quite stable in a person, but this doesn't mean stored fat is stagnant. New triglycerides are constantly synthesized and stored as others are hydrolyzed and released into circulation. Thus, there is a constant turnover of stored triglyceride, with an equilibrium between synthesis and hydrolysis, energy storage and energy use.

There are two kinds of fat in humans—white (or yellow) fat and brown fat. **White fat** is the more abundant and is the most significant adipose tissue of the adult body. Its adipocytes are usually 70 to 120 μm in diameter, but may be five times as large in obese people. They have a single large, central globule of triglyceride. Their cytoplasm is restricted to a thin layer immediately beneath the plasma membrane, and the nucleus is pushed against the edge of the cell. Since the triglyceride is dissolved out by most histological fixatives, fat cells in most specimens look empty and somewhat collapsed, with a resemblance to chicken wire.

White fat provides thermal insulation, anchors and cushions such organs as the eyeballs and kidneys, and contributes to body contours such as the female breasts and hips. On average, women have more fat relative to body weight than men do. It helps to meet the caloric needs of pregnancy and nursing an infant, and having too little fat reduces female fertility.

**Brown fat** is found mainly in fetuses, infants, and children, but adults also have small deposits of brown fat; it accounts for up to 6% of an infant's weight, and is concentrated especially in fat pads in the shoulders, upper back, and around the kidneys. It stores lipid in the form of multiple globules rather than one large one. It gets its color from an unusual abundance of blood vessels and certain enzymes in its mitochondria. Brown fat is a heat-generating tissue. It has numerous mitochondria, but their oxidative pathway is not linked to ATP synthesis. Therefore, when these cells oxidize fats, they release all of the energy as heat. Hibernating animals accumulate brown fat in preparation for winter.

**▶▶▶APPLY WHAT YOU KNOW**

*Why would infants and children have more need for brown fat than adults do?* (Hint: *Smaller bodies have a higher ratio of surface area to volume than larger bodies do.*)

**TABLE 5.6 Adipose Tissue**

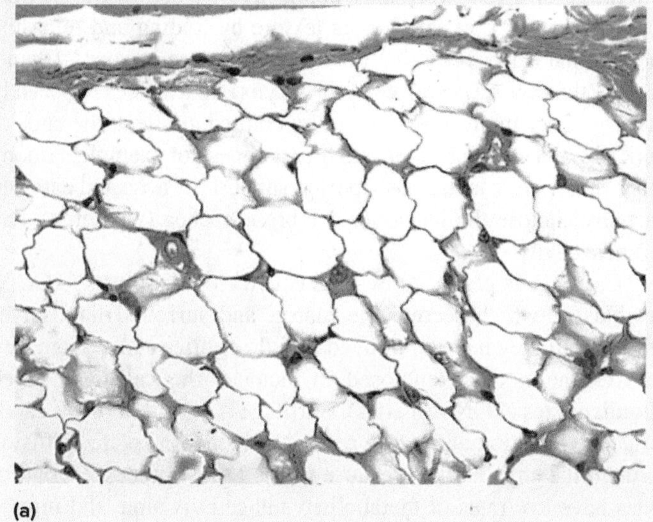

(a)

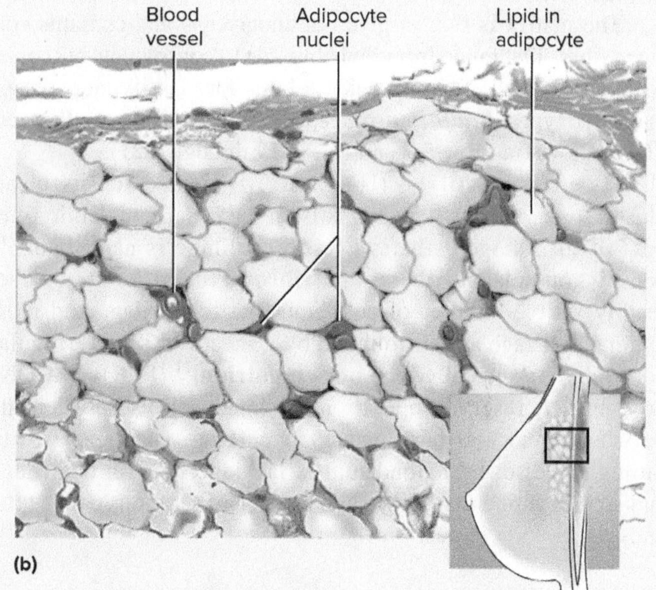


(b)

**FIGURE 5.18 Adipose Tissue.** Breast (×100). (a) Light micrograph. (b) Labeled drawing. APR

a: Dennis Strete/McGraw-Hill Education

**Microscopic appearance:** Dominated by adipocytes—large, empty-looking cells with thin margins; tissue sections often very pale because of scarcity of stained cytoplasm; adipocytes shrunken; nucleus pressed against plasma membrane; blood vessels present

**Representative locations:** Subcutaneous fat beneath skin; breast; heart surface; mesenteries; surrounding organs such as kidneys and eyes

**Functions:** Energy storage; thermal insulation; heat production by brown fat; protective cushion for some organs; filling space, shaping body

## 5.3d Cartilage

**Cartilage** is a relatively stiff connective tissue with a flexible rubbery matrix; you can feel its texture by folding and releasing the external ear or palpating the tip of your nose or your "Adam's apple" (the *thyroid cartilage* of the larynx). It is also easily seen in many grocery items—it is the milky-colored gristle at the ends of pork ribs and on chicken leg and breast bones, for example. Among other functions, cartilages shape and support the nose and ears and partially enclose the larynx (voice box), trachea (windpipe), and thoracic cavity.

Cartilage is produced by cells called **chondroblasts**[18] (CON-dro-blasts), which secrete the matrix and surround themselves with it until they become trapped in little cavities called **lacunae**[19] (la-CUE-nee). Once enclosed in lacunae, the cells are called **chondrocytes** (CON-dro-sites). Cartilage is devoid of blood capillaries, so nutrition and waste removal depend on solute diffusion through the stiff matrix. Because this is a slow process, chondrocytes have low rates of metabolism and cell division, and injured cartilage heals slowly.

The matrix is rich in glycosaminoglycans and contains collagen fibers that range from invisibly fine to conspicuously coarse. Differences in the fibers provide a basis for classifying cartilage into three types: *hyaline cartilage, elastic cartilage,* and *fibrocartilage* (shown in **table 5.7** and **figs. 5.19** through **5.21**).

**Hyaline**[20] **cartilage** (HY-uh-lin) is named for its clear, glassy appearance, which stems from the usually invisible fineness of its collagen fibers. **Elastic cartilage** is named for its conspicuous elastic fibers, and **fibrocartilage** for its coarse, readily visible bundles of collagen. Elastic cartilage and most hyaline cartilage are surrounded by a sheath of dense irregular connective tissue called the **perichondrium**[21] (PERR-ih-CON-dree-um). A reserve population of chondroblasts between the perichondrium and cartilage contributes to cartilage growth throughout life. Perichondrium is lacking from fibrocartilage and some hyaline cartilage, such as the cartilaginous caps at the ends of the long bones.

## 5.3e Bone

**Bone,** or **osseous tissue (table 5.8, fig. 5.22),** is a hard, calcified connective tissue that composes the skeleton. The term *bone* has two meanings in anatomy—an entire organ such as the femur and mandible, or just the osseous tissue. Bones are composed of not only **osseous tissue,** but also cartilage, bone marrow, dense irregular connective tissue, and other tissue types.

There are two forms of osseous tissue: (1) **Spongy bone** fills the heads of the long bones and forms the middle layer of flat bones such as the sternum and cranial bones. Although it is calcified and hard, its delicate slivers and plates give it a spongy appearance (see fig. 7.4a). (2) **Compact (dense) bone** is a denser calcified tissue with no spaces visible to the naked eye. It forms the external surfaces of all bones, so spongy bone, when present, is always covered by a shell of compact bone.

Further differences between compact and spongy bone are described in sections 7.2c and 7.2d. Here, we examine only compact bone. Most specimens you study will probably be chips of dead, dried bone ground to microscopic thinness. In such preparations, the cells are absent but spaces reveal their former locations. Most compact bone is arranged in cylinders of tissue that surround **central (osteonic) canals,** which run longitudinally through the shafts of long bones such as the femur. Blood vessels and nerves travel through these canals. The bone matrix is deposited in **concentric lamellae**—onionlike layers around each canal. A central canal and its surrounding lamellae are called an **osteon.** Tiny lacunae between the lamellae are occupied by mature bone cells, or **osteocytes.**[22] Delicate channels called **canaliculi** radiate from each lacuna to its neighbors and allow the osteocytes to contact each other. The bone as a whole is covered with a tough fibrous **periosteum** (PERR-ee-OSS-tee-um) similar to the perichondrium of cartilage.

About one-third of the dry weight of bone is composed of collagen fibers and glycosaminoglycans, which enable a bone to bend slightly under stress. Two-thirds of its weight is minerals (mainly calcium and phosphate salts) that enable bones to withstand compression by the weight of the body.

## 5.3f Blood

**Blood (table 5.9, fig. 5.23)** is a fluid connective tissue that travels through tubular blood vessels. Its primary function is to transport cells and dissolved matter from place to place. It may seem odd that a tissue as fluid as blood and another as rock hard as bone are both considered connective tissues, but they have more in common than first meets the eye. Like other connective tissues, blood is composed of more ground substance than cells. Its ground substance is the **blood plasma** and its cellular components are collectively called the **formed elements.** Another factor placing blood in the connective tissue category is that it is produced by the connective tissues of the bone marrow and lymphatic organs. Unlike other connective tissues, blood doesn't exhibit fibers except when it clots.

The formed elements are of three kinds—erythrocytes, leukocytes, and platelets. **Erythrocytes**[23] (eh-RITH-ro-sites), or **red blood cells (RBCs),** are the most abundant. In stained blood films, they look like pink discs with thin, pale centers and no nuclei. Erythrocytes transport oxygen and carbon dioxide. **Leukocytes,** or **white blood cells (WBCs),** serve various roles in defense against infection and other diseases. They travel from one organ to another in the bloodstream and lymph but spend most of their lives in the connective tissues. Leukocytes are somewhat larger than erythrocytes and have conspicuous nuclei that usually appear violet in stained preparations. There are five kinds, distinguished partly by variations in nuclear shape: *neutrophils, eosinophils, basophils,*

[18] *chondro* = cartilage, gristle; *blast* = forming
[19] *lacuna* = lake, cavity
[20] *hyal* = glass
[21] *peri* = around; *chondri* = cartilage
[22] *osteo* = bone; *cyte* = cell
[23] *erythro* = red; *cyte* = cell

## TABLE 5.7 Cartilage

### Hyaline Cartilage

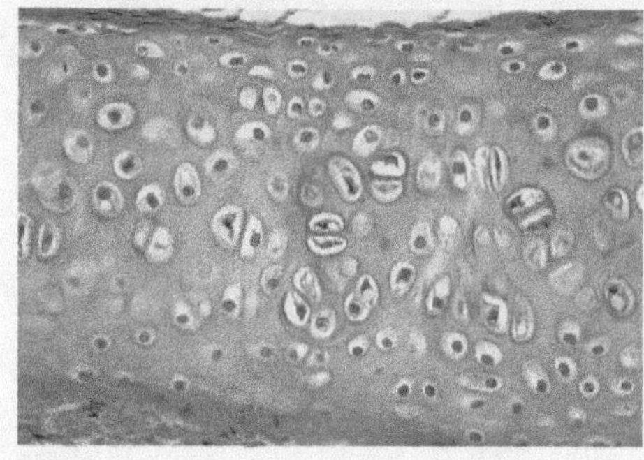

(a)



(b)

**FIGURE 5.19 Hyaline Cartilage.** Bronchus (×400). (a) Light micrograph. (b) Labeled drawing. APR

a: ©Ed Reschke

**Microscopic appearance:** Clear, glassy matrix, often stained light blue or pink in tissue sections; fine, dispersed collagen fibers, not usually visible; chondrocytes enclosed in lacunae, often in small clusters of three or four cells *(cell nests)*; usually covered by perichondrium

**Representative locations:** A thin *articular cartilage*, lacking perichondrium, over the ends of bones at movable joints; supportive rings and plates around trachea and bronchi; a boxlike enclosure around the larynx; much of the fetal skeleton; and a *costal cartilage* attaches the end of a rib to the breastbone

**Functions:** Eases joint movements; holds airway open during respiration; moves vocal cords during speech; a precursor of bone in the fetal skeleton and the growth zones of long bones of children

### Elastic Cartilage

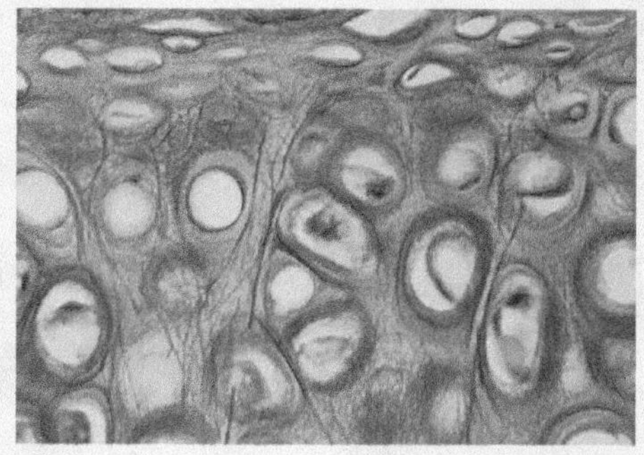

(a)



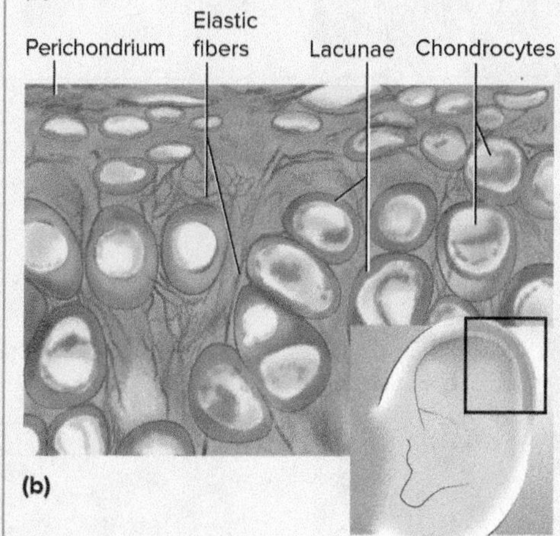

(b)

**FIGURE 5.20 Elastic Cartilage.** External ear (×1,000). (a) Light micrograph. (b) Labeled drawing. APR

a: ©Ed Reschke

**Microscopic appearance:** Elastic fibers form weblike mesh amid lacunae; always covered by perichondrium

**Representative locations:** External ear; epiglottis

**Functions:** Provides flexible, elastic support

### Fibrocartilage

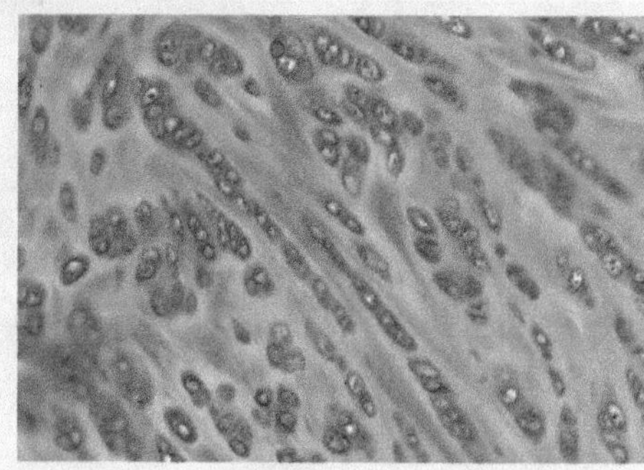

(a)



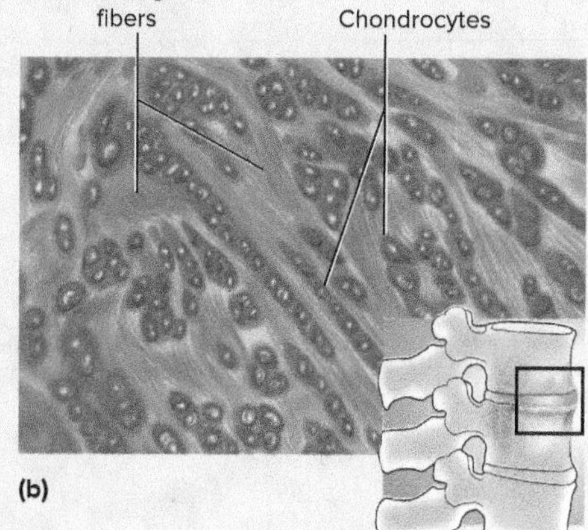

(b)

**FIGURE 5.21 Fibrocartilage.** Intervertebral disc (×400). (a) Light micrograph. (b) Labeled drawing. APR

a: Dr. Alvin Telser

**Microscopic appearance:** Parallel collagen fibers similar to those of tendon; rows of chondrocytes in lacunae between collagen fibers; never has a perichondrium

**Representative locations:** Pubic symphysis (anterior joint between two halves of pelvic girdle); intervertebral discs, which separate bones of vertebral column; menisci, or pads of shock-absorbing cartilage, in knee joint; at points where tendons insert on bones near articular hyaline cartilage

**Functions:** Resists compression and absorbs shock in some joints; often a transitional tissue between dense connective tissue and hyaline cartilage (for example, at some tendon–bone junctions)

## TABLE 5.8 Bone

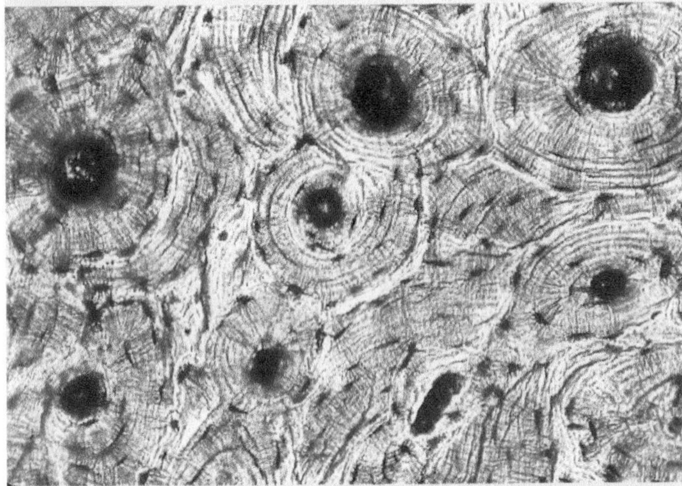

(a)

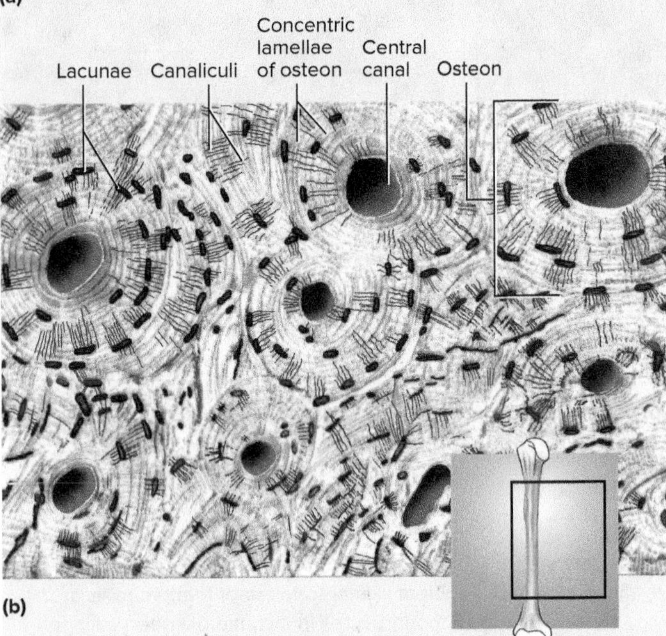


(b)

**FIGURE 5.22 Compact Bone (×100).** (a) Light micrograph. (b) Labeled drawing. APR

a: Dennis Strete/McGraw-Hill Education

**Microscopic appearance (compact bone):** Calcified matrix arranged in concentric lamellae around central canals; osteocytes in lacunae between adjacent lamellae; lacunae interconnected by delicate canaliculi

**Representative location:** Skeleton

**Functions:** Physical support of body; leverage for muscle action; protective enclosure of viscera; reservoir of calcium and phosphorus

## TABLE 5.9 Blood

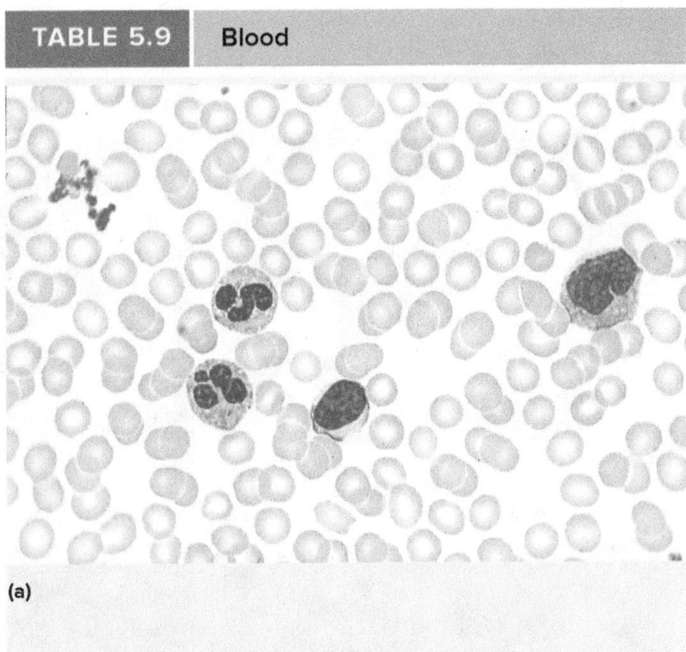

(a)

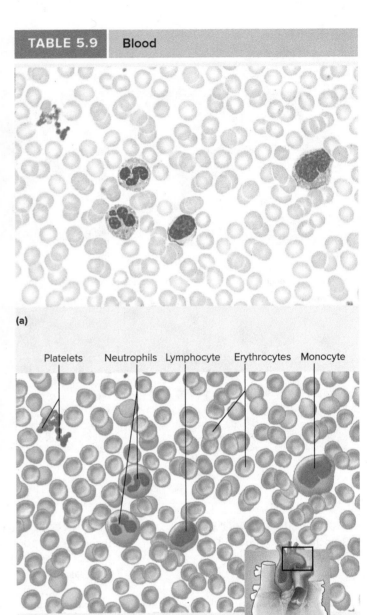

Platelets
Neutrophils
Lymphocyte
Erythrocytes
Monocyte

(b)

**FIGURE 5.23 Blood Smear (×1,000).** (a) Light micrograph. (b) Labeled drawing. APR

a: ©Ed Reschke

**Microscopic appearance:** Erythrocytes appear as pale pink discs with light centers and no nuclei; leukocytes are slightly larger, are much fewer, and have variously shaped nuclei, usually stained violet; platelets are cell fragments with no nuclei, about one-quarter the diameter of erythrocytes

**Representative locations:** Contained in heart and blood vessels

**Functions:** Transports gases, nutrients, wastes, chemical signals, and heat throughout body; provides defensive leukocytes; contains clotting agents to minimize bleeding; platelets secrete growth factors that promote tissue maintenance and repair

*lymphocytes,* and *monocytes.* Their individual characteristics are considered in detail in table 18.6. **Platelets** are small cell fragments scattered amid the blood cells. They are involved in clotting and other mechanisms for minimizing blood loss, and in secreting growth factors that promote blood vessel growth and maintenance.

**BEFORE YOU GO ON**

Answer the following questions to test your understanding of the preceding section:

9. What features do most or all connective tissues have in common to set this class apart from nervous, muscular, and epithelial tissue?
10. List the cell and fiber types found in fibrous connective tissues and state their functional differences.
11. What substances account for the gelatinous consistency of connective tissue ground substance?
12. What is areolar tissue? How can it be distinguished from any other kind of connective tissue?
13. Discuss the difference between dense regular and dense irregular connective tissue as an example of the relationship between form and function.
14. Describe some similarities, differences, and functional relationships between hyaline cartilage and bone.
15. What are the three basic kinds of formed elements in blood, and what are their respective functions?

## 5.4 Nervous and Muscular Tissues—Excitable Tissues

**Expected Learning Outcomes**

When you have completed this section, you should be able to

a. explain what distinguishes excitable tissues from other tissues;
b. name the cell types that compose nervous tissue;
c. identify the major parts of a nerve cell;
d. visually recognize nervous tissue from specimens or photographs;
e. name the three kinds of muscular tissue and describe the differences between them; and
f. visually identify any type of muscular tissue from specimens or photographs.

Excitability is a characteristic of all living cells, but it is developed to its highest degree in nervous and muscular tissues, which are therefore described as **excitable tissues.** The basis for their excitation is an electrical charge difference (voltage) called the *membrane potential,* which occurs across the plasma membranes of all cells. Nervous and muscular tissues respond quickly to outside stimuli by means of changes in membrane potential. In nerve cells, these changes result in the rapid transmission of signals to other cells. In muscle cells, they result in contraction, or shortening of the cell.

### 5.4a Nervous Tissue

**Nervous tissue (table 5.10, fig. 5.24)** is specialized for communication by means of electrical and chemical signals. It consists of **neurons** (NOOR-ons), or nerve cells, and a much greater number of **neuroglia** (noo-ROG-lee-uh), or **glial cells** (GLEE-ul), which protect and assist the neurons. Neurons detect stimuli, respond quickly, and transmit coded information rapidly to other cells. Each neuron has a prominent **neurosoma,** or cell body, that houses the nucleus and most other organelles. This is the cell's center of genetic control and protein synthesis. Neurosomas are usually round, ovoid, or stellate in shape. Extending from the neurosoma, there are usually multiple short, branched processes called **dendrites,**[24] which receive signals from other cells and conduct messages to the neurosoma; and a single, much longer **axon,** or **nerve fiber,** which sends outgoing signals to other cells. Some axons are more than a meter long and extend from the brainstem to the foot.

Glial cells constitute most of the volume of the nervous tissue. They are usually much smaller than neurons. There are six types of glial cells, described in section 12.3a, which provide a variety of supportive, protective, and "housekeeping" functions for the nervous system. Although they communicate with neurons and each other, they don't transmit long-distance signals.

Nervous tissue is found in the brain and spinal cord (central nervous system), nerves, and ganglia, which are knotlike swellings in nerves where the neurosomas outside the central nervous system are concentrated. Local variations in the structure of nervous tissue are described in chapters 12 to 16.

### 5.4b Muscular Tissue

**Muscular tissue** is specialized to contract when stimulated, and thus to exert a physical force on other tissues, organs, or fluids—for example, a skeletal muscle pulls on a bone, the heart contracts and expels blood, and the bladder contracts and expels urine. Not only do movements of the body and its limbs depend on muscle, but so do such processes as digestion, waste elimination, breathing, speech, and blood circulation. The muscles are also an important source of body heat.

There are three types of muscular tissue—*skeletal, cardiac,* and *smooth*—which differ in appearance, physiology, and function (as shown in **table 5.11** and **figs. 5.25** through **5.27**). **Skeletal muscle** consists of long threadlike cells called **muscle fibers.** Most skeletal muscle is attached to bones, but there are exceptions in the tongue, upper esophagus, some facial muscles, and some **sphincter**[25] (SFINK-tur) muscles (muscular rings or cuffs that open and close body passages). Each cell contains multiple nuclei adjacent to the plasma membrane. Skeletal muscle is described as striated and voluntary. The first term refers to alternating light and

[24]*dendr* = tree; *ite* = little
[25]*sphinc* = squeeze, bind tightly

**TABLE 5.10 Nervous Tissue**

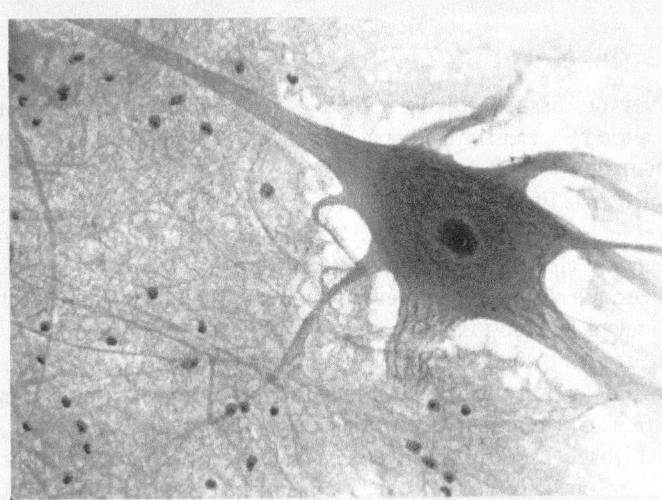

(a)

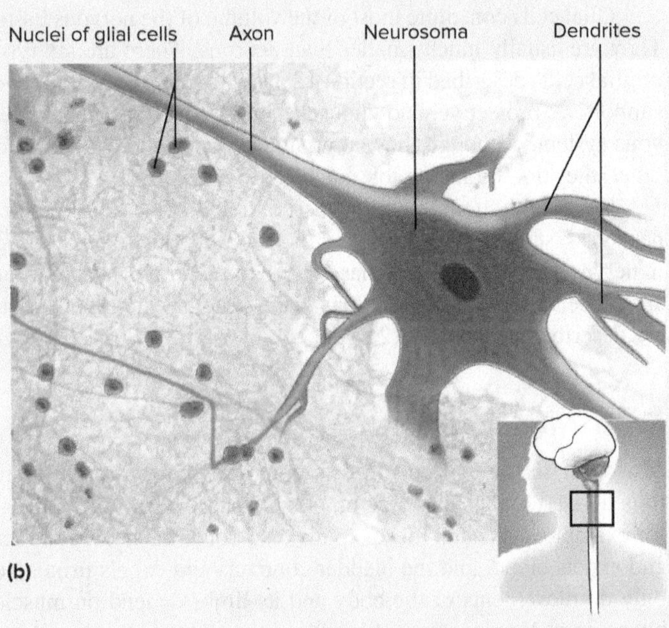


(b)

**FIGURE 5.24 Neuron and Glial Cells.** Spinal cord smear (×400). (a) Light micrograph. (b) Labeled drawing. APR

a: ©Ed Reschke

**Microscopic appearance:** Most sections show a few large neurons, usually with rounded or stellate cell bodies (neurosomas) and fibrous processes (axon and dendrites) extending from the neurosomas; neurons are surrounded by a greater number of much smaller glial cells, which lack dendrites and axons.

**Representative locations:** Brain, spinal cord, nerves, ganglia

**Function:** Internal communication

dark bands, or **striations** (stry-AY-shuns), created by the overlapping pattern of cytoplasmic protein filaments that cause muscle contraction. The second term, *voluntary,* refers to the fact that we usually have conscious control over skeletal muscle.

**Cardiac muscle** is limited to the heart. It too is striated, but it differs from skeletal muscle in its other features. Its cells are much shorter, so they are commonly called **cardiomyocytes**[26] rather than fibers. They are branched or notched at the ends. They contain only one nucleus, which is located near the center and often surrounded by a light-staining region of glycogen. Cardiomyocytes are joined end to end by junctions called **intercalated discs**[27] (in-TUR-kuh-LAY-ted). Mechanical connections in these discs keep the cells from pulling apart when the heart contracts. Electrical junctions in the discs allow a wave of electrical excitation to travel rapidly from cell to cell so that all the cardiomyocytes of a heart chamber are stimulated and contract almost simultaneously. Intercalated discs appear as dark transverse lines separating each cell from the next. They may be only faintly visible, however, unless the tissue has been specially stained for them. Cardiac muscle is considered *involuntary* because it is not usually under conscious control; it contracts even if all nerve connections to it are severed.

**Smooth muscle** lacks striations and is involuntary. Smooth muscle cells are fusiform and relatively short. They have only one, centrally placed nucleus. Small amounts of smooth muscle are found in the iris of the eye and in the skin, but most of it, called **visceral muscle,** forms layers in the walls of the digestive, respiratory, and urinary tracts; blood vessels; the uterus; and other viscera. In locations such as the esophagus and small intestine, smooth muscle forms adjacent layers, with the cells of one layer encircling the organ and the cells of the other layer running longitudinally. When the circular smooth muscle contracts, it may propel contents such as food through the organ. By regulating the diameter of blood vessels, smooth muscle is very important in controlling blood pressure and flow. Both smooth and skeletal muscle form sphincters that control the emptying of the bladder and rectum.

**▶▶▶APPLY WHAT YOU KNOW**

*How does the meaning of the word* fiber *differ in the following uses:* muscle fiber, nerve fiber, *and* connective tissue fiber?

**BEFORE YOU GO ON**

Answer the following questions to test your understanding of the preceding section:

16. What do nervous and muscular tissue have in common? What is the primary function of each?
17. What kinds of cells compose nervous tissue, and how can they be distinguished from each other?
18. Name the three kinds of muscular tissue, describe how to distinguish them from each other in microscopic appearance, and state a location and function for each.

[26]*cardio* = heart; *myo* = muscle; *cyte* = cell
[27]*inter* = between; *calated* = inserted

**TABLE 5.11 Muscular Tissue**

| Skeletal Muscle | Cardiac Muscle | Smooth Muscle |
|---|---|---|
| 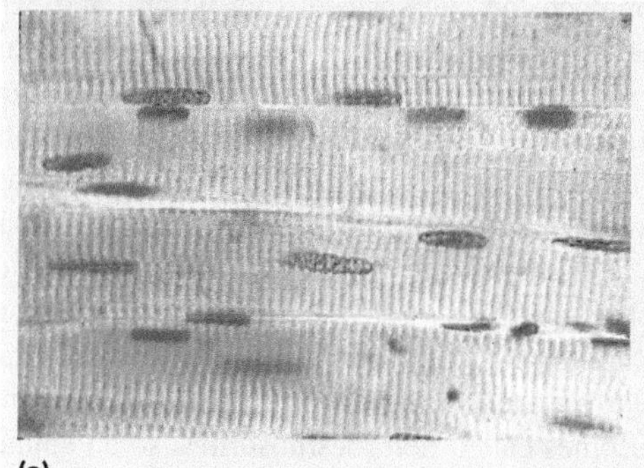 (a) | 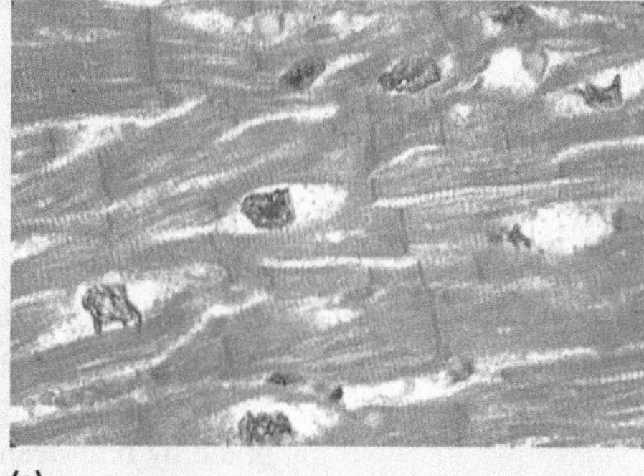 (a) | 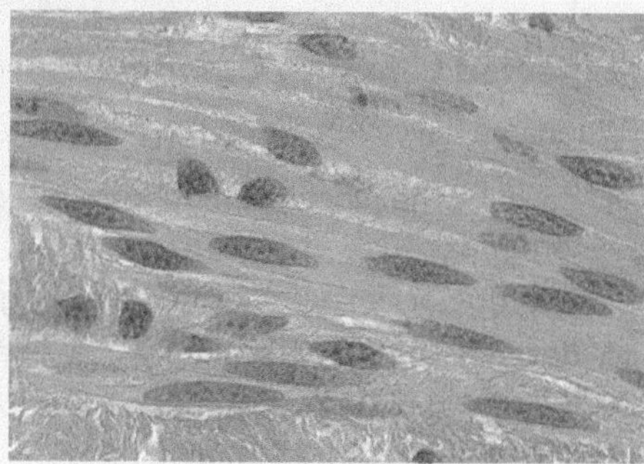 (a) |
| 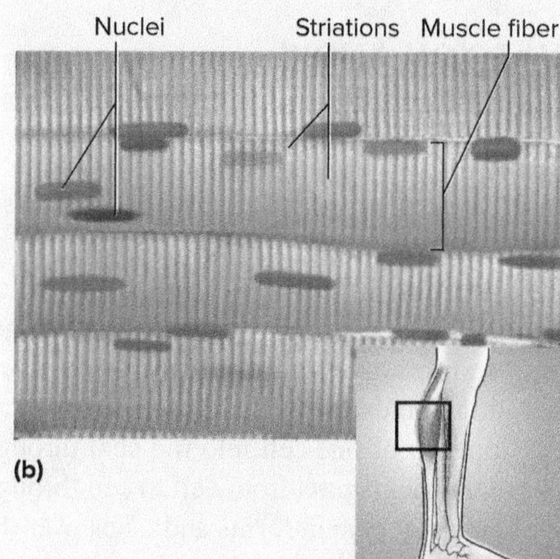  (b) | 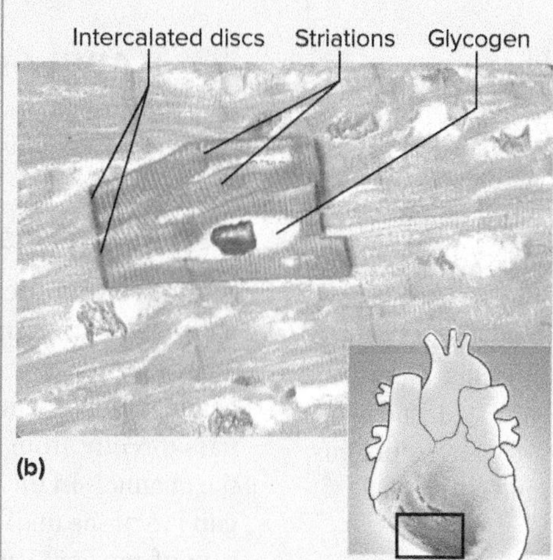  (b) | 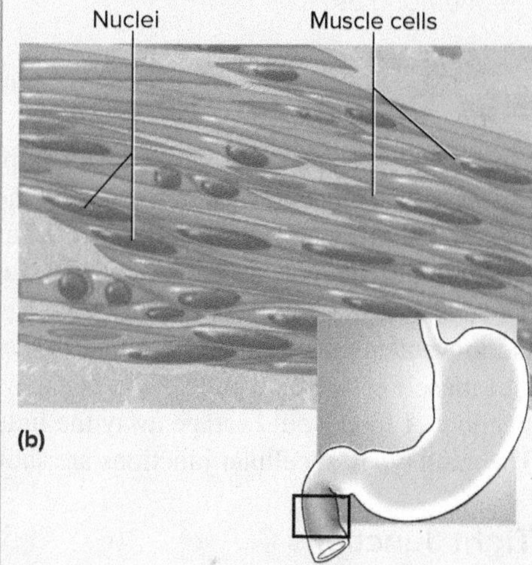  (b) |
| **FIGURE 5.25 Skeletal Muscle (×400).** (a) Light micrograph. (b) Labeled drawing. APR<br>a: ©Ed Reschke | **FIGURE 5.26 Cardiac Muscle (×400).** (a) Light micrograph. (b) Labeled drawing. APR<br>a: ©Ed Reschke | **FIGURE 5.27 Smooth Muscle.** Intestinal wall (×1,000). (a) Light micrograph. (b) Labeled drawing. APR<br>a: McGraw-Hill Education/Dennis Strete, photographer |
| **Microscopic appearance:** Long, threadlike, unbranched cells (fibers), relatively parallel in longitudinal tissue sections; striations; multiple nuclei per cell, near plasma membrane<br>**Representative locations:** Skeletal muscles, mostly attached to bones but also in the tongue, esophagus, and encircling the lips, eyelids, urethra, and anus<br>**Functions:** Body movements, facial expression, posture, breathing, speech, swallowing, control of urination and defecation, and assistance in childbirth; under voluntary control | **Microscopic appearance:** Short cells (cardiomyocytes) with notched or slightly branched ends; less parallel appearance in tissue sections; striations; intercalated discs; one nucleus per cell, centrally located and often surrounded by a light zone<br>**Representative location:** Heart<br>**Functions:** Pumping of blood; under involuntary control | **Microscopic appearance:** Short fusiform cells overlapping each other; nonstriated; one nucleus per cell, centrally located<br>**Representative locations:** Usually found as sheets of tissue in walls of blood vessels and viscera such as the digestive tract; also in iris and associated with hair follicles; involuntary sphincters of urethra and anus<br>**Functions:** Swallowing; contractions of stomach and intestines; expulsion of feces and urine; labor contractions; control of blood pressure and flow; control of respiratory airflow; control of pupillary diameter; erection of hairs; under involuntary control |

## 5.5 Cellular Junctions, Glands, and Membranes

**Expected Learning Outcomes**

When you have completed this section, you should be able to

a. describe the junctions that hold cells and tissues together;
b. describe or define different types of glands;
c. describe the typical anatomy of a gland;
d. name and compare different modes of glandular secretion; and
e. describe the types and composition of the body's membranes.

### 5.5a Cellular Junctions

Most cells—except for blood cells, macrophages, and metastatic cancer cells—must be anchored to each other and to the matrix if they are to grow and divide normally. The connections between one cell and another are called **cellular junctions.** They enable the cells to resist stress, communicate with each other, and control the movement of substances through tissues. Without them, cardiac muscle cells would pull apart when they contracted, and every swallow of food would scrape away the lining of your esophagus. The main types of cellular junctions are shown in **figure 5.28.**

#### Tight Junctions

A **tight junction** completely encircles an epithelial cell near its apical surface and joins it tightly to the neighboring cells, somewhat like the plastic harness on a six-pack of beverage cans. At a tight junction, the plasma membranes of two adjacent cells come very close together and are linked by transmembrane cell-adhesion proteins. These zipperlike interlocking proteins seal off the intercellular space and make it difficult or impossible for substances to pass between cells.

In the stomach and intestines, tight junctions prevent digestive juices from seeping between epithelial cells and digesting the underlying connective tissue. They also help to prevent bacteria from invading the tissues, and they ensure that most nutrients pass *through* the epithelial cells and not *between* them. In addition, some membrane proteins function in the apical domain of the cell, and others in the lateral or basal domains; tight junctions limit how far drifting proteins can travel and keep them segregated in the appropriate domains of the membrane where they are needed to perform their tasks.

#### Desmosomes

A **desmosome**[28] (DEZ-mo-some) is a patch that holds cells together somewhat like the snap on a pair of jeans. They are not continuous and cannot prevent substances from passing around them and going between the cells, but serve to keep cells from pulling apart and enable a tissue to resist mechanical stress. Desmosomes are common in the epidermis, the epithelium of the uterine cervix, other epithelia, and cardiac muscle. Hooklike J-shaped proteins arise from the cytoskeleton, approach the cell surface from within, and penetrate into a thick protein plaque on the inner face of the plasma membrane; then the short arm of the J turns back into the cell—thus anchoring the cytoskeleton to the membrane plaque. Proteins of the plaque are linked to transmembrane proteins that, in turn, are linked to transmembrane proteins of the next cell, forming a zone of strong cell adhesion. Each cell mirrors the other and contributes half of the desmosome. Such connections create a strong structural network that binds cells together throughout the tissue. The basal cells of an epithelium are similarly linked to the underlying basement membrane by half-desmosomes called **hemidesmosomes,** so an epithelium cannot easily peel away from the underlying tissue.

**▶▶▶APPLY WHAT YOU KNOW**

*Why would desmosomes not be suitable as the sole type of cell junction between epithelial cells of the stomach?*

#### Gap Junctions

A **gap (communicating) junction** is formed by a *connexon,* which consists of six transmembrane proteins arranged in a ring, somewhat like the segments of an orange, surrounding a water-filled channel. Ions, glucose, amino acids, and other small solutes can pass directly from the cytoplasm of one cell into the next through the channel. In the embryo, nutrients pass from cell to cell through gap junctions until the circulatory system forms and takes over the role of nutrient distribution. In cardiac muscle and most smooth muscle, gap junctions allow electrical excitation to pass directly from cell to cell so that the cells contract in near unison. (Gap junctions are absent from skeletal muscle.) In the lens and cornea of the eye, which lack blood vessels, gap junctions allow nutrients and other material to pass from cell to cell.

### 5.5b Glands

A **gland** is a cell or organ that secretes substances for use elsewhere in the body or for elimination as waste. The gland product may be something synthesized by its cells (such as digestive enzymes) or something removed from the tissues and modified by the gland (such as urine and bile pigments). The product is called a **secretion** if it is useful to the body (such as an enzyme or hormone) and an **excretion** if it is a waste product (such as urine and bile). Glands are composed mostly of epithelial tissue, but usually have a supportive connective tissue framework and capsule.

#### Endocrine and Exocrine Glands

Glands are classified as endocrine or exocrine. Both types originate as invaginations of a surface epithelium **(fig. 5.29). Exocrine**[29] **glands** (EC-so-crin) usually maintain their contact with the surface by way of a **duct,** an epithelial tube that conveys

[28] *desmo* = band, bond, ligament; *som* = body

[29] *exo* = out; *crin* = to separate, secrete

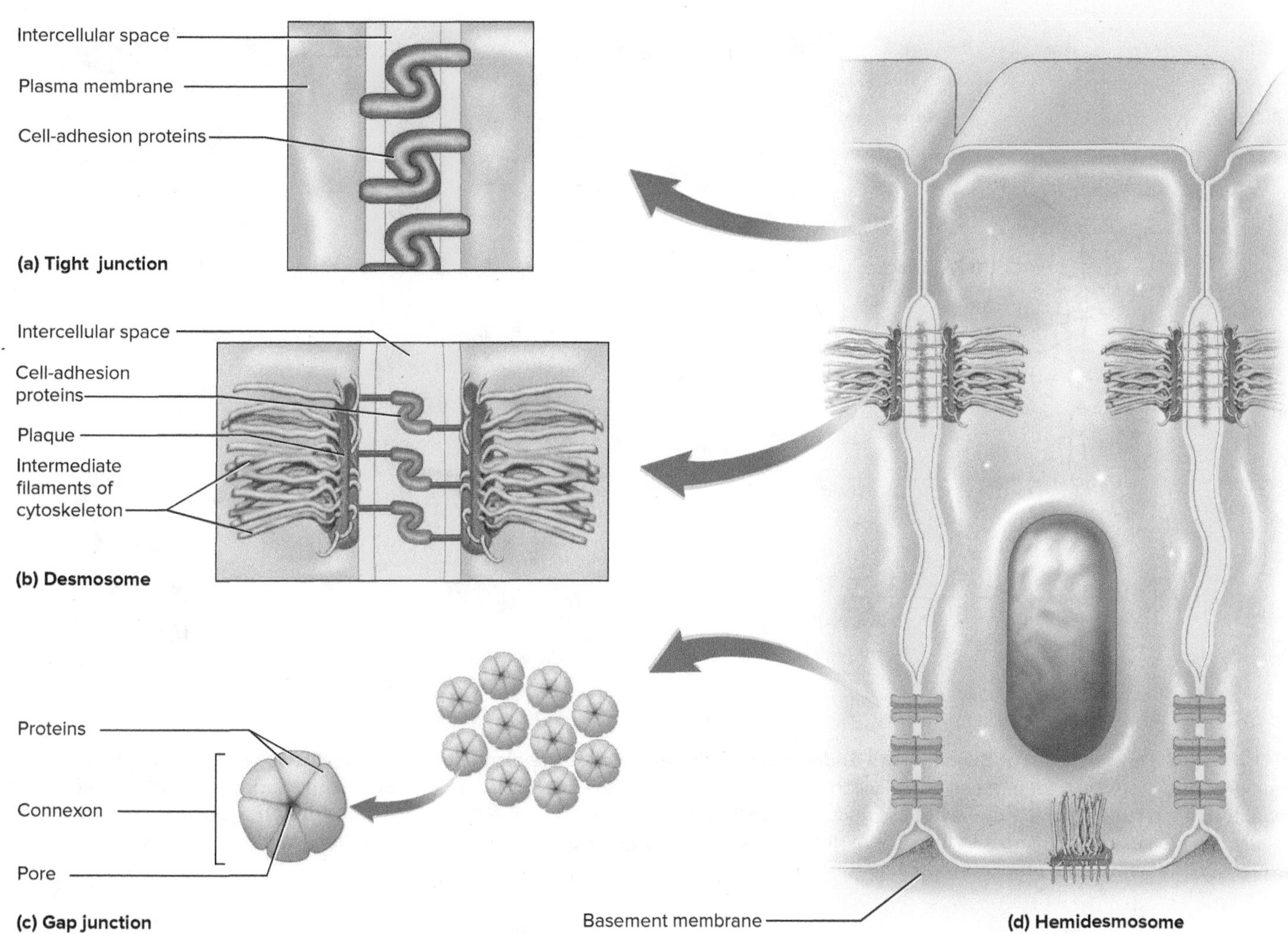


**FIGURE 5.28 Structure of Four Kinds of Cellular Junctions.** (a) Tight junction. (b) Desmosome. (c) Gap junction. (d) Hemidesmosome between cell and basement membrane.

*Which of these junctions allows material to pass from one cell directly into the next?*

their secretion to the surface. The secretion may be released to the body surface, as in the case of sweat, mammary, and tear glands. More often, however, it is released into the cavity (lumen) of another organ such as the mouth or intestine; this is the case with salivary glands, the liver, and the pancreas.

**Endocrine**[30] **glands** lose contact with the surface and have no ducts. They do, however, have a high density of blood capillaries and secrete their products directly into the blood **(fig. 5.30a).** The secretions of endocrine glands, called *hormones,* function as chemical messengers to stimulate cells elsewhere in the body. Endocrine glands include the pituitary, thyroid, and adrenal glands.

The exocrine–endocrine distinction isn't always clear. The liver is an exocrine gland that secretes one of its products, bile, through a system of ducts, but secretes hormones, albumin, and other products directly into the blood. Several glands, such as the pancreas and kidney, have both exocrine and endocrine components. Nearly all of the viscera have at least some cells that secrete hormones, even though most of these organs are not usually thought of as glands (for example, the brain and heart).

**Unicellular glands** are secretory cells found in an epithelium that is predominantly nonsecretory. They can be endocrine or exocrine. For example, the respiratory tract, which is lined mainly by ciliated cells, also has a liberal scattering of exocrine goblet cells (see figs. 5.6 and 5.7). The stomach and small intestine have scattered endocrine cells, which secrete hormones that regulate digestion.

Endocrine glands are the subject of chapter 17 and are not further considered here.

## Exocrine Gland Structure

Multicellular exocrine glands such as the pancreas and salivary glands are usually enclosed in a fibrous **capsule (fig. 5.30b).** The capsule often gives off extensions called **septa** (singular, *septum*),

[30] *endo* = in, into; *crin* = to separate, secrete

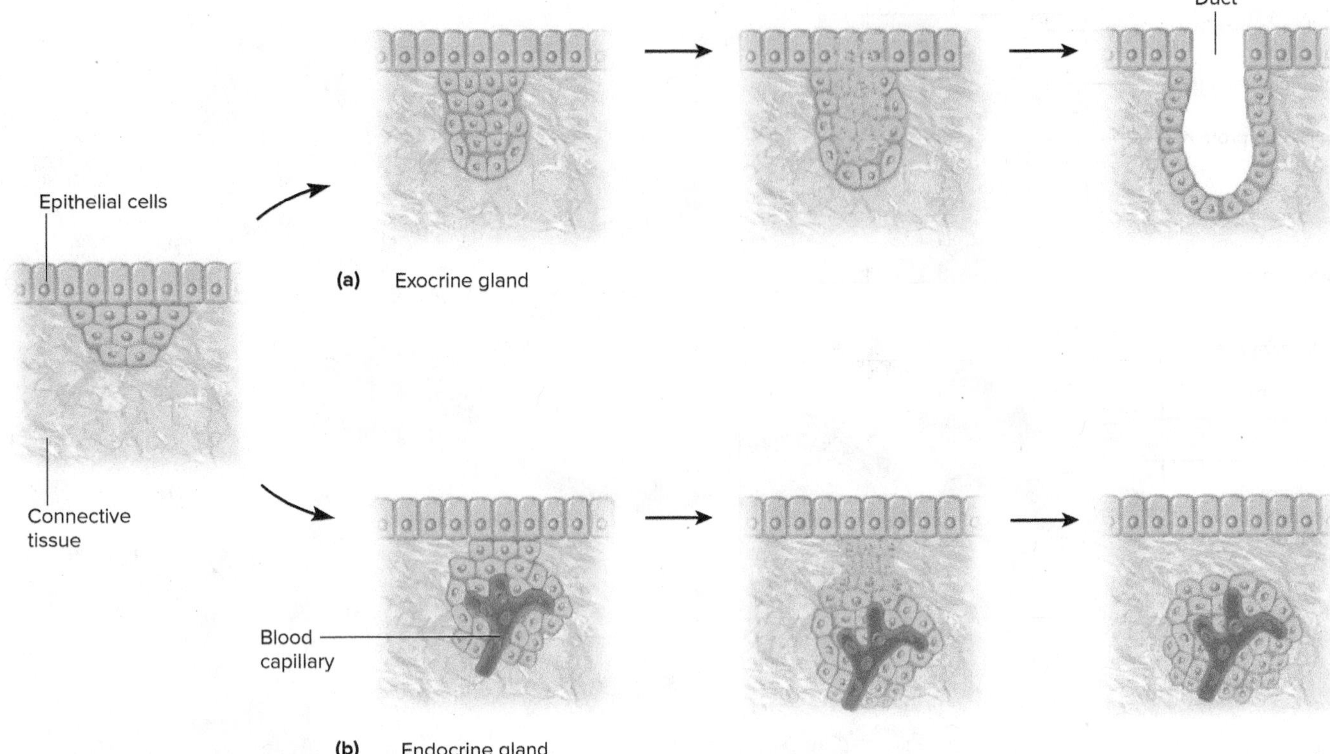


**FIGURE 5.29 Development of Exocrine and Endocrine Glands.** (a) An exocrine gland begins with epithelial cells proliferating into the connective tissue below. A form of cell death called *apoptosis* hollows out the core and creates a duct to the surface. The gland remains connected to the surface for life by way of this duct and releases its secretions onto the epithelial surface. (b) An endocrine gland begins similarly, but the cells connecting it to the surface degenerate while the secretory tissue becomes infiltrated with blood capillaries. The secretory cells secrete their products (hormones) into the blood.

or **trabeculae** (trah-BEC-you-lee), that divide the interior of the gland into compartments called **lobes,** which are visible to the naked eye. Finer connective tissue septa may further subdivide each lobe into microscopic **lobules.** Blood vessels, nerves, and the gland's own ducts generally travel through these septa. The connective tissue framework of the gland, called its **stroma,** supports and organizes the glandular tissue. The cells that perform the tasks of synthesis and secretion are collectively called the **parenchyma** (pa-REN-kih-muh). This is typically simple cuboidal or simple columnar epithelium.

Exocrine glands are classified according to their "architecture"—the branching of their ducts and the appearance and extent of their secretory portions (**fig. 5.31**). They are called **simple** if they have a single unbranched duct and **compound** if they have a branched duct. If the duct and secretory portion are of uniform diameter, the gland is called **tubular.** If the secretory cells form a dilated sac, the gland is called acinar and the sac is an **acinus**[31] (ASS-ih-nus), or **alveolus**[32] (AL-vee-OH-lus) (**fig. 5.30c**). A gland with secretory cells in both the tubular and acinar portions is called a **tubuloacinar (tubuloalveolar) gland.**

## Types of Secretions

Glands are classified not only by their structure but also by the nature of their secretions. **Serous glands** (SEER-us) produce relatively thin, watery fluids such as perspiration, milk, tears, and digestive juices. **Mucous glands,** found in the oral and nasal cavities among other places, secrete a glycoprotein called *mucin* (MEW-sin). After it is secreted, mucin absorbs water and forms the sticky product *mucus.* Goblet cells are unicellular mucous glands. (Note that *mucus,* the secretion, is spelled differently from *mucous,* the adjective form of the word.) **Mixed glands,** such as the two pairs of salivary glands in the chin, contain both serous and mucous cells and produce a mixture of the two types of secretions.

## Modes of Secretion

Exocrine glands are classified into *eccrine, apocrine,* and *holocrine* types according to how they release their secretions. **Eccrine**[33] **glands** (EC-rin), also called **merocrine**[34] **glands** (MERR-oh-crin), release their products by means of exocytosis. These include the tear glands, salivary glands, pancreas, and most others. Mammary glands

[31] *acinus* = berry
[32] *alveol* = cavity, pit

[33] *ec* = *ex* = out; *crin* = to separate, secrete
[34] *mero* = part; *crin* = to separate, secrete

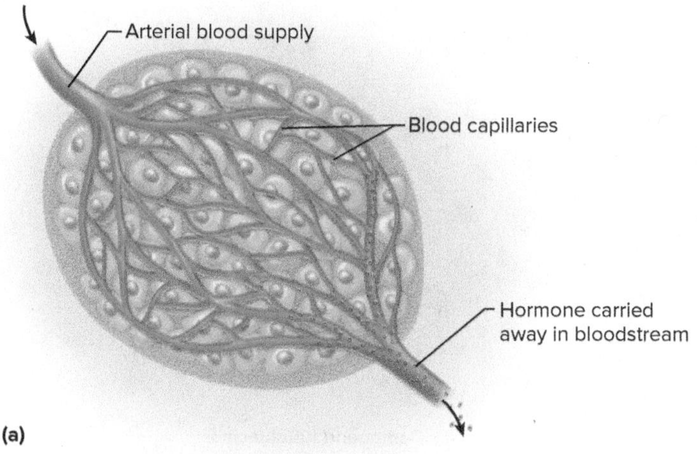


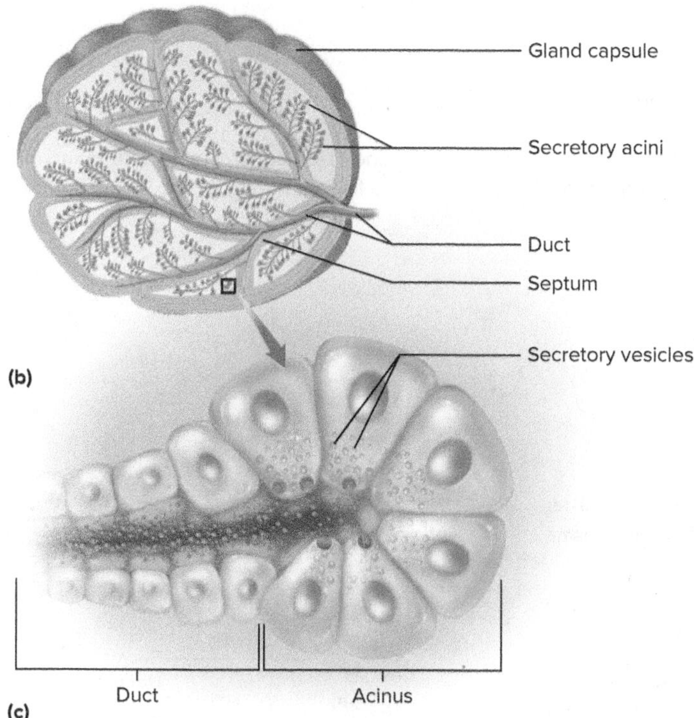


**FIGURE 5.30 General Structure of Endocrine and Exocrine Glands.** (a) Endocrine glands have no ducts but have a high density of blood capillaries and secrete their products (hormones) directly into the bloodstream. (b) Exocrine glands usually have a system of ducts, which often follow connective tissue septa, until their finest divisions end in saccular acini of secretory cells. (c) Detail of an acinus and the beginning of a duct.

*What membrane transport process are the cells of the acinus in (c) carrying out? (Review section 3.3.)*

secrete milk sugar (lactose) and proteins (casein, lactalbumin) by this method **(fig. 5.32a),** but secrete the milk fat by another method called **apocrine**[35] secretion **(fig. 5.32b).** Lipids coalesce from the cytosol into a droplet that buds from the cell surface, covered by a layer of plasma membrane and a very thin film of cytoplasm. Sweat glands of the axillary (armpit) region were once thought to use the apocrine method as well. Closer study showed this to be untrue; they are eccrine, but they're nevertheless different from other merocrine glands in function and histological appearance (see figure 6.10) and are still referred to as apocrine sweat glands.

In **holocrine**[36] **glands,** cells accumulate a product and then the entire cell disintegrates, *becoming* the secretion instead of *releasing* one **(fig. 5.32c).** Holocrine secretions tend to be relatively thick and oily, composed of cell fragments and the substances the cells had synthesized before disintegrating. Only a few glands use this method, such as the oil-producing glands of the scalp and other areas of skin, and certain glands of the eyelid.

## 5.5c Membranes

Atlas A (section A.3) describes the major body cavities and the membranes that line them and cover their viscera. We now consider some histological aspects of these membranes. Membranes may be composed of epithelial tissue only; connective tissue only; or epithelial, connective, and muscular tissue.

The largest membrane of the body is the **cutaneous membrane**—or more simply, the skin (detailed in chapter 6). It consists of a stratified squamous epithelium (epidermis) resting on a layer of connective tissue (dermis). Unlike the other membranes to be considered, it is relatively dry. It resists dehydration of the body and provides an inhospitable environment for the growth of infectious organisms.

The two principal kinds of internal membranes are mucous and serous membranes. A **mucous membrane (mucosa) (fig. 5.33a)** lines passages that open to the exterior environment: the digestive, respiratory, urinary, and reproductive tracts. A mucous membrane consists of two to three layers: (1) an epithelium; (2) an areolar connective tissue layer called the **lamina propria**[37] (LAM-ih-nuh PRO-pree-uh); and (3) often a layer of smooth muscle called the **muscularis mucosae** (MUSK-you-LAIR-iss mew-CO-see). Mucous membranes have absorptive, secretory, and protective functions. They are often covered with mucus secreted by goblet cells, multicellular mucous glands, or both. The mucus traps bacteria and foreign particles, which keeps them from invading the tissues and aids in their removal from the body. The epithelium of a mucous membrane may also include absorptive, ciliated, and other types of cells.

A **serous membrane (serosa)** is composed of a simple squamous epithelium resting on a thin layer of areolar connective tissue **(fig. 5.33b).** Serous membranes produce watery **serous fluid,** which arises from the blood and derives its name from the fact that it is similar to blood serum in composition. Serous membranes line the insides of some body cavities and form a smooth outer surface on some of the viscera, such as the digestive tract. The pleurae, pericardium, and peritoneum described in atlas A are serous membranes. Their epithelial component is called **mesothelium.**

The circulatory system is lined with a simple squamous epithelium called **endothelium,** derived from mesoderm. The endothelium rests on a thin layer of areolar tissue, which often rests in turn on an elastic sheet. Collectively, these tissues make

[35]*apo* = from, off, away; *crin* = to separate, secrete

[36]*holo* = whole, entire; *crin* = to separate, secrete

[37]*lamina* = layer; *propria* = of one's own

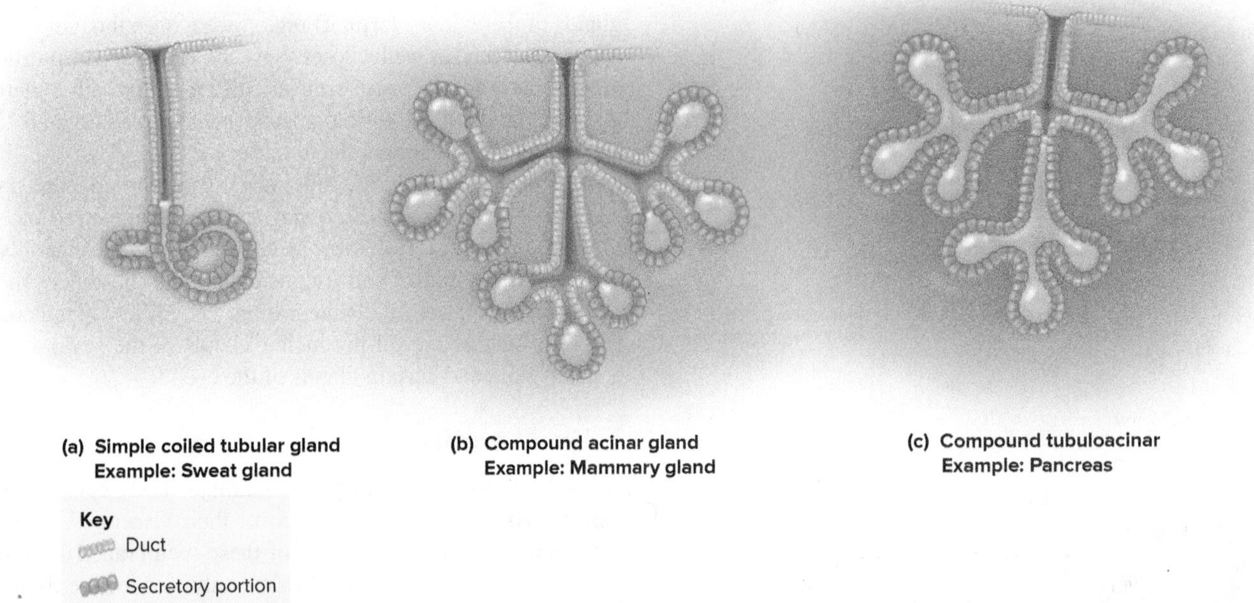


**FIGURE 5.31 Some Types of Exocrine Glands.** (a) A simple coiled tubular gland such as a sweat gland. (b) A compound acinar gland such as the mammary gland. (c) A compound tubuloacinar gland such as the pancreas. These are only a few examples of the 10 or so types of gland architecture.

*Predict and sketch the appearance of a simple acinar gland.*

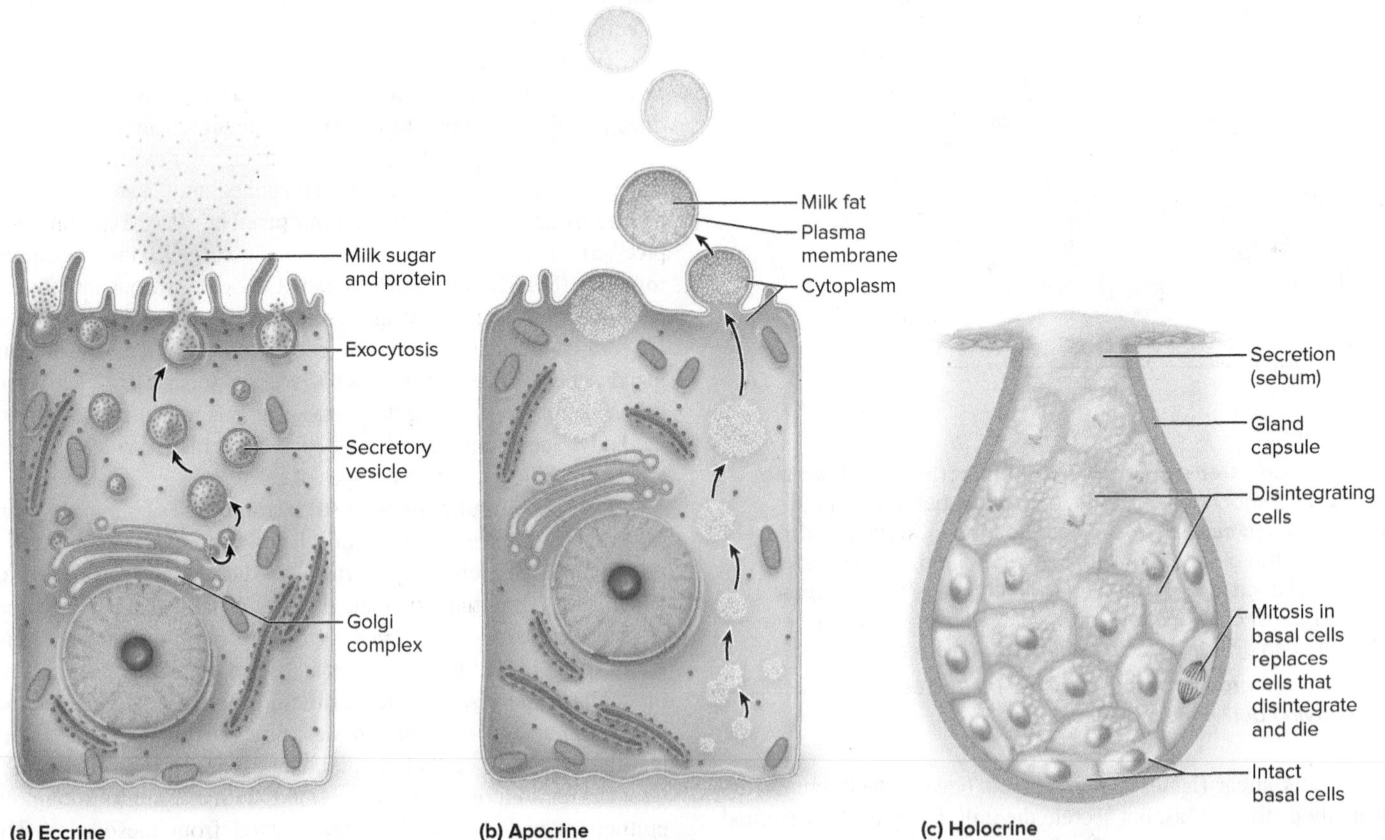


**FIGURE 5.32 The Three Modes of Exocrine Secretion.** (a) Eccrine secretion in a cell of the mammary gland, secreting milk sugar (lactose) and proteins (casein, lactalbumin) by exocytosis. (b) Apocrine secretion of fat by a cell of the mammary gland. Fat droplets coalesce in the cytosol, then bud from the cell surface with a thin coat of cytoplasm and plasma membrane. (c) Holocrine secretion by a sebaceous (oil) gland of the scalp. In this method, entire gland cells break down and become the secretion (sebum).

*Which of these three glands would require the highest rate of mitosis? Why?*

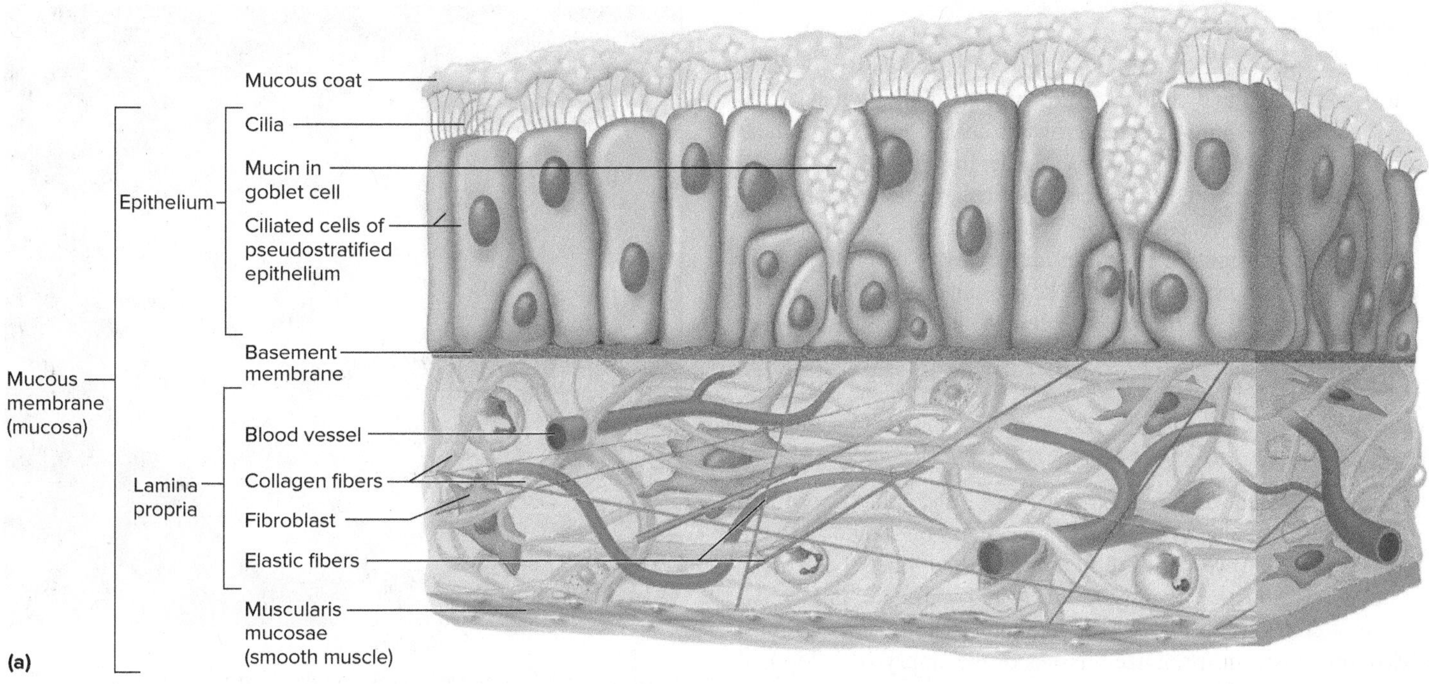


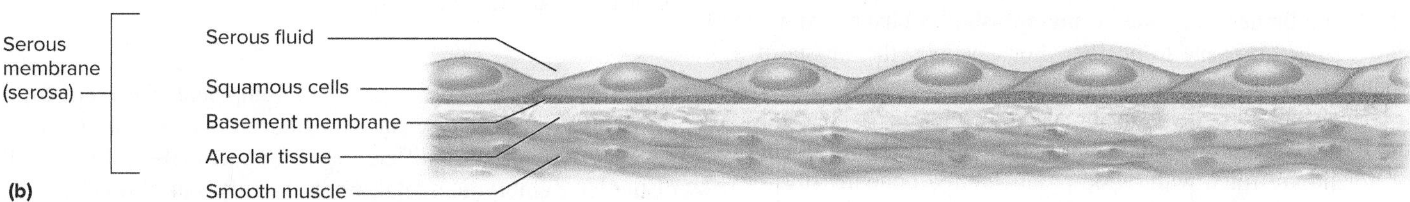


**FIGURE 5.33 Histology of Mucous and Serous Membranes.** (a) A mucous membrane such as the inner lining of the trachea. (b) A serous membrane such as the external surface of the small intestine.

up a membrane called the *tunica interna* of the blood vessels and *endocardium* of the heart.

The foregoing membranes are composed of two to three tissue types. By contrast, some membranes composed only of connective tissue include the *dura mater* around the brain, *synovial membranes* that enclose joints of the skeletal system, and the *periosteum* that covers each bone. Some membranes composed only of epithelium include the anterior surfaces of the lens and cornea of the eye. All of these are described in later chapters.

**BEFORE YOU GO ON**

Answer the following questions to test your understanding of the preceding section:

**19.** Compare the structure of tight junctions and gap junctions. Relate their structural differences to their functional differences.

**20.** Distinguish between a simple gland and a compound gland, and give an example of each. Distinguish between a tubular gland and an acinar gland, and give an example of each.

**21.** Contrast the eccrine, apocrine, and holocrine methods of secretion, and name a gland product produced by each method.

**22.** Describe the differences between a mucous and a serous membrane.

**23.** Name the layers of a mucous membrane, and state which of the four primary tissue classes composes each layer.

## 5.6 Tissue Growth, Development, Repair, and Degeneration

### Expected Learning Outcomes

When you have completed this section, you should be able to

a. name and describe the modes of tissue growth;

b. define *adult* and *embryonic stem cells* and their varied degrees of developmental plasticity;

c. name and describe the ways that a tissue can change from one type to another;

d. name and describe the modes and causes of tissue shrinkage and death; and

e. name and describe the ways the body repairs damaged tissues.

### 5.6a Tissue Growth

Tissues grow because their cells increase in number or size. Most embryonic and childhood growth occurs by **hyperplasia**[38] (HY-pur-PLAY-zhuh)—tissue growth through cell multiplication. Skeletal muscles and adipose tissue grow, however, through **hypertrophy**[39] (hy-PUR-truh-fee)—the enlargement of preexisting cells. Even a very muscular or fat adult has essentially the same number of muscle fibers or adipocytes as he or she had in late adolescence, but the cells may be substantially larger. **Neoplasia**[40] (NEE-oh-PLAY-zhuh) is the development of a tumor *(neoplasm)*—whether benign or malignant—composed of abnormal, nonfunctional tissue.

### 5.6b Tissue Development

You have studied the form and function of more than two dozen discrete types of human tissue in this chapter. You should not leave this subject, however, with the impression that once these tissue types are established, they never change. Tissues are, in fact, capable of changing from one type to another within certain limits. Most obviously, unspecialized tissues of the embryo develop into more diverse and specialized types of mature tissue—mesenchyme to cartilage and bone, for example. This development of a more specialized form and function is called **differentiation.**

Some tissues can undergo **metaplasia,**[41] a change from one type of mature tissue to another. For example, the vagina of a young girl is lined with a simple cuboidal epithelium. At puberty, it changes to a stratified squamous epithelium, better adapted to the future demands of intercourse and childbirth. The long bones of a child are filled with blood-producing red bone marrow, but by adulthood, most of this changes to adipose tissue. In smokers, the pseudostratified columnar epithelium of the bronchi may transform into a stratified squamous epithelium.

**APPLY WHAT YOU KNOW**

*What functions of a ciliated pseudostratified columnar epithelium could not be served by a stratified squamous epithelium? In light of this, what might be some consequences of bronchial metaplasia in heavy smokers?*

### 5.6c Stem Cells

The growth and differentiation of tissues depend upon a supply of reserve **stem cells.** These are undifferentiated cells that are not yet performing any specialized function, but have the potential to differentiate into one or more types of mature functional cells, such as liver, brain, cartilage, or skin cells. Such cells have various degrees of **developmental plasticity,** or diversity of mature cell types to which they can give rise.

There are two types of stem cells: embryonic and adult. **Embryonic stem cells** compose the early human embryo

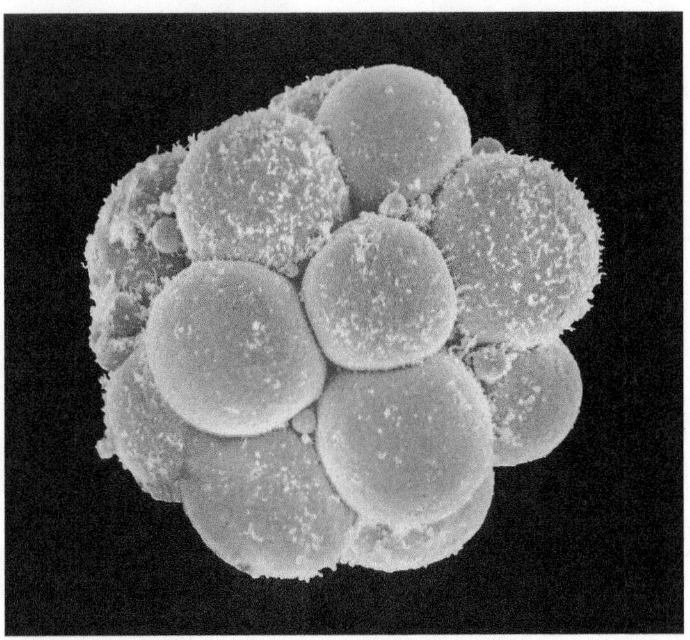

**FIGURE 5.34 The Morula Stage of Human Development.** This stage consists of about 16 to 32 totipotent stem cells with unlimited developmental plasticity.

Dr Yorgos Nikas/Science Photo Library/Getty Images

**(fig. 5.34).** In the early stages of development, these are called **totipotent stem cells,** because they have the potential to develop into any type of fully differentiated human cell—not only cells of the later embryonic, fetal, or adult body, but also cells of the temporary structures of pregnancy, such as the placenta and amniotic sac. Totipotency is unlimited developmental plasticity. About 4 days after fertilization, the developing embryo enters the *blastocyst* stage. The blastocyst is a hollow ball with an *outer cell mass* that helps form the placenta and other accessory organs of pregnancy, and an *inner cell mass (embryoblast)* that becomes the embryo itself (see fig. 29.4). Cells of the inner cell mass are called **pluripotent stem** cells; they can still develop into any cell type of the embryo, but not into the accessory organs of pregnancy. Thus their developmental plasticity is already somewhat limited.

**Adult stem cells** occur in small numbers in mature organs and tissues throughout a person's life. Typically an adult stem cell divides mitotically; one of its daughter cells remains a stem cell and the other one differentiates into a mature specialized cell. The latter cell may replace another that has grown old and died, contribute to the development of growing organs (as in a child), or help to repair damaged tissue. Some adult stem cells are **multipotent**—able to develop into two or more different cell lines, but not just any type of body cell. Certain multipotent bone marrow stem cells, for example, can give rise to red blood cells, five kinds of white blood cells, and platelet-producing cells. **Unipotent** stem cells have the most limited plasticity, as they can produce only one mature cell type. Examples include the cells that give rise to sperm, eggs, and keratinocytes (the majority cell type of the epidermis).

Both embryonic and adult stem cells have enormous potential for therapy, but advances in the field (see Deeper Insight 5.4) have

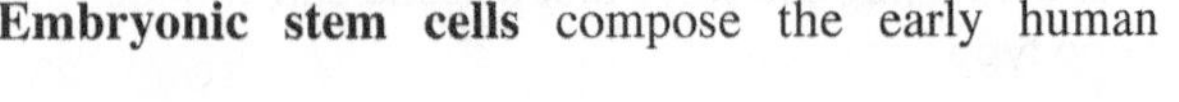

[38]*hyper* = excessive; *plas* = growth
[39]*hyper* = excessive; *trophy* = nourishment
[40]*neo* = new; *plas* = form, growth
[41]*meta* = change; *plas* = form, growth

## DEEPER INSIGHT 5.3
### CLINICAL APPLICATION

#### *Stem-Cell Therapy*

Cell biologists, clinicians, and hopeful patients look to stem cells as a possible treatment for diseases arising from the loss of functional tissue. Conceivably, with the right biochemical coaxing, adult stem cells (AS cells) may be induced to differentiate into various kinds of mature, differentiated cells to replace cardiac muscle damaged by heart attack, restore an injured spinal cord, cure neurodegenerative diseases such as parkinsonism, or cure diabetes by replacing lost insulin-secreting cells. AS cells have limited developmental potential, however, and may be unable to make many of the cell types needed to treat a broad range of degenerative diseases. In addition, they are present in very small numbers and are difficult to harvest from a tissue and culture in the quantities needed for therapy.

Embryonic stem cells (ES cells) could overcome these shortcomings. They are obtained from surplus embryos of about 16 to 32 cells (fig. 5.34) produced by *in vitro fertilization (IVF)* clinics, putting them to good use instead of discarding them. Unfortunately, though, stem-cell research has yet to produce many safe and proven therapies. Questions remain as to whether implanted stem cells may lodge in the wrong place in the body or grow into tumors instead of healthy functional tissue. Stem cells have proven their value as a "workhorse" of laboratory research in mechanisms of disease, toxicity screening, and drug testing; so far, however, the only therapies proven safe and effective, and approved by the U.S. Food and Drug Administration, are treatments using bone marrow and umbililcal cord blood for certain leukemias and other blood- and immune-related diseases (see Deeper Insight 18.3). Typically, the lag from a medical discovery to clinical use is about 20 years, and stem-cell therapy seems to be no exception. We may be in for a long wait to see if stem-cell technology will yield wider applications.

Meanwhile, unfortunately, fradulent stem-cell "clinics" have sprung up around the world charging vulnerable people tens of thousands of dollars (in nonrefundable cash, of course) for worthless and even life-threatening treatments. Such reports have emerged as a patient blinded by supposed stem-cell injections into the eyes and another in whom injected stem cells developed into a spinal tumor. The FDA is attempting to crack down on illegal treatments in the United States, but many vulnerable patients continue to be victimized by illicit providers in Mexico, South America, India, East Asia, and elsewhere.

---

been slowed both by technical difficulties and controversy over the use of embryonic cells.

## 5.6d Tissue Repair

Damaged tissues can be repaired in two ways: *regeneration* or *fibrosis*. **Regeneration** is the replacement of dead or damaged cells by the same type of cells as before; it restores normal function to the organ. Most skin injuries (cuts, scrapes, and minor burns) heal by regeneration. The liver also regenerates remarkably well. **Fibrosis** is the replacement of damaged tissue with scar tissue, composed mainly of collagen produced by fibroblasts. Scar tissue helps to hold an organ together, but it doesn't restore normal function. Examples include the healing of severe cuts and burns, the healing of muscle injuries, and scarring of the lungs in tuberculosis.

**Figure 5.35** illustrates the following stages in the healing of a cut in the skin, where both regeneration and fibrosis are involved:

1. Severed blood vessels bleed into the cut. Mast cells and cells damaged by the cut release histamine, which dilates blood vessels, increases blood flow to the area, and makes blood capillaries more permeable. Blood plasma seeps into the wound, carrying antibodies and clotting proteins.
2. A blood clot forms in the tissue, loosely knitting the edges of the cut together and inhibiting the spread of pathogens from the site of injury into healthy tissues. The surface of the blood clot dries and hardens in the air, forming a scab that temporarily seals the wound and blocks infection. Beneath the scab, macrophages begin to phagocytize and digest tissue debris.
3. New blood capillaries sprout from nearby vessels and grow into the wound. The deeper portions of the clot become infiltrated by capillaries and fibroblasts and transform into a soft mass called **granulation tissue.** Macrophages remove the blood clot while fibroblasts deposit new collagen to replace it. This *fibroblastic (reconstructive) phase* of repair begins 3 to 4 days after the injury and lasts up to 2 weeks.
4. Surface epithelial cells around the wound multiply and migrate into the wounded area, beneath the scab. The scab loosens and eventually falls off, and the epithelium grows thicker. Thus, the epithelium *regenerates* while the underlying connective tissue undergoes *fibrosis,* or scarring. Capillaries withdraw from the area as fibrosis progresses. The scar tissue may or may not show through the epithelium, depending on the severity of the wound. The wound may exhibit a depressed area at first, but this is often filled in by continued fibrosis and remodeling from below, until the scar becomes unnoticeable. This *remodeling (maturation) phase* of tissue repair begins several weeks after injury and may last as long as 2 years.

## 5.6e Tissue Degeneration and Death

**Atrophy**[42] (AT-ro-fee) is the shrinkage of a tissue through a loss in cell size or number. It results from both normal aging *(senile atrophy)* and lack of use of an organ *(disuse atrophy).* Muscles that are not exercised exhibit disuse atrophy as their cells become smaller. This was a serious problem for the first astronauts who participated in prolonged microgravity space flights. Upon return to normal gravity, they were sometimes too weak from muscular atrophy to walk. Space stations and shuttles now include exercise equipment to maintain the crew's muscular condition. Disuse atrophy also occurs when a limb is immobilized in a cast or by

---

[42] *a* = without; *trophy* = nourishment

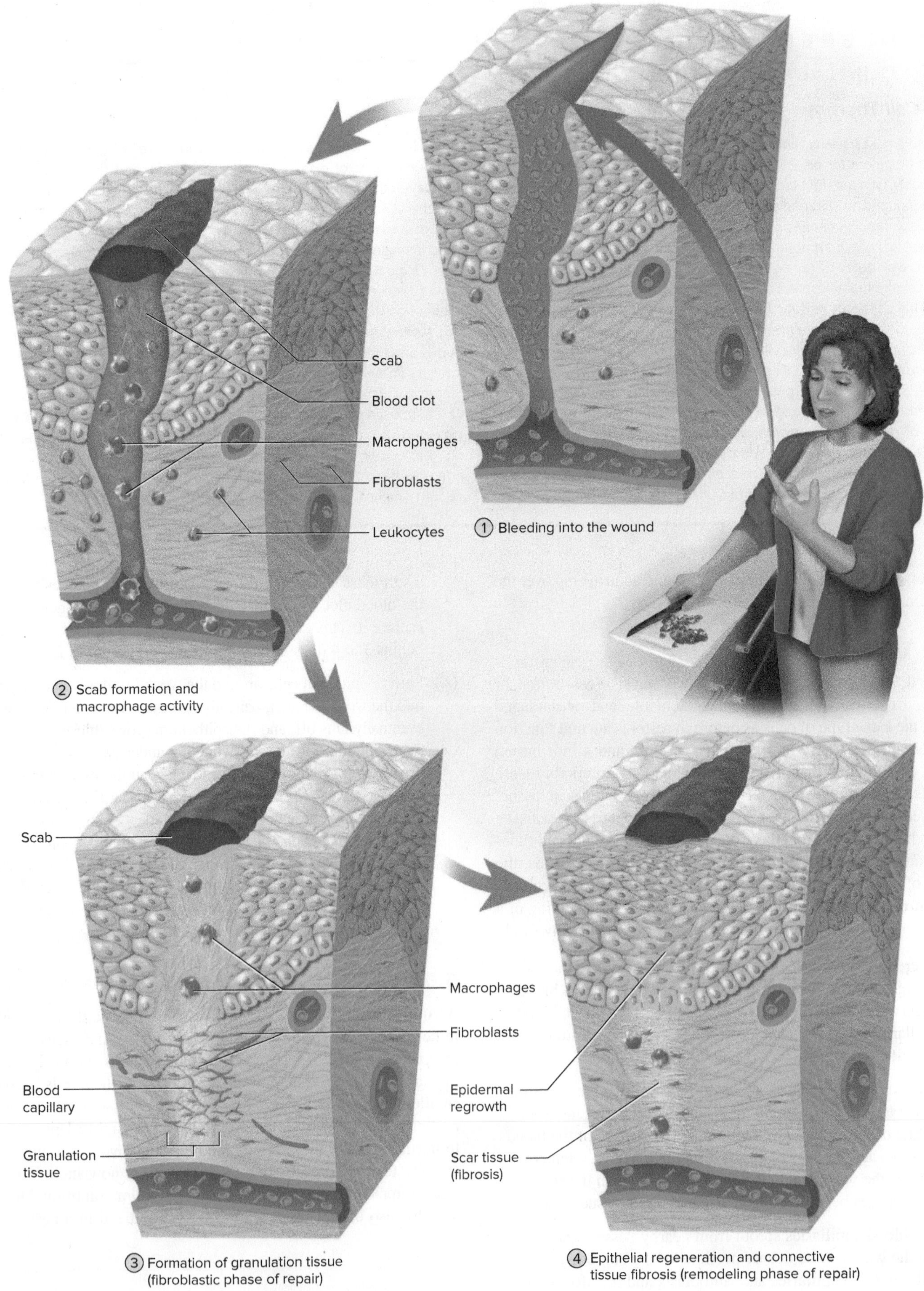


**FIGURE 5.35 Stages in the Healing of a Skin Wound.**

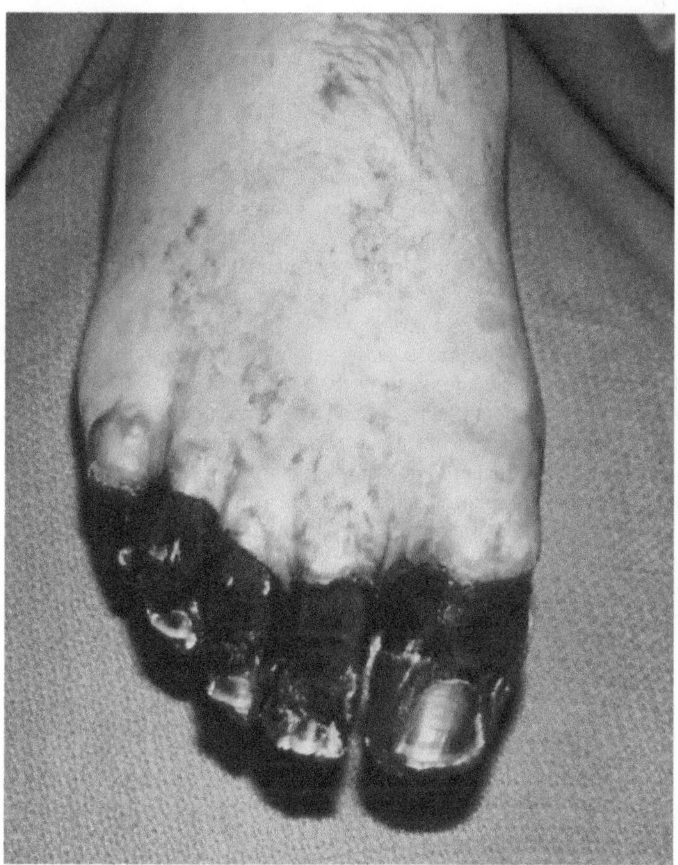

**FIGURE 5.36 Dry Gangrene of the Foot Caused by Diabetes Mellitus.**

Source: William Archibald/CDC

paralysis, or a person is confined to bed or a wheelchair by an illness or disability.

**Necrosis**[43] (neh-CRO-sis) is premature, pathological tissue death due to trauma, toxins, infection, and so forth; infarction and gangrene are two types of necrosis. **Infarction** is the sudden death of tissue, such as cardiac muscle *(myocardial infarction)* or brain tissue *(cerebral infarction),* that occurs when its blood supply is cut off. **Gangrene** is tissue necrosis resulting from infection or an obstructed blood supply. *Dry gangrene* often occurs in diabetics, especially in the feet. It is characterized by dry, shrunken skin with bluish-purple, brown, or black discoloration **(fig. 5.36).** A lack of sensation due to diabetic nerve damage can make a person oblivious to injury and infection, and poor blood circulation due to diabetic arterial damage results in slow healing and rapid spread of infection. This often necessitates the amputation of toes, feet, or legs. A **decubitus ulcer (bed sore** or **pressure sore)** is a form of dry gangrene that occurs when immobilized persons, such as those confined to a hospital bed or wheelchair, are unable to move, and continual pressure on the skin cuts off blood flow to an area. Pressure sores occur most often in places where a bone comes close to the body surface, such as the hips, sacral region, and ankles. Here, the thin layer of skin and connective tissue is especially prone to compression between the bone and a bed or wheelchair.

*Wet gangrene* typically occurs in internal organs and involves neutrophil invasion, liquefaction of the tissue, pus, and a foul odor. It can result from appendicitis or an obstructed colon, for example. *Gas gangrene* is necrosis of a wound resulting from infection with certain bacteria of the genus *Clostridium,* usually introduced when a wound is contaminated with soil. The disorder is named for bubbles of gas (mainly hydrogen) that accumulate in the tissues. This is a deadly condition that requires immediate intervention, often including amputation.

Cells dying by necrosis usually swell, exhibit *blebbing* (bubbling) of their plasma membranes, and then rupture. The cell contents released into the tissues trigger an inflammatory response in which macrophages phagocytize the cellular debris.

**Apoptosis**[44] (AP-op-TOE-sis), or **programmed cell death,** is often the normal death of cells that have completed their function and best serve the body by dying and getting out of the way. Cells can be induced to undergo apoptosis in some pathological conditions, however. Cells undergoing apoptosis shrink and are quickly phagocytized by macrophages and other cells. The cell contents never escape, so there is no inflammatory response. Although billions of cells die every hour by apoptosis, they are engulfed so quickly that they are almost never seen except within macrophages.

Apparently, nearly every cell has a built-in "suicide program" that enables the body to dispose of it when necessary. In some cases, an extracellular suicide signal binds to a receptor protein in the plasma membrane, which then activates enzymes that degrade the cell's DNA and proteins. In other cases, cells seem to undergo apoptosis automatically if they stop receiving growth factors from other cells. For example, in embryonic development we produce about twice as many neurons as we need. Those that make connections with target cells survive, while the excess neurons die for lack of *nerve growth factor.* Apoptosis also dissolves the webbing between the fingers and toes during embryonic development; it frees the earlobe from the side of the head in people with the genotype for detached earlobes; and it causes shrinkage of the breasts after lactation ceases.

**BEFORE YOU GO ON**

Answer the following questions to test your understanding of the preceding section:

**24.** Distinguish between differentiation and metaplasia.

**25.** Tissues can grow through an increase in cell size or cell number. What are the respective terms for these two kinds of growth?

**26.** Distinguish between atrophy, necrosis, and apoptosis, and describe a circumstance under which each of these forms of tissue loss may occur.

**27.** Distinguish between regeneration and fibrosis. Which process restores normal cellular function? What good is the other process if it does not restore function?

[43] *necr* = death; *osis* = process

[44] *apo* = away; *ptosis* = falling

## DEEPER INSIGHT 5.4

### CLINICAL APPLICATION

### *Regenerative Medicine*

As the population ages while science progresses in knowledge and technical skill, people look to the medical community with hopes of repairing or replacing body parts that are damaged, lost, defective from birth, or worn-out by age. Is it possible to repair brain or heart tissue; or a nose, ear, or finger; or even larger body parts lost to injury? The science of **regenerative medicine,** still in its infancy, seeks to do just that.

One of its approaches is **tissue engineering**—growing tissues and organs in the laboratory, ideally from the patient's own cells, and implanting them into the body. To produce something like a blood vessel or bronchus, tissue engineers start with an organ from a donor body and *decellularize* it—strip it of all living cells, leaving only its collagenous connective tissue framework, or scaffold. While preserving the shape and mechanical properties of the organ to be replaced, this cell-free scaffold eliminates the likelihood of immune rejection by the patient to receive it. It is then seeded with cells from the patient's body, such as chrondrocytes, fibroblasts, or keratinocytes. The product is maintained in an incubator called a *bioreactor,* which provides nutrients, oxygen, and growth factors while the cells repopulate the scaffold. Some treatments use synthetic polymer scaffolds and even artificial organs produced by 3D inkjet bioprinters. One of the most daunting problems in growing artificial organs is producing the microvascular blood supply needed to sustain an organ such as a liver.

Tissue engineering has succeeded in the laboratory in producing liver, bone, cartilage, ureter, tendon, intestine, and breast tissue, and even a beating rodent heart. "Bench to bedside" translation to the clinic and real patients is another matter. Early successes, however, include nasofacial reconstruction, engineered skin for covering burns and diabetic foot ulcers, repair of damaged knee cartilages, and even urinary bladders grown from patients' own cells and transplanted into their bodies. Preclinical trials are underway on producing bioengineered blood vessels for coronary bypass surgery, and hopes for future development include heart valves and patches of cardiac muscle.

# STUDY GUIDE

## ▶ Assess Your Learning Outcomes

*To test your knowledge, discuss the following topics with a study partner or in writing, ideally from memory.*

### 5.1 The Study of Tissues

1. Two names for the branch of biology concerned with tissue structure
2. The four primary tissue classes that constitute the body
3. The roles of cells, matrix, fibers, and ground substance in tissue composition, and how these terms relate to each other
4. Primary germ layers of the embryo and their relationship to mature tissues
5. How and why tissues are prepared as stained histological sections; the three common planes of section; and some ways that tissues are prepared other than sectioning

### 5.2 Epithelial Tissue

1. Characteristics that distinguish epithelium from the other three primary tissue classes
2. Functions of the basement membrane and its relationship to an epithelium
3. Defining characteristics of a simple epithelium
4. Four types of simple epithelium and the appearance, functions, and representative locations of each
5. Defining characteristics of a stratified epithelium
6. Four types of stratified epithelium and the appearance, functions, and representative locations of each
7. Distinctions between keratinized and nonkeratinized stratified squamous epithelium, including differences in histology, locations, and functions
8. The special protective property and mechanism of urothelium
9. Epithelial exfoliation and its clinical relevance

### 5.3 Connective Tissue

1. Characteristics that distinguish connective tissue from the other three primary tissue classes
2. Functions of connective tissues
3. Cell types found in fibrous connective tissue, and the functions of each
4. Fiber types found in fibrous connective tissue, their composition, and the functions of each
5. The composition and variations in the ground substance of fibrous connective tissue
6. The appearance, functions, and locations of areolar, reticular, dense irregular, and dense regular connective tissue
7. The appearance, functions, and locations of adipose tissue, including the differences between white fat and brown fat
8. Defining characteristics of cartilage as a class; the three types of cartilage and how they differ in histology, function, and location; the relationship of the perichondrium to cartilage; and where perichondrium is absent
9. Defining characteristics of osseous tissue as a class; the distinction between spongy and compact bone; and the relationship of the periosteum to bone
10. The appearance of cross sections of compact bone
11. Why blood is classified as connective tissue; the term for its matrix; and the major categories of formed elements in blood

### 5.4 Nervous and Muscular Tissues—Excitable Tissues

1. Why nervous and muscular tissues are called *excitable tissues* even though excitability is a property of all living cells
2. The two basic types of cells in nervous tissue and their functional differences
3. The general structure of neurons
4. Defining characteristics of muscular tissue as a class
5. Three types of muscle and how they differ in histology, function, and location

### 5.5 Cellular Junctions, Glands, and Membranes

1. The general function of cellular junctions
2. Differences in the structure and function of tight junctions, desmosomes, hemidesmosomes, and gap junctions
3. The definition of a *gland* and the two basic functions of glands
4. The developmental, structural, and functional distinctions between exocrine and endocrine glands; examples of each; and why some glands cannot be strictly classified into one category or the other
5. Examples of unicellular glands in both the exocrine and endocrine categories
6. General histology of a typical exocrine gland
7. The scheme for classifying exocrine glands according to the anatomy of their duct systems and their distribution of secretory cells
8. Differences between serous, mucous, and mixed glands, and examples of each
9. Comparison of the mode of secretion of eccrine, apocrine, and holocrine glands
10. The variety of serous, mucous, and other membranes in the body, and names of some specialized membranes of the skin, blood vessels, and joints

### 5.6 Tissue Growth, Development, Repair, and Degeneration

1. Differences between hyperplasia, hypertrophy, and neoplasia as normal and pathological modes of tissue growth
2. Differences between differentiation and metaplasia as modes of transformation from one tissue type to another
3. What stem cells are and how they relate to developmental plasticity; differences between embryonic and adult stem cells; and differences between totipotent, pluripotent, multipotent, and unipotent stem cells
4. Differences between regeneration and fibrosis as modes of tissue repair
5. Steps in the healing of a wound such as a cut in the skin
6. The general meaning of tissue *atrophy* and two forms or causes of atrophy
7. Differences between necrosis and apoptosis as modes of cell death and tissue shrinkage; some normal functions of apoptosis
8. Varieties of necrosis including infarction, dry gangrene, and gas gangrene

# STUDY GUIDE

## ▶ Testing Your Recall

*Answers in Appendix A*

1. Urothelium is found in
   a. the urinary system.
   b. the respiratory system.
   c. the digestive system.
   d. the reproductive system.
   e. all of the above.

2. The external surface of the stomach is covered by
   a. a mucosa.
   b. a serosa.
   c. the parietal peritoneum.
   d. a lamina propria.
   e. a basement membrane.

3. Which of these is a primary germ layer?
   a. epidermis
   b. mucosa
   c. ectoderm
   d. endothelium
   e. epithelium

4. A seminiferous tubule of the testis is lined with ______ epithelium.
   a. simple cuboidal
   b. pseudostratified columnar ciliated
   c. stratified squamous
   d. transitional
   e. stratified cuboidal

5. ______ prevent fluids from seeping between epithelial cells.
   a. Glycosaminoglycans
   b. Hemidesmosomes
   c. Tight junctions
   d. Communicating junctions
   e. Basement membranes

6. A fixative serves to
   a. stop tissue decay.
   b. improve contrast.
   c. repair a damaged tissue.
   d. bind epithelial cells together.
   e. bind cardiac myocytes together.

7. The collagen of areolar tissue is produced by
   a. macrophages.
   b. fibroblasts.
   c. mast cells.
   d. leukocytes.
   e. chondrocytes.

8. Tendons are composed of ______ connective tissue.
   a. skeletal
   b. areolar
   c. dense irregular
   d. yellow elastic
   e. dense regular

9. The shape of the external ear is due to
   a. skeletal muscle.
   b. elastic cartilage.
   c. fibrocartilage.
   d. articular cartilage.
   e. hyaline cartilage.

10. The most abundant formed element(s) of blood is/are
    a. plasma.
    b. erythrocytes.
    c. platelets.
    d. leukocytes.
    e. proteins.

11. Any form of pathological tissue death is called ______.

12. The simple squamous epithelium that lines the peritoneal cavity is called ______.

13. Osteocytes and chondrocytes occupy little cavities called ______.

14. Muscle cells and axons are often called ______ because of their shape.

15. Tendons and ligaments are made mainly of the protein ______.

16. Of the three major categories of muscle, the only one that never has gap junctions is ______.

17. An epithelium rests on a layer called the ______ between its deepest cells and the underlying connective tissue.

18. Fibers and ground substance make up the ______ of a connective tissue.

19. A/An ______ adult stem cell can differentiate into two or more mature cell types.

20. Any epithelium in which every cell touches the basement membrane is called a/an ______ epithelium.

## ▶ Building Your Medical Vocabulary

*Answers in Appendix A*

*State a meaning of each word element, and give a medical term from this chapter that uses it or a slight variation of it.*

1. apo-
2. chondro-
3. ecto-
4. -gen
5. histo-
6. holo-
7. hyalo-
8. necro-
9. plas-
10. squamo-

# STUDY GUIDE

## ▶ What's Wrong with These Statements?

*Answers in Appendix A*

*Briefly explain why each of the following statements is false, or reword it to make it true.*

1. The esophagus is protected from abrasion by a keratinized stratified squamous epithelium.
2. Only the basal cells of a pseudostratified columnar epithelium contact the basement membrane.
3. Skeletal muscle is defined by the fact that it is always attached to bones.
4. The secretions of a gland are produced by the cells of its stroma.
5. In all connective tissues, the matrix occupies more space than the cells do.
6. Adipocytes are limited to adipose tissue.
7. Tight junctions function primarily to prevent cells from pulling apart.
8. The development of mature tissue types from the immature tissues of a neonate (newborn) is called neoplasia.
9. Nerve and muscle cells are the body's only electrically excitable cells.
10. Cartilage is always covered by a fibrous perichondrium.

## ▶ Testing Your Comprehension

1. A woman in labor is often told to push. In doing so, is she consciously contracting her uterus to expel the baby? Justify your answer based on the muscular composition of the uterus.
2. A major tenet of the cell theory is that all bodily structure and function are based on cells. The structural properties of bone, cartilage, and tendons, however, are due more to their extracellular material than to their cells. Is this an exception to the cell theory? Why or why not?
3. When cartilage is compressed, water is squeezed out of it, and when pressure is taken off, water flows back into the matrix. This being the case, why do you think cartilage at weight-bearing joints such as the knees can degenerate from lack of exercise?
4. The epithelium of the respiratory tract is mostly of the pseudostratified columnar ciliated type, but in the alveoli—the tiny air sacs where oxygen and carbon dioxide are exchanged between the blood and inhaled air—the epithelium is simple squamous. Explain the functional significance of this histological difference. That is, why don't the alveoli have the same kind of epithelium as the rest of the respiratory tract?
5. Which do you think would heal faster, cartilage or bone? Stratified squamous or simple columnar epithelium? Why?

CHAPTER 6

# THE INTEGUMENTARY SYSTEM

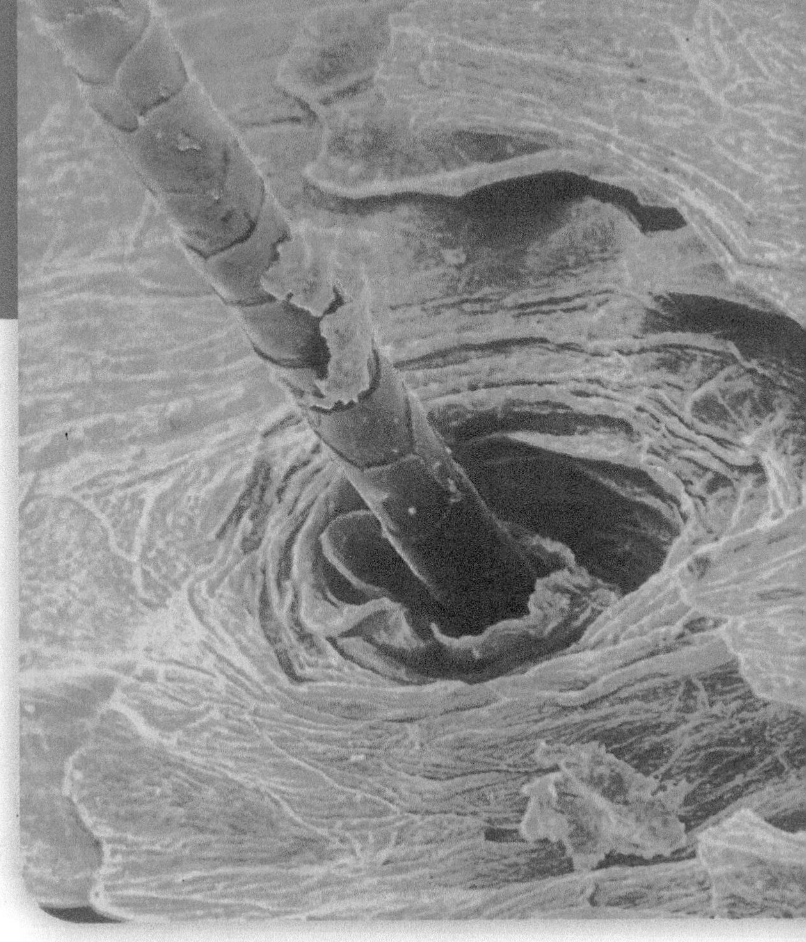

A human hair emerging from its follicle (SEM)

SPL/Science Source

## CHAPTER OUTLINE



## DEEPER INSIGHTS

Module 4: Integumentary System

## BRUSHING UP

- The epidermis of the skin is a keratinized stratified squamous epithelium, introduced in table 5.3.
- The dermis is composed of the areolar and dense irregular connective tissues described in tables 5.4 and 5.5. Its main protein is collagen, introduced in section 5.3b.
- The well-known durability of the epidermis depends in part on its desmosomes, depicted in figure 5.28b.
- Reviewing eccrine, apocrine, and holocrine gland types (see fig. 5.32) will help in understanding the types of sweat glands and oil glands of the skin in this chapter.
- Understanding some characteristics of the integumentary system, such as skin color and baldness, requires familiarity with dominant and recessive gene alleles (see section 4.4b).

We pay more daily attention to our skin, hair, and nails than to any other organ system. It is, after all, the most visible one, and its appearance strongly affects our social interactions. Few people venture out of the house without first looking in a mirror to see if their skin and hair are presentable. Social considerations aside, the integumentary system is important to one's self-image, and a positive self-image is important to the attitudes that promote overall good health. Care of the integumentary system is thus a particularly important part of the total plan of patient care.

**Dermatology**[1] is the branch of medicine specializing in the care and treatment of the skin. Even a general physical examination, however, should include inspection of the skin, hair, and nails. Their appearance can provide clues not only to their own health, but also to deeper disorders such as liver cancer, anemia, and heart failure. The skin also is the most vulnerable of our organs, exposed to radiation, trauma, infection, and injurious chemicals. Consequently, it needs and receives more medical attention than any other organ system.

## 6.1 Skin and Subcutaneous Tissue

### Expected Learning Outcomes

When you have completed this section, you should be able to

a. list the functions of the skin and relate them to its structure;
b. describe the histological structure of the epidermis, dermis, and subcutaneous tissue;
c. describe the normal and pathological colors that the skin can have, and explain their causes; and
d. describe the common markings of the skin.

The **integumentary**[2] **system** consists of the skin, hair, nails, and their associated glands. The **skin (integument)** is the body's largest and heaviest organ. In adults, it covers an area of 1.5 to 2.0 $m^2$ and accounts for about 8% of the body weight. It consists of two layers: a stratified squamous epithelium called the *epidermis* and a deeper connective tissue layer called the *dermis* **(fig. 6.1).** Below the dermis is another connective tissue layer, the *hypodermis,* which is not part of the skin but is customarily studied in conjunction with it.

Most of the skin is 1 to 2 mm thick, but it ranges from less than 0.5 mm on the eyelids to 6 mm between the shoulder blades. The difference is due mainly to variation in thickness of the dermis, although skin is classified as thick or thin based on the relative thickness of the epidermis alone. **Thick skin** covers the palms, soles, and corresponding surfaces of the fingers and toes. Its epidermis alone is about 0.5 mm thick, due to a very thick surface layer of dead cells called the *stratum corneum* (see fig. 6.3). Thick skin has sweat glands but no hair follicles or sebaceous (oil) glands. The rest of the body is covered with **thin skin,** which has an epidermis about 0.1 mm thick, with a thin stratum corneum (see fig. 6.5). It possesses hair follicles, sebaceous glands, and sweat glands.

### 6.1a Functions of the Skin

The skin is much more than a container for the body. It has a variety of important functions that go well beyond appearance, as we shall see here.

1. **Resistance to trauma and infection.** The skin suffers the most physical injuries to the body, but it resists and recovers from trauma better than other organs do. The epidermal cells are packed with the tough protein **keratin** and linked by strong desmosomes that give this epithelium its durability. Few infectious organisms can penetrate the intact skin. Bacteria and fungi colonize the surface, but their numbers are kept in check by its relative dryness, its slight acidity (pH 4–6), and defensive antimicrobial peptides called *dermcidin* and *defensins.* The protective acidic film is called the *acid mantle.*
2. **Other barrier functions.** The skin is important as a barrier to water. It prevents the body from absorbing excess water when you are swimming or bathing, but even more importantly, it prevents the body from losing excess water. The epidermis is also a barrier to ultraviolet (UV) rays, blocking much of this cancer-causing radiation from reaching deeper tissue layers; and it is a barrier to many potentially harmful chemicals. It is, however, permeable to several drugs and poisons (see Deeper Insight 6.1).
3. **Vitamin D synthesis.** The skin carries out the first step in the synthesis of vitamin D, which is needed for bone development and maintenance. The liver and kidneys complete the process. This is further detailed in figure 7.16.
4. **Sensation.** The skin is our most extensive sense organ. It is equipped with a variety of nerve endings that react to heat,

[1]*dermat* = skin; *logy* = study of

[2]*integument* = covering

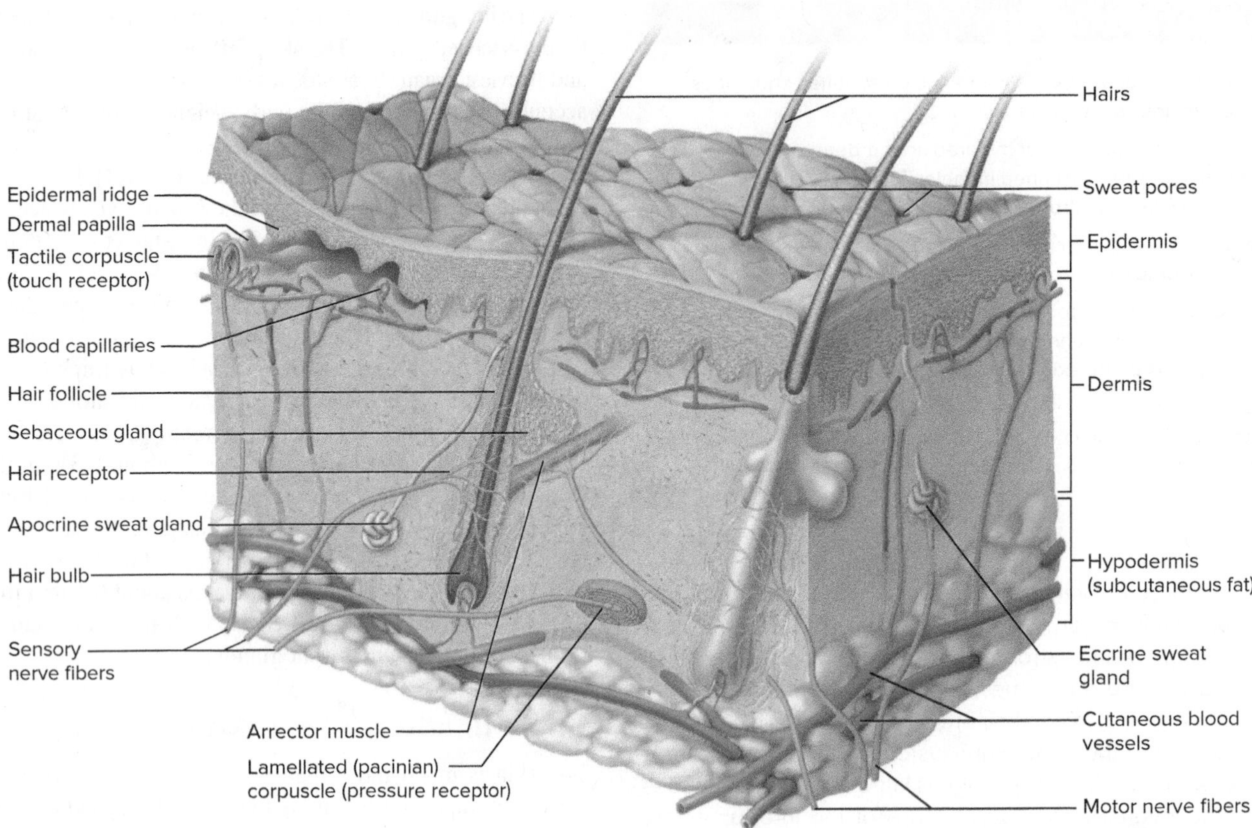


**FIGURE 6.1 Structure of the Skin and Subcutaneous Tissue.** The epidermis is peeled up at the upper left corner to show the dermal–epidermal boundary.

cold, touch, texture, pressure, vibration, and tissue injury (see section 16.2). These sensory receptors are especially abundant on the face, palms, fingers, soles, nipples, and genitals. There are relatively few on the back and in skin overlying joints such as the knees and elbows.

## DEEPER INSIGHT 6.1

### CLINICAL APPLICATION

### *Transdermal Absorption*

The ability of the skin to absorb chemicals makes it possible to administer several medicines as ointments or lotions, or by means of adhesive patches that release the medicine steadily through a membrane. For example, inflammation can be treated with a hydrocortisone ointment, nitroglycerine patches are used to relieve heart pain, nicotine patches are used to help overcome tobacco addiction, and other medicated patches are used to control high blood pressure and motion sickness.

Unfortunately, the skin can also be a route for absorption of poisons. These include toxins from poison ivy and other plants; metals such as mercury, arsenic, and lead; and solvents such as acetone (nail polish remover) and paint thinner; and pesticides. Some of these can cause brain damage, liver failure, or kidney failure, which is good reason for using protective gloves when handling such substances.

5. **Thermoregulation.** The skin receives 10 times as much blood flow as it needs for its own maintenance, and is richly supplied with nerve endings called thermoreceptors, which monitor the body surface temperature. All of this relates to its great importance in regulating body temperature. In response to chilling, the body retains heat by constricting blood vessels of the dermis *(cutaneous vasoconstriction),* keeping warm blood deeper in the body. In response to overheating, it loses excess heat by dilating those vessels *(cutaneous vasodilation),* allowing more blood to flow close to the surface and lose heat through the skin. If this is insufficient to restore normal temperature, sweat glands secrete perspiration. The evaporation of sweat can have a powerful cooling effect. Thus, the skin plays roles in both warming and cooling the body.
6. **Nonverbal communication.** The skin is an important means of nonverbal communication. Humans, like most other primates, have much more expressive faces than other mammals **(fig. 6.2).** Complex skeletal muscles insert in the dermis and pull on the skin to create subtle and varied facial expressions. The general appearance of the skin, hair, and nails—whether the ravages of adolescent acne, the presence of a birthmark or scar, or just a "bad hair day"—is also important to social acceptance and to a person's self-image and emotional state.

(a)

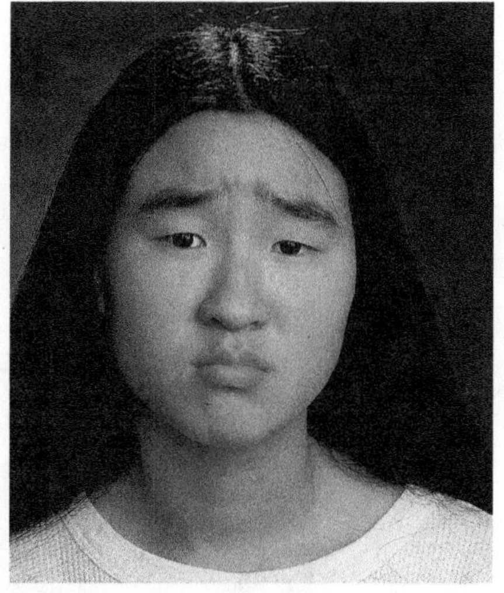

(b)

**FIGURE 6.2 Importance of the Skin in Nonverbal Expression.** (a) Primates such as humans and this chimpanzee differ from other mammals in having very expressive faces due to facial muscles that insert on the collagen fibers of the dermis and move the skin. (b) Human facial expression, reflecting the actions of complex facial muscles surveyed in chapter 10.

a: DLILLC/Corbis/VCG/Getty Images; b: Joe DeGrandis/McGraw-Hill Education

## 6.1b The Epidermis

The **epidermis**[3] is a keratinized stratified squamous epithelium, as described in table 5.3. That is, its surface consists of dead cells packed with the tough protein keratin. Like other epithelia, the epidermis lacks blood vessels and depends on the diffusion of nutrients from the underlying connective tissue. It has sparse nerve endings for touch and pain, but most sensations of the skin are due to nerve endings in the dermis.

### Cells of the Epidermis

The epidermis is composed of five types of cells **(fig. 6.3):**

1. **Keratinocytes** (keh-RAT-ih-no-sites) are the great majority of epidermal cells. They are named for their role in synthesizing keratin. In ordinary histological specimens, nearly all visible epidermal cells are keratinocytes.
2. **Stem cells** are undifferentiated cells that divide and give rise to the keratinocytes. They are found only in the deepest layer of the epidermis, called the *stratum basale.*
3. **Melanocytes** also occur only in the stratum basale, amid the stem cells and deepest keratinocytes. They synthesize the brown to black pigment *melanin.* They have branching processes that spread among the keratinocytes and continually shed melanin-containing fragments *(melanosomes)* from their tips. The keratinocytes phagocytize these and gather the melanin granules on the "sunny side" of their nucleus. Like a parasol, the dark granules shield the DNA from ultraviolet rays.
4. **Tactile cells,** relatively few in number, are receptors for touch. They, too, are found in the basal layer of the epidermis and are associated with an underlying dermal nerve fiber. The tactile cell and its nerve fiber are collectively called a *tactile disc.*
5. **Dendritic**[4] **cells** are found in two layers of the epidermis called the *stratum spinosum* and *stratum granulosum* (described in the next section). They are immune cells that originate in the bone marrow but migrate to the epidermis and epithelia of the oral cavity, esophagus, and vagina. The epidermis has as many as 800 dendritic cells per square millimeter. They stand guard against toxins, microbes, and other pathogens that penetrate into the skin. When they detect such invaders, they alert the immune system so the body can defend itself (see section 21.1b).

### Layers of the Epidermis

Cells of the epidermis are arranged in four to five zones, or strata (five in thick skin) (fig. 6.3). The following description progresses from deep to superficial, and from the youngest to the oldest keratinocytes.

1. The **stratum basale** (bah-SAY-lee) consists mainly of a single layer of cuboidal to low columnar stem cells and keratinocytes resting on the basement membrane. Scattered among these are the melanocytes, tactile cells, and stem cells. As stem cells divide, they give rise to keratinocytes that migrate toward the surface and replace lost epidermal cells.
2. The **stratum spinosum** (spy-NO-sum) consists of several layers of keratinocytes. In most places, this is the thickest stratum, but on the palms and soles it is usually exceeded by the stratum corneum. The deepest cells of the stratum spinosum continue dividing, but as they're pushed farther upward, they cease. Instead, they produce more and more keratin filaments, which cause the cells to flatten. Therefore, the higher up you look in the stratum spinosum, the flatter the cells appear. Dendritic cells are also found throughout the stratum spinosum, but are not usually identifiable in routinely stained tissue sections.

[3]*epi* = above, upon; *derm* = skin

[4]*dendr* = tree, branch

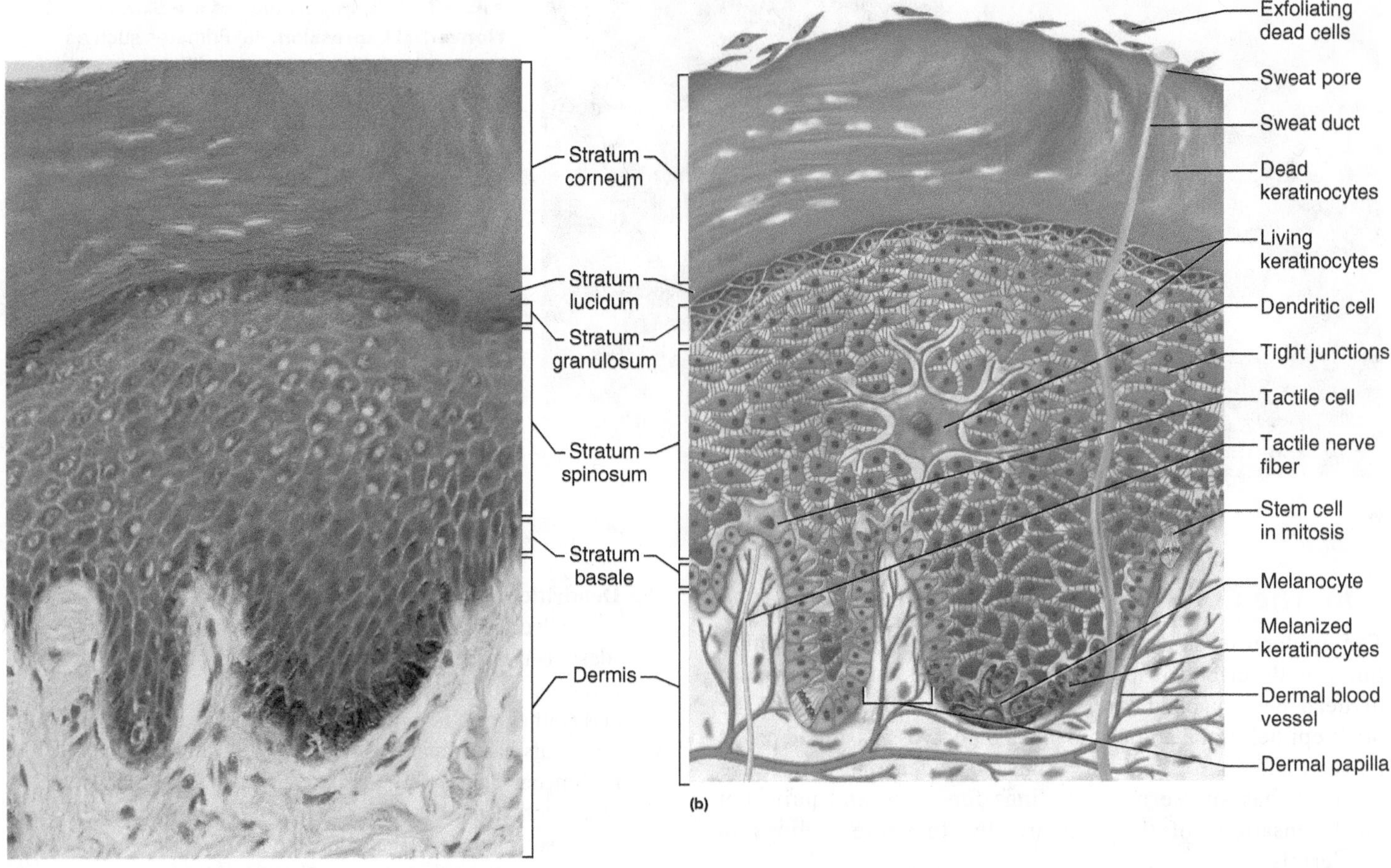


**FIGURE 6.3 Layers and Cell Types of the Epidermis.** (a) Photo. (b) Drawing with added features of skin not visible in the photo. Gaps between the keratinocytes are an artifact created by cell shrinkage during fixation, but are typically seen in microscope slides of skin. The drawing accentuates the ladderlike tight junctions that bridge these gaps. APR

a: Biophoto Associates/Science Source

The stratum spinosum is named for an artificial appearance *(artifact)* created by the histological fixation of skin specimens. Keratinocytes are firmly attached to each other by numerous desmosomes, which partly account for the toughness of the epidermis. Histological fixatives shrink the keratinocytes so they pull away from each other, but they remain attached by the desmosomes—like two people holding hands while they step farther apart. The desmosomes thus create bridges from cell to cell, giving each cell a spiny appearance from which we derive the word *spinosum.* Keratinocytes are also bound to each other by tight junctions, which make an essential contribution to water retention by the skin.

3. The **stratum granulosum** consists of three to five layers of flat keratinocytes—more in thick skin than in thin skin. The keratinocytes of this layer contain coarse, dark-staining *keratohyalin granules* that give the layer its name.
4. The **stratum lucidum**[5] (LOO-sih-dum) is a thin zone superficial to the stratum granulosum, seen only in thick skin. Here, the keratinocytes are densely packed with a clear protein named *eleidin* (ee-LEE-ih-din). The cells have no nuclei or other organelles. This zone has a pale, featureless appearance with indistinct cell boundaries.
5. The **stratum corneum** consists of up to 30 layers of dead, scaly, keratinized cells that form a durable surface layer. It is especially resistant to abrasion, penetration, and water loss.

## The Life History of a Keratinocyte

Dead cells constantly flake off the skin surface. Because we constantly lose these epidermal cells, they must be continually replaced. Keratinocytes are produced deep in the epidermis by the mitosis of stem cells in the stratum basale. Some of the deepest keratinocytes in the stratum spinosum also continue dividing. Mitosis requires an abundant supply of oxygen and nutrients, which these deep cells acquire from the blood vessels in the nearby dermis. Once the epidermal cells migrate more than two or three cells away from the dermis, their mitosis ceases. Mitosis is seldom seen in prepared slides of the skin, because it occurs mainly at night and most tissue specimens are taken during the day.

[5] *stratum* = layer; *lucid* = light, clear

As new keratinocytes form, they push the older ones toward the surface. In 30 to 40 days, a keratinocyte makes its way to the surface and flakes off. This migration is slower in old age and faster in skin that has been injured or stressed. Injured epidermis regenerates more rapidly than any other tissue in the body. Mechanical stress from manual labor or tight shoes accelerates keratinocyte multiplication and results in *calluses* or *corns,* thick accumulations of dead keratinocytes on the hands or feet.

As keratinocytes are shoved upward by the dividing cells below, they flatten and produce more keratin filaments and lipid-filled **lamellar granules.** In the stratum granulosum, four important developments occur: (1) Keratohyalin granules release a protein called *filaggrin* that binds the cytoskeletal keratin filaments together into coarse, tough bundles. (2) The cells produce a tough layer of *envelope proteins* just beneath the plasma membrane, resulting in a nearly indestructible protein sac around the keratin bundles. (3) Lamellar granules release a lipid mixture that spreads out over the cell surface and waterproofs it. (4) Finally, as these barriers cut the keratinocytes off from the supply of nutrients from below, their organelles degenerate and the cells die, leaving just the tough waterproof sac enclosing coarse bundles of keratin. These processes, along with the tight junctions between keratinocytes, result in an **epidermal water barrier** that is crucial to the retention of body water.

The stratum corneum consists of compact layers of dead keratinocytes and keratinocyte fragments. The dead cells soon **exfoliate** (flake off) from the epidermal surface as specks called **dander.** Dander floats around as tiny white specks in the air, settles on household surfaces, and forms much of the house dust that accumulates there. *Dandruff* is composed of clumps of dander stuck together by sebum (oil).

A curious effect of the epidermal water barrier is the way our skin wrinkles when we linger in the bath or a lake. The keratin of the stratum corneum absorbs water and swells, but the deeper layers of the skin do not. The thickening of the stratum corneum forces it to wrinkle. This is especially conspicuous on the fingers and toes ("prune fingers") because they have such a thick stratum corneum and they lack the sebaceous glands that produce water-resistant oil elsewhere on the body. There may be more to the story than this, however, because the wrinkles do not form when the nerves to the fingers are severed, indicating some role for the nervous system. It has recently been hypothesized that this buckling of the skin may serve a function similar to the tread on a car tire, to channel water away and improve our grip when we press our fingertips to wet surfaces.

## 6.1c The Dermis

Beneath the epidermis is a connective tissue layer, the **dermis.** It ranges from 0.2 mm thick in the eyelids to about 4 mm thick in the palms and soles. It is composed mainly of collagen, but also contains elastic and reticular fibers, fibroblasts, and the other cells typical of fibrous connective tissue (described in section 5.3b). It is well supplied with blood vessels, cutaneous glands, and nerve endings. The hair follicles and nail roots are embedded in the dermis. In the face, skeletal muscles attach to dermal collagen fibers and produce such expressions as a smile, a wrinkle of the forehead, or the lifting of an eyebrow (see fig. 6.2).

The boundary between the epidermis and dermis is histologically conspicuous and usually wavy. The upward waves are fingerlike extensions of the dermis called **dermal papillae**[6] (see fig. 6.3), and the downward epidermal waves between the papillae are called **epidermal ridges.** The dermal and epidermal boundaries thus interlock like corrugated cardboard, an arrangement that resists slippage of the epidermis across the dermis. If you look closely at your hand and wrist, you will see delicate furrows that divide the skin into tiny rectangular to rhomboidal areas. The dermal papillae produce the raised areas between the furrows. On the fingertips, this wavy boundary forms the *friction ridges* that produce fingerprints. In highly sensitive areas such as the lips and genitals, exceptionally tall dermal papillae allow blood capillaries and nerve fibers to reach close to the surface. This imparts a redder color and more sensitivity to touch in such areas.

### ▶▶▶APPLY WHAT YOU KNOW

*Dermal papillae are relatively high and numerous in palmar and plantar skin but low and few in number in the skin of the face and abdomen. What do you think is the functional significance of this difference?*

There are two zones of dermis called the papillary and reticular layers **(fig. 6.4).** The **papillary layer** (PAP-ih-lerr-ee) is a thin zone of areolar tissue in and near the dermal papillae. This loosely organized tissue allows for mobility of leukocytes and other defenses against organisms introduced through breaks in the epidermis. This layer is especially rich in small blood vessels.

The **reticular**[7] **layer** of the dermis is deeper and much thicker. It consists of dense irregular connective tissue; it is much more fibrous than cellular, and thus tougher than the papillary layer. The boundary between the papillary and reticular layers is often vague. In the reticular layer, the collagen forms thicker bundles with less room for ground substance, and there are often small clusters of adipocytes. Stretching of the skin in obesity and pregnancy can tear the collagen fibers and produce *striae* (STRY-ee), or stretch marks. These occur especially in areas most stretched by weight gain: the thighs, buttocks, abdomen, and breasts.

There are extensive plexuses of blood vessels at the dermal–epidermal boundary, in mid-dermis, and between the dermis and hypodermis. When dermal blood vessels are damaged by such causes as burns and friction from tight shoes, serous fluid can seep out of the vessels and accumulate as a **blister,** separating the epidermis from the dermis until the fluid is either reabsorbed or expelled by rupture of the blister.

## 6.1d The Hypodermis

Beneath the skin is a layer called the **hypodermis**[8] or **subcutaneous tissue** (see fig. 6.1). The boundary between the dermis and hypodermis is indistinct, but the hypodermis generally has more areolar and adipose tissue. It pads the body and binds the skin to the underlying tissues. Drugs are introduced into the hypodermis

[6] *pap* = nipple; *illa* = little
[7] *reti* = network; *cul* = little
[8] *hypo* = below; *derm* = skin

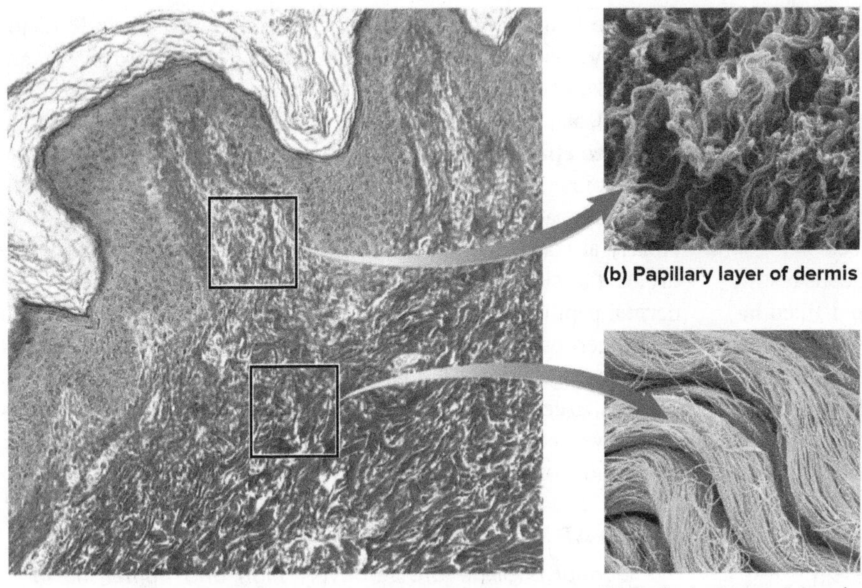


**FIGURE 6.4 The Dermis.** (a) Light micrograph (LM) of axillary skin, with the epidermis stained pink and dermal collagen stained blue. (b) The papillary layer, composed of loosely organized, random-seeming bundles of collagen fibers; open fluid-filled space; and numerous small blood vessels that nourish both dermis and epidermis. (c) The reticular layer, composed of coarser, tougher bundles of collagen and less open space. Parts (b) and (c) are scanning electron micrographs (SEMs).

a: Dennis Strete/McGraw-Hill Education; b: David M. Phillips/Science Source; c: Susumu Nishinaga/Science Source

by injection because the subcutaneous tissue is highly vascular and absorbs them quickly.

**Subcutaneous fat** is hypodermis composed predominantly of adipose tissue. It serves as an energy reservoir and thermal insulation, and it is compressible and protects deeper tissue by absorbing pressure and blows to the body. It is not uniformly distributed; for example, it is virtually absent from the scalp but relatively abundant in the abdomen, hips, thighs, and female breasts. The subcutaneous fat averages about 8% thicker in women than in men, and varies with age. Infants and elderly people have less subcutaneous fat than other people and are therefore more sensitive to cold.

**Table 6.1** summarizes the layers of the skin and hypodermis, from superficial to deep.

## 6.1e Skin Color

The most significant factor in skin color is **melanin.** This is produced by the melanocytes but accumulates in the keratinocytes of the stratum basale and stratum spinosum **(fig. 6.5).** There are two forms of melanin: a brownish black **eumelanin**[9] and a reddish yellow sulfur-containing pigment, **pheomelanin.**[10] People of different skin colors have essentially the same number of melanocytes, but in dark skin, the melanocytes produce greater quantities of melanin, the melanin granules in the keratinocytes

[9] *eu* = true; *melan* = black; *in* = substance
[10] *pheo* = dusky; *melan* = black; *in* = substance

**TABLE 6.1 Stratification of the Skin and Hypodermis**

| Layer | Description |
|---|---|
| **Epidermis** | Keratinized stratified squamous epithelium |
| Stratum corneum | Dead, keratinized cells of the skin surface |
| Stratum lucidum | Clear, featureless, narrow zone seen only in thick skin |
| Stratum granulosum | Two to five layers of cells with dark-staining keratohyalin granules; scanty in thin skin |
| Stratum spinosum | Many layers of keratinocytes, typically shrunken in fixed tissues but attached to each other by desmosomes, which give them a spiny look; progressively flattened the farther they are from the dermis. Dendritic cells are abundant here but are not distinguishable in routinely stained preparations. |
| Stratum basale | Single layer of cuboidal to columnar cells resting on basement membrane; site of most mitosis; consists of stem cells, keratinocytes, melanocytes, and tactile cells, but these are difficult to distinguish with routine stains. Melanin is conspicuous in keratinocytes of this layer in black to brown skin. |
| **Dermis** | Fibrous connective tissue, richly endowed with blood vessels and nerve endings. Sweat glands and hair follicles originate here and in hypodermis. |
| Papillary layer | Superficial one-fifth of dermis; composed of areolar tissue; often extends upward as dermal papillae |
| Reticular layer | Deeper four-fifths of dermis; dense irregular connective tissue |
| **Hypodermis** | Areolar or adipose tissue between skin and muscle |

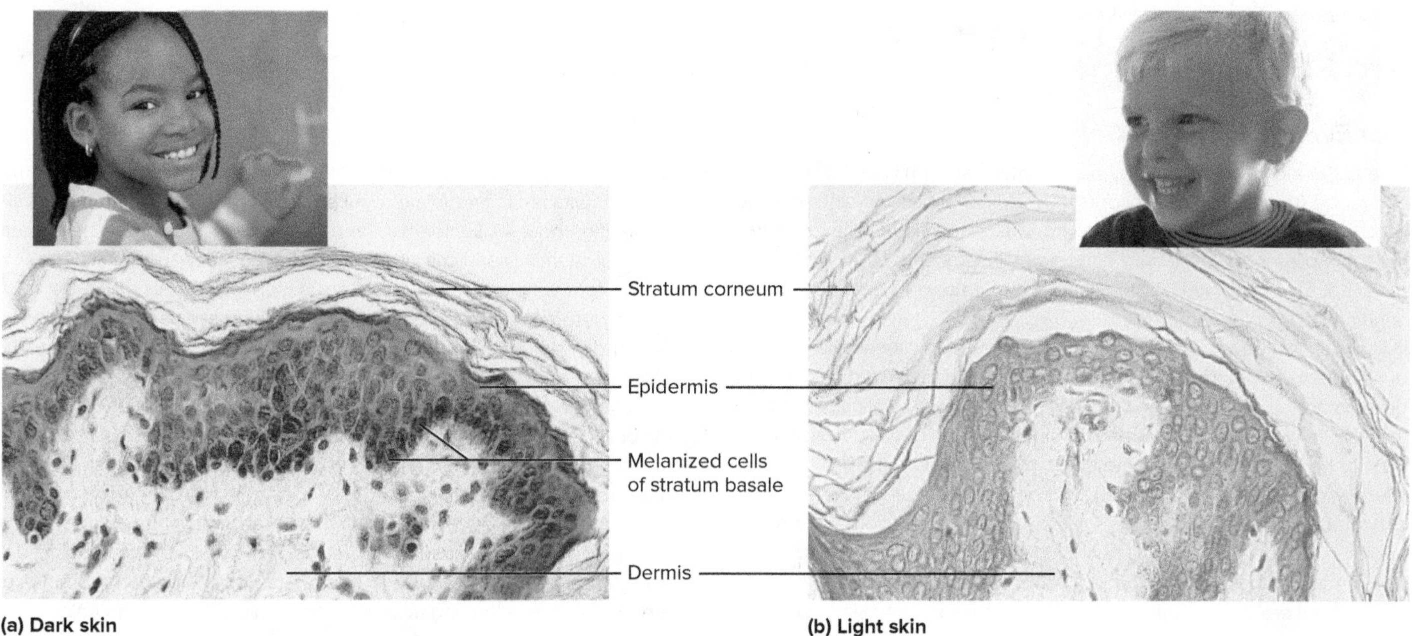


**FIGURE 6.5 Variations in Skin Pigmentation.** (a) The stratum basale shows heavy deposits of melanin in dark skin. (b) Light skin shows little to no visible melanin.

*Which of the five types of epidermal cells are the melanized cells in part (a)?*

a: Dennis Strete/McGraw-Hill Education; **(girl):** Tom & Dee Ann McCarthy/Corbis/Getty Images Plus; **b:** ©Dennis Strete/McGraw-Hill Education; **(boy):** Arthur Tilley/Stockbyte/Getty Images

are more spread out than tightly clumped, and the melanin breaks down more slowly. Thus, melanized cells may be seen throughout the epidermis, from stratum basale to stratum corneum. In light skin, the melanin is clumped near the keratinocyte nucleus, so it imparts less color to the cells. It also breaks down more rapidly, so little of it is seen beyond the stratum basale, if even there.

Skin color also varies with exposure to the UV rays of sunlight, which stimulate melanin synthesis and darken the skin. A suntan fades as melanin is degraded in older keratinocytes and as keratinocytes migrate to the surface and exfoliate. The amount of melanin also varies from place to place on the body. It is relatively concentrated in freckles and moles, on the dorsal surfaces of the hands and feet as compared with the palms and soles, on the nipple and surrounding area (areola) of the breast, around the anus, on the scrotum and penis, and on the lateral surfaces of the female genital folds (labia majora). The contrast between heavily melanized and lightly melanized regions of the skin is more pronounced in some people than others, but it exists to some extent in nearly everyone. Variation in ancestral exposure to UV is the primary reason for the geographic and ethnic variation in skin color today (see Deeper Insight 6.2).

Other factors in skin color are hemoglobin and carotene. **Hemoglobin,** the red pigment of blood, imparts reddish to pinkish hues as blood vessels show through the skin. Its color is lightened by the white of the dermal collagen. The skin is redder in places such as the lips, where blood capillaries come closer to the surface and the hemoglobin shows through more vividly. **Carotene**[11] is a yellow pigment acquired from egg yolks and yellow and orange vegetables. Depending on the diet, carotene or related compounds can become concentrated to various degrees in the stratum corneum and subcutaneous fat, imparting a yellow color. This is often most conspicuous in skin of the heel and in calluses of the feet, because this is where the stratum corneum is thickest.

The skin may also exhibit abnormal colors of diagnostic value:

- **Cyanosis**[12] is blueness of the skin resulting from a deficiency of oxygen in the circulating blood. Oxygen deficiency turns the hemoglobin a reddish violet color, which is lightened to blue-violet as it shows through the white dermal collagen. Oxygen deficiency can result from conditions that prevent the blood from picking up a normal load of oxygen in the lungs, such as airway obstructions in drowning and choking, lung diseases such as emphysema, and respiratory arrest. Cyanosis also occurs in situations such as cold weather and cardiac arrest, when blood flows so slowly through the skin that the tissues consume its oxygen faster than freshly oxygenated blood arrives.
- **Erythema**[13] (ERR-ih-THEE-muh) is abnormal redness of the skin. It occurs in such situations as exercise, hot weather,

[11] *carot* = carrot
[12] *cyan* = blue; *osis* = condition
[13] *eryth* = red; *em* = blood

## DEEPER INSIGHT 6.2
## EVOLUTIONARY MEDICINE

### *The Evolution of Skin Color*

One of the most conspicuous signs of human variation is skin color, which can range from the color of espresso or milk chocolate to café au lait or light peach. Such variation results from a combination of evolutionary selection pressures, especially differences in exposure to ultraviolet (UV) radiation. Environmental UV levels account for up to 77% of the variation in human skin color.

UV can have two adverse effects: It causes skin cancer and it breaks down folate, a B vitamin needed for normal cell division, fertility, and fetal development. It also has a desirable effect: It stimulates keratinocytes to synthesize vitamin D, which is needed for the absorption of dietary calcium and thus for healthy bone development. Too much UV raises the risk of cancer, infertility, and fetal deformities such as spina bifida; too little and one is at risk of bone deformities such as rickets. Consequently, populations native to the tropics and people descended from them tend to have well-melanized skin to screen out excessive UV. Populations native to far northern and southern latitudes, where the sunlight is weak, tend to have light skin to allow for adequate UV penetration. Ancestral skin color is thus partly a compromise between vitamin D and folate requirements. Worldwide, women have skin averaging about 4% lighter than men do, perhaps because of their greater need for vitamin D and calcium to support pregnancy and lactation.

But for multiple reasons, there are exceptions to this trend. UV exposure is determined by more than latitude. It increases at higher elevations and in dry air, because the thinner, drier atmosphere filters out less UV. This helps to explain the darker skin of people indigenous to such localities as deserts, the Andes Mountains, and the high plateaus of Tibet and Ethiopia. Some other exceptions may be the result of human migrations from one latitude to another occurring too recently for their skin color to have adapted to the new level of UV exposure. Variation may also result from cultural differences in clothing and shelter, intermarriage among people of different geographic ancestries, and darwinian sexual selection—a preference in mate choice for partners of light or dark complexion, thereby perpetuating and accentuating ethnic differences in color.

sunburn, anger, and embarrassment. Erythema is caused by increased blood flow in dilated cutaneous blood vessels or by dermal pooling of red blood cells that have escaped from abnormally permeable capillaries, as in sunburn.

- **Pallor** is a pale or ashen color that occurs when there is so little blood flow through the skin that the white of the dermal collagen shows through. It can result from emotional stress, low blood pressure, circulatory shock, cold temperatures, or severe anemia.
- **Albinism**[14] **(fig. 6.6a)** is a genetic lack of melanin that usually results in milky white hair and skin, and blue-gray eyes. Melanin is synthesized from the amino acid tyrosine by the enzyme tyrosinase. People with albinism have inherited a recessive, nonfunctional tyrosinase allele from both parents.
- **Jaundice**[15] **(fig. 6.6b)** is yellowing of the skin and whites of the eyes resulting from high levels of bilirubin in the blood. Bilirubin is a hemoglobin breakdown product. When erythrocytes get old, they disintegrate and release their hemoglobin. The liver and spleen convert hemoglobin to bilirubin, which the liver excretes in the bile. Bilirubin can accumulate enough to discolor the skin, however, in such situations as a rapid rate of erythrocyte destruction; when diseases such as cancer, hepatitis, and cirrhosis compromise liver function; and in premature infants, where the liver is not well enough developed to dispose of bilirubin efficiently.
- A **hematoma,**[16] or bruise, is a mass of clotted blood showing through the skin. It is usually due to accidental trauma (blows to the skin), but it may indicate hemophilia, other metabolic or nutritional disorders, or physical abuse.

[14]*alb* = white; *ism* = state, condition
[15]*jaun* = yellow
[16]*hemat* = blood; *oma* = mass

**APPLY WHAT YOU KNOW**

*An infant brought to a clinic shows abnormally yellow skin. What sign could you look for to help decide whether this was due to jaundice or to a large amount of carotene from strained vegetables in the diet?*

### 6.1f Skin Markings

The skin is marked by many lines, creases, ridges, and patches of accentuated pigmentation. **Friction ridges** are the markings on the fingertips that leave distinctive oily fingerprints on surfaces we touch. They are characteristic of most primates, though their function has long been obscure. When we stroke an uneven surface, friction ridges enhance fingertip sensitivity to texture by vibrating and stimulating sense organs called *lamellar corpuscles* deeper in the skin. They are also thought to improve one's grasp and aid in the manipulation of small and rough-surfaced objects. Friction ridges form during fetal development and remain essentially unchanged for life. Their patterns result from a combination of heredity and the surfaces that the fetus randomly touches with its fingertips before birth. Thus, everyone has a unique pattern of friction ridges; not even identical twins produce identical fingerprints.

**Flexion lines (flexion creases)** are the lines on the flexor surfaces of the digits, palms, wrists, elbows, and other places (see atlas B, fig. B.19). They mark sites where the skin folds during flexion of the joints. The skin is tightly bound to deeper connective tissues along these lines.

Freckles and moles are tan to black aggregations of melanized keratinocytes. **Freckles** are flat patches that vary with heredity and exposure to the sun. A **mole (nevus)** is an elevated patch of melanized skin, often with hair. Moles are harmless and sometimes even regarded as "beauty marks," but they should be watched for changes in color, diameter, or contour that may suggest malignancy (skin cancer) (see section 6.4a).

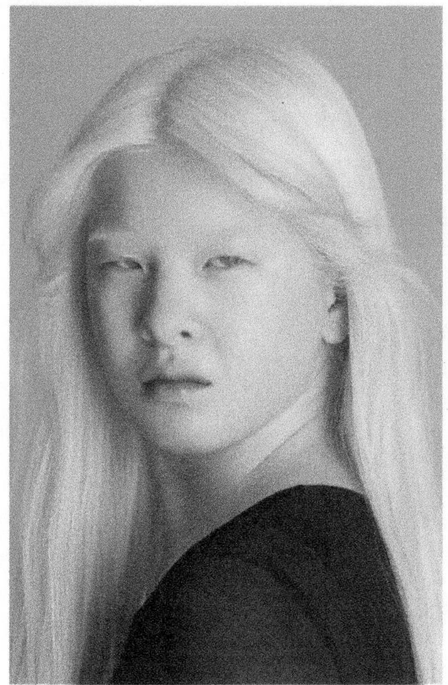

(a)

(b)

**FIGURE 6.6 Two Abnormal Skin Colors.**
(a) Albinism. (b) Jaundice.

a: Jonathan Knowles/Getty Images; b: Dr P. Marazzi/Science Source

Birthmarks, or **hemangiomas,**[17] are patches of skin discolored by benign tumors of the blood capillaries. *Capillary hemangiomas* (strawberry birthmarks) usually develop about a month after birth. They become bright red to deep purple and develop small capillary-dense elevations that give them a strawberry-like appearance. About 90% of capillary hemangiomas disappear by the age of 5 or 6 years. *Cavernous hemangiomas* are flatter and duller in color. They are present at birth, enlarge up to 1 year of age, and then regress. About 90% disappear by the age of 9 years. A *port-wine stain* is flat and pinkish to dark purple in color. It can be quite large and remains for life.

**BEFORE YOU GO ON**

Answer the following questions to test your understanding of the preceding section:

1. What is the major histological difference between thick and thin skin? Where on the body is each type of skin found?
2. How does the skin help to adjust body temperature?
3. List the five cell types of the epidermis. Describe their locations and functions.
4. List the five layers of epidermis from deep to superficial. What are the distinctive features of each layer? Which layer is often absent?
5. What are the two layers of the dermis? What type of tissue composes each layer?
6. Name the pigments responsible for normal skin colors and explain how certain conditions can produce discolorations of the skin.

[17] *hem* = blood; *angi* = vessels; *oma* = mass, tumor

## 6.2 Hair and Nails

**Expected Learning Outcomes**

When you have completed this section, you should be able to

a. distinguish between three types of hair;
b. describe the histology of a hair and its follicle;
c. discuss some theories of the purposes served by various kinds of hair; and
d. describe the structure and function of nails.

The hair, nails, and cutaneous glands are the **accessory organs (appendages)** of the skin. Hair and nails are composed mostly of dead, keratinized cells. The stratum corneum of the skin is made of pliable **soft keratin,** but the hair and nails are composed mostly of **hard keratin.** This is more compact than soft keratin and is toughened by numerous cross-linkages between the keratin molecules.

### 6.2a Hair

A hair is also known as a **pilus** (PY-lus); in the plural, *pili* (PY-lye). It is a slender filament of keratinized cells that grows from an oblique tube in the skin called a **hair follicle (fig. 6.7).**

#### Distribution and Types

Hair occurs almost everywhere on the body except palms and soles; palmar, plantar, and lateral surfaces and distal segments of the fingers and toes; and the lips, nipples, and parts of the genitals. The limbs and trunk have about 55 to 70 hairs per square centimeter, and the face has about 10 times as many.

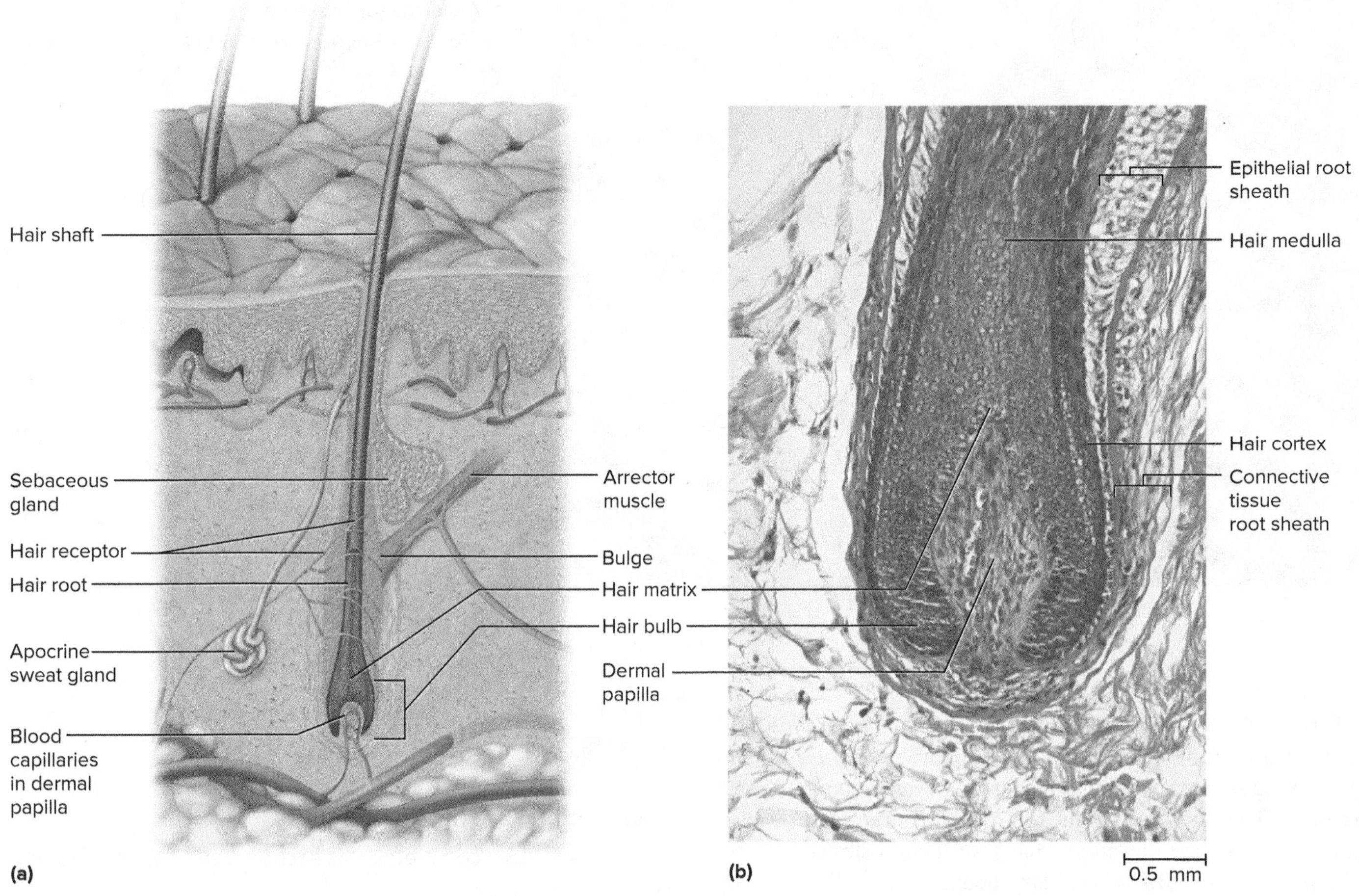


**FIGURE 6.7 Structure of a Hair and Its Follicle.** (a) Anatomy of the follicle and associated structures. (b) Light micrograph of the base of a hair follicle. APR

b: Ed Reschke/Getty Images

There are about 30,000 hairs in a man's beard and about 100,000 hairs in the average person's scalp. The density of hair doesn't differ much from one person to another or even between the sexes; indeed, it is virtually the same in humans, chimpanzees, and gorillas. Differences in apparent hairiness are due mainly to differences in texture and pigmentation.

Not all hair is alike, even on one person. Over the course of our lives, we grow three kinds of hair: downy, vellus, and terminal hair. **Downy hair (lanugo**[18]**)** is fine, unpigmented hair that appears on the fetus in the last 3 months of development. By the time of birth, most of it is replaced by similar fine, pale hair called **vellus hair.**[19] Vellus hair constitutes about two-thirds of the hair of women, one-tenth of the hair of men, and all the hair of children except for the eyebrows, eyelashes, and hair of the scalp. **Terminal hair** is longer, coarser, and usually more heavily pigmented. It forms the eyebrows and eyelashes and covers the scalp; after puberty, it also forms the axillary and pubic hair, all facial hair, and some of the hair on the trunk and limbs.

[18]*lan* = down, wool
[19]*vellus* = fleece

## Structure of the Hair and Follicle

The portion of a hair above the skin is called the **shaft,** and all that beneath the surface is the **root.** The root penetrates deeply into the dermis or hypodermis and ends with a dilation called the **bulb.** The only living cells of a hair are in and near the bulb. The bulb grows around a bud of vascular connective tissue called the **dermal papilla,** which provides the hair with its sole source of nutrition. Immediately above the papilla is a region of mitotically active cells, the **hair matrix,** which is the hair's growth center. All cells higher up are dead.

In cross section, a hair reveals up to three layers. From the inside out, these are the medulla, cortex, and cuticle. The **medulla** is a core of loosely arranged cells and air spaces. It is most prominent in thick hairs such as those of the eyebrows, but narrower in hairs of medium thickness and absent from the thinnest hairs of the scalp and elsewhere. The **cortex** constitutes most of the bulk of a hair. It consists of several layers of elongated keratinized cells that appear cuboidal to flattened in cross sections. The **cuticle** is composed of multiple layers of thin, scaly cells that overlap each other like roof shingles with their free edges directed upward (see this chapter's opening photo). Cells lining the follicle are like shingles facing in the opposite direction. They interlock with the scales of the hair cuticle and resist pulling on the hair. When a hair is pulled out, this layer of follicle cells comes with it. The scaly cuticle also helps keep the hairs separated so they don't become matted together.

The follicle is a diagonal tube that contains the hair root. It has two principal layers: an **epithelial root sheath** and a **connective tissue root sheath.** The epithelial root sheath is an extension of the epidermis; it consists of stratified squamous epithelium and lies immediately adjacent to the hair root. Toward the deep end of the follicle, it widens to form a **bulge,** a source of stem cells for follicle growth. The connective tissue root sheath, which is derived from the dermis and composed of collagenous connective tissue, surrounds the epithelial sheath and is somewhat denser than the adjacent dermis.

Associated with the follicle are nerve and muscle fibers. Nerve fibers called **hair receptors** entwine each follicle and respond to hair movements. You can feel their effect by carefully moving a single hair with a pin or by lightly running your finger over the hairs of your forearm without touching the skin. Each hair has an **arrector muscle**—also known as a *pilomotor muscle* or *arrector pili*[20]—a bundle of smooth muscle cells extending from dermal collagen fibers to the connective tissue root sheath of the follicle (see figs. 6.1 and 6.7a). In response to cold, fear, touch, or other stimuli, the sympathetic nervous system stimulates the arrector to contract, making the hair stand on end and wrinkling the skin in such areas as the scrotum and areola. In other mammals, piloerection traps an insulating layer of warm air next to the skin or makes the animal appear larger and less vulnerable to a potential enemy. In humans, it pulls the follicles into a vertical position and causes "goose bumps," but serves no useful purpose.

[20]*arrect* = erect; *pili* = of hair

## Hair Texture and Color

The texture of hair is related to differences in cross-sectional shape **(fig. 6.8)**—straight hair is round, wavy hair is oval, and tightly curled hair is relatively flat. Hair color is due to pigment granules in the cells of the cortex. Brown and black hair are rich in eumelanin. Red hair has a slight amount of eumelanin but a high concentration of pheomelanin. Blond hair has an intermediate amount of pheomelanin but very little eumelanin. Gray and white hair result from a scarcity or absence of melanins in the cortex and the presence of air in the medulla.

## Hair Growth and Loss

Each hair follicle goes through three developmental phases called the **hair cycle.** At any given time, about 90% of the scalp follicles

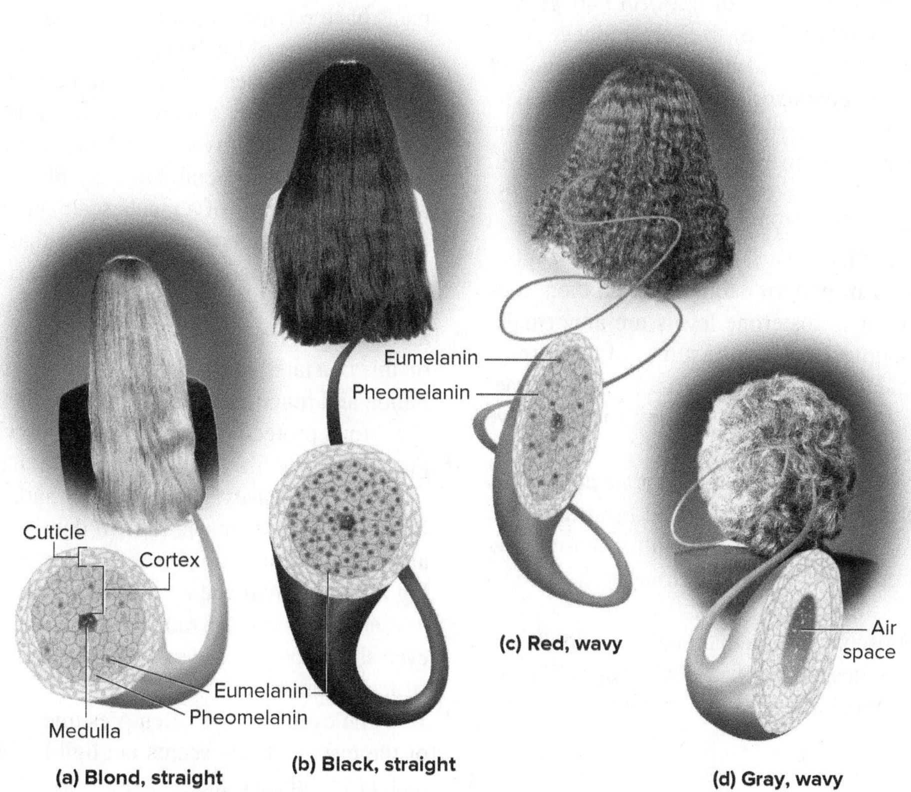


**FIGURE 6.8 The Basis of Hair Color and Texture.** Note the round cross-sectional shape of straight hair (a, b) compared to the flatter shape of wavy hair (c, d). Also note the proportions of pigments in the cortex in relation to hair color.

? *Which of the hair layers illustrated here corresponds to the scales seen in this chapter's opening photo?*

a–d: Joe DeGrandis/McGraw-Hill Education

are in a growth stage called **anagen.**[21] Stem cells in the hair bulge multiply, the follicle deepens, and the hair grows in length during this time. Anagen lasts about 6 to 8 years for any given follicle. This is followed by **catagen,**[22] in which mitosis ceases, the follicle shrinks, and the hair dies and loses its anchorage. The hair becomes a **club hair,** named for a hard keratinized knot at its base. Club hairs are easily pulled out by brushing the hair, and the hard club can be felt at the end. Catagen lasts for about 2 to 3 weeks, then is followed by a **telogen**[23] stage, in which the follicle rests for 1 to 3 months. It then begins the process anew, starting over with anagen and the growth of a new hair, often alongside the old club hair. We lose 50 to 100 scalp hairs daily, but fortunately, the follicles are asynchronous, so we don't lose all our hairs at once.

Scalp hairs grow fastest from adolescence until the 40s, at a rate of about 1 mm per 3 days (10–18 cm/year). After that, an increasing percentage of follicles are in the catagen and telogen phases rather than the growing anagen phase. Follicles also shrink and begin producing wispy vellus hairs instead of thicker terminal hairs. Thinning of the hair, or baldness, is called **alopecia**[24] (AL-oh-PEE-she-uh). It occurs to some degree in both sexes and may be worsened by disease, poor nutrition, fever, emotional stress, radiation, or chemotherapy. In the great majority of cases, however, it is simply a matter of aging.

**Pattern baldness** is the condition in which hair is lost unevenly across the scalp rather than thinning uniformly. It results from a combination of genetic and hormonal influences. The relevant gene has two alleles: one for uniform hair growth and a baldness allele for patchy hair growth. The baldness allele is dominant in males and is expressed only in the presence of the high level of testosterone characteristic of men. In men who are either heterozygous or homozygous for the baldness allele, testosterone causes terminal hair to be replaced by vellus hair, beginning on top of the head and later the sides. In women, the baldness allele is recessive. Homozygous dominant and heterozygous women show normal hair distribution; only homozygous recessive women are at risk of pattern baldness. Even then, they exhibit the trait only if their testosterone levels are abnormally high for a woman (for example, because of a tumor of the adrenal gland, a woman's principal source of testosterone). Such characteristics in which an allele is dominant in one sex and recessive in the other are called *sex-influenced traits.*

Excessive or undesirable hairiness in areas that are not usually hairy, especially in women and children, is called **hirsutism.**[25] It tends to run in families and usually results from either masculinizing ovarian tumors or hypersecretion of testosterone by the adrenal cortex. It is often associated with menopause.

Contrary to popular misconceptions, hair and nails don't continue to grow after a person dies, cutting hair doesn't make it grow faster or thicker, and emotional stress cannot make the hair turn white overnight.

[21]*ana* = up; *gen* = build, produce
[22]*cata* = down
[23]*telo* = end
[24]*alopecia* = fox mange
[25]*hirsut* = shaggy

## Functions of Hair

Compared with other mammals, the relative hairlessness of humans is so unusual that it raises the question, Why do we have any hair at all? What purpose does it serve? There are different answers for the different types of hair; furthermore, some of the answers would make little sense if we limited our frame of reference to industrialized societies, where barbers and hairdressers are engaged to alter the natural state of the hair. It is more useful to take a comparative approach to this question and consider the purposes hair serves in other species of mammals.

Most hair of the human trunk and limbs is probably best interpreted as vestigial, with little present function. Body hair undoubtedly served to keep our ancestors warm, but in modern humans it is too scanty. Stimulation of the hair receptors, however, alerts people to parasites crawling on the skin, such as fleas and ticks. Thus, we are less likely to become unknowingly infested with parasites.

The scalp is normally the only place where the hair is thick enough to retain heat. Heat loss from a bald scalp can be substantial and quite uncomfortable. The brain receives a rich supply of warm blood, and most of the scalp lacks an insulating fat layer. Heat is easily conducted through the bones of the skull and lost to the surrounding air. In addition, without hair there is nothing to break the wind and stop it from carrying away heat. Hair also protects the scalp from sunburn, since the scalp is otherwise most directly exposed to the sun's rays. These may be the reasons humans have retained thick hair on their heads while losing most of it from the rest of the body.

Tufts and patches of hair, sometimes with contrasting colors, are important among mammals for advertising species, age, sex, and individual identity. For the less groomed members of the human species, scalp and facial hair may play a similar role. The indefinitely growing hair of a man's scalp and beard, for example, could provide a striking contrast to a face that is otherwise almost hairless. It creates a badge of recognition instantly visible at a distance.

The beard and pubic and axillary hair signify sexual maturity and aid in the transmission of sexual scents. We will further reflect on this in a later discussion of apocrine sweat glands, whose distribution and function add significant evidence to support this theory.

Stout protective **guard hairs,** or **vibrissae** (vy-BRISS-ee), guard the nostrils and ear canals and prevent foreign particles from entering easily. The eyelashes and blink reflex shield the eye from dust and other windblown debris. The eyelashes of humans and other mammals also seem to be perfectly adapted for reducing airflow across the eye surface, thus reducing evaporation and dryness. In windy or rainy conditions, we can squint so that the eyelashes protect the eyes even further, but without completely obstructing our vision.

The eyebrows are often presumed to keep sweat or debris out of the eyes, but this seems negligible. More likely, they function mainly to enhance facial expression. Movements of the eyebrows are an important means of nonverbal communication in humans of all cultures, and we even have special *frontalis* muscles for this purpose. Eyebrow expressiveness is not unique to humans; even monkeys and apes use quick eyebrow flashes to greet each other, assert their dominance, and break up quarrels.

### 6.2b Nails

Fingernails and toenails are clear, hard derivatives of the stratum corneum. They are composed of thin, dead, scaly cells, densely packed together and filled with parallel fibers of hard keratin. Most mammals have claws, whereas flat nails are one of the distinguishing characteristics of humans and other primates. Flat nails serve as strong keratinized "tools" that can be used for grooming, picking apart food, and other manipulations. In addition, they allow for more fleshy and sensitive fingertips. Imagine touching a few grains of salt on a table. The nail, by providing a counterforce or resistance from the other side, enhances one's sensitivity to such tiny objects.

The hard part of the nail is the **nail plate (fig. 6.9),** which includes the **free edge** overhanging the tip of the finger or toe; the **nail body,** which is the visible attached part of the nail; and the **nail root,** which extends proximally under the overlying skin. The surrounding skin rises a bit above the nail as a **nail fold,** separated from the margin of the nail plate by a **nail groove.** The groove and the space under the free edge accumulate dirt and bacteria and require special attention when scrubbing for duty in an operating room or nursery.

The skin underlying the nail plate is the **nail bed;** its epidermis is called the **hyponychium**[26] (HIPE-o-NICK-ee-um). At the proximal end of the nail, the stratum basale thickens into a growth zone called the **nail matrix.** Mitosis in the matrix accounts for the growth of the nail—about 1 mm per week in the fingernails and slightly slower in the toenails. The thickness of the matrix obscures the underlying dermal blood vessels and is the reason why an opaque white crescent, the **lunule**[27] (LOON-yule), often appears at the proximal end of a nail. A narrow zone of dead skin, the **cuticle** or **eponychium**[28] (EP-o-NICK-ee-um), commonly overhangs this end of the nail.

The appearance of the fingertips and nails can be valuable in medical diagnosis. The fingertips become swollen or *clubbed* in response to long-term hypoxemia—a deficiency of oxygen in the blood stemming from conditions such as congenital heart defects and emphysema. Dietary deficiencies may be reflected in the appearance of the nails. An iron deficiency, for example, may cause them to become flat or concave (spoonlike) rather than convex. Contrary to popular belief, adding gelatin to the diet has no effect on the growth or hardness of the nails.

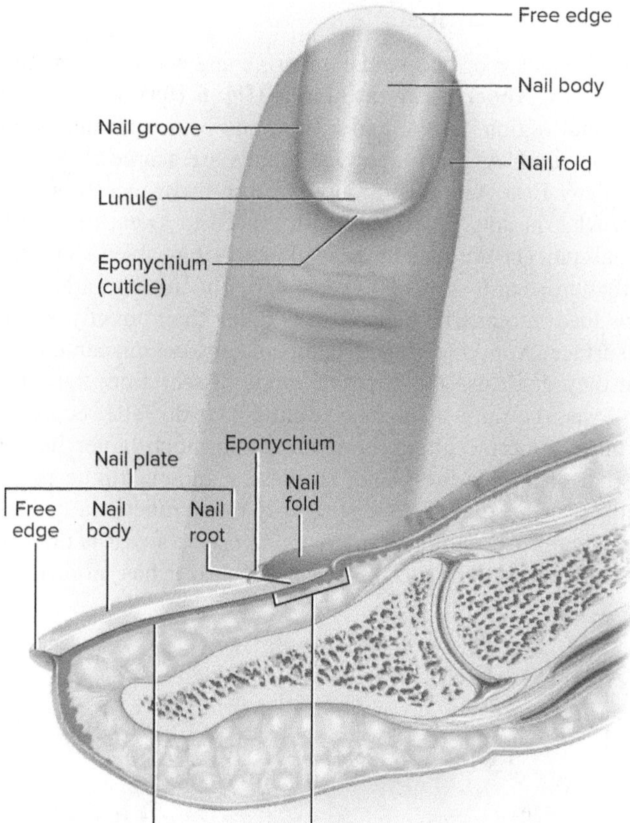


**FIGURE 6.9 Anatomy of a Fingernail.** APR

**BEFORE YOU GO ON**

Answer the following questions to test your understanding of the preceding section:

7. What is the difference between vellus hair and terminal hair?
8. State the functions of the hair papilla, hair receptors, and arrector muscle.
9. Describe what happens in the anagen, catagen, and telogen phases of the hair cycle.
10. State some reasonable theories for the different functions of hair of the eyebrows, eyelashes, scalp, nostrils, and axilla.
11. Define or describe the *nail plate, nail fold, eponychium, hyponychium,* and *nail matrix.*

## 6.3 Cutaneous Glands

**Expected Learning Outcomes**

When you have completed this section, you should be able to

a. name two types of sweat glands, and describe the structure and function of each;
b. describe the location, structure, and function of sebaceous and ceruminous glands; and
c. discuss the distinction between breasts and mammary glands, and explain their respective functions.

The skin has five kinds of glands: *eccrine sweat glands, apocrine sweat glands, sebaceous glands, ceruminous glands,* and *mammary glands.*

[26] *hypo* = below; *onych* = nail
[27] *lun* = moon; *ule* = little
[28] *ep* = above; *onych* = nail

## 6.3a Sweat Glands

Sweat glands are of two kinds: apocrine and eccrine (compare figure 5.32). **Apocrine sweat glands (fig. 6.10a)** occur in the groin, anal region, axilla, and areola, and in mature males, in the beard area. Axillary apocrine glands are scarce or absent from many East Asians, possibly because their ancestors, living in what is now Siberia, had little need to sweat in such a cold habitat. The absence of these glands is traceable to a mutation that arose at least 40,000 years ago. The ducts of apocrine glands lead into nearby hair follicles rather than directly to the skin surface. Apocrine glands, unfortunately, are misnamed because they don't use the apocrine mode of secretion; they use exocytosis, the same as eccrine sweat glands do. The secretory part of an apocrine gland, however, has a much larger lumen than that of an eccrine gland, so these glands continue to be called apocrine glands to distinguish them functionally and histologically from the eccrine type. Apocrine sweat is thicker and more milky than eccrine sweat because it has more fatty acids in it.

Apocrine sweat glands are scent glands that respond especially to stress and sexual stimulation. They are not active until puberty, and in women, they enlarge and shrink in phase with the menstrual cycle. These facts, as well as experimental evidence, suggest that they secrete *sex pheromones*—chemicals that exert subtle effects on the sexual behavior and physiology of other people. They apparently correspond to the scent glands that develop in other mammals as they approach sexual maturity. Fresh apocrine sweat doesn't have a disagreeable odor; indeed, it is considered attractive or arousing in some cultures, where it is as much a part of courtship as artificial perfume is to others. Clothing, however, traps stale sweat long enough for bacteria to degrade the secretion and release free fatty acids with a rancid odor. Disagreeable body odor is called *bromhidrosis*.[29] It occasionally indicates a metabolic disorder, but more often reflects inadequate hygiene.

Many mammals have apocrine scent glands associated with specialized tufts of hair. In humans, apocrine glands are found

[29]*brom* = stench; *hidros* = sweat

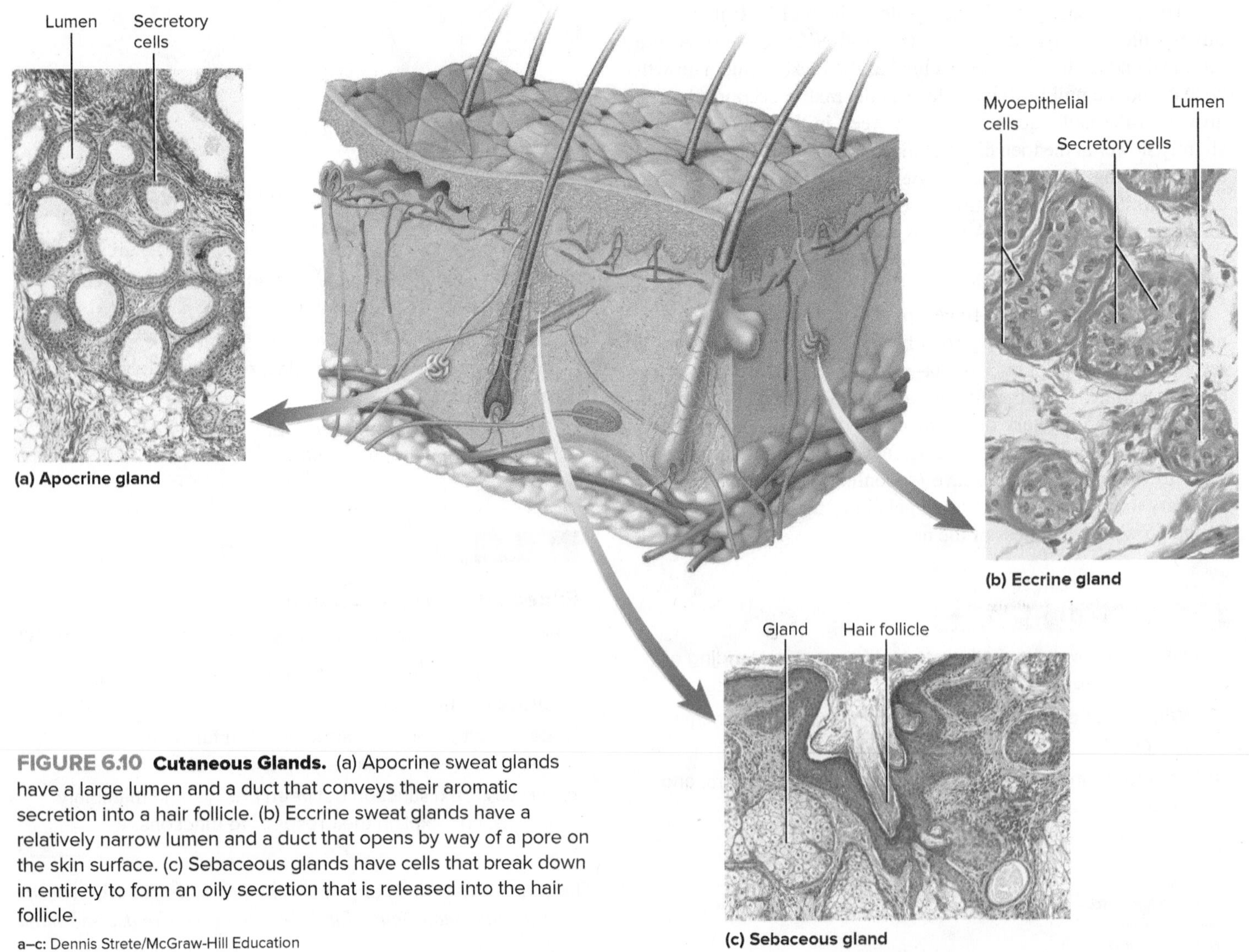


**FIGURE 6.10 Cutaneous Glands.** (a) Apocrine sweat glands have a large lumen and a duct that conveys their aromatic secretion into a hair follicle. (b) Eccrine sweat glands have a relatively narrow lumen and a duct that opens by way of a pore on the skin surface. (c) Sebaceous glands have cells that break down in entirety to form an oily secretion that is released into the hair follicle.

a–c: Dennis Strete/McGraw-Hill Education

mainly in the regions covered by the pubic hair, axillary hair, and beard. This supports the interpretation that they are pheromone glands. The hair serves to retain the aromatic secretion and regulate its rate of evaporation from the skin. Thus, it seems no mere coincidence that women's faces lack both apocrine scent glands and a beard.

**Eccrine (merocrine) sweat glands** (EK-rin) **(fig. 6.10b)** are widely distributed over the entire body, but are especially abundant on the palms, soles, and forehead. Their primary function is to cool the body. Overheating activates sweating through the sympathetic nervous system. Then, because of the high heat capacity of water (see section 2.2), the evaporation of sweat carries away a substantial amount of body heat, cooling one down. Each is a simple tubular gland with a twisted coil in the dermis or hypodermis, and an undulating or coiled duct leading to a sweat pore on the skin surface. The duct is lined by a stratified cuboidal epithelium in the dermis and by keratinocytes in the epidermis.

In both apocrine and eccrine sweat glands, specialized **myoepithelial**[30] **cells** are found amid the secretory cells at the deep end of the gland. They have contractile properties similar to those of smooth muscle. The sympathetic nervous system stimulates them to contract, squeeze the base of the gland, and force perspiration up the duct—particularly under conditions of overheating, nervousness, or arousal.

Sweat production begins in the deep secretory portion of the gland. Protein-free fluid filters from the blood capillaries into the lumen of the gland. Most sodium chloride is reabsorbed from the filtrate as it passes up the duct, but some remains, along with potassium, urea, lactic acid, and ammonia. Some drugs are also excreted in the perspiration. Thus, the eccrine sweat glands excrete some of the same wastes as the kidneys. The contribution of an individual sweat gland to this is minuscule, but there are 3 or 4 million eccrine sweat glands in the adult skin, with a total mass about equal to one kidney.

Perspiration is about 99% water and has a pH ranging from 4 to 6, contributing the earlier-mentioned *acid mantle* that inhibits bacterial growth on the skin. Usually, perspiration evaporates about as fast as it is produced, so it isn't noticed; this is called **insensible perspiration.** But under such conditions as heat, exercise, and circulatory shock, more copious sweat is produced and noticeably wets the skin; this is called **diaphoresis**[31] (DY-uh-foe-REE-sis). Insensible perspiration typically amounts to about 500 mL/day, but in diaphoresis, a person can lose a liter or more of sweat per hour. In heavy sweating, fluid loss from the bloodstream can be so great as to cause circulatory shock. Sweating, however, isn't the only way the skin loses water. A significant amount also diffuses between the keratinocytes and evaporates from the skin surface—a process called *cutaneous transpiration* (see section 24.1b).

## 6.3b Sebaceous Glands

**Sebaceous**[32] **glands** (see-BAY-shus) produce an oily secretion called **sebum** (SEE-bum). They are flask-shaped, with short ducts that usually open into a hair follicle **(fig. 6.10c),** although some of them open directly onto the skin surface. These are holocrine glands with little visible lumen. Their secretion consists of broken-down cells that are replaced by mitosis at the base of the gland. Sebum keeps the skin and hair from becoming dry, brittle, and cracked. The sheen of well-brushed hair is due to sebum distributed by the hairbrush. Ironically, we go to great lengths to wash sebum from the skin, only to replace it with various skin creams and hand lotions made of little more than lanolin, which is sheep sebum.

## 6.3c Ceruminous Glands

**Ceruminous glands** (seh-ROO-mih-nus) are modified apocrine glands found only in the external ear canal. Their yellow, waxy secretion combines with sebum and dead epidermal cells to form earwax, or **cerumen.**[33] They are coiled, simple tubular glands with ducts leading to hair follicles or the skin surface of the ear canal. Cerumen keeps the eardrum pliable, waterproofs the canal, kills bacteria, and coats the guard hairs of the ear, making them sticky and more effective in blocking foreign particles from entering the canal.

## 6.3d Mammary Glands

The **mammary glands** and breasts *(mammae)* are often mistakenly regarded as one and the same. Breasts, however, are present in both sexes, and even in females they rarely contain more than small traces of mammary gland. The mammary glands, by contrast, are the milk-producing glands that develop within the female breast during pregnancy and lactation. They are modified apocrine sweat glands that produce a richer secretion and channel it through ducts to a nipple for more efficient conveyance to the offspring. The anatomy and physiology of the mammary gland are discussed in more detail in section 28.1c.

In most mammals, two rows of mammary glands form along lines called the *mammary ridges,* or *milk lines.* Primates have dispensed with all but two of these glands. A few people of both sexes, however, develop additional nipples or mammae along the milk line inferior to the primary mammae. In the Middle Ages and colonial America, this condition, called *polythelia,*[34] was used to incriminate women as supposed witches.

The glands of the skin are summarized in **table 6.2.**

**BEFORE YOU GO ON**

Answer the following questions to test your understanding of the preceding section:

12. How do eccrine and apocrine sweat glands differ in structure and function?
13. What other type of gland is associated with hair follicles? How does its mode of secretion differ from that of sweat glands?
14. What is the difference between the breast and mammary gland?

[30] *myo* = muscle
[31] *dia* = through; *phoresis* = carrying
[32] *seb* = fat, tallow; *aceous* = possessing
[33] *cer* = wax
[34] *poly* = many; *theli* = nipples

**TABLE 6.2 Cutaneous Glands**

| Gland Type | Definition |
|---|---|
| Sweat glands | Glands that produce perspiration |
| Eccrine glands | Sweat glands that function in evaporative cooling; widely distributed over the body surface; open by ducts onto the skin surface |
| Apocrine glands | Sweat glands that function as scent glands; found in the regions covered by the pubic, axillary, and male facial hair; open by ducts into hair follicles |
| Sebaceous glands | Oil glands associated with hair follicles |
| Ceruminous glands | Glands of the ear canal that contribute to the cerumen (earwax) |
| Mammary glands | Milk-producing glands located in the breasts |

## 6.4 Skin Disorders

**Expected Learning Outcomes**

When you have completed this section, you should be able to

a. describe the three most common forms of skin cancer; and
b. describe the three classes of burns and the priorities in burn treatment.

Because it is the most exposed of all our organs, skin is not only the most vulnerable to injury and disease, but it is also the one place where we are most likely to notice anything out of the ordinary. Skin diseases become increasingly common in old age, and most people over age 70 have complaints about their integumentary system. Aging of the skin is discussed more fully in section 29.4a. The healing of cuts and other injuries to the skin occurs by the process described in section 5.6d. We focus here on two particularly common and serious disorders: skin cancer and burns. Other skin diseases are briefly summarized in **table 6.3.**

### 6.4a Skin Cancer

Skin cancer befalls about one out of five people in the United States at some time in their lives. Most cases are caused by UV radiation from the sun, which damages DNA and disables protective tumor suppressor genes in the epidermal cells. Consequently, most tumors occur on the head, neck, and hands, where exposure to the sun is greatest. It is most common in fair-skinned people and the elderly, who have had the longest lifetime UV exposure (see Deeper Insight 6.3). The ill-advised popularity of suntanning, however, has caused an alarming increase in skin cancer among younger people. Skin cancer is one of the most common cancers, but it is also one of the easiest to treat and has one of the highest survival rates when it is detected and treated early.

**▶▶▶APPLY WHAT YOU KNOW**

*Skin cancer is relatively rare in people with dark skin. Other than possible differences in behavior, such as less intentional suntanning, why do you think this is so?*

There are three types of skin cancer named for the epidermal cells in which they originate: *basal cell carcinoma, squamous cell carcinoma,* and *melanoma.* The three types are also distinguished from each other by the appearance of their **lesions**[35] (zones of tissue injury).

**Basal cell carcinoma**[36] **(fig. 6.11a)** is the most common type. It is the least deadly because it seldom metastasizes, but if neglected, it can severely disfigure the face. It arises from cells of the stratum basale and eventually invades the dermis. On the surface, the lesion first appears as a small, shiny bump. As the bump enlarges, it often develops a central depression and a beaded "pearly" edge.

**Squamous cell carcinoma (fig. 6.11b)** arises from keratinocytes of the stratum spinosum. Lesions usually appear on the scalp, ears, lower lip, or back of the hand. They have a raised, reddened, scaly appearance, later forming a concave ulcer with raised edges. The chance of recovery is good with early detection and surgical removal, but if it goes unnoticed or is neglected, this cancer tends to metastasize to the lymph nodes and can be lethal.

**Melanoma (fig. 6.11c)** is a skin cancer that arises from the melanocytes. It accounts for no more than 5% of skin cancers, but it is the sixth most frequently diagnosed cancer in the United States and is extremely aggressive. It can be treated surgically if caught early, but if it metastasizes—which it does quickly—it is unresponsive to chemotherapy. The prognosis for metastatic melanoma has generally been grim, with the average patient living only 6 months after diagnosis and only 5% to 14% surviving for 5 years. Hope is arising, however, from new targeted therapies for melanoma. One of these treatments uses the radioisotope rhenium-188 ($^{188}$Re) bonded to melanocyte-stimulating hormone (MSH). MSH selectively binds to melanocyte receptors, thus accumulating selectively in the very cells that compose metastatic melanoma. $^{188}$Re emits alpha particles, a highly potent ionizing radiation that is lethal to the tumor cells. Yet alpha particles are too large and heavy to penetrate very far, and are thus harmless to healthy cells around the tumor. $^{188}$Re, bound to other peptides, has also been used to treat liver cancer and is in clinical trials for pancreatic cancer.

The greatest risk factor for melanoma is a family history of the disease. It has a relatively high incidence in men, in redheads, and in people who experienced severe sunburns in childhood. About two-thirds of cases of melanoma in men result from an oncogene called *BRAF.* In women, *BRAF* does not appear to trigger melanoma, but it has been linked to some breast and ovarian cancers. *BRAF* mutations are commonly found in moles.

It is important to distinguish a mole from a melanoma. A mole usually has a uniform color and even contour, and it is no larger in diameter than the eraser of a new wooden pencil (about 6 mm). If it becomes malignant, however, it forms a large, flat, spreading

[35] *lesio* = injure
[36] *carcin* = cancer; *oma* = tumor

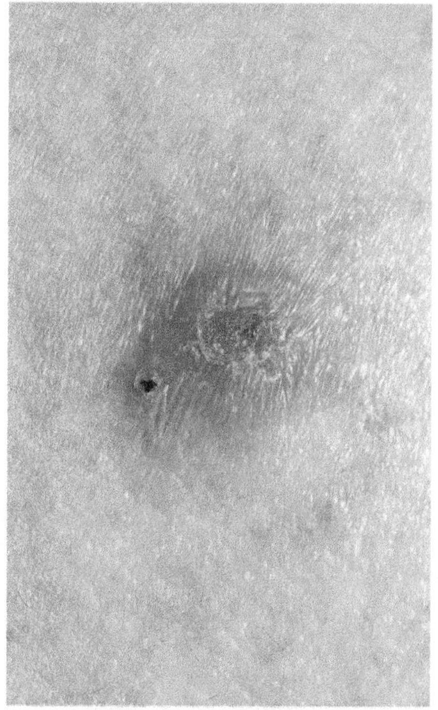
(a) Basal cell carcinoma

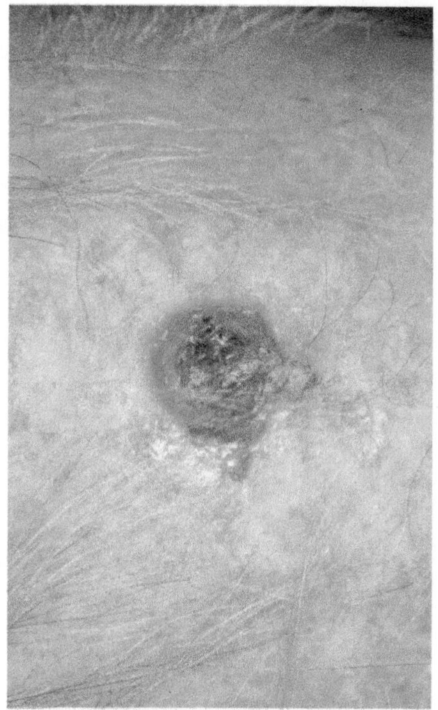
(b) Squamous cell carcinoma

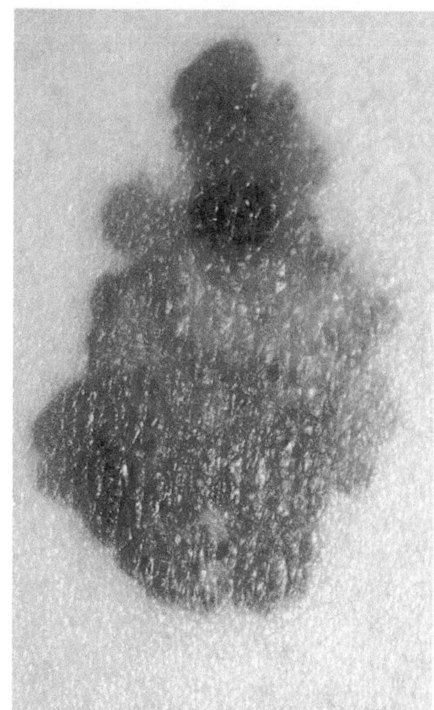
(c) Melanoma

**FIGURE 6.11 Skin Cancer.** (a) Basal cell carcinoma. (b) Squamous cell carcinoma. (c) Melanoma.

*Which of the ABCD rules can you identify in part (c)?*

a: jax10289/Shutterstock; b: DR P. Marazzi/Science Photo Library/Alamy; c: Source: National Cancer Institute (NCI)/U.S. Department of Health and Human Services (USHSS)

lesion with a scalloped border. The American Cancer Society suggests an "ABCD rule" for recognizing melanoma: *A* for asymmetry (irregular shape, unlike the rounded lesions of the other forms of skin cancer); *B* for border irregularity (the contour is not smooth but wavy or scalloped); *C* for color (often a mixture of brown, black, tan, and sometimes red and blue); and *D* for diameter (greater than 6 mm).

Depending on the type of cancer and its location (local lesion or metastatic spread), skin cancers are treated by surgical excision, radiation therapy, or destruction of the lesion by heat (electrodesiccation) or cold (cryosurgery).

## 6.4b Burns

**Burns** are usually caused by fires, kitchen spills, or excessively hot bath water, but they also can be caused by sunlight, ionizing radiation, strong acids and bases, or electrical shock. Burn deaths result primarily from fluid loss, infection, and the toxic effects of **eschar** (ESS-car)—the burned, dead tissue.

Burns are classified according to the depth of tissue involvement. **First-degree burns (fig. 6.12a)** involve only the epidermis and are marked by redness, slight edema, and pain. They heal in a few days and seldom leave scars. Most sunburns are first-degree burns.

**Second-degree burns (fig. 6.12b)** involve the epidermis and part of the dermis but leave at least some of the dermis intact. First- and second-degree burns are therefore also known as **partial-thickness burns.** A second-degree burn may be red, tan, or white and is blistered and very painful. It may take from 2 weeks to several months to heal and may leave scars. The epidermis regenerates by division of epithelial cells in the hair follicles and sweat glands and around the edges of the lesion. Severe sunburns and many scalds are second-degree burns.

**Third-degree burns (fig. 6.12c)** are a leading cause of accidental death. They are also called **full-thickness burns** because the epidermis, all of the dermis, and often some deeper tissues (muscle and bone) are destroyed. (Some authorities call burns that extend to the bone *fourth-degree burns.*) Since no dermis remains, the skin can regenerate only from the edges of the wound. Third-degree burns often require skin grafts (see Deeper Insight 6.4). If a third-degree burn is left to itself to heal, contracture (abnormal connective tissue fibrosis) and severe disfigurement may result.

### ▶▶▶APPLY WHAT YOU KNOW

*A third-degree burn may be surrounded by painful areas of first- and second-degree burns, but the region of the third-degree burn is painless. Explain the reason for this lack of pain.*

The two most urgent considerations in treating a burn patient are fluid replacement and infection control. A patient can lose several liters of water, electrolytes, and protein each day from the burned area. As fluid is lost from the tissues, more is transferred from the bloodstream to replace it, and the volume of circulating blood declines. A patient may lose up to 75% of the blood plasma

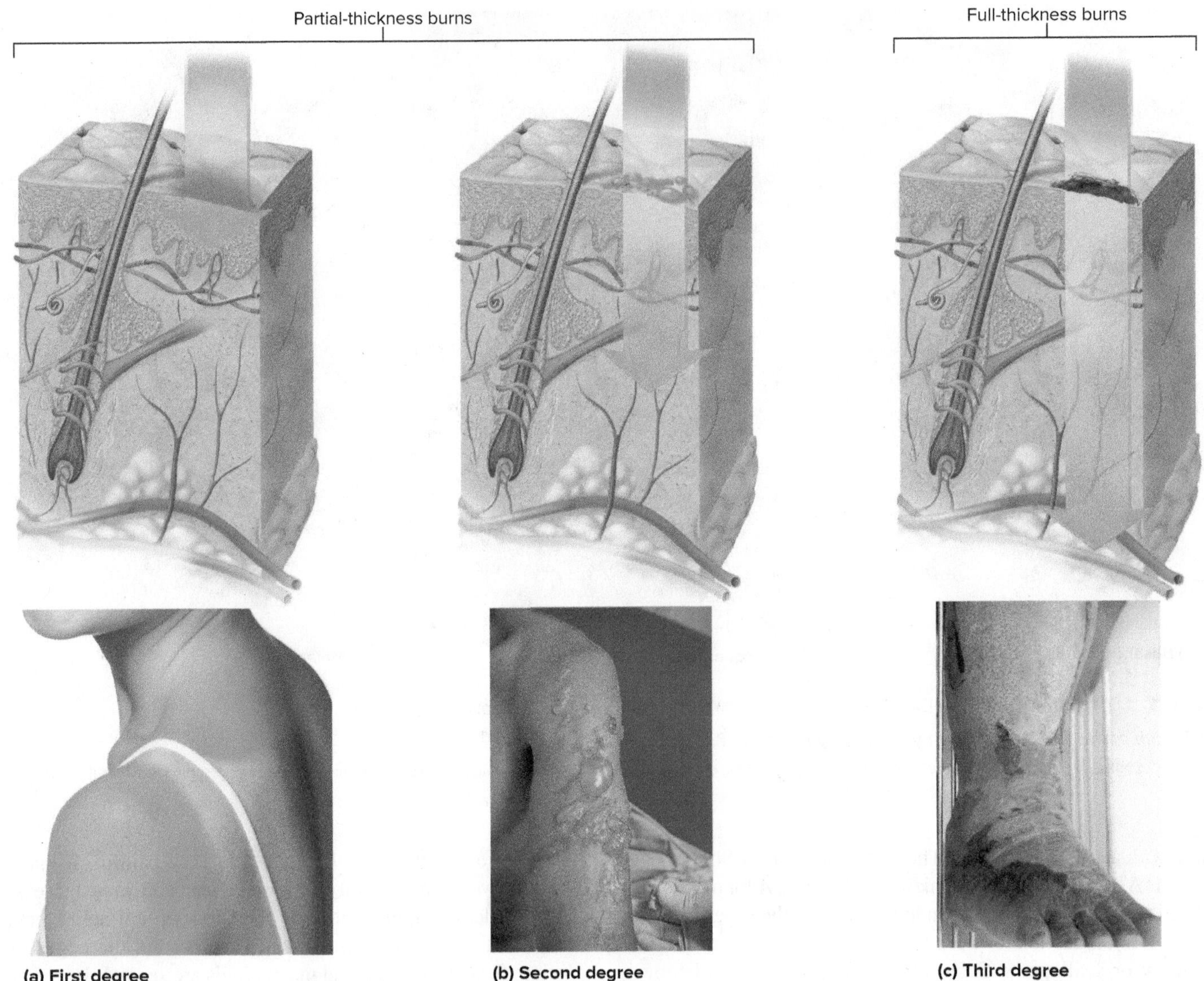


**FIGURE 6.12 Burns.** (a) First-degree burn, involving only the epidermis. (b) Second-degree burn, involving the epidermis and part of the dermis and often with blistering. (c) Third-degree burn, extending through the entire dermis and often involving even deeper tissue.

a: Dmitrii Kotin/Alamy Stock Photo; b: thawatchai_bandit/Shutterstock; c: Anukool Manoton/Shutterstock

within a few hours, potentially leading to circulatory shock and cardiac arrest—the principal cause of death in burn patients. Intravenous fluid must be given to make up for this loss. A severely burned patient may also require thousands of extra calories daily to compensate for protein loss and the demands of tissue repair. Supplemental nutrients are given intravenously or via gastric tube.

Infection is controlled by keeping the patient in an aseptic (germ-free) environment and administering antibiotics. The eschar is sterile for the first 24 hours, but then it quickly becomes infected and may have toxic effects on the digestive, respiratory, and other systems. Its removal, called **debridement**[37] (deh-BREED-ment), is essential to infection control.

[37] *de* = un; *bride* = bridle

**BEFORE YOU GO ON**

Answer the following questions to test your understanding of the preceding section:

15. What types of cells are involved in each type of skin cancer?
16. Which type of skin cancer is most dangerous? What are its early warning signs?
17. What are the differences between first-, second-, and third-degree burns?
18. What are the two most urgent priorities in treating a burn victim? How are these needs addressed?

| TABLE 6.3 | Some Disorders of the Integumentary System |
|---|---|
| Acne | Inflammation of the sebaceous glands, especially beginning at puberty; follicle becomes blocked with keratinocytes and sebum and develops into a whitehead *(comedo)* composed of these and bacteria; continued inflammation of follicle results in pus production and appearance of pimples, and oxidation of sebum turns a whitehead into a blackhead. |
| Dermatitis | Any inflammation of the skin, typically marked by itching and redness; often *contact dermatitis,* caused by exposure to toxic foliage such as poison ivy. |
| Eczema (ECK-zeh-mah) | Itchy, red, "weeping" skin lesions caused by an allergy, usually beginning before age 5; may progress to thickened, leathery, darkly pigmented patches of skin. |
| Psoriasis (so-RY-ah-sis) | Recurring, reddened plaques covered with silvery scale; sometimes disfiguring; possibly caused by an autoimmune response; runs in families. |
| Rosacea (ro-ZAY-she-ah) | A red rashlike area, often in the area of the nose and cheeks, marked by fine networks of dilated blood vessels; worsened by hot drinks, alcohol, and spicy food. |
| Seborrheic dermatitis (seb-oh-REE-ik) | Recurring patches of scaly white or yellowish inflammation often on the head, face, chest, and back; called *cradle cap* (a yellow, crusty scalp lesion) in infants. Cause unknown, but correlated with genetic and climatic factors. |
| Tinea | Any fungal infection of the skin; common in moist areas such as the axilla, groin, and foot *(athlete's foot)*. Misnamed *ringworm* because of the circular, wormlike growth pattern sometimes exhibited. |

***You can find other integumentary system disorders described in the following places:***

*Genital warts* in Deeper Insight 27.5; and in the present chapter, *pathological skin colors* and *birthmarks* in sections 6.1e and 6.1f; *baldness* and *hirsutism* in section 6.2a; *polythelia* in section 6.3d; and *skin cancer* and *burns* in section 6.4.

## DEEPER INSIGHT 6.3

## CLINICAL APPLICATION

### *UVA, UVB, and Sunscreens*

Ultraviolet radiation is divided into two wavelength ranges, UVA and UVB. UVA, so-called "tanning rays," have the longer wavelength (320–400 nm) and lower energy of the two. UVA lies just below the visible spectrum of light, where 400 nm is on the borderline between black and the deepest violet we can see. UVB, so-called "burning rays," have a shorter wavelength (290–320 nm) and higher energy level. Tanning salons often advertise that they only use "safe" UVA rays, but public health authorities are skeptical. UVA can burn as well as tan, it is responsible for most of the undesirable photoaging effects on the skin (see section 29.4a), and it inhibits one's immune system. Both UVA and UVB are now thought to initiate skin cancer. As dermatologists like to say, there is no such thing as a healthy tan.

Many people buy sunscreen according to its sun protection factor (SPF), but may be misled by the concept. SPF is a laboratory measure of protection from UVB radiation. It is advisable to use a minimum SPF of 15 for meaningful protection. It might seem that an SPF of 30 would give twice as much protection as SPF 15, but the relationship between protection and SPF is not linear. An SPF 15 sunscreen protects the skin from 93% of UVB, but SPF 30 protects only slightly more—97%. Although manufacturers compete to produce high-SPF products, higher numbers create a false sense of much greater protection. SPF values above 30 are considered to be misleading by the Australian government.

Furthermore, effectiveness varies with the amount applied, frequency of reapplication, skin type, and sweating, and sunscreen is washed off by swimming. People tend to use only one-quarter to one-half as much as needed to provide the SPF rating on the label, and wait too long between reapplications. For effective protection, one should divide the SPF by 2 and reapply sunscreen that many minutes after the onset of sun exposure—that is, every 15 minutes for an SPF of 30. Some products claim "broad spectrum UVA/UVB protection," but there is no good evidence that they protect adequately against UVA.

It was once assumed that sunscreens protect against skin cancer, but more careful studies have cast doubt on this. Sunburn and skin cancer are caused by different mechanisms, and even if sunscreen protects against burning, it provides little protection against cancer. Ironically, as the sale of sunscreen has risen, so has the incidence of skin cancer—perhaps because people falsely assume that when they use sunscreen, they can safely stay in the sun longer.

## DEEPER INSIGHT 6.4
### CLINICAL APPLICATION

### *Skin Grafts and Artificial Skin*

Third-degree burns leave no dermal tissue to regenerate what was lost; therefore, they generally require skin grafts. The ideal graft is an *autograft*[38]—taking epidermis and part of the dermis from an undamaged area of the patient's own body, such as the thigh or buttock, and grafting it to a burned area. This is called a *split-skin* graft because part of the dermis is left behind to proliferate and replace the epidermis that was removed—the same way a second-degree burn heals. The advantage of an autograft is that it is not rejected by the immune system. Relatively small areas of healthy skin can be made to cover much larger lesions by means of *meshed skin grafts* **(fig. 6.13).** The donor skin is cut into a mesh pattern and stretched over the lesion. Regenerating skin cells fill in the gaps in the mesh.

The next-best method, if the burns are too extensive for autografting, is to use skin from an identical twin to avoid immune rejection. Since identical twins are rare, however, the best one can usually hope for is another close relative as donor.

An *allograft*[39] is a graft from any other person, usually obtained from a skin bank. The immune system attempts to reject allografts, but they suffice as temporary coverings for the burned area. They can be replaced by autografts when the patient is well enough for healthy skin to be removed from an undamaged area of the body.

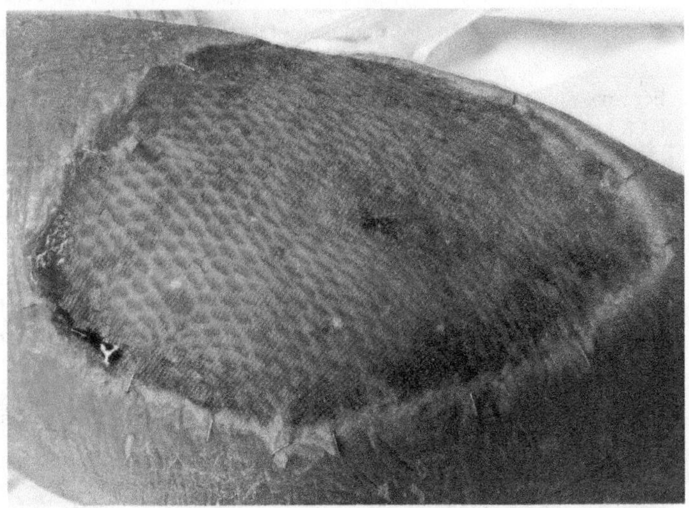

**FIGURE 6.13 A Meshed Skin Graft.**
Barry Slaven/Science Source

Pig skin is sometimes used on burn patients but presents the same problem of immune rejection. A graft of tissue from a different species is called a *xenograft*[40]. A xenograft is a short-term method of maintaining a patient until a better, long-term solution is possible. The immune reaction can be suppressed by drugs called *immunosuppressants,* but these lower one's resistance to infection, which is already compromised in a burn patient.

Some alternatives to skin grafts are also being used. Tiny keratinocyte patches cultured with growth stimulants have produced sheets of epidermal tissue as large as the entire body surface. These can replace large areas of burned tissue. Dermal fibroblasts also have been successfully cultured and used for autografts. A drawback to these approaches is that the culture process requires 3 or 4 weeks, which is too long a wait for some patients with severe burns.

Several bioengineering companies now produce artificial skin for both temporary and permanent coverings. A temporary silicone–nylon synthetic membrane can provide covering and a moist environment for wound healing. Another method called *cultured epithelial autograft (CEA)* uses the patient's own keratinocytes from a small skin biopsy and cultures these in the laboratory for 2 to 3 weeks to produce sheets of tissue that can cover large burn areas. Another method cultures fibroblasts on a collagen gel to produce a dermis, then keratinocytes to produce an overlying epidermis. Still another technology available in some countries is a spray-on skin graft. A bit of epidermis the size of a postage stamp is taken from the patient and enzymatically broken up into separate cells. The cell suspension is then sprayed onto areas of second-degree burns or other skin lesions. Within a week, this can grow into an area of healthy skin the size of a textbook page.

[38] *auto* = self
[39] *allo* = different, other
[40] *xeno* = strange, alien, foreign

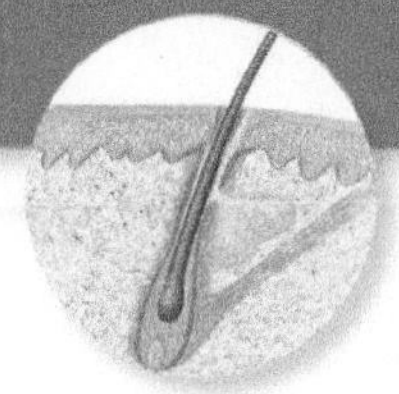

# CONNECTIVE ISSUES

## Effects of the **INTEGUMENTARY SYSTEM** on Other Organ Systems

**ALL SYSTEMS**
Skin covers the body and provides a barrier to pathogens and to excessive water loss; epidermal keratinocytes initiate synthesis of calcitriol, with effects on multiple other organ systems as noted.

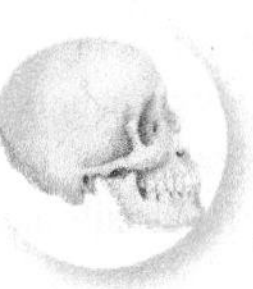

**SKELETAL SYSTEM**
Bone growth and maintenance depend on calcium, which is absorbed from the diet under the influence of calcitriol.

**LYMPHATIC AND IMMUNE SYSTEMS**
Dendritic cells of the skin alert the immune system when pathogens breach the epidermal barrier.

**MUSCULAR SYSTEM**
Muscle contraction depends on calcium, which is absorbed from the diet under the influence of calcitriol.

**RESPIRATORY SYSTEM**
Nasal guard hairs block some airborne debris from being inhaled; calcium is required for the secretion of respiratory mucus, which therefore depends on calcitriol.

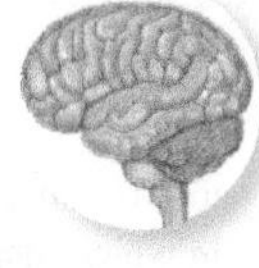

**NERVOUS SYSTEM**
The transmission of nerve signals across synapses depends on calcium, which is absorbed from the diet under the influence of calcitriol.

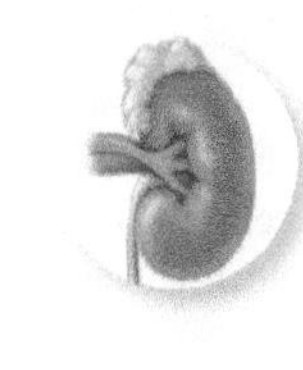

**URINARY SYSTEM**
Skin complements the urinary system by excreting salts and some nitrogenous waste in the sweat; calcitriol promotes reabsorption of calcium by the kidneys.

**ENDOCRINE SYSTEM**
Hormone secretion depends on calcium as a trigger for exocytosis and, therefore, on calcitriol; the role of epidermal keratinocytes in synthesizing calcitriol is itself an endocrine function.

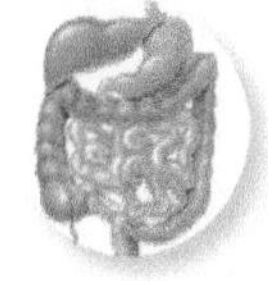

**DIGESTIVE SYSTEM**
By their role in calcitriol synthesis, keratinocytes influence intestinal absorption of calcium; calcium is needed for the secretion of all digestive enzymes and mucus.

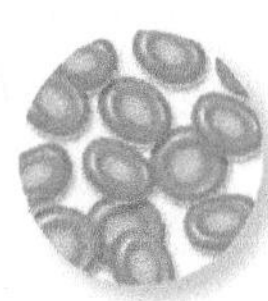

**CIRCULATORY SYSTEM**
The skin is a major blood reservoir; cutaneous vasoconstriction diverts blood to other organs; skin supports blood volume by retarding fluid loss; dermal vasoconstriction and vasodilation help to regulate blood temperature.

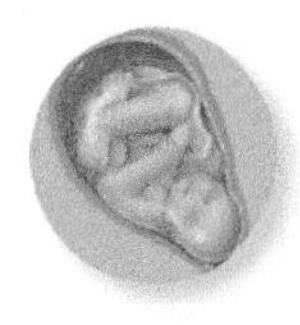

**REPRODUCTIVE SYSTEM**
Cutaneous nerve endings are important in sexual stimulation; mammary glands produce milk; apocrine sweat glands secrete pheromones that affect sexual behavior and physiology; skin stretches to accommodate abdominal growth in pregnancy.

# STUDY GUIDE

## Assess Your Learning Outcomes

*To test your knowledge, discuss the following topics with a study partner or in writing, ideally from memory.*

### 6.1 The Skin and Subcutaneous Tissue

1. The name of the branch of medicine that deals with the integumentary system
2. The difference between the terms *integumentary system* and *integument;* organs that belong to the integumentary system
3. The two principal layers of the skin, and the name of the connective tissue layer that lies between the skin and the deeper muscle or other tissue
4. Normal thickness of the skin, and differences in histology and location between thick and thin skin
5. Functions of the skin
6. Five histological layers of thick skin and which of them is lacking from thin skin
7. Five kinds of epidermal cells, their respective functions, and the epidermal layers in which they occur
8. The life history of a keratinocyte from the time it is "born" by mitosis at the base of the epidermis to the time it exfoliates from the surface
9. Fiber and cell types of the dermis, other dermal structures, and the typical thickness of the dermis
10. Dermal papillae, epidermal ridges, their function, and their relationship to the surface appearance of skin
11. The two layers of the dermis, and how they differ histologically and functionally
12. Composition and functions of the hypodermis, and an alternative name for it when it is composed predominantly of adipose tissue
13. Factors that account for the variety of normal skin colors; abnormal skin colors and their causes
14. Friction ridges, flexion lines, freckles, moles, and hemangiomas

### 6.2 Hair and Nails

1. How the keratin of hair and nails differs from keratin of the epidermis
2. Three kinds of hair, including fetal and adult types
3. The three regions of a hair from base to tip, and the three layers of a hair from core to surface
4. Location of a hair's growth zone and of its source of nourishment
5. The two layers of a hair follicle; their composition; and the specialized nerve endings and smooth muscle associated with a follicle
6. The basis for differences between straight, wavy, and curly hair and for differences in hair color
7. Events of the anagen, catagen, and telogen stages of a hair's life; the typical life span and growth rate of scalp hairs
8. Alopecia, pattern baldness, and hirsutism
9. Functions and body distribution of the various kinds of hair
10. The anatomy of fingernails and toenails; location of their growth zone; and a typical rate of nail growth

### 6.3 Cutaneous Glands

1. Apocrine and eccrine sweat gland distribution, development, structure, and function
2. The same characteristics of sebaceous glands; the name of their product; and how their mode of secretion differs from that of the sweat glands
3. Ceruminous gland distribution, development, structure, and function
4. Mammary gland structure and development and how mammary glands relate to a type of sweat glands

### 6.4 Skin Disorders

1. Three forms of skin cancer and differences in their appearance, the cells in which they originate, their frequency of occurrence, and their severity
2. Three degrees of burns and how they are treated

## Testing Your Recall

*Answers in Appendix A*

1. Cells of the ______ are keratinized and dead.
   a. papillary layer
   b. stratum spinosum
   c. stratum basale
   d. stratum corneum
   e. stratum granulosum

2. The epidermal water barrier is formed at the point where epidermal cells
   a. pass from stratum basale to stratum spinosum.
   b. enter the telogen phase.
   c. pass from stratum spinosum to stratum granulosum.
   d. form the epidermal ridges.
   e. exfoliate.

3. Which of the following skin conditions or appearances would most likely result from liver failure?
   a. pallor
   b. erythema
   c. seborrheic dermatitis
   d. jaundice
   e. melanization

4. All of the following interfere with microbial invasion of the body *except*
   a. the acid mantle.
   b. melanization.
   c. dendritic cells.
   d. keratinization.
   e. sebum.

5. The hair on a 6-year-old's arms is
   a. vellus hair.
   b. terminal hair.
   c. alopecia.
   d. downy hair.
   e. rosacea.

6. Which of the following terms is *least* related to the rest?
   a. lunule
   b. nail plate
   c. hyponychium
   d. free edge
   e. cortex

# STUDY GUIDE

7. Which of the following is a scent gland?
   a. eccrine gland
   b. sebaceous gland
   c. apocrine gland
   d. ceruminous gland
   e. eccrine gland
8. _____ are skin cells with a sensory role.
   a. Tactile cells
   b. Dendritic cells
   c. Stem cells
   d. Melanocytes
   e. Keratinocytes
9. Which of the following glands produce the acid mantle?
   a. eccrine sweat glands
   b. apocrine sweat glands
   c. mammary glands
   d. ceruminous glands
   e. sebaceous glands
10. Which of the following skin cells alert the immune system to pathogens?
    a. fibroblasts
    b. melanocytes
    c. keratinocytes
    d. dendritic cells
    e. tactile cells
11. _____ is sweating without noticeable wetness of the skin.
12. A muscle that causes a hair to stand on end is called a/an _____.
13. The process of removing burned skin from a patient is called _____.
14. Blueness of the skin due to low oxygen concentration in the blood is called _____.
15. Projections of the dermis toward the skin surface are called _____.
16. Cerumen is more commonly known as _____.
17. The holocrine glands that secrete into a hair follicle are called _____.
18. Hairs grow only during the _____ phase of the hair cycle.
19. A hair is nourished by blood vessels in a connective tissue projection called the _____.
20. A _____ burn destroys the entire dermis.

## Building Your Medical Vocabulary

*Answers in Appendix A*

*State a meaning of each word element, and give a medical term from this chapter that uses it or a slight variation of it.*

1. -in
2. albo-
3. dermato-
4. dia-
5. homo-
6. lesio-
7. melano-
8. -oma
9. onycho-
10. pilo-

## What's Wrong with These Statements?

*Answers in Appendix A*

*Briefly explain why each of the following statements is false, or reword it to make it true.*

1. Basal cell carcinoma is the rarest form of skin cancer and the least likely to metastasize.
2. Brown or black skin owes its color to a great abundance of melanocytes.
3. The dermis is composed mainly of keratin.
4. Vitamin D synthesis begins in certain cutaneous glands.
5. Epidermal cells multiply rapidly in the stratum granulosum to produce the thick, protective stratum corneum.
6. The hair cuticle is composed of dead cells; the living hair cells constitute the cortex.
7. The three layers of the skin are the epidermis, dermis, and hypodermis.
8. People of African descent have a much higher density of epidermal melanocytes than do people of northern European descent.
9. Pallor indicates a genetic lack of melanin.
10. Eccrine and apocrine sweat glands are present from birth.

## Testing Your Comprehension

1. Many organs of the body contain numerous smaller organs, perhaps even thousands. Describe an example of this in the integumentary system.
2. Certain aspects of human form and function are easier to understand when viewed from the perspective of comparative anatomy and evolution. Discuss examples of this in the integumentary system.
3. Explain how the complementarity of form and function is reflected in the fact that the dermis has two histological layers and not just one.
4. Cold weather does not normally interfere with oxygen uptake by the blood, but it can cause cyanosis anyway. Why?
5. Why is it important for the epidermis to be effective, but not *too* effective, in screening out UV radiation?

CHAPTER 7

# BONE TISSUE

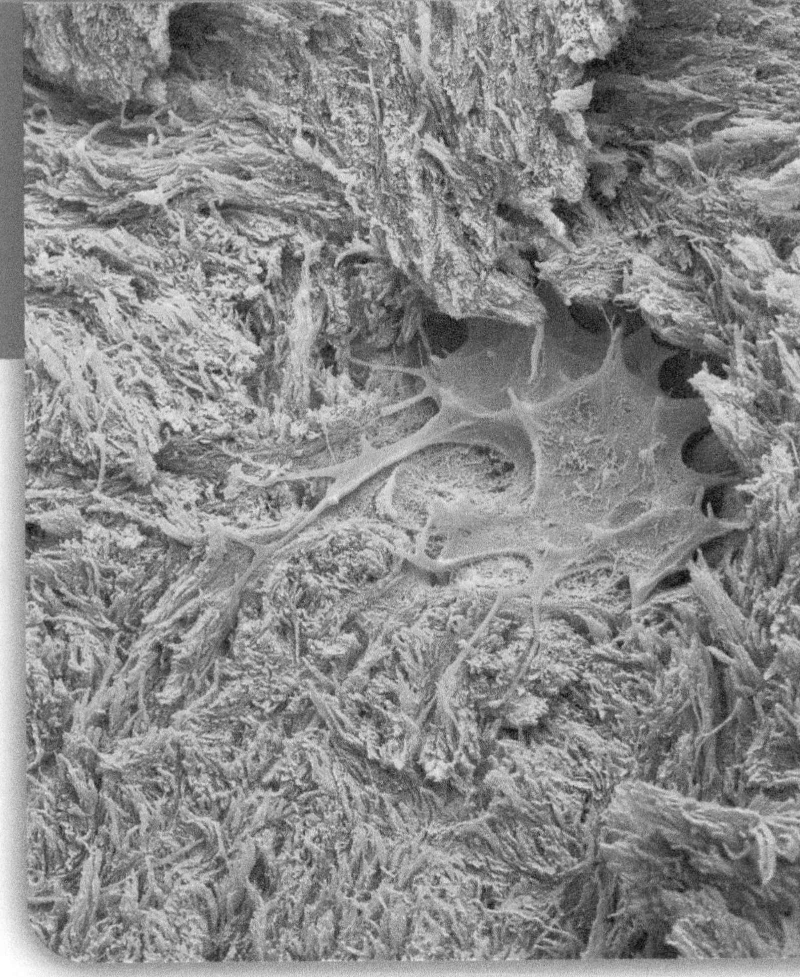

A bone cell (osteocyte) surrounded by calcified bone matrix
Eye of Science/Science Source

## CHAPTER OUTLINE



## DEEPER INSIGHTS

**Module 5: Skeletal System**

**BRUSHING UP**

- Bones develop from an embryonic connective tissue called mesenchyme, described in section 5.1b.
- Hyaline cartilage histology (see table 5.7) is important for understanding bone development and certain features of the mature skeleton.
- Review stem cells (section 5.6c) to best understand bone cells and their origins.

In art and history, nothing has so often symbolized death as a skull or skeleton.[1] Bones and teeth are the most durable remains of a once-living body and the most vivid reminder of the impermanence of life.

The dry bones presented for laboratory study may wrongly suggest that the skeleton is a nonliving scaffold for the body, like the steel girders of a building. Seeing it in such a sanitized form makes it easy to forget that the living skeleton is made of dynamic tissues, full of cells—that it continually remodels itself and interacts physiologically with all of the other organ systems of the body. The skeleton is permeated with nerves and blood vessels, which attests to its sensitivity and metabolic activity.

**Osteology,**[2] the study of bone, is the subject of these next three chapters. In this chapter, we study bone as a tissue—its composition, its functions, how it develops and grows, how its metabolism is regulated, and some of its disorders. This will provide a basis for understanding the skeleton, joints, and muscles in the chapters that follow.

## 7.1 Tissues and Organs of the Skeletal System

**Expected Learning Outcomes**

When you have completed this section, you should be able to

a. name the tissues and organs that compose the skeletal system;
b. state several functions of the skeletal system;
c. distinguish between bone as a tissue and as an organ; and
d. describe the general features of a long bone and a flat bone.

The **skeletal system** is composed of bones, cartilages, and ligaments joined tightly to form a strong, flexible framework for the body. Cartilage, the forerunner of most bones in embryonic and childhood development, covers many joint surfaces in the mature skeleton. Ligaments hold bones together at the joints and are discussed in chapter 9. Tendons are structurally similar to ligaments but attach muscle to bone; they are discussed with the muscular system in chapter 10. Here, we focus on the bones.

### 7.1a Functions of the Skeleton

The skeleton plays at least six roles:

1. **Support.** Bones of the limbs and vertebral column support the body; the mandible and maxilla support the teeth; and some viscera are supported by nearby bones.
2. **Protection.** Bones enclose and protect the brain, spinal cord, heart, lungs, pelvic viscera, and bone marrow.
3. **Movement.** Limb movements, breathing, and other movements are produced by the action of muscles on the bones.
4. **Electrolyte balance.** The skeleton stores calcium and phosphate ions and releases them into the tissue fluid and blood according to the body's physiological needs.
5. **Acid–base balance.** Bone tissue buffers the blood against excessive pH changes by absorbing or releasing alkaline phosphate and carbonate salts.
6. **Blood formation.** Red bone marrow is the major producer of blood cells, including cells of the immune system.

### 7.1b Bones and Osseous Tissue

Bone, or **osseous**[3] **tissue,** is a connective tissue in which the matrix is hardened by the deposition of calcium phosphate and other minerals. The hardening process is called **mineralization** or **calcification.** (Bone is not the hardest substance in the body; that distinction goes to tooth enamel.) Osseous tissue is only one of the tissues that make up a bone. Also present are blood, bone marrow, cartilage, adipose tissue, nervous tissue, and fibrous connective tissue. The word *bone* can denote an organ composed of all these tissues, or it can denote just the osseous tissue.

### 7.1c General Features of Bones

Bones have a wide variety of shapes correlated with their varied protective and locomotor functions. Most of the cranial bones are in the form of thin curved plates called **flat bones,** such as the paired parietal bones that form the dome of the top of the head. The sternum (breastbone), scapula (shoulder blade), ribs, and hip bones are also flat bones. The most important bones in movement are the **long bones** of the limbs—the humerus, radius, and ulna of the arm and forearm; the femur, tibia, and fibula of the thigh and leg; and the metacarpals, metatarsals, and phalanges of the hands and feet. Like crowbars, long bones serve as rigid levers that are acted upon by skeletal muscles to produce the major body movements. Various bones that don't fit the flat or long

[1] *skelet* = dried up
[2] *osteo* = bone; *logy* = study of
[3] *os, osse, oste* = bone

bone groups are sometimes called *short bones* (such as those of the wrist and ankle) or *irregular bones* (such as the vertebrae and some skull bones).

**Figure 7.1** shows the general anatomy of a long bone. Much of it is composed of an outer shell of dense white osseous tissue called **compact (dense) bone** or **cortical bone.** The shell encloses a space called the **marrow cavity,** or **medullary cavity** (MED-you-lerr-ee), which contains bone marrow. At the ends of the bone, the central space is occupied by a more loosely organized form of osseous tissue called **spongy (cancellous) bone.** A narrow zone of spongy bone also occurs just inside the cortical bone of the shaft and in the middle of most flat, irregular, and short bones. The skeleton is about three-quarters compact bone and one-quarter spongy bone in dry weight. Spongy bone is always enclosed by a shell of more durable compact bone.

The principal features of a long bone are its shaft, called the **diaphysis**[4] (dy-AF-ih-sis), and an expanded head at each end called the **epiphysis**[5] (eh-PIF-ih-sis). The diaphysis provides leverage, and the epiphysis is enlarged to strengthen the joint and provide added surface area for the attachment of tendons and ligaments. Mature bones often exhibit an *epiphysial line* of slightly denser spongy bone between the epiphysis and diaphysis. This is a remnant of a childhood growth zone called an *epiphysial plate,* detailed later. The joint surface where one bone meets another is covered with a layer of hyaline cartilage called the **articular cartilage.** Together with a lubricating fluid secreted between the bones, this cartilage enables a joint to move far more easily than it would if one bone rubbed directly against the other. Blood vessels penetrate into the bone through minute holes called **nutrient foramina** (for-AM-ih-nuh); we will trace where they go when we consider the histology of bone.

Externally, a bone is covered with a sheath called the **periosteum.**[6] This has a tough, outer *fibrous layer* of collagen and an inner *osteogenic layer* of bone-forming cells described in the next section. Some collagen fibers of the outer layer are continuous with the tendons that bind muscle to bone, and some penetrate into the bone matrix as **perforating fibers.** The periosteum thus provides strong attachment and continuity from muscle to tendon to bone. The osteogenic layer is important to the growth of bone and healing of fractures. There is no periosteum over the articular cartilage.

A thin layer of reticular connective tissue called the **endosteum**[7] lines the internal marrow cavity, covers all the honeycombed surfaces of spongy bone, and lines a canal system found throughout the compact bone.

Flat bones have a sandwichlike construction with two layers of compact bone, called the *inner* and *outer tables,* enclosing a middle layer of spongy bone **(fig. 7.2).** The spongy layer in the cranium is called **diploe**[8] (DIP-lo-ee). A moderate blow to the skull can fracture the outer table of compact bone, but the diploe may absorb the impact and leave the inner table and brain unharmed. Both surfaces of a flat bone are covered with periosteum, and the marrow spaces amid the spongy bone are lined with endosteum.

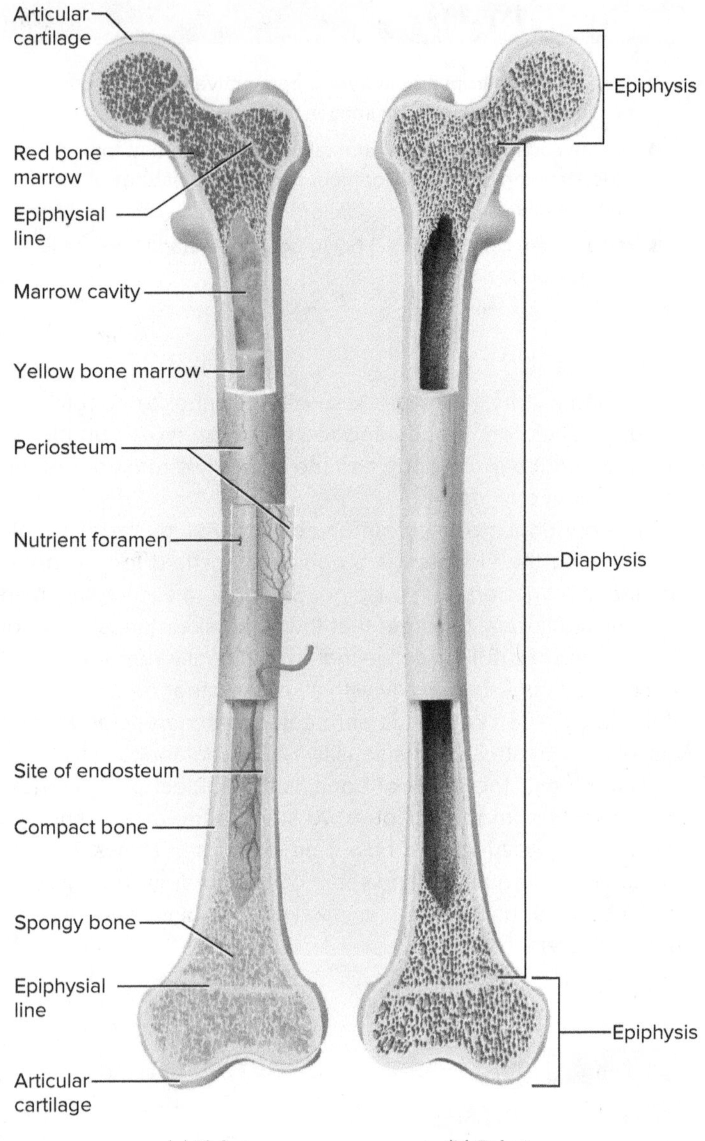


**FIGURE 7.1 Anatomy of a Long Bone.** (a) The femur, with its soft tissues including bone marrow, articular cartilage, blood vessels, and periosteum. (b) A dried femur in longitudinal section.

? *What is the functional significance of a long bone being wider at the epiphyses than at the diaphysis?*

[4]*dia* = across; *physis* = growth; originally named for a ridge on the shaft of the tibia
[5]*epi* = upon, above; *physis* = growth
[6]*peri* = around; *oste* = bone
[7]*endo* = within; *oste* = bone
[8]*diplo* = double

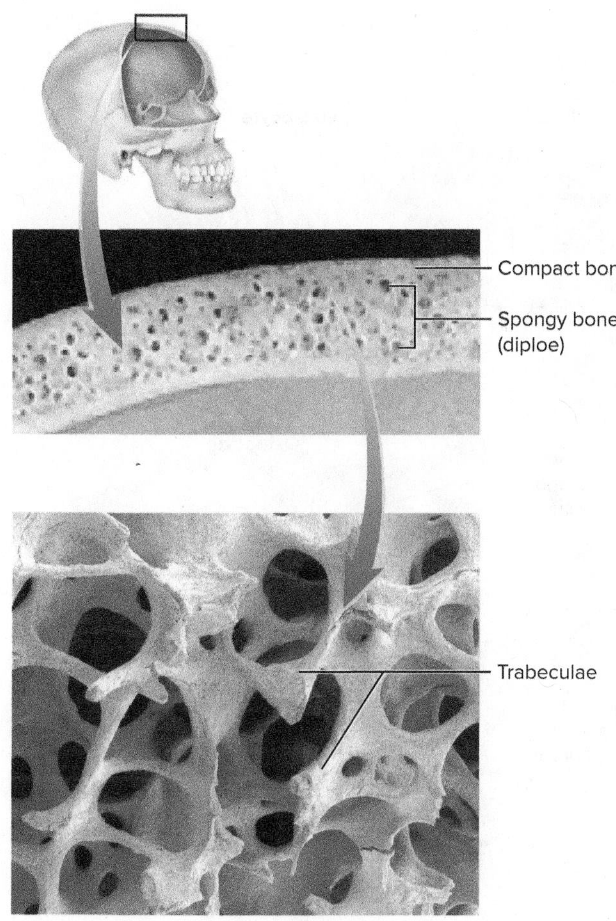


**FIGURE 7.2 Anatomy of a Flat Bone.**

**Middle:** Christine Eckel/McGraw-Hill Education; **Lower:** Steve Gschmeissner/Science Photo Library/Alamy Stock Photo

**BEFORE YOU GO ON**

Answer the following questions to test your understanding of the preceding section:

1. Name at least five tissues found in a bone.
2. List three or more functions of the skeletal system other than supporting the body and protecting some of the internal organs.
3. Describe the anatomical differences between compact and spongy bone, and their spatial relationship to each other in a long bone and a flat bone.
4. State the anatomical terms for the shaft, head, growth zone, and fibrous covering of a long bone.

## 7.2 Histology of Osseous Tissue

### Expected Learning Outcomes

When you have completed this section, you should be able to

a. list and describe the cells, fibers, and ground substance of bone tissue;
b. state the importance of each constituent of bone tissue;
c. compare the histology of the two types of bone tissue; and
d. distinguish between the two types of bone marrow.

### 7.2a Bone Cells

Like any other connective tissue, bone consists of cells, fibers, and ground substance. There are four principal types of bone cells **(fig. 7.3):**

1. **Osteogenic**[9] **cells** are stem cells that develop from embryonic mesenchyme and then give rise to most other bone cell types. They occur in the endosteum and inner layer of the periosteum. They multiply continually, and some go on to become the *osteoblasts* described next.
2. **Osteoblasts**[10] are bone-forming cells that synthesize the organic matter of the bone and then promote its mineralization. This bone-building activity is called **osteogenesis.** Osteoblasts form rows in the endosteum and inner layer of the periosteum and resemble a cuboidal epithelium on the bone surface (see fig. 7.8). They are nonmitotic, so the only source of new osteoblasts is the osteogenic cells. Stress and fractures stimulate accelerated mitosis of those cells and therefore a rapid rise in the number of osteoblasts, which then reinforce or rebuild the bone. Osteoblasts also have an endocrine function: They secrete the hormone *osteocalcin,* which stimulates insulin secretion by the pancreas, increases insulin sensitivity in adipocytes, and limits the growth of adipose tissue.
3. **Osteocytes** are former osteoblasts that have become trapped in the matrix they deposited (see this chapter's opening photo). They reside in tiny cavities called **lacunae,**[11] which are interconnected by slender channels called **canaliculi**[12] (CAN-uh-LIC-you-lye). Each osteocyte has delicate cytoplasmic processes that reach into the canaliculi to contact the processes from neighboring osteocytes. Some of them also contact osteoblasts on the bone surface. Neighboring osteocytes are connected by gap junctions where their processes meet, so they can pass nutrients and chemical signals to one another and pass their metabolic wastes to the nearest blood vessel for disposal.

   Osteocytes have multiple functions. Some resorb bone matrix and others deposit it, so they contribute to the homeostatic maintenance of bone density and blood concentrations of calcium and phosphate ions. Perhaps even more importantly, they are strain sensors. When a load is applied to a bone, it produces a flow in the extracellular fluid of the lacunae and canaliculi. This stimulates sensory cilia on the osteocytes and induces the cells to secrete signals that regulate bone remodeling—adjustments in bone shape and density to adapt to stress.

[9] *osteo* = bone; *genic* = producing
[10] *osteo* = bone; *blast* = form, produce
[11] *lac* = lake, hollow; *una* = little
[12] *canal* = canal, channel; *icul* = little

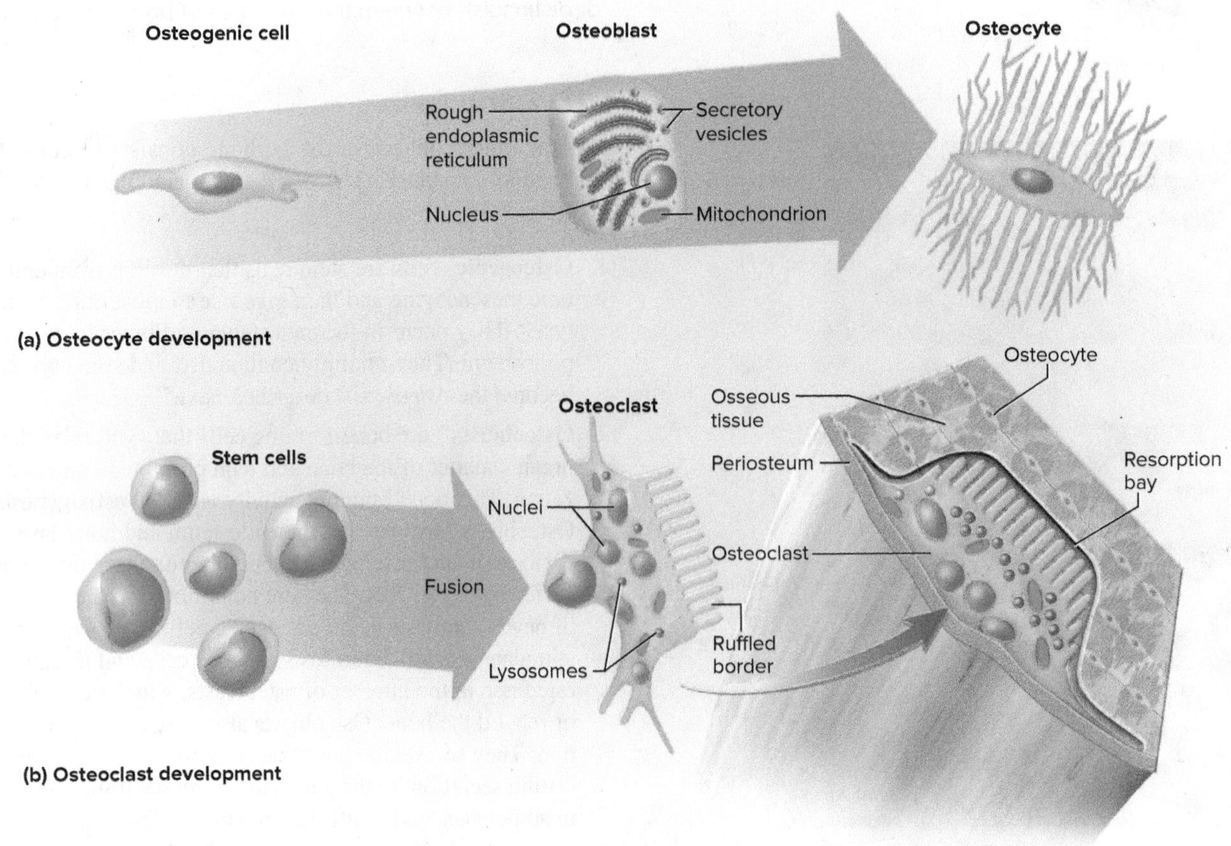


**FIGURE 7.3 Bone Cells and Their Development.** (a) Osteogenic cells give rise to osteoblasts, which deposit matrix around themselves and transform into osteocytes. (b) Bone marrow stem cells fuse to form osteoclasts.

4. **Osteoclasts**[13] are bone-dissolving cells on the bone surfaces. Their action is called **osteolysis,** the opposite of osteogenesis. They develop from the same bone marrow stem cells as blood cells. Thus, osteogenic cells, osteoblasts, and osteocytes all belong to one cell lineage, but osteoclasts have an independent origin (fig. 7.3). Several stem cells fuse to form each osteoclast, so osteoclasts are unusually large (up to 150 μm) and typically have 3 or 4 nuclei, but sometimes up to 50. The side of the osteoclast facing the bone surface has a *ruffled border* with many deep infoldings of the plasma membrane that increase surface area and the efficiency of bone resorption. Osteoclasts often reside in pits called *resorption bays* that they etch into the bone surface. Bone remodeling results from the combination of osteogenesis by osteoblasts and osteolysis by osteoclasts.

[13]*osteo* = bone; *clast* = destroy, break down

## 7.2b The Matrix

The matrix of osseous tissue averages, by dry weight, about one-third organic and two-thirds inorganic matter. The organic matter, synthesized by the osteoblasts, includes collagen and various protein–carbohydrate complexes such as glycosaminoglycans, proteoglycans, and glycoproteins (all described in section 2.4c). The inorganic matter is about 85% **hydroxyapatite,** a crystallized calcium phosphate salt [$Ca_{10}(PO_4)_6(OH)_2$]; 10% calcium carbonate ($CaCO_3$); and lesser amounts of magnesium, sodium, potassium, fluoride, sulfate, carbonate, and hydroxide ions. Several foreign elements behave chemically like bone minerals and become incorporated into osseous tissue as contaminants, sometimes with deadly results (see Deeper Insight 7.1).

**▶▶▶APPLY WHAT YOU KNOW**

*What two organelles do you think are especially prominent in osteoblasts?* (Hint: *Consider the major substances that osteoblasts synthesize.*)

Bone is in a class of materials that engineers call a **composite,** a combination of two basic structural materials—in this case, a ceramic and a polymer. A composite can combine the optimal mechanical properties of each component. Consider a fiberglass fishing rod, for example, made of a ceramic (glass fibers) embedded in a polymer (resin). The resin alone would be too brittle and the fibers alone too flexible and limp to serve the purpose of a fishing rod, but together they produce a material of great strength and flexibility.

In bone, the polymer is collagen and the ceramic is hydroxyapatite and other minerals. The ceramic component enables a bone to support the weight of the body without sagging. When the bones are deficient in calcium salts, they are soft and bend easily. One way to demonstrate this is to soak a clean dry bone, such as a chicken bone, in vinegar for a few days. As the mild acid of the vinegar dissolves the minerals, the bone becomes flexible and rubbery. Such mineral deficiency and flexibility are the central problems in the childhood disease *rickets,* in which the soft bones of the lower limbs bend under the body's weight and become permanently deformed (see Deeper Insight 7.3).

The protein component gives bone a degree of flexibility. Without protein, a bone is excessively brittle, as in *osteogenesis imperfecta,* or *brittle bone disease* (see table 7.2). Without collagen, a jogger's bones would shatter under the impact of running. But normally, when a bone bends slightly toward one side, the tensile strength of the collagen fibers on the opposite side holds the bone together and prevents it from snapping like a stick of chalk. Collagen molecules have *sacrificial bonds* that break under stress, protecting a bone from fracture by dissipating some of the shock. The bonds re-form when the collagen is relieved of stress.

## DEEPER INSIGHT 7.1
## MEDICAL HISTORY

### *Bone Contamination*

When Marie and Pierre Curie and Henri Becquerel received their 1903 Nobel Prize for the discovery of radioactivity (see Deeper Insight 2.1), radiation captured the public imagination. Not for several decades did anyone realize its dangers. For example, factories employed women to paint luminous numbers on watch and clock dials with radium paint. The women moistened their paint brushes with their tongues to keep them finely pointed and ingested radium in the process. The radium accumulated in their bones and caused many of them to develop a bone cancer called osteosarcoma. History remembers these women as the tragic "radium girls."

Even more horrific, in the wisdom of hindsight, was a deadly health fad in which people drank "tonics" made of radium-enriched water. One famous enthusiast was the millionaire playboy and championship golfer Eben Byers (1880–1932), who drank several bottles of radium tonic each day and praised its virtues as a wonder drug and aphrodisiac. Like the factory women, Byers contracted osteosarcoma. By the time of his death, holes had formed in his skull and doctors had removed his entire upper jaw and most of his mandible in an effort to halt the spreading cancer. Byers' bones and teeth were so radioactive they could expose photographic film in the dark. Brain damage left him unable to speak, but he remained mentally alert to the bitter end. His tragic decline and death shocked the world and helped put an end to the radium tonic fad.

Unlike fiberglass, bone varies from place to place in its ratio of minerals to collagen. The middle-ear bones, for example, are about 90% mineral, giving them the necessary stiffness to efficiently conduct sound vibrations to the inner ear. The limb bones, by contrast, have a higher percentage of collagen so they can bend slightly under the body's weight. Osseous tissue is thus adapted to different amounts of tension and compression exerted on different parts of the skeleton.

## 7.2c Compact Bone

The histological study of compact bone usually uses slices that have been dried, cut with a saw, and ground to translucent thinness. This procedure destroys the cells but reveals fine details of the matrix **(fig. 7.4).** Such sections show onionlike **concentric lamellae**—layers of matrix concentrically arranged around a **central (haversian[14]) canal** and connected with each other by canaliculi. A central canal and its lamellae constitute an **osteon (haversian system)**—the basic structural unit of compact bone. In longitudinal views and three-dimensional reconstructions, we can see that an osteon is actually a cylinder of tissue surrounding a central canal. Along their length, central canals are joined by transverse or diagonal passages called **perforating canals.** The central and perforating canals are lined with endosteum. Each osteon is separated from its neighbors by a thin *cement line,* which blocks microfractures of the bone from spreading and minimizes the chance of them causing a large-scale fracture.

Collagen fibers "corkscrew" down the matrix of a given lamella in a helical arrangement like the threads of a screw. The helices coil in one direction in one lamella and in the opposite direction in the next lamella (fig. 7.4b). This enhances the strength of bone on the same principle as plywood, made of thin layers of wood with the grain running in different directions from one layer to the next. In areas where the bone must resist tension (bending), the helix is loosely coiled like the threads on a wood screw and the fibers are more stretched out on the longitudinal axis of the bone. In weight-bearing areas where resistance to compression is more important, the helix is tightly coiled like the closely spaced threads on a bolt, and the fibers are more nearly transverse.

The skeleton receives about half a liter of blood per minute. Blood vessels, along with nerves, enter the bone tissue through nutrient foramina on the surface. These foramina open into the perforating canals that cross the matrix and feed into the central canals. The innermost osteocytes around each central canal receive nutrients from these blood vessels and pass them along through their gap junctions to neighboring osteocytes. They also receive wastes from their neighbors and convey them to the central canal for removal by the bloodstream. Thus, the cytoplasmic processes of the osteocytes maintain a two-way flow of nutrients and wastes between the central canal and the outermost cells of the osteon.

Not all of the matrix is organized into osteons. The inner and outer boundaries of dense bone are arranged in *circumferential lamellae* that run parallel to the bone surface. Between osteons, we can find irregular regions called *interstitial lamellae,* the remains of old osteons that broke down as the bone grew and remodeled itself.

[14]Clopton Havers (1650–1702), English anatomist

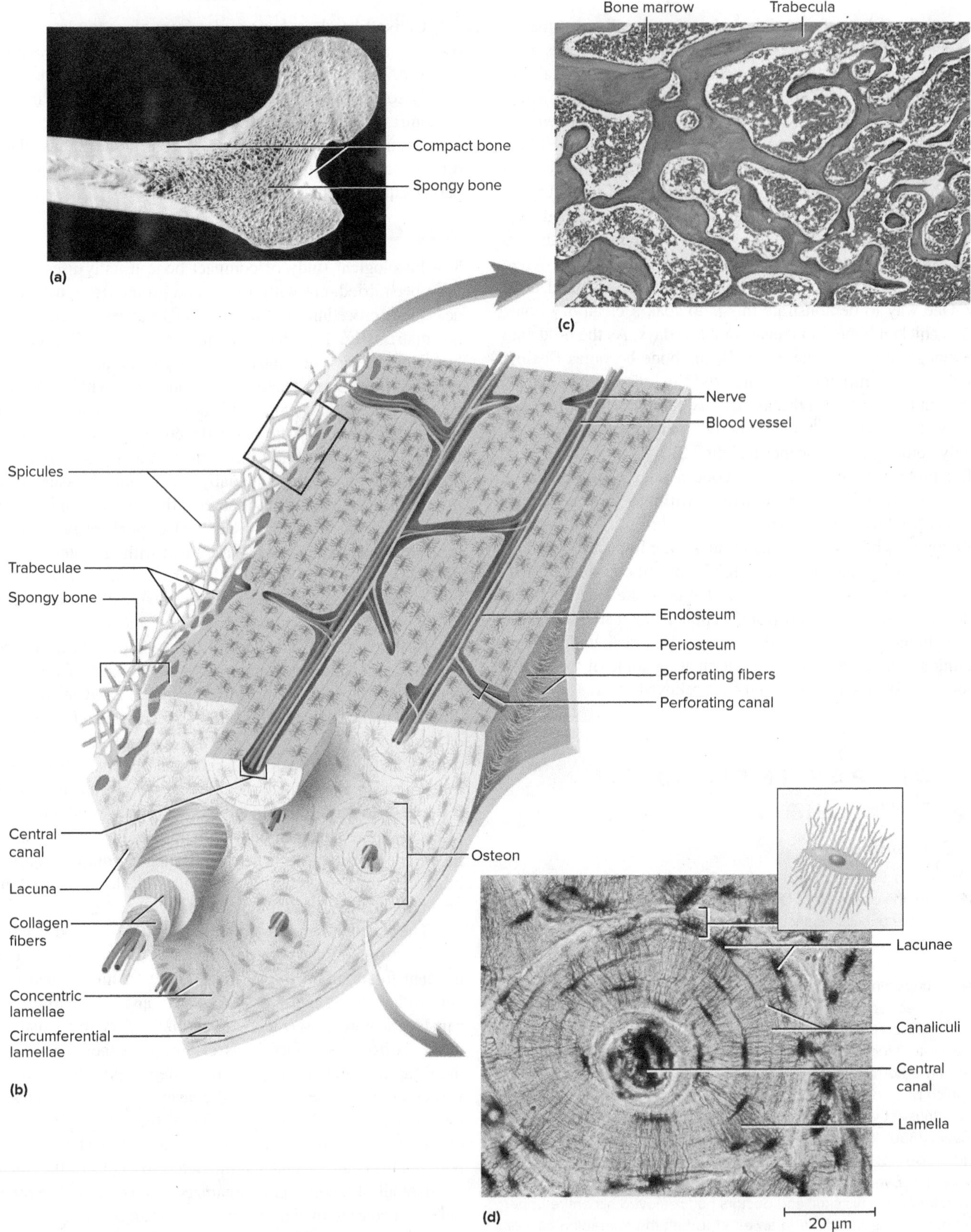


**FIGURE 7.4 The Histology of Osseous Tissue.** (a) Compact and spongy bone in a longitudinal section of the femur. (b) The three-dimensional structure of compact bone. Lamellae of one osteon are telescoped to show their alternating arrangement of collagen fibers. (c) Histology of decalcified spongy bone and red bone marrow. (d) Microscopic appearance of a cross section of an osteon of dried compact bone. The art inset relates osteocyte structure to the shapes of the lacunae and canaliculi of the bone. APR

a: B Christopher/Alamy Stock Photo; c: Biophoto Associates/Science Source; d: Ed Reschke/Getty Images

## 7.2d Spongy Bone

Spongy bone (fig. 7.4a–c) consists of a lattice of delicate slivers called **spicules**[15] (rods or spines) and **trabeculae**[16] (thin plates or beams). Although calcified and hard, it is named for its spongelike appearance. It is covered with endosteum and permeated by spaces filled with bone marrow. The matrix is arranged in lamellae like those of compact bone, but there are few osteons. Central canals are not needed here because no osteocyte is very far from the marrow. Spongy bone is well designed to impart strength to a bone while adding a minimum of weight. Its trabeculae aren't randomly arranged as they may seem at a glance, but develop along the bone's lines of stress **(fig. 7.5).** Spongy bone has much more surface area exposed to osteoclast action than compact bone does. Therefore, when osteoclasts resorb bone tissue, it comes largely from the spongy bone, as we see in osteoporosis (see Deeper Insight 7.4 at the end of this chapter).

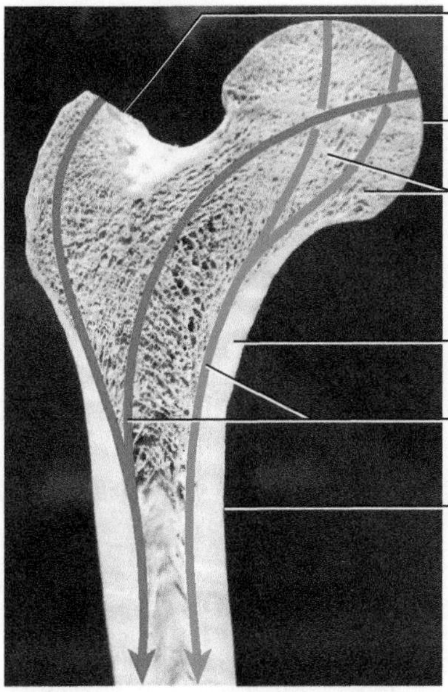

## 7.2e Bone Marrow

**Bone marrow** is a general term for soft tissue that occupies the marrow cavity of a long bone, the spaces amid the trabeculae of spongy bone, and the larger central canals. There are two kinds of marrow—red and yellow. We can best appreciate their differences by considering how marrow changes over a person's lifetime.

In a child, the marrow cavity of nearly every bone is filled with **red bone marrow (myeloid tissue).** This is often described as *hematopoietic*[17] *tissue* (he-MAT-o-poy-ET-ic)—tissue that produces blood cells—but it is actually composed of multiple tissues in a delicate but intricate arrangement, and is properly considered an organ unto itself. Its structure is further described in section 21.1d.

In adults, most of the red marrow is replaced by fatty **yellow bone marrow,** like the fat at the center of a ham bone. Red marrow is then limited to the skull, vertebrae, ribs, sternum, part of the pelvic (hip) girdle, and the proximal heads of the humerus and femur **(fig. 7.6).** Yellow bone marrow no longer produces blood, although in the event of severe or chronic anemia, it can transform back into red marrow and resume its hematopoietic function.

**BEFORE YOU GO ON**

Answer the following questions to test your understanding of the preceding section:

5. Suppose you had unlabeled electron micrographs of the four kinds of bone cells and their neighboring tissues. Name the four cells and explain how you could visually distinguish each one from the other three.
6. Name three organic components of the bone matrix.
7. What are the mineral crystals of bone called, and what are they made of?

[15]*spic* = dart, point; *ule* = little
[16]*trabe* = beam; *cul* = little
[17]*hemato* = blood; *poietic* = forming



**FIGURE 7.5 Spongy Bone Structure in Relation to Mechanical Stress.** In this frontal section of the femur, the trabeculae of spongy bone can be seen oriented along lines of mechanical stress applied by the weight of the body or the pull of a muscle.

B Christopher/Alamy Stock Photo

8. Sketch a cross section of an osteon and label its major parts.
9. What are the two kinds of bone marrow? What does *hematopoietic tissue* mean? Which type of bone marrow fits this description?

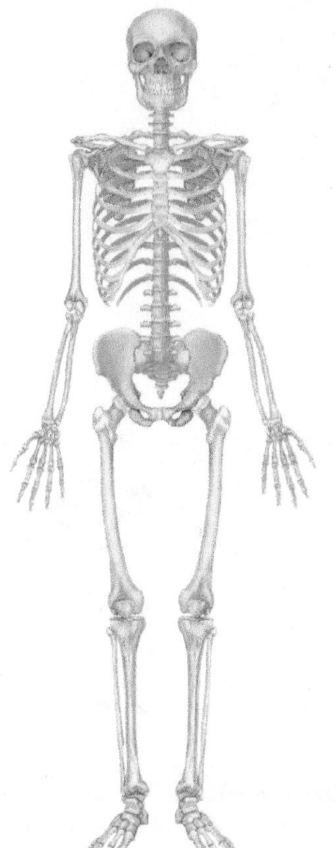

**FIGURE 7.6 Adult Distribution of Red and Yellow Bone Marrow.**

 *What would be the most accessible places to draw red bone marrow from an adult?*

## 7.3 Bone Development

**Expected Learning Outcomes**

When you have completed this section, you should be able to

a. describe two mechanisms of bone formation; and
b. explain how mature bone continues to grow and remodel itself.

The formation of bone is called **ossification** (OSS-ih-fih-CAY-shun) or **osteogenesis.** There are two methods of ossification—*intramembranous* and *endochondral*. Both begin with embryonic *mesenchyme* (MEZ-en-kime).

### 7.3a Intramembranous Ossification

**Intramembranous**[18] **ossification** (IN-tra-MEM-bra-nus) produces the flat bones of the skull, most of the clavicle (collarbone), and part of the mandible. Follow its stages in **figure 7.7** as you read the correspondingly numbered descriptions here.

(1) Mesenchyme first condenses into a soft sheet of tissue permeated with blood vessels—the *membrane* to which *intramembranous* refers. Mesenchymal cells line up along the blood vessels, become osteoblasts, and secrete a soft collagenous *osteoid*[19] *tissue (prebone)* (**fig. 7.8**) in the direction away from the vessel. Osteoid tissue resembles bone but is not yet calcified.

(2) Calcium phosphate and other minerals crystallize on the collagen fibers of the osteoid tissue and harden the matrix. Continued osteoid deposition and mineralization squeeze the blood vessels and future bone marrow into narrower and narrower spaces. As osteoblasts become trapped in their own hardening matrix, they become osteocytes.

(3) While the foregoing processes are occurring, more mesenchyme adjacent to the developing bone condenses and forms a fibrous periosteum on each surface. The spongy bone becomes a honeycomb of slender calcified trabeculae.

(4) At the surfaces, osteoblasts beneath the periosteum deposit layers of bone, fill in the spaces between trabeculae, and create a zone of compact bone on each side as well as thicken the bone overall. This process gives rise to the sandwichlike structure typical of a flat cranial bone—a layer of spongy bone between two layers of compact bone.

[18] *intra* = within; *membran* = membrane

[19] *oste* = bone; *oid* = like, resembling

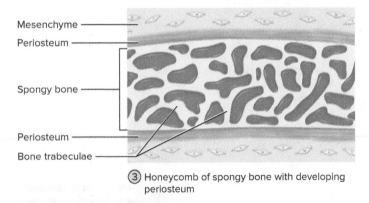

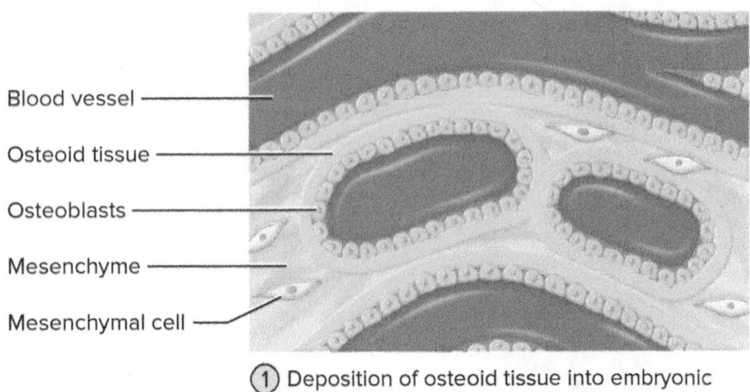


(1) Deposition of osteoid tissue into embryonic mesenchyme

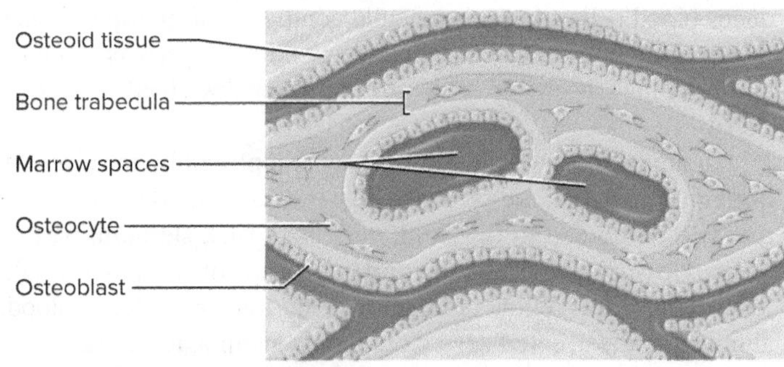


(2) Calcification of osteoid tissue and entrapment of osteocytes

Mesenchyme
Periosteum
Spongy bone
Periosteum
Bone trabeculae

(3) Honeycomb of spongy bone with developing periosteum

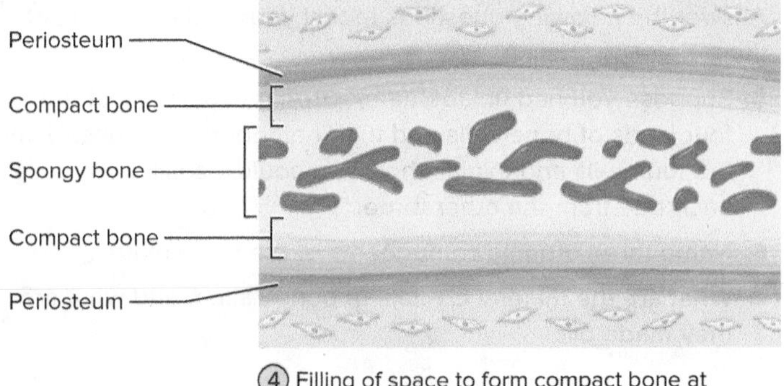


(4) Filling of space to form compact bone at surfaces, leaving spongy bone in middle

**FIGURE 7.7 Intramembranous Ossification.** The figures are drawn to different scales, with the highest magnification and detail at the beginning and backing off for a broader overview at the end of the process.

*With the aid of chapter 8, name at least two specific bones other than the clavicle that would form by this process.*

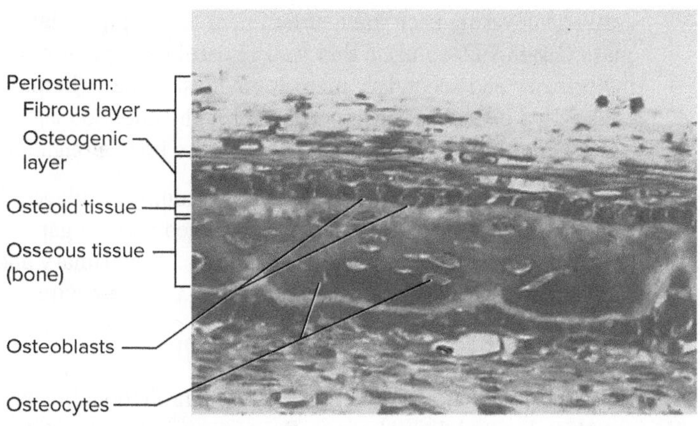


**FIGURE 7.8 Intramembranous Ossification in the Fetal Cranium.** Note the layers of osteoid tissue, osteoblasts, and fibrous periosteum on both sides of the bone.
Ken Saladin

Intramembranous ossification also plays an important role in the lifelong thickening, strengthening, and remodeling of the long bones discussed next. Throughout the skeleton, it is the method of depositing new tissue on the bone surface even past the age where the bones can no longer grow in length.

## 7.3b Endochondral Ossification

**Endochondral**[20] **ossification** (EN-doe-CON-drul) is a process in which a bone develops from a preexisting model composed of hyaline cartilage. It begins around the sixth week of fetal development and continues into a person's 20s. Most bones of the body develop in this way, including the vertebrae, ribs, sternum, scapula, pelvic girdle, and bones of the limbs.

**Figure 7.9** shows the following steps in endochondral ossification. This figure uses a metacarpal bone from the palmar region of the hand as an example because of its relative simplicity, having only one *epiphysial plate* (growth center). Many other bones develop in more complex ways, having an epiphysial plate at both ends or multiple plates at each end, but the basic process is the same.

1. Mesenchyme develops into a body of hyaline cartilage, covered with a fibrous perichondrium, in the location of a future bone. For a time, the perichondrium produces chondrocytes and the cartilage model grows in thickness.

2. In a **primary ossification center** near the middle of this cartilage, chondrocytes begin to inflate and die, while the thin walls between them calcify. The perichondrium stops producing chondrocytes and begins producing osteoblasts. These deposit a thin collar of bone around the middle of the cartilage model,

[20]*endo* = within; *chondr* = cartilage

Perichondrium
Hyaline cartilage
(1) Early cartilage model

Enlarging chondrocytes
Bony collar
Primary ossification center
Periosteum
(2) Formation of primary ossification center, bony collar, and periosteum

Secondary ossification center
Blood vessel
Primary marrow cavity
(3) Vascular invasion, formation of primary marrow cavity, and appearance of secondary ossification center

Secondary marrow cavity
Epiphysis
Metaphysis
Diaphysis
Secondary ossification center
(4) Bone at birth, with enlarged primary marrow cavity and appearance of secondary marrow cavity in one epiphysis

Epiphysial plate
Nutrient foramen
Compact bone
Metaphysis
Cartilage
(5) Bone of child, with epiphysial plate at distal end

Articular cartilage
Spongy bone
Epiphysial line
Periosteum
Marrow cavity
(6) Adult bone with a single marrow cavity and closed epiphysial plate

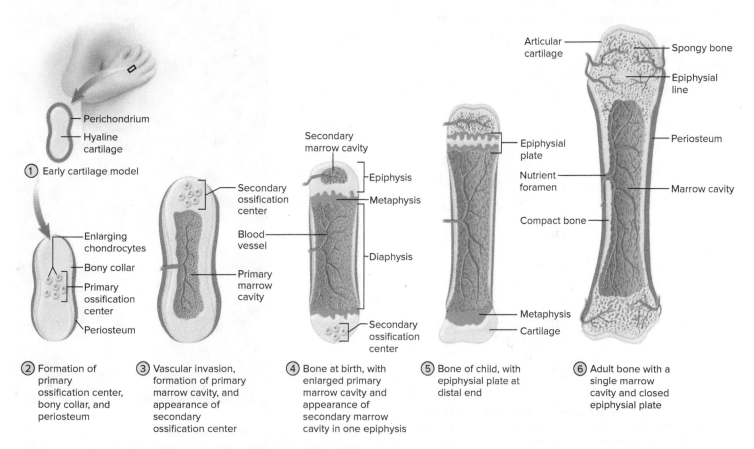

**FIGURE 7.9 Stages of Endochondral Ossification.** A metacarpal bone of the hand.

*With the aid of chapter 8, name at least two specific bones that would have two epiphysial plates (proximal and distal) at stage 5.*

reinforcing it like a napkin ring. The former perichondrium is now considered to be a periosteum. As chondrocytes in the middle of the model die, their lacunae merge into a single cavity.

3. Blood vessels invade the primary ossification center, delivering blood-borne osteoclasts that digest the calcified tissue. This creates a hollowed-out center called the **primary marrow cavity.** Osteoblasts also arrive and deposit layers of bone lining the cavity, thickening the shaft. As the bony collar under the periosteum thickens and elongates, a wave of cartilage death progresses toward each end of the bone. Osteoclasts in the marrow cavity follow this wave, dissolving calcified cartilage remnants and enlarging the marrow cavity of the diaphysis. The region of transition from cartilage to bone at each end of the primary marrow cavity is called a **metaphysis** (meh-TAFF-ih-sis). Soon, chondrocyte enlargement and death and vascular invasion occur in the epiphysis of the model as well, creating a **secondary ossification center.** In the metacarpal bones, as illustrated in the figure, this occurs in only one epiphysis. In longer bones of the arms, forearms, legs, and thighs, it occurs at both ends.

4. The secondary ossification center hollows out by the same process as the diaphysis, generating a **secondary marrow cavity** in the epiphysis. This cavity expands outward from the center in all directions. At the time of birth, the bone typically looks like step 4 in the figure. In bones with two secondary ossification centers, one center lags behind the other, so at birth there is a secondary marrow cavity at one end while chondrocyte growth has just begun at the other. The joints of the limbs are still cartilaginous at birth, much as they are in the 12-week fetus in **figure 7.10.**

5. During infancy and childhood, the epiphyses fill with spongy bone. Cartilage is then limited to the articular cartilage covering each joint surface, and to an **epiphysial plate** (EP-ih-FIZ-ee-ul), a thin wall of cartilage separating the primary and secondary marrow cavities at one or both ends of the bone. The plate persists through childhood and adolescence and serves as a growth zone for bone elongation.

6. By the late teens to early twenties, all remaining cartilage in the epiphysial plate is generally consumed and the gap between the epiphysis and diaphysis closes. The primary and secondary marrow cavities then unite into a single cavity.

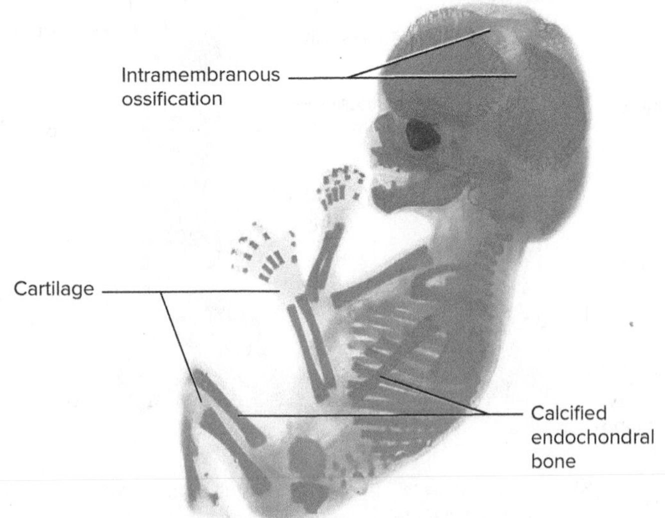


**FIGURE 7.10 The Fetal Skeleton at 12 Weeks.** The red-stained regions are calcified at this age, whereas the elbow, wrist, knee, and ankle joints appear translucent because they are still cartilaginous.

? *Why are the joints of an infant weaker than those of an older child?*

Biophoto Associates/Science Source

## 7.3c Bone Growth and Remodeling

Ossification doesn't end at birth, but continues throughout life with the growth and remodeling of bones. Bones grow in two directions: length and width.

### Bone Elongation

To understand growth in length, we must return to the epiphysial plates mentioned earlier (see fig. 7.9, step 5). From infancy through adolescence, an epiphysial plate is present at one or both ends of a long bone, at the junction between the diaphysis and epiphysis. On X-rays, it appears as a translucent line across the end of a bone, since it is not yet ossified (**fig. 7.11;** compare the X-ray of an adult hand in fig. 8.35). The epiphysial plate is a region of

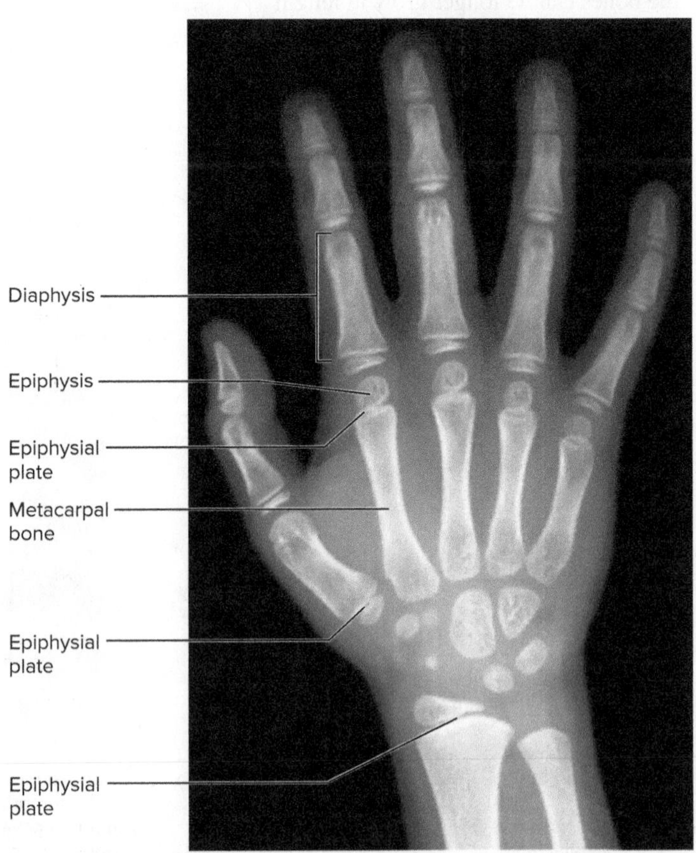


**FIGURE 7.11 X-Ray of a Child's Hand.** The cartilaginous epiphysial plates are evident at the ends of the long bones. Long bones of the hand and fingers develop only one epiphysial plate. Notice that the wrist is still largely cartilaginous (X-ray translucent).

Puwadol Jaturawutthichai/Shutterstock

transition from cartilage to bone, and functions as a growth zone where the bones elongate. Growth here is responsible for a person's increase in height.

The epiphysial plate consists of typical hyaline cartilage in the middle, with a transitional zone on each side where cartilage is being replaced by bone. The transitional zone, facing the marrow cavity, is called the **metaphysis** (meh-TAF-ih-sis). In figure 7.9, step 4, the cartilage is the blue region and each metaphysis is violet. **Figure 7.12** shows the histological structure of the metaphysis and the following steps in the replacement of cartilage by bone.

1. **Zone of reserve cartilage.** This region, farthest from the marrow cavity, consists of typical hyaline cartilage with resting chondrocytes, not yet showing any sign of transformation into bone.
2. **Zone of cell proliferation.** A little closer to the marrow cavity, chondrocytes multiply and arrange themselves into longitudinal columns of flattened lacunae.
3. **Zone of cell hypertrophy.** Next, the chondrocytes cease to multiply and begin to hypertrophy (enlarge), much like they do in the primary ossification center of the fetus. The walls of matrix between lacunae become very thin.
4. **Zone of calcification.** Minerals are deposited in the matrix between the columns of lacunae and calcify the cartilage. These are not the permanent mineral deposits of bone, but only a temporary support for the cartilage that would otherwise soon be weakened by the breakdown of the enlarged lacunae.
5. **Zone of bone deposition.** Within each column, the walls between the lacunae break down and the chondrocytes die. This converts each column into a longitudinal channel (clear spaces in the figure), which is immediately invaded by blood vessels and marrow from the marrow cavity. Osteoblasts line up along the walls of these channels and begin depositing concentric lamellae of matrix, while osteoclasts dissolve the temporarily calcified cartilage.

The process of bone deposition in zone 5 creates a region of spongy bone at the end of the marrow cavity facing the metaphysis. This spongy bone remains for life, although with extensive lifelong

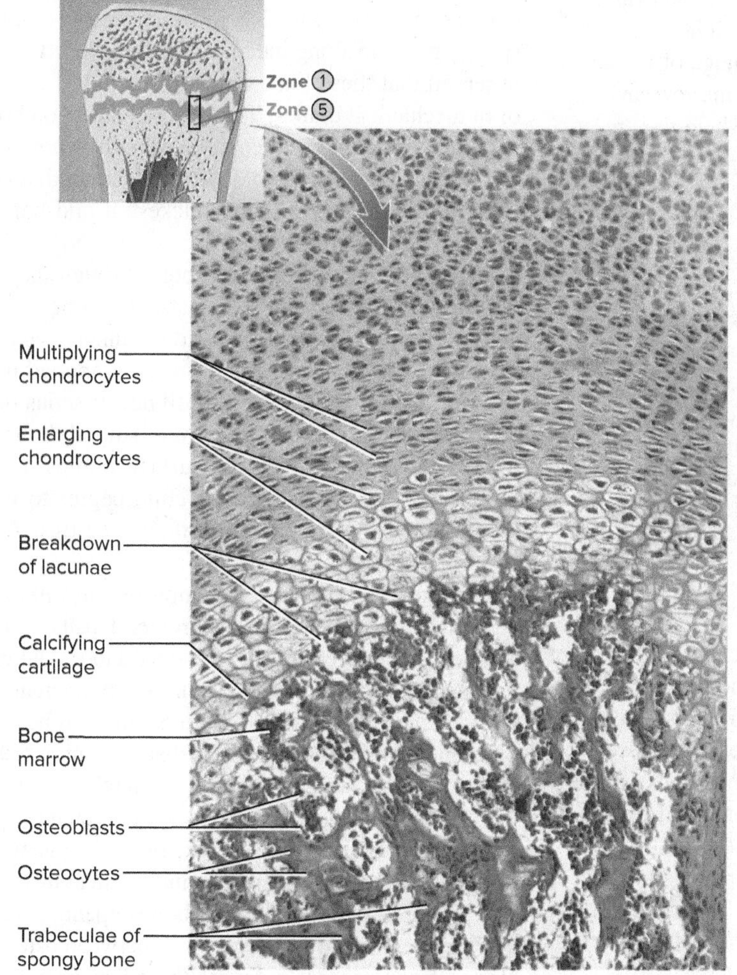


FIGURE 7.12 **Zones of the Metaphysis.** This micrograph shows the transition from cartilage to bone in the growth zone of a long bone.

? *Which two zones in this figure account for a child's growth in height?*

Victor Eroschenko

remodeling. But around the perimeter of the marrow cavity, continuing ossification converts this spongy bone to compact bone. Osteoblasts lining the aforementioned channels deposit layer after layer of bone matrix, so the channel grows narrower and narrower. These layers become the concentric lamellae of an osteon. Finally only a slender channel persists, the central canal of a new osteon. Osteoblasts trapped in the matrix become osteocytes.

**APPLY WHAT YOU KNOW**

*In a given osteon, which lamellae are the oldest—those immediately adjacent to the central canal or those around the perimeter of the osteon? Explain your answer.*

How does a child or adolescent grow in height? Chondrocyte multiplication in zone 2 and hypertrophy in zone 3 continually push the zone of reserve cartilage (1) toward the ends of the bone, so the bone elongates. In the lower limbs, this process causes a person to grow in height, while bones of the upper limbs grow proportionately.

Thus, bone elongation is really a result of cartilage growth. Cartilage growth from within, by the multiplication of chondrocytes and deposition of new matrix in the interior, is called **interstitial**[21] **growth.** The most common form of dwarfism results from a failure of cartilage growth in the long bones (see Deeper Insight 7.2).

In the late teens to early twenties, all the cartilage of the epiphysial plate is depleted. The primary and secondary marrow cavities now unite into one cavity. The junctional region where they meet is filled with spongy bone, and the site of the original epiphysial plate is marked with a line of slightly denser spongy bone called the **epiphysial line** (see figs. 7.1; 7.5; and 7.9, step 6). Often a delicate ridge on the bone surface marks the location of this line. When the epiphysial plate is depleted, we say that the epiphyses have "closed" because no gap between the epiphysis and diaphysis is visible on an X-ray. Once the epiphyses have all closed in the lower limbs, a person can grow no taller. The epiphysial plates close at different ages in different bones and in different regions of the same bone. The processes and rates of elongation and epiphysial closure are influenced especially by growth hormone and sex steroids (see section 7.4d). The state of closure in various bones of a subadult skeleton is often used in forensic science to estimate the individual's "bone age" at death.

## Bone Widening and Thickening

Bones also continually grow in diameter and thickness. This involves a process called **appositional growth,**[22] the deposition of new tissue at the surface. Cartilages grow by both interstitial and appositional growth. In bone, however, osteocytes embedded in calcified matrix have little room to spare for the deposition of more matrix internally. Bone is therefore limited to appositional growth.

Appositional growth occurs by intramembranous ossification at the bone surface. Osteoblasts in the inner layer of periosteum deposit osteoid tissue on the bone surface, calcify it, and become trapped in it as osteocytes—much like the process in figure 7.8. They lay down matrix in layers parallel to the surface, not in cylindrical osteons like those deeper in the bone. This process produces the surface layers of bone called *circumferential lamellae,* described earlier. As a bone increases in diameter, its marrow cavity also widens. This is achieved by osteoclasts of the endosteum dissolving tissue on the inner bone surface. Thus, flat bones develop by intramembranous ossificaton alone, whereas long bones develop by a combination of the intramembranous and endochondral methods.

## Bone Remodeling

In addition to their growth, bones are continually remodeled throughout life by the absorption of old bone and deposition of new. This process replaces about 10% of the skeletal tissue per year. It releases minerals into the blood for uses elsewhere; reshapes bones in response to use and disuse; and repairs microfractures, preventing them from developing into catastrophic bone failure similar to metal fatigue.

**Wolff's**[23] **law of bone** states that the architecture of a bone is determined by the mechanical stresses placed upon it, and the bone thereby adapts to withstand them. Wolff's law is a fine example of the complementarity of form and function, showing that the form of a bone is shaped by its functional experience. It is admirably demonstrated by figure 7.5, in which we see that the trabeculae of spongy bone lie along the lines of stress placed on the femur. Wolff observed that these lines were similar to the ones engineers knew of in mechanical cranes. The effect of stress on bone development is quite evident in elite tennis players, in whom the cortical bone of the racket arm is up to 35% thicker than that of the other arm. Long bones of the limbs are thickest at midshaft, where they are subjected to the greatest stress.

Bone remodeling comes about through the collaborative action of osteoblasts and osteoclasts. If a bone is little used, osteoclasts remove matrix and get rid of unnecessary mass. If a bone is heavily used or stress is consistently applied to a particular region of a bone, osteoblasts deposit new osseous tissue and thicken it. Consequently, the comparatively smooth bones of an infant or toddler develop a variety of surface bumps, ridges, and spines (described in chapter 8) as the child begins to walk. The greater trochanter of the femur, for example (see figs. 7.5 and 8.39), is a massive outgrowth of bone stimulated by the pull of tendons from several powerful hip muscles employed in walking.

On average, bones have a greater density and mass in athletes and people engaged in heavy manual labor than they do in sedentary people. Anthropologists who study ancient skeletal remains use evidence of this sort to help distinguish between members of different social classes, such as distinguishing aristocrats from laborers. Even in studying modern skeletal remains, as in investigating a suspicious death, Wolff's law comes into play as the bones give evidence of a person's sex, race, height, weight, nutritional status, work or exercise habits, and medical history.

The orderly remodeling of bone depends on a precise balance between deposition and resorption, between osteoblasts and osteoclasts. If one process outpaces the other, or both processes occur

[21] *inter* = between; *stit* = to place, stand

[22] *ap* = *ad* = to, near; *posit* = to place

[23] Julius Wolff (1836–1902), German anatomist and surgeon

## DEEPER INSIGHT 7.2
### CLINICAL APPLICATION

### Achondroplastic Dwarfism

*Achondroplastic*[24] *dwarfism* (a-con-dro-PLAS-tic) is a condition in which the long bones of the limbs stop growing in childhood, while the growth of other bones is unaffected. As a result, a person has a short stature but a normal-size head and trunk **(fig. 7.13).** As its name implies, achondroplastic dwarfism results from a failure of cartilage growth—specifically, failure of the chondrocytes in zones 2 and 3 of the metaphysis to multiply and enlarge. This is different from *pituitary dwarfism,* in which a deficiency of growth hormone stunts the growth of all of the bones, and a person has short stature but normal proportions throughout the skeletal system.

Achondroplastic dwarfism results from a spontaneous mutation that can arise any time DNA is replicated. Two people of normal height with no family history of dwarfism can therefore have a child with achondroplastic dwarfism. The mutant allele is dominant, so the offspring of a heterozygous achondroplastic dwarf have at least a 50% chance of exhibiting dwarfism, depending on the genotype of the other parent. Persons homozygous for the trait (those who inherit it from both parents) are usually stillborn or die soon after birth.

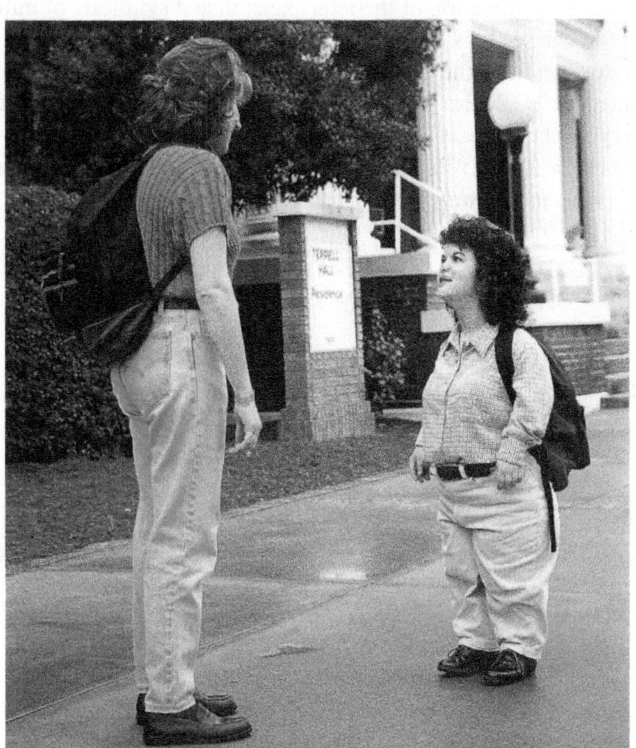

**FIGURE 7.13 Achondroplastic Dwarfism.** The student on the right, pictured with her roommate of normal height, is an achondroplastic dwarf with a height of about 122 cm (48 in.). Her parents were of normal height. Note the normal proportion of head to trunk but shortening of the limbs.

Joe DeGrandis/McGraw-Hill Education

[24]*a* = without; *chondr* = cartilage; *plast* = growth

too rapidly, various bone deformities, developmental abnormalities, and other disorders occur, such as *osteitis deformans* (Paget disease), *osteogenesis imperfecta* (brittle bone disease), and *osteoporosis* (see table 7.2 and Deeper Insight 7.4).

**BEFORE YOU GO ON**

Answer the following questions to test your understanding of the preceding section:

**10.** Describe the stages of intramembranous ossification. Name a bone that forms in this way.

**11.** Describe how a cartilage model transforms into a long bone in endochondral ossification.

**12.** Describe the five zones of a metaphysis and the major distinctions between them.

**13.** How does Wolff's law explain some of the structural differences between the bones of a young child and the bones of a young adult?

## 7.4 Physiology of Osseous Tissue

**Expected Learning Outcomes**

When you have completed this section, you should be able to

a. describe the processes by which minerals are added to and removed from bone tissue;

b. discuss the role of the bones in regulating blood calcium and phosphate levels; and

c. name the main hormones that regulate bone physiology, and describe their effects.

Even after a bone is fully formed, it remains a metabolically active organ with many roles to play. Not only is it involved in its own maintenance, growth, and remodeling, but it also exerts a profound influence on the rest of the body by exchanging minerals with the tissue fluid. Disturbances of calcium homeostasis in the skeleton can disrupt the functioning of other organ systems, especially the nervous and muscular systems. For reasons explained later, such disturbances can even cause death by suffocation.

### 7.4a Mineral Deposition and Resorption

**Mineral deposition (mineralization)** is a crystallization process in which calcium, phosphate, and other ions are taken from the blood plasma and deposited in bone tissue, mainly as needlelike crystals of hydroxyapatite. Deposition begins in fetal ossification and continues throughout life.

Osteoblasts begin the process by laying down collagen fibers in a helical pattern along the length of the osteon. These fibers then become encrusted with minerals that harden the matrix. The first few hydroxyapatite crystals to form act as "seed crystals" that attract more calcium and phosphate from solution. The more hydroxyapatite that forms, the more it attracts additional minerals from the tissue fluid, until the matrix is thoroughly calcified.

▶▶▶ **APPLY WHAT YOU KNOW**

*What positive feedback process can you recognize in bone deposition?*

Abnormal calcification of tissues, called **ectopic**[25] **ossification,** sometimes occurs in the lungs, brain, eyes, muscles, tendons, arteries, and other organs. One example of this is arteriosclerosis, or "hardening of the arteries," which results from calcification of the arterial walls. A calcified mass in an otherwise soft organ such as the lungs is called a **calculus.**[26]

**Mineral resorption** is the process of dissolving bone. It releases minerals into the blood and makes them available for other uses. Resorption is carried out by osteoclasts. They have surface receptors for calcium and respond to falling levels of calcium in the tissue fluid. Hydrogen pumps in the ruffled border of the osteoclast secrete hydrogen ions into the tissue fluid, and chloride ions follow by electrical attraction. The space between the osteoclast and the bone thus becomes filled with concentrated hydrochloric acid with a pH of about 4. The acid dissolves the bone minerals. The osteoclast also secretes an acid-tolerant enzyme (protease) that digests the collagen of the bone matrix.

When orthodontic appliances (braces) are used to reposition teeth, a tooth moves because osteoclasts dissolve bone ahead of the tooth (where the appliance creates greater pressure of the tooth against the bone) and osteoblasts deposit bone in the low-pressure zone behind it.

[25]*ec* = out of; *top* = place
[26]*calc* = stone; *ulus* = little

## 7.4b Calcium Homeostasis

The adult body contains about 1,100 g of calcium, with 99% of it in the bones. Calcium is needed for much more than bone structure. It also plays roles in communication among neurons and in muscle contraction, blood clotting, and exocytosis. Calcium is deposited in the skeleton when the supply is ample and withdrawn when needed for these other purposes. The skeleton exchanges about 18% of its calcium with the blood each year.

This exchange is tightly regulated by hormones to maintain a blood calcium concentration of 9.2 to 10.4 mg/dL. This is a narrow margin of safety. A calcium deficiency, called **hypocalcemia**[27] (HY-po-cal-SEE-me-uh), causes excessive excitability of the nervous system and can lead to muscle tremors, spasms, or tetany—inability of the muscles to relax. Tetany of the muscles of the larynx can cause death by suffocation. A calcium excess, called **hypercalcemia,**[28] makes nerve and muscle cells less excitable than normal. This can be manifested in nervous system depression, emotional disturbances, muscle weakness, sluggish reflexes, and sometimes cardiac arrest.

Hypercalcemia is rare, but hypocalcemia can result from a wide variety of causes including vitamin D deficiency, diarrhea, thyroid tumors, or underactive parathyroid glands. Pregnancy and lactation put women at risk of hypocalcemia because of the calcium demanded by ossification of the fetal skeleton and synthesis of milk.

You can see how critical blood calcium level is, but what causes it to deviate from the norm, and how does the body correct such imbalances? Calcium homeostasis depends on a balance between dietary intake, urinary and fecal losses, and exchanges with the osseous tissue **(fig. 7.14).** It is regulated by three hormones: *calcitriol, calcitonin,* and *parathyroid hormone.*

[27]*hypo* = below normal; *calc* = calcium; *emia* = blood condition
[28]*hyper* = above normal; *calc* = calcium; *emia* = blood condition

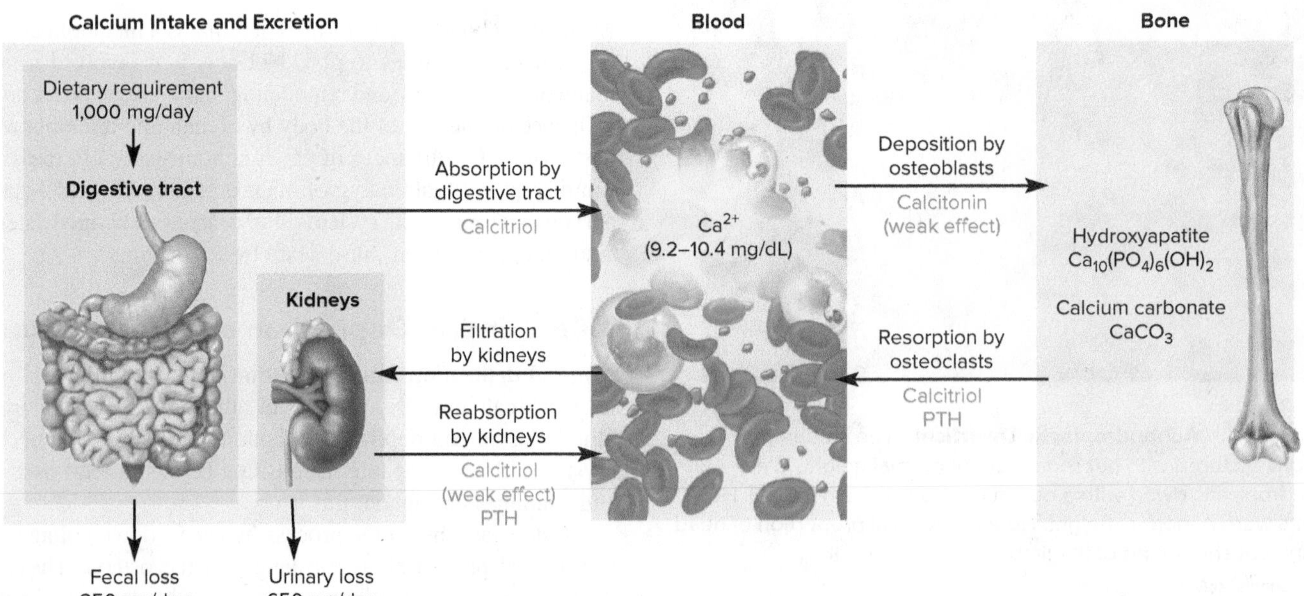


FIGURE 7.14 **Hormonal Control of Calcium Balance.** The central panel represents the blood reservoir of calcium and shows its normal (safe) range. Calcitriol and PTH regulate calcium exchanges between the blood and the small intestine and kidneys (left). Calcitonin, calcitriol, and PTH regulate calcium exchanges between blood and bone (right).

## DEEPER INSIGHT 7.3

### CLINICAL APPLICATION

### *Rickets and Osteomalacia*

Rickets is a childhood disease in which the bones are soft and deformed as a result of vitamin D and calcium deficiency. It is characterized by fragile bones, bone pain, and frequent fractures; deformity of the chest, pelvis, and spine; and bowed legs **(fig. 7.15).** It is one of the most common childhood diseases of developing countries, but usually preventable by exposure to sunlight. Even 15 minutes per day is usually enough for adequate vitamin D synthesis. Vitamin D can also be obtained from fortified milk and dairy products, eggs, oily fish, and some mushrooms.

Rickets is common in areas wracked with warfare and famine. It also develops in infants who are breast-fed and kept from the sun without receiving supplemental vitamin D. In London during the early 1800s, it occurred in 80% to 90% of children who were kept indoors because of the heavy smog in the air and who were often exploited for long hours of factory work. The United States mandated the addition of vitamin D to milk in 1930 and outlawed child labor in 1937, greatly reducing rickets and other health problems. Yet rickets is increasing again as children spend more time indoors and even because of the increased use of sunscreen. The highest incidence today is in the Mideast, owing to covering of most or all of the body for religious or other cultural reasons.

Osteomalacia is a similar bone-softening, vitamin D deficiency disease of adults. It is especially common in nursing home residents and the homebound elderly. It often begins with lumbar aches and pains and progresses to bone and joint pain, muscle weakness, difficulty walking and stair climbing, loss of height because of vertebral compression, a waddling gait due to spinal deformity, and pathological bone fractures.

FIGURE 7.15 **Rickets in a Boy of Eastern Kenya.**

Jeff Rotman / Alamy Stock Photo

## Calcitriol

**Calcitriol** (CAL-sih-TRY-ol) is a form of vitamin D produced by the sequential action of the skin, liver, and kidneys **(fig. 7.16):**

1. Epidermal keratinocytes use ultraviolet radiation from sunlight to convert a steroid, 7-dehydrocholesterol, to previtamin $D_3$. Over another 3 days, the warmth of sunlight on the skin further converts this to vitamin $D_3$ *(cholecalciferol),* and a transport protein carries this to the bloodstream.
2. The liver adds a hydroxyl group, converting it to *calcidiol.*
3. The kidneys then add another hydroxyl group, converting calcidiol to calcitriol, the most active form of vitamin D.

Calcitriol behaves as a hormone—a blood-borne chemical messenger from one organ to another. It is called a vitamin only because it is added to the diet, mainly in fortified milk, as a safeguard for people who don't get enough sunlight to initiate adequate synthesis in the skin.

The principal function of calcitriol is to raise the blood calcium concentration. It does this in three ways (fig. 7.14), especially the first of these:

1. It increases calcium absorption by the small intestine, using mechanisms detailed in chapter 25 (see section 25.6f).
2. It increases calcium resorption from the skeleton. Calcitriol binds to osteoblasts, which then stimulate stem cells to differentiate into osteoclasts. The new osteoclasts liberate calcium and phosphate ions from bone.
3. It weakly promotes the reabsorption of calcium ions by the kidneys, so less calcium is lost in the urine.

Although calcitriol promotes bone resorption, it is also necessary for bone deposition. Without it, calcium and phosphate levels in the blood are too low for normal deposition. The result is a softness of the bones called **rickets** in children and **osteomalacia**[29] in adults (see Deeper Insight 7.3).

## Calcitonin

**Calcitonin** is produced by *parafollicular (clear) cells* of the thyroid gland (see fig. 17.9). It is secreted when the blood calcium concentration rises too high, and it lowers the concentration by two principal mechanisms (figs. 7.14 and **7.17a**):

1. **Osteoclast inhibition.** Within 15 minutes after it is secreted, calcitonin reduces osteoclast activity by as much as 70%, so osteoclasts liberate less calcium from the skeleton.
2. **Osteoblast stimulation.** Within an hour, calcitonin increases the number and activity of osteoblasts, which deposit calcium into the skeleton.

Calcitonin plays an important role in children but has only a weak effect in most adults. The osteoclasts of children are highly active in skeletal remodeling and release 5 g or more of calcium into the blood each day. By inhibiting this, calcitonin

[29] *osteo* = bone; *malacia* = softening

7-dehydrocholesterol

Ultraviolet light

Vitamin $D_3$ (cholecalciferol)

Calcidiol

Calcitriol

Bone resorption

Reduced excretion of $Ca^{2+}$

Absorption of $Ca^{2+}$ and phosphate

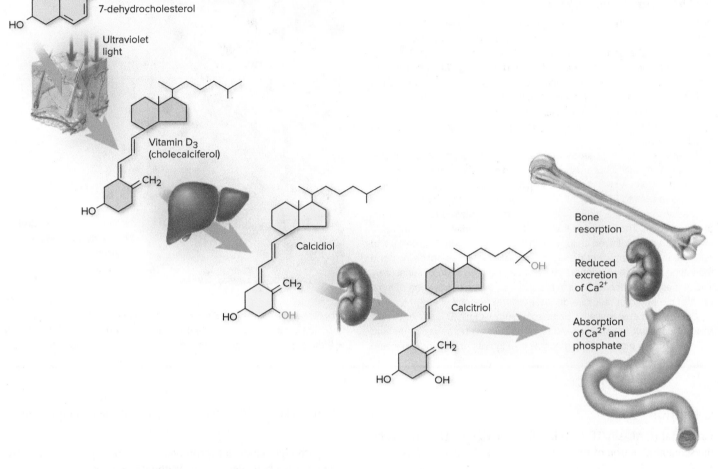

**FIGURE 7.16 Calcitriol (Vitamin D) Synthesis and Action.** See text for explanation.

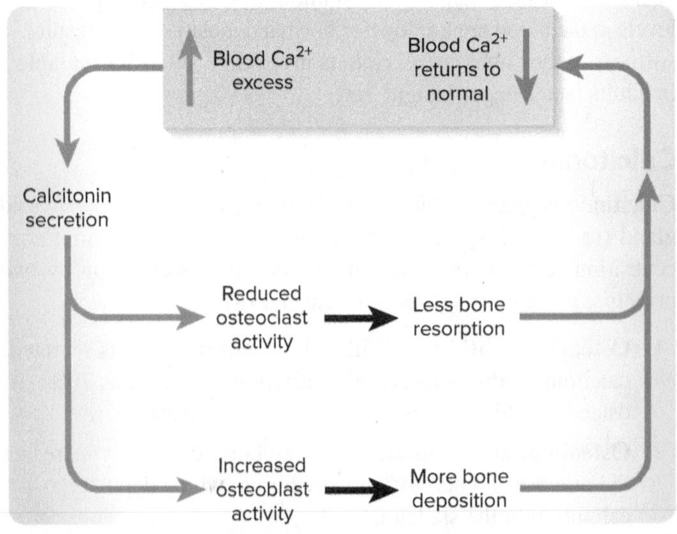


**(a) Correction for hypercalcemia**

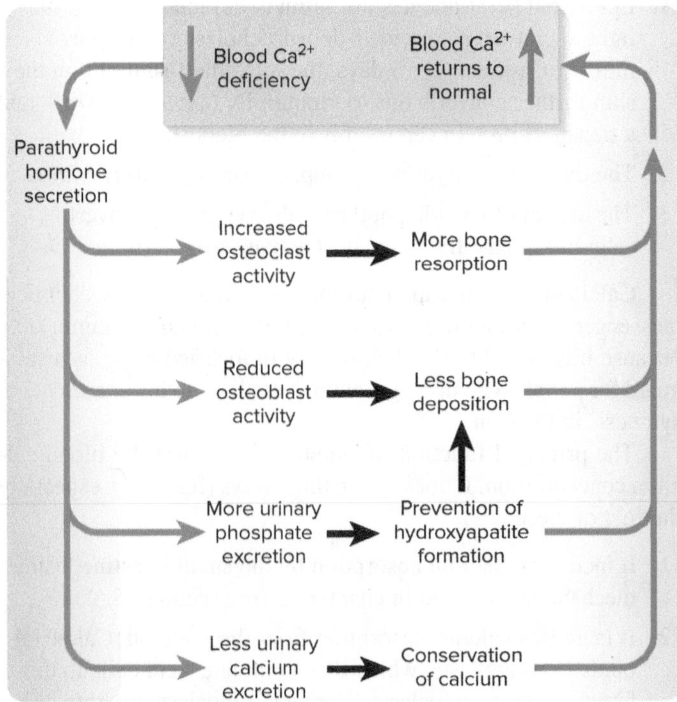


**(b) Correction for hypocalcemia**

**FIGURE 7.17 Negative Feedback Loops in Calcium Homeostasis.** (a) The correction of hypercalcemia by calcitonin. (b) The correction of hypocalcemia by parathyroid hormone.

can significantly lower the blood calcium level in children. In adults, however, the osteoclasts release only about 0.8 g of calcium per day. Calcitonin cannot change adult blood calcium very much by suppressing this lesser contribution. Calcitonin deficiency isn't known to cause any adult disease. Calcitonin may, however, help to maintain bone density in pregnant and lactating women.

### Parathyroid Hormone

**Parathyroid hormone (PTH)** is secreted by the parathyroid glands, which adhere to the posterior surface of the thyroid gland. These glands release PTH when blood calcium is low. A mere 1% drop in the calcium level doubles PTH secretion. PTH raises the calcium level by four mechanisms (figs. 7.14 and **7.17b**):

1. It binds to receptors on the osteoblasts, which in turn stimulate the osteoclast population and promote bone resorption.
2. It promotes calcium reabsorption by the kidneys, so less calcium is lost in the urine.
3. It promotes the final step of calcitriol synthesis in the kidneys, thus enhancing the calcium-raising effect of calcitriol.
4. It inhibits collagen synthesis by osteoblasts, thus inhibiting bone deposition.

## 7.4c Phosphate Homeostasis

The average adult has 500 to 800 g of phosphorus, of which 85% to 90% is in the bones. Phosphate is required not only for bone strength but also as a component of DNA, RNA, ATP, phospholipids, and other compounds. Plasma phosphorus concentration ranges from 3.5 to 4.0 mg/dL. Its level is not as tightly regulated as calcium. Nor, apparently, does it need to be; changes in plasma phosphate level are not associated with any immediate functional disorder. Calcitriol raises the phosphate level by promoting its absorption from the diet by the small intestine. This makes sense, because one effect of calcitriol is to promote bone deposition, and that requires both calcium and phosphate. Parathyroid hormone, on the other hand, lowers the blood phosphate level by promoting its urinary excretion.

**▶▶▶APPLY WHAT YOU KNOW**

*While raising the blood calcium level, PTH lowers the phosphate level. Explain why this is important for achieving the purpose of PTH.*

## 7.4d Other Factors Affecting Bone

At least 20 more hormones, growth factors, and vitamins affect osseous tissue in complex ways that are still not well understood **(table 7.1).** Bone growth is especially rapid in

**TABLE 7.1 Agents Affecting Calcium and Bone Metabolism**

| Name | Effect |
|---|---|
| **Hormones** | |
| Calcitonin | Promotes mineralization and lowers blood $Ca^{2+}$ concentration in children, but usually has little effect in adults; may prevent bone loss in pregnant and lactating women |
| Calcitriol (vitamin D) | Promotes intestinal absorption of $Ca^{2+}$ and phosphate; reduces urinary excretion of both; promotes both resorption and mineralization; stimulates osteoclast activity |
| Cortisol | Inhibits osteoclast activity, but if secreted in excess (Cushing disease), can cause osteoporosis by reducing bone deposition (inhibiting cell division and protein synthesis), inhibiting growth hormone secretion, and stimulating osteoclasts to resorb bone |
| Estrogen | Stimulates osteoblasts and adolescent growth; prevents osteoporosis |
| Growth hormone | Stimulates bone elongation and cartilage proliferation at epiphysial plate; increases urinary excretion of $Ca^{2+}$ but also increases intestinal $Ca^{2+}$ absorption, which compensates for the loss |
| Insulin | Stimulates bone formation; significant bone loss occurs in untreated diabetes mellitus |
| Parathyroid hormone | Indirectly activates osteoclasts, which resorb bone and raise blood $Ca^{2+}$ concentration; inhibits urinary $Ca^{2+}$ excretion; promotes calcitriol synthesis |
| Testosterone | Stimulates osteoblasts and promotes protein synthesis, thus promoting adolescent growth and epiphysial closure |
| Thyroid hormone | Essential to bone growth; enhances synthesis and effects of growth hormone, but excesses can cause hypercalcemia, increased $Ca^{2+}$ excretion in urine, and osteoporosis |
| **Growth Factors** | At least 12 hormonelike substances produced in bone itself that stimulate neighboring bone cells, promote collagen synthesis, stimulate epiphysial growth, and produce many other effects |
| **Vitamins** | |
| Vitamin A | Promotes glycosaminoglycan (chondroitin sulfate) synthesis |
| Vitamin C (ascorbic acid) | Required for collagen synthesis, bone growth, and fracture repair |
| Vitamin D | Normally functions as a hormone (see calcitriol) |

puberty and adolescence, when surges of growth hormone, estrogen, and testosterone promote ossification. These hormones stimulate rapid multiplication of osteogenic cells, matrix deposition by osteoblasts, and multiplication and hypertrophy of the chondrocytes in the metaphyses. Adolescent girls grow faster than boys and attain their full height earlier, not only because they begin puberty earlier but also because estrogen has a stronger effect than testosterone. Since males grow for a longer time, however, they usually grow taller. Sex steroids eventually deplete the cartilage of the epiphysial plates, bring about closure of the epiphyses, and put an end to one's growth in height. A deficiency or excess of these steroids can therefore cause abnormalities ranging from stunted growth to very tall stature. The use of anabolic steroids by adolescent athletes can cause premature closure and result in abnormally short adult stature (see Deeper Insight 2.6). The excessive consumption of cola (more than three 12-ounce servings per day) is associated with loss of bone density in women, but not in men. The effect is thought to be due to the phosphoric acid in cola, which binds intestinal calcium and interferes with its absorption. Other soft drinks don't contain phosphoric acid or affect bone density.

**BEFORE YOU GO ON**

Answer the following questions to test your understanding of the preceding section:

14. Describe the role of collagen and seed crystals in bone mineralization.
15. Why is it important to regulate blood calcium concentration within such a narrow range?
16. What effect does calcitonin have on blood calcium concentration, and how does it produce this effect? Answer the same questions for parathyroid hormone.
17. How is vitamin D synthesized, and what effect does it have on blood calcium concentration?

## 7.5 Bone Disorders

**Expected Learning Outcomes**

When you have completed this section, you should be able to

a. name and describe several bone diseases;
b. name and describe the types of fractures;
c. explain how a fracture is repaired; and
d. discuss some clinical treatments for fractures and other skeletal disorders.

Most people probably give little thought to their skeletal systems unless they break a bone. This section describes bone fractures, their healing, and their treatment, followed by a summary of other bone diseases. Bone disorders are among the concerns of **orthopedics**,[30] a branch of medicine that originated as the treatment of skeletal deformities in children. It is now much more extensive and deals with the prevention and correction of injuries and disorders of the bones, joints, and muscles. It includes the design of artificial joints and limbs and the treatment of athletic injuries.

### 7.5a Fractures and Their Repair

There are multiple ways of classifying bone fractures. A **stress fracture** is a break caused by abnormal trauma to a bone, such as fractures incurred in falls, athletics, auto accidents, and military combat. A **pathological fracture** is a break in a bone weakened by some other disease, such as bone cancer or osteoporosis, usually caused by a stress that would not normally fracture a bone. Fractures are also classified according to the direction of the fracture line, whether the skin is broken, and whether a bone is merely cracked or broken into separate pieces. For example, a *nondisplaced* fracture is one in which the bone pieces remain in proper anatomical alignment, whereas a *displaced* fracture is one in which at least one piece is shifted out of alignment with the other **(fig. 7.18a, b).** A *comminuted* fracture is one in which a bone is broken into three or more pieces **(fig. 7.18c).** A *greenstick* fracture is one in which the bone is incompletely broken on one side but merely bent on the opposite side **(fig. 7.18d),** the way a green twig breaks only partially and not into separate pieces. Several other types of fractures are routinely taught in clinical and first aid courses.

#### The Healing of Fractures

An uncomplicated fracture heals in about 8 to 12 weeks, but complex fractures take longer and all fractures heal more slowly in older people. The healing process occurs in the following stages **(fig. 7.19):**

1. **Formation of hematoma and granulation tissue.** A bone fracture severs blood vessels of the bone and periosteum, causing bleeding and the formation of a blood clot *(fracture hematoma).* Blood capillaries soon grow into the clot, while fibroblasts, macrophages, osteoclasts, and osteogenic cells invade the tissue from both the periosteal and medullary sides of the fracture. Osteogenic cells become very abundant within 48 hours of the injury. All of this capillary and cellular invasion converts the blood clot to a soft fibrous mass called **granulation tissue.**

2. **Formation of a soft callus.**[31] Fibroblasts deposit collagen in the granulation tissue, while some osteogenic cells become chondroblasts and produce patches of fibrocartilage called the **soft callus.**

[30] *ortho* = straight; *ped* = child, foot
[31] *call* = hard, tough

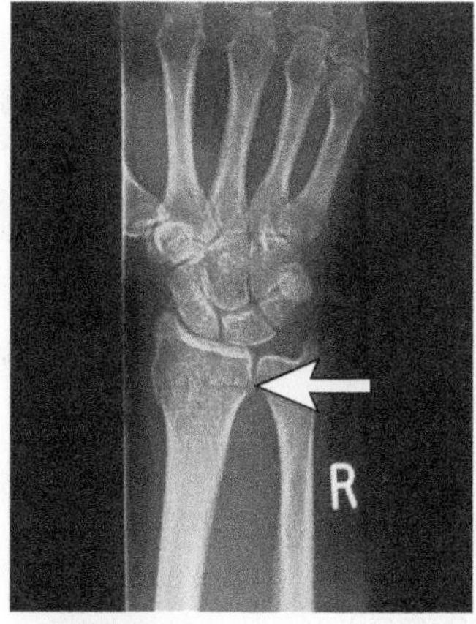


(a) Nondisplaced

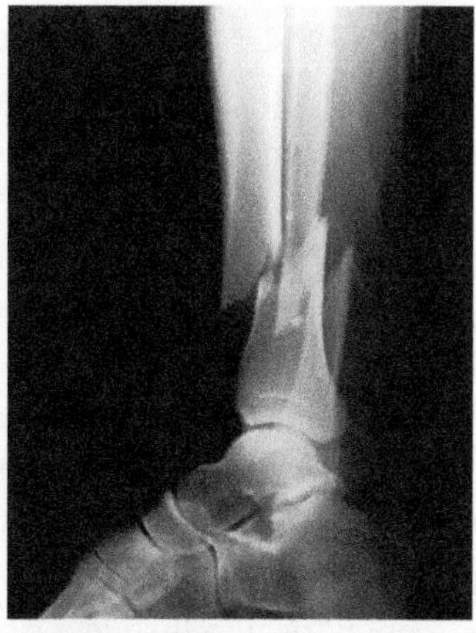

(b) Displaced

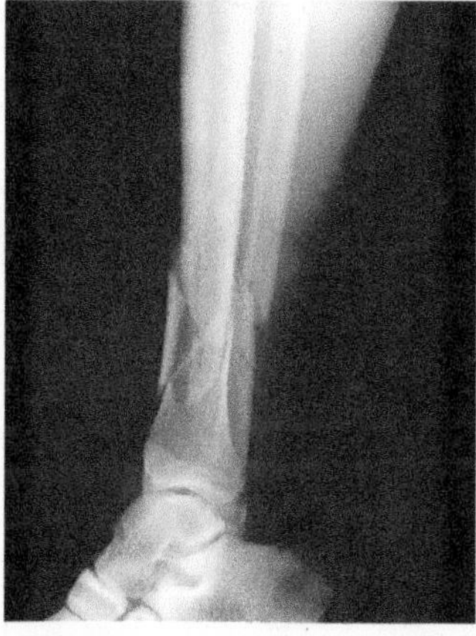

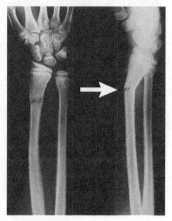

(c) Comminuted

(d) Greenstick

**FIGURE 7.18 X-Rays of Representative Fracture Types.** (a) Nondisplaced fracture of the distal humerus in a 3-year-old. (b) Displaced fracture of the tibia and fibula. (c) Comminuted fracture of the tibia and fibula. (d) Greenstick fracture of the ulna.

a: Watney Collection/Medical Images; b: Howard Kingsnorth/The Image Bank/Getty Images; c: Lester V. Bergman/Corbis NX/Getty Images; d: Biophoto Associates/Science Source

③ **Conversion to hard callus.** Other osteogenic cells differentiate into osteoblasts, which produce a bony collar called the **hard callus** around the fracture. The hard callus is cemented to dead bone around the injury site and acts as a temporary splint to join the broken ends or bone fragments together. It takes about 4 to 6 weeks for a hard callus to form. During this period, it is important that a broken bone be immobilized by traction or a cast to prevent reinjury.

④ **Remodeling.** The hard callus persists for 3 to 4 months. Meanwhile, osteoclasts dissolve small fragments of broken bone, and osteoblasts deposit spongy bone to bridge the gap between the broken ends. This spongy bone gradually fills in to become compact bone, in a manner similar to intramembranous ossification. Usually the fracture leaves a slight thickening of the bone visible by X-ray; such thickenings may serve as forensic evidence of child abuse. In some cases, however, healing is so complete that no trace of the fracture can be found.

## The Treatment of Fractures

Most fractures are set by **closed reduction,** a procedure in which the bone fragments are manipulated into their normal positions without surgery. **Open reduction** involves the surgical exposure of the bone and the use of plates, screws, or pins to realign the fragments **(fig. 7.20).** To stabilize the bone during healing, fractures are often set in casts. Traction is used to treat fractures of the femur in children. It aids in the alignment of the bone fragments by overriding the force of the strong thigh muscles. Traction is rarely used for elderly patients, however, because the risks from long-term confinement to bed outweigh the benefits. Hip fractures are usually pinned, and early ambulation (walking) is encouraged because it promotes blood circulation and healing. Fractures that take longer than 2 months to heal may be treated with electrical stimulation, which accelerates repair by suppressing the effects of parathyroid hormone.

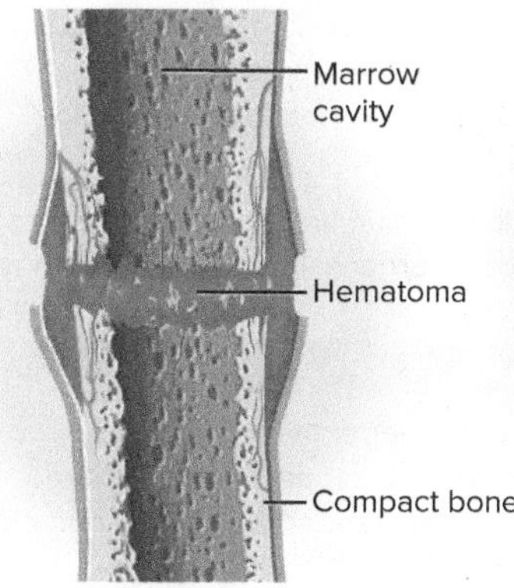


① **Hematoma formation**
The hematoma is converted to granulation tissue by invasion of cells and blood capillaries.

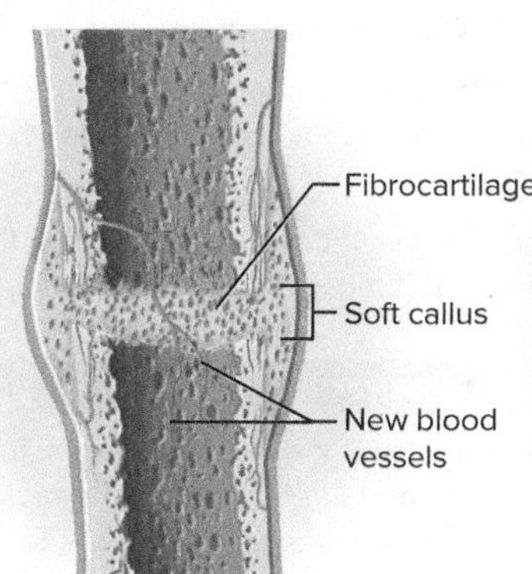


② **Soft callus formation**
Deposition of collagen and fibrocartilage converts granulation tissue to a soft callus.

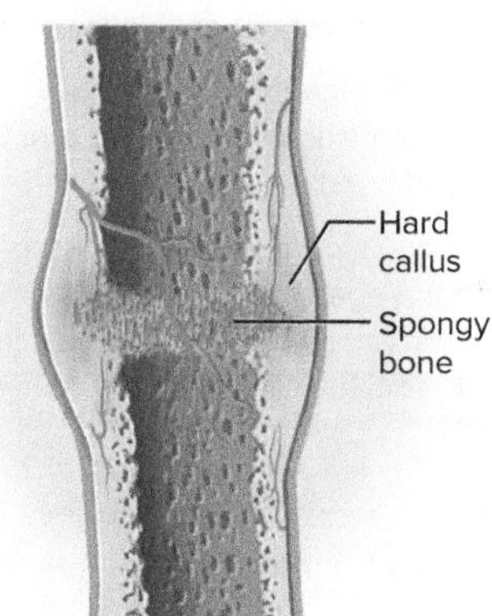


③ **Hard callus formation**
Osteoblasts deposit a temporary bony collar around the fracture to unite the broken pieces while ossification occurs.

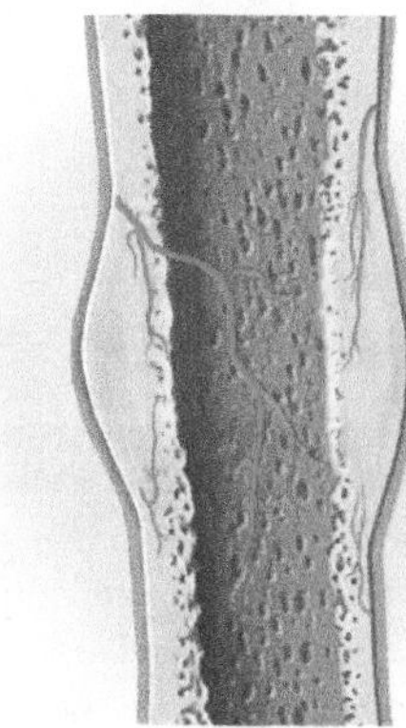

④ **Bone remodeling**
Small bone fragments are removed by osteoclasts, while osteoblasts deposit spongy bone and then convert it to compact bone.

**FIGURE 7.19 The Healing of a Bone Fracture.**

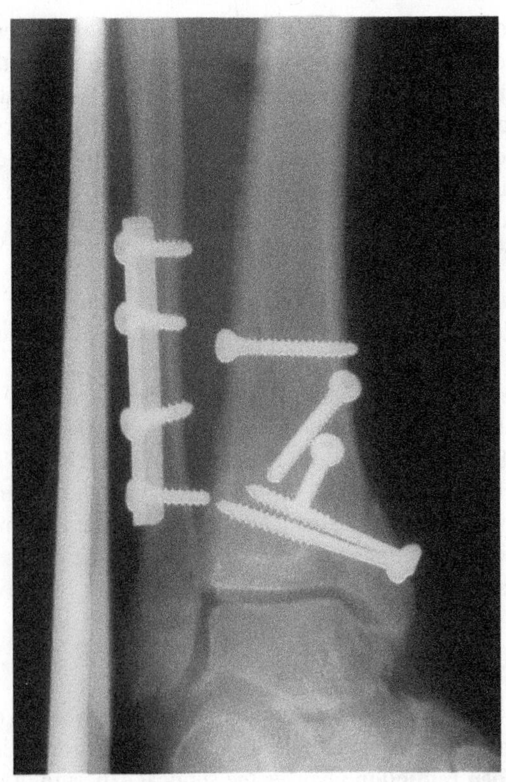

**FIGURE 7.20 Open Reduction of an Ankle Fracture.**
Southern Illinois University/Science Source

### 7.5b Other Bone Disorders

Several additional bone disorders are summarized in **table 7.2.** The most common bone disease, **osteoporosis,**[32] receives special consideration in Deeper Insight 7.4. The effects of aging on the skeletal system are described in section 29.4a.

**BEFORE YOU GO ON**

Answer the following questions to test your understanding of the preceding section:

**18.** Name and describe four types of bone fractures.

**19.** Why would osteomyelitis be more likely to occur in an open fracture than in a closed fracture?

**20.** What is a callus? How does it contribute to fracture repair?

**TABLE 7.2 Bone Diseases**

| Disease | Description |
|---|---|
| Osteitis deformans (Paget[33] disease) | Excessive proliferation of osteoclasts and resorption of excess bone, with osteoblasts attempting to compensate by depositing extra bone. This results in rapid, disorderly bone remodeling and weak, deformed bones. Osteitis deformans usually passes unnoticed, but in some cases it causes pain, disfiguration, and fractures. It is most common in males over the age of 50. |
| Osteomyelitis[34] | Inflammation of osseous tissue and bone marrow as a result of bacterial infection. This disease was often fatal before the discovery of antibiotics and is still very difficult to treat. |
| Osteogenesis imperfecta (brittle bone disease) | A defect in collagen deposition that renders bones exceptionally brittle, resulting in fractures present at birth or occurring with extraordinary frequency during childhood; also causing tooth deformity, and hearing loss due to deformity of middle-ear bones. |
| Osteosarcoma[35] (osteogenic sarcoma) | The most common and deadly form of bone cancer. It occurs most often in the tibia, femur, and humerus of males between the ages of 10 and 25. In 10% of cases, it metastasizes to the lungs or other organs; if untreated, death typically occurs within 1 year. |

***You can find other skeletal system disorders described in the following places:***

*Achondroplastic dwarfism* in Deeper Insight 7.2; *ectopic ossification* in section 7.4; *rickets* and *osteomalacia* in Deeper Insight 7.3; *bone fractures* (in general) in section 7.5a; *osteoporosis* in Deeper Insight 7.4; *mastoiditis* in section 8.2a; *herniated discs* in Deeper Insight 8.4; *abnormal spinal curvatures* in Deeper Insight 8.3; *fractured clavicle* in section 8.4a; *fallen arches* in section 8.5b; *arthritis* in Deeper Insight 9.5; and cleft palate in Deeper Insight 29.4.

[32] *osteo* = bone; *por* = porous; *osis* = condition
[33] Sir James Paget (1814–99), English surgeon
[34] *osteo* = bone; *myel* = marrow; *itis* = inflammation
[35] *osteo* = bone; *sarc* = flesh; *oma* = tumor

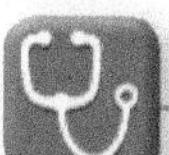

## DEEPER INSIGHT 7.4
### CLINICAL APPLICATION

### *Osteoporosis*

Osteoporosis is the most common of all bone diseases. It can be defined as a disorder in which bone density declines to the extent that the bones become brittle and subject to pathological fractures. Starting around age 40, bone resorption outpaces deposition, so we lose overall bone density. The loss comes especially from spongy bone, because it has the greatest surface area exposed to osteoclast action **(fig. 7.21a).** Proportionate amounts of organic matrix and minerals are lost, so the bone that remains is normal in composition. By old age, however, it may be insufficient in quantity to support the body's weight and withstand normal stresses.

People with osteoporosis are especially vulnerable to fractures of the hip, wrist, and spine. Their bones may break under stresses as slight as sitting down too quickly. Among the elderly, slowly healing hip fractures can impose prolonged immobility and lead to fatal complications such as pneumonia. Those who survive often face a long, costly recovery. Spinal deformity is also a common consequence of osteoporosis. As the bodies of the vertebrae lose spongy bone, they become compressed by body weight **(fig. 7.21b)** and the spine can develop an exaggerated thoracic curvature called hyperkyphosis **(fig. 7.21c).**

Postmenopausal women of European and Asian ancestry are at the greatest risk for osteoporosis. About 30% of U.S. women suffer a fracture due to osteoporosis at some point in their lives. Compared to men, they have less initial bone mass and begin to lose it at an earlier age. Since estrogen supports bone mass, the risk of osteoporosis rises sharply after menopause, when the ovaries cease to produce it. By age 70, the average white woman has lost 30% of her bone mass, and some as much as 50%. Osteoporosis is less common among women of African ancestry because of their greater initial bone density.

Other risk factors include family history; a light body build; dietary deficiencies of calcium, vitamin D, and protein; inadequate exercise; smoking; and overuse of alcohol. Osteoporosis is surprisingly common in young female runners, dancers, and gymnasts in spite of their vigorous exercise. They sometimes have such a low percentage of body fat that they stop ovulating, and without developing follicles, their ovaries secrete low levels of estrogen. About 20% of osteoporosis sufferers are men. In early long-term space missions, astronauts developed osteoporosis because in a microgravity environment, their bones were subjected to too little of the stress that normally stimulates bone deposition. This and the prevention of muscle atrophy are reasons why exercise equipment is now standard on space stations.

Osteoporosis is now diagnosed by *bone mineral density (BMD)* tests using low-dose X-rays. This has enabled earlier diagnosis and more effective treatment. However, the severity of osteoporosis depends not on bone density alone, but also on the degree of connectivity between the spongy bone trabeculae, which is lost as trabeculae deteriorate. Neither BMD testing nor any other diagnostic method yet available can detect this.

Treatment is aimed at promoting bone deposition with drugs that either stimulate osteoblasts or slow the rate of bone resorption. Osteoblasts can be stimulated to build bone by pulsed treatment with a synthetic parathyroid hormone (PTH) or by selective estrogen–receptor modulators (SERMs), which mimic the effects of estrogen without producing undesirable estrogen side effects such as the risk of stroke or breast cancer. Resorption can be inhibited with a family of drugs called bisphosphanates. This is an intensive area of clinical research and new drugs are brought to market often.

As with so many other disorders, prevention is far preferable to treatment. Prevention is best begun in the young, bone-forming years of one's 20s and 30s, but continued even into old age. It includes weight-bearing exercise; ample dietary intake of calcium, vitamin D, and protein; and of course avoiding such risk factors as smoking and a sedentary lifestyle. For the elderly, such weight-bearing exercises as dancing, stair climbing, walking, and running can be pleasurable ways of minimizing the risk of osteoporosis.

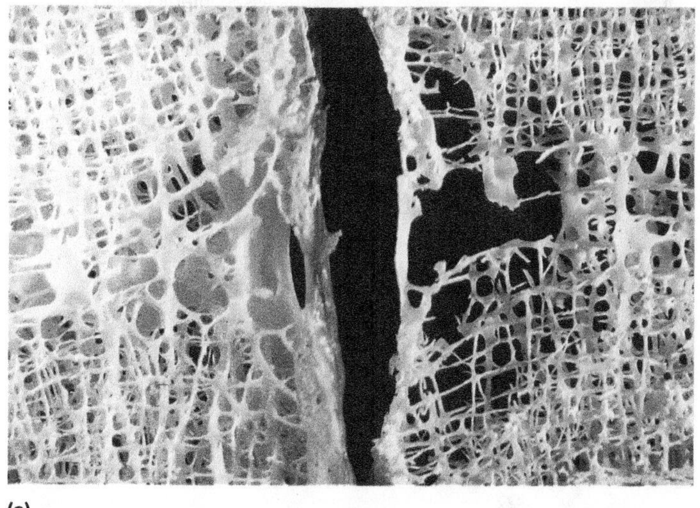

(a)

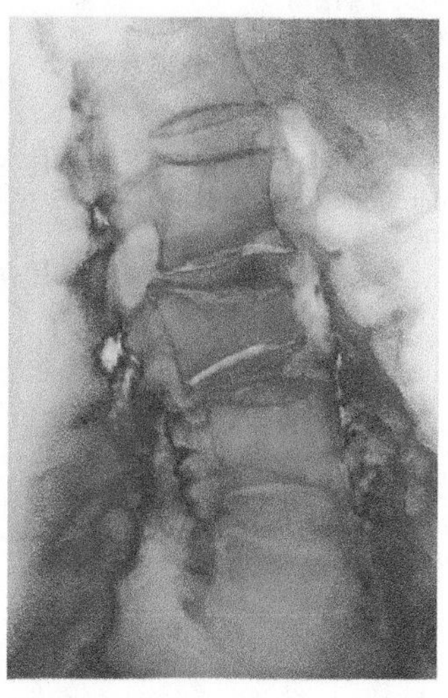

(b)

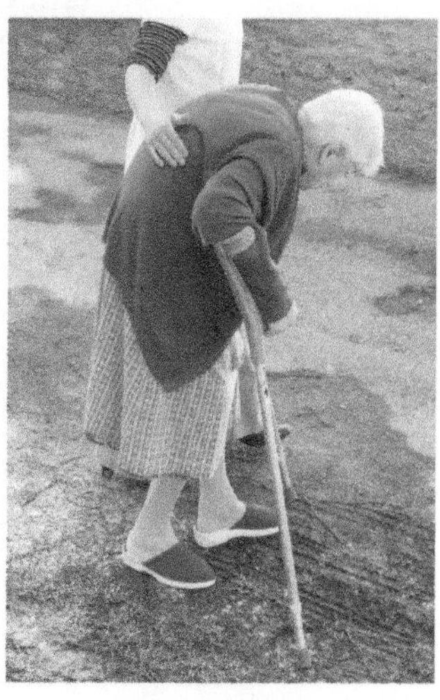

(c)

**FIGURE 7.21 Spinal Osteoporosis.** (a) Spongy bone in the body of a vertebra in good health (left) and with osteoporosis (right). (b) X-ray of lumbar vertebrae severely damaged by osteoporosis. (c) Woman with severe hyperkyphosis due to compression of thoracic vertebrae.

a: Michael Klein/Photolibrary/Getty Images; b: Dr. P. Marazzi/Science Source; c: Phanie/Alamy

# CONNECTIVE ISSUES

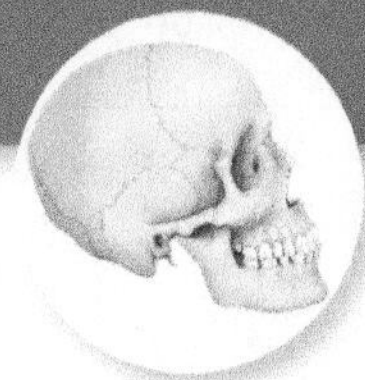

## Effects of the SKELETAL SYSTEM on Other Organ Systems

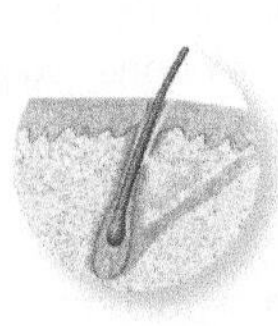

**INTEGUMENTARY SYSTEM**
Bones lying close to the body surface support and shape the skin.

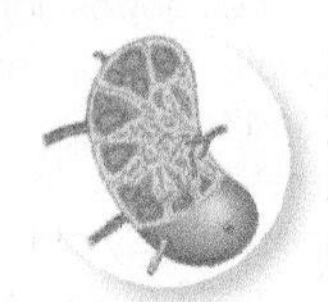

**LYMPHATIC AND IMMUNE SYSTEMS**
White blood cells produced in the bone marrow carry out the body's immune functions.

**MUSCULAR SYSTEM**
Bones are the attachment sites for most skeletal muscles and provide leverage for muscle action; calcium homeostasis, important for muscle contraction, is achieved partly through a balance between bone deposition and resorption.

**RESPIRATORY SYSTEM**
Ventilation of the lungs is achieved by musculoskeletal actions of the thoracic cage; the thoracic cage protects the delicate lungs from trauma; bones support and shape the nasal cavity.

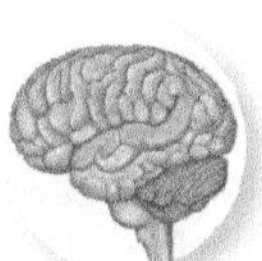

**NERVOUS SYSTEM**
The cranium and vertebral column protect the brain and spinal cord; osseous tissue provides the calcium homeostasis needed for nerve function.

**URINARY SYSTEM**
The thoracic cage partially protects the kidneys, and the pelvic girdle protects the lower urinary tract.

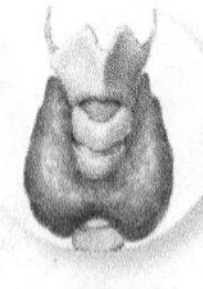

**ENDOCRINE SYSTEM**
Bones protect endocrine glands in the head, thorax, and pelvis; bones secrete the hormone osteocalcin, which promotes insulin action; hormone secretion depends on calcium homeostasis.

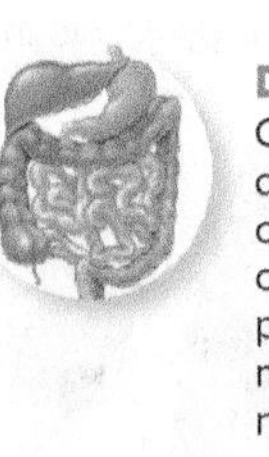

**DIGESTIVE SYSTEM**
Osseous tissue interacts with the digestive system in maintaining calcium homeostasis; the thoracic cage and pelvic girdle protect portions of the digestive tract; musculoskeletal movements are necessary for chewing.

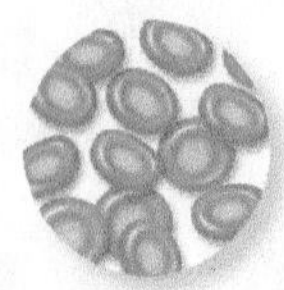

**CIRCULATORY SYSTEM**
Bone marrow forms blood cells and platelets; osseous tissue provides the calcium homeostasis needed for cardiac function and blood clotting.

**REPRODUCTIVE SYSTEM**
The pelvic girdle protects the internal reproductive organs; childbirth is adapted to the anatomy of the female pelvic girdle; ligaments anchor the penis, clitoris, uterus, and ovaries to the pelvic girdle.

# STUDY GUIDE

## Assess Your Learning Outcomes

*To test your knowledge, discuss the following topics with a study partner or in writing, ideally from memory.*

### 7.1 Tissues and Organs of the Skeletal System

1. The branch of medicine and biology that deals with the skeleton and bone tissue
2. Organs and tissues that constitute the skeletal system
3. Functions of the skeletal system
4. Which primary tissue category includes bone, and how bone differs from other tissues in that category
5. The relationship of compact bone, spongy bone, and the marrow cavity in the anatomy of a long bone
6. Other anatomical features of a long bone including the diaphysis, epiphysis, epiphysial plate, articular cartilage, periosteum, and endosteum
7. Structure of a typical flat bone

### 7.2 Histology of Osseous Tissue

1. The four cell types in bone tissue; their functions, origins, and locations in the tissue
2. Organic and inorganic components of the bone matrix; their respective contributions to bone strength; and the significance of the helical arrangement of collagen fibers in bone
3. Osteon structure and the relationship of osteonic bone to interstitial and circumferential lamellae
4. The route by which nerves and blood vessels penetrate throughout a bone
5. Comparisons of the histology of spongy bone with that of compact bone; where spongy bone is found; and why bones are not composed solely of compact bone
6. Location and functions of the bone marrow; the composition and childhood versus adult distribution of the two types of marrow

### 7.3 Bone Development

1. Stages of intramembranous ossification; some bones that form in this way; and how far this process has progressed by birth
2. The same points concerning endochondral ossification
3. Histology, cell transformations, and tissue zones of the metaphysis; which zones and processes account for a child's or adolescent's growth in height
4. How stresses on bones remodel them throughout life; the difference between interstitial and appositional growth

### 7.4 Physiology of Osseous Tissue

1. The purpose and process of mineralization of osseous tissue, and the identity of the cells that carry it out
2. The purpose and process of bone resorption, and the identity of the cells and cell secretions that carry it out
3. Functions of calcium in the body; the normal range of blood calcium concentration; and causes and consequences of hypocalcemia and hypercalcemia
4. The role of the skeleton as a calcium reservoir in regulating blood calcium levels
5. How calcitriol is synthesized and the mechanisms by which it supports or raises blood calcium level
6. The source of calcitonin and how it corrects hypercalcemia
7. The source of parathyroid hormone and multiple mechanisms by which it corrects hypocalcemia
8. Two forms of phosphate ions in the blood; the bodily functions of phosphate; and how calcitriol and parathyroid hormone affect blood phosphate levels
9. Effects of dietary vitamins A, C, and D on bone metabolism
10. Effects of cortisol, estrogen, testosterone, growth hormone, insulin, and thyroid hormone on bone metabolism

### 7.5 Bone Disorders

1. The difference between a stress fracture and a pathological fracture; stages in the healing of a fractured bone; and approaches to the clinical treatment of fractures
2. Causes of osteoporosis; its risk factors, pathological effects, diagnosis, treatment, and prevention

## Testing Your Recall

*Answers in Appendix A*

1. Which cells have a ruffled border and secrete hydrochloric acid?
   a. C cells
   b. osteocytes
   c. osteogenic cells
   d. osteoblasts
   e. osteoclasts

2. The marrow cavity of an adult bone may contain
   a. myeloid tissue.
   b. hyaline cartilage.
   c. periosteum.
   d. osteocytes.
   e. articular cartilages.

3. The spurt of growth in puberty results from cell proliferation and hypertrophy in
   a. the epiphysis.
   b. the epiphysial line.
   c. compact bone.
   d. the epiphysial plate.
   e. spongy bone.

4. Osteoclasts are most closely related, by common descent, to
   a. osteoprogenitor cells.
   b. osteogenic cells.
   c. blood cells.
   d. fibroblasts.
   e. osteoblasts.

5. The walls between cartilage lacunae break down in the zone of
   a. cell proliferation.
   b. calcification.
   c. reserve cartilage.
   d. bone deposition.
   e. cell hypertrophy.

6. Which of these is *not* an effect of PTH?
   a. rise in blood phosphate level
   b. reduction of calcium excretion
   c. increased intestinal calcium absorption
   d. increased number of osteoclasts
   e. increased calcitriol synthesis

# STUDY GUIDE

7. A child jumps to the ground from the top of a playground "jungle gym." His leg bones do not shatter mainly because they contain
   a. an abundance of glycosaminoglycans.
   b. young, resilient osteocytes.
   c. an abundance of calcium phosphate.
   d. collagen fibers.
   e. hydroxyapatite crystals.
8. One long bone meets another at its
   a. diaphysis.
   b. epiphysial plate.
   c. periosteum.
   d. metaphysis.
   e. epiphysis.
9. Calcitriol is made from
   a. calcitonin.
   b. 7-dehydrocholesterol.
   c. hydroxyapatite.
   d. estrogen.
   e. PTH.
10. One sign of osteoporosis is
    a. osteosarcoma.
    b. osteomalacia.
    c. osteomyelitis.
    d. a spontaneous wrist fracture.
    e. hypocalcemia.
11. Calcium phosphate crystallizes in bone as a mineral called ______.
12. Osteocytes contact each other through channels called ______ in the bone matrix.
13. A bone increases in diameter only by ______ growth, the addition of new surface lamellae.
14. Seed crystals of hydroxyapatite form only when the levels of calcium and phosphate in the tissue fluid exceed the ______.
15. A calcium deficiency called ______ can cause death by suffocation.
16. ______ are cells that secrete collagen and stimulate calcium phosphate deposition.
17. The most active form of vitamin D, produced mainly by the kidneys, is ______.
18. The most common bone disease is ______.
19. The transitional region between epiphysial cartilage and the primary marrow cavity of a young bone is called the ______.
20. A pregnant, poorly nourished woman may suffer a softening of the bones called ______.

## Building Your Medical Vocabulary

*Answers in Appendix A*

*State a meaning of each word element, and give a medical term from this chapter that uses it or a slight variation of it.*

1. calc-
2. -clast
3. -malacia
4. myelo-
5. ortho-
6. osse-
7. osteo-
8. -physis
9. spic-
10. topo-

## What's Wrong with These Statements?

*Answers in Appendix A*

*Briefly explain why each of the following statements is false, or reword it to make it true.*

1. The flat cranial bones are composed of compact bone only, with no spongy bone.
2. In endochondral ossification, bone tissue is formed by the calcification of preexisting cartilage.
3. Fractures are the most common bone disorder.
4. The growth zone of the long bones of adolescents is the articular cartilage.
5. Osteoclasts develop from osteoblasts.
6. Osteoblasts are multipotent stem cells.
7. The protein of the bone matrix is called hydroxyapatite.
8. Osteocytes are nourished by blood capillaries in the canaliculi of the osteons.
9. Vitamin D promotes bone deposition, not resorption.
10. Parathyroid hormone stimulates bone deposition by osteoblasts.

## Testing Your Comprehension

1. Most osteocytes of an osteon are far removed from blood vessels, but still receive blood-borne nutrients. Explain how this is possible.
2. A 50-year-old business executive decides he has not been getting enough exercise for the last several years. He takes up hiking and finds that he really loves it. Within 2 years, he is spending many of his weekends hiking with a heavy backpack and camping in the mountains. Explain what changes in his anatomy could be predicted from Wolff's law of bone.
3. How does the regulation of blood calcium concentration exemplify negative feedback and homeostasis?
4. Describe how the arrangement of trabeculae in spongy bone demonstrates the unity of form and function.
5. Identify two bone diseases you would expect to see if the epidermis were a completely effective barrier to UV radiation and a person took no dietary supplements to compensate for this. Explain your answer.

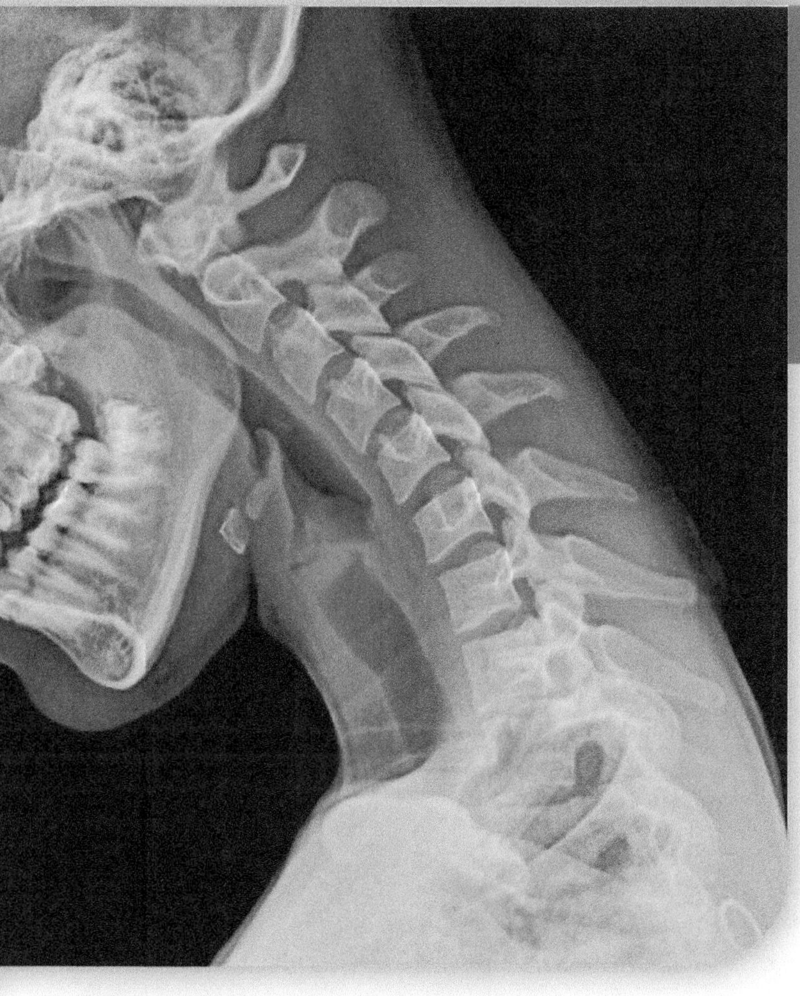

CHAPTER

# 8

# THE SKELETAL SYSTEM

X-ray of the cervical spine of a 20-year-old female

Science Photo Library - Zephyr/Getty Images

## CHAPTER OUTLINE



## DEEPER INSIGHTS

**Module 5: Skeletal System**

**BRUSHING UP**

- Anatomical descriptions of the skeletal system depend heavily on the directional terminology introduced in atlas A, table A.1.
- Understanding skeletal anatomy also depends on knowledge of the terms for body regions and cavities described in atlas A.

Knowledge of skeletal anatomy will be useful as you study later chapters. It provides a point of reference for studying the gross anatomy of other organ systems because many organs are named for their relationships to nearby bones. The subclavian artery and vein, for example, lie adjacent to the clavicle; the temporalis muscle is attached to the temporal bone; the ulnar nerve and radial artery travel beside the ulna and radius of the forearm; and the frontal, parietal, temporal, and occipital lobes of the brain are named for adjacent bones of the cranium. Understanding how the muscles produce body movements also depends on knowledge of skeletal anatomy. Additionally, the positions, shapes, and processes of bones can serve as landmarks for clinicians in determining where to give an injection or record a pulse, what to look for in an X-ray, and how to perform physical therapy and other clinical procedures.

## 8.1 Overview of the Skeleton

**Expected Learning Outcomes**

When you have completed this section, you should be able to

a. define the two subdivisions of the skeleton;
b. state the approximate number of bones in the adult body;
c. explain why this number varies with age and from one person to another; and
d. define several terms that denote surface features of bones.

The skeleton **(fig. 8.1)** is divided into two regions: the axial skeleton and appendicular skeleton. The **axial skeleton,** which forms the central supporting axis of the body, includes the skull, auditory ossicles (middle-ear bones), hyoid bone, vertebral column, and thoracic cage (ribs and sternum). The **appendicular skeleton** includes the bones of the upper limb and pectoral girdle and the bones of the lower limb and pelvic girdle.

### 8.1a Bones of the Skeletal System

It is often stated that there are 206 bones in the skeleton, but this is only a typical adult count, not an invariable number. At birth there are about 270, and even more bones form during childhood. With age, however, the number decreases as separate bones gradually fuse. For example, each side of a child's pelvic girdle has three bones—the *ilium, ischium,* and *pubis*—but in adults, these are fused into a single *hip bone* on each side. The fusion of several bones, completed by late adolescence to the mid-20s, brings about the average adult number of 206. These bones are listed in **table 8.1.**

This number varies even among adults. One reason is the development of **sesamoid**[1] **bones**—bones that form within

[1] *sesam* = sesame seed; *oid* = resembling

**TABLE 8.1 Bones of the Adult Skeletal System**

| | |
|---|---|
| **Axial Skeleton** | |
| ***Skull (22 bones)*** | |
| Cranial bones | |
| Frontal bone (1) | Temporal bones (2) |
| Parietal bones (2) | Sphenoid bone (1) |
| Occipital bone (1) | Ethmoid bone (1) |
| Facial bones | |
| Maxillae (2) | Nasal bones (2) |
| Palatine bones (2) | Vomer (1) |
| Zygomatic bones (2) | Inferior nasal conchae (2) |
| Lacrimal bones (2) | Mandible (1) |
| ***Auditory ossicles (6 bones)*** | |
| Malleus (2) | Stapes (2) |
| Incus (2) | |
| ***Hyoid bone (1 bone)*** | |
| ***Vertebral column (26 bones)*** | |
| Cervical vertebrae (7) | Sacrum (1) |
| Thoracic vertebrae (12) | Coccyx (1) |
| Lumbar vertebrae (5) | |
| ***Thoracic cage (25 bones plus thoracic vertebrae)*** | |
| Ribs (24) | |
| Sternum (1) | |
| **Appendicular Skeleton** | |
| ***Pectoral girdle (4 bones)*** | |
| Scapulae (2) | Clavicles (2) |
| ***Upper limbs (60 bones)*** | |
| Humerus (2) | Carpal bones (16) |
| Radius (2) | Metacarpal bones (10) |
| Ulna (2) | Phalanges (28) |
| ***Pelvic girdle (2 bones)*** | |
| Hip bones (2) | |
| ***Lower limbs (60 bones)*** | |
| Femurs (2) | Tarsal bones (14) |
| Patellae (2) | Metatarsal bones (10) |
| Tibiae (2) | Phalanges (28) |
| Fibulae (2) | |
| **Grand Total: 206 Bones** | |

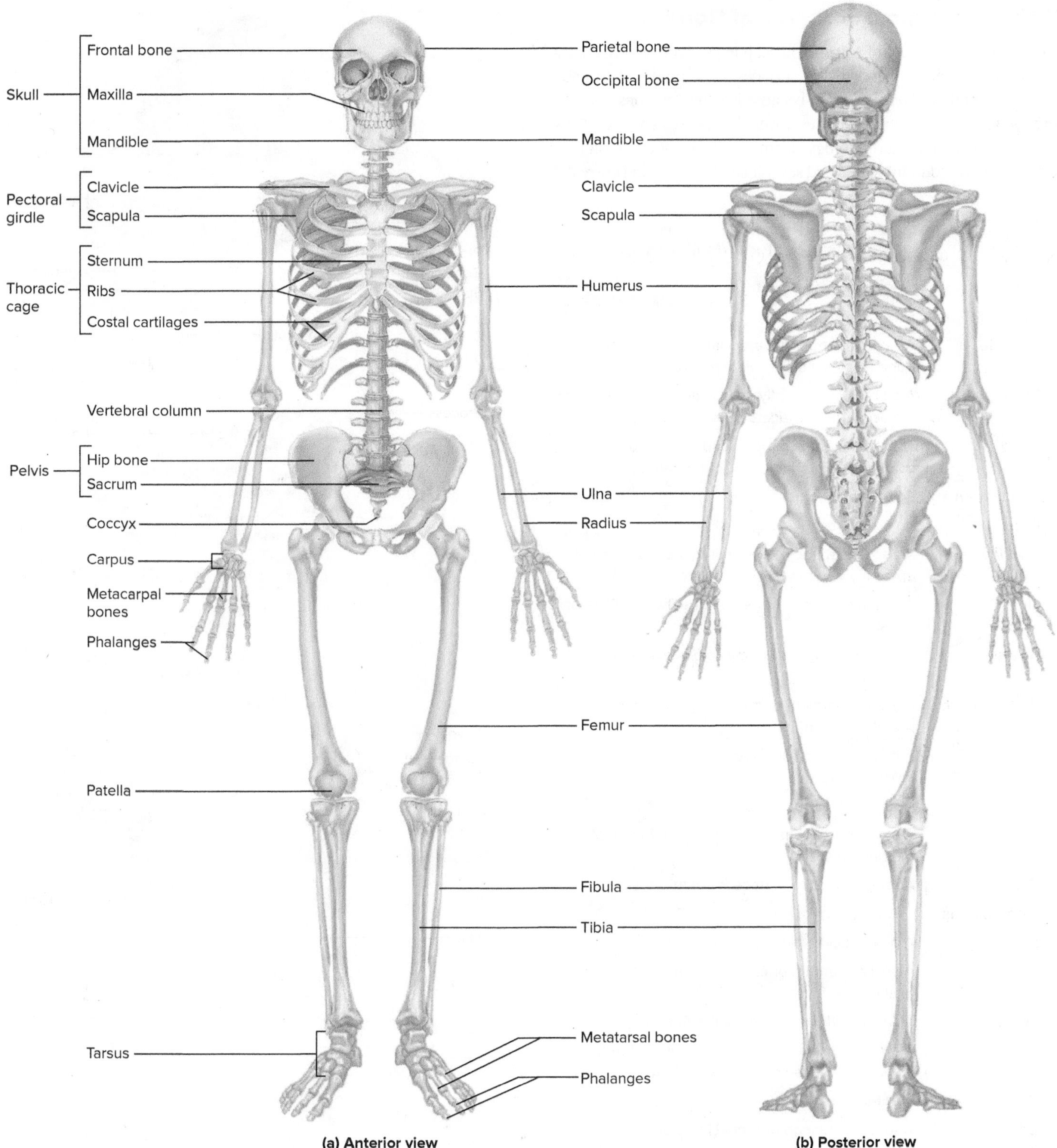


**FIGURE 8.1 The Adult Skeleton.** (a) Anterior view. (b) Posterior view. The appendicular skeleton is colored green, and the rest is axial skeleton. APR

some tendons in response to strain. The patella (kneecap) is the largest of these; most of the others are small, rounded bones in such locations as the hands and feet (see fig. 8.35c). Another reason for adult variation is that some people have extra bones in the skull called **sutural bones** (SOO-chur-ul) (see fig. 8.6).

## 8.1b Anatomical Features of Bones

Bones exhibit a variety of ridges, spines, bumps, depressions, canals, pores, slits, cavities, and articular surfaces. It is important to know the names of these *bone markings* because later descriptions of joints, muscle attachments, and the routes traveled by nerves and blood vessels are based on this terminology. Terms for the most common bone features are listed in **table 8.2,** and several are illustrated in **figure 8.2.**

**TABLE 8.2 Anatomical Features (Markings) of Bones**

| Term | Description and Example |
|---|---|
| **Articulations (Joint Surfaces)** | |
| Condyle | A rounded knob that articulates with another bone (occipital condyles of the skull) |
| Facet | A smooth, flat, slightly concave or convex articular surface (articular facets of the vertebrae) |
| Head | The prominent expanded end of a bone, sometimes rounded (head of the femur) |
| **Extensions and Projections** | |
| Crest | A narrow ridge (iliac crest of the pelvis) |
| Epicondyle | An expanded region superior to a condyle (medial epicondyle of the femur) |
| Line | A slightly raised, elongated ridge (nuchal lines of the skull) |
| Process | Any bony prominence (mastoid process of the skull) |
| Protuberance | A bony outgrowth or protruding part (mental protuberance of the chin) |
| Spine | A sharp, slender, or narrow process (mental spines of the mandible) |
| Trochanter | Two massive processes unique to the femur |
| Tubercle | A small, rounded process (greater tubercle of the humerus) |
| Tuberosity | A rough elevated surface (tibial tuberosity) |
| **Depressions** | |
| Alveolus | A pit or socket (tooth socket) |
| Fossa | A shallow, broad, or elongated basin (mandibular fossa) |
| Fovea | A small pit (fovea capitis of the femur) |
| Sulcus | A groove for a tendon, nerve, or blood vessel (intertubercular sulcus of the humerus) |
| **Passages and Cavities** | |
| Canal | A tubular passage or tunnel in a bone (auditory canal of the skull) |
| Fissure | A slit through a bone (orbital fissures behind the eye) |
| Foramen | A hole through a bone, usually round (foramen magnum of the skull) |
| Meatus | A canal (external acoustic meatus of the ear) |
| Sinus | An air-filled space in a bone (frontal sinus of the forehead) |

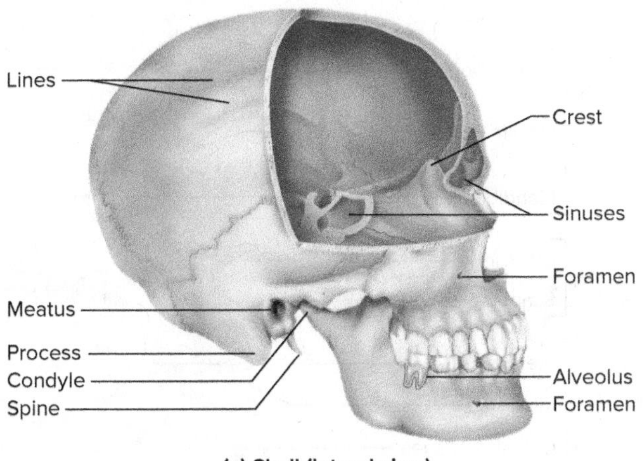

(a) Skull (lateral view)

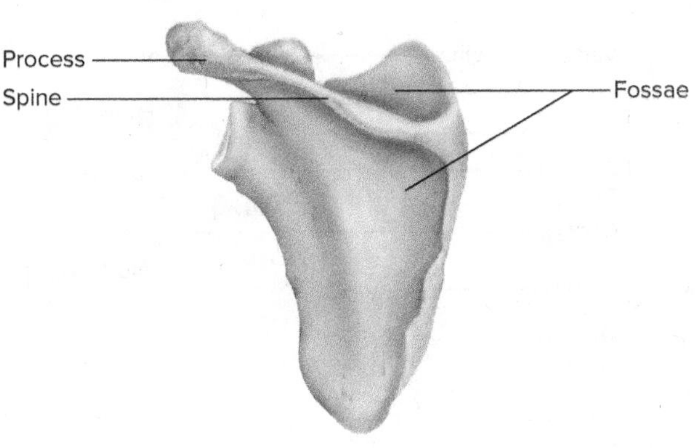

(b) Scapula (posterior view)

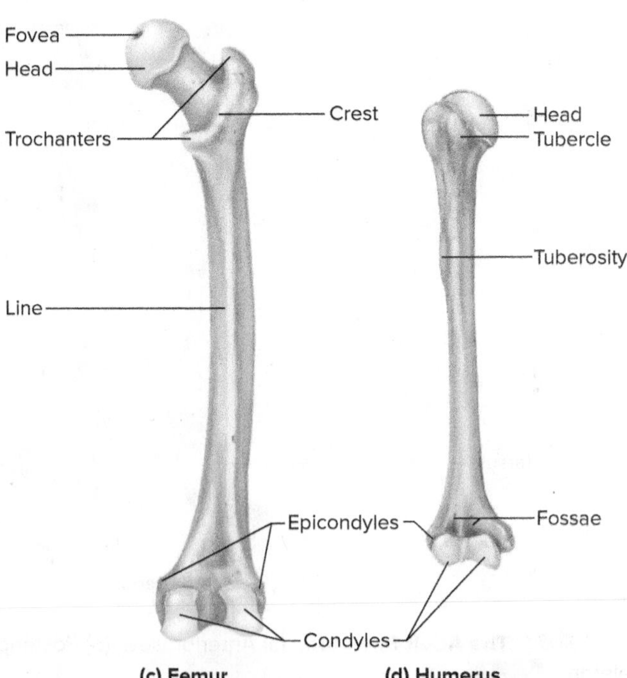

(c) Femur (posterior view)
(d) Humerus (anterior view)

**FIGURE 8.2 Anatomical Features of Bones.** (a) Skull, lateral view. (b) Scapula, posterior view. (c) Femur, posterior view. (d) Humerus, anterior view. Most of these features also occur on many other bones of the body.

You will probably study both **articulated** skeletons (dried bones held together by wires and rods to show their spatial relationships to each other) and **disarticulated** bones (bones taken apart so their surface features can be studied in more detail). As you study this chapter, also use yourself as a model. You can easily palpate (feel) many of the bones and some of their details through the skin. Rotate your forearm, cross your legs, palpate your skull and wrist, and think about what is happening beneath the surface or what you can feel through the skin. You will gain the most from this chapter (and indeed, the entire book) if you are conscious of your own body in relation to what you are studying.

**BEFORE YOU GO ON**

Answer the following questions to test your understanding of the preceding section:

1. Name the major components of the axial skeleton. Name those of the appendicular skeleton.
2. Explain why an adult does not have as many bones as a child does. Explain why one adult may have more bones than another.
3. Briefly describe each of the following bone features: a condyle, crest, tubercle, fossa, sulcus, and foramen.

## 8.2 The Skull

### Expected Learning Outcomes

When you have completed this section, you should be able to

a. distinguish between cranial and facial bones;
b. name the bones of the skull and their anatomical features;
c. identify the cavities in the skull and in some of its individual bones;
d. name the principal sutures that join the bones of the skull;
e. describe some bones that are closely associated with the skull; and
f. describe the development of the skull from infancy through childhood.

The skull is the most complex part of the skeleton. **Figures 8.3** through **8.6** present an overview of the skull's general anatomy. Although it may seem to consist only of the mandible (lower jaw) and "the rest," it is composed of 22 bones and sometimes more. Most of these are connected by immovable joints called **sutures** (SOO-chures), which are visible as seams on the surface (fig. 8.4). These are important landmarks in the descriptions that follow.

The skull contains several prominent cavities **(fig. 8.7).** The largest, with an adult volume of about 1,350 mL, is the **cranial cavity,** which encloses the brain. Other cavities include the **orbits** (eye sockets), **nasal cavity, oral (buccal) cavity, middle-** and **inner-ear cavities,** and **paranasal sinuses.** The sinuses are named for the bones in which they occur **(fig. 8.8)**—the **frontal, sphenoidal, ethmoidal,** and **maxillary sinuses.** They are connected with the nasal cavity, lined by mucous membranes, and filled with air. They lighten the anterior portion of the skull and act as chambers that add resonance to the voice. The latter effect can be sensed in the way your voice changes when you have a cold and mucus obstructs the travel of sound into the sinuses and back.

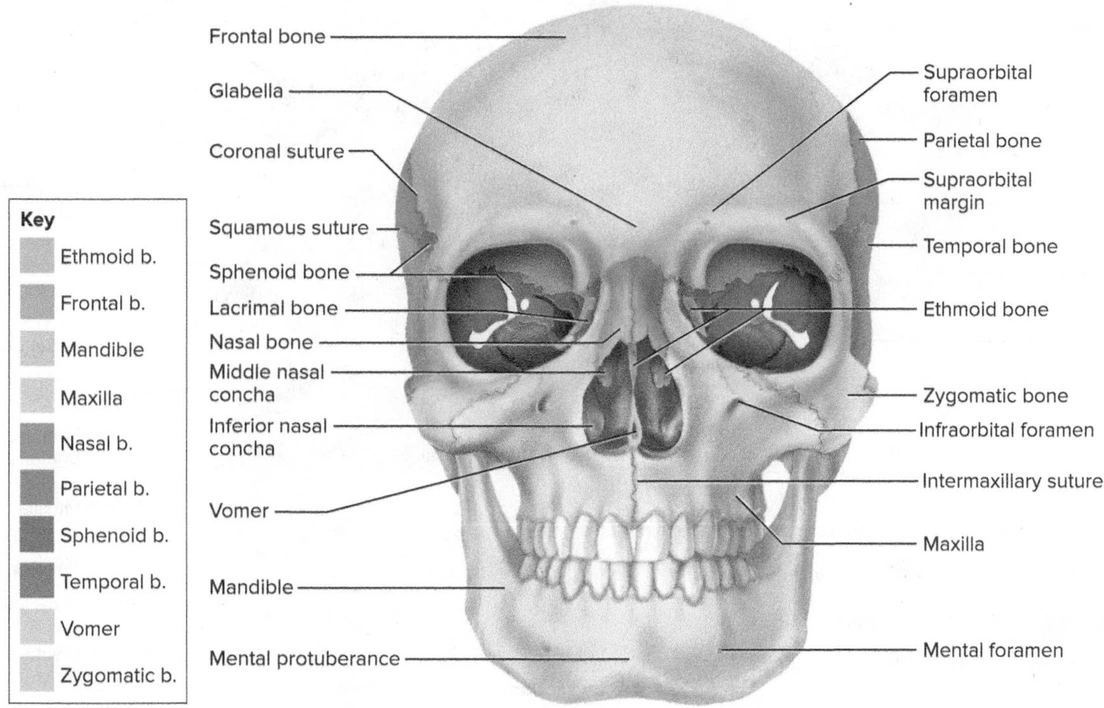


**FIGURE 8.3 The Skull (Anterior View).** APR

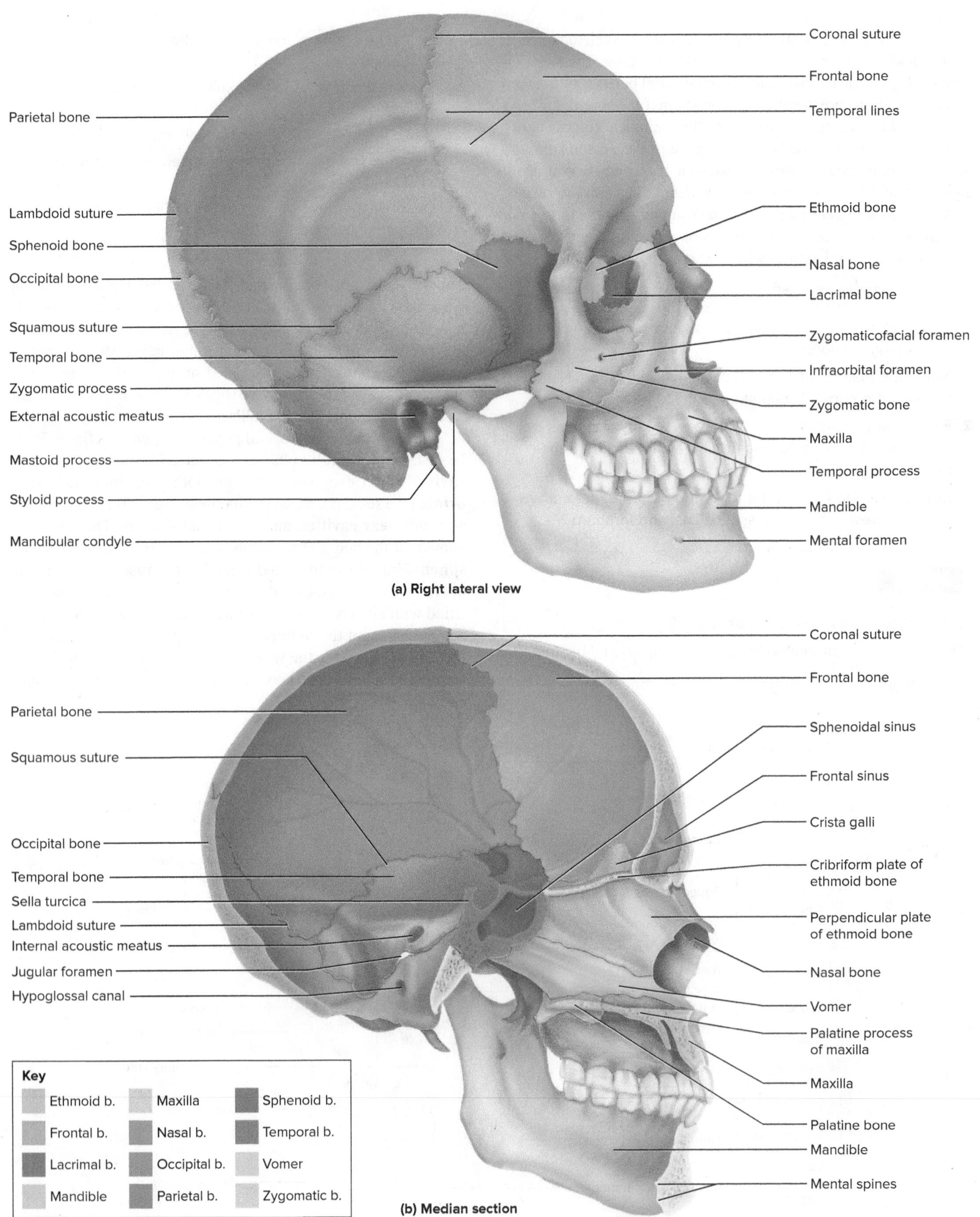
Coronal suture
Frontal bone
Parietal bone
Temporal lines
Lambdoid suture
Ethmoid bone
Sphenoid bone
Nasal bone
Occipital bone
Lacrimal bone
Squamous suture
Zygomaticofacial foramen
Temporal bone
Infraorbital foramen
Zygomatic process
Zygomatic bone
External acoustic meatus
Maxilla
Mastoid process
Temporal process
Styloid process
Mandible
Mandibular condyle
Mental foramen
(a) Right lateral view
Coronal suture
Frontal bone
Parietal bone
Sphenoidal sinus
Squamous suture
Frontal sinus
Crista galli
Occipital bone
Cribriform plate of ethmoid bone
Temporal bone
Sella turcica
Perpendicular plate of ethmoid bone
Lambdoid suture
Internal acoustic meatus
Nasal bone
Jugular foramen
Hypoglossal canal
Vomer
Palatine process of maxilla
Maxilla
Palatine bone
Mandible
Mental spines
Key
Ethmoid b.
Maxilla
Sphenoid b.
Frontal b.
Nasal b.
Temporal b.
Lacrimal b.
Occipital b.
Vomer
Mandible
Parietal b.
Zygomatic b.
(b) Median section

**FIGURE 8.4 The Skull.** (a) Right lateral surface anatomy. (b) Internal anatomy, median section. APR

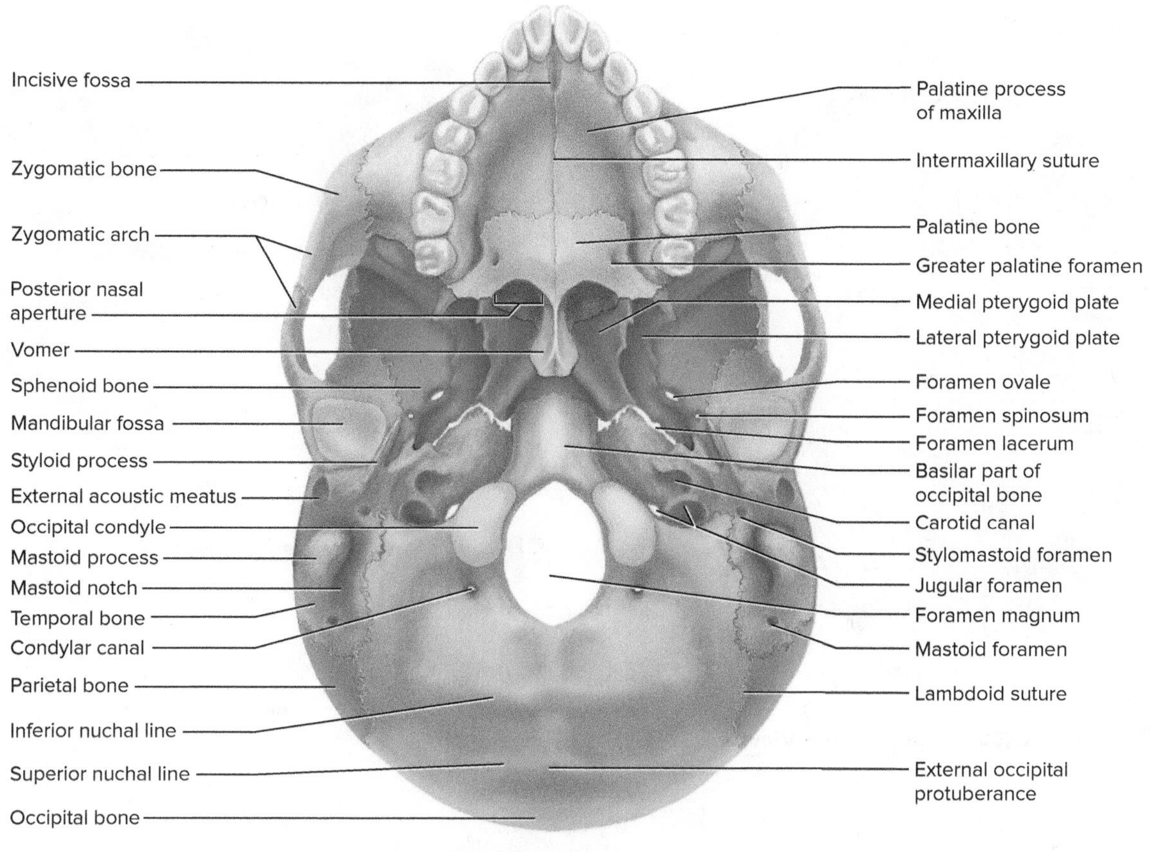


(a) Inferior view

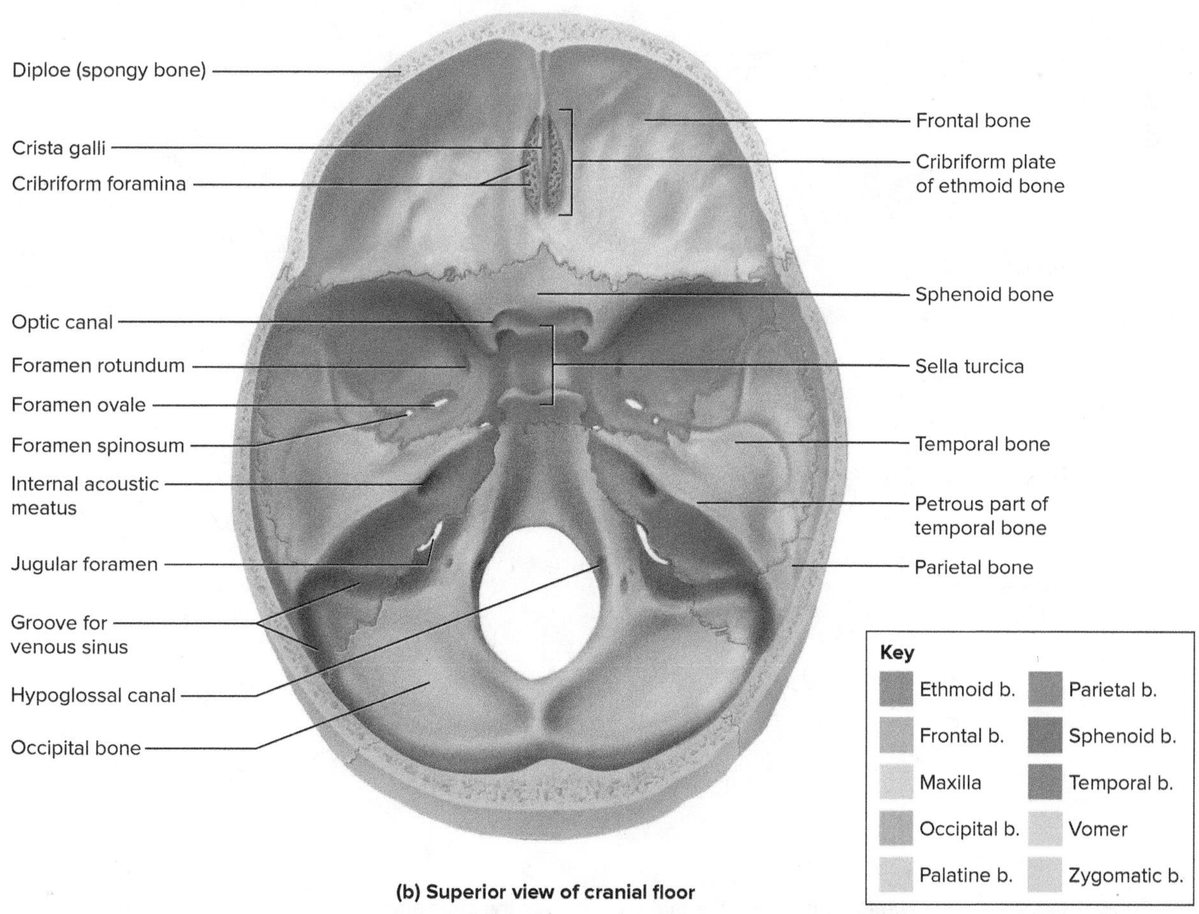


(b) Superior view of cranial floor

**FIGURE 8.5 The Base of the Skull.** (a) Inferior view. (b) Superior view of the cranial floor. APR

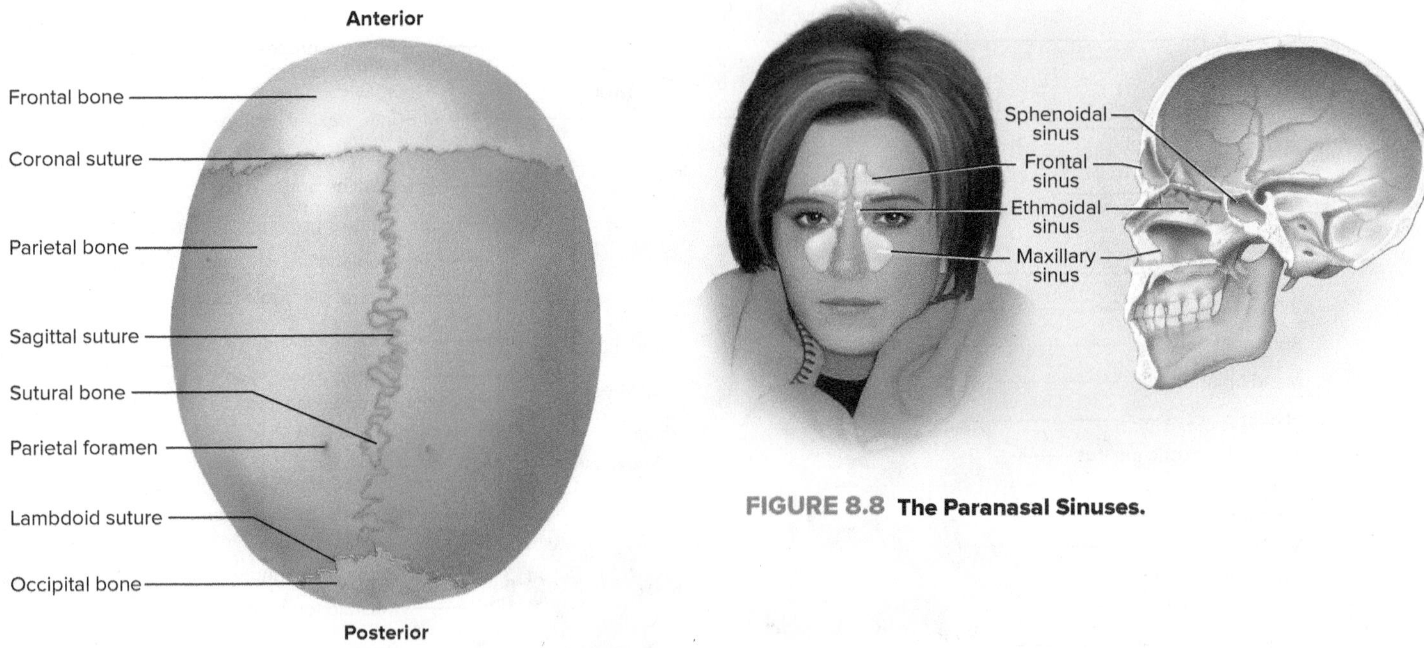


**FIGURE 8.8 The Paranasal Sinuses.**

**FIGURE 8.6 The Calvaria (Skullcap) (Superior View).** APR

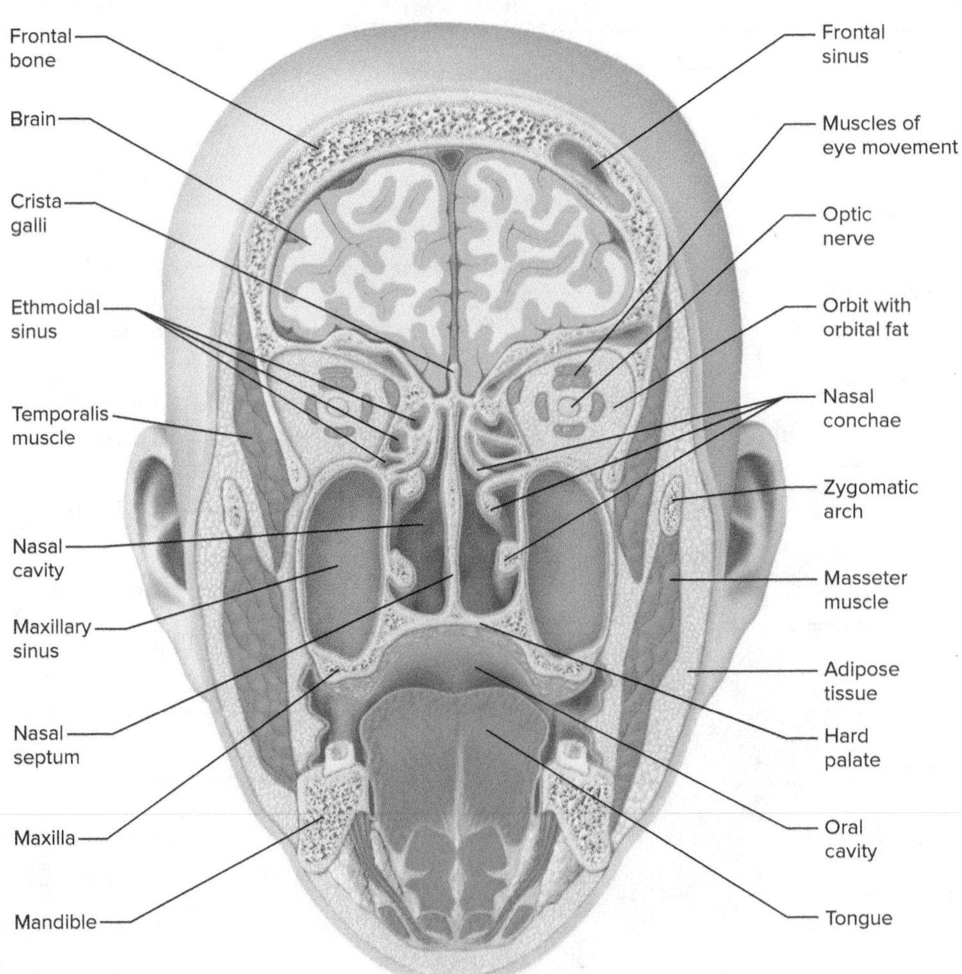


**FIGURE 8.7 Frontal Section of the Head.** This shows the major cavities of the skull and their contents.

Bones of the skull have especially conspicuous **foramina**—singular, *foramen* (fo-RAY-men)—holes that allow passage for nerves and blood vessels. Some major foramina are summarized in **table 8.3.** Some of the details will mean more after you study cranial nerves and blood vessels in later chapters.

## 8.2a Cranial Bones

**Cranial bones** are those that enclose the brain; collectively, they compose the **cranium**[2] (braincase). The delicate brain tissue doesn't come directly into contact with the bones, but is separated from them by three membranes called the *meninges* (meh-NIN-jeez) (see section 14.2a). The thickest and toughest of these, the *dura mater*[3] (DUE-rah MAH-tur), is pressed against the inside of the cranium in most places and firmly attached to it at a few points.

The cranium is a rigid structure with an opening, the *foramen magnum* (literally "large hole"), where the spinal cord meets the brain. The cranium consists of two major parts—the calvaria and the base. The **calvaria**[4] (skullcap) isn't a single bone but simply the dome of the top of the skull; it is composed of parts of multiple bones that form the roof and walls (see fig. 8.6). In skulls prepared for study, the calvaria is often sawed so that part of it can be lifted off for examination of the interior. This reveals the **base** (floor) of the cranial cavity (see fig. 8.5b), which exhibits three paired depressions called cranial fossae. These correspond to the contour of the inferior surface of the brain **(fig. 8.9).** The relatively shallow **anterior cranial fossa** is crescent-shaped and accommodates the frontal lobes of the brain. The **middle cranial fossa,** which drops abruptly deeper, is shaped like a pair of outstretched bird's wings and accommodates the temporal lobes. The **posterior cranial fossa** is deepest and houses a large posterior division of the brain called the cerebellum.

There are eight cranial bones:

| | |
|---|---|
| 1 frontal bone | 1 occipital bone |
| 2 parietal bones | 1 sphenoid bone |
| 2 temporal bones | 1 ethmoid bone |

### The Frontal Bone

The **frontal bone** extends from the forehead back to a prominent *coronal suture,* which crosses the crown of the head from right to left and joins the frontal bone to the parietal bones (see figs. 8.3 and 8.4). The frontal bone forms the anterior wall and about one-third of the roof of the cranial cavity, and it turns inward to form nearly all of the anterior cranial fossa and the roof of the orbit.

[2]*crani* = helmet
[3]*dura* = tough, strong; *mater* = mother
[4]*calvar* = bald, skull

**TABLE 8.3 Foramina of the Skull and the Nerves and Blood Vessels Transmitted Through Them**

| Bones and Their Foramina | Structures Transmitted |
|---|---|
| **Frontal Bone** | |
| Supraorbital foramen or notch | Supraorbital nerve, artery, and vein; ophthalmic nerve |
| **Temporal Bone** | |
| Carotid canal | Internal carotid artery |
| External acoustic meatus | Sound waves to eardrum |
| Jugular foramen | Internal jugular vein; glossopharyngeal, vagus, and accessory nerves |
| **Occipital Bone** | |
| Foramen magnum | Spinal cord; accessory nerve; vertebral arteries |
| Hypoglossal canal | Hypoglossal nerve to muscles of tongue |
| **Sphenoid Bone** | |
| Foramen ovale | Mandibular division of trigeminal nerve; accessory meningeal artery |
| Foramen rotundum | Maxillary division of trigeminal nerve |
| Optic canal | Optic nerve; ophthalmic artery |
| Superior orbital fissure | Oculomotor, trochlear, and abducens nerves; ophthalmic division of trigeminal nerve; ophthalmic veins |
| **Maxilla** | |
| Inferior orbital fissure | Infraorbital nerve; zygomatic nerve; infraorbital vessels |
| Infraorbital foramen | Infraorbital nerve and vessels |
| **Mandible** | |
| Mental foramen | Mental nerve and vessels |
| Mandibular foramen | Inferior alveolar nerves and vessels to the lower teeth |

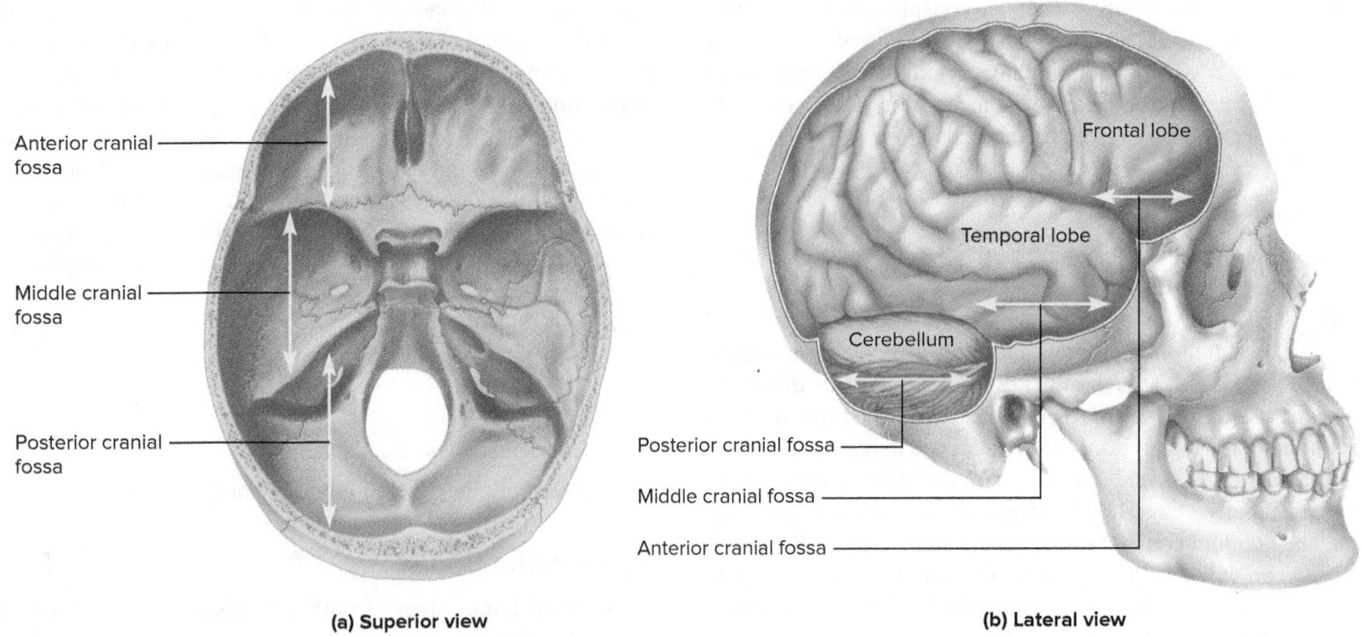


**FIGURE 8.9 Cranial Fossae.** (a) Superior view. (b) Lateral view showing how the three fossae conform to the contours of the base of the brain.

Deep to the eyebrows it has a ridge called the **supraorbital margin.** Each margin is perforated by a single **supraorbital foramen** (see figs. 8.3 and 8.14), which provides passage for a nerve, artery, and veins. In some people, the edge of this foramen breaks through the margin of the orbit and forms a *supraorbital notch.* A person may have a foramen on one supraorbital margin and a notch on the other. The smooth area of the frontal bone just above the root of the nose is called the **glabella.**[5] The frontal bone also contains the frontal sinus. You may not see this sinus on all skulls. On some, the calvaria is cut too high to show it, and some people simply don't have one. Along the cut edge of the calvaria, you can also see the diploe (DIP-lo-ee)—the layer of spongy bone in the middle of the cranial bones (see fig. 8.5b).

## The Parietal Bones

The right and left **parietal bones** (pa-RY-eh-tul) form most of the cranial roof and part of its walls (see figs. 8.4 and 8.6). Each is bordered by four sutures that join it to the neighboring bones: (1) a **sagittal suture** between the parietal bones; (2) the **coronal**[6] **suture** at the anterior margin; (3) the **lambdoid**[7] **suture** (LAM-doyd) at the posterior margin; and (4) the **squamous suture** laterally. Small sutural bones are often seen along the sagittal and lambdoid sutures, like little islands of bone with the suture lines passing around them. Internally, the parietal and frontal bones have markings that look a bit like aerial photographs of river tributaries (see fig. 8.4b). These represent places where the bone molded itself around blood vessels of the meninges.

Externally, the parietal bones have few features. A **parietal foramen** sometimes occurs near the corner of the lambdoid and sagittal sutures (see fig. 8.6). It is an exit for a small vein from a blood sinus atop the brain. A pair of slight lateral thickenings, the superior and inferior **temporal lines,** form an arc across the parietal and frontal bones (see fig. 8.4a). They mark the attachment of the large, fan-shaped *temporalis muscle,* a chewing muscle that converges on the mandible.

## The Temporal Bones

If you palpate your skull just above and anterior to the ear—that is, the temporal region—you can feel the **temporal bone,** which forms the lower wall and part of the floor of the cranial cavity **(fig. 8.10).** The temporal bone derives its name from the fact that people often develop their first gray hairs on the temples with the passage of time.[8] The relatively complex shape of the temporal bone is best understood by dividing it into four parts:

1. The **squamous**[9] **part** (which you just palpated) is relatively flat and vertical. It is encircled by the squamous suture. It bears two prominent features: (a) the **zygomatic process,** which extends anteriorly to form part of the *zygomatic arch,* described later; and (b) the **mandibular fossa,** a depression where the mandible articulates with the cranium.
2. The **tympanic**[10] **part** is a small ring of bone that borders the opening of the **external acoustic meatus** (me-AY-tus), or ear canal. It has a pointed spine on its inferior surface,

[5] *glab* = smooth
[6] *corona* = crown
[7] Shaped like the Greek letter lambda (λ)
[8] *tempor* = time
[9] *squam* = flat; *ous* = characterized by
[10] *tympan* = drum (eardrum); *ic* = pertaining to

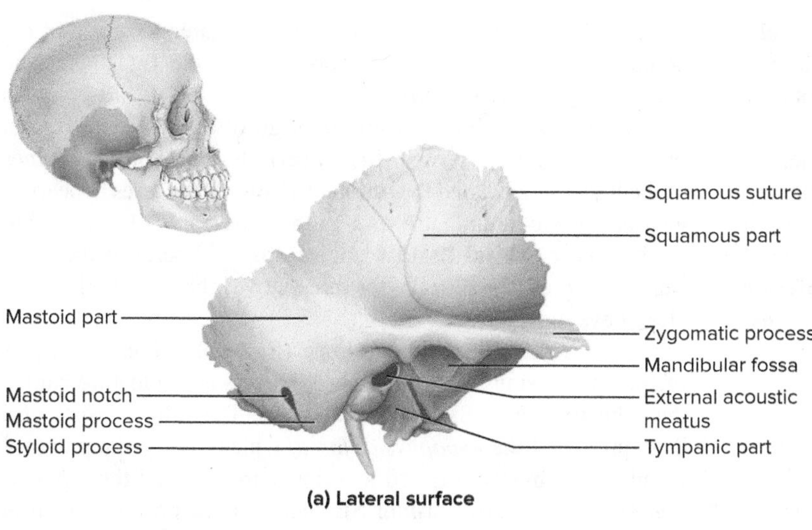


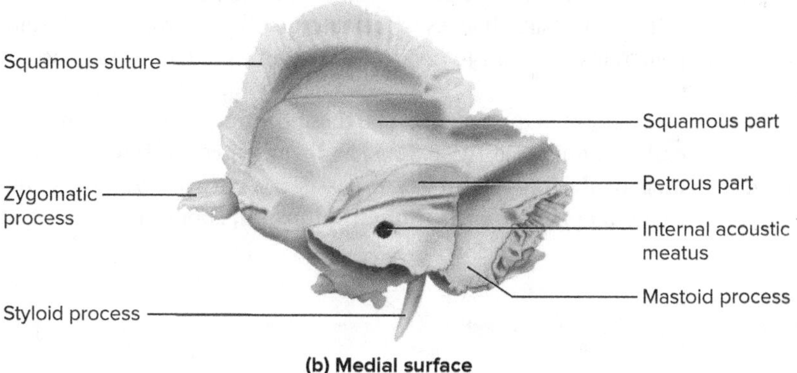


**FIGURE 8.10 The Right Temporal Bone.** (a) The lateral surface, facing the scalp and external ear. (b) The medial surface, facing the brain. APR

*List five bones that articulate with the temporal bone.*

the **styloid process,** named for its resemblance to the stylus used by ancient Greeks and Romans to write on wax tablets. The styloid process provides attachment for muscles of the tongue, pharynx, and hyoid bone.

3. The **mastoid**[11] **part** lies posterior to the tympanic part. It bears a heavy **mastoid process,** which you can palpate as a prominent lump behind the earlobe. It is filled with small air sinuses that communicate with the middle-ear cavity. These sinuses are subject to infection and inflammation *(mastoiditis),* which can erode the bone and spread to the brain. A groove called the **mastoid notch** lies medial to the mastoid process (see fig. 8.5a). It is the origin of the *digastric muscle,* which opens the mouth. The notch is perforated at its anterior end by the **stylomastoid foramen,** which is a passage for the facial nerve, and at its posterior end by the **mastoid foramen,** which passes a small artery and vein from the brain.

4. The **petrous**[12] **part** can be seen in the cranial floor, where it resembles a little mountain range separating the middle cranial fossa from the posterior fossa (fig. 8.10b). It houses the middle- and inner-ear cavities. The **internal acoustic meatus,** an opening on its posteromedial surface, allows passage of a nerve that carries signals for hearing and balance from the inner ear to the brain. On the inferior surface of the petrous part are two prominent foramina named for the major blood vessels that pass through them (see fig. 8.5a): (a) The **carotid canal** is a passage for the internal carotid artery, a major blood supply to the brain. This artery is so close to the inner ear that one can sometimes hear the pulsing of its blood when the ear is resting on a pillow or the heart is beating hard. (b) The **jugular foramen** is a large, irregular opening just medial to the styloid process, between the temporal and occipital bones. Blood from the brain drains through this foramen into the internal jugular vein of the neck. Three cranial nerves also pass through this foramen (see table 8.3).

## The Occipital Bone

The **occipital bone** (oc-SIP-ih-tul) forms the rear of the skull *(occiput)* and much of its base (see fig. 8.5). Its most conspicuous feature, the **foramen magnum,** admits the spinal cord to the cranial cavity; the dura mater is attached to the rim of this foramen. An important consideration in head injuries is swelling of the brain. Since the cranium cannot expand, swelling puts pressure on the brain and results in even more tissue damage. Severe swelling can force the brainstem out through the foramen magnum, usually with fatal consequences.

The occipital bone continues anterior to this as a thick median plate, the **basilar part.** On either side of the foramen magnum is a smooth knob called the **occipital condyle** (CON-dile), where the skull rests on the vertebral column. Passing like a tunnel beneath each condyle is a **hypoglossal**[13] **canal,** named for the *hypoglossal nerve* that passes through it to innervate the muscles of the tongue. In some people, a **condylar canal** (CON-dih-lur) is found posterior to each occipital condyle. A small vein from a blood sinus of the brain passes through here.

Internally, the occipital bone displays impressions left by large venous sinuses that drain blood from the brain (see fig. 8.5b). One of these grooves travels along the midsagittal line. Just before reaching the foramen magnum, it branches into right and left grooves that wrap around the occipital bone like outstretched arms before terminating at the jugular foramina. The venous sinuses that occupy these grooves are described in table 20.4.

Other features of the occipital bone can be palpated on the back of your head. One is a prominent medial bump called the

[11]*mast* = breast; *oid* = shaped like

[12]*petr* = stone, rock; *ous* = like

[13]*hypo* = below; *gloss* = tongue

**external occipital protuberance**—the attachment for the **nuchal**[14] **ligament** (NEW-kul), which binds the skull to the vertebral column. A ridge, the **superior nuchal line,** can be traced horizontally from this protuberance toward the mastoid process (see fig. 8.5a). It defines the superior limit of the neck and provides attachment to the skull for several neck and back muscles. It forms the boundary where, in palpating the upper neck, you feel the transition from muscle to bone. By pulling down on the occipital bone, some of these muscles help to keep the head erect. The deeper **inferior nuchal line** provides attachment for some of the deep neck muscles. This inconspicuous ridge cannot be palpated on the living body but is visible on an isolated skull.

## The Sphenoid Bone

The **sphenoid**[15] **bone** (SFEE-noyd) has a complex shape with a thick median **body** and outstretched **greater** and **lesser wings,** which give the bone as a whole a ragged mothlike shape. Most of it is best seen from the superior perspective **(fig. 8.11a).** In this view, the lesser wings form the posterior margin of the anterior cranial fossa and end at a sharp bony crest, where the sphenoid drops abruptly to the greater wings. The greater wings form about half of the middle cranial fossa (the temporal bone forming the rest) and are perforated by several foramina.

The greater wing also forms part of the lateral surface of the cranium just anterior to the temporal bone (see fig. 8.4a). The lesser wing forms the posterior wall of the orbit and contains the **optic canal,** which permits passage of the optic nerve and ophthalmic artery (see fig. 8.14). Superiorly, a pair of bony spines of the lesser wing called the **anterior clinoid processes** appears to guard the optic foramina. A gash in the posterior wall of the orbit, the **superior orbital fissure,** angles upward lateral to the optic canal. It serves as a passage for three nerves that supply the muscles of eye movement.

The body of the sphenoid bone **(fig. 8.11b)** contains a pair of sphenoidal sinuses and has a saddlelike surface feature named the **sella turcica**[16] (SEL-la TUR-sih-ca). The sella consists of a deep pit called the *hypophysial fossa,* which houses the pituitary gland (hypophysis); a raised anterior margin called the *tuberculum sellae* (too-BUR-cu-lum SEL-lee); and a posterior margin called the *dorsum sellae.* In life, the dura mater stretches over the sella turcica and attaches to the anterior clinoid processes. A stalk penetrates the dura to connect the pituitary gland to the base of the brain.

Lateral to the sella turcica, the sphenoid is perforated by several foramina (see fig. 8.5a). The **foramen rotundum** and **foramen ovale** (oh-VAY-lee) are passages for two branches of the trigeminal nerve. The **foramen spinosum,** about the diameter of

[14]*nucha* = back of the neck
[15]*sphen* = wedge; *oid* = resembling
[16]*sella* = saddle; *turcica* = Turkish

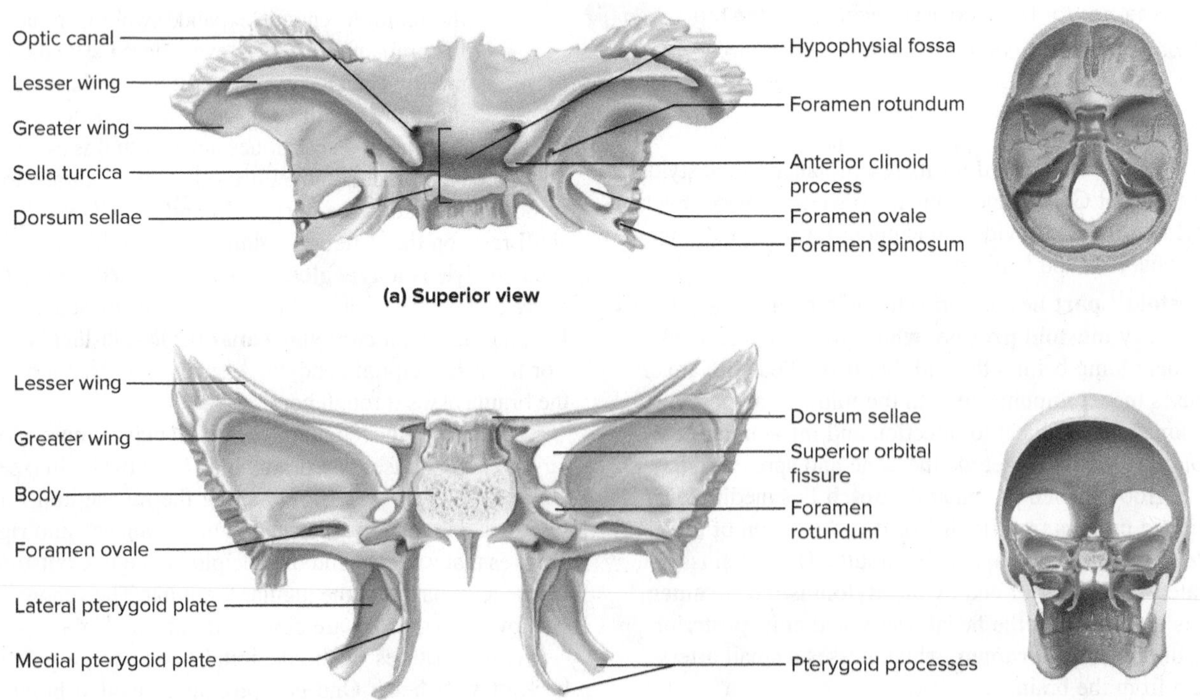


**FIGURE 8.11 The Sphenoid Bone.** (a) Superior view. (b) Posterior view, as if looking from the back of the head into the opened skull. APR

a pencil lead, provides passage for an artery of the meninges. An irregular gash called the **foramen lacerum**[17] (LASS-eh-rum) occurs at the junction of the sphenoid, temporal, and occipital bones. It is filled with cartilage in life and transmits no major vessels or nerves.

In an inferior view of the skull, the sphenoid can be seen just anterior to the basilar part of the occipital bone. The internal openings of the nasal cavity seen here are called the **posterior nasal apertures,** or **choanae**[18] (co-AH-nee). Lateral to each aperture, the sphenoid bone exhibits a pair of parallel plates—the **medial** and **lateral pterygoid**[19] **plates** (TERR-ih-goyd) (see fig. 8.5a). Each plate has a narrower inferior extension called the **pterygoid process.** These plates and processes provide attachment for some of the jaw muscles.

## The Ethmoid Bone

The **ethmoid**[20] **bone** (ETH-moyd) is an anterior cranial bone located between the eyes (figs. 8.7 and **8.12**). It contributes to the medial wall of the orbit, the roof and walls of the nasal cavity, and the nasal septum. It is a very porous and delicate bone, with three major portions:

1. The vertical **perpendicular plate,** a thin median plate of bone that forms the superior two-thirds of the nasal septum (see fig. 8.4b). (The lower part is formed by the *vomer,* discussed later.) The septum divides the nasal cavity into right and left air spaces called the **nasal fossae** (FOSS-ee). The septum is often curved, or deviated, toward one nasal fossa or the other.
2. A horizontal **cribriform**[21] **plate** (CRIB-rih-form), which forms the roof of the nasal cavity. This plate has a median blade called the **crista galli**[22] (GAL-eye), an attachment point for the dura mater. On each side of the crista is an elongated depressed area perforated with numerous holes, the **cribriform (olfactory) foramina.** A pair of *olfactory bulbs* of the brain, concerned with the sense of smell, rests in these depressions, and the foramina allow passage for olfactory nerves from the nasal cavity to the bulbs.
3. The **ethmoidal labyrinth,** a large mass on each side of the perpendicular plate. The labyrinth is named for the fact that internally, it has a maze of air spaces called the **ethmoidal cells.** Collectively, these constitute the *ethmoidal sinus* discussed earlier. The lateral surface of the labyrinth is a smooth, slightly concave **orbital plate** seen on the medial wall of the orbit (see fig. 8.14). The medial surface of the labyrinth gives rise to two curled, scroll-like plates of bone called the **superior** and **middle nasal conchae**[23] (CON-kee). These project into the nasal fossa from its lateral wall toward the septum (see figs. 8.7 and **8.13**). There is also a separate bone, the *inferior nasal concha,* discussed later. The three conchae occupy most of the nasal cavity, leaving little open space. By filling space and creating turbulence in the flow of inhaled air, they ensure that the air contacts the mucous membranes that cover these bones, which cleanse, humidify, and warm the inhaled air before it reaches the lungs. The superior concha and adjacent part of the nasal septum also bear the sensory cells of smell.

Usually, all that can be seen of the ethmoid is the perpendicular plate, by looking into the nasal cavity (see fig. 8.3); the orbital plate, by looking at the medial wall of the orbit **(fig. 8.14);** and the crista galli and cribriform plate, seen from within the cranial cavity (see fig. 8.5b).

[17]*lacerum* = torn, lacerated
[18]*choana* = funnel
[19]*pteryg* = wing; *oid* = resembling
[20]*ethmo* = sieve, strainer; *oid* = resembling

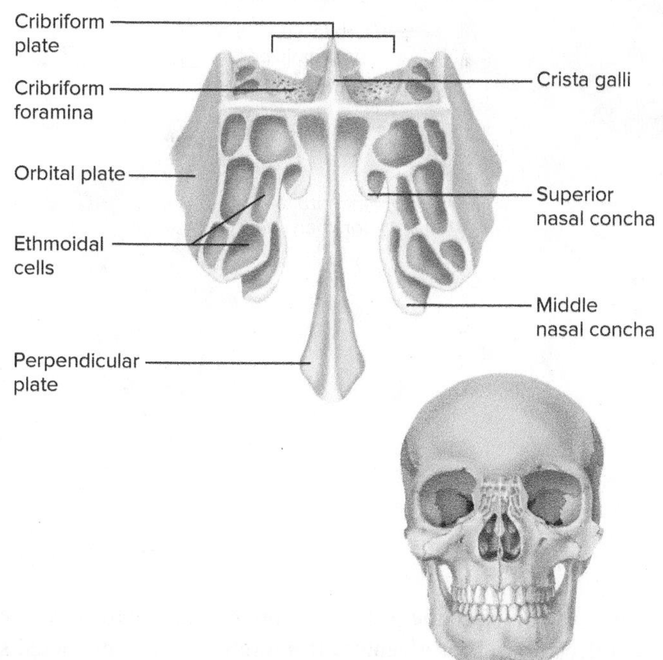


**FIGURE 8.12 The Ethmoid Bone (Anterior View).** 

*List five bones that articulate with the ethmoid bone.*

## 8.2b Facial Bones

**Facial bones** do not enclose the brain but lie anterior to the cranial cavity. They support the orbital, nasal, and oral cavities, shape the face, and provide attachment for the muscles of facial expression and mastication. There are 14 facial bones:

| | |
|---|---|
| 2 maxillae | 2 nasal bones |
| 2 palatine bones | 2 inferior nasal conchae |
| 2 zygomatic bones | 1 vomer |
| 2 lacrimal bones | 1 mandible |

[21]*cribri* = sieve; *form* = in the shape of
[22]*crista* = crest; *galli* = of a rooster
[23]*concha* = conch (large marine snail)

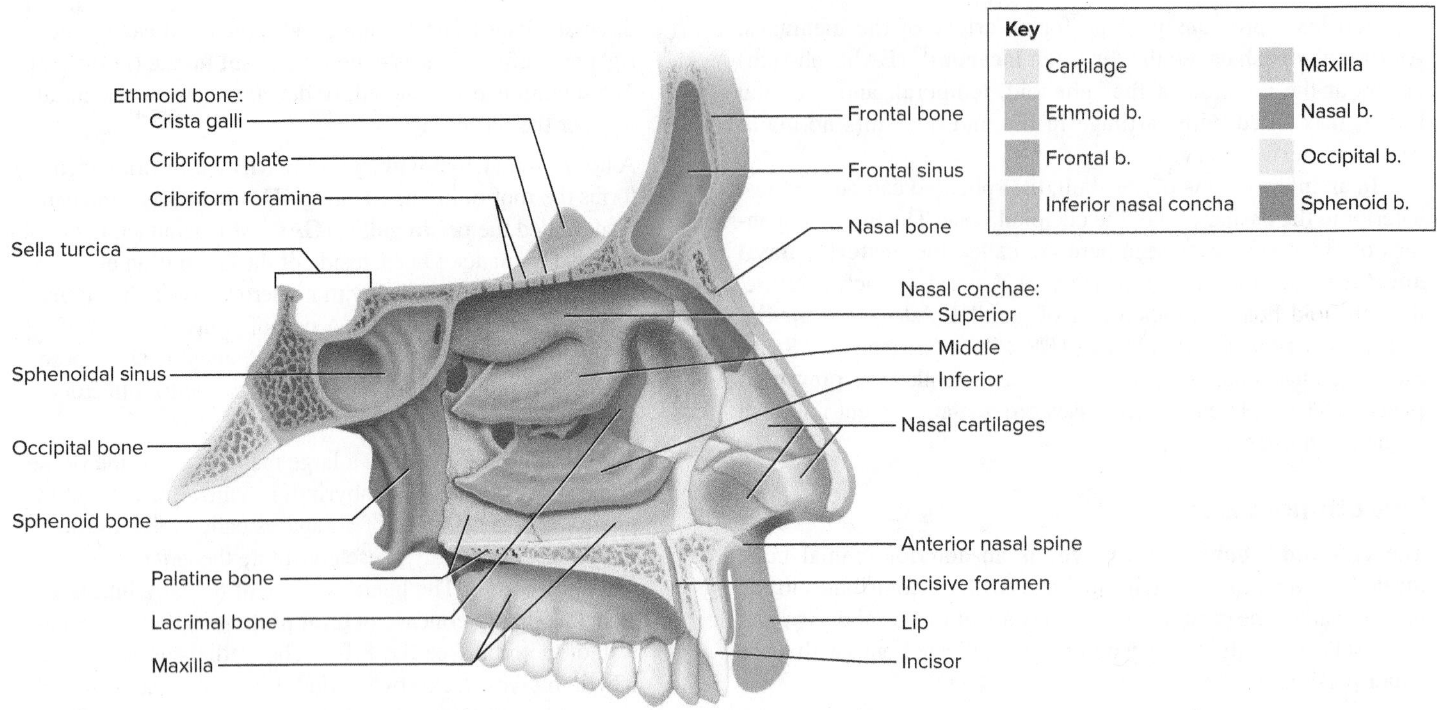


**FIGURE 8.13 The Left Nasal Cavity, Sagittal Section with Nasal Septum Removed.** APR

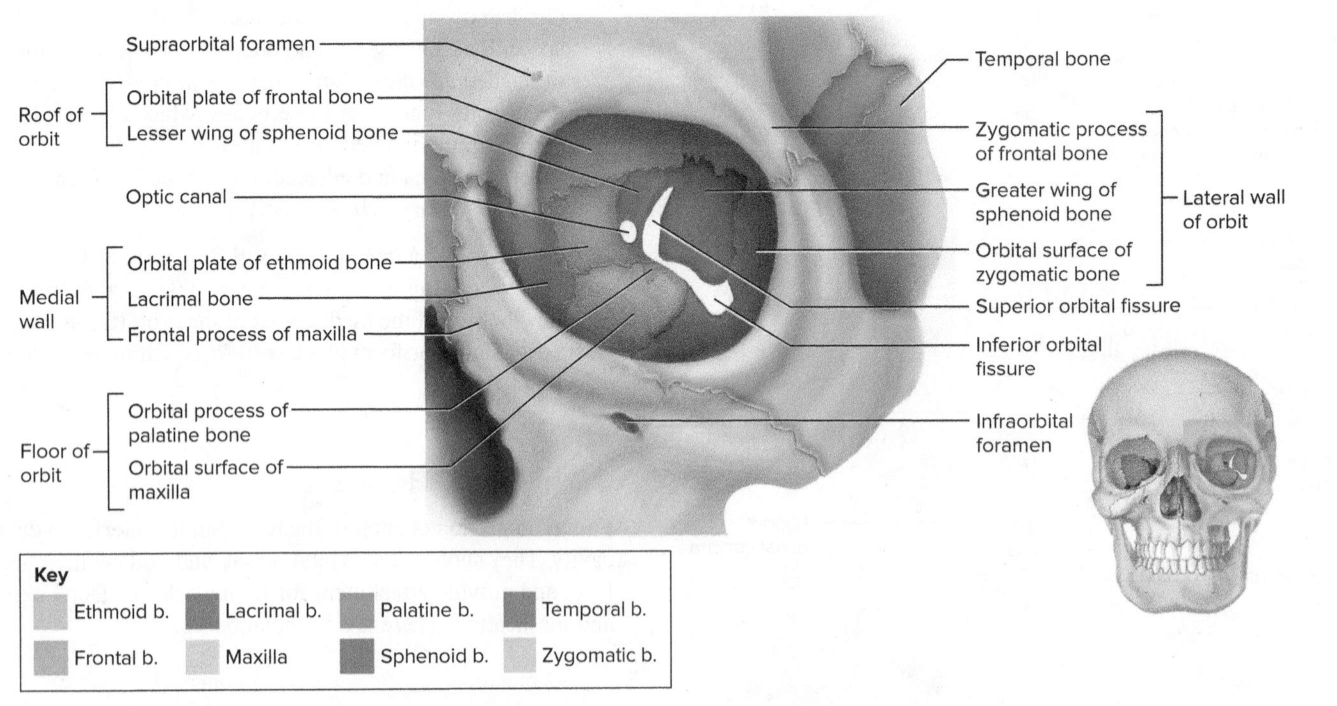


**FIGURE 8.14 The Left Orbit (Anterior View).** APR

## The Maxillae

The **maxillae** (mac-SILL-ee) are the largest facial bones. They form the upper jaw and meet each other at a median *intermaxillary suture* (see figs. 8.3, 8.4a, and 8.5a). Small points of maxillary bone called **alveolar processes** grow into the spaces between the bases of the teeth. The root of each tooth is inserted into a deep socket, or **alveolus.** If a tooth is lost or extracted so that chewing no longer puts stress on the maxilla, the alveolar processes are resorbed and the alveolus fills in with new bone, leaving a smooth area on the maxilla.

Although they are preserved with the skull, the teeth are not bones. They are discussed in detail in section 25.2a.

**APPLY WHAT YOU KNOW**

*Suppose you were studying a skull with some teeth missing. How could you tell whether the teeth had been lost after the person's death or years before it?*

Each maxilla extends from the teeth to the inferomedial wall of the orbit. Just below the orbit, it exhibits an **infraorbital foramen,** which provides passage for a blood vessel to the face and a nerve that receives sensations from the nasal region and cheek. This nerve emerges through the foramen rotundum into the cranial cavity. The maxilla forms part of the floor of the orbit, where it exhibits a gash called the **inferior orbital fissure** that angles downward and medially (fig. 8.14). The inferior and superior orbital fissures form a sideways V whose apex lies near the optic canal. The inferior orbital fissure is a passage for blood vessels and sensory nerves from the face.

The **palate** forms the roof of the mouth and floor of the nasal cavity. Its function is to separate the nasal cavity from the oral cavity, enabling us (and other mammals) to continue breathing while chewing. The high metabolic rate of humans requires rapid digestion of food, which in turn is aided by prolonged and thorough mastication into small, easily digested particles. This would be difficult if such prolonged mastication required an interruption of airflow.

The palate consists of a bony **hard palate** anteriorly and a fleshy **soft palate** posteriorly. Most of the hard palate is formed by horizontal extensions of the maxilla called **palatine processes** (PAL-uh-tine) (see fig. 8.5a). Just behind the incisors (front teeth) is a median pit, the **incisive fossa,** which is a passage for an artery to the palate and a nerve to the lower part of the nasal septum and the six front teeth of the maxilla. One or two pairs of *incisive foramina* open into this fossa (fig. 8.13) but are difficult to see. The palatine processes normally meet at the intermaxillary suture at about 12 weeks of gestation. Failure to join results in a *cleft palate* (see Deeper Insight 8.1).

### Cleft Palate and Lip

Failure of the fetal maxillae to join results in a cleft palate—a median fissure between the oral and nasal cavities, often accompanied by an upper lip cleft on one or both sides. A cleft palate makes it difficult for an infant to generate the suction needed for nursing, and may be accompanied by frequent ear infections and difficulties in hearing and speech. Cleft palate and lip can be surgically corrected with good cosmetic results, but may require follow-up speech therapy. Correction by 18 months of age can improve language acquisition and avoid the psychosocial problems often faced by school-age children with the condition.

## The Palatine Bones

The **palatine bones** divide the oral and nasal cavities from each other posteriorly (fig. 8.13). Each has an L shape formed by a *horizontal plate* and a *perpendicular plate.* The horizontal plates form the posterior one-third of the bony palate. Each is marked by a large **greater palatine foramen,** a nerve passage to the palate. The perpendicular plate is a thin, delicate, irregularly shaped plate that forms part of the wall between the nasal cavity and the orbit (see figs. 8.5a and 8.13).

## The Zygomatic Bones

The **zygomatic**[24] **bones,** colloquially called the cheekbones, form the angles of the cheeks at the inferolateral margins of the orbits and part of the lateral wall of each orbit; they extend about halfway to the ear (see figs. 8.4a and 8.5a). Each zygomatic bone has an inverted T shape and usually a small **zygomaticofacial foramen** (ZY-go-MAT-ih-co-FAY-shul) near the intersection of the stem and crossbar of the T. A nerve passes through here to supply the skin on the prominence of the cheek. The prominent zygomatic arch that flares from each side of the skull is formed mainly by the union of the zygomatic bone, temporal bone, and maxilla (see fig. 8.4a).

## The Lacrimal Bones

The **lacrimal**[25] **bones** (LACK-rih-mul) form part of the medial wall of each orbit (fig. 8.14). They are the smallest bones of the skull, about the size of the little fingernail. A depression called the **lacrimal fossa** houses a membranous *lacrimal sac* in life. Tears from the eye collect in this sac and drain into the nasal cavity.

## The Nasal Bones

Two small rectangular **nasal bones** form the bridge of the nose (see fig. 8.3) and support cartilages that shape its lower portion. If you palpate the bridge, you can easily feel where the nasal bones end and the cartilages begin. The nasal bones are often fractured by blows to the nose.

## The Inferior Nasal Conchae

There are three conchae in the nasal cavity. The superior and middle conchae, as discussed earlier, are parts of the ethmoid bone. The **inferior nasal concha**—the largest of the three—is a separate bone (fig. 8.13).

## The Vomer

The **vomer** forms the inferior half of the nasal septum (see figs. 8.3 and 8.4b). Its name literally means "plowshare," which refers to its resemblance to the blade of a plow. The superior half of the nasal septum is formed by the perpendicular plate of the ethmoid bone, as mentioned earlier. The vomer and perpendicular plate support a wall of *septal cartilage* that forms most of the anterior part of the septum.

[24]*zygo* = to join, unite
[25]*lacrim* = tear, to cry

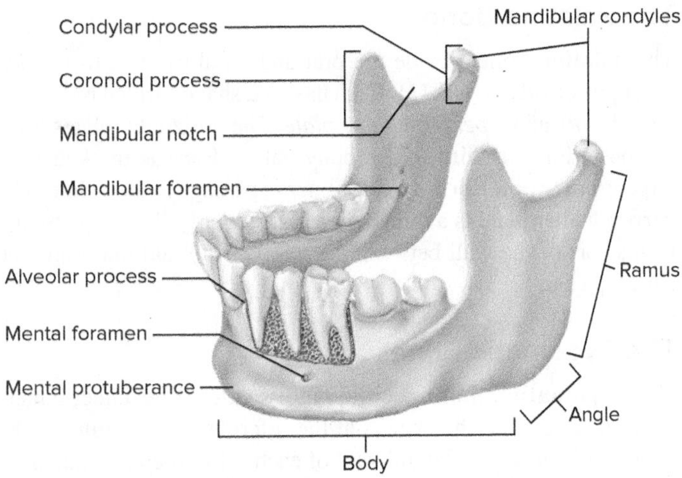


FIGURE 8.15 **The Mandible.** APR

## The Mandible

The **mandible (fig. 8.15)** is the strongest bone of the skull and the only one that can move significantly. It supports the lower teeth and provides attachment for muscles of mastication and facial expression. The horizontal portion, bearing the teeth, is called the **body;** the vertical to oblique posterior portion is the **ramus** (RAY-mus) (plural, *rami*); and these two portions meet at a corner called the **angle.** The mandible develops as separate right and left bones in the fetus, joined by a median cartilaginous joint called the **mental symphysis** (SIM-fih-sis) at the point of the chin. This joint ossifies in early childhood, uniting the two halves into a single bone. The point of the chin itself is called the **mental protuberance.** The inner (posterior) surface of the mandible in this region has a pair of small points, the **mental spines,** which serve for attachment of certain chin muscles (see fig. 8.4b).

On the anterolateral surface of the body, the **mental foramen** permits the passage of nerves and blood vessels of the chin. The inner surface of the body has a number of shallow depressions and ridges to accommodate muscles and salivary glands. The angle of the mandible has a rough lateral surface for insertion of the *masseter,* a muscle of mastication. Like the maxilla, the mandible has pointed alveolar processes between the teeth.

The ramus is somewhat Y-shaped. Its posterior branch, called the **condylar process** (CON-dih-lur), bears the **mandibular condyle**—an oval knob that articulates with the mandibular fossa of the temporal bone. The meeting of this condyle with the temporal bone forms a hinge, the **temporomandibular joint (TMJ).** The anterior branch of the ramus is a blade called the **coronoid process.** It is the point of insertion for the temporalis muscle, which pulls the mandible upward when you bite. The U-shaped arch between the two processes is the **mandibular notch.** Just below the notch, on the medial surface of the ramus, is the **mandibular foramen.** The nerve and blood vessels that supply the lower teeth enter this foramen and then travel through the bone of the mandibular body, giving off branches to each tooth along the way. Dentists commonly inject lidocaine near the mandibular foramen to deaden sensation from the lower teeth.

## 8.2c Bones Associated with the Skull

Seven bones are closely associated with the skull but not considered part of it. These are the three auditory ossicles in each middle-ear cavity and the hyoid bone beneath the chin. The **auditory ossicles**[26]—named the **malleus** (hammer), **incus** (anvil), and **stapes** (STAY-peez) (stirrup)—are discussed in connection with hearing in "Anatomy of the Ear" in section 16.4.

The **hyoid**[27] **bone** is a slender U-shaped bone between the chin and larynx **(fig. 8.16).** It is one of the few bones that doesn't articulate with any other. It is suspended from the styloid processes of the skull, somewhat like a hammock, by the small *stylohyoid muscles* and *stylohyoid ligaments.* The median **body** of the hyoid is flanked on either side by hornlike projections called the **greater** and **lesser horns (cornua).** The larynx (voice box) is suspended from the hyoid bone by a broad ligament (see fig. 22.4a), and the hyoid serves for attachment of several muscles that control the mandible, tongue, and larynx. Forensic pathologists look for a fractured hyoid as evidence of strangulation.

## 8.2d The Skull in Infancy and Childhood

The head of an infant couldn't fit through the mother's pelvic outlet at birth if not for the fact that the bones of its skull are not yet fused. The shifting of the cranial bones during birth may cause the infant's head to appear deformed, but it soon assumes a more normal shape. Spaces between the unfused cranial bones are called **fontanelles,**[28] after the fact that pulsation of the infant's blood can be felt there. The bones are joined at these points only by fibrous membranes, in which intramembranous ossification is completed later (see fig. 7.10). Four of these sites are especially prominent and regular in location: the **anterior, posterior, sphenoid (anterolateral),**

[26] *os* = bone; *icle* = little
[27] *hy* = the letter U; *oid* = resembling
[28] *fontan* = fountain; *elle* = little

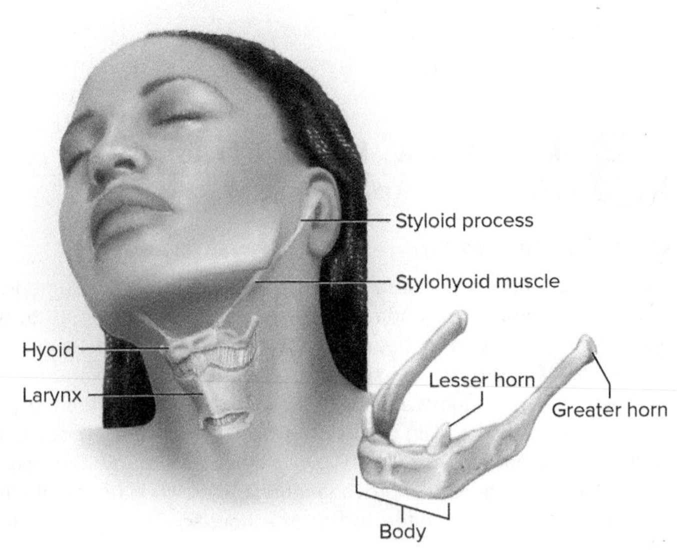


FIGURE 8.16 **The Hyoid Bone.**

## DEEPER INSIGHT 8.2
### CLINICAL APPLICATION

### *Cranial Assessment of the Newborn*

Obstetric nurses routinely assess the fontanelles of newborns by palpation. In a difficult delivery, one cranial bone may override another along a suture line, which calls for close monitoring of the infant. Abnormally wide sutures may indicate hydrocephalus, the accumulation of excessive amounts of cerebrospinal fluid, which causes the cranium to swell. Bulging fontanelles suggest abnormally high intracranial pressure, while depressed fontanelles indicate dehydration.

and **mastoid (posterolateral) fontanelles (fig. 8.17).** Most fontanelles ossify by the time the infant is a year old, but the largest one—the anterior fontanelle—can still be palpated 18 to 24 months after birth.

The frontal bone and mandible are separate right and left bones at birth, but fuse medially in early childhood. The frontal bones usually fuse by age 5 or 6, but in some children a *metopic*[29] *suture* persists between them. Traces of this suture are evident in some adult skulls.

The face of a newborn is flat and the cranium relatively large. To accommodate the growing brain, the skull grows more rapidly than the rest of the skeleton during childhood. It reaches about half its adult size by 9 months of age, three-quarters by age 2, and nearly final size by 8 or 9 years. The heads of babies and children are therefore much larger in proportion to the trunk than the heads of adults—an attribute thoroughly exploited by cartoonists and advertisers who draw big-headed characters to give them a more endearing or immature appearance. In humans and other animals, the large, rounded heads of the young are thought to promote survival by stimulating parental caregiving instincts.

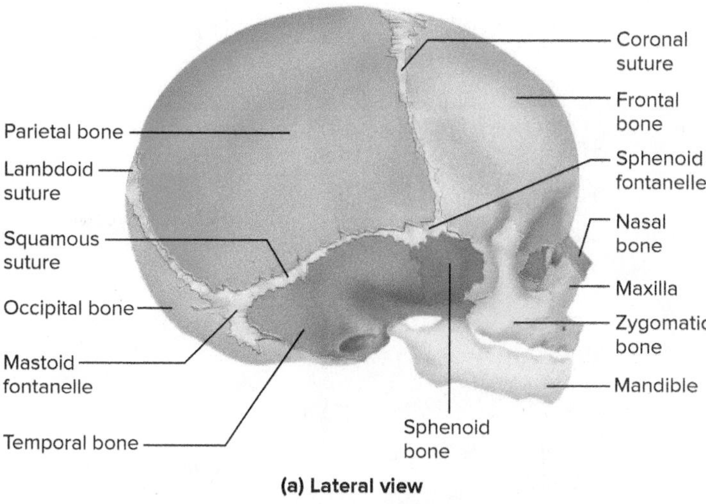


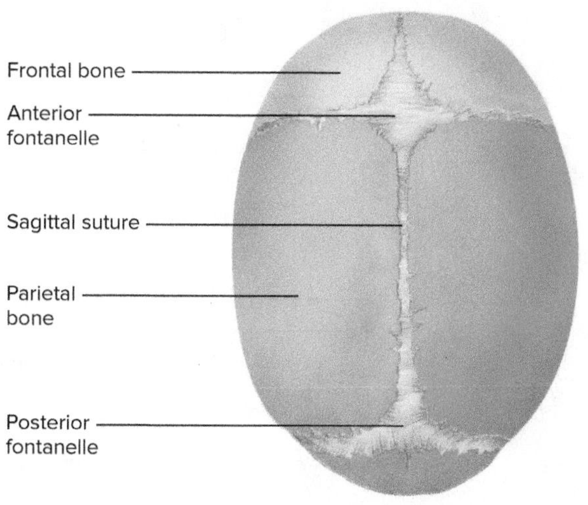


**FIGURE 8.17 The Fetal Skull Near the Time of Birth.** (a) Lateral view. (b) Superior view of the calvaria.

**BEFORE YOU GO ON**

Answer the following questions to test your understanding of the preceding section:

4. Name the paranasal sinuses and state their locations. Name any four other cavities in the skull.
5. Explain the difference between a cranial bone and a facial bone. Give four examples of each.
6. Draw an oval representing a superior view of the calvaria. Draw lines representing the coronal, lambdoid, and sagittal sutures. Label the four bones separated by these sutures.
7. State which bone has each of these features: a squamous part, hypoglossal canal, greater horn, greater wing, condylar process, and cribriform plate.
8. Determine which of the following structures cannot normally be palpated on a living person: the mastoid process, crista galli, superior orbital fissure, palatine processes, zygomatic bone, mental protuberance, and stapes. You may find it useful to palpate some of these on your own skull as you try to answer.

## 8.3 The Vertebral Column and Thoracic Cage

### Expected Learning Outcomes

When you have completed this section, you should be able to

a. describe the general features of the vertebral column and those of a typical vertebra;
b. describe the structure of the intervertebral discs and their relationship to the vertebrae;
c. describe the special features of vertebrae in different regions of the vertebral column, and discuss the functional significance of the regional differences; and
d. describe the anatomy of the sternum and ribs and how the ribs articulate with the thoracic vertebrae.

[29] *met* = beyond; *op* = the eyes

## 8.3a General Features of the Vertebral Column

The **vertebral column,** or **spine,** physically supports the skull and trunk, allows for their movement, protects the spinal cord, and absorbs stresses produced by walking, running, and lifting. It also provides attachment for the limbs, thoracic cage, and postural muscles. Although commonly called the backbone, it consists of not a single bone but a flexible chain of 33 **vertebrae** with **intervertebral discs** of fibrocartilage between most of them.

The adult vertebral column averages about 71 cm (28 in.) long, with the intervertebral discs accounting for about one-quarter of the length. Most people are about 1% shorter when they go to bed at night than when they first rise in the morning. This is because during the day, the weight of the body compresses the intervertebral discs and squeezes water out of them. When one is sleeping, with the weight off the spine, the discs reabsorb water and swell.

As shown in **figure 8.18,** the vertebrae are divided into five groups, usually numbering 7 *cervical vertebrae* (SUR-vih-cul) in the neck, 12 *thoracic vertebrae* in the chest, 5 *lumbar vertebrae* in the lower back, 5 *sacral vertebrae* at the base of the spine, and 4 tiny *coccygeal vertebrae* (coc-SIDJ-ee-ul). To help remember the numbers of cervical, thoracic, and lumbar vertebrae—7, 12, and 5—think of a typical workday: Go to work at 7, have lunch at 12, and go home at 5. All mammals have 7 cervical vertebrae, even in the famously long necks of giraffes.

Variations in this arrangement occur in about 1 person in 20. For example, the last lumbar vertebra is sometimes incorporated into the sacrum, producing four lumbar and six sacral vertebrae. In other cases, the first sacral vertebra fails to fuse with the second, producing six lumbar and four sacral vertebrae. The coccyx usually has four but sometimes five vertebrae. The cervical and thoracic vertebrae are more constant in number.

Beyond the age of 3 years, the vertebral column has four bends that give it an undulating S shape **(fig. 8.19).** A bend that is concave in the anterior direction (curved outward toward the back) is called a **kyphosis.**[30] There are two of these, the *thoracic kyphosis* and *pelvic kyphosis.* A bend toward the front,

[30]*kypho* = crooked, bent; *osis* = condition

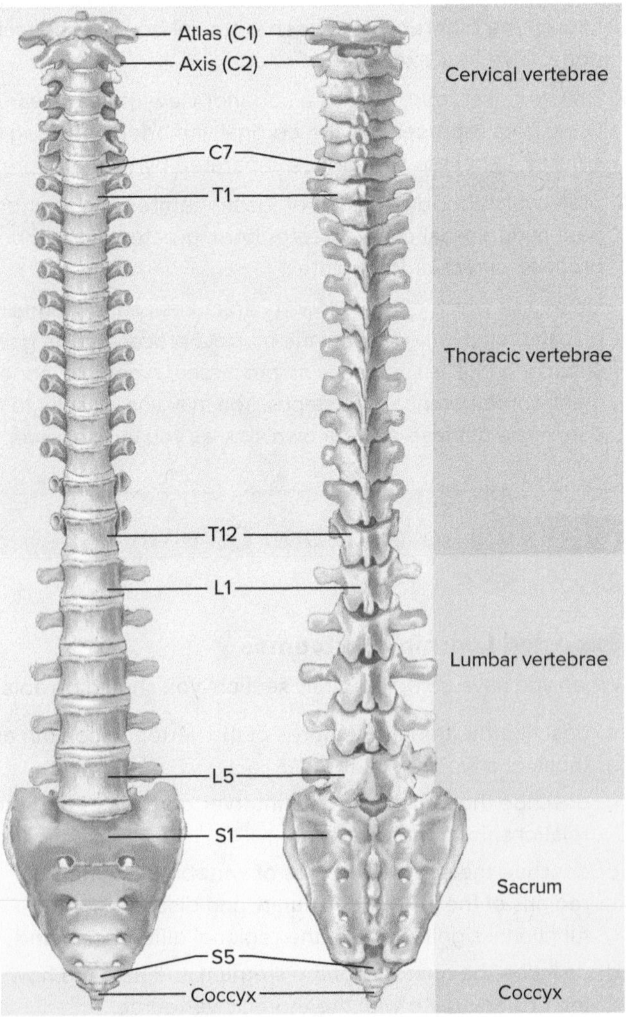

**(a) Anterior view** **(b) Posterior view**

FIGURE 8.18 **The Vertebral Column.** (a) Anterior view. (b) Posterior view. APR

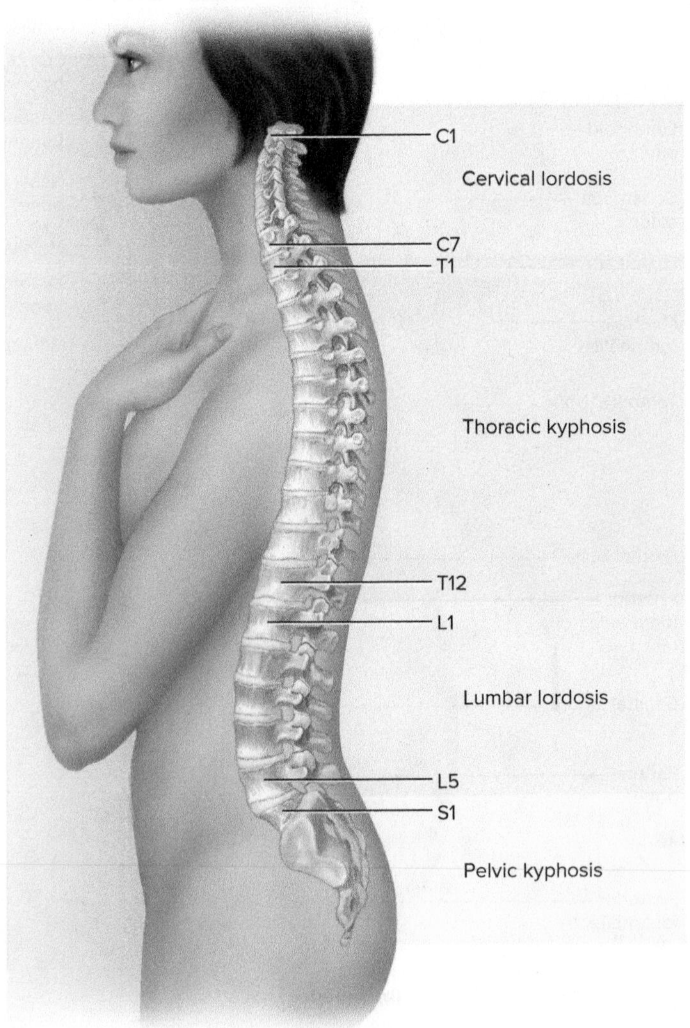


FIGURE 8.19 **Curvatures of the Adult Vertebral Column.**

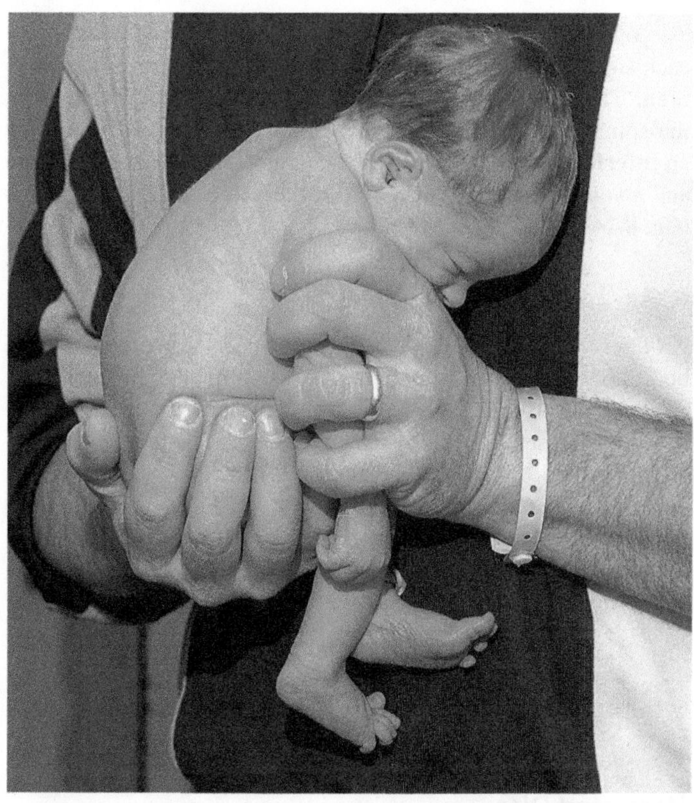

FIGURE 8.20 **Spinal Curvature of the Newborn Infant.** At this age, the spine forms a single C-shaped curve.

Bob Coyle/McGraw-Hill Education

concave posteriorly, is called a **lordosis,**[31] and there are also two of these—the *cervical lordosis* and *lumbar lordosis.* These are not present in the newborn, whose spine exhibits one continuous C-shaped curve, as it does in monkeys, apes, and most other four-legged animals **(fig. 8.20).** As an infant begins to crawl and lift its head, the cervical region becomes curved toward the posterior side, enabling an infant on its belly to look up. As a toddler begins walking, another curve develops in the same direction in the lumbar region. The resulting S shape makes sustained bipedal walking possible (see Deeper Insight 8.5). The thoracic and pelvic kyphoses are called *primary curvatures* because they exist from birth. The cervical and lumbar lordoses are called *secondary curvatures* because they develop later, in the child's first few years of crawling and walking. Abnormal lateral and anteroposterior curvatures are among the most common disorders of the spine (see Deeper Insight 8.3).

### 8.3b General Structure of a Vertebra

A representative vertebra and intervertebral disc are shown in **figure 8.22.** The most obvious feature of a vertebra is the **body (centrum)**—a mass of spongy bone and red bone marrow covered with a thin shell of compact, cortical bone. This is the weight-bearing portion of the vertebra. Its rough superior and inferior surfaces provide firm attachment to the intervertebral discs.

[31]*lordo* = backward; *osis* = condition

## DEEPER INSIGHT 8.3

### CLINICAL APPLICATION

### *Abnormal Spinal Curvatures*

Abnormal spinal curvatures **(fig. 8.21)** can result from disease, weakness or paralysis of the trunk muscles, poor posture, pregnancy, or congenital defects in vertebral anatomy. The most common deformity is an abnormal lateral curvature called *scoliosis.* It occurs most often in the thoracic region, particularly among adolescent girls. It sometimes results from a developmental abnormality in which the body and arch fail to develop on one side of a vertebra. If the person's skeletal growth is not yet complete, scoliosis can be corrected with a back brace.

An exaggerated thoracic curvature is called *hyperkyphosis.* It is usually a result of osteoporosis (see fig. 7.21), but it also occurs in people with osteomalacia or spinal tuberculosis and in adolescents who engage heavily in such spine-loading sports as wrestling and weight lifting. An exaggerated lumbar curvature is called *hyperlordosis.* It may have the same causes as hyperkyphosis, or it may result from added abdominal weight in pregnancy or obesity.

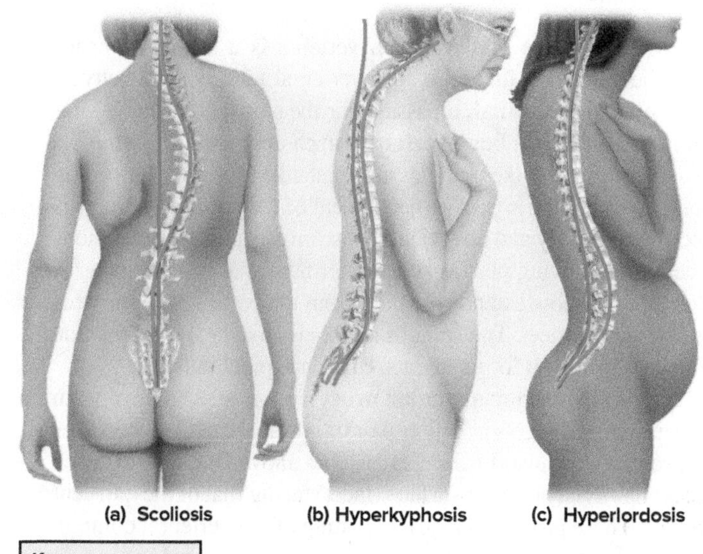


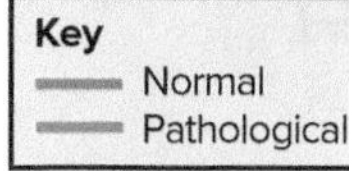


FIGURE 8.21 **Abnormal Spinal Curvatures.** (a) Scoliosis. (b) Hyperkyphosis. (c) Hyperlordosis.

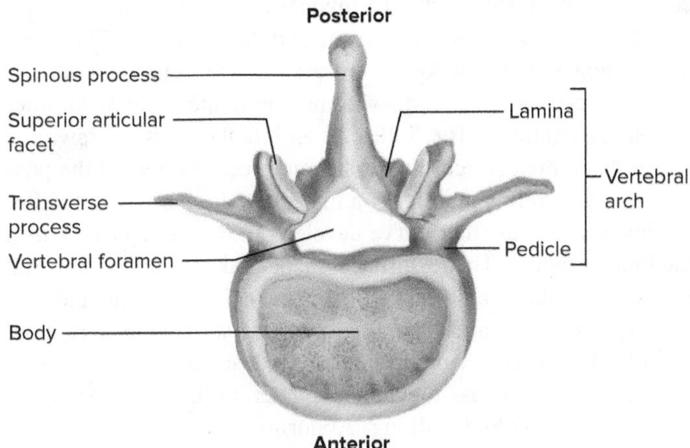


**(a) 2nd lumbar vertebra (L2)**

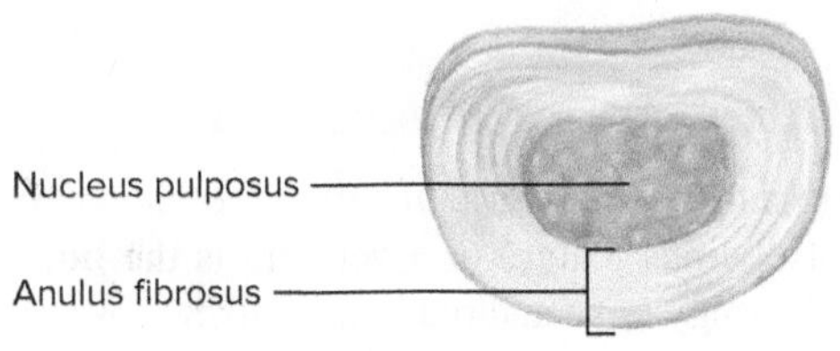


**(b) Intervertebral disc**

**FIGURE 8.22 A Representative Vertebra and Intervertebral Disc (Superior Views).** (a) A typical vertebra. (b) An intervertebral disc, oriented the same way as the vertebral body in part (a) for comparison.

**APPLY WHAT YOU KNOW**

*The vertebral bodies and intervertebral discs get progressively larger as we look lower and lower on the vertebral column. What is the functional significance of this trend?*

Posterior to the body of each vertebra is a triangular space called the **vertebral foramen.** The vertebral foramina collectively form the **vertebral canal,** a passage for the spinal cord. Each foramen is bordered by a bony **vertebral arch** composed of two parts on each side: a pillarlike **pedicle**[32] and platelike **lamina.**[33] Extending from the apex of the arch, a projection called the **spinous process** is directed posteriorly and downward. You can see and feel the spinous processes on a living person as a row of bumps along the spine. A **transverse process** extends laterally from the point where the pedicle and lamina meet. The spinous and transverse processes provide points of attachment for ligaments, ribs, and spinal muscles.

A pair of **superior articular processes** projects upward from one vertebra and meets a similar pair of inferior articular processes that projects downward from the vertebra above **(fig. 8.24a).** Each process has a flat articular surface (facet) facing that of the adjacent vertebra. These processes restrict twisting of the vertebral column, which could otherwise severely damage the spinal cord.

When two vertebrae are joined, they exhibit an opening on each side between their pedicles called the **intervertebral foramen.** These allow passage for spinal nerves that connect with the spinal cord at regular intervals. Each foramen is formed by an **inferior vertebral notch** in the pedicle of the upper vertebra and a **superior vertebral notch** in the pedicle of the lower one **(fig. 8.24b).**

## 8.3c Intervertebral Discs

An intervertebral disc is a cartilaginous pad located between the bodies of two adjacent vertebrae. It consists of an inner gelatinous **nucleus pulposus** surrounded by a ring of fibrocartilage, the **anulus fibrosus** (see fig. 8.22b). There are 23 discs—the first one between cervical vertebrae 2 and 3 (C2–C3) and the last one between the last lumbar vertebra and the sacrum (L5–S1). They help to bind adjacent vertebrae together, support the weight of the body, allow spinal mobility, and absorb shock. Discs can rupture painfully when subjected to excessive stress (see Deeper Insight 8.4).

### DEEPER INSIGHT 8.4
**CLINICAL APPLICATION**

### *Herniated Disc*

Stress on the vertebral column, as in lifting a heavy weight, compresses the intervertebral discs and makes them bulge laterally. Excessive stress can crack the anulus fibrosus, allowing the gelatinous nucleus pulposus to ooze out **(fig. 8.23).** This is called a *herniated disc* (colloquially, a "ruptured disc," or more inaccurately, "slipped disc"). Herniation usually occurs at the posterolateral corners of the discs because the anulus fibrosus is thinnest on the posterior side and corners are least supported by nearby spinal ligaments. About 95% of herniations are at the L4–L5 or L5–S1 level because these bear the most weight. Disc herniation rarely occurs in young people because of their well-hydrated, thick, resilient discs. Herniated discs are one of the most common causes of lower back pain, stemming from inflammation stimulated by the nucleus and pressure of the oozing nucleus on spinal nerve roots passing through this tight space. Over 80% of patients recover from the pain with only oral analgesics, requiring no surgery; up to 76% of cases resolve partially or completely within 1 year.

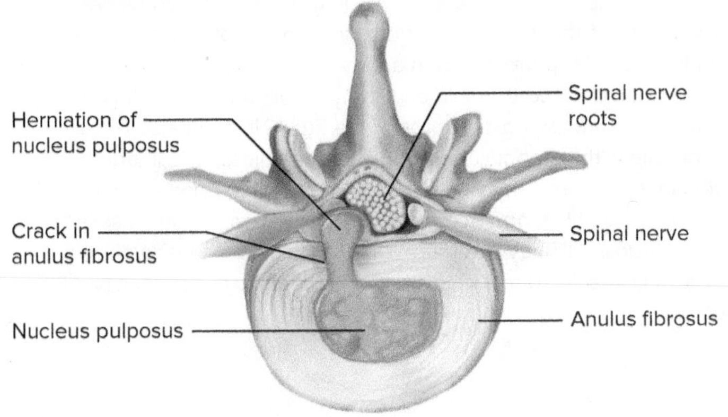


**FIGURE 8.23 Herniated Disc.**

[32]*ped* = foot; *icle* = little
[33]*lamina* = plate

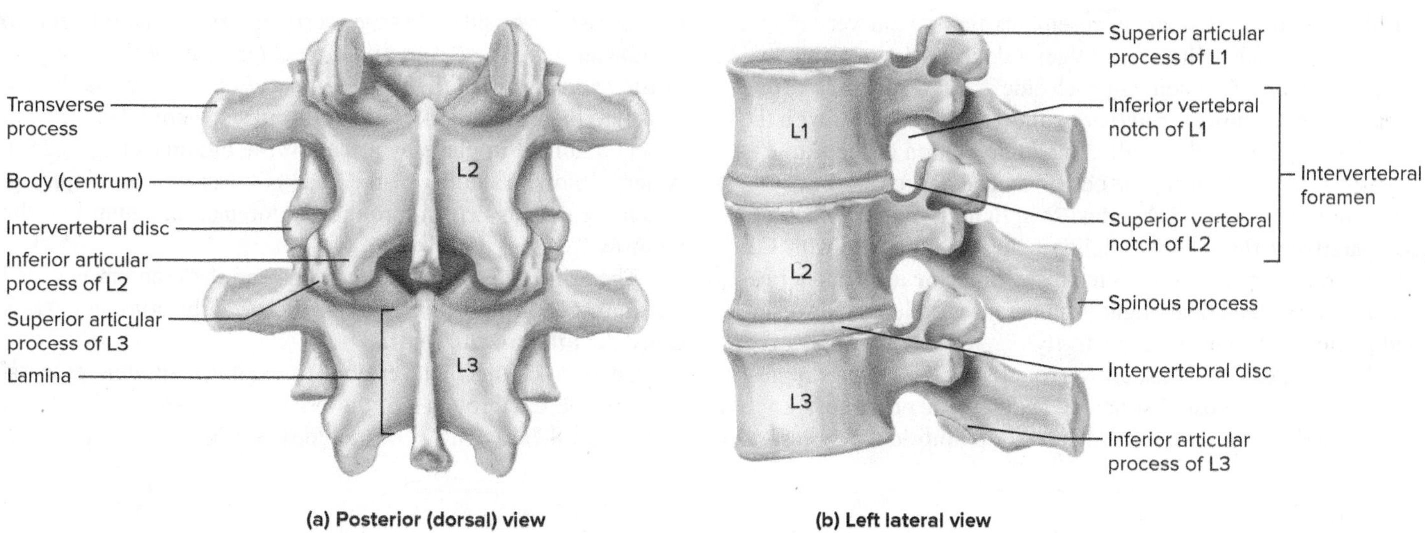


**FIGURE 8.24 Articulated Vertebrae.** (a) Posterior view. (b) Left lateral view.

## 8.3d Regional Characteristics of Vertebrae

We are now prepared to consider how vertebrae differ from one region of the vertebral column to another and from the generalized anatomy just described. Knowing these variations will enable you to identify the region of the spine from which an isolated vertebra was taken. More importantly, these modifications in form reflect functional differences among the vertebrae.

### The Cervical Vertebrae

The cervical vertebrae (C1–C7) are relatively small. Their function is to support the head and allow for its movements. The first two (C1 and C2) have unique structures for this purpose **(fig. 8.25).** Vertebra C1 is called the **atlas** because it supports the head in a manner reminiscent of Atlas, the giant of Greek mythology who was condemned by Zeus to carry the heavens

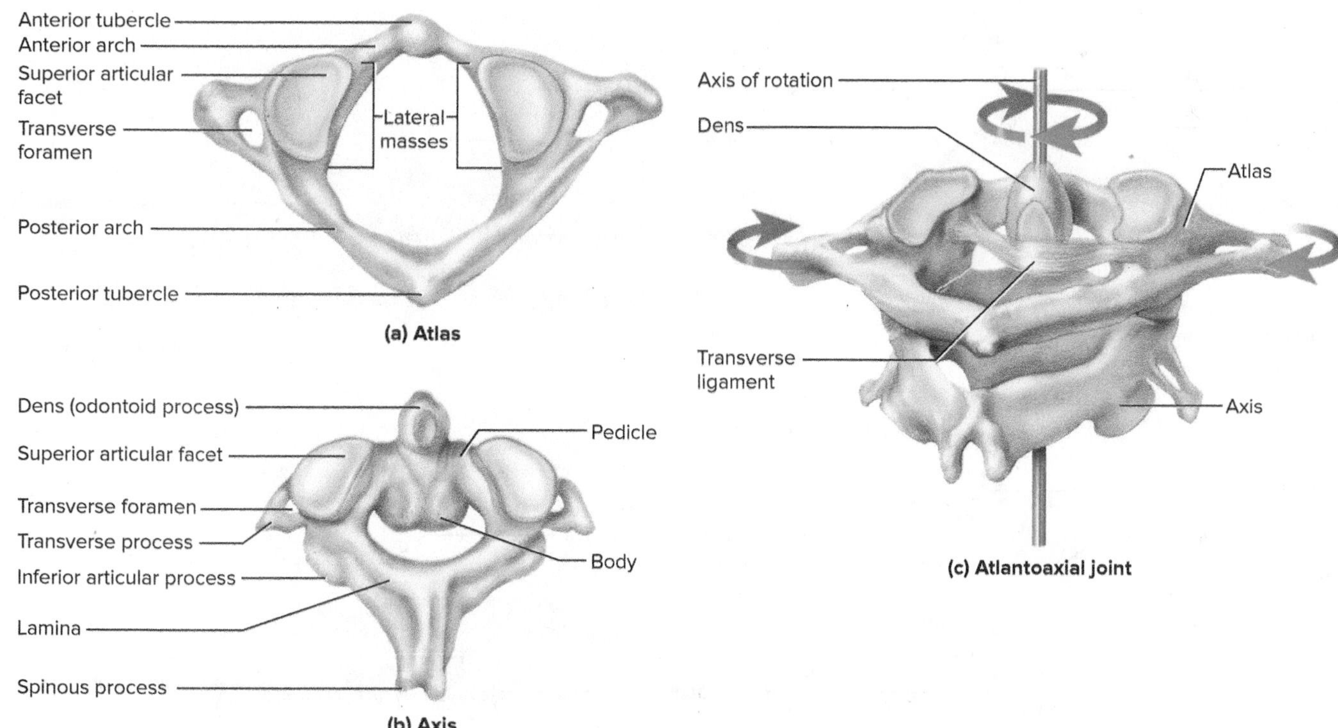


**FIGURE 8.25 The Atlas and Axis, Cervical Vertebrae C1 and C2.** (a) The atlas, superior view. (b) The axis, posterosuperior view. (c) Articulation of the atlas and axis and rotation of the atlas. This movement turns the head from side to side, as in gesturing "no." Note the transverse ligament holding the dens of the axis in place. APR

? *What serious consequence could result from a rupture of the transverse ligament?*

on his shoulders. It scarcely resembles the typical vertebra; it has no body, and is little more than a delicate ring surrounding a large vertebral foramen. On each side is a **lateral mass** with a deeply concave **superior articular facet** that articulates with the occipital condyle of the skull. A nodding motion of the skull, as in gesturing "yes," causes the occipital condyles to rock back and forth on these facets. The **inferior articular facets,** which are comparatively flat or only slightly concave, articulate with C2. The lateral masses are connected by an **anterior arch** and a **posterior arch,** which bear slight protuberances called the **anterior** and **posterior tubercle,** respectively.

Vertebra C2, the **axis,** allows rotation of the head as in gesturing "no." Its most distinctive feature is a prominent knob called the **dens** (pronounced "denz"), or **odontoid**[34] **process,** on its anterosuperior side. No other vertebra has a dens. It begins to form as an independent ossification center during the first year of life and fuses with the axis by the age of 3 to 6 years. It projects into the vertebral foramen of the atlas, where it is nestled in a facet and held in place by a **transverse ligament** (fig. 8.25c). A heavy blow to the top of the head can cause a fatal injury in which the dens is driven through the foramen magnum into the brainstem.

The articulation between the atlas and the cranium is called the **atlanto–occipital joint;** the one between the atlas and axis is called the **atlantoaxial joint.**

The axis is the first vertebra to exhibit a spinous process. In vertebrae C2 through C6, the process is forked, or *bifid,*[35] at its tip **(fig. 8.26a).** This fork provides attachment for the *nuchal*

[34] *dens* = *odont* = tooth; *oid* = resembling

[35] *bifid* = branched, cleft into two parts

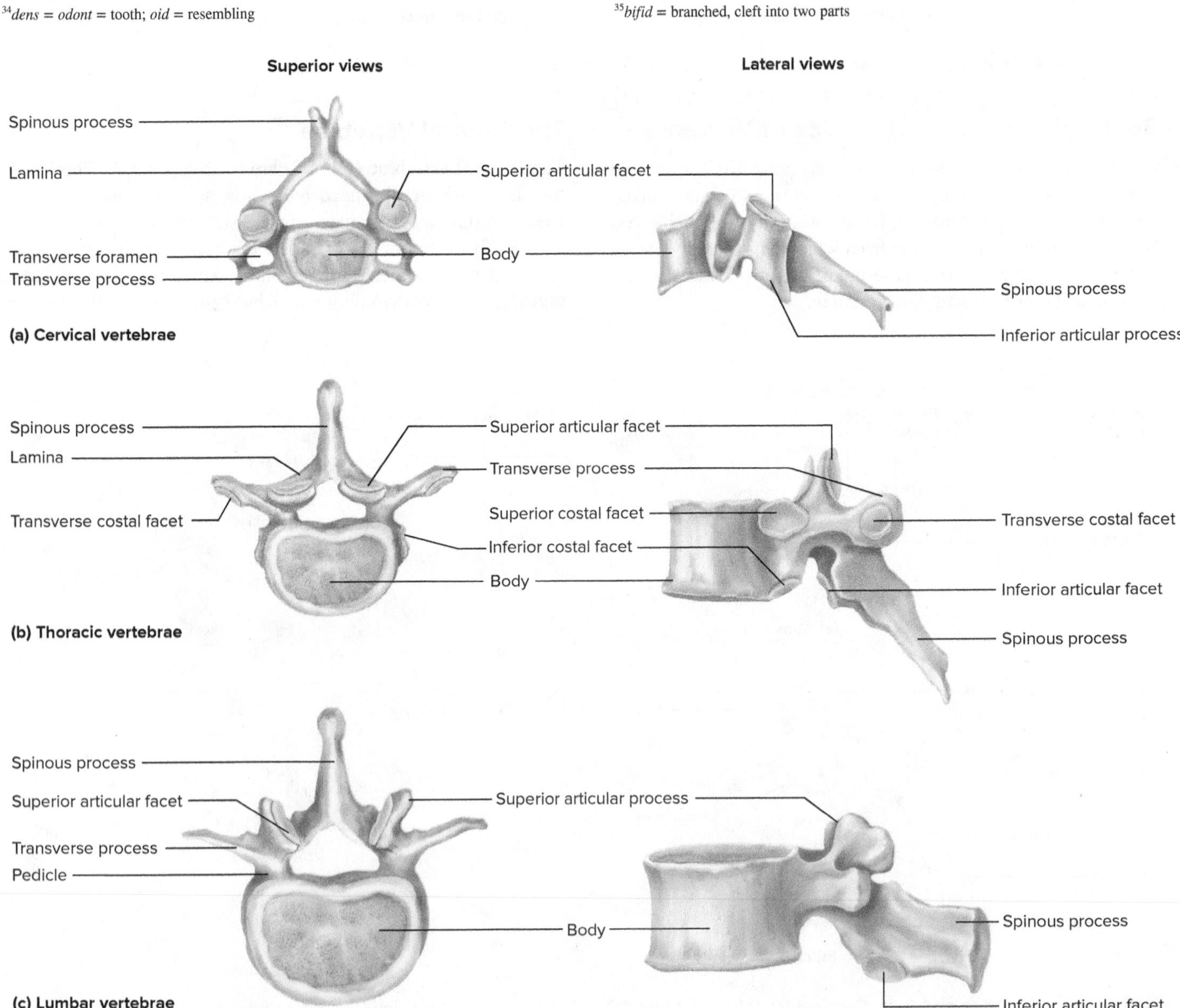


**FIGURE 8.26 Regional Differences in Vertebrae.** (a) Cervical vertebrae. (b) Thoracic vertebrae. (c) Lumbar vertebrae. The left-hand figures are superior views and the right-hand figures are left lateral views. APR

*ligament* of the back of the neck. All seven cervical vertebrae have a prominent round **transverse foramen** in each transverse process. These foramina provide passage and protection for the *vertebral arteries,* which supply blood to the brain, and *vertebral veins,* which drain blood from various neck structures (but not from the brain). Transverse foramina occur in no other vertebrae and thus provide an easy means of recognizing a cervical vertebra.

Cervical vertebrae C3 through C6 are similar to the typical vertebra depicted in figure 8.22a, with the addition of the transverse foramina and bifid spinous processes. Vertebra C7 is a little different—its spinous process is not bifid, but is especially long and forms a prominent bump on the lower back of the neck. C7 is sometimes called the *vertebra prominens* because of this conspicuous spinous process. This feature is a convenient landmark for counting vertebrae by palpation. One can easily identify the largest bump on the neck as C7, then count up or down from there to identify others.

## The Thoracic Vertebrae

There are 12 **thoracic vertebrae** (T1–T12), corresponding to the 12 pairs of ribs attached to them; no other vertebrae have ribs. One function of the thoracic vertebrae is to support the thoracic cage enclosing the heart and lungs. They lack the transverse foramina and bifid processes that distinguish the cervical vertebrae, but possess the following distinctive features of their own **(fig. 8.26b):**

- The spinous processes are relatively pointed and angle sharply downward.
- The body is somewhat heart-shaped, more massive than in the cervical vertebrae but less than in the lumbar vertebrae.
- The body has small, smooth, slightly concave spots called *costal facets* for attachment of the ribs.
- Vertebrae T1 through T10 have a shallow, cuplike **transverse costal**[36] **facet** at the end of each transverse process. These provide a second point of articulation for ribs 1 to 10. There are no transverse costal facets on T11 and T12 because ribs 11 and 12 attach only to the bodies of those two vertebrae.

Thoracic vertebrae vary among themselves mainly in the mode of articulation with the ribs (see fig. 8.30). In most cases, a rib inserts between two vertebrae, so each vertebra contributes one-half of the articular surface. A rib articulates with the **inferior costal facet** of the upper vertebra and the **superior costal facet** of the vertebra below that. This terminology may be a little confusing, but note that the superior and inferior facets are named for their position on the vertebral body, not for which part of the rib's articulation they provide. Vertebrae T1 and T10 through T12, however, have complete costal facets on the bodies for ribs 1 and 10 through 12, which articulate on the vertebral bodies instead of between vertebrae. Vertebrae T11 and T12, as noted, have no transverse costal facets. These variations will be more functionally understandable after you have studied the anatomy of the ribs, so we will return then to the details of these articular surfaces.

Each thoracic vertebra has a pair of superior articular facets that face posteriorly and a pair of inferior articular facets that face anteriorly (except in vertebra T12). Thus, the superior facets of one vertebra articulate with the inferior facets of the next one above it. In vertebra T12, however, the inferior articular facets face somewhat laterally instead of anteriorly. This positions them to articulate with the medially facing superior articular facets of the first lumbar vertebra. T12 thus shows an anatomical transition between the thoracic and lumbar pattern, described next.

## The Lumbar Vertebrae

There are five **lumbar vertebrae** (L1–L5). Their most distinctive features are a thick, stout body and a blunt, squarish spinous process for attachment of the strong lumbar muscles **(fig. 8.26c).** In addition, their articular processes are oriented differently than on other vertebrae. The superior processes face medially (like the palms of your hands about to clap), and the inferior processes face laterally, toward the superior processes of the next vertebra. This arrangement resists twisting of the lower spine. These differences are best observed on an articulated skeleton.

## The Sacrum

The **sacrum** (SACK-rum, SAY-krum) is a bony plate that forms the posterior wall of the pelvic girdle **(fig. 8.27).** It was named *sacrum* for its prominence as the largest and most durable bone of the vertebral column.[37] There are five separate **sacral vertebrae** (S1–S5) in children, but they begin to fuse around age 16 and are fully fused by age 26.

The anterior surface of the sacrum is relatively smooth and concave and has four transverse lines that indicate where the five vertebrae have fused. This surface exhibits four pairs of large **anterior sacral foramina,** which allow for passage of nerves and arteries to the pelvic organs. The posterior surface is very rough. The spinous processes of the vertebrae fuse into a ridge called the **median sacral crest.** The transverse processes fuse into a less prominent **lateral sacral crest** on each side of the median crest. Again on the posterior side of the sacrum, there are four pairs of openings for spinal nerves, the **posterior sacral foramina.** The nerves that emerge here supply the gluteal region and lower limbs.

A **sacral canal** runs through the sacrum and ends in an inferior opening called the **sacral hiatus** (hy-AY-tus). This canal contains spinal nerve roots. On each side of the sacrum is an ear-shaped region called the **auricular**[38] **surface** (aw-RIC-you-lur). This articulates with a similarly shaped surface on the hip bone (see fig. 8.37b) and forms the strong, nearly immovable **sacroiliac**

[36]*costa* = rib; *al* = pertaining to

[37]*sacr* = great, prominent

[38]*auri* = ear; *cul* = little; *ar* = pertaining to

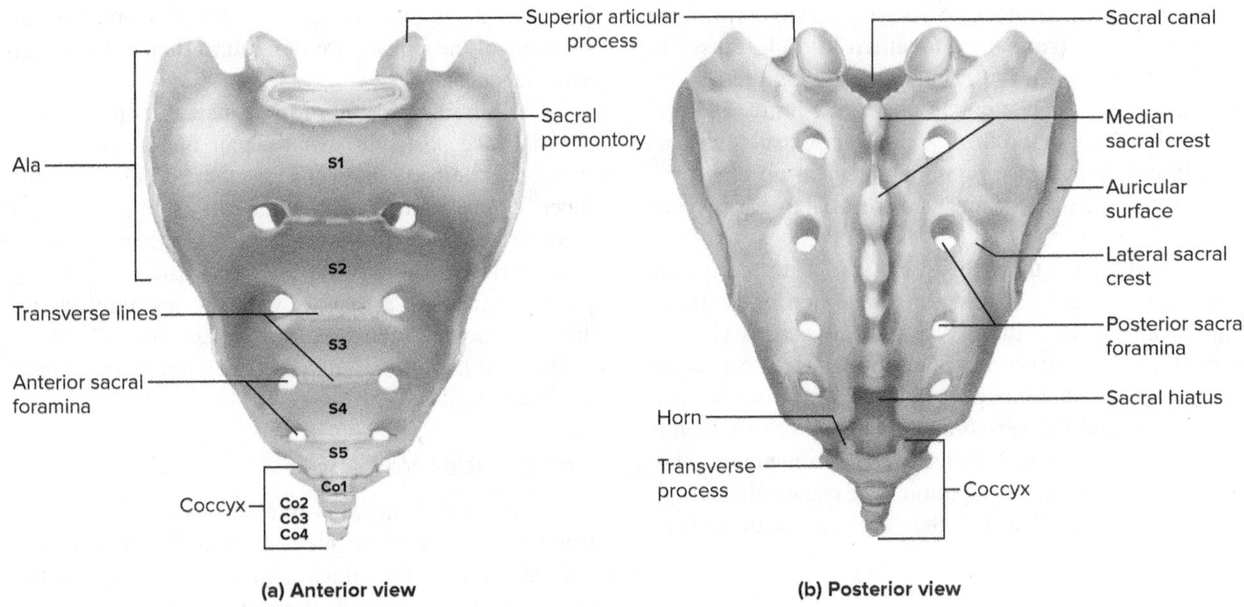


**FIGURE 8.27 The Sacrum and Coccyx.** (a) The anterior surface, which faces the viscera of the pelvic cavity. (b) The posterior surface. The processes of this surface can be palpated in the sacral region. APR

**(SI) joint** (SACK-ro-ILL-ee-ac). The body of vertebra S1 juts anteriorly to form a **sacral promontory,** which supports the body of vertebra L5. Lateral to the median sacral crest, S1 also has a pair of **superior articular processes** that articulate with vertebra L5. Lateral to these is a pair of large, rough, winglike extensions called the **alae**[39] (AIL-ee).

## The Coccyx

Four (sometimes five) tiny **coccygeal vertebrae** (Co1 to Co4 or Co5) fuse by the age of 20 to 30 years to form the **coccyx**[40] (COC-six) (fig. 8.27), colloquially called the tailbone. Although it is indeed the vestige of an ancestral tail, it is not entirely useless; it provides attachment for the muscles of the pelvic floor. Vertebra Co1 has a pair of **horns (cornua)** that serve as attachment points for ligaments that bind the coccyx to the sacrum. The coccyx can be fractured by a difficult childbirth or a hard fall on the buttocks.

## 8.3e The Thoracic Cage

The **thoracic cage (fig. 8.28)** consists of the thoracic vertebrae, sternum, and ribs. It forms a roughly conical enclosure for the lungs and heart and provides attachment for the pectoral girdle and upper limb. It has a broad base and a somewhat narrower superior apex. Its inferior border is the arc of the lower ribs, called the **costal margin.** The cage protects not only the thoracic organs but also the spleen, most of the liver, and to some extent the kidneys. Most important is its role in breathing; it is rhythmically expanded by the respiratory muscles to create a vacuum that draws air into the lungs, and then compressed to expel air.

## The Sternum

The **sternum** (breastbone) is a bony plate anterior to the heart. It is subdivided into three regions: the manubrium, body, and xiphoid process. The **manubrium**[41] (ma-NOO-bree-um) is the broad superior portion, shaped like the knot of a necktie. It lies at the level of vertebrae T3 to T4. It has a median **suprasternal (jugular) notch,** which you can easily palpate between your clavicles (collarbones), and right and left **clavicular notches** where it articulates with the clavicles. The dagger-shaped **body,** or **gladiolus,**[42] is the longest part of the sternum, lying at the level of vertebrae T5 through T9. It joins the manubrium at the **sternal angle,** which can be palpated as a transverse ridge at the point where the sternum projects farthest forward. In some people, however, the angle is rounded or concave. The second rib attaches here, making the sternal angle a useful landmark for counting ribs by palpation. The manubrium and body have scalloped lateral margins where cartilages of the ribs are attached. At the inferior end (vertebral level T10 to T11) is a small, pointed **xiphoid**[43] **process** (ZIF-oyd) that provides attachment for some of the abdominal muscles. In cardiopulmonary resuscitation,

[39] *alae* = wings
[40] *coccyx* = cuckoo (named for resemblance to a cuckoo's beak)
[41] *manubrium* = handle
[42] *gladiolus* = sword
[43] *xipho* = sword; *oid* = resembling

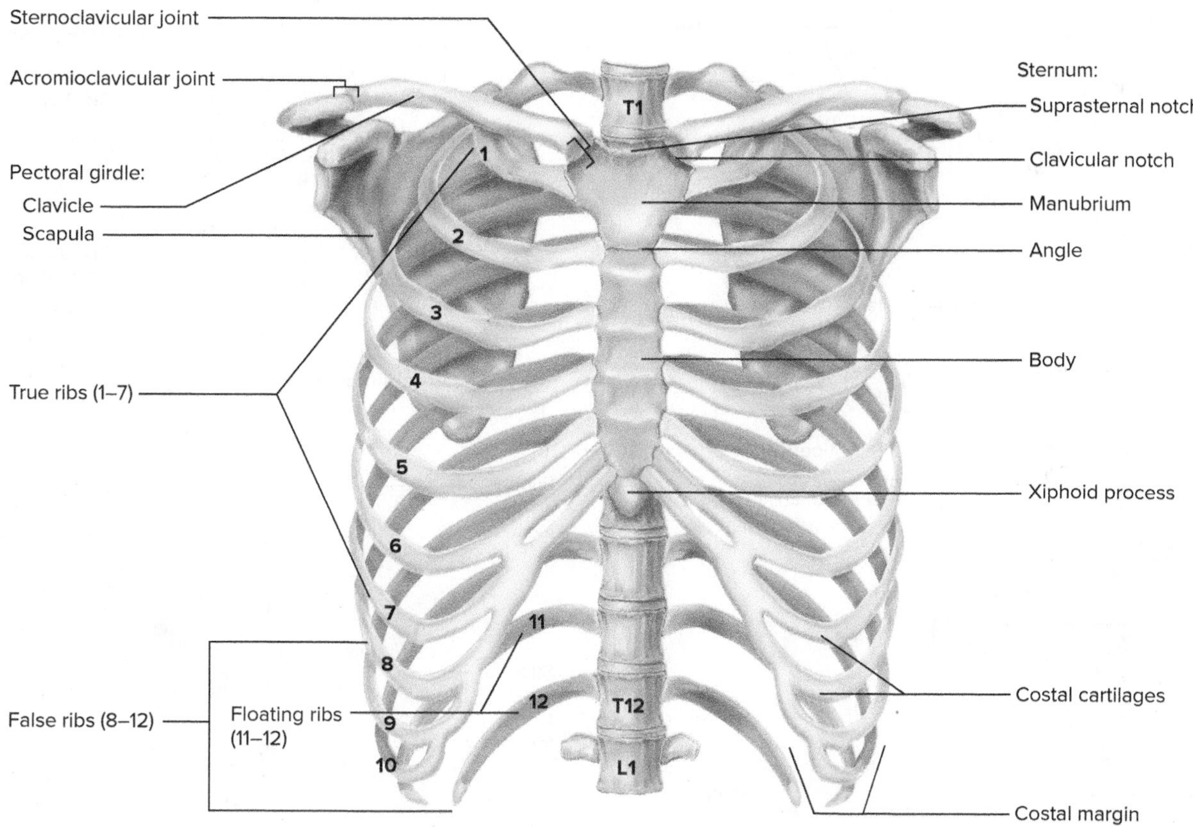


**FIGURE 8.28 The Thoracic Cage and Pectoral Girdle (Anterior View).** APR

improperly performed chest compressions can drive the xiphoid process into the liver and cause a fatal hemorrhage.

## The Ribs

There are 12 pairs of **ribs,** with no difference in number between the sexes (despite popular religious belief). Each is attached at its posterior (proximal) end to the vertebral column, and most of them are also attached at the anterior (distal) end to the sternum. The anterior attachment is by way of a long strip of hyaline cartilage called the **costal cartilage** (COSS-tul).

As a rule, the ribs increase in length from 1 through 7 and become progressively smaller again through rib 12. They are increasingly oblique (slanted) in orientation from 1 through 9, then less so from 10 through 12. They also differ in their individual structure and attachments at different levels of the thoracic cage, so we will examine them in order as we descend the chest, taking note of their universal characteristics as well as their individual variations.

Rib 1 is peculiar. On an articulated skeleton, you must look for its vertebral attachment just below the base of the neck; much of this rib lies above the level of the clavicle (fig. 8.28). It is a short, flat, C-shaped plate of bone **(fig. 8.29a).** At the vertebral end, it exhibits a knobby **head** that articulates with the body of vertebra T1. On an isolated vertebra, you can find a smooth costal facet for this attachment on the middle of the body. Immediately distal to the head, the rib narrows to a **neck** and then widens again to form a rough area called the **tubercle.** This is its point of attachment to the transverse costal facet of the same vertebra. Beyond the tubercle, the rib flattens and widens into a gently sloping bladelike **shaft.** The shaft ends distally in a squared-off, rough area. In the living individual, the costal cartilage begins here and spans the rest of the distance to the upper sternum. The superior surface of rib 1 has a pair of shallow grooves that serve as platforms for the subclavian artery and subclavian vein.

Ribs 2 through 7 present a more typical appearance **(fig. 8.29b).** At the proximal end, each exhibits a head, neck, and tubercle. The head is wedge-shaped and inserts between two vertebrae. Each margin of the wedge has a smooth surface called an *articular facet.* The **superior articular facet** joins the inferior costal facet of the vertebra above; the **inferior articular facet** joins the superior costal facet of vertebra below. The tubercle of the rib articulates with the transverse costal facet of each same-numbered vertebra. **Figure 8.30** details the rib–vertebra attachments typical of this region of the rib cage.

Beyond the tubercle, each rib makes a sharp curve around the side of the chest and then progresses anteriorly to approach the sternum (see fig. 8.28). The curve is called the **angle** of the rib and the rest of the bony blade distal to it is the **shaft.** The inferior margin of the shaft has a **costal groove** that marks the path of the

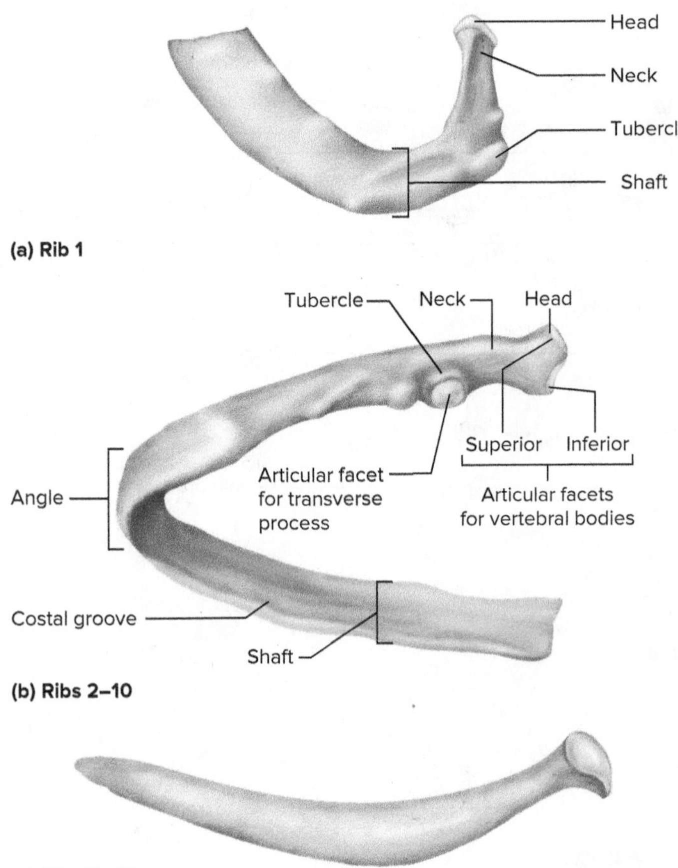


**FIGURE 8.29 Anatomy of the Ribs.** (a) Rib 1 (superior view) is an atypical flat plate. (b) Typical features of ribs 2 to 10. (c) Appearance of the floating ribs, 11 and 12.

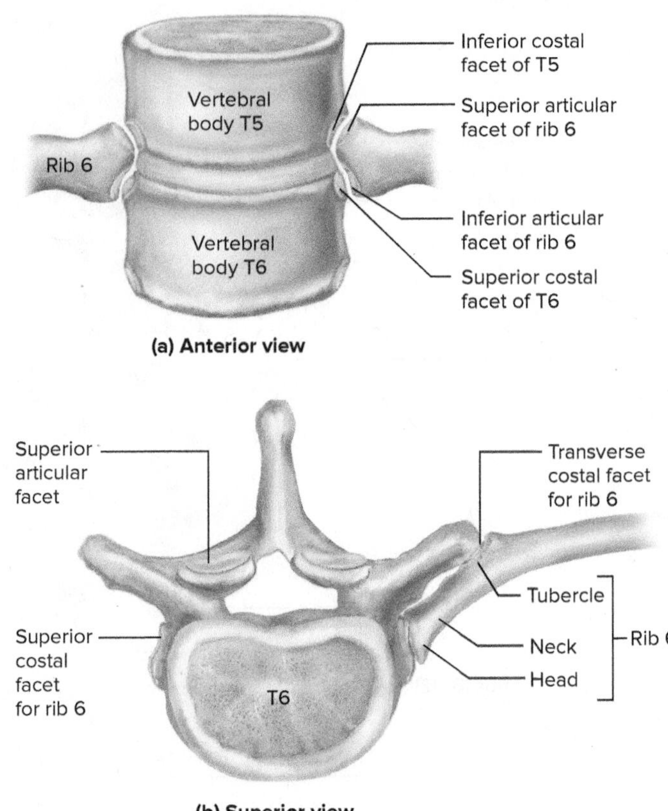


**FIGURE 8.30 Articulation of Rib 6 with Vertebrae T5 and T6.** (a) Anterior view. Note the relationship of the articular facets of the rib with the costal facets of the two vertebrae. (b) Superior view. Note that the rib articulates with a vertebra at two points: the costal facet on the vertebral body and the transverse costal facet on the transverse process.

intercostal blood vessels and nerve. Each of these ribs, like rib 1, ends in a blunt, rough area where the costal cartilage begins. Each has its own costal cartilage connecting it to the sternum; because of this feature, ribs 1 through 7 are called **true ribs.**

Ribs 8 through 12 are called **false ribs** because they lack independent cartilaginous connections to the sternum. In 8 through 10, the costal cartilages sweep upward and end on the costal cartilage of rib 7 (see fig. 8.28). Rib 10 also differs from 2 through 9 in that it attaches to the body of a single vertebra (T10) rather than between vertebrae. Thus, vertebra T10 has a complete costal facet on its body for rib 10.

Ribs 11 and 12 are again unusual **(fig. 8.29c).** Posteriorly, they articulate with the bodies of vertebrae T11 and T12, but they do not have tubercles and do not attach to the transverse processes of the vertebrae. Those two vertebrae therefore have no transverse costal facets. At the distal end, these two relatively small, delicate ribs taper to a point and are capped by a small cartilaginous tip, but there is no cartilaginous connection to the sternum or to any of the higher costal cartilages. The ribs are merely embedded in lumbar muscle at this end. Consequently, 11 and 12 are also called **floating ribs.** In people of Japanese and some other ancestries, rib 10 is also usually floating. **Table 8.4** summarizes these variations in rib anatomy and their vertebral and sternal attachments.

**BEFORE YOU GO ON**

Answer the following questions to test your understanding of the preceding section:

9. Discuss the contribution of the intervertebral discs to the length and flexibility of the spine.
10. Construct a three-column table headed C4, T4, and L4. In each column, list all anatomical features that would distinguish that vertebra from the other two.
11. Name the three parts of the sternum. How many ribs attach (directly or indirectly) to each part?
12. Describe how rib 5 articulates with the spine. How do ribs 1 and 12 differ from this and from each other in their modes of articulation?
13. Distinguish between true, false, and floating ribs. Which ribs fall into each category?
14. Name the three divisions of the sternum and list the sternal features that can be palpated on a living person.

**TABLE 8.4 Articulations of the Ribs**

| Rib | Type | Costal Cartilage | Articulating Vertebral Bodies | Articulating with a Transverse Costal Facet? | Rib Tubercle |
|---|---|---|---|---|---|
| 1 | True | Individual | T1 | Yes | Present |
| 2 | True | Individual | T1 and T2 | Yes | Present |
| 3 | True | Individual | T2 and T3 | Yes | Present |
| 4 | True | Individual | T3 and T4 | Yes | Present |
| 5 | True | Individual | T4 and T5 | Yes | Present |
| 6 | True | Individual | T5 and T6 | Yes | Present |
| 7 | True | Individual | T6 and T7 | Yes | Present |
| 8 | False | Shared with rib 7 | T7 and T8 | Yes | Present |
| 9 | False | Shared with rib 7 | T8 and T9 | Yes | Present |
| 10 | False | Shared with rib 7 | T10 | Yes | Present |
| 11 | False, floating | None | T11 | No | Absent |
| 12 | False, floating | None | T12 | No | Absent |

## 8.4 The Pectoral Girdle and Upper Limb

**Expected Learning Outcome**

When you have completed this section, you should be able to

a. identify and describe the features of the clavicle, scapula, humerus, radius, ulna, and bones of the wrist and hand.

### 8.4a The Pectoral Girdle

The **pectoral girdle** (shoulder girdle) supports the arm and links it to the axial skeleton. It consists of two bones on each side of the body: the *clavicle* (collarbone) and *scapula* (shoulder blade). The medial end of the clavicle articulates with the sternum at the **sternoclavicular joint,** and its lateral end articulates with the scapula at the **acromioclavicular joint** (see fig. 8.28). The scapula also articulates with the humerus at the **glenohumeral joint.** These are loose attachments that result in a shoulder far more flexible than that of most other mammals, but they also make the shoulder joint easy to dislocate.

**APPLY WHAT YOU KNOW**

*How is the unusual flexibility of the human shoulder joint related to the habitat of our primate ancestors?*

#### The Clavicle

The **clavicle**[44] **(fig. 8.31)** is slightly S-shaped, somewhat flattened from the upper to lower surface, and easily seen and palpated on the upper thorax (see atlas B, fig. B.1b). The superior surface is relatively smooth and rounded, whereas the inferior surface is flatter and marked by grooves and ridges for muscle attachment. The medial **sternal end** has a rounded, hammerlike head, and the lateral **acromial end** is markedly flattened. Near the acromial end is a rough tuberosity called the **conoid tubercle**—a ligament attachment that faces toward the rear and slightly downward.

The clavicle braces the shoulder, keeping the upper limb away from the midline of the body, and is an attachment for some of the muscles of head movement (sternocleidomastoid and trapezius). It also transfers force from the arm to the axial region of the body, as when doing pushups. It is thickened in people who do heavy manual labor, and in right-handed people, the right clavicle is usually stronger and shorter than the left because of the workload placed on it. Without the clavicles, the pectoralis major muscles would pull the shoulders forward and medially—which indeed happens when a clavicle is fractured. The clavicle is one of the

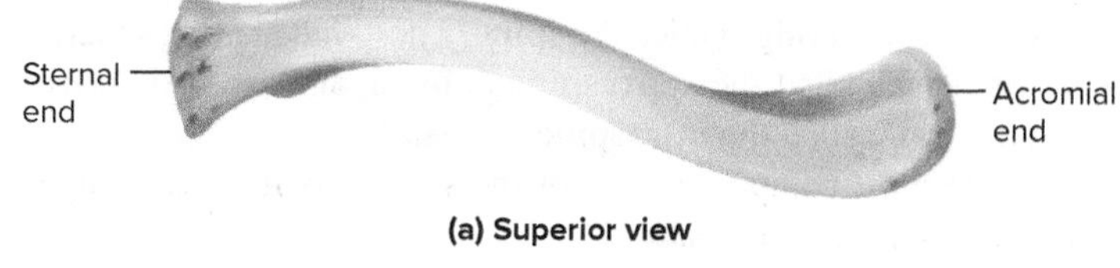


(a) Superior view

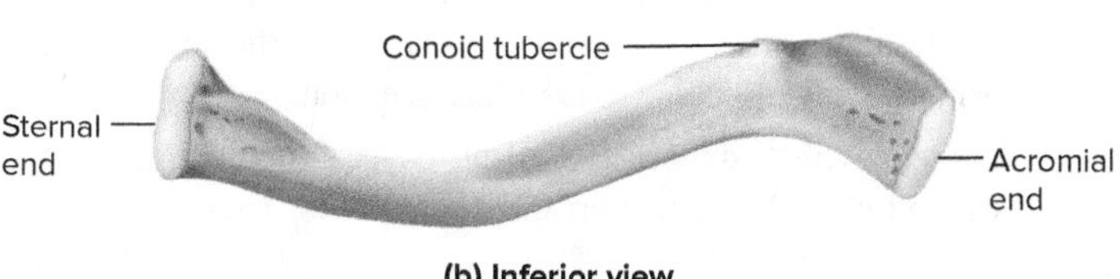


(b) Inferior view

**FIGURE 8.31 The Right Clavicle.** (a) Superior view. (b) Inferior view. APR

[44]*clav* = hammer, club, key; *icle* = little

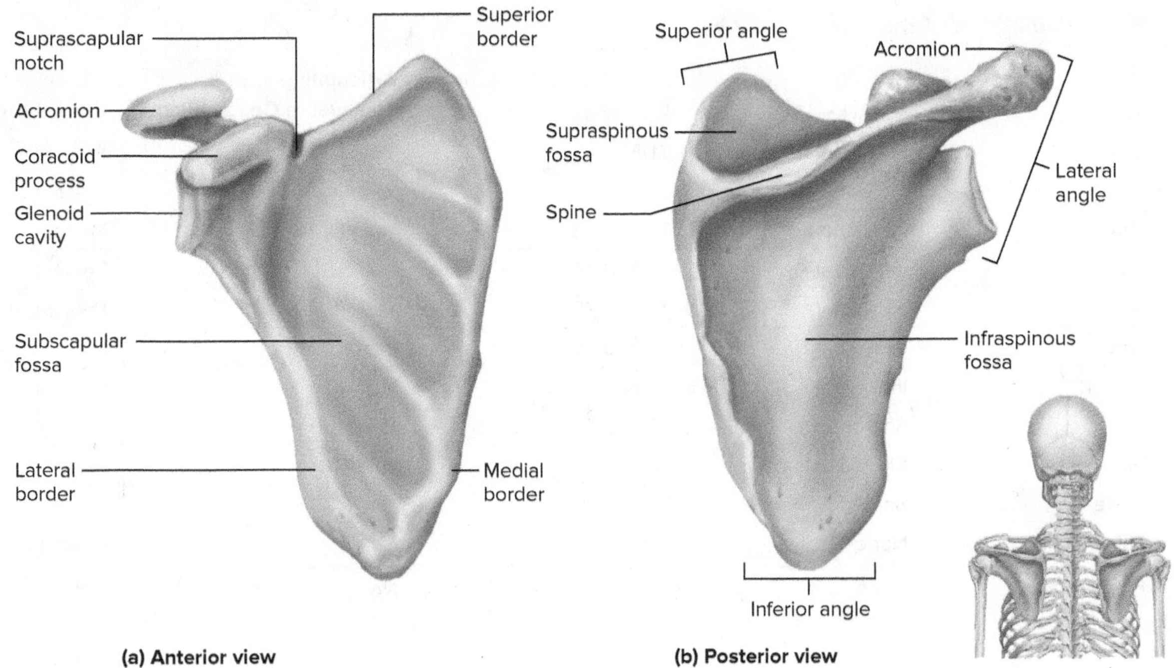


**FIGURE 8.32 The Right Scapula.** (a) Anterior view. (b) Posterior view. 

most commonly fractured bones in the body because it is so close to the surface and because people often reach out with their arms to break a fall.

## The Scapula

The **scapula**[45] **(fig. 8.32),** named for its resemblance to a spade or shovel, is a triangular plate that posteriorly overlies ribs 2 through 7. Its only direct attachment to the thorax is by muscles; it glides across the rib cage as the arm and shoulder move. The three sides of the triangle are called the **superior, medial (vertebral),** and **lateral (axillary) borders,** and its three angles are the **superior, inferior,** and **lateral angles.** A conspicuous **suprascapular notch** in the superior border provides passage for a nerve. The broad anterior surface of the scapula, called the **subscapular fossa,** is slightly concave and relatively featureless. The posterior surface has a transverse ridge called the **spine,** a deep indentation superior to the spine called the **supraspinous fossa,** and a broad surface inferior to it called the **infraspinous fossa.**[46]

The most complex region of the scapula is its lateral angle, which has three main features:

1. The **acromion**[47] (ah-CRO-me-on) is a platelike extension of the scapular spine that forms the apex of the shoulder. It articulates with the clavicle, which forms the sole bridge from the appendicular to the axial skeleton.
2. The **coracoid**[48] **process** (COR-uh-coyd) is named for a vague resemblance to a crow's beak, but is shaped more like a bent finger; it provides attachment for tendons of the *biceps brachii* and other muscles of the arm.
3. The **glenoid**[49] **cavity** (GLEN-oyd) is a shallow socket that articulates with the head of the humerus, forming the glenohumeral joint. The anatomy of this joint is detailed in section 9.3b and figure 9.24.

## 8.4b The Upper Limb

Each upper limb contains 30 bones distributed in the following three limb segments:

1. The arm proper (**brachial region** or **brachium**[50] [BRAY-kee-um]) extends from shoulder to elbow. It contains only one bone, the *humerus.*
2. The forearm **(antebrachial region** or **antebrachium**[51]**)** extends from elbow to wrist and contains two bones: the *radius* and *ulna.* In anatomical position, these bones are parallel and the radius is lateral to the ulna.
3. The hand consists of the **carpal**[52] **region,** with 8 small carpal bones arranged in two rows in the base of the hand; the **metacarpal region** in the palm, with 5 bones; and the fingers **(digits),** with 14 bones. The two hands together contain 54 of the 206 bones in the body—over one-quarter of the total.

Note that what we colloquially call the wrist—the narrow region where one may wear a bracelet or wristwatch—is not what

[45] *scap* = spade, shovel; *ula* = little
[46] *supra* = above; *infra* = below
[47] *acr* = extremity, point, apex; *omi* = shoulder
[48] *corac* = crow; *oid* = resembling
[49] *glen* = pit, socket; *oid* = resembling
[50] *brachi* = arm
[51] *ante* = before
[52] *carp* = wrist

anatomists call the wrist (carpal region): the thick, fleshy base of the hand proximal to the hollow of the palm.

## The Humerus

The **humerus** has a hemispherical **head** that articulates with the glenoid cavity of the scapula **(fig. 8.33).** The smooth surface of the head (covered with articular cartilage in the living state) is bordered by a groove called the **anatomical neck.** Other prominent features of the proximal end are muscle attachments called the **greater** and **lesser tubercles** and an **intertubercular sulcus** between them that accommodates a tendon of the biceps muscle. The **surgical neck,** a common fracture site, is a narrowing of the bone just distal to the tubercles, at the transition from the head to the shaft. The shaft has a rough area called the **deltoid tuberosity** on its lateral surface. This is an insertion for the *deltoid muscle* of the shoulder.

The distal end of the humerus has two smooth condyles. The lateral one, called the **capitulum**[53] (ca-PIT-you-lum), is shaped like a wide tire and articulates with the radius. The medial one, called the **trochlea**[54] (TROCK-lee-uh), is pulleylike and articulates with the ulna. Immediately proximal to these condyles, the humerus flares out to form two bony processes, the **lateral** and **medial epicondyles,** which are the bumps you can palpate at the widest point of your elbow. The medial epicondyle protects the *ulnar nerve,* which passes close to the surface across the back of the elbow. This epicondyle is popularly known as the "funny bone" because striking the elbow on the edge of a table stimulates the ulnar nerve and produces a sharp tingling sensation. Immediately proximal to the epicondyles, the margins of the humerus are called the **lateral** and **medial supracondylar ridges.** These are attachments for certain forearm muscles described in chapter 10.

The distal end of the humerus also shows three deep pits: two anterior and one posterior. The posterior pit, called the **olecranon fossa** (oh-LEC-ruh-non), accommodates a process of the ulna called the *olecranon* when the elbow is extended. On the anterior surface, a medial pit called the **coronoid fossa** accommodates the *coronoid process* of the ulna when the forearm is flexed. The lateral pit is the **radial fossa,** named for the nearby head of the radius.

## The Radius

The **radius** has a distinctive discoidal **head** at its proximal end **(fig. 8.34).** When the forearm is rotated so the palm turns forward

[53]*capit* = head; *ulum* = little
[54]*troch* = wheel, pulley

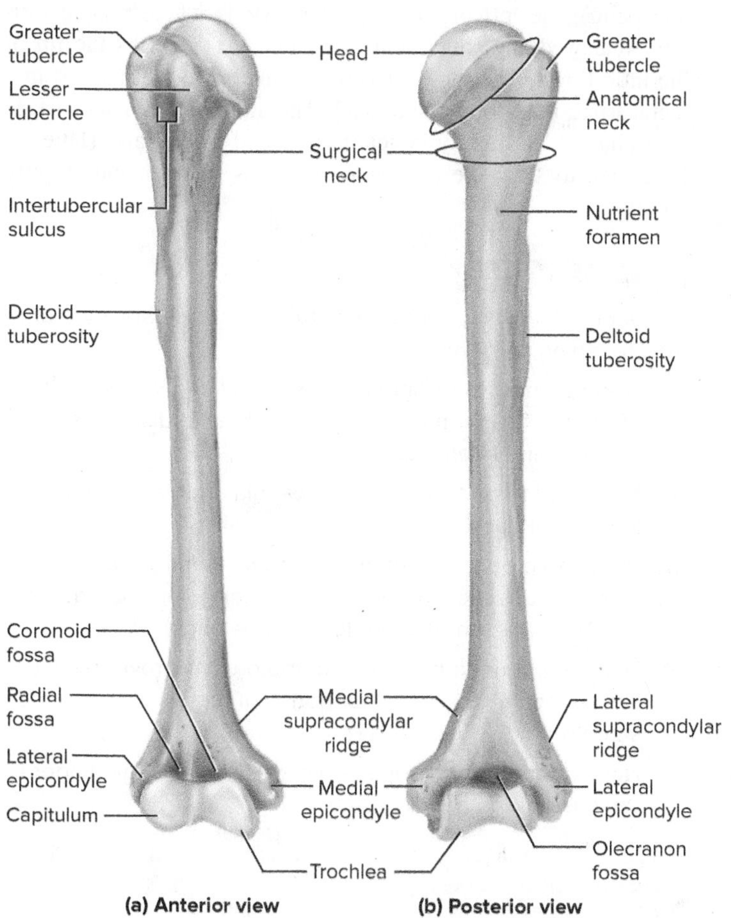


**FIGURE 8.33 The Right Humerus.** (a) Anterior view. (b) Posterior view. APR

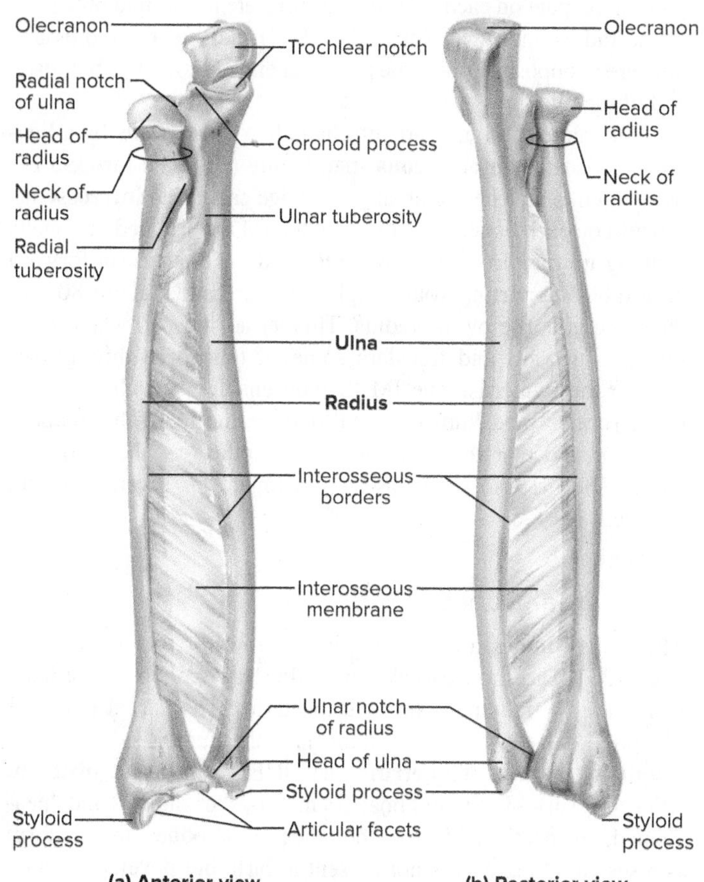


**FIGURE 8.34 The Right Radius and Ulna.** (a) Anterior view. (b) Posterior view. APR

and back, the circular superior surface of this disc spins on the capitulum of the humerus, and the edge of the disc spins on the radial notch of the ulna. Immediately distal to the head, the radius has a narrower **neck** and then widens to a rough prominence, the **radial tuberosity,** on its medial surface. The distal tendon of the biceps muscle terminates on this tuberosity.

The distal end of the radius has the following features, from lateral to medial:

1. a bony point, the **styloid process,** which can be palpated proximal to the thumb;
2. two shallow depressions (articular facets) that articulate with the scaphoid and lunate bones of the wrist; and
3. the **ulnar notch,** which articulates with the end of the ulna.

## The Ulna

At the proximal end of the **ulna** (fig. 8.34) is a deep, C-shaped **trochlear notch** that wraps around the trochlea of the humerus. The posterior side of this notch is formed by a prominent **olecranon**—the bony point where you rest your elbow on a table. The anterior side is formed by a less prominent **coronoid process.** Laterally, the head of the ulna has a less conspicuous **radial notch,** which accommodates the edge of the head of the radius. At the distal end **(head)** of the ulna is a medial **styloid process.** The bony lumps you can palpate on each side of your wrist are the styloid processes of the radius and ulna. Notice that the "heads" of the radius and ulna are at opposite ends—the proximal end of the radius but distal end of the ulna.

The radius and ulna are attached along their shafts by a ligament called the **interosseous membrane (IM)** (IN-tur-OSS-ee-us), which is attached to an angular ridge called the **interosseous margin** on each bone. Most fibers of the IM are oriented obliquely, slanting upward from the ulna to the radius. If you lean forward on a table supporting your weight on your hands, about 80% of the force is borne by the radius. This tenses the IM, which pulls the ulna upward and transfers some of this force through the ulna to the humerus. The IM thereby enables two elbow joints (humeroradial and humeroulnar) to share the load; this reduces the wear and tear that one joint would otherwise have to bear alone. The IM also serves as an attachment for several forearm muscles.

## The Carpal Bones

The **carpal bones** are arranged in two rows of four bones each **(fig. 8.35).** The short carpal bones allow movements of the hand from side to side and anterior to posterior. The carpal bones of the proximal row, starting at the lateral (thumb) side, are the **scaphoid, lunate, triquetrum** (tri-QUEE-trum), and **pisiform** (PY-sih-form)—Latin for "boat-," "moon-," "triangle-," and "pea-shaped," respectively. Unlike the other carpal bones, the pisiform is a sesamoid bone; it is not present at birth but develops around the age of 9 to 12 years within the tendon of the *flexor carpi ulnaris muscle.*

The bones of the distal row, again starting on the lateral side, are the **trapezium,**[55] **trapezoid, capitate,**[56] and **hamate.**[57] The hamate can be recognized by a prominent hook called the **hamulus** on the palmar side (fig. 8.35b). The hamulus is an attachment for the *flexor retinaculum,* a fibrous sheet in the wrist that covers the carpal tunnel (see fig. 10.31).

## The Metacarpal Bones

The **metacarpal**[58] **bones** span the palmar region of the hand. Metacarpal I is located proximal to the base of the thumb and metacarpal V proximal to the base of the little finger. On a skeleton, the metacarpal bones look like extensions of the fingers, making the fingers seem much longer than they really are. The proximal end of a metacarpal bone is called the **base,** the shaft is called the **body,** and the distal end is called the **head.** The heads of the metacarpal bones form the knuckles when you clench your fist.

## The Phalanges

The bones of the fingers are called **phalanges** (fah-LAN-jeez), in the singular, *phalanx* (FAY-lanks). There are two phalanges in the thumb and three in each of the other digits. Phalanges are identified by roman numerals preceded by *proximal, middle,* and *distal.* For example, proximal phalanx I is in the basal segment of the thumb (the first segment beyond the web between the thumb and palm); the left proximal phalanx IV is where people usually wear wedding rings; and distal phalanx V forms the tip of the little finger. The three parts of a phalanx are the same as in a metacarpal: base, body, and head. The anterior (palmar) surface of a phalanx is slightly concave from end to end and flattened from side to side; the posterior surface is rounder and slightly convex.

**BEFORE YOU GO ON**

Answer the following questions to test your understanding of the preceding section:

15. Describe how to distinguish the medial and lateral ends of the clavicle from each other, and how to distinguish its superior and inferior surfaces.
16. Name the three fossae of the scapula and describe the location of each.
17. What three bones meet at the elbow? Identify the fossae, articular surfaces, and processes of this joint and state to which bone each of these features belongs.
18. Name the four carpal bones of the proximal row from lateral to medial, then the four bones of the distal row in the same order.
19. Name the four long bones from the tip of the little finger to the base of the hand.

---

[55]*trapez* = table, grinding surface
[56]*capit* = head; *ate* = possessing
[57]*ham* = hook; *ate* = possessing
[58]*meta* = beyond; *carp* = wrist

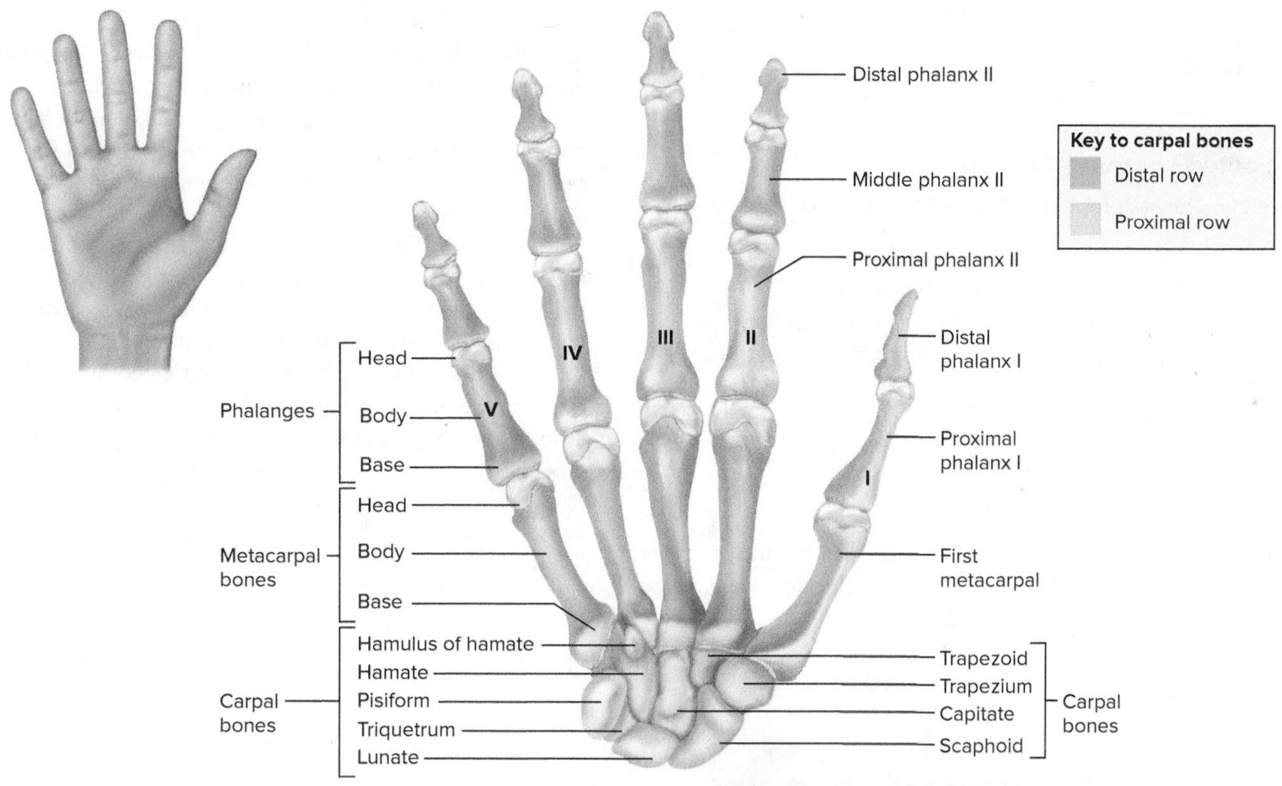


**(a) Anterior view**

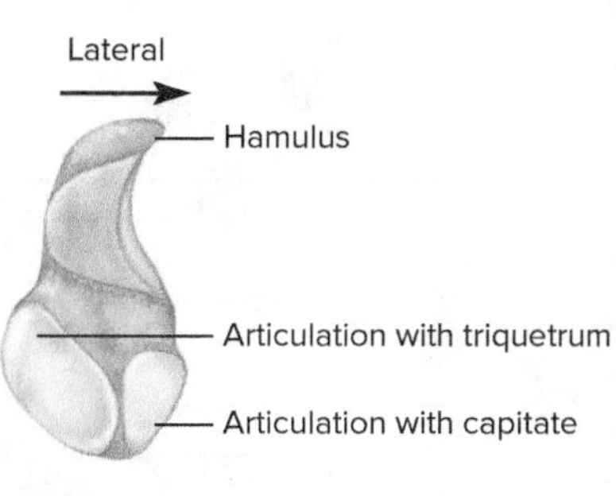


**(b) Hamate bone**

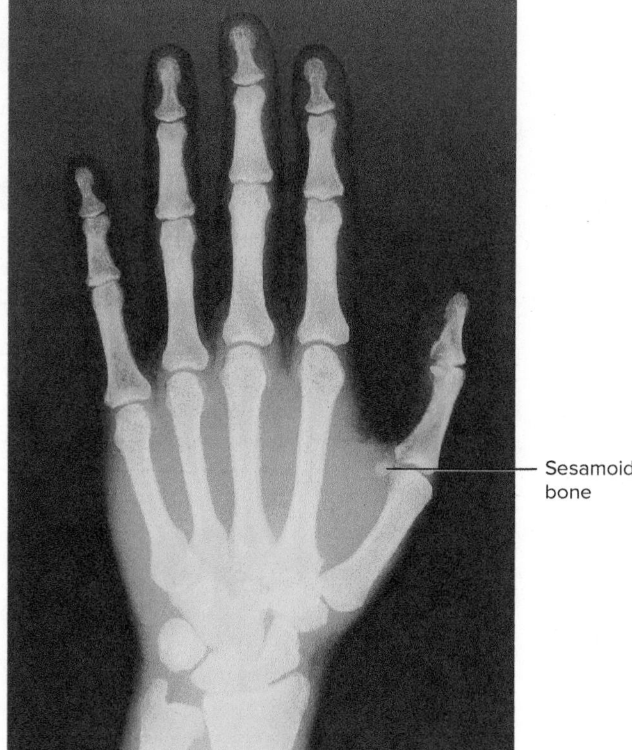


**(c) X-ray of adult hand**

**FIGURE 8.35 The Right Hand.** (a) Carpal bones color-coded to distinguish the proximal and distal rows. (b) The right hamate bone, viewed from the palmar side to show its distinctive hook. This unique bone is a useful landmark for locating the others when studying the skeleton. (c) X-ray of an adult hand. Identify the unlabeled bones in the X-ray by comparing it with the drawing in part (a). A small sesamoid bone is visible at the base of the thumb. The pisiform bone in part (a) is also a sesamoid bone. APR

? *How does part (c) differ from the X-ray of a child's hand in figure 7.11?*

**c:** RNHRD NHS Trust/The Image Bank/Getty Images

## 8.5 The Pelvic Girdle and Lower Limb

**Expected Learning Outcomes**

When you have completed this section, you should be able to

a. identify and describe the features of the pelvic girdle, femur, patella, tibia, fibula, and bones of the foot; and
b. compare the anatomy of the male and female pelvic girdles and explain the functional significance of the differences.

### 8.5a The Pelvic Girdle

The terms *pelvis* and *pelvic girdle* are used in contradictory ways by various anatomical authorities. Here we will follow the practice of *Gray's Anatomy* and the *Terminologia Anatomica* in considering the **pelvic girdle** to consist of a complete ring composed of three bones **(fig. 8.36)**—two **hip (coxal) bones** and the sacrum (which, as you know, is also part of the vertebral column). The hip bones are also frequently called the *ossa coxae*[59] (OS-sa COC-see). The **pelvis**[60] is a bowl-shaped structure composed of these bones as well as the ligaments and muscles that line the pelvic cavity and form its floor. The pelvic girdle supports the trunk on the lower limbs and encloses and protects the viscera of the pelvic cavity—mainly the lower colon, urinary bladder, and internal reproductive organs.

Each hip bone is joined to the vertebral column at one point, the sacroiliac joint, where its ear-shaped **auricular surface** matches the auricular surface of the sacrum. The two hip bones articulate with each other on the anterior side of the pelvis, where they are joined by a pad of fibrocartilage called the **interpubic**

[59]*os* = bone; *coxae* = of the hip
[60]*pelv* = basin, bowl

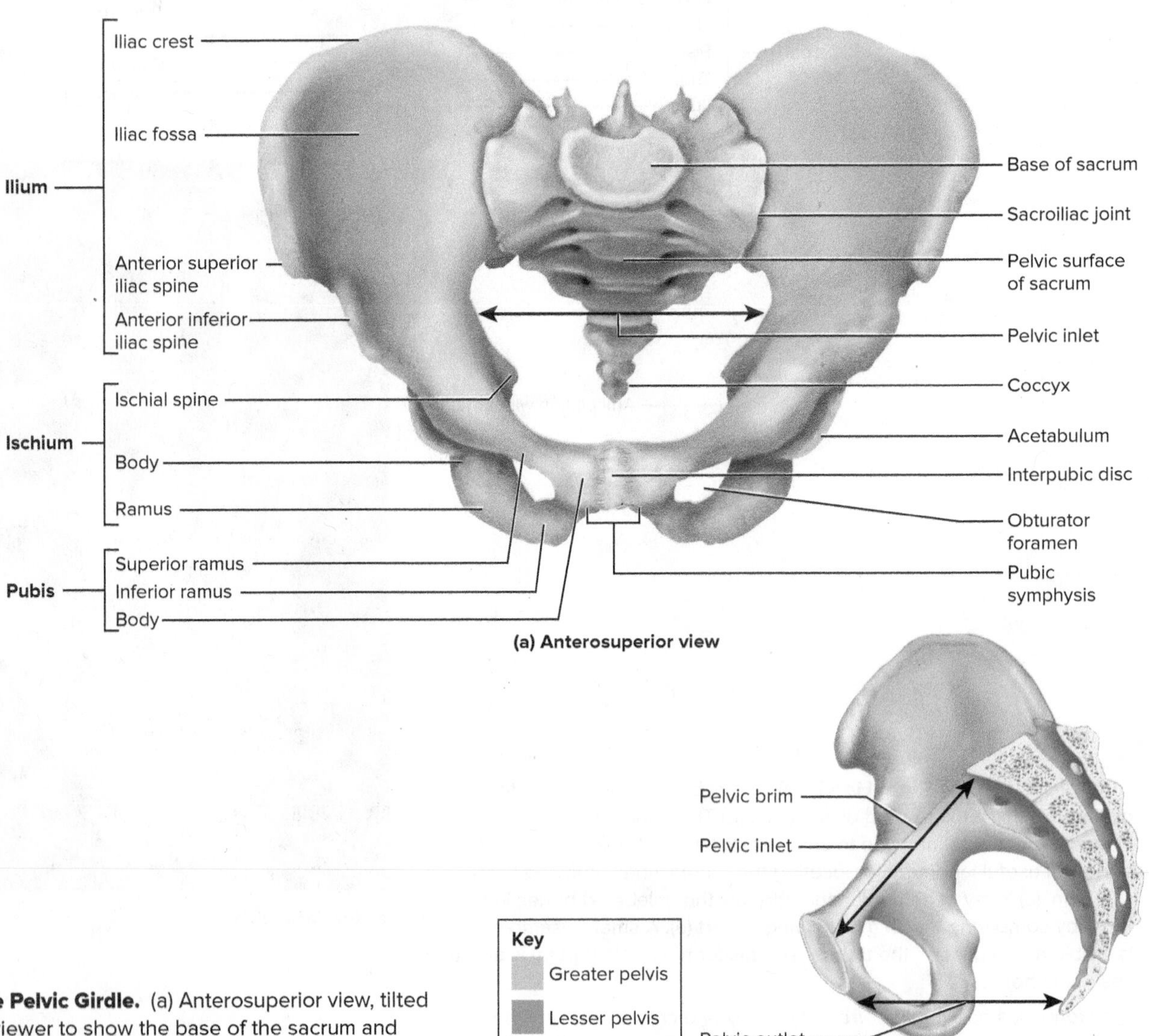


**FIGURE 8.36 The Pelvic Girdle.** (a) Anterosuperior view, tilted slightly toward the viewer to show the base of the sacrum and the pelvic inlet. (b) Median section, to show the greater and lesser pelvis and the pelvic inlet and outlet. APR

**disc.** The disc and the adjacent region of each pubic bone constitute the **pubic symphysis,**[61] which can be palpated as a hard prominence immediately above the genitalia.

The pelvis is divided into the broad **greater (false) pelvis** between the flare of the hips and the narrower **lesser (true) pelvis** below. The two are separated by a round margin called the **pelvic brim.** The opening circumscribed by the brim is called the **pelvic inlet**—an entry into the lesser pelvis through which an infant's head passes during birth. The lower margin of the lesser pelvis is called the **pelvic outlet.**

The hip bones have three distinctive features that will serve as landmarks for further description. These are the **iliac**[62] **crest** (superior crest of the hip); **acetabulum**[63] (ASS-eh-TAB-you-lum) (the hip socket—named for its resemblance to vinegar cups used on ancient Roman dining tables); and **obturator**[64] **foramen** (a large round-to-triangular hole below the acetabulum, closed by a ligament called the *obturator membrane* in living persons).

The adult hip bone forms by the fusion of three childhood bones called the *ilium* (ILL-ee-um), *ischium* (ISS-kee-um), and *pubis* (PEW-biss), identified by color in **figure 8.37.** The largest of these is the **ilium,** which extends from the iliac crest to the center of the acetabulum. The iliac crest extends from an anterior point or angle called the **anterior superior iliac spine** to a sharp posterior angle called the **posterior superior iliac spine.** In a lean person, the anterior superior spines form visible anterior protrusions at a point where the front pockets usually open on a pair of pants, and the posterior superior spines are sometimes marked by dimples above the buttocks where connective tissue attached to the spines pulls inward on the skin (see atlas B, fig. B.15). The latter is a genetic trait like cheek dimples.

Below the superior spines are the **anterior** and **posterior inferior iliac spines.** Below the latter is a deep **greater sciatic notch** (sy-AT-ic), named for the thick sciatic nerve that passes through it and continues down the posterior side of the thigh.

The posterolateral surface of the ilium is relatively rough-textured because it serves for attachment of several muscles of the buttocks and thighs. The anteromedial surface, by contrast, is the smooth, slightly concave **iliac fossa,** covered in life by the broad *iliacus muscle.* Medially, the ilium exhibits an auricular surface that matches the one on the sacrum, so that the two bones form the sacroiliac (SI) joint.

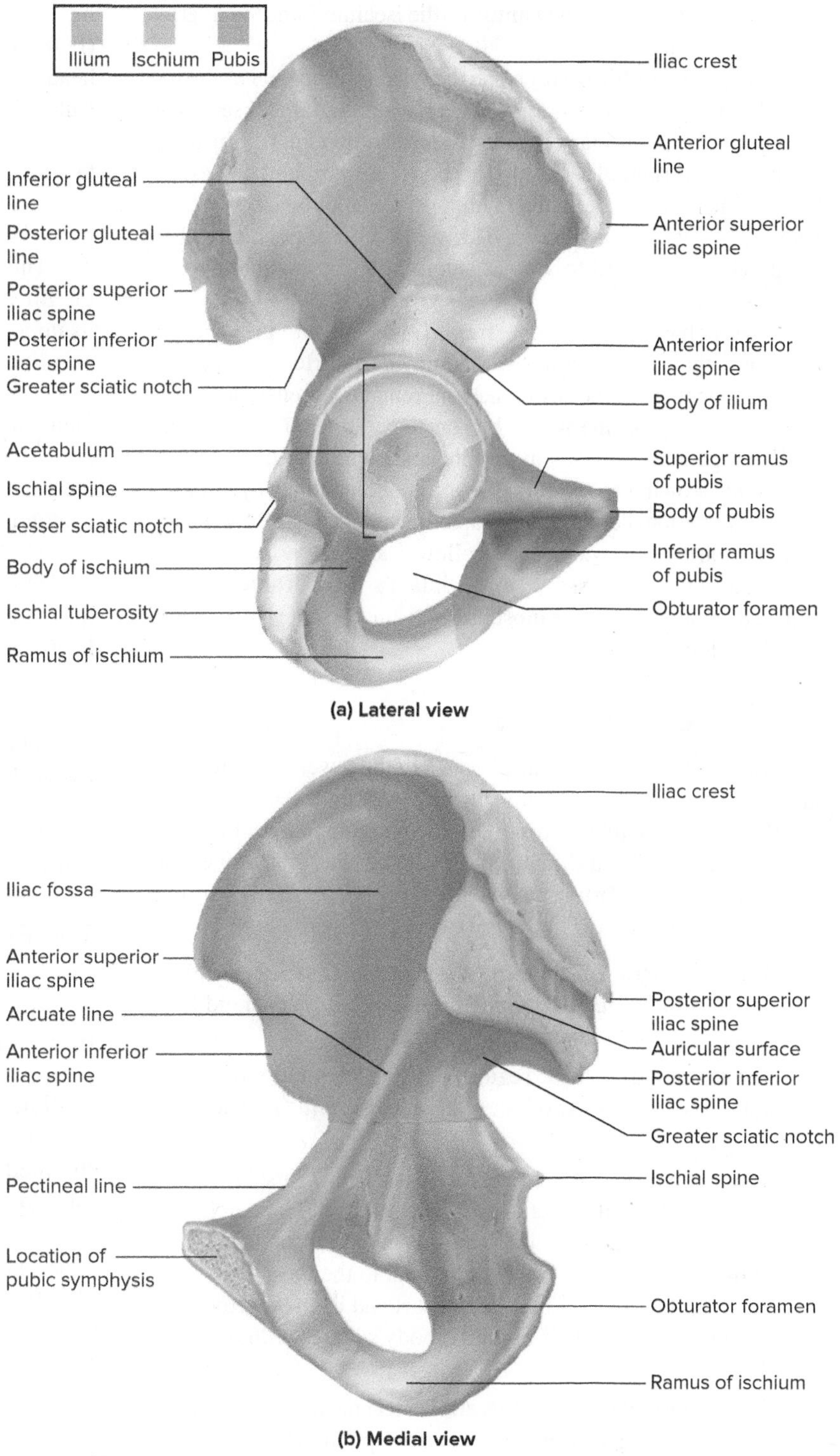

**FIGURE 8.37 The Right Hip Bone.** (a) Lateral view. (b) Medial view. The three childhood bones that fuse to form the adult hip bone are identified by color according to the key. APR

The **ischium** is the inferoposterior portion of the hip bone. Its heavy **body** is marked with a prominent **ischial spine.** Inferior to the spine is a slight indentation, the **lesser sciatic notch,** and then the thick, rough-surfaced **ischial tuberosity,** which supports your body when you are sitting. The tuberosity can be palpated by

[61] *sym* = together; *physis* = growth
[62] *ili* = flank, loin; *ac* = pertaining to
[63] *acetabulum* = vinegar cup
[64] *obtur* = to close, stop up; *ator* = that which

sitting on your fingers. The **ramus** of the ischium joins the inferior ramus of the pubis anteriorly.

The **pubis (pubic bone)** is the most anterior portion of the hip bone. In anatomical position, it is nearly horizontal and serves as a platform for the urinary bladder. It has a **superior** and **inferior ramus** and a triangular **body.** The body of one pubis meets the body of the other at the pubic symphysis. The pubis and ischium encircle the obturator foramen. The pubis is often fractured when the pelvis is subjected to violent anteroposterior compression, as in seat-belt injuries.

The pelvis is the most *sexually dimorphic* part of the skeleton—that is, the one whose anatomy most differs between the sexes. In identifying the sex of skeletal remains, forensic scientists focus especially on the pelvis but on many other bones as well. The average male pelvis is more robust (heavier and thicker) than the female's owing to the forces exerted on the bones by stronger muscles. The female pelvis is adapted to the needs of pregnancy and childbirth. It is wider and shallower and has a larger pelvic inlet and outlet for passage of the infant's head. **Table 8.5** and **figure 8.38** summarize the most useful features of the pelvis in sex identification.

## 8.5b The Lower Limb

The number and arrangement of bones in the lower limb are similar to those of the upper limb. In the lower limb, however, they are adapted for weight bearing and locomotion and are therefore shaped and articulated differently. The femur and tibia are essentially pillars for supporting the weight of the body. Each lower limb has 30 bones distributed in the following three segments.

1. The thigh **(femoral region)** extends from hip to knee and contains the *femur.* The *patella* (kneecap) is a sesamoid bone at the junction of the femoral and crural regions.
2. The leg proper **(crural region)** extends from knee to ankle and contains two bones, the medial *tibia* and lateral *fibula.*
3. The foot consists of the **tarsal region,** with 7 tarsal bones extending from the heel to the midpoint of the foot arch; **metatarsal region,** with 5 bones extending from there to the "balls" of the feet just proximal to the toes; and toes **(digits),** with 14 bones. The feet and hands together contain more than half of all the body's bones (106 of the total 206).

As with the colloquial versus anatomical meaning of *wrist,* the colloquial meaning of *ankle* (the narrow point where one may wear an ankle bracelet) is different from the anatomical meaning: the posterior half of the foot containing the seven tarsal (ankle) bones. In anatomical terms, the wrist is part of the hand and the ankle is part (indeed, about half) of the foot.

### The Femur

The **femur** (FEE-mur) is the longest and strongest bone of the body, measuring about one-quarter of one's height **(fig. 8.39).** It has a hemispherical head that articulates with the acetabulum of the pelvis, forming a quintessential *ball-and-socket joint.* A ligament extends from the acetabulum to a pit, the **fovea capitis**[65] (FOE-vee-uh CAP-ih-tiss), in the head of the femur. Distal to the head is a constricted **neck** and then two massive, rough processes called the **greater** and **lesser trochanters**[66] (tro-CAN-turs), which are insertions for the powerful muscles of the hip. The trochanters are connected on the posterior side by a thick oblique ridge of bone, the **intertrochanteric crest,** and on the anterior side by a more delicate **intertrochanteric line.**

The primary feature of the shaft is a posterior ridge called the **linea aspera**[67] (LIN-ee-uh ASS-peh-ruh) at its midpoint. At its upper end, the linea aspera forks into a medial **spiral (pectineal) line** and a lateral **gluteal tuberosity.** The gluteal tuberosity is a rough ridge (sometimes a depression) that serves for attachment of the powerful *gluteus maximus* muscle of the buttock. At its lower end, the linea aspera forks into **medial** and **lateral supracondylar lines,** which continue down to the respective epicondyles.

The **medial** and **lateral epicondyles** are the widest points of the femur, easily palpated at the knee. These and the supracondylar lines are attachments for certain thigh and leg muscles and knee ligaments. At the distal end of the femur are two smooth round surfaces of the knee joint, the **medial** and **lateral condyles,** separated by a groove called the **intercondylar fossa** (IN-tur-CON-dih-lur). During knee flexion and extension, the condyles rock on the superior surface of the tibia. On the anterior side of the femur, a smooth medial depression called the **patellar surface** articulates with the patella. On the posterior side is a flat or slightly depressed area called the **popliteal surface.**

### The Patella

The **patella,**[68] or kneecap (fig. 8.39), is a roughly triangular sesamoid bone embedded in the tendon of the knee. It is cartilaginous at birth and ossifies at 3 to 6 years of age. It has a broad superior **base,** a pointed inferior **apex,** and a pair of shallow **articular facets** on its posterior surface where it articulates with the femur. The lateral facet is usually larger than the medial. The *quadriceps femoris tendon* extends from the anterior *quadriceps femoris muscle* of the thigh to the patella, and it continues as the *patellar ligament* from the patella to the tibia. This is a change in terminology more than a change in structure or function, as a tendon connects muscle to bone and a ligament connects bone to bone. Because of the way the quadriceps tendon loops over the patella, the patella acts like a pulley, modifying the direction of pull by the quadriceps muscle. This improves its efficiency in extending the knee, hence the efficiency of walking and running.

### The Tibia

The leg has two bones: a thick strong tibia (TIB-ee-uh) on the medial side and a slender fibula (FIB-you-luh) on the lateral side

[65]*fovea* = pit; *capitis* = of the head
[66]*trochanter* = to run
[67]*linea* = line; *asper* = rough
[68]*pat* = pan; *ella* = little

**TABLE 8.5 Comparison of the Male and Female Pelvic Girdles**

| Feature | Male | Female |
|---|---|---|
| General appearance | More massive; rougher; heavier processes | Less massive; smoother; more delicate processes |
| Tilt | Upper end of pelvis relatively vertical | Upper end of pelvis tilted forward |
| Depth of greater pelvis | Deeper; ilium projects farther above sacroiliac joint | Shallower; ilium does not project as far above sacroiliac joint |
| Width of greater pelvis | Hips less flared; anterior superior spines closer together | Hips more flared; anterior superior spines farther apart |
| Pelvic inlet | Heart-shaped | Round or oval |
| Pelvic outlet | Smaller | Larger |
| Subpubic angle | Narrower, usually 90° or less | Wider, usually 100° or more |
| Pubic symphysis | Taller | Shorter |
| Body of pubis | More triangular | More rectangular |
| Greater sciatic notch | Narrower | Wider |
| Obturator foramen | Rounder | More oval to triangular |
| Acetabulum | Larger, faces more laterally | Smaller, faces slightly anteriorly |
| Sacrum | Narrower and deeper | Wider and shallower |
| Coccyx | Less movable; more vertical | More movable; tilted posteriorly |

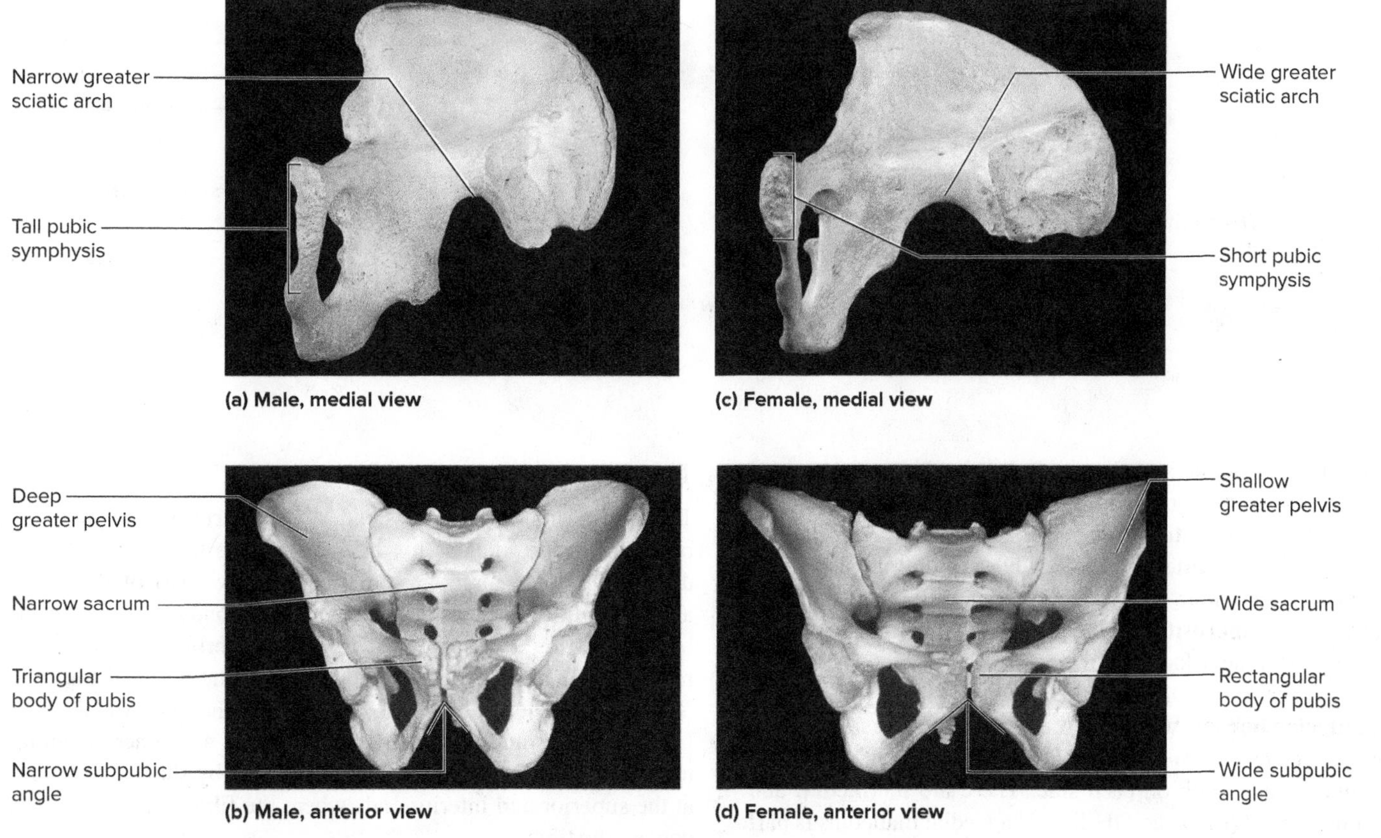


**FIGURE 8.38 Comparison of the Male and Female Pelvic Girdles.** (a) Male, medial view. (b) Male, anterior view. (c) Female, medial view. (d) Female, anterior view. Compare with table 8.5.

**(top, both):** David Hunt/specimens from the National Museum of Natural History, Smithsonian Institution; **(bottom, both):** VideoSurgery/Science Source

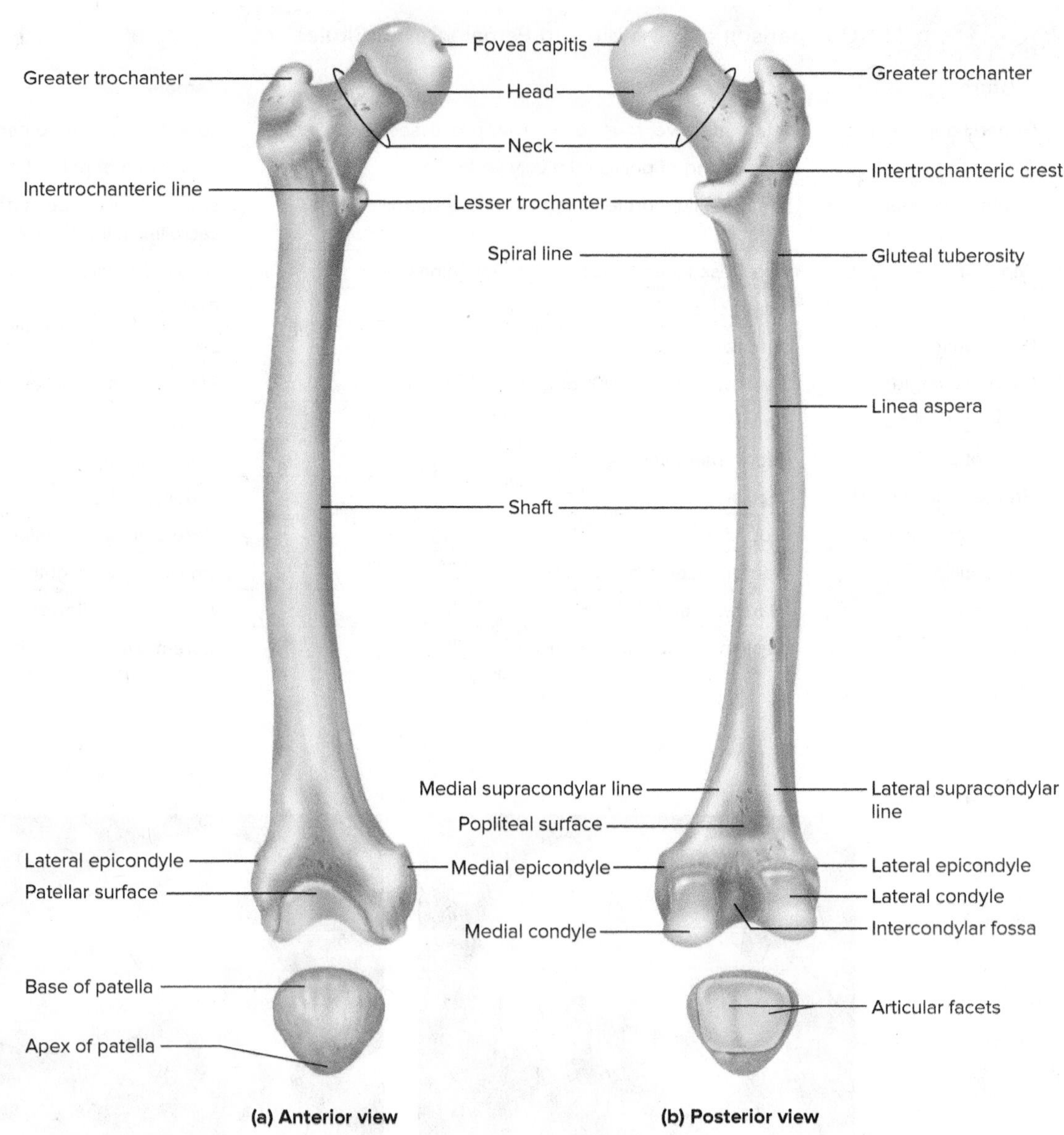


**FIGURE 8.39 The Right Femur and Patella.** (a) Anterior view. (b) Posterior view. APR

**(fig. 8.40).** The **tibia** is the only weight-bearing bone of the crural region. Its broad superior head has two fairly flat articular surfaces, the **medial** and **lateral condyles,** separated by a ridge called the **intercondylar eminence.** The condyles of the tibia articulate with those of the femur. The rough anterior surface of the upper tibia, the **tibial tuberosity,** can be palpated just below the patella. This is an attachment for the powerful thigh muscles that extend (straighten) the knee. Distal to this, the shaft has a sharply angular **anterior border,** which can be palpated in the shin. At the ankle, just above the rim of a standard dress shoe, you can palpate a prominent bony knob on each side. These are the **medial** and **lateral malleoli**[69] (MAL-ee-OH-lie). The medial malleolus is part of the tibia, and the lateral malleolus is the part of the fibula.

## The Fibula

The **fibula**[70] (fig. 8.40) is a slender lateral strut that helps to stabilize the ankle. It does not bear any of the body's weight; indeed, orthopedic surgeons sometimes remove part of the fibula and use it to replace damaged or missing bone elsewhere in the body. The fibula is somewhat thicker and broader at its proximal end, the **head,** than at the distal end. The point of the head is called the **apex.** The distal expansion is the lateral malleolus. Like the radius and ulna, the tibia and fibula are joined by an interosseous membrane along their shafts, and by shorter ligaments at the superior and inferior ends where the fibular head and apex contact the tibia.

[69] *malle* = hammer; *olus* = little

[70] *fibula* = little pin or clasp; from a garment pin in ancient Greece and Rome

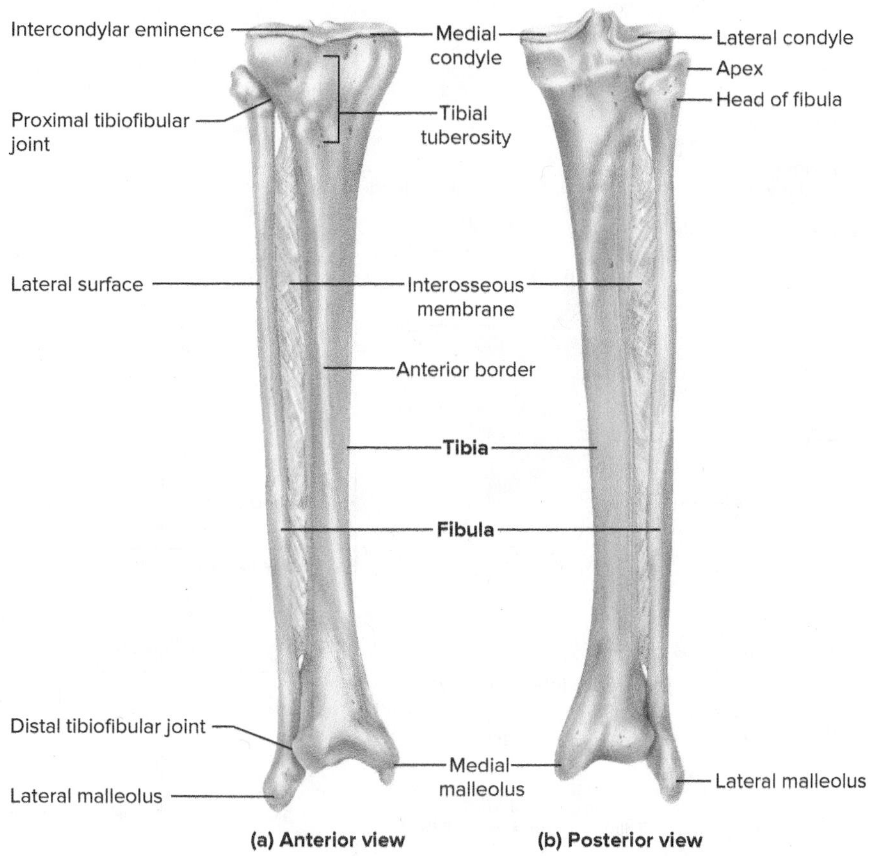


**FIGURE 8.40 The Right Tibia and Fibula.** (a) Anterior view. (b) Posterior view. APR

## The Ankle and Foot

The **tarsal bones** of the ankle are arranged in proximal and distal groups somewhat like the carpal bones of the wrist **(fig. 8.41).** Because of the load-bearing role of the ankle, however, their shapes and arrangement are conspicuously different from those of the carpal bones, and they are fully integrated into the structure of the foot. The largest tarsal bone is the **calcaneus**[71] (cal-CAY-nee-us), which forms the heel. Its posterior end is the point of attachment for the **calcaneal (Achilles) tendon** from the calf muscles. The second-largest tarsal bone, and the most superior, is the **talus.** It has three articular surfaces: an inferoposterior one that articulates with the calcaneus, a superior **trochlear surface** that articulates with the tibia, and an anterior surface that articulates with a short, wide tarsal bone called the **navicular.**[72] The talus, calcaneus, and navicular are considered the proximal row of tarsal bones.

The distal group forms a row of four bones. Proceeding from the medial to lateral, these are the **medial, intermediate,** and **lateral cuneiforms**[73] (cue-NEE-ih-forms) and the **cuboid.** The cuboid is the largest.

[71]*calc* = stone, chalk
[72]*navi* = boat; *cul* = little; *ar* = like
[73]*cunei* = wedge; *form* = in the shape of

### ▶▶▶APPLY WHAT YOU KNOW

*The upper and lower limbs each contain 30 bones, yet we have 8 carpal bones in the upper limb and only 7 tarsal bones in the lower limb. What makes up the difference in the lower limb?*

The remaining bones of the foot are similar in arrangement and name to those of the hand. The proximal **metatarsal**[74] **bones** are similar to the metacarpals. They are **metatarsals I** through **V** from medial to lateral, metatarsal I being proximal to the great toe. Metatarsals I to III articulate with the first through third cuneiforms; metatarsals IV and V both articulate with the cuboid.

Bones of the toes, like those of the fingers, are called phalanges. The great toe contains only two bones, the proximal and distal phalanx I. The other toes each contain a proximal, middle, and distal phalanx, and are numbered II through V from medial to lateral. Thus middle phalanx V, for example, would be the middle bone of the smallest toe. The metatarsal and phalangeal bones each have a base, body, and head, like the bones of the hand. All of them, especially the phalanges, are slightly concave on the inferior (plantar) side.

Note that roman numeral I represents the *medial* group of bones in the foot but the *lateral* group in the hand. In both cases,

[74]*meta* = beyond; *tars* = ankle

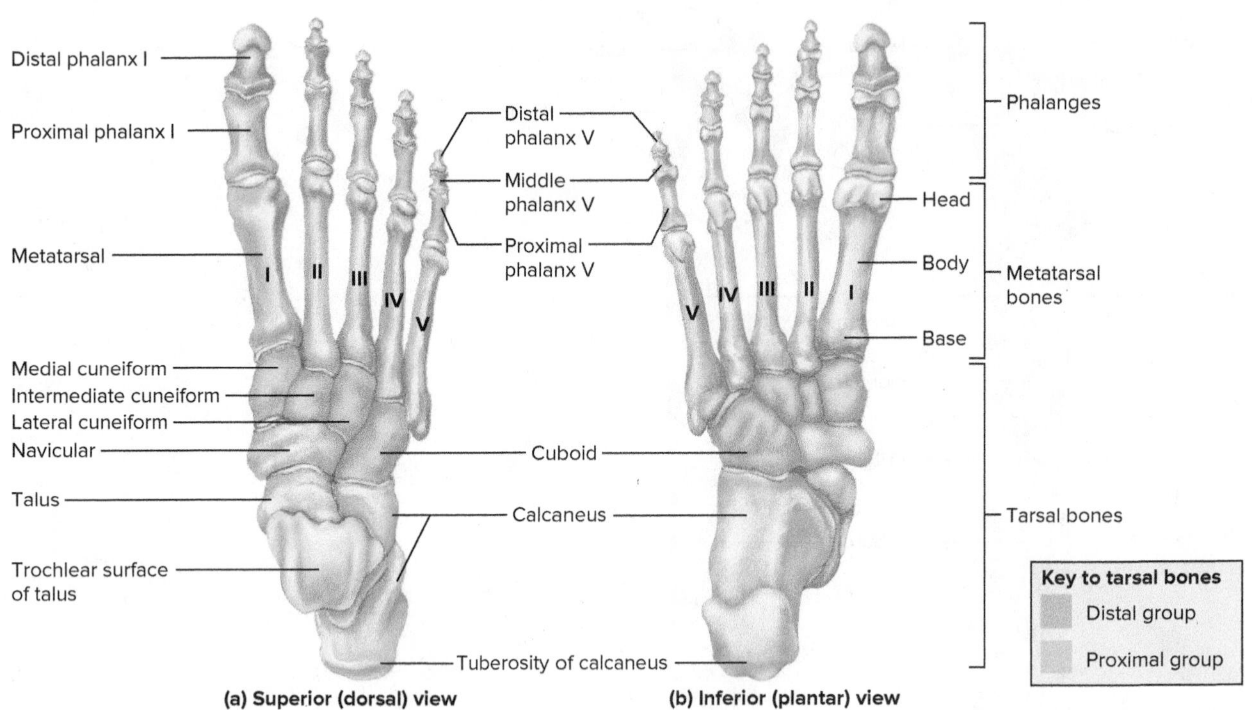


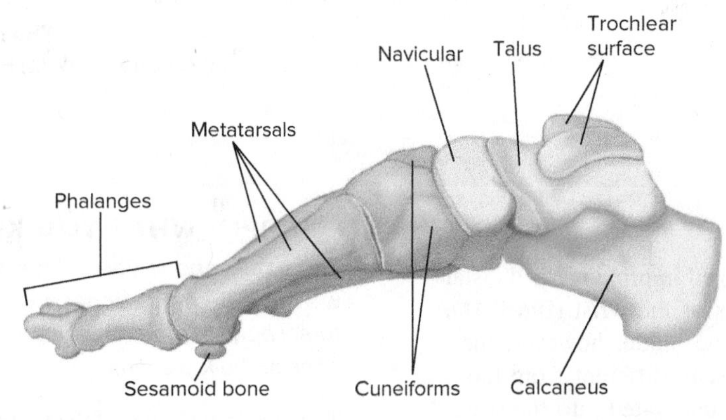


**FIGURE 8.41 The Right Foot.** (a) Superior (dorsal) view. (b) Inferior (plantar) view. (c) Medial view. APR

*Contrast the tarsal bones with the carpal bones. Which ones are similar in location? Which ones are different?*

however, it refers to the largest digit of the limb. The reason for the difference between the hand and foot lies in a rotation of the limbs that occurs in the seventh week of embryonic development. Early in the seventh week, the limbs extend anteriorly from the body, the foot is a paddlelike *foot plate,* and the *hand plate* is also more or less paddlelike with the finger buds showing early separation **(fig. 8.42a).** The future thumb and great toe are both directed superiorly, and the future palms and soles face each other medially. But then each limb rotates about 90° in opposite directions. The upper limb rotates laterally. To visualize this, hold your hands straight out in front of you with the palms facing each other as if

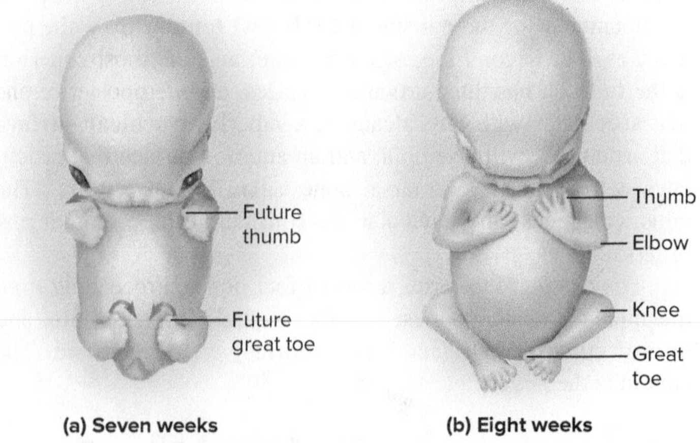


**FIGURE 8.42 Embryonic Limb Rotation.** (a) Rotation of the hands and feet in opposite directions in week 7. (b) Resulting orientation of hands and feet established by week 8.

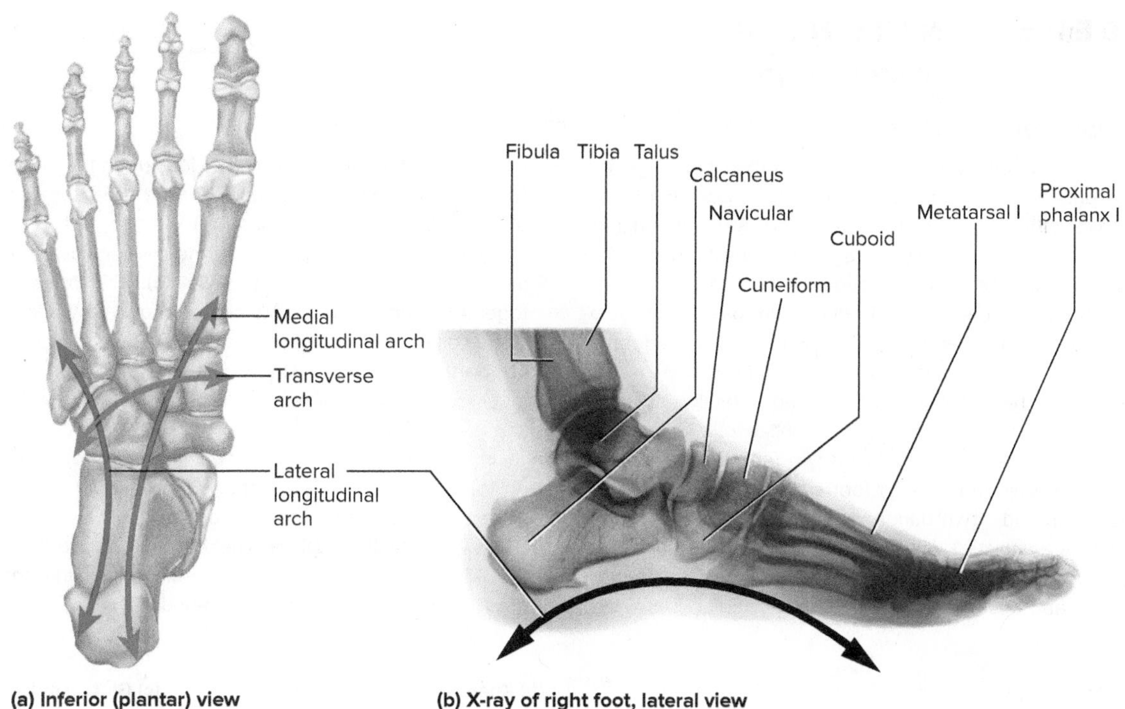


**FIGURE 8.43 Arches of the Foot.** (a) Inferior (plantar) view. (b) X-ray of right foot, lateral view.
b: stockdevil/123RF

you were about to clap. Then rotate your forearms so the thumbs face away from each other (laterally) and the palms face upward. The lower limbs rotate in the opposite direction, medially, so that the soles face downward and the great toes become medial. So even though the thumb and great toe (digit I of the hand and foot) start out facing in the same direction, these opposite rotations result in their being on opposite sides of the hand and foot **(fig. 8.42b).** This rotation also explains why the elbow flexes posteriorly and the knee flexes anteriorly, and why (as you will see in chapter 10) the muscles that flex the elbow are on the anterior side of the arm, whereas those that flex the knee are on the posterior side of the thigh.

The foot normally doesn't rest flat on the ground, but has three springy arches that distribute the body's weight between the heel and the heads of the metatarsal bones and absorb the stress of walking **(fig. 8.43).** The **medial longitudinal arch,** which essentially extends from heel to great toe, is formed from the calcaneus, talus, navicular, cuneiforms, and metatarsals I to III. It is normally well above the ground, as evidenced by the shape of a wet footprint. The **lateral longitudinal arch** extends from heel to little toe and includes the calcaneus, cuboid, and metatarsals IV and V. The **transverse arch** includes the cuboid, cuneiforms, and proximal heads of the metatarsal bones. These arches are held together by short, strong ligaments. Excessive weight, repetitious stress, or congenital weakness of these ligaments can stretch them, resulting in *pes planus* (commonly called flat feet or fallen arches). This condition makes a person less tolerant of prolonged standing and walking. A comparison of the flat-footed apes with humans underscores the significance of the human foot arches (see Deeper Insight 8.5).

**BEFORE YOU GO ON**

Answer the following questions to test your understanding of the preceding section:

20. Name the bones of the adult pelvic girdle. What three bones of a child fuse to form the hip bone of an adult?
21. Name any four structures of the pelvis that you can palpate and describe where to palpate them.
22. Describe several ways in which the male and female pelvic girdles differ.
23. What parts of the femur are involved in the hip joint? What parts are involved in the knee joint?
24. Name the prominent knobs on each side of your ankle. What bones contribute to these structures?
25. Name all the bones that articulate with the talus and describe the location of each.

## DEEPER INSIGHT 8.5
### EVOLUTIONARY MEDICINE

### *Skeletal Adaptations for Bipedalism*

Some mammals can stand, hop, or walk briefly on their hind legs, but humans are the only mammals that are habitually bipedal. Footprints preserved in a layer of volcanic ash in Tanzania indicate that hominids walked upright as early as 3.6 million years ago. This bipedal locomotion is possible only because of several adaptations of the human feet, legs, spine, and skull. These features are so distinctive that paleoanthropologists (those who study human fossil remains) can tell with considerable certainty whether a fossil species was able to walk upright.

As important as the hand has been to human evolution, the foot may be an even more significant adaptation. Unlike other mammals, humans support their entire body weight on two feet. While apes are flat-footed, humans have strong, springy foot arches that absorb shock as the body jostles up and down during walking and running. The tarsal bones are tightly articulated with one another, and the calcaneus is strongly developed. The great toe is not opposable as it is in most Old World monkeys and apes, but it is highly developed so it provides the "toe-off" that pushes the body forward in the last phase of the stride **(fig. 8.44a).** For this reason, loss of the great toe has a more crippling effect than the loss of any other toe.

While the femurs of apes are nearly vertical, in humans they angle medially from hip to knee **(fig. 8.44b).** This places our knees closer together, beneath the body's center of gravity. We lock our knees when standing, allowing us to stand erect with little muscular effort. Apes cannot do this and cannot stand on two legs for very long without tiring—much as you would if you tried to maintain an erect posture with your knees slightly bent.

In apes and other quadrupedal (four-legged) mammals, the abdominal viscera are supported by the muscular abdominal wall. In humans, the viscera bear down on the floor of the pelvic cavity, and a bowl-shaped pelvis with an inturned floor is necessary to support their weight. This has resulted in a narrower pelvic outlet—a condition that creates pain and difficulty in giving birth to such large-brained infants. The pain of childbirth

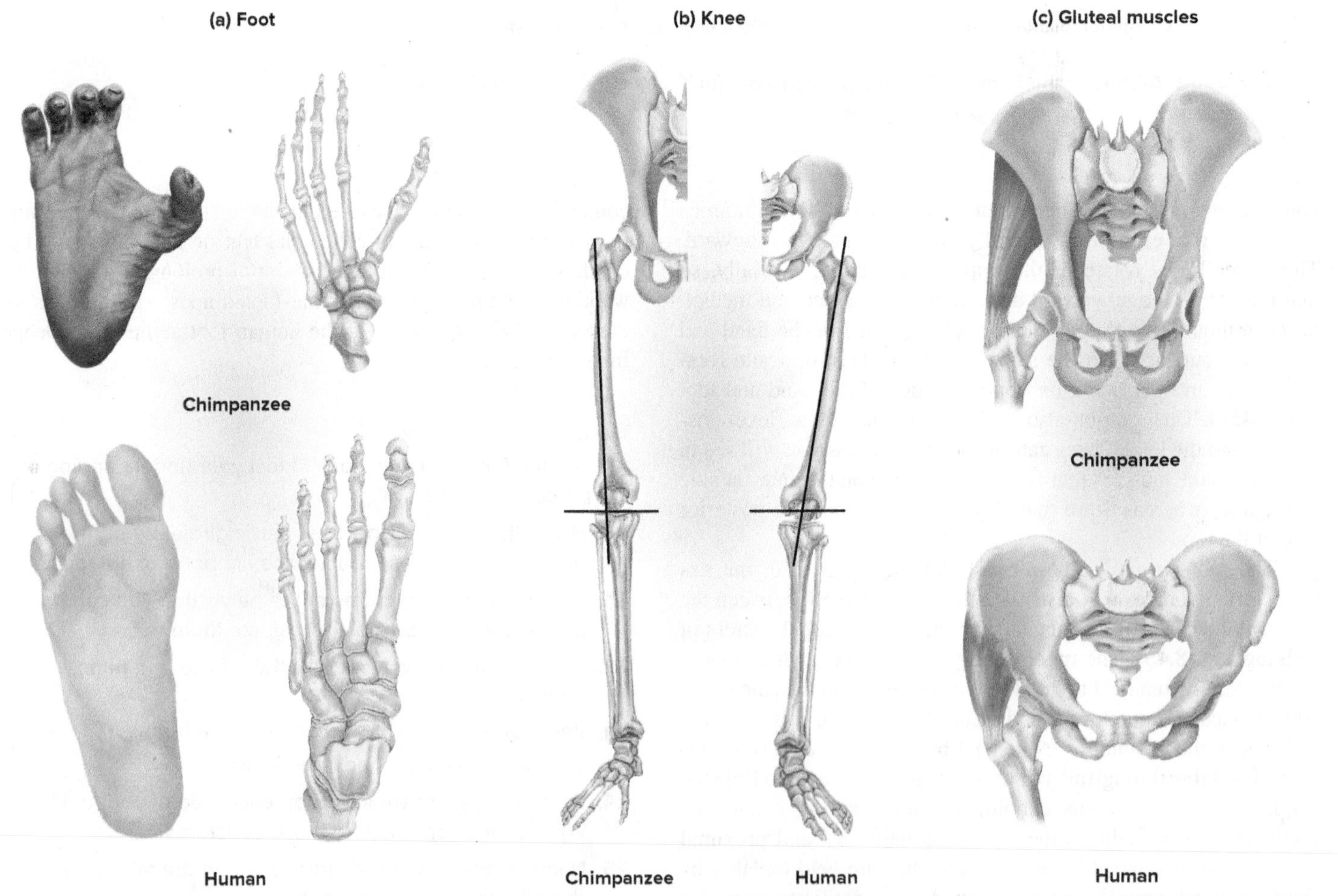

**FIGURE 8.44 Skeletal Adaptations for Bipedalism.** Human adaptations for bipedalism are best understood by comparison to our close living relative, the chimpanzee, which is not adapted for a comfortable or sustained erect stance. See the text for the relevance of each comparison. (a) Foot. (b) Knee. (c) Gluteal muscles. (d) Pelvis. (e) Vertebral column. (f) Skull.

*(figure continues)*

seems unique to humans and, one could say, is a price we must pay for having both a large brain and a bipedal stance.

The largest muscle of the buttock, the *gluteus maximus,* serves in apes primarily as an abductor of the thigh—that is, it moves the leg laterally. In humans, however, the ilium has expanded posteriorly, so the gluteus maximus originates behind the hip joint. This changes the function of the muscle—instead of abducting the thigh, it pulls the thigh back in the second half of a stride (pulling back on your right thigh, for example, when your left foot is off the ground and swinging forward). Two other buttock muscles, the *gluteus medius* and *gluteus minimus,* extend laterally in humans from the surface of the ilium to the greater trochanter of the femur **(fig. 8.44c).** In walking, when one foot is lifted from the ground, these muscles shift the body weight over the other foot so we don't fall over. The actions of all three gluteal muscles, and the corresponding evolutionary remodeling of the pelvis, account for the smooth, efficient stride of a human as compared with the awkward, shuffling gait of a chimpanzee or gorilla when walking upright. The posterior growth of the ilium **(fig. 8.44d)** is the reason the greater sciatic notch is so deeply concave.

The lumbar lordosis of the human spine allows for efficient bipedalism by shifting the body's center of gravity to the rear, above and slightly behind the hip joint **(fig. 8.44e).** Because of their C-shaped spines, chimpanzees cannot stand as easily. Their center of gravity is anterior to the hip joint when they stand; they must make a constant muscular effort to keep from falling forward, and they fatigue quickly. Humans, by contrast, require little effort to keep their balance. Our australopithecine ancestors probably could travel all day with relatively little fatigue.

The human head is balanced on the vertebral column with the gaze directed forward. The cervical curvature of the spine and remodeling of the skull have made this possible. The foramen magnum has moved to a more inferior and anterior location, and the face is much flatter than an ape's face **(fig. 8.44f),** so there is less weight anterior to the occipital condyles. Being balanced on the spine, the head doesn't require strong muscular attachments to hold it erect.

The forelimbs of apes are longer than the hindlimbs; indeed, some species such as the orangutan and gibbons hold their long forelimbs over their heads when they walk on their hind legs. By contrast, our forelimbs are shorter than our hindlimbs and far less muscular than the forelimbs of apes. No longer needed for locomotion, our forelimbs have become better adapted for carrying objects, holding things closer to the eyes, and manipulating them more precisely.

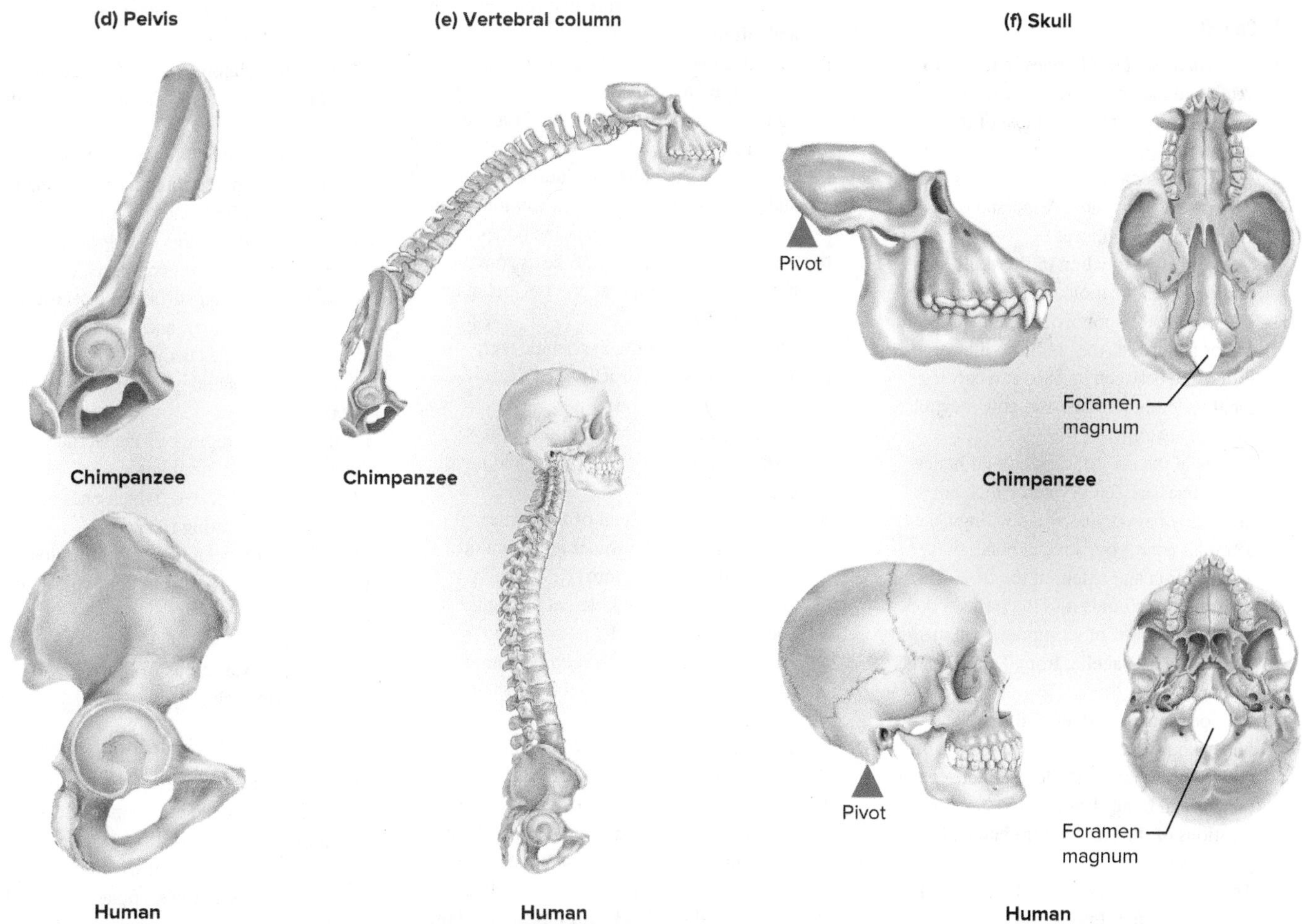


**FIGURE 8.44 Skeletal Adaptations for Bipedalism *(continued).***

# STUDY GUIDE

## Assess Your Learning Outcomes

*To test your knowledge, discuss the following topics with a study partner or in writing, ideally from memory.*

### 8.1 Overview of the Skeleton

1. The difference between the axial and appendicular skeletons, and the bones in each category
2. The typical number of named bones in an adult; why this number differs in newborns and children; and why the number varies among adults
3. Sutural and sesamoid bones, and examples of the latter
4. Names of the various outgrowths, depressions, articular surfaces, cavities, and passages in bones

### 8.2 The Skull

1. The usual number of bones in the adult skull, and the collective name of the seams or joints that bind most of them together
2. Names and locations of the cavities that enclose the brain, nose, ears, and eyes, and of the paranasal sinuses
3. The collective function of the skull foramina; the location and function of the largest one, the foramen magnum
4. Major features of the cranium; the difference between its base and calvaria; the three cranial fossae and how they relate to brain anatomy
5. Names of the six different cranial bones; which ones are solitary and which are bilaterally paired; and what distinguishes a cranial bone from a facial bone
6. The location and extent of the frontal bone; the suture that binds it to the parietal bones; and the locations of its supraorbital margin and foramen, glabella, frontal sinus, and diploe
7. The location and extent of the parietal bones; the suture formed where they meet the occipital bone and the one that separates the parietal bones from each other; and the locations of the parietal foramen and temporal lines
8. The location and extent of the temporal bones; the suture that borders them; and the names and boundaries of their four major parts
9. The location and extent of the occipital bone, its basilar part, and the names and locations of its foramina, canals, and surface protrusions
10. The location and extent of the sphenoid bone; its wings, body, pterygoid plates, clinoid processes, and foramina; its relationships with the pituitary gland and nasal apertures
11. The location and extent of the ethmoid bone; its part in defining the nasal fossae; and the locations of its plates, foramina, air cells, and nasal conchae
12. Names of the eight different facial bones; which ones are solitary and which are bilaterally paired
13. The location and extent of the maxilla; its foramina, alveoli, and alveolar and palatine processes; and the suture that joins the right and left maxillae
14. The location and extent of the palatine bones; their foramina; and their part in partially defining the walls of the nasal cavity and orbit
15. Structure of the palate, including the hard and soft regions and the contributions of the palatine processes and palatine bones
16. The location and extent of the zygomatic bones, and the temporal process and main foramen of each
17. The three parts of the zygomatic arch
18. The locations and structures of the tiny lacrimal and nasal bones
19. The inferior nasal concha and why it is distinguished from the superior and middle conchae
20. The location and extent of the vomer; contributions of the vomer and ethmoid bone to the nasal septum
21. Structure of the mandible, including the body, ramus, and angle; its two main processes and the notch between them; its foramina, symphysis, protuberance, and spines
22. The bones, and their specific features, that form the temporomandibular joint
23. The locations and names of the auditory ossicles; location and features of the hyoid bone; and functions of these bones
24. Names and locations of the fontanelles of the neonatal skull; why they exist; and how a child's skull changes between birth and 9 years of age

### 8.3 The Vertebral Column and Thoracic Cage

1. The number of vertebrae and intervertebral discs in the vertebral column (spine)
2. Four curvatures of the adult spine; which ones are present at birth; and when and how the others develop
3. Features of a typical vertebra
4. The five classes of vertebrae and the number of vertebrae in each class; the system of numbering them; and why the number of vertebrae in a child differs from the number at 30 years of age and beyond
5. Features that identify an isolated vertebra as cervical, thoracic, or lumbar
6. How the anatomy of the first two vertebrae (C1–C2) relates to movements of the head
7. How the anatomy of the thoracic vertebrae (T1–T12) relates to the articulations of the ribs
8. The structure and function of intervertebral discs; which vertebrae have discs between them and which ones do not
9. Anatomical features of the sacrum, including its foramina, crests, canal and hiatus, auricular surface and sacroiliac joint, promontory, and alae
10. Features of the coccyx
11. Components and general shape of the thoracic cage
12. Three main regions of the sternum; its notches and sternal angle
13. The number of ribs; which ones are true, false, and floating ribs
14. All features seen in most of the ribs
15. Which ribs differ from that typical anatomy, and how
16. How the ribs articulate with the vertebrae, including variations from the top to bottom of the rib cage

### 8.4 The Pectoral Girdle and Upper Limb

1. Names and locations of the 4 bones of the pectoral girdle and 30 bones of each upper limb
2. Names of the joints at which the humerus articulates with the scapula, the scapula with the clavicle, and the clavicle with the axial skeleton

# STUDY GUIDE

3. Features of the clavicle, including the sternal and acromial ends and conoid tubercle; function of the clavicles
4. Features of the scapula, including its borders and angles, fossae, suprascapular notch, acromion, coracoid process, and glenoid cavity
5. Names of the four regions of the upper limb and the bones contained in each
6. Features of the humerus, including the head, necks, tubercles, intertubercular sulcus, deltoid tuberosity, capitulum, trochlea, epicondyles, supracondylar ridges, and three fossae
7. Features of the radius, including the head, neck, radial tuberosity, styloid process, and ulnar notch
8. Features of the ulna, including the trochlear and radial notches, coronoid and styloid processes, and olecranon; and the relationship of the radius and ulna to the interosseous membrane
9. Names of the carpal bones, in order, from lateral to medial in the proximal row and lateral to medial in the distal row; the unusual structure of the hamate bone
10. The system of naming and numbering the 5 metacarpal bones of the palmar region and 5 sets of phalanges in the digits; why there are 5 digits but only 14 phalanges; the base, body, and head of all 19 metacarpals and phalanges

**8.5 The Pelvic Girdle and Lower Limb**

1. Names and locations of the 3 bones of the pelvic girdle and 30 bones of each lower limb
2. Names of the joints at which the lower limb articulates with the pelvic girdle and the pelvic girdle articulates with the axial skeleton
3. The distinction between the pelvic girdle and pelvis
4. Three childhood bones that fuse to form each adult hip (coxal) bone, and the boundaries of each on the hip bone
5. Features of the hip (coxal) bones and pelvic girdle including the auricular surfaces; interpubic disc and pubic symphysis; greater and lesser pelves; pelvic brim, inlet, and outlet; iliac crest; acetabulum; obturator foramen; four ischial spines; two sciatic notches; iliac fossa; and parts of the ischium and pubis
6. Differences between the male and female pelvic girdles and the essential reason for these differences
7. Names of the four regions of the lower limb and the bones contained in each
8. Features of the femur, including the head, neck, fovea capitis, trochanters, intertrochanteric crest, gluteal tuberosity, condyles, intercondylar fossa, epicondyles, lines, and patellar and popliteal surfaces
9. Features of the patella, including the base, apex, and articular facets
10. Features of the tibia, including the lateral and medial condyles and intercondylar eminence; tibial tuberosity; anterior crest; and medial malleolus
11. Features of the fibula, including the head, apex, and lateral malleolus
12. Names of the tarsal bones from posterior to anterior, and from lateral to medial in the distal row; why they are more fully integrated into the foot than the carpal bones are into the hand
13. The system of naming and numbering the 5 metatarsal bones of the foot and 5 sets of phalanges in the digits; why there are 5 digits but only 14 phalanges; the base, body, and head of all 19 metatarsals and phalanges
14. Why the elbows and knees flex in opposite directions, and why the largest digit is lateral in the hand but medial in the foot
15. Names and locations of the three foot arches

## Testing Your Recall

Answers in Appendix A

1. Which of these is *not* a paranasal sinus?
   a. frontal
   b. temporal
   c. sphenoidal
   d. ethmoidal
   e. maxillary

2. Which of these is a facial bone?
   a. frontal
   b. ethmoid
   c. occipital
   d. temporal
   e. lacrimal

3. Which of these *cannot* be palpated on a living person?
   a. the crista galli
   b. the mastoid process
   c. the zygomatic arch
   d. the superior nuchal line
   e. the hyoid bone

4. All of the following are groups of vertebrae *except* for ______, which is a spinal kyphosis.
   a. thoracic
   b. cervical
   c. lumbar
   d. pelvic
   e. sacral

5. Thoracic vertebrae do *not* have
   a. transverse foramina.
   b. costal facets.
   c. spinous processes.
   d. transverse processes.
   e. pedicles.

6. The tubercle of a rib articulates with
   a. the sternal notch.
   b. the margin of the gladiolus.
   c. the costal facets of two vertebrae.
   d. the body of a vertebra.
   e. the transverse process of a vertebra.

7. The disc-shaped head of the radius articulates with the ______ of the humerus.
   a. radial tuberosity
   b. trochlea
   c. capitulum
   d. olecranon
   e. glenoid cavity

8. All of the following are carpal bones, *except* the ______, which is a tarsal bone.
   a. trapezium
   b. cuboid
   c. trapezoid
   d. triquetrum
   e. pisiform

9. The bone that supports your body weight when you are sitting down is
   a. the acetabulum.
   b. the pubis.
   c. the ilium.
   d. the coccyx.
   e. the ischium.

# STUDY GUIDE

10. Which of these is the bone of the heel?
    a. cuboid
    b. calcaneus
    c. navicular
    d. trochlear
    e. talus
11. Gaps between the cranial bones of an infant are called ______.
12. The external auditory canal is a passage in the ______ bone.
13. Bones of the skull are joined along lines called ______.
14. The ______ bone has greater and lesser wings and protects the pituitary gland.
15. A herniated disc occurs when a ring called the ______ cracks.
16. The transverse ligament of the atlas holds the ______ of the axis in place.
17. The sacroiliac joint is formed where the ______ surface of the sacrum articulates with that of the ilium.
18. The ______ processes of the radius and ulna form bony protuberances on each side of the wrist.
19. Nerves and blood vessels pass through small holes in the skull called ______. The singular form of this word is ______.
20. The ______ arch of the foot extends from the heel to the great toe.

## Building Your Medical Vocabulary

*Answers in Appendix A*

*State a meaning of each word element, and give a medical term from this chapter that uses it or a slight variation of it.*

1. costo-
2. cranio-
3. dura
4. glosso-
5. -icle
6. masto-
7. pedo-
8. pterygo-
9. supra-
10. tarso-

## What's Wrong with These Statements?

*Answers in Appendix A*

*Briefly explain why each of the following statements is false, or reword it to make it true.*

1. The internal jugular vein passes out the foramen magnum of the skull and down the neck.
2. The hands have more phalanges than the feet.
3. As an adaptation to pregnancy, the female's pelvis is deeper than the male's.
4. A wristwatch or bracelet normally encircles the area of the carpal (wrist) bones.
5. On a living person, it would be possible to palpate the acromion and spine of the scapula but not the muscles of the infraspinous fossa.
6. If you rest your chin on your hands and your elbows on a table, the coronoid process of the ulna rests on the table.
7. The lumbar vertebrae do not articulate with any ribs and therefore do not have transverse processes.
8. The most frequently broken bone is the humerus.
9. In strict anatomical terminology, the words *arm* and *leg* both refer to regions with only one bone.
10. Sesamoid bones are found along the sutures between cranial bones in some people.

## Testing Your Comprehension

1. Most bones form joints with at least two others. For example, there are 12 joints between vertebra T6 and other, adjacent bones. Identify at least 10 of them.
2. By palpating the hind leg of a cat or dog or by examining a laboratory skeleton, you can see that cats and dogs stand on the heads of their metatarsal bones; the calcaneus does not touch the ground. How is this similar to the stance of a woman wearing high-heeled shoes? How is it different?
3. Between any two of the unfused vertebrae (cervical through lumbar), there is an intervertebral disc—except between C1 and C2. Give some reasons for the unique absence of a disc at that location.
4. In adolescents, trauma sometimes separates the head of the femur from the neck. Why do you think this is more common in adolescents than in adults?
5. Discuss all the ways you can in which the differences between vertebrae C5 and L3 exemplify this book's theme of the unity of form and function.

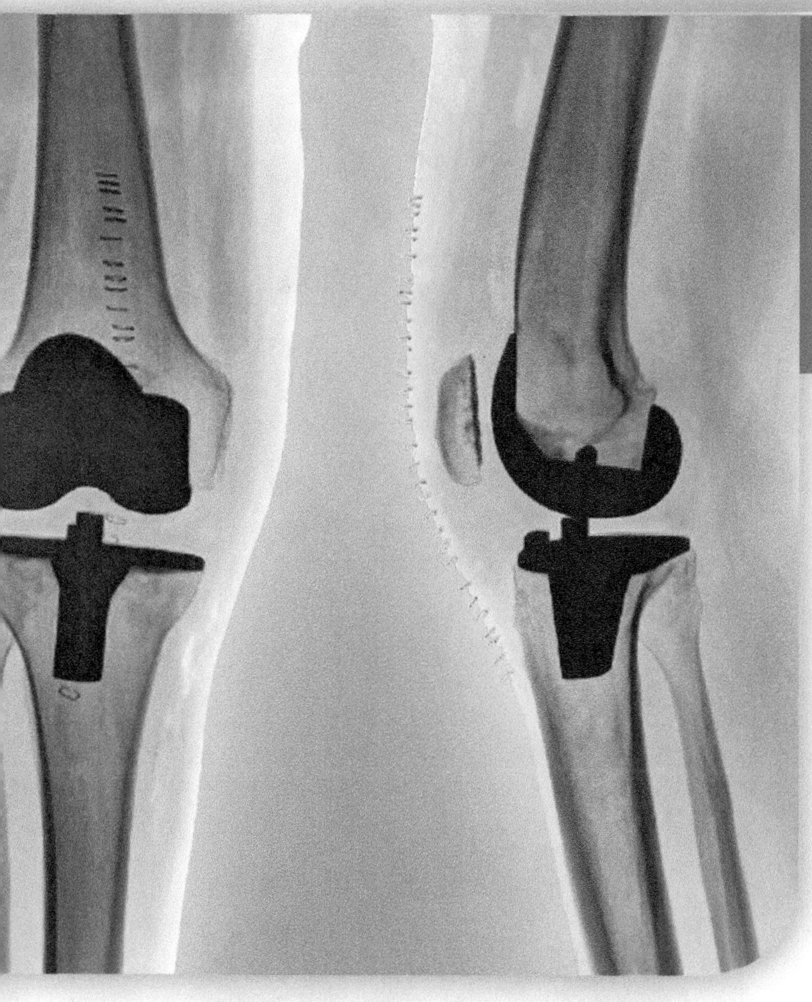

X-ray of knee replacement prosthesis, frontal and lateral views
Zephyr/Getty Images

# CHAPTER 9

# JOINTS

## CHAPTER OUTLINE



## DEEPER INSIGHTS

**Module 5: Skeletal System**

## BRUSHING UP

- Understanding the anatomy and function of the joints requires familiarity with the names of all the major bones (see table 8.1 and fig. 8.1).
- Understanding joint action also requires knowledge of the surface features of bones, especially at the articular surfaces of the limb bones, described throughout chapter 8 and itemized in general terms in table 8.2.
- Movements of the joints are described with reference to the basic anatomical planes defined in atlas A, figure A.1.

Joints, or articulations, link the bones of the skeletal system into a functional whole—a system that supports the body, permits effective movement, and protects the softer organs. Joints such as the shoulder, elbow, and knee are remarkable specimens of biological design—self-lubricating, almost frictionless, and able to bear heavy loads and withstand compression while executing smooth and precise movements **(fig. 9.1).** Yet it is equally important that other joints be less movable or even immobile. Such joints are better able to support the body and protect delicate organs. The vertebral column, for example, is only moderately mobile, for it must allow for flexibility of the torso and yet protect the delicate spinal cord and support much of the body's weight. Bones of the cranium must protect the brain and sense organs, but need not allow for movement (except during birth); thus, they are locked together by immobile joints, the sutures studied in chapter 8.

In everyday life, we take the greatest notice of the most freely mobile joints of the limbs, and it is here that people feel most severely compromised by such disabling diseases as arthritis. Much of the work of physical therapists focuses on limb mobility. In this chapter, we will survey all types of joints, from the utterly immobile to the most mobile, but with an emphasis on the latter. This survey of joint anatomy and movements will provide a foundation for the study of muscle actions in chapter 10.

**FIGURE 9.1 Joint Flexibility.**
Rubberball/Erik Isakson/Getty Images

## 9.1 Joints and Their Classification

### Expected Learning Outcomes

When you have completed this section, you should be able to

a. explain what joints are, how they are named, and what functions they serve;
b. name and describe the four major categories of joints;
c. describe the three types of fibrous joints and give an example of each;
d. distinguish between the three types of sutures;
e. describe the two types of cartilaginous joints and give an example of each; and
f. explain, with examples, why some joints change categories as a person ages.

Any point where two bones meet is called a **joint (articulation),** whether or not the bones are mobile at that interface. The science of joint structure, function, and dysfunction is called **arthrology.**[1] The study of musculoskeletal movement is **kinesiology**[2] (kih-NEE-see-OL-oh-jee).

The name of a joint is typically derived from the names of the bones involved. For example, the *atlanto–occipital joint* is where the atlas meets the occipital condyles; the *glenohumeral joint* is where the glenoid cavity of the scapula meets the humerus; and the *radioulnar joint* is where the radius meets the ulna.

Joints can be classified according to the manner in which the adjacent bones are bound to each other, with corresponding differences in how freely the bones can move. Authorities differ in their classification schemes, but one common view places the

[1] *arthro* = joint; *logy* = study of
[2] *kinesio* = movement; *logy* = study of

joints in four major categories: *bony, fibrous, cartilaginous,* and *synovial joints*. This section describes the first three of these and the subclasses of each. The remainder of the chapter will then be concerned primarily with synovial joints.

## 9.1a Bony Joints

A **bony joint,** or **synostosis**[3] (SIN-oss-TOE-sis), is an immobile joint formed when the gap between two bones ossifies and they become, in effect, a single bone. Bony joints can form by ossification of either fibrous or cartilaginous joints. An infant is born with right and left frontal and mandibular bones, for example, but these soon fuse seamlessly into a single frontal bone and mandible. Three childhood bones—the ilium, ischium, and pubis—fuse to form a single hip bone on each side of an adult. The epiphyses and diaphyses of the long bones are joined by cartilaginous joints in childhood and adolescence, and these become bony joints in early adulthood. In old age, the first rib often fuses with the sternum and the two parietal bones sometimes fuse along the sagittal suture.

[3]*syn* = together; *ost* = bone; *osis* = condition

## 9.1b Fibrous Joints

A **fibrous joint** is also called a **synarthrosis**[4] (SIN-ar-THRO-sis). It is a point at which adjacent bones are bound by collagen fibers that emerge from one bone, cross the space between them, and penetrate into the other **(fig. 9.2).** There are three kinds of fibrous joints: *sutures, gomphoses,* and *syndesmoses*. In sutures and gomphoses, the fibers are very short and allow for little or no movement. In syndesmoses, the fibers are longer and the attached bones are more mobile.

[4]*syn* = together; *arthr* = joined; *osis* = condition

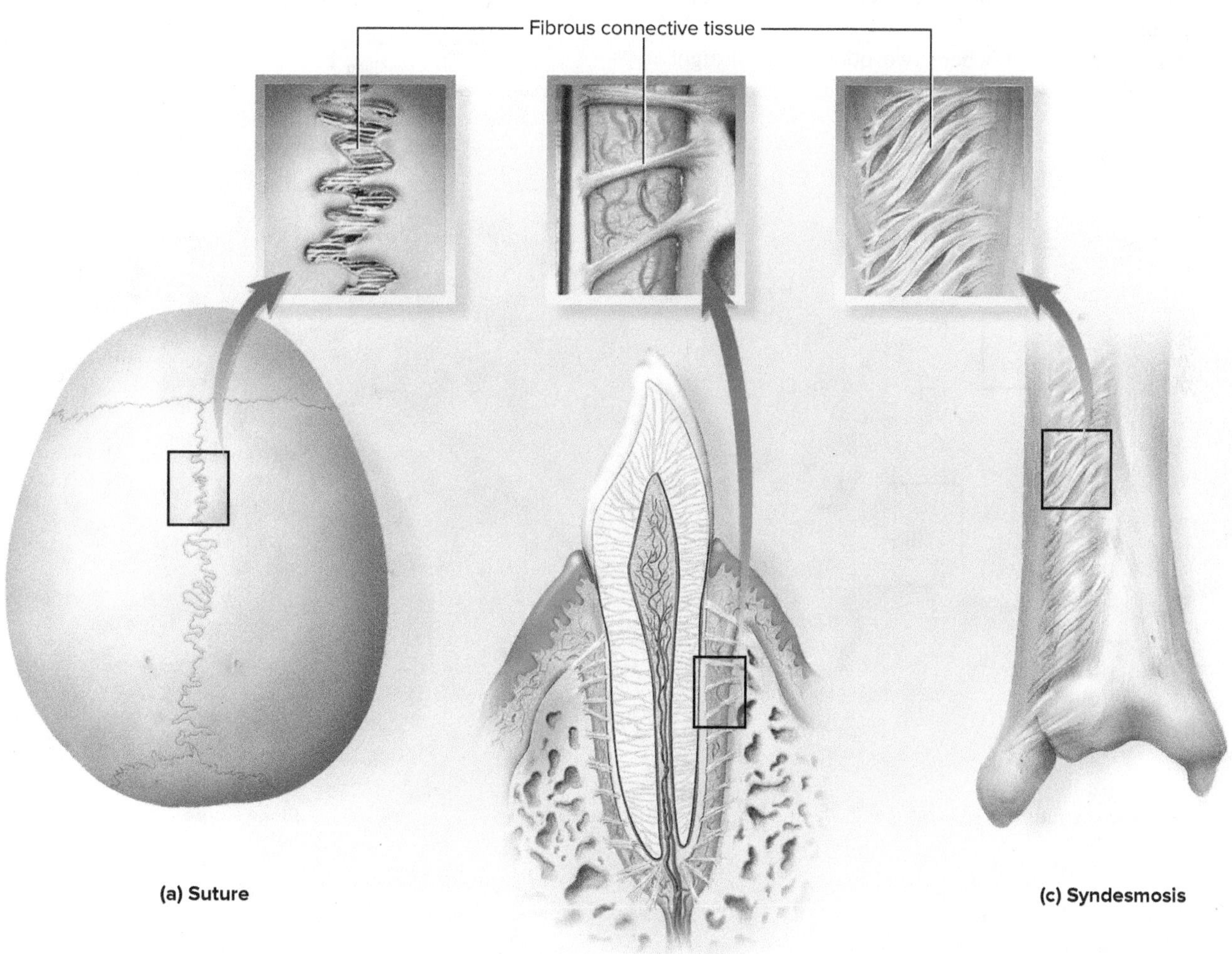


**FIGURE 9.2 Fibrous Joints.** (a) A suture between the parietal bones. (b) A gomphosis between a tooth and the jaw. (c) A syndesmosis between the tibia and fibula.

*If we narrowly define a joint as an attachment of one bone to another, one of these three would not qualify. Which one and why?*

## Sutures

**Sutures** are immobile or only slightly mobile fibrous joints that closely bind the bones of the skull to each other; they occur nowhere else. In chapter 8, we didn't take much notice of the differences between one suture and another, but some differences may have caught your attention as you studied the diagrams in that chapter or examined laboratory specimens. Sutures can be classified as *serrate, lap,* and *plane sutures.* Readers with some knowledge of woodworking may recognize that the structures and functional properties of these sutures have something in common with basic types of carpentry joints **(fig. 9.3).**

**Serrate sutures** appear as wavy lines along which the adjoining bones firmly interlock with each other by their serrated margins, like pieces of a jigsaw puzzle. Serrate sutures are analogous to a dovetail wood joint. Examples include the coronal, sagittal, and lambdoid sutures that border the parietal bones.

**Lap (squamous) sutures** occur where two bones have overlapping beveled edges, like a miter joint in carpentry. On the surface, a lap suture appears as a relatively smooth (nonserrated) line. An example is the squamous suture where the temporal bone meets the sphenoid and parietal bones. The beveled edge of the temporal bone can be seen in figure 8.10b.

**Plane (butt) sutures** occur where two bones have straight nonoverlapping edges. The two bones merely border on each other, like two boards glued together in a butt joint. This type of joint is represented by the intermaxillary suture in the roof of the mouth (see fig. 8.5a).

## Gomphoses

Even though the teeth are not bones, the attachment of a tooth to its socket is classified as a joint called a **gomphosis** (gom-FOE-sis). The term refers to its similarity to a nail hammered into wood.[5] The tooth is held firmly in place by a fibrous **periodontal ligament,** which consists of collagen fibers that extend from the bone matrix of the jaw into the dental tissue (see fig. 9.2b). The periodontal ligament allows the tooth to move or give a little under the stress of chewing. Along with associated nerve endings, this slight tooth movement allows us to sense how hard we're biting and to sense a particle of food stuck between the teeth.

## Syndesmoses

A **syndesmosis**[6] (SIN-dez-MO-sis) is a fibrous joint at which two bones are bound by relatively long collagenous fibers. The

[5]*gomph* = nail, bolt; *osis* = condition
[6]*syn* = together; *desm* = band; *osis* = condition

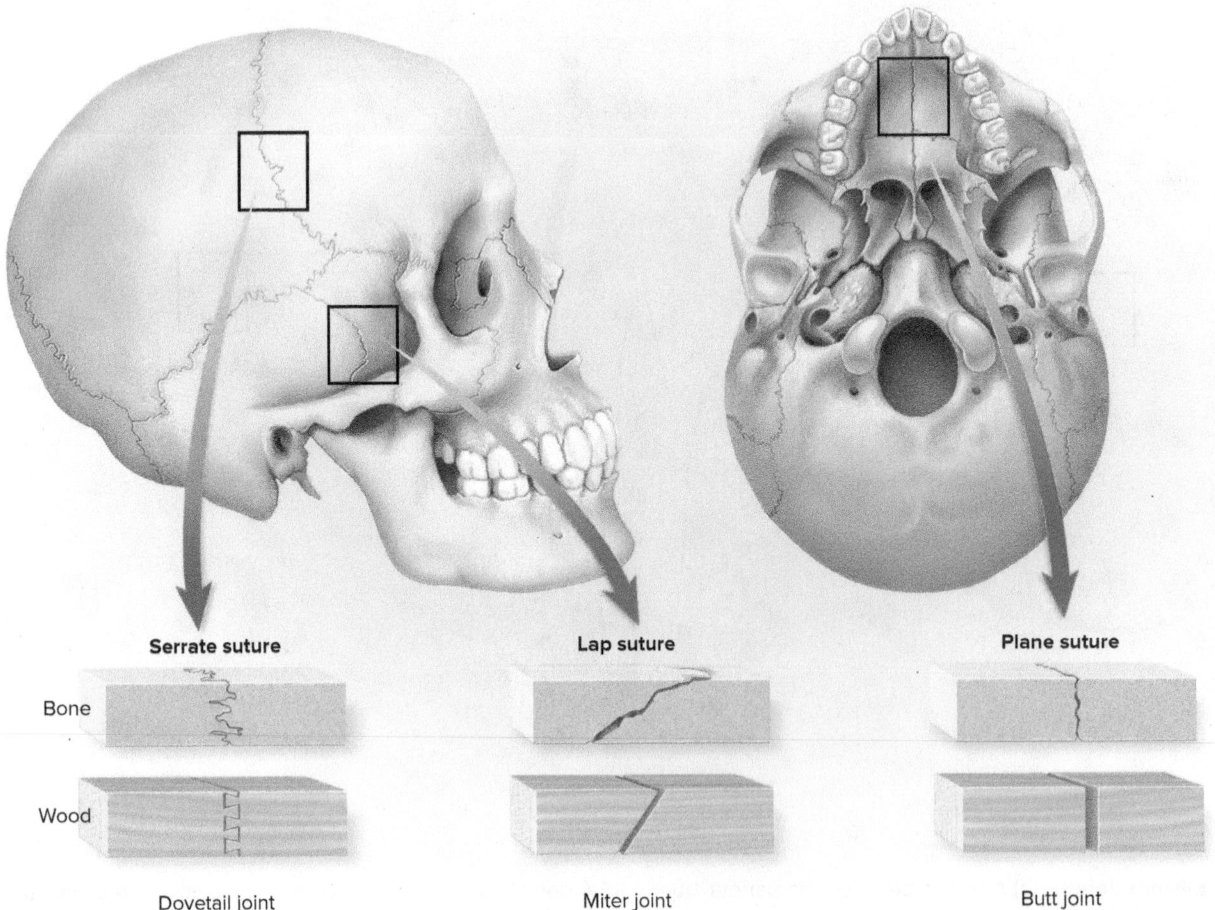


**FIGURE 9.3 Sutures.** Serrate, lap, and plane sutures compared to some common wood joints.

separation between the bones and length of the fibers give these joints more mobility than a suture or gomphosis has. An especially mobile syndesmosis exists between the shafts of the radius and ulna, which are joined by a broad fibrous *interosseous membrane.* This permits such movements as pronation and supination of the forearm. A less mobile syndesmosis is the one that binds the distal ends of the tibia and fibula together, side by side (see fig. 9.2c).

## 9.1c Cartilaginous Joints

A **cartilaginous joint** is also called an **amphiarthrosis**[7] (AM-fee-ar-THRO-sis). In these joints, two bones are linked by cartilage **(fig. 9.4).** The two types of cartilaginous joints are *synchondroses* and *symphyses.*

### Synchondroses

A **synchondrosis**[8] (SIN-con-DRO-sis) is a joint in which the bones are bound by hyaline cartilage. An example is the temporary joint between the epiphysis and diaphysis of a long bone in a child, formed by the cartilage of the epiphysial plate. Another is the attachment of the first rib to the sternum by a hyaline costal cartilage (fig. 9.4a). (The other costal cartilages are joined to the sternum by synovial joints.)

### Symphyses

In a **symphysis**[9] (SIM-fih-sis), two bones are joined by fibrocartilage (fig. 9.4b, c). One example is the pubic symphysis, in which the right and left pubic bones are joined anteriorly by the cartilaginous interpubic disc. Another is the joint between the bodies of two vertebrae, united by an intervertebral disc. The surface of each vertebral body is covered with hyaline cartilage. Between the vertebrae, this cartilage becomes infiltrated with collagen bundles to form fibrocartilage. Each intervertebral disc permits only slight movement between adjacent vertebrae, but the collective effect of all 23 discs gives the spine considerable flexibility.

**▶▶▶APPLY WHAT YOU KNOW**

*The intervertebral joints are symphyses only in the cervical through the lumbar region. How would you classify the intervertebral joints of the sacrum and coccyx in a middle-aged adult?*

[7]*amphi* = on all sides; *arthr* = joined; *osis* = condition
[8]*syn* = together; *chondr* = cartilage; *osis* = condition
[9]*sym* = together; *physis* = growth

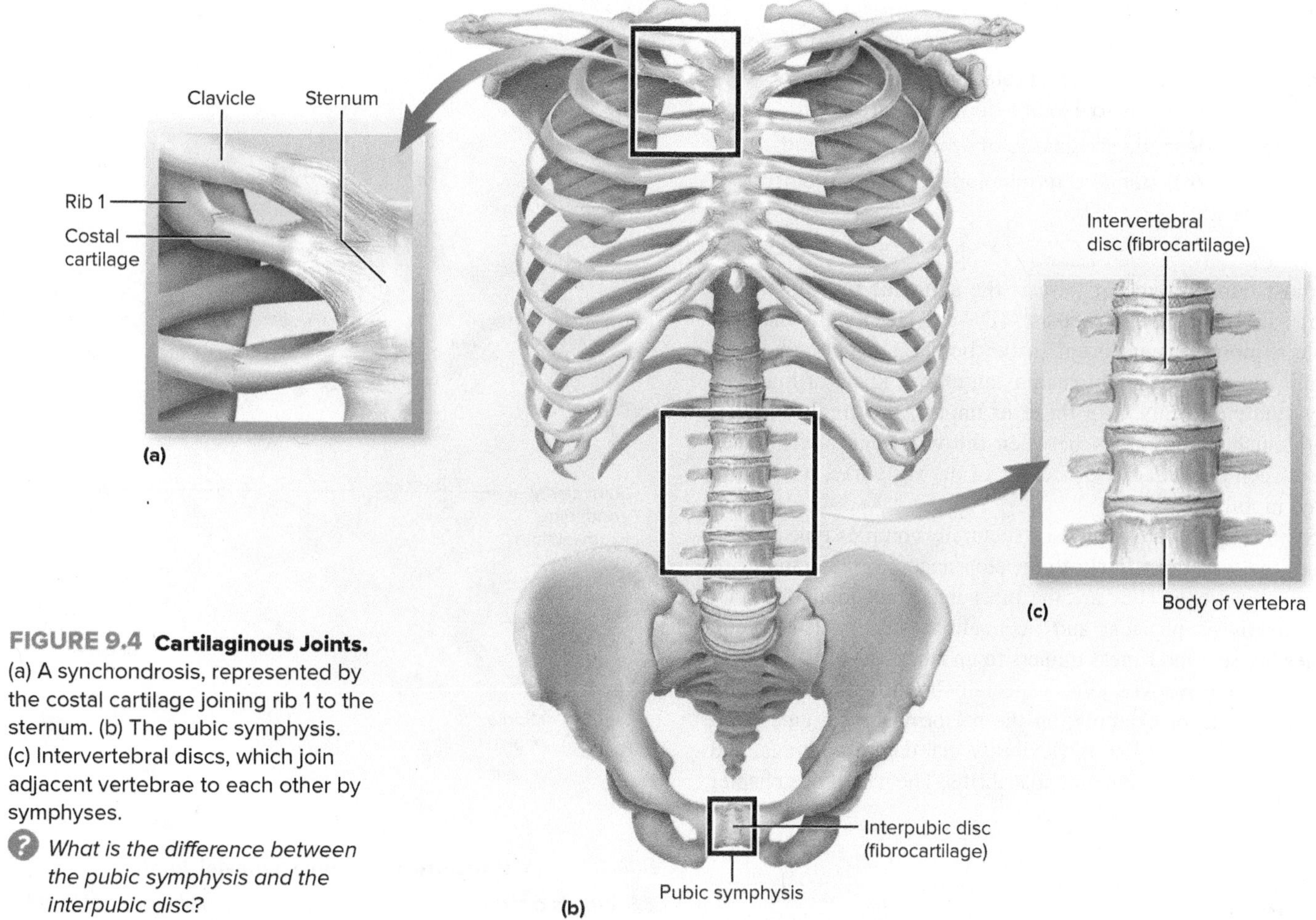


**FIGURE 9.4 Cartilaginous Joints.** (a) A synchondrosis, represented by the costal cartilage joining rib 1 to the sternum. (b) The pubic symphysis. (c) Intervertebral discs, which join adjacent vertebrae to each other by symphyses.

*What is the difference between the pubic symphysis and the interpubic disc?*

**BEFORE YOU GO ON**

Answer the following questions to test your understanding of the preceding section:

1. What is the difference between arthrology and kinesiology?
2. Distinguish between a synostosis, synarthrosis, and amphiarthrosis.
3. Define *suture, gomphosis,* and *syndesmosis,* and explain what these three joints have in common.
4. Name the three types of sutures and describe how they differ.
5. Name two synchondroses and two symphyses.
6. Give some examples of joints that become synostoses with age.

## 9.2 Synovial Joints

### Expected Learning Outcomes

When you have completed this section, you should be able to

a. identify the anatomical components of a typical synovial joint;
b. classify any given joint action as a first-, second-, or third-class lever;
c. explain how mechanical advantage relates to the power and speed of joint movement;
d. discuss the factors that determine a joint's range of motion;
e. describe the primary axes of rotation that a bone can have and relate this to a joint's degrees of freedom;
f. name and describe six classes of synovial joints; and
g. use the correct standard terminology for various joint movements.

The most familiar type of joint is the **synovial joint** (sih-NO-vee-ul), also called a **diarthrosis**[10] (DY-ar-THRO-sis). Ask most people to point out any joint in the body, and they are likely to point to a synovial joint such as an elbow, knee, or knuckle. Many synovial joints, like these examples, are freely mobile. Others, such as the joints between the wrist and ankle bones and between the articular processes of the vertebrae, have more limited mobility.

Synovial joints are the most structurally complex type of joint and are the type most likely to develop uncomfortable and crippling dysfunctions. They are the most important joints for such professionals as physical and occupational therapists, athletic coaches, nurses, and fitness trainers to understand well. Their mobility makes the synovial joints especially important to the quality of life. Reflect, for example, on the performance extremes of a young athlete, the decline in flexibility that comes with age, and the crippling effect of rheumatoid arthritis. The rest of this chapter is concerned with synovial joints.

[10]*dia* = separate, apart; *arthr* = joint; *osis* = condition

### 9.2a General Anatomy

In synovial joints, the facing surfaces of the two bones are covered with **articular cartilage,** a layer of hyaline cartilage up to 2 or 3 mm thick. These surfaces are separated by a narrow space, the **joint (articular) cavity,** containing a slippery lubricant called **synovial fluid (fig. 9.5).** This fluid, for which the joint is named, is rich in albumin and hyaluronic acid, which give it a viscous, slippery texture similar to raw egg white.[11] It nourishes the articular cartilages, removes their wastes, and makes movements at synovial joints almost friction-free. A connective tissue **joint (articular) capsule** encloses the cavity and retains the fluid. It has an outer **fibrous capsule** continuous with the periosteum of the adjoining bones, and an inner, cellular **synovial membrane.** The synovial membrane is composed mainly of fibroblast-like cells that secrete the fluid, and is populated by macrophages that remove debris from the joint cavity. Joint capsules and ligaments are well supplied with *lamellar corpuscles* (see section 16.2b) and other sensory nerve endings that enable the brain to monitor limb positions and joint movements.

In a few synovial joints, fibrocartilage grows inward from the joint capsule and forms a pad between the articulating bones. In the jaw (temporomandibular) joint, at both ends of the clavicle (sternoclavicular and acromioclavicular joints), and between the ulna and carpal bones, the pad crosses the entire joint capsule and

[11]*ovi* = egg

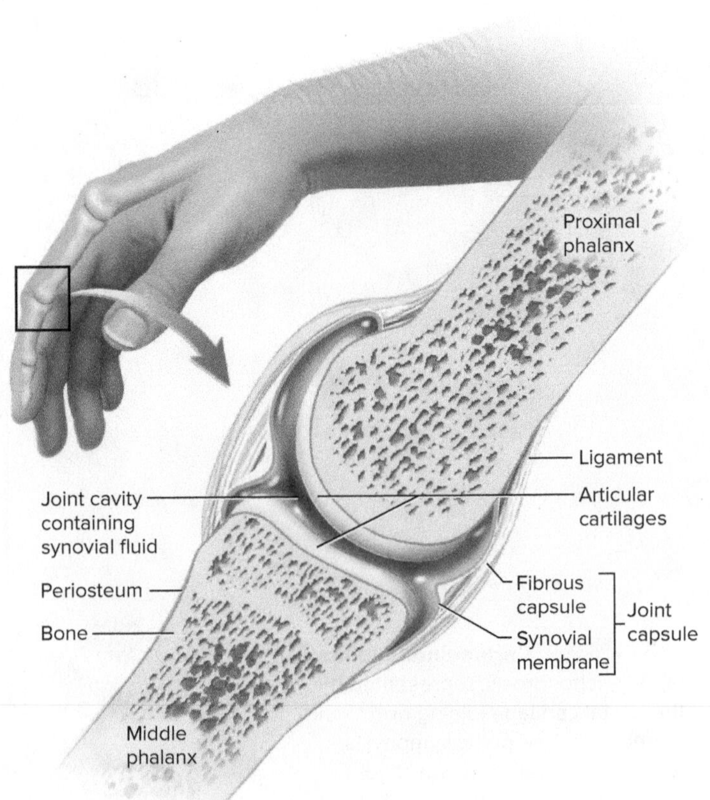


**FIGURE 9.5 Structure of a Simple Synovial Joint.**

 *Why is a meniscus unnecessary in an interphalangeal joint?*

is called an **articular disc** (see fig. 9.23c). In the knee, two cartilages extend inward from the left and right but don't entirely cross the joint (see fig. 9.28d). Each is called a **meniscus**[12] because of its crescent-moon shape. These cartilages absorb shock and pressure, guide the bones across each other, improve the fit between the bones, and stabilize the joint, reducing the chance of dislocation.

Accessory structures associated with a synovial joint include tendons, ligaments, and bursae. A **tendon** is a strip or sheet of tough collagenous connective tissue that attaches a muscle to a bone. Tendons are often the most important structures in stabilizing a joint. A **ligament** is a similar tissue that attaches one bone to another. Several ligaments are named and illustrated in our discussion of individual joints later in this chapter, and tendons are more fully considered in chapter 10 along with the gross anatomy of muscles.

A **bursa**[13] is a fibrous sac of synovial fluid located between adjacent muscles, where a tendon passes over a bone, or between bone and skin (see fig. 9.24). Bursae cushion muscles, help tendons slide more easily over the joints, and sometimes enhance the mechanical effect of a muscle by modifying the direction in which its tendon pulls. **Tendon (synovial) sheaths** are elongated cylindrical bursae wrapped around a tendon, seen especially in the hand and foot **(fig. 9.6).** They enable tendons to move back and forth more freely in such tight spaces as the wrist and ankle.

[12] *men* = moon, crescent; *isc* = little
[13] *bursa* = purse

## DEEPER INSIGHT 9.1

### CLINICAL APPLICATION

### *Exercise and Articular Cartilage*

When synovial fluid is warmed by exercise, it becomes thinner (less viscous), like warm oil, and more easily absorbed by the articular cartilage. The cartilage then swells and provides a more effective cushion against compression. For this reason, a warm-up period before vigorous exercise helps protect the articular cartilage from undue wear and tear.

Because cartilage is nonvascular, repetitive compression during exercise is important to its nutrition and waste removal. Each time a cartilage is compressed, fluid and metabolic wastes are squeezed out of it. When weight is taken off the joint, the cartilage absorbs synovial fluid like an expanding sponge, and the fluid carries oxygen and nutrients to the chondrocytes. Without exercise, articular cartilages deteriorate more rapidly from inadequate nutrition, oxygenation, and waste removal.

Weight-bearing exercise builds bone mass and strengthens the muscles that stabilize many of the joints, thus reducing the risk of joint dislocations. Excessive joint stress, however, can hasten the progression of osteoarthritis by damaging the articular cartilage (see Deeper Insight 9.5). Swimming and bicycling are good ways of exercising the joints with minimal damage.

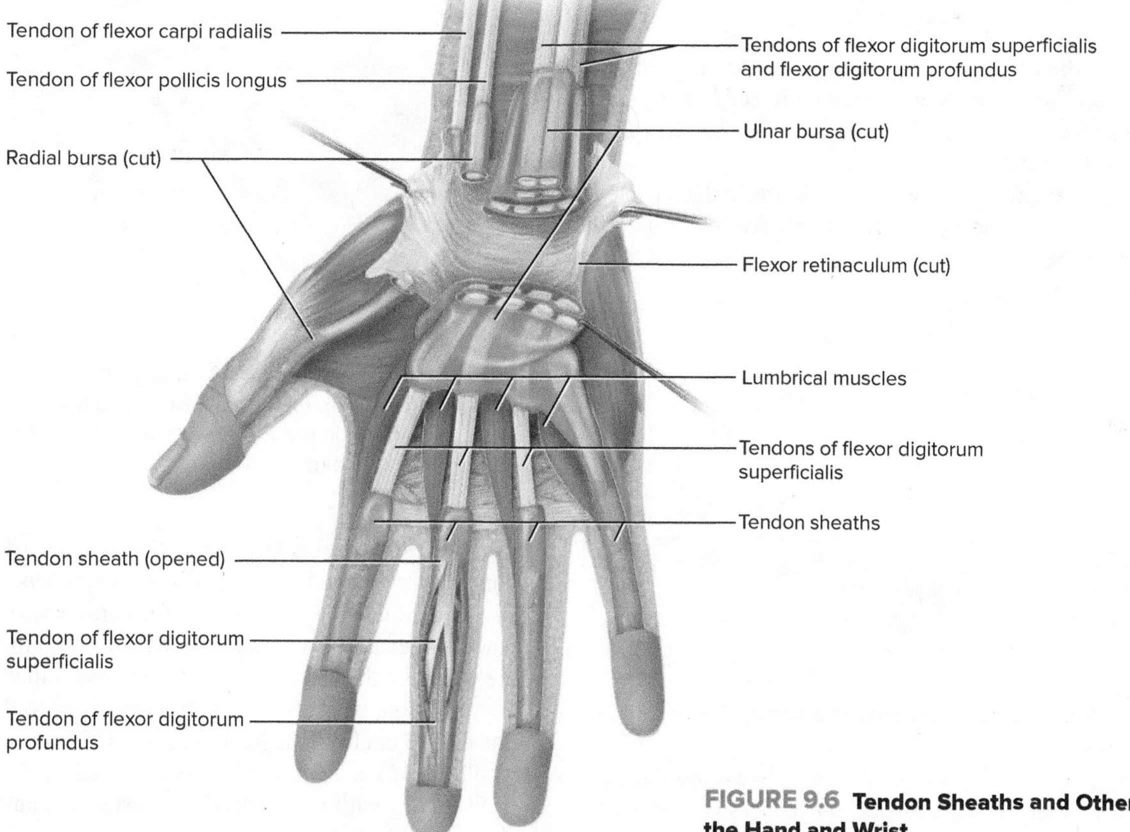


**FIGURE 9.6 Tendon Sheaths and Other Bursae in the Hand and Wrist.**

### 9.2b Joints and Lever Systems

Many bones, especially the long bones, act as levers to enhance the speed or power of limb movements. A lever is any elongated, rigid object that rotates around a fixed point called the **fulcrum (fig. 9.7).** Rotation occurs when an effort applied to one point on the lever overcomes a resistance (load) at some other point. The portion of a lever from the fulcrum to the point of effort is called the **effort arm,** and the part from the fulcrum to the point of resistance is called the **resistance arm.** In skeletal anatomy, the fulcrum is a joint; the effort is applied by a muscle; and the resistance can be an object against which the body is working (as in weight lifting), the weight of the limb itself, or the tension in an opposing muscle.

#### Levers, Speed, and Force

The function of a lever is to produce a gain in the speed, distance, or force of a motion—either to exert more force against a resisting object than the force applied to the lever (for example, in moving a heavy object with a crowbar), or to move the resisting object farther or faster than the effort arm is moved (as in rowing a boat, where the blade of the oar moves much farther and faster than the handle). A single lever cannot confer both advantages. There is a trade-off between force on one hand and speed or distance on the other—as one increases, the other decreases.

The **mechanical advantage** ***(MA)*** of a lever is the ratio of its output force to its input force. If $L_E$ is the length of the effort arm and $L_R$ is the length of the resistance arm,

$$MA = L_E/L_R.$$

If *MA* is greater than 1.0, the lever produces more force, but less speed or distance, than the force exerted on it. If *MA* is less than 1.0, the lever produces more speed or distance, but less force, than the input **(fig. 9.8a, b).**

Consider, for example, the action of the brachialis muscle on the ulna when it flexes the elbow **(fig. 9.8c).** We will regard the ulna as the lever and the hand, along with whatever is in it, as the load or resistance being moved. The fulcrum of this lever is the humeroulnar joint. The brachialis tendon attaches to the ulna only slightly distal to the joint, so the effort arm is very short. The resistance arm extends from the joint to the load on the muscle (such as the weight in the hand), so $L_E$ is much greater than $L_R$. Considering a typical ulna measuring 5 cm from the joint to the brachialis tendon and 33 cm from the joint to the load, the mechanical advantage would be $MA = 5/33 = 0.15$. As expected, with this $MA < 1$, the hand travels with more speed and distance than the point of brachialis attachment.

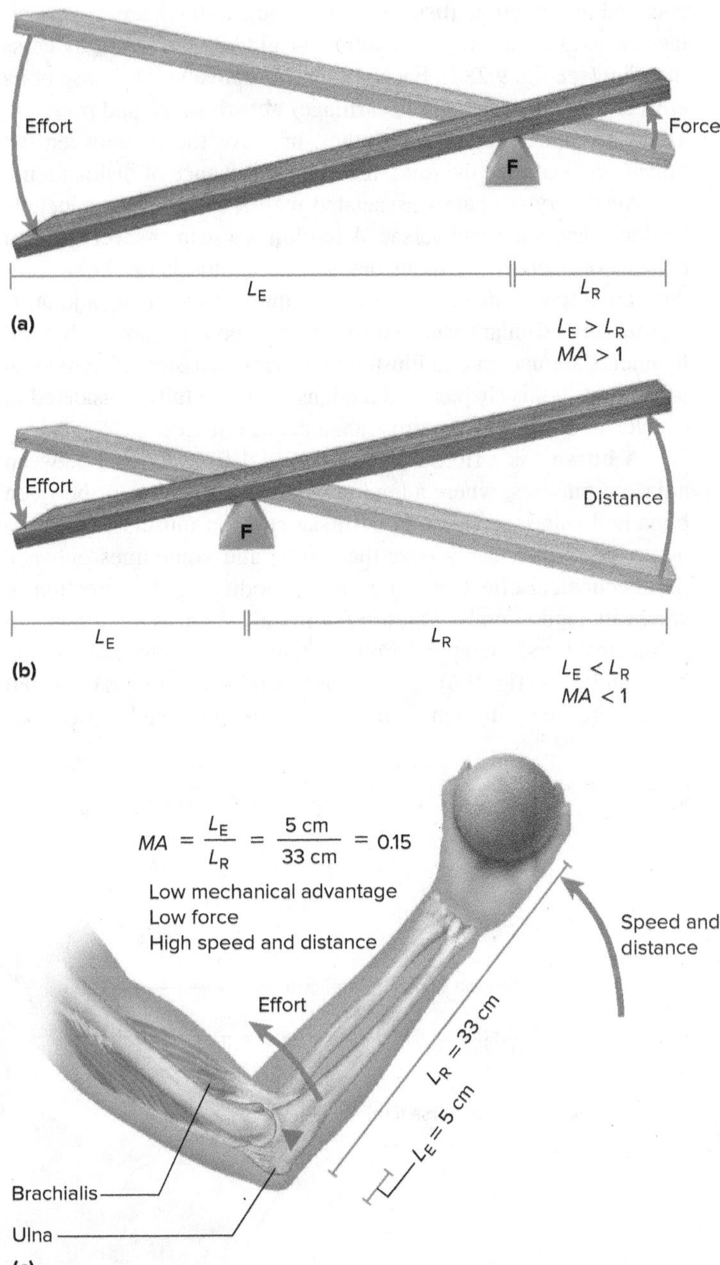


**FIGURE 9.8 Mechanical Advantage *(MA)*.** (a) $MA > 1$ in a first-class lever with $L_E > L_R$. (b) $MA < 1$ in a first-class lever with $L_E < L_R$. (c) $MA < 1$ in the forearm; when acted upon by the brachialis muscle, this is a third-class lever.

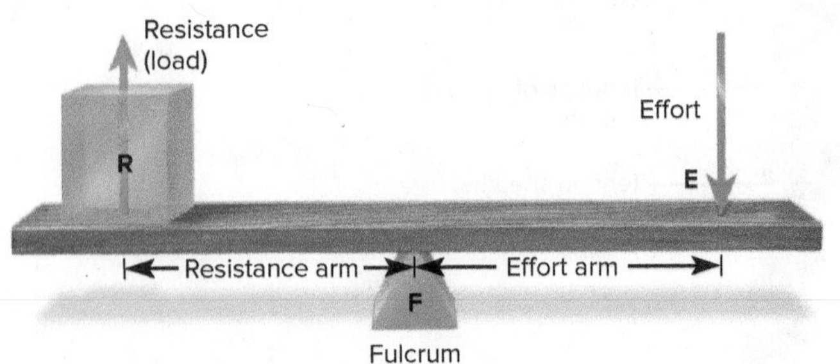


**FIGURE 9.7 The Basic Components of a Lever.** This example is a first-class lever.

*What would be the mechanical advantage of the lever shown here? Where would you put the fulcrum to increase the mechanical advantage without changing the lever class?*

In chapter 10, you will often find that two or more muscles act on the same joint, seemingly producing the same effect. This may seem redundant, but it makes sense if the tendinous attachments of the muscles are at different points on a bone and produce different mechanical advantages. A sprinter taking off from the starting line, for example, uses "low-gear" (high-*MA*) muscles that don't generate much speed, but have the power to overcome the inertia of the body. The runner then "shifts into high gear" by using muscles with different attachments that confer a lower mechanical advantage but produce more speed at the feet. This is analogous to the way an automobile transmission uses one gear to get a car moving and other gears to cruise at higher speeds.

## Types of Levers

There are three classes of levers that differ with respect to which component is in the middle—the fulcrum (F), effort (E), or resistance (R) **(fig. 9.9).**

1. A **first-class lever** is one with the fulcrum in the middle (EFR), such as a seesaw. An anatomical example is the atlanto–occipital joint of the neck, where the muscles of the back of the neck pull down on the occipital bone of the skull and oppose the tendency of the head to tip forward. Loss of muscle tone here can be embarrassing if you nod off in class. Rocking of the foot on the tibia as the toes are raised and lowered also exemplifies a first-class lever. (It is often misinterpreted as a second-class lever because of a superficial resemblance between standing on tiptoes and the wheelbarrow example that follows.)
2. A **second-class lever** has the resistance in the middle (FRE). Lifting the handles of a wheelbarrow, for example, causes it to pivot on the axle of the wheel at the opposite end and lift a load in the middle. If you sit in a chair and raise one thigh, like bouncing a small child on your knee, the femur pivots on the hip joint (the fulcrum), the quadriceps femoris muscle of the anterior thigh elevates the tibia like the wheelbarrow handles, and the resistance is the weight of the child or the thigh itself.
3. In a **third-class lever,** the effort is applied between the fulcrum and resistance (REF). For example, in paddling a canoe, the relatively stationary grip at the upper end of the paddle is the fulcrum, the effort is applied to the middle of the shaft, and the resistance is produced by the water against the blade. Most musculoskeletal levers are third class. The forearm acts as a third-class lever when you flex your elbow. The fulcrum is the joint between the ulna and humerus, the effort is applied partly by the biceps brachii muscle, and the resistance can be any weight in the hand or the weight of the forearm itself.

The classification of a lever changes as it performs different actions. We use the forearm as a third-class lever when we flex the elbow, as in weight lifting, but we use it as a first-class lever when we extend it, as in hammering nails. The mandible is a second-class lever when we open the mouth and a third-class lever when we close it to bite off a piece of food.

## Range of Motion

One aspect of joint performance and physical assessment of a patient is a joint's flexibility, or **range of motion *(ROM)***—the degrees through which a joint can move. The knee, for example, can flex through an arc of 130° to 140°, the metacarpophalangeal joint of the index finger about 90°, and the ankle about 74°. *ROM* obviously affects a person's functional independence and quality of life. It is also an important consideration in training for athletics or dance, in clinical diagnosis, and in monitoring the progress of rehabilitation. The *ROM* of a joint is normally determined by the following factors:

- **Structure of the articular surfaces of the bones.** In many cases, joint movement is limited by the shapes of the bone surfaces. For example, you cannot straighten your elbow beyond 180° or so because, as it straightens, the olecranon of the ulna swings into the olecranon fossa of the humerus and the fossa prevents it from moving any farther.
- **Strength and tautness of ligaments and joint capsules.** Some bone surfaces impose little if any limitation on joint movement. The articulations of the phalanges are an example; as one can see by examining a dry skeleton, an interphalangeal joint can bend through a broad arc. In the living body, however, these bones are joined by ligaments that limit their movement. As you flex one of your knuckles, ligaments on the anterior (palmar) side of the joint go slack, but ligaments on the posterior (dorsal) side tighten and prevent the joint from flexing beyond 90° or so. The knee is another case in point. In kicking a football, the knee rapidly extends to about 180°, but it can go no farther. Its motion is limited in part by a *cruciate ligament* and other knee ligaments described later. Gymnasts, dancers, and acrobats increase the *ROM* of their synovial joints by gradually stretching their ligaments during training. "Double-jointed" people have unusually large *ROMs* at some joints, not because the joint is actually double or fundamentally different from normal in its anatomy, but because the ligaments are unusually long or slack.
- **Action of the muscles and tendons.** Extension of the knee is also limited by the *hamstring muscles* on the posterior side of the thigh. In many other joints, too, pairs of muscles oppose each other and moderate the speed and range of joint motion. Even a resting muscle maintains a state of tension called *muscle tone,* which serves in many cases to stabilize a joint. One of the major factors preventing dislocation of the shoulder joint, for example, is tension in the *biceps brachii* muscle, whose tendons cross the joint, insert on the scapula, and hold the head of the humerus against the glenoid cavity. The nervous system continually monitors and adjusts joint angles and muscle tone to maintain joint stability and limit unwanted movements.

## Axes of Rotation

In solid geometry, we recognize three mutually perpendicular axes, *x, y,* and *z.* In anatomy, these correspond to the transverse, frontal, and sagittal planes of the body. Just as we can describe any point

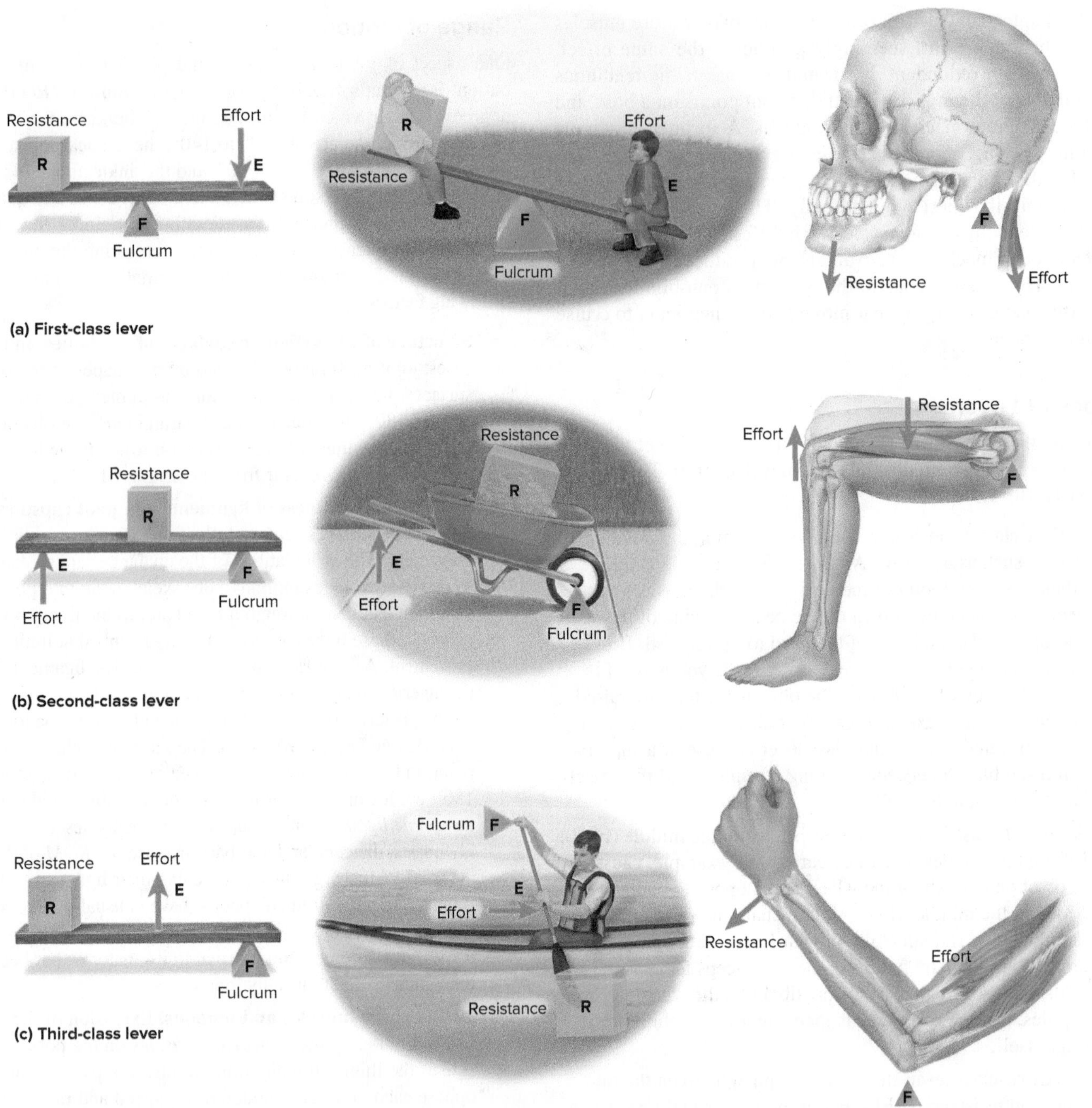


**FIGURE 9.9 The Three Classes of Levers.** Left: The lever classes defined by the relative positions of the resistance (load), fulcrum, and effort. Center: Mechanical examples. Right: Anatomical examples. (a) Muscles of the back of the neck pull down on the occipital bone to oppose the tendency of the head to drop forward. The fulcrum is the occipital condyles. (b) The quadriceps muscle of the anterior thigh elevates the knee. The fulcrum is the hip joint. (c) In flexing the elbow, the biceps brachii muscle exerts an effort on the radius. Resistance is provided by the weight of the forearm or anything held in the hand. The fulcrum is the elbow joint.

in space by its *x*, *y*, and *z* coordinates, we can describe any joint movement by reference to the transverse, frontal, or sagittal anatomical planes.

A moving bone has a relatively stationary **axis of rotation** that passes through the bone in a direction perpendicular to the plane of movement. Think of a door for comparison; it moves horizontally as it opens and closes, and it rotates on hinges that are oriented on the vertical axis. Now consider the shoulder joint **(fig. 9.10),** where the convex head of the humerus inserts into the concave glenoid cavity of the scapula. If you raise your arm to one side of your body, the head of the humerus rotates on an axis that passes from anterior to posterior; the arm rises in the frontal plane whereas its axis of rotation is in the sagittal plane. If you lift your arm to point at something straight in front of you, it moves through the sagittal plane whereas its axis of rotation is on the frontal plane, passing through the shoulder from lateral to medial. And if you swing your

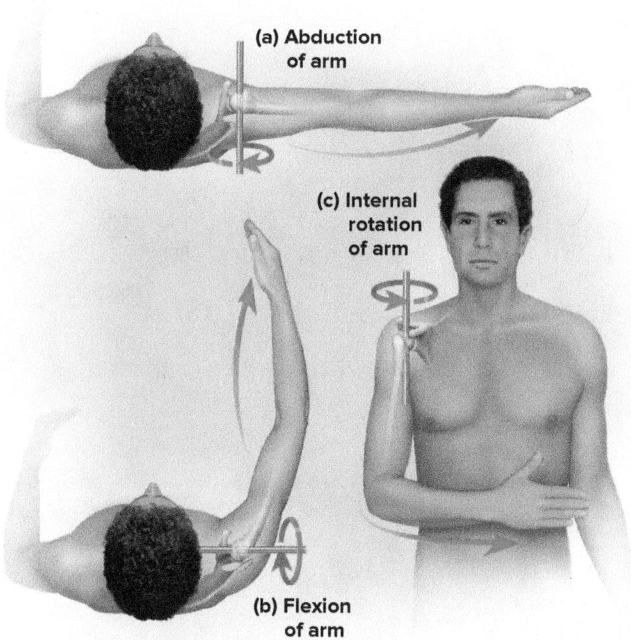


**FIGURE 9.10 Axes of Joint Rotation.** (a) Abduction of the arm in the frontal plane. (b) Flexion of the arm in the sagittal plane. (c) Internal rotation of the arm. All three axes are represented in movements of the multiaxial ball-and-socket joint of the shoulder.

arm in a horizontal arc, for example to grasp the opposite shoulder, the humeral head rotates in the transverse plane and its axis of rotation passes vertically through the joint.

Because the arm can move in all three anatomical planes, the shoulder joint is said to have three **degrees of freedom,** or to be a **multiaxial** joint. Other joints move through only one or two planes; they have one or two degrees of freedom and are called **monaxial** and **biaxial** joints, respectively. Degrees of freedom are a factor used in classifying the synovial joints.

## Classes of Synovial Joints

There are six fundamental types of synovial joints, distinguished by the shapes of their articular surfaces and their degrees of freedom. We will begin by looking at these six types in simple terms, but then see that this is an imperfect classification for reasons discussed at the end. All six types can be found in the upper limb **(fig. 9.11).** They are listed here in descending order of mobility: one multiaxial type (ball-and-socket), three biaxial types (condylar, saddle, and plane), and two monaxial types (hinge and pivot).

1. **Ball-and-socket joints.** These are the shoulder and hip joints—the only multiaxial joints in the body. In both cases, one bone (the humerus or femur) has a smooth hemispherical head that fits into a cuplike socket on the other (the glenoid cavity of the scapula or the acetabulum of the hip bone).
2. **Condylar (ellipsoid) joints.** These joints exhibit an oval convex surface on one bone that fits into a complementary-shaped depression on the other. The radiocarpal joint of the wrist and metacarpophalangeal (MET-uh-CAR-po-fah-LAN-jee-ul) joints at the bases of the fingers are examples. They are biaxial joints, capable of movement in two planes. To demonstrate this, hold your hand with the palm facing you. Make a fist, and these joints flex in the sagittal plane. Fan your fingers apart, and they move in the frontal plane.
3. **Saddle joints.** Here, both bones have a saddle-shaped surface—concave in one direction (like the front-to-rear curvature of a horse's saddle) and convex in the other (like the left-to-right curvature of a saddle). The clearest example of this is the trapeziometacarpal joint between the trapezium of the wrist and metacarpal I at the base of the thumb. Saddle joints are biaxial. The thumb, for example, moves in a frontal plane when you spread the fingers apart, and in a sagittal plane when you move it as if to grasp a tool such as a hammer. This range of motion gives us and other primates that invaluable anatomical hallmark, the opposable thumb. Another saddle joint is the sternoclavicular joint, where the clavicle articulates with the sternum. The clavicle moves vertically in the frontal plane at this joint when you lift a suitcase, and moves horizontally in the transverse plane when you reach forward to push open a door.
4. **Plane (gliding) joints.** Here the bone surfaces are flat or only slightly concave and convex. The adjacent bones slide over each other and have relatively limited movement. Plane joints are found between the carpal bones of the wrist, the tarsal bones of the ankle, and the articular processes of the vertebrae. Their movements, although slight, are complex. They are usually biaxial. For example, when the head is tilted forward and back, the articular facets of the vertebrae slide anteriorly and posteriorly; when the head is tilted from side to side, the facets slide laterally. Although any one joint moves only slightly, the combined action of the many joints in the wrist, ankle, and vertebral column allows for a significant amount of overall movement.
5. **Hinge joints.** These are essentially monaxial joints, moving freely in one plane with very little movement in any other, like a door hinge. Some examples are the elbow, knee, and interphalangeal (finger and toe) joints. In these cases, one bone has a convex (but not hemispherical) surface, such as the trochlea of the humerus and the condyles of the femur. This fits into a concave depression on the other bone, such as the trochlear notch of the ulna and the condyles of the tibia.
6. **Pivot joints.** These are monaxial joints in which a bone spins on its longitudinal axis like the axle of a bicycle wheel. There are two principal examples: the atlantoaxial joint between the first two vertebrae, and the radioulnar joint at the elbow. At the atlantoaxial joint, the dens of the axis projects into the vertebral foramen of the atlas and is held against the anterior arch of the atlas by the transverse ligament (see fig. 8.25c). As the head rotates left and right, the skull and atlas pivot around the dens. At the radioulnar joint, the anular ligament of the ulna wraps around the neck of the radius. During pronation and supination of the forearm, the disclike radial head pivots like a wheel turning on its axle. The edge of the wheel spins against the radial notch of the ulna like a car tire spinning in snow.

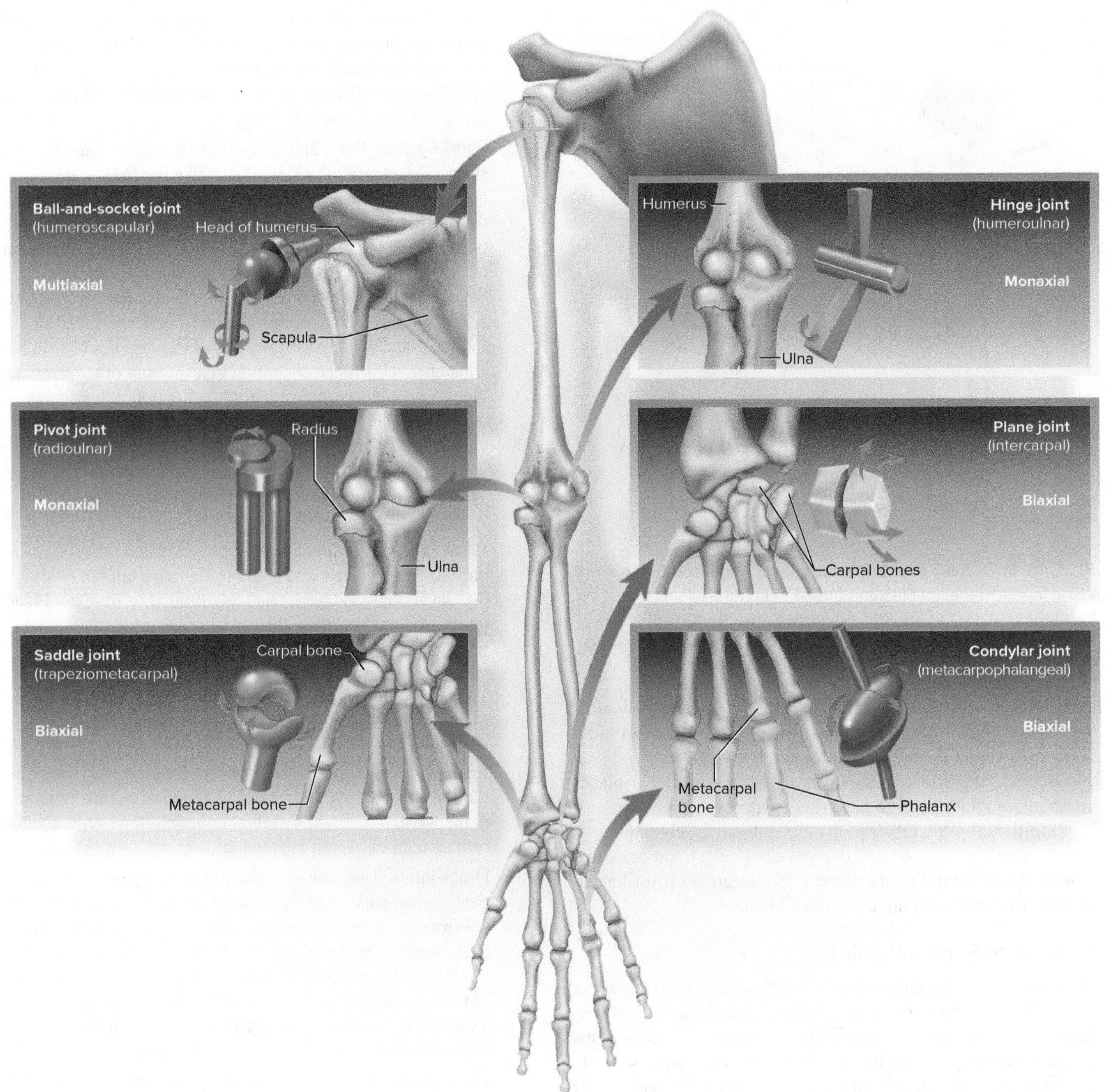


**FIGURE 9.11 The Six Types of Synovial Joints.** All six have representatives in the forelimb. Mechanical models show the types of motion possible at each joint.

Some joints cannot be easily classified into any one of these six categories. The jaw joint, for example, has some aspects of condylar, hinge, and plane joints. It clearly has an elongated condyle where it meets the temporal bone of the cranium, but it moves in a hingelike fashion when the mandible moves up and down in speaking, biting, and chewing; it glides slightly forward when the jaw juts forward to take a bite; and it glides from side to side to grind food between the molars. To observe the importance of the forward glide, try to open your mouth while pushing the jaw posteriorly with the heel of your hand; it is difficult to open the mouth more than 1 or 2 cm when there is resistance to protraction of the mandible.

The knee is a classic hinge joint, but has an element of the pivot type; when we lock our knees to stand more effortlessly, the femur pivots slightly on the tibia. The humeroradial joint acts as a hinge joint when the elbow flexes and a pivot joint when the forearm pronates.

## 9.2c Movements of Synovial Joints

Kinesiology, physical therapy, and other medical and scientific fields have a specific vocabulary for the movements of synovial joints. The following terms form a basis for describing the muscle actions in chapter 10 and may also be indispensable to your advanced coursework or intended career. This section introduces the terms for joint movements, many of which are presented in pairs or groups with opposite or contrasting meanings. This section relies on familiarity with the three cardinal anatomical planes and the directional terms in atlas A, table A.1. All directional terms used here refer to a person in standard anatomical position. When one is standing in anatomical position, each joint is said to be in its **zero position.** Joint movements can be described as deviating from the zero position or returning to it.

### Flexion and Extension

**Flexion (fig. 9.12)** is a movement that decreases a joint angle, usually in the sagittal plane. This is particularly common at hinge joints—for example, bending the elbow so that the arm and forearm go from a 180° angle to 90° or less. It occurs in other types of joints as well. For example, if you hold out your hands with the palms up, flexion of the wrist tips your palms toward you. The meaning of *flexion* is perhaps least obvious in the ball-and-socket joints of the shoulder and hip. At the shoulder, it means to raise your arm as if pointing at something directly in front of you or to continue in that arc and point toward the sky. At the hip, it means to raise the thigh, for example to place your foot on the next higher step when ascending a flight of stairs.

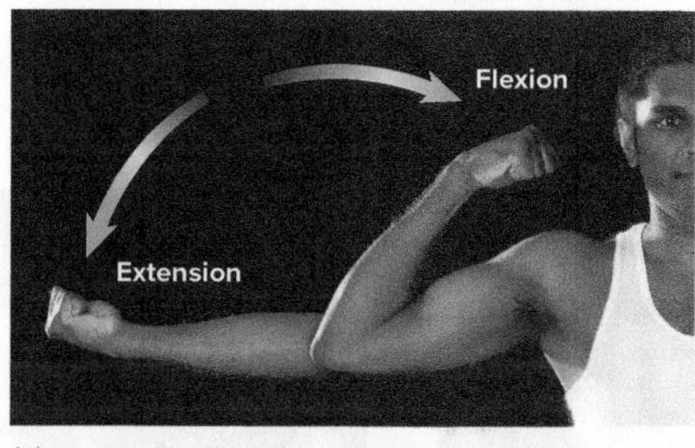

(a)

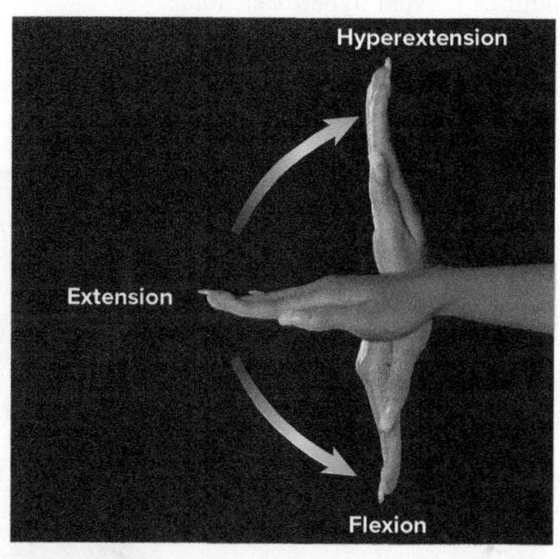

(b)

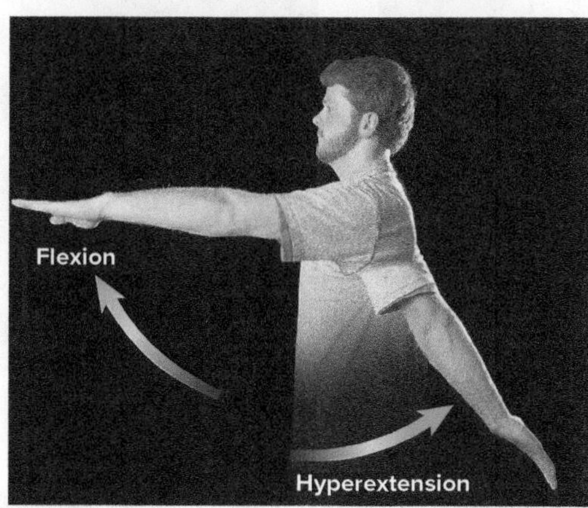


(c)

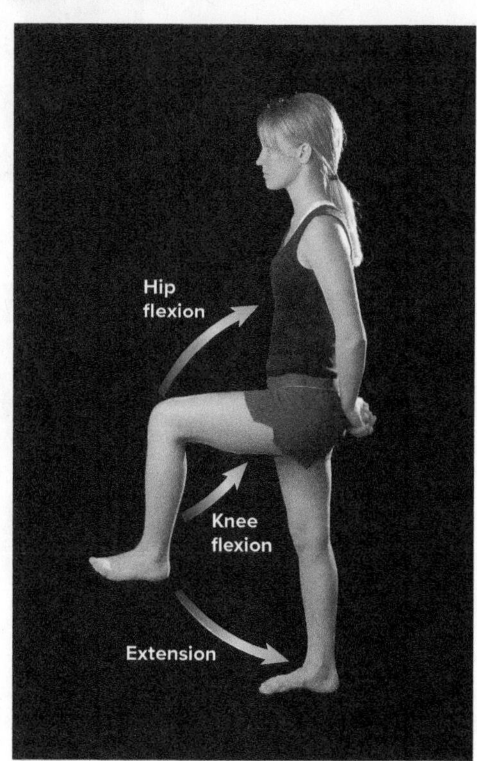


(d)

**FIGURE 9.12 Flexion and Extension.** (a) Flexion and extension of the elbow. (b) Flexion, extension, and hyperextension of the wrist. (c) Flexion and hyperextension of the shoulder. (d) Flexion and extension of the hip and knee.

a–d: Timothy L. Vacula/McGraw-Hill Education

**Extension** (fig. 9.12) is a movement that straightens a joint and generally returns a body part to the zero position—for example, straightening the elbow, wrist, or knee, or returning the arm or thigh back to zero position. In stair climbing, both the hip and knee extend when lifting the body to the next higher step.

Further extension of a joint beyond the zero position is called **hyperextension.**[14] For example, if you hold your hand in front of you with the palm down, then raise the back of your hand as if you were admiring a new ring, you hyperextend the wrist. Hyperextension of the upper or lower limb means to move the limb to a position behind the frontal plane of the trunk, as if reaching around with your arm to scratch your back. Each backswing of the lower limb when you walk hyperextends the hip.

Flexion and extension occur at nearly all diarthroses, but hyperextension is limited to only a few. At most diarthroses, ligaments or bone structures prevent hyperextension.

[14]*hyper* = excessive, beyond normal

## Abduction and Adduction

**Abduction**[15] (ab-DUC-shun) **(fig. 9.13a)** is the movement of a body part in the frontal plane away from the midline of the body—for example, moving the feet apart to stand spread-legged, or raising an arm to one side of the body. **Adduction**[16] **(fig. 9.13b)** is movement in the frontal plane back toward the midline. Some joints can be **hyperadducted,** as when you stand with your ankles crossed, cross your fingers, or hyperadduct the shoulder to stand with your elbows straight and your hands clasped below your waist. You **hyperabduct** the arm if you raise it high enough to cross slightly over the front or back of your head.

## Elevation and Depression

**Elevation (fig. 9.14a)** is a movement that raises a body part vertically in the frontal plane. **Depression (fig. 9.14b)** lowers a

[15]*ab* = away; *duc* = to lead or carry
[16]*ad* = toward; *duc* = to lead or carry

(a) Abduction

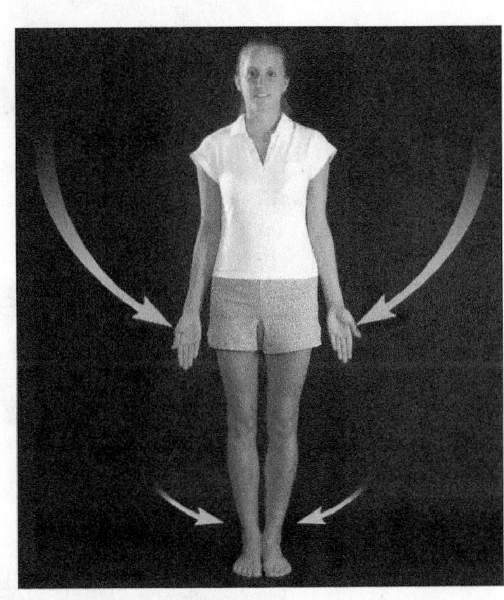

(b) Adduction

**FIGURE 9.13 Abduction and Adduction.** (a) Abduction of the limbs. (b) Adduction of the limbs, returning them to zero position.

a, b: Timothy L. Vacula/McGraw-Hill Education

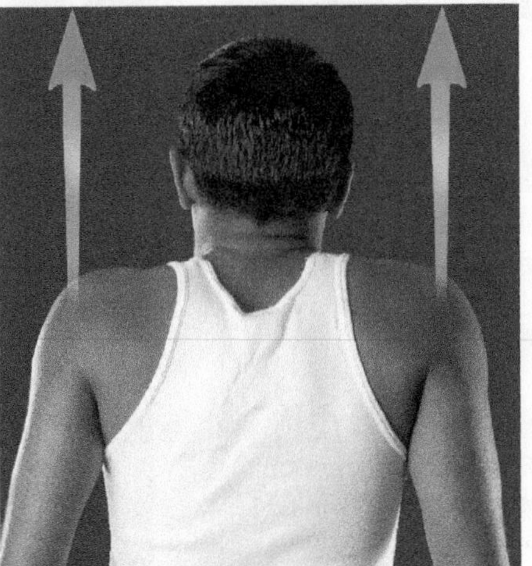

(a) Elevation

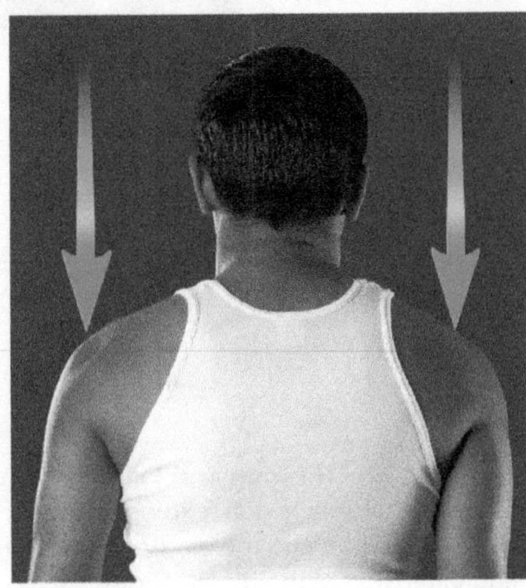

(b) Depression

**FIGURE 9.14 Elevation and Depression.** (a) Elevation of the shoulders. (b) Depression of the shoulders.

a, b: Timothy L. Vacula/McGraw-Hill Education

(a) Protraction

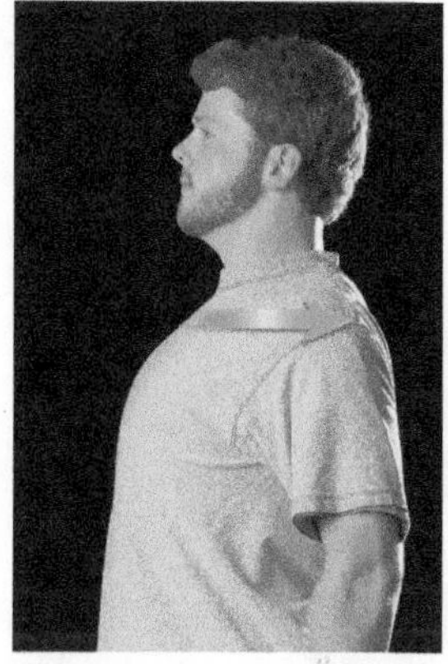

(b) Retraction

**FIGURE 9.15 Protraction and Retraction.** (a) Protraction of the shoulder, as in pushing open a door. (b) Retraction of the shoulder.

a, b: Timothy L. Vacula/McGraw-Hill Education

body part in the same plane. For example, to lift a suitcase from the floor, you elevate your scapula; in setting it down again, you depress the scapula. These are also important jaw movements in biting.

## Protraction and Retraction

**Protraction**[17] **(fig. 9.15a)** is the anterior movement of a body part in the transverse (horizontal) plane, and **retraction**[18] **(fig. 9.15b)** is posterior movement. Your shoulder protracts, for example, when you reach in front of you to push a door open. It retracts when you return it to the resting (zero) position or pull the shoulders back to stand at military attention. Such exercises as rowing a boat, bench presses, and push-ups involve repeated protraction and retraction of the shoulders.

## Circumduction

In **circumduction**[19] **(fig. 9.16),** one end of an appendage remains fairly stationary while the other end makes a circular motion. If an artist standing at an easel reaches forward and draws a circle on a canvas, she circumducts the upper limb; the shoulder remains stationary while the hand moves in a circle. A baseball player winding up for the pitch circumducts the upper limb in a more extreme "windmill" fashion. One can also circumduct an individual finger, the hand, the thigh, the foot, the trunk, and the head.

[17]*pro* = forward; *trac* = to pull or draw
[18]*re* = back; *trac* = to pull or draw
[19]*circum* = around; *duc* = to carry, lead

**FIGURE 9.16 Circumduction.**

Timothy L. Vacula/McGraw-Hill Education

**APPLY WHAT YOU KNOW**

*Choose any example of circumduction and explain why this motion is actually a sequence of flexion, abduction, extension, and adduction.*

## Rotation

**Rotation (fig. 9.17)** is a movement in which a bone spins on its longitudinal axis, like the axle of a bicycle wheel. For example, if you stand with bent elbow and move your forearm to grasp your opposite arm, your humerus spins in a motion called **medial (internal) rotation.** If you make the opposite action, so the forearm points away from your trunk, your humerus undergoes **lateral**

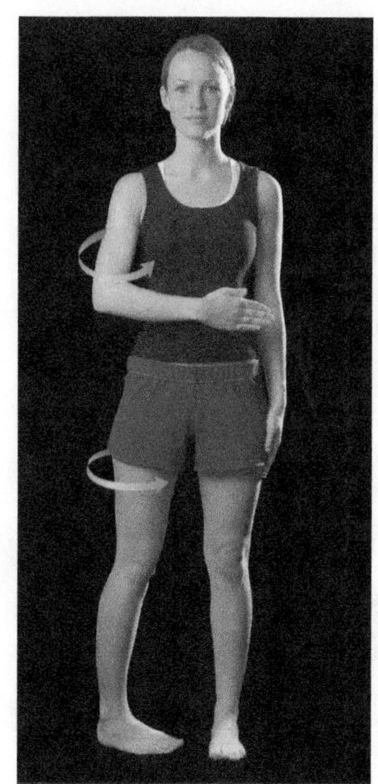

(a) Medial (internal) rotation

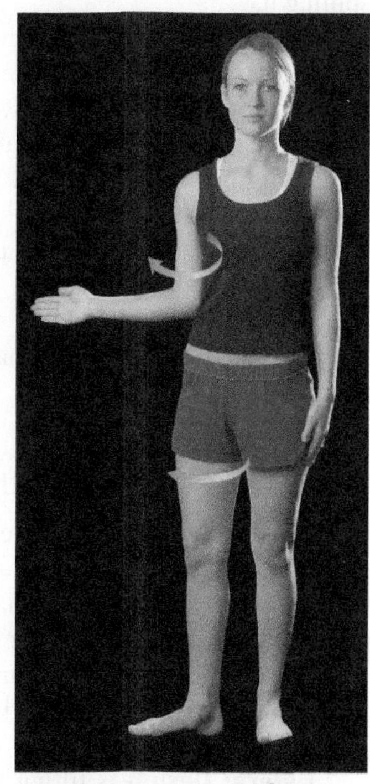

(b) Lateral (external) rotation

**FIGURE 9.17 Medial (Internal) and Lateral (External) Rotation.** (a) Medial (internal) rotation of the humerus and femur. (b) Lateral (external) rotation of both.

a, b: Timothy L. Vacula/McGraw-Hill Education

**(external) rotation.** Good examples of lateral and medial rotation of the humerus are its movements in the forehand and backhand strokes of tennis. The femur can also rotate. If you stand and turn your right foot so your toes point toward your left foot, then turn it so your toes point away from the left food, your femur undergoes medial and lateral rotation, respectively. Powerful left and right rotation at the waist is important in such actions as baseball pitching and golf. Other examples are given in the coming discussions of forearm and head movements.

## Supination and Pronation

Supination and pronation are known primarily as forearm movements, but see also the later discussion of foot movements. **Supination**[20] (SOO-pih-NAY-shun) **(fig. 9.18a)** of the forearm is a movement that turns the palm to face anteriorly or upward; in anatomical position, the forearm is supinated and the radius is parallel to the ulna. **Pronation**[21] **(fig. 9.18b)** is the opposite movement, causing the palm to face posteriorly or downward, and the radius to cross the ulna like an X. During these movements, the concave end of the disc-shaped head of the radius spins on the capitulum of the humerus, and the edge of the disc spins in the radial notch of the ulna. The ulna remains relatively stationary.

As an aid to remembering these terms, think of it this way: You are *prone* to stand in the most comfortable position, which is with the forearm *pronated.* But if you were holding a bowl of *soup* in your palm, you would need to *supinate* the forearm to keep from spilling it.

Chapter 10 describes the muscles that perform these actions (see table 10.10). Of these, the *supinator* is the most powerful. Supination is the type of movement you would usually make with your right hand to turn a doorknob clockwise or to drive a screw into a piece of wood. The threads of screws and bolts are designed with the relative strength of the supinator in mind, so the greatest power can be applied when driving them with a screwdriver in the right hand.

We will now consider a few body regions that combine the foregoing motions, or that have unique movements and terminology.

## Special Movements of the Head and Trunk

*Flexion* of the spine produces forward-bending movements, as in tilting the head forward or bending at the waist in a toe-touching exercise **(fig. 9.19a).** *Extension* of the vertebral column straightens the trunk or the neck, as in standing up or returning the head to a forward-looking zero position. *Hyperextension* is employed in looking up toward the sky or bending over backward **(fig. 9.19b).**

**Lateral flexion** is tilting the head or trunk to the right or left of the midline **(fig. 9.19c).** Twisting at the waist or turning of the head is called **right rotation** or **left rotation** when the chest or the face turns to the right or left of the forward-facing zero position **(fig. 9.19d, e).** Powerful right and left rotation at the waist is important in baseball pitching, golf, discus throwing, and other sports.

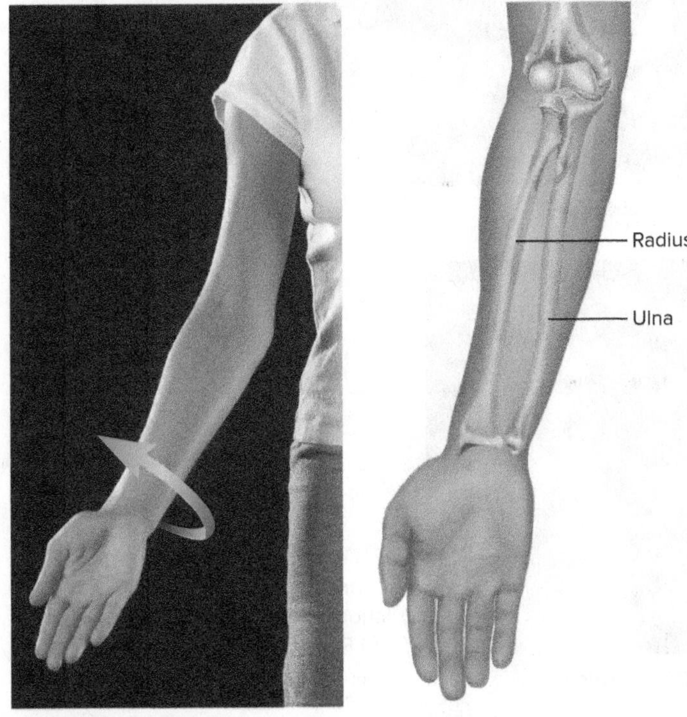


(a) Supination

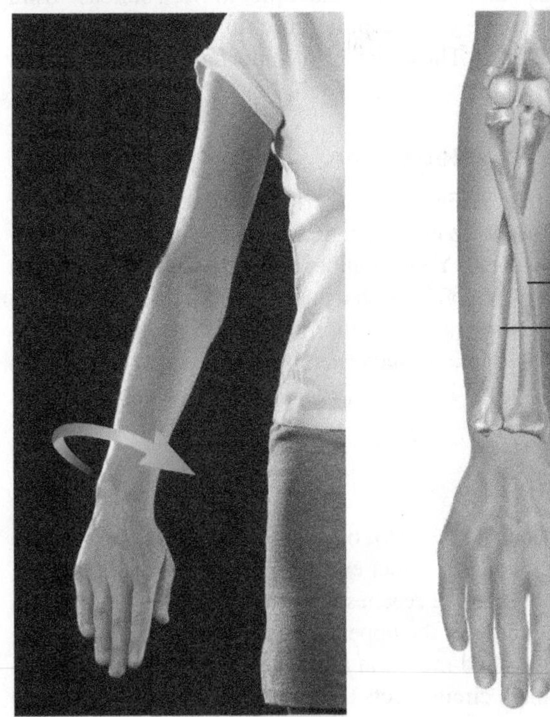


(b) Pronation

**FIGURE 9.18 Supination and Pronation of the Forearm.** (a) Supination. (b) Pronation. Note the way these forearm rotations affect the relationship of the radius and ulna. Relative positions of muscles, nerves, and blood vessels are similarly affected.

a, b: Timothy L. Vacula/McGraw-Hill Education

[20] *supin* = to lay back
[21] *pron* = to bend forward

(a) Flexion

(b) Hyperextension

(c) Lateral flexion

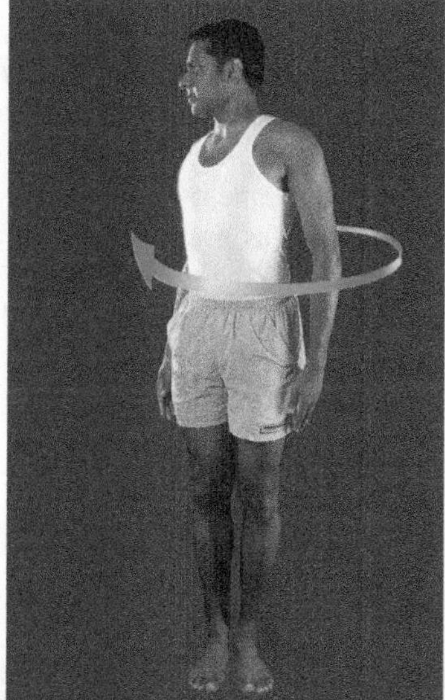
(d) Right rotation

(e) Rotation

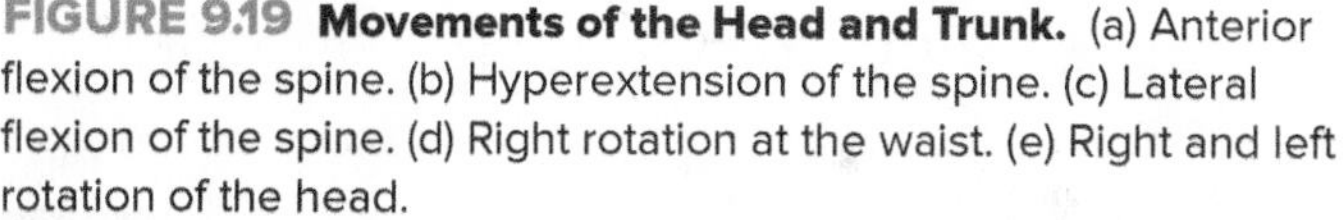
**FIGURE 9.19 Movements of the Head and Trunk.** (a) Anterior flexion of the spine. (b) Hyperextension of the spine. (c) Lateral flexion of the spine. (d) Right rotation at the waist. (e) Right and left rotation of the head.

? *In rotation of the head (e), what bone spins on its axis?*

a–e: Timothy L. Vacula/McGraw-Hill Education

## Special Movements of the Mandible

Movements of the mandible are concerned especially with biting and chewing. Imagine taking a bite of raw carrot. Most people have some degree of overbite; at rest, the upper incisors (front teeth) overhang the lower ones. For effective biting, however, the chisel-like edges of the incisors must meet. In preparation to bite, we therefore *protract* the mandible to bring the lower incisors forward. After the bite is taken, we *retract* it **(fig. 9.20a, b).** To actually take the bite, we must *depress* the mandible to open the mouth, then *elevate* it so the incisors cut off the piece of food.

Next, to chew the food, we don't simply raise and lower the mandible as if hammering away at the food between the teeth; rather, we exercise a grinding action that shreds the food between the broad, bumpy surfaces of the premolars and molars. This entails a side-to-side movement of the mandible called **lateral excursion** (movement to the left or right of the zero position) and **medial excursion** (movement back to the median, zero position) **(fig. 9.20c, d).**

## Special Movements of the Hand and Digits

The hand moves anteriorly and posteriorly by flexion and extension of the wrist. It can also move in the frontal plane. **Ulnar flexion** tilts the hand toward the little finger, and **radial flexion** tilts it toward the thumb **(fig. 9.21a, b).** We often use such motions when waving hello to someone with a side-to-side wave of the hand, or when washing windows, polishing furniture, or keyboarding.

Movements of the digits are more varied, especially those of the thumb. *Flexion* of the fingers is curling them; *extension* is straightening them. Most people cannot hyperextend their fingers. Spreading the fingers apart is *abduction* **(fig. 9.21c),** and bringing them together again so they touch along their surfaces is *adduction* (as in fig. 9.21a, b).

The thumb is different, however, because in embryonic development it rotates nearly 90° from the rest of the hand. If you hold your hand in a completely relaxed position (but not resting on a table), you will probably see that the plane that contains your thumb and index finger is about 90° to the plane that contains the index through little fingers. Much of the terminology of thumb movement therefore differs from that of the other four fingers. *Flexion* of the thumb is bending the joints so the tip of the thumb is directed toward the palm, and *extension* is straightening it. If you now place the palm of your hand on a tabletop with all five digits parallel and touching, the thumb is extended. Keeping your hand there, if you move your thumb away from the index finger so they

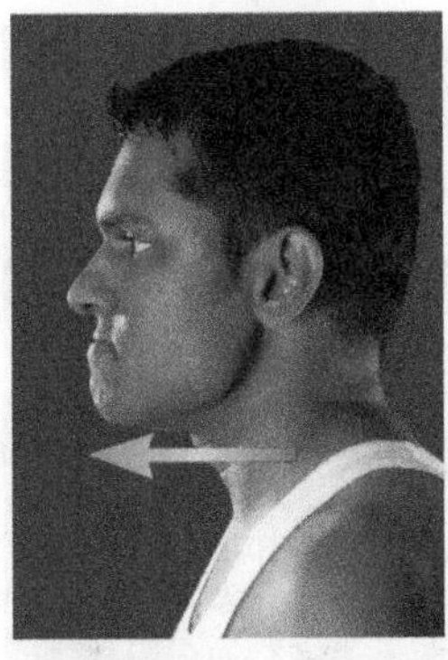

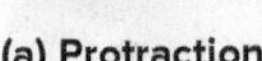

(a) Protraction

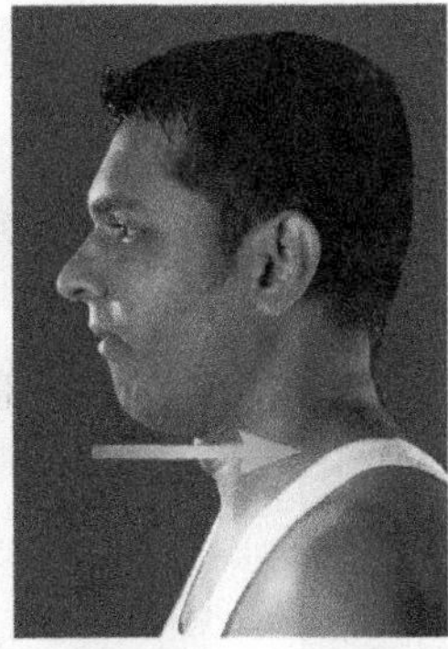

(b) Retraction

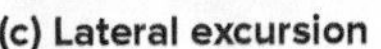

(c) Lateral excursion

(d) Medial excursion

**FIGURE 9.20 Movements of the Mandible.** (a) Protraction and (b) retraction. (c) Lateral and (d) medial excursion, as in chewing food.

a–d: Timothy L. Vacula/McGraw-Hill Education

form a 90° angle (but both are on the plane of the table), the thumb movement is called **radial abduction** (as in fig. 9.21c). Another movement, **palmar abduction,** moves the thumb away from the plane of the hand so it points anteriorly, as you would do if you were about to wrap your hand around a tool handle **(fig. 9.21d).** From either position—radial or palmar abduction—*adduction* of the thumb means to bring it back to zero position, touching the base of the index finger.

Two terms are unique to the thumb: **Opposition**[22] means to move the thumb to approach or touch the tip of any of the other four fingers **(fig. 9.21e). Reposition**[23] is the return to zero position.

## Special Movements of the Foot

A few additional movement terms are unique to the foot. **Dorsiflexion** is a movement in which the toes are elevated, as you might do to trim your toenails **(fig. 9.22a).** In each step you take, the foot dorsiflexes as it comes forward. This prevents you from scraping your toes on the ground and results in the characteristic *heel strike* of human locomotion when the foot touches down in front of you. **Plantar flexion** is movement of the foot so the toes point downward, as in pressing the gas pedal of a car or standing on tiptoes. This motion also produces the *toe-off* in each step you take, as the heel of the foot behind you lifts off the ground. Plantar flexion can be a very powerful motion, epitomized by high jumpers and the jump shots of basketball players.

[22]*op* = against; *posit* = to place
[23]*re* = back; *posit* = to place

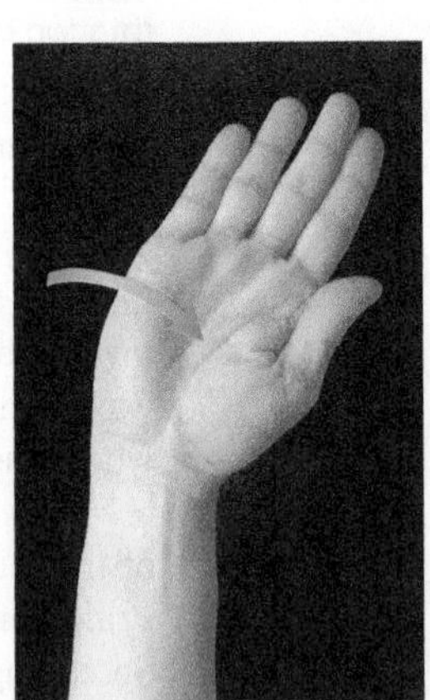

(a) Radial flexion

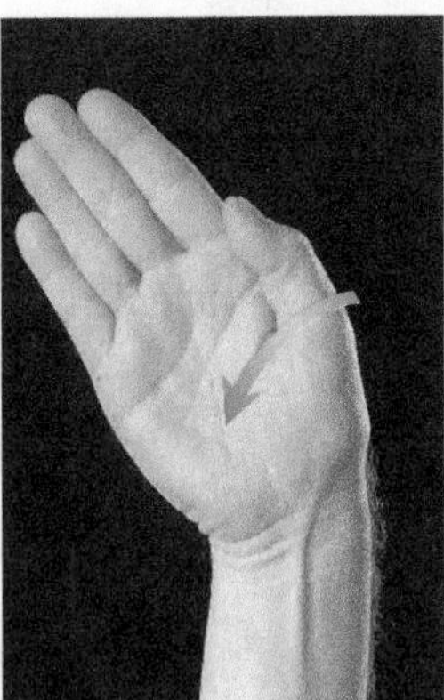

(b) Ulnar flexion

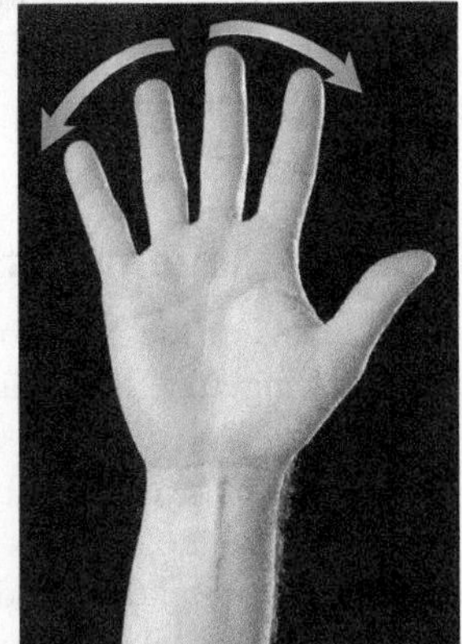

(c) Abduction of fingers

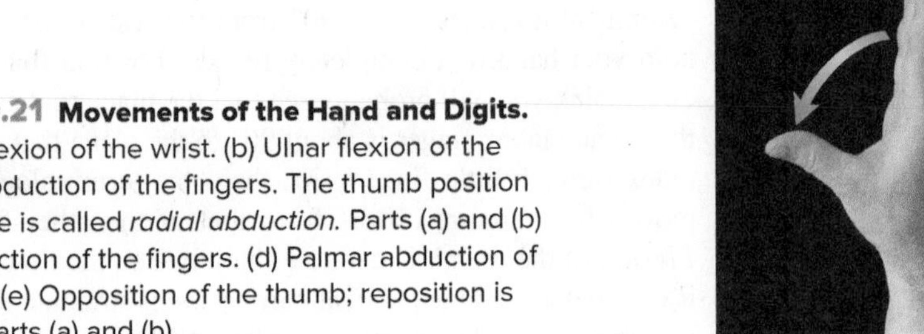

(d) Palmar abduction of thumb

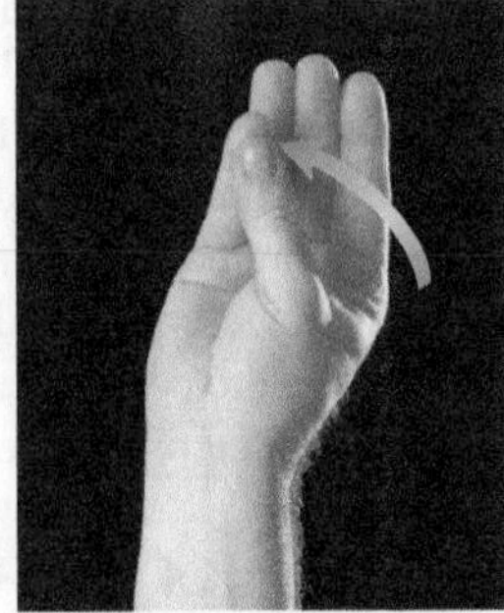

(e) Opposition of thumb

**FIGURE 9.21 Movements of the Hand and Digits.** (a) Radial flexion of the wrist. (b) Ulnar flexion of the wrist. (c) Abduction of the fingers. The thumb position in this figure is called *radial abduction.* Parts (a) and (b) show adduction of the fingers. (d) Palmar abduction of the thumb. (e) Opposition of the thumb; reposition is shown in parts (a) and (b).

a–e: Timothy L. Vacula/McGraw-Hill Education

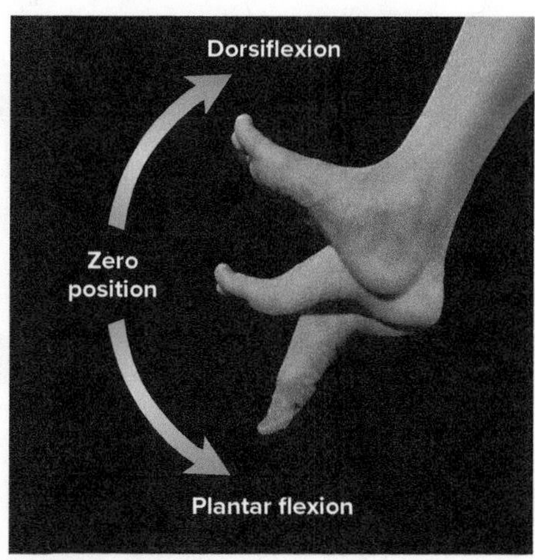

(a) Flexion of ankle

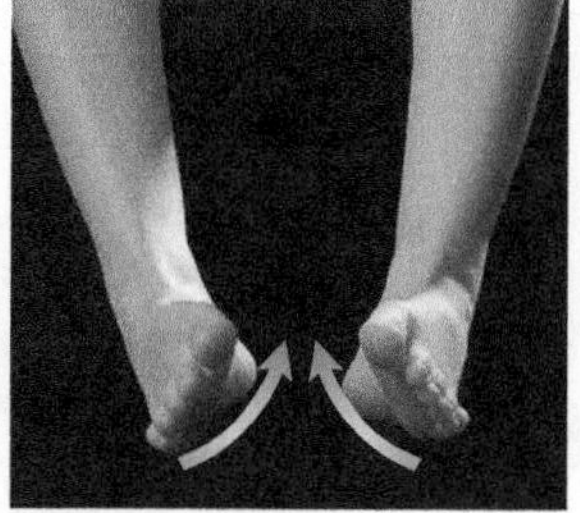
(b) Inversion

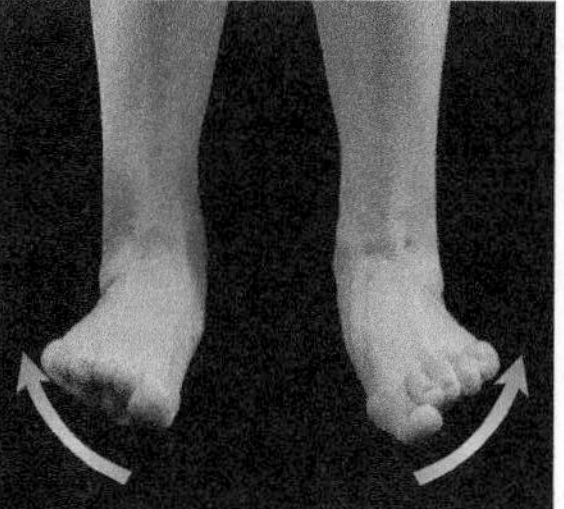
(c) Eversion

**FIGURE 9.22 Movements of the Foot.** (a) Plantar flexion and dorsiflexion of the ankle. (b) Inversion of the feet. (c) Eversion of the feet.

a–c: Timothy L. Vacula/McGraw-Hill Education

**Inversion**[24] is a foot movement that tips the soles medially, somewhat facing each other, and **eversion**[25] is a movement that tips the soles laterally, away from each other **(fig. 9.22b, c).** These movements are important in walking on uneven surfaces such as a rocky trail. They are common in fast sports such as tennis and football, and sometimes cause ankle sprains. These terms also refer to congenital deformities of the feet, which are often corrected by orthopedic shoes or braces.

*Pronation* and *supination,* referring mainly to forearm movements, also apply to the feet but refer here to a more complex combination of movements. Pronation of the foot is a combination of dorsiflexion, eversion, and abduction—that is, the toes are elevated and turned away from the other foot and the sole is tilted away from the other foot. Supination of the foot is a combination of plantar flexion, inversion, and adduction—the toes are lowered and turned toward the other foot and the sole is tilted toward it. These may seem a little difficult to visualize and consciously perform, but they are common motions in walking, running, ballet, and crossing uneven surfaces.

You can perhaps understand why these terms apply to the feet if you place the palms of your hands on a table and pretend they are your soles. Tilt your hands so the inner edge (thumb side) of each is raised from the table. This is like raising the medial edge of your foot from the ground, and as you can see, it involves a slight supination of your forearms. Resting your hands palms down on a table, your forearms are already pronated; but if you raise the outer edges of your hands (the little finger side), like pronating the feet, you will see that it involves a continuation of the pronation movement of the forearm.

**BEFORE YOU GO ON**

Answer the following questions to test your understanding of the preceding section:

7. Describe the roles of articular cartilage and synovial fluid in joint mobility.
8. Give an anatomical example of each class of levers and explain why each example belongs in that class.
9. Give an example of each of the six classes of synovial joints and state how many axes of rotation each example has.
10. Suppose you reach overhead and screw a lightbulb into a ceiling fixture. Name each joint that would be involved and the joint actions that would occur.
11. Where are the effort, fulcrum, and resistance in the act of dorsiflexion? What class of lever does the foot act as during dorsiflexion? Would you expect it to have a mechanical advantage greater or less than 1.0? Why?

[24]*in* = inward; *version* = turning
[25]*e* = outward; *version* = turning

## 9.3 Anatomy of Selected Diarthroses

**Expected Learning Outcomes**

When you have completed this section, you should be able to

a. identify the major anatomical features of the jaw, shoulder, elbow, hip, knee, and ankle joints; and
b. explain how the anatomical differences between these joints are related to differences in function.

We now examine the gross anatomy of certain diarthroses. It is beyond the scope of this book to discuss all of them, but the ones selected here most often require medical attention and many of them have a strong bearing on athletic performance and everyday mobility.

### 9.3a The Jaw Joint

The **temporomandibular (jaw) joint (TMJ)** is the articulation of the condyle of the mandible with the mandibular fossa of the temporal bone **(fig. 9.23).** You can feel its action by pressing your fingertips against the jaw immediately anterior to the ear while opening and closing your mouth.

The synovial cavity of the TMJ is divided into superior and inferior chambers by an articular disc, which permits lateral and

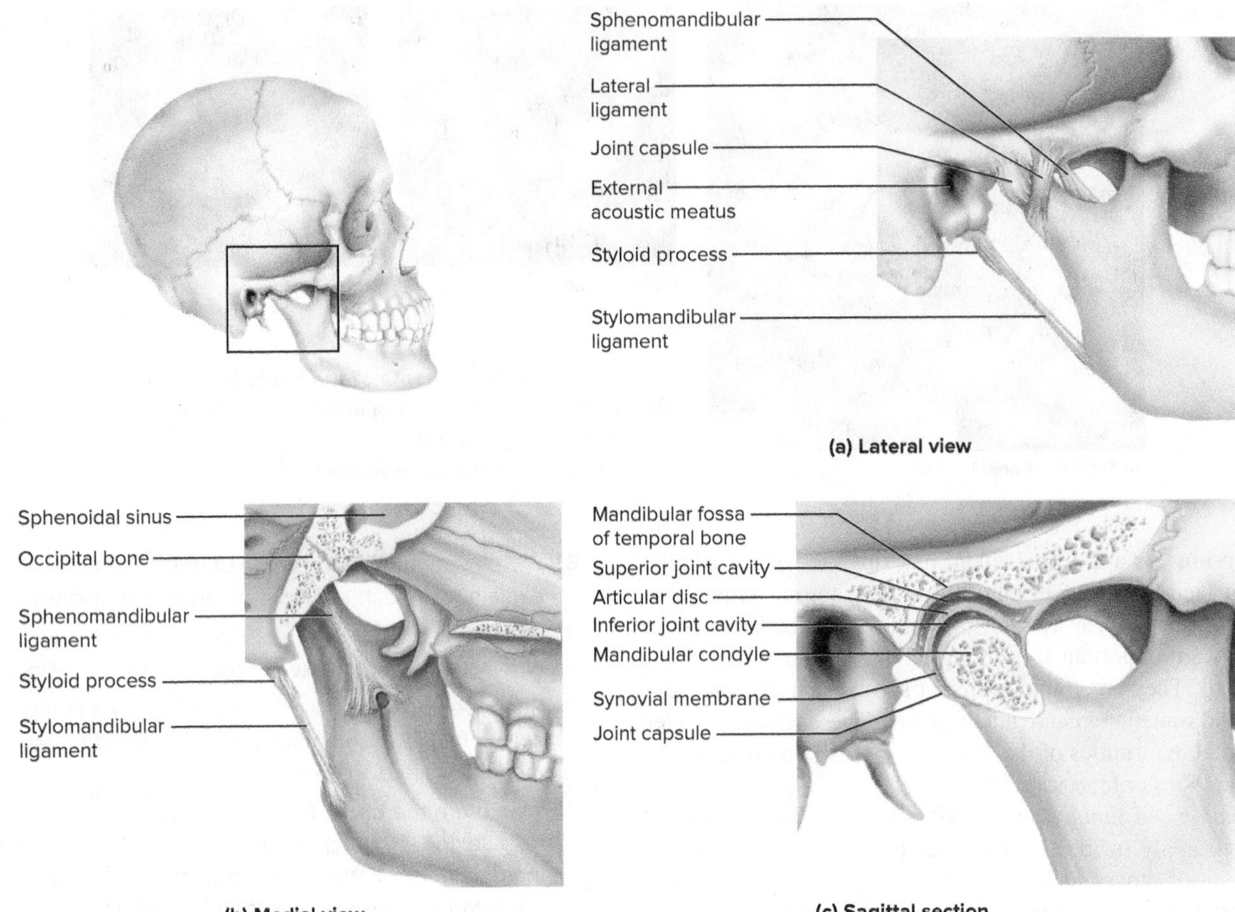


**FIGURE 9.23 The Temporomandibular (Jaw) Joint (TMJ).** (a) Lateral view. (b) Medial view of bisected skull. (c) Sagittal section of joint. APR

medial excursion of the mandible. Two ligaments support the joint. The **lateral ligament** prevents posterior displacement of the mandible. If the jaw receives a hard blow, this ligament normally prevents the condylar process from being driven upward and fracturing the base of the skull. The **sphenomandibular ligament** on the medial side of the joint extends from the sphenoid bone to the ramus of the mandible. A *stylomandibular ligament* extends from the styloid process to the angle of the mandible but is not part of the TMJ proper.

A deep yawn or other strenuous depression of the mandible can dislocate the TMJ by making the condyle pop out of the fossa and slip forward. The joint is relocated by pressing down on the molars while pushing the jaw posteriorly.

## DEEPER INSIGHT 9.2
## CLINICAL APPLICATION

### TMJ Dysfunction

*Temporomandibular joint dysfunction (TMD)* afflicts 20% to 30% of the adult population worldwide, and ranks second only to toothache among the most common causes of orofacial pain. It seems to be a cluster of disorders with symptoms that include clicking, popping, or grating noises; restricted jaw movements that may cause problems eating or speaking; and aching pain in the TMJ and associated chewing muscles that intensifies in chewing and yawning. The causes of TMD are so poorly understood that there is no agreement on the best treatment and there are, indeed, more than a dozen different names for it. Pain medication (analgesics) can be helpful. Since TMD is often associated with anxiety, depression, or stress, some patients and physicians report success with behavioral therapies as diverse as meditation, biofeedback, and yoga.

## 9.3b The Shoulder Joint

The **glenohumeral (humeroscapular) joint,** or shoulder joint, is where the hemispherical head of the humerus articulates with the glenoid cavity of the scapula **(fig. 9.24).** Together, the shoulder and elbow joints serve to position the hand for the performance of a task; without a hand, shoulder and elbow movements are almost useless. The relatively loose shoulder joint capsule and shallow glenoid cavity sacrifice joint stability for freedom of movement (see Deeper Insight 9.3). The cavity, however, has a ring of fibrocartilage called the **glenoid labrum**[26] around its margin, making it somewhat deeper than it looks on a dried skeleton.

[26] *glen* = socket; *oid* = resembling; *labrum* = lip

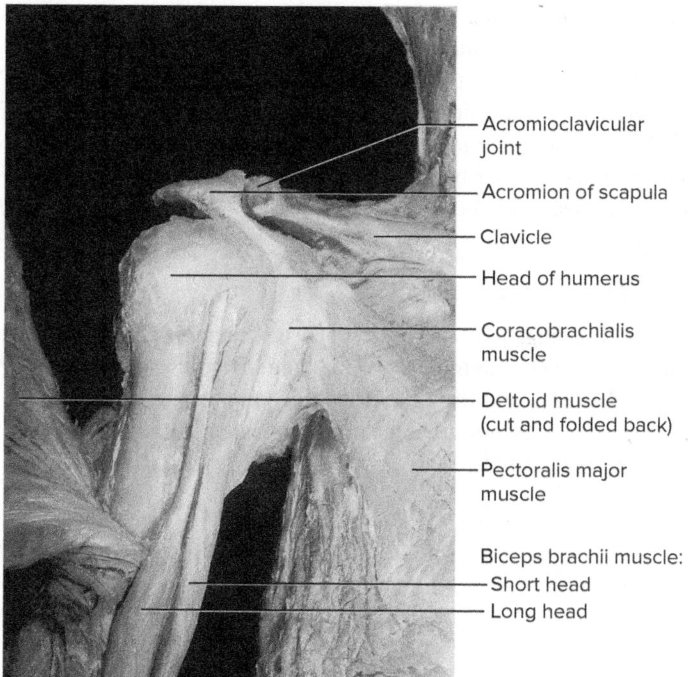


(a) Anterior dissection

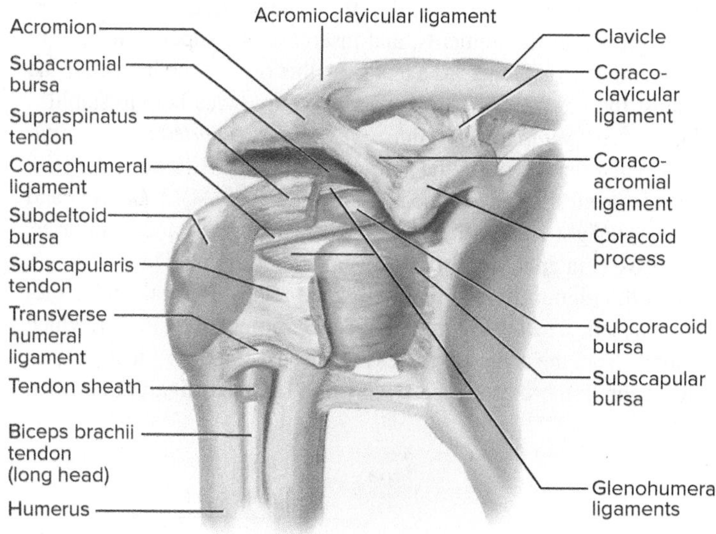


(b) Anterior view

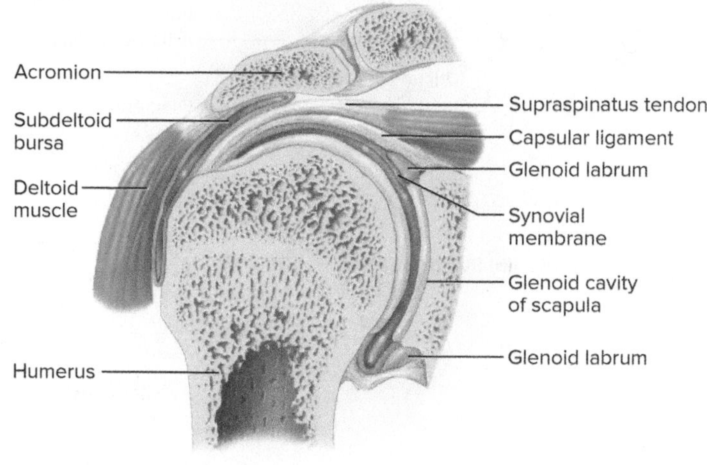


(c) Frontal section

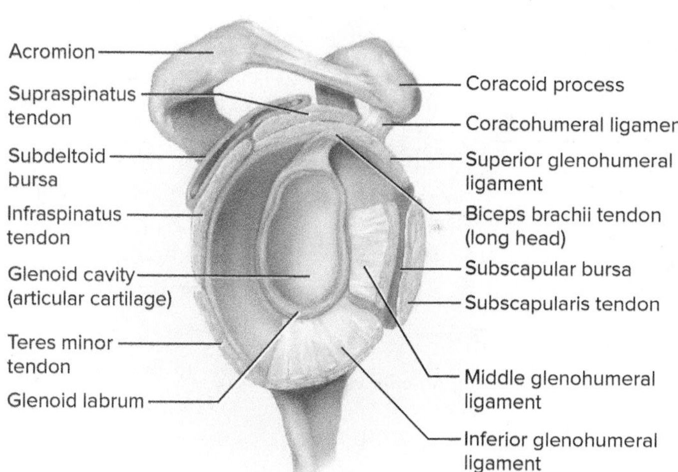


(d) Lateral view, humerus removed

**FIGURE 9.24 The Glenohumeral (Shoulder) Joint.** (a) Anterior view of dissected cadaver shoulder. (b) Anterior view of shoulder ligaments and bursae. (c) Frontal section, showing joint cavity. (d) Lateral view of the shoulder socket (glenoid cavity of the scapula) with the humerus removed. APR

a: Rebecca Gray/McGraw-Hill Education

## DEEPER INSIGHT 9.3
### CLINICAL APPLICATION

### *Shoulder Dislocation*

The anatomy and mobility of the shoulder joint make it especially susceptible to dislocation. Over 95% of cases are classified as *anterior dislocation* (displacement of the humeral head in the anterior direction). Such dislocations are usually caused when the arm is abducted and receives a blow from above—for example, by heavy objects falling from a shelf. A complex of nerves and blood vessels traverses the axillary region, and shoulder dislocation can easily damage the axillary nerve or artery (see figs. 13.17 and 20.39). Left untreated, this can lead to muscle atrophy, weakness, or paralysis. Greek physician Hippocrates taught students to treat shoulder dislocation by placing a heel in the patient's axilla and pulling on the arm, but this can cause even worse nerve damage and is never done anymore by professionals. Because the shoulder is so easily dislocated, one also should never attempt to move an unconscious or immobilized person by pulling on his or her arm.

The shoulder is stabilized mainly by the biceps brachii muscle on the anterior side of the arm. One of its tendons arises from the *long head* of the muscle (see table 10.10), passes through the intertubercular groove of the humerus, and inserts on the superior margin of the glenoid cavity. It acts as a taut strap that presses the humeral head against the glenoid cavity. Four additional muscles help to stabilize this joint: the *supraspinatus, infraspinatus, teres minor,* and *subscapularis.* Their tendons form the **rotator cuff,** which is fused to the joint capsule on all sides except the inferior (see fig. 10.24). Table 10.9 and Deeper Insight 10.4 further describe the rotator cuff and its injuries.

Five principal ligaments also support this joint. Three of them, called the **glenohumeral ligaments,** are relatively weak and sometimes absent. The other two are the **coracohumeral ligament,** which extends from the coracoid process of the scapula to the greater tubercle of the humerus, and the **transverse humeral ligament,** which extends from the greater to the lesser tubercle of the humerus and forms a tunnel housing the tendon from the long head of the biceps.

Four bursae occur at the shoulder. Their names describe their locations: the **subdeltoid, subacromial, subcoracoid,** and **subscapular bursae.** The *deltoid* is the large muscle that caps the shoulder, and the other bursae are named for parts of the scapula described in section 8.4a.

## 9.3c The Elbow Joint

The elbow is a hinge joint composed of two articulations: the **humeroulnar joint** where the trochlea of the humerus joins the trochlear notch of the ulna, and the **humeroradial joint** where the capitulum of the humerus meets the head of the radius **(fig. 9.25).** Both are enclosed in a single joint capsule. On the posterior side of the

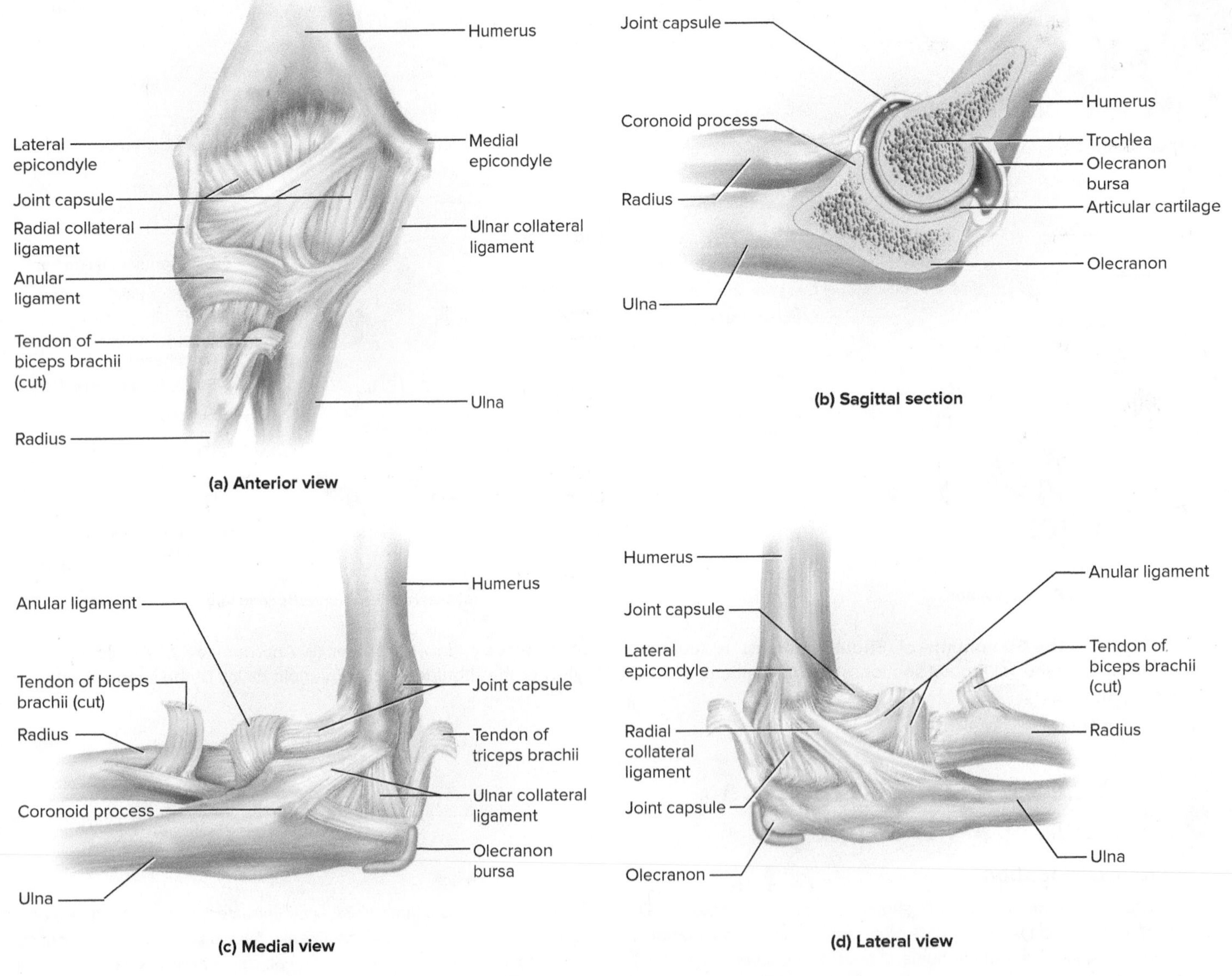


**FIGURE 9.25 The Elbow Joint.** This region includes two joints that form the elbow hinge—the humeroulnar and humeroradial—and one joint, the radioulnar, not involved in the hinge. (a) Anterior elbow ligaments. (b) Sagittal section, showing joint cavity. (c) Medial elbow ligaments. (d) Lateral elbow ligaments. APR

elbow, there is a prominent **olecranon bursa** to ease the movement of tendons over the joint. Side-to-side motions of the elbow joint are restricted by a pair of ligaments: the **radial (lateral) collateral ligament** and **ulnar (medial) collateral ligament.**

Another joint occurs in the elbow region, the **proximal radioulnar joint,** but it is not involved in the hinge. At this joint, the edge of the disclike head of the radius fits into the radial notch of the ulna. It is held in place by the **anular ligament,** which encircles the radial head and is attached at each end to the ulna. The radial head rotates like a wheel against the ulna as the forearm is pronated or supinated.

## 9.3d The Hip Joint

The **coxal (hip) joint** is the point where the head of the femur inserts into the acetabulum of the hip bone **(fig. 9.26).** Because the coxal joints bear much of the body's weight, they have deep sockets

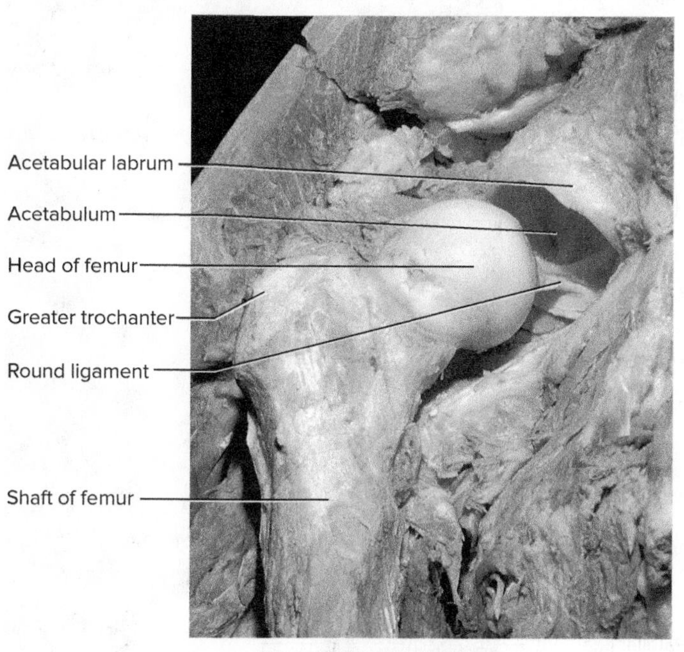


(a) Anterior dissection

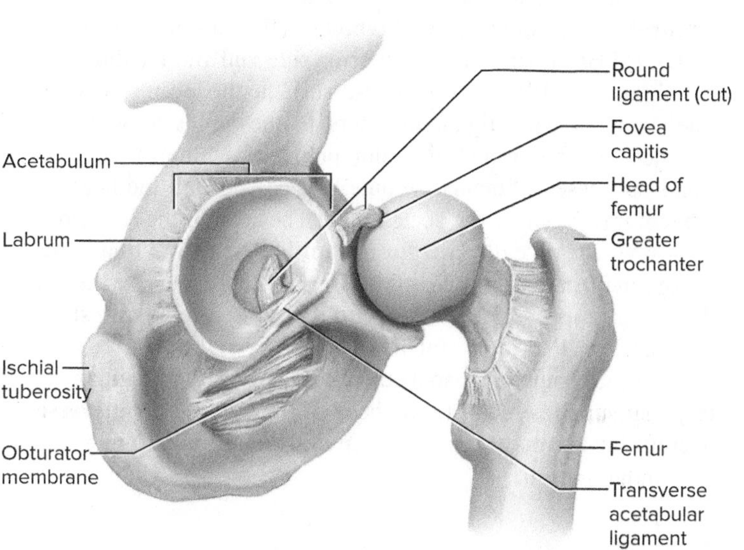


(b) Lateral view, femur retracted

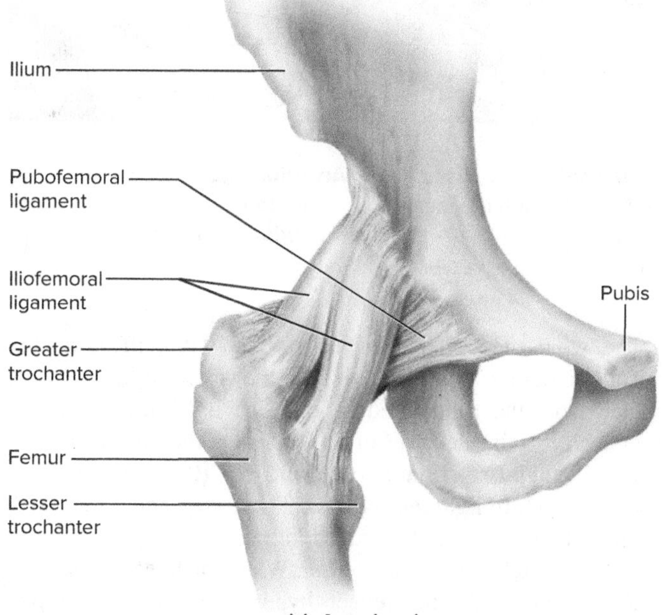

(c) Anterior view

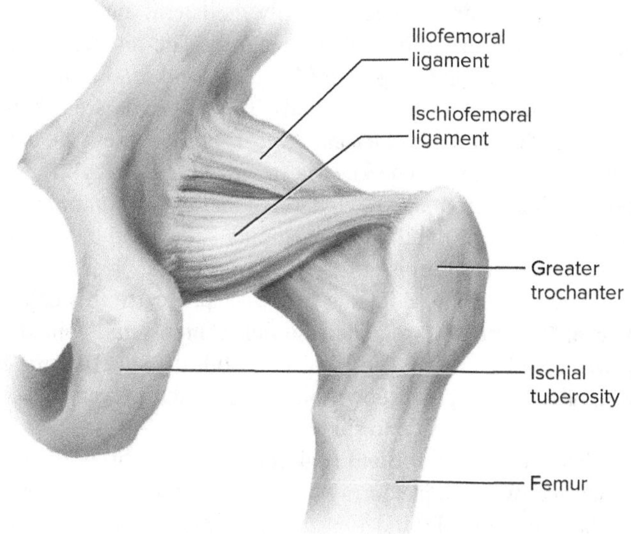


(d) Posterior view

**FIGURE 9.26 The Coxal (Hip) Joint.** (a) Anterior view of dissected cadaver hip. (b) Lateral view of hip joint with femur retracted from acetabulum. (c) Anterior hip ligaments. (d) Posterior hip ligaments.

a: Rebecca Gray/McGraw-Hill Education

and are much more stable than the shoulder joint. The depth of the socket is somewhat greater than you see on dried bones because of a horseshoe-shaped ring of fibrocartilage, the **acetabular labrum,** attached to its rim. Dislocations of the hip are therefore rare.

**APPLY WHAT YOU KNOW**

*Where else in the body is there a structure similar to the acetabular labrum? What do those two locations have in common?*

Ligaments that support the coxal joint include the **iliofemoral** and **pubofemoral ligaments** (ILL-ee-oh-FEM-o-rul, PYU-bo-FEM-o-rul) on the anterior side and the **ischiofemoral ligament** (ISS-kee-oh-FEM-o-rul) on the posterior side. The name of each ligament refers to the bones to which it attaches—the femur and the ilium, pubis, or ischium. When you stand up, these ligaments become twisted and pull the head of the femur tightly into the acetabulum. The head of the femur has a conspicuous pit called the **fovea capitis.** The **round ligament,** or **ligamentum teres**[27] (TERR-eez), arises here and attaches to the lower margin of the acetabulum. This is a relatively slack ligament, so it is doubtful that it plays a significant role in holding the femur in its socket. It does, however, contain an artery that supplies blood to the head of the femur. A **transverse acetabular ligament** bridges a gap in the inferior margin of the acetabular labrum.

## 9.3e The Knee Joint

The **tibiofemoral (knee) joint** is the largest and most complex diarthrosis of the body **(figs. 9.27** and **9.28).** It is primarily a hinge joint, but when the knee is flexed it is also capable of slight rotation and lateral gliding. The patella and patellar ligament also articulate with the femur to form a gliding **patellofemoral joint.**

The joint capsule encloses only the lateral and posterior aspects of the knee joint, not the anterior. The anterior aspect is covered by the patella, patellar ligament, and *lateral* and *medial patellar retinacula* (not illustrated). The retinacula are extensions of the tendon of the *quadriceps femoris muscle,* the large anterior muscle of the thigh. The knee is stabilized mainly by the quadriceps tendon in front and the tendon of the *semimembranosus muscle* on the rear of the thigh. Developing strength in these muscles therefore reduces the risk of knee injury.

The joint cavity contains two C-shaped cartilages called the **lateral** and **medial menisci** (singular, **meniscus**) joined by a **transverse ligament.** The menisci absorb the shock of the body weight jostling up and down on the knee and prevent the femur from rocking from side to side on the tibia.

The posterior **popliteal region** (pop-LIT-ee-ul) of the knee is supported by a complex array of *extracapsular ligaments* external to the joint capsule and two *intracapsular ligaments* within it. The extracapsular ligaments include two collateral ligaments that prevent the knee from rotating when the joint is extended—the **fibular (lateral) collateral ligament** and the **tibial (medial) collateral ligament**—and other ligaments not illustrated.

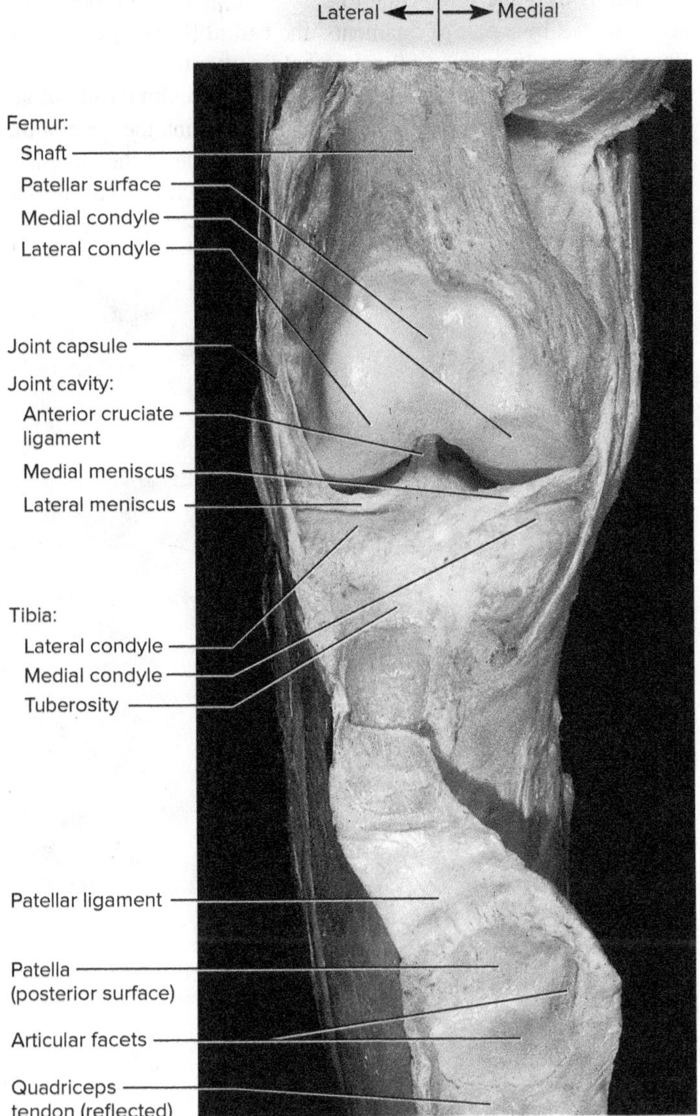


**FIGURE 9.27 The Right Knee, Anterior Dissection.** The quadriceps tendon has been cut and folded (reflected) downward to expose the joint cavity and the posterior surface of the patella.

Rebecca Gray/McGraw-Hill Education

The two intracapsular ligaments lie deep within the joint. The synovial membrane folds around them, however, so that they are excluded from the fluid-filled synovial cavity. These ligaments cross each other in the form of an X; hence, they are called the **anterior cruciate**[28] **ligament (ACL)** (CROO-she-ate) and **posterior cruciate ligament (PCL).** These are named according to whether they attach to the anterior or posterior side of the tibia, not for their attachments to the femur. When the knee is extended, the ACL is pulled tight and prevents hyperextension. The PCL prevents the femur from sliding off the front of the tibia and prevents the tibia from being displaced backward. The ACL is one of the most common sites of knee injury (see Deeper Insight 9.4).

[27] *teres* = round

[28] *cruci* = cross; *ate* = characterized by

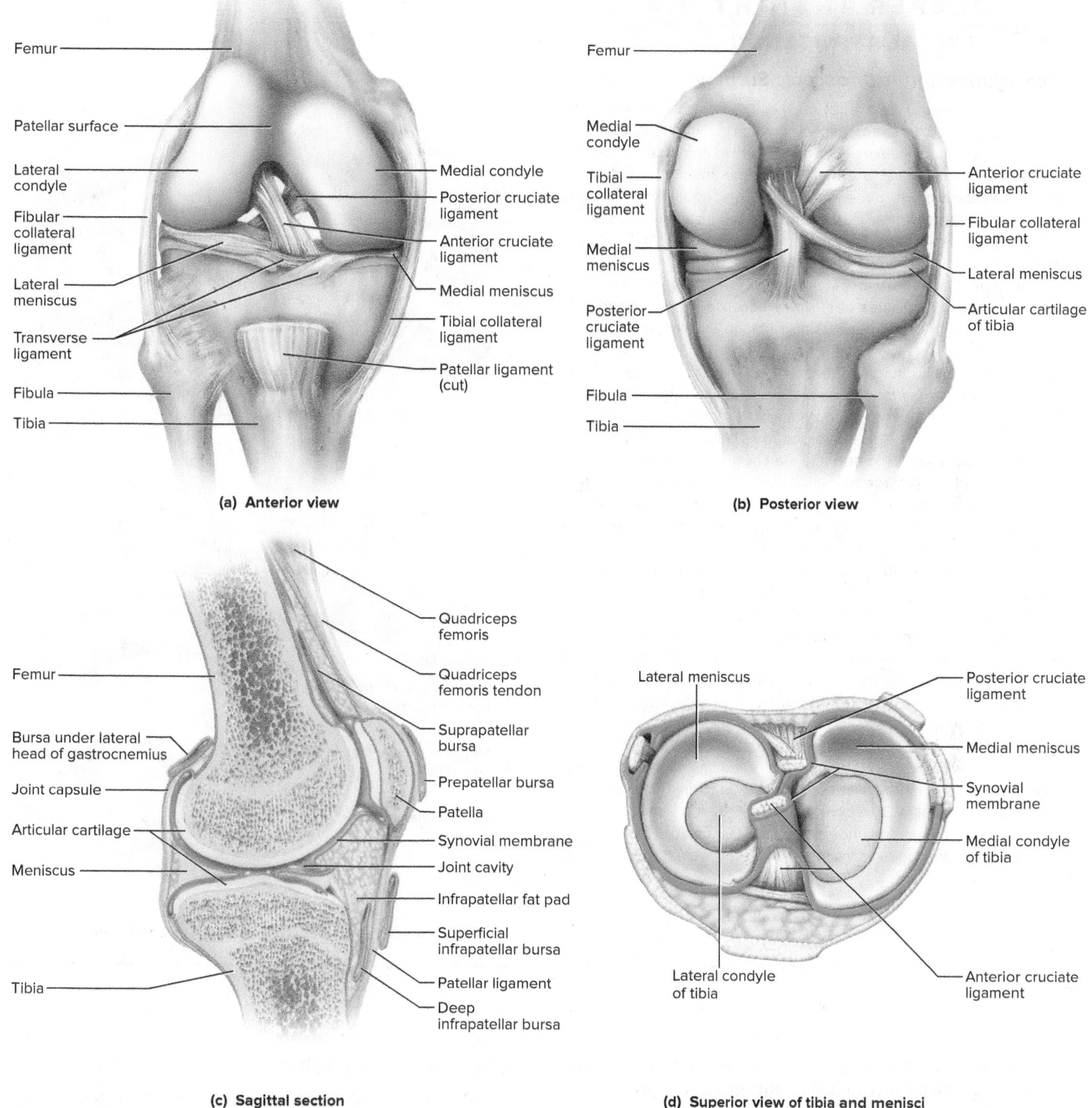


**FIGURE 9.28 The Right Tibiofemoral (Knee) Joint.** (a) Anterior view of knee joint with patella removed. (b) Posterior view. (c) Sagittal section of knee showing joint cavity and bursae. (d) Superior view of tibia showing the menisci. APR

**▶▶▶APPLY WHAT YOU KNOW**

*What structure in the elbow joint serves the same function as the ACL of the knee?*

An important aspect of human bipedalism is the ability to lock the knees and stand erect without tiring the extensor muscles of the leg. When the knee is extended to the fullest degree allowed by the ACL, the femur rotates medially on the tibia. This action locks the knee, and in this state, all the major knee ligaments are twisted and taut. To unlock the knee, the *popliteus* muscle rotates the femur laterally and untwists the ligaments.

## DEEPER INSIGHT 9.4

### CLINICAL APPLICATION

### *Knee Injuries and Arthroscopic Surgery*

Although the knee can bear a lot of weight, it is highly vulnerable to rotational and horizontal stress, especially when the knee is flexed (as in skiing or running) and receives a blow from behind or from the side. The most common injuries are to a meniscus or the anterior cruciate ligament (ACL). Lateral blows to the knee or body, especially when the foot is firmly planted on the ground, sometimes cause a so-called "unhappy triad" of injuries: tears in the tibial collateral ligament, medial meniscus, and anterior cruciate ligament **(fig. 9.29).** These three structures are strongly interconnected, so an injurious force is easily transferred from one to another. Knee injuries heal slowly because ligaments and tendons have a scanty blood supply and cartilage usually has no blood vessels at all.

The diagnosis and surgical treatment of knee injuries have been greatly improved by *arthroscopy,* a procedure in which the interior of a joint is viewed with a pencil-thin instrument, the *arthroscope,* inserted through a small incision. The arthroscope has a light, a lens, and fiber optics that allow a viewer to see into the cavity and take photographs or video recordings. A surgeon can also withdraw samples of synovial fluid by arthroscopy or inject saline into the joint cavity to expand it and provide a clearer view. If surgery is required, additional small incisions can be made for the surgical instruments and the procedures can be observed through the arthroscope or on a monitor. Arthroscopic surgery produces much less tissue damage than conventional surgery and enables patients to recover more quickly.

Orthopedic surgeons now often replace a damaged ACL with a graft from the patellar ligament or a hamstring tendon. The surgeon "harvests" a strip from the middle of the patient's ligament (or tendon), drills a hole into the femur and tibia within the joint cavity, threads the ligament through the holes, and fastens it with biodegradable screws. The grafted ligament is more taut and "competent" than the damaged ACL. It becomes ingrown with blood vessels and serves as a substrate for the deposition of more collagen, which further strengthens it in time. Following arthroscopic ACL reconstruction, a patient typically must use crutches for 7 to 10 days and undergo physical therapy for 6 to 10 weeks, followed by self-directed exercise therapy. Healing is completed in about 9 months.

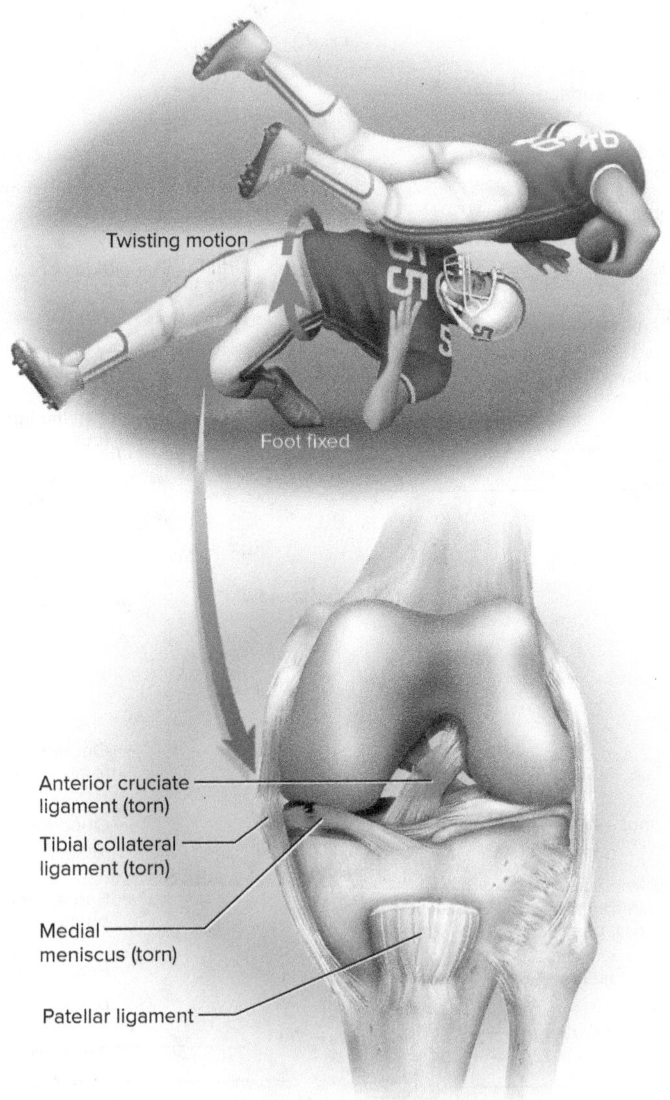


**FIGURE 9.29 The "Unhappy Triad" of Knee Injuries.**

The knee joint has about 13 bursae. Four of these are anterior: the **superficial infrapatellar, suprapatellar, prepatellar,** and **deep infrapatellar.** Located in the popliteal region are the *popliteal bursa* and *semimembranosus bursa* (not illustrated). At least seven more bursae are found on the lateral and medial sides of the knee joint. From figure 9.28c, your knowledge of the relevant word elements *(infra-, supra-, pre-),* and the terms *superficial* and *deep,* you should be able to work out the reasoning behind most of these names and develop a system for remembering the locations of these bursae.

## 9.3f The Ankle Joint

The **talocrural**[29] **(ankle) joint** includes two articulations—a medial joint between the tibia and talus and a lateral joint between the fibula and talus, both enclosed in one joint capsule **(fig. 9.30).** The malleoli of the tibia and fibula overhang the talus on each side like a cap and prevent most side-to-side motion. The ankle therefore has a more restricted range of motion than the wrist.

[29] *talo* = ankle; *crural* = pertaining to the leg

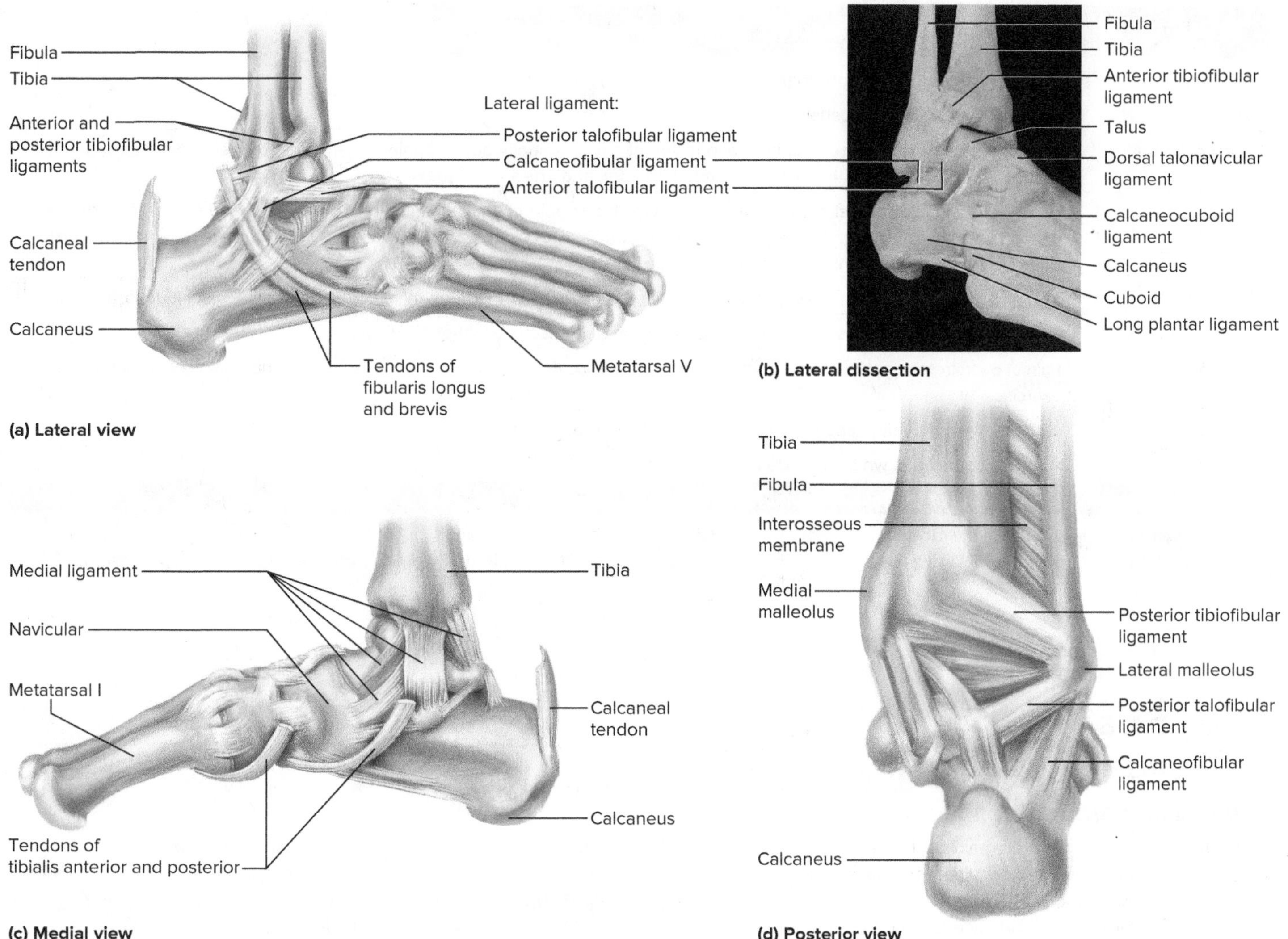


**FIGURE 9.30 The Talocrural (Ankle) Joint and Ligaments of the Right Foot.** (a) Lateral view. (b) Lateral ligaments in dissected cadaver ankle. (c) Medial view. (d) Posterior view. APR

b: Christine Eckel/McGraw-Hill Education

The ligaments of the ankle include (1) **anterior** and **posterior tibiofibular ligaments,** which bind the tibia to the fibula; (2) a multipart **medial (deltoid[30]) ligament,** which binds the tibia to the foot on the medial side; and (3) a multipart **lateral (collateral) ligament,** which binds the fibula to the foot on the lateral side. The **calcaneal (Achilles) tendon** extends from the calf muscles to the calcaneus. It plantarflexes the foot and limits dorsiflexion. Plantar flexion is limited by extensor tendons on the anterior side of the ankle and by the anterior part of the joint capsule.

Sprains (torn ligaments and tendons) are common at the ankle, especially when the foot is suddenly inverted or everted to excess. They are painful and usually accompanied by immediate swelling. They are best treated by immobilizing the joint and reducing swelling with an ice pack, but in extreme cases may require a cast or surgery. Sprains and other joint disorders are briefly described in **table 9.1.**

[30]*delt* = triangular, Greek letter delta (Δ); *oid* = resembling

**BEFORE YOU GO ON**

Answer the following questions to test your understanding of the preceding section:

12. What keeps the mandibular condyle from slipping out of its fossa in a posterior direction?
13. Explain how the biceps brachii tendon braces the shoulder joint.
14. Identify the three joints found at the elbow and name the movements in which each joint is involved.
15. What keeps the femur from slipping backward off the tibia?
16. What keeps the tibia from slipping sideways off the talus?

**TABLE 9.1 Some Common Joint Disorders**

| | |
|---|---|
| Arthritis | Broad term embracing more than 100 types of joint rheumatism. |
| Bursitis | Inflammation of a bursa, usually due to overuse of a joint. |
| Dislocation | Displacement of a bone from its normal position at a joint, usually accompanied by a sprain of the adjoining connective tissues. Most common at the fingers, thumb, shoulder, and knee. |
| Gout | A hereditary disease, most common in men, in which uric acid crystals accumulate in the joints and irritate the articular cartilage and synovial membrane. Causes gouty arthritis, with swelling, pain, tissue degeneration, and sometimes fusion of the joint. Most commonly affects the great toe. |
| Rheumatism | Broad term for any pain in the supportive and locomotory organs of the body, including bones, ligaments, tendons, and muscles. |
| Sprain | Torn ligament or tendon, sometimes with damage to a meniscus or other cartilage. |
| Strain | Painful overstretching of a tendon or muscle without serious tissue damage. Often results from inadequate warm-up before exercise. |
| Synovitis | Inflammation of a joint capsule, often as a complication of a sprain. |
| Tendinitis | A form of bursitis in which a tendon sheath is inflamed. |

***You can find other joint disorders in the following places:***

*Temporomandibular joint (TMJ) dysfunction* in Deeper Insight 9.2; *jaw dislocation* in section 9.3a; *shoulder dislocation* in Deeper Insight 9.3; *knee injuries* in Deeper Insight 9.4; *arthritis* in Deeper Insight 9.5; *hip dislocation* in section 9.3d; and *rotator cuff injury* in Deeper Insight 10.4.

## DEEPER INSIGHT 9.5
### CLINICAL APPLICATION

### *Arthritis and Artificial Joints*

**Arthritis**[31] is a broad term for pain and inflammation of a joint and embraces more than a hundred different diseases of largely obscure or unknown causes. In all of its forms, it is the most common crippling disease in the United States; nearly everyone past middle age develops arthritis to some degree. Physicians who treat arthritis and other joint disorders are called *rheumatologists.*

The most common form of arthritis is *osteoarthritis (OA),* also called "wear-and-tear arthritis" because it is apparently a normal consequence of years of wear on the joints. As joints age, the articular cartilages soften and degenerate. As the cartilage becomes roughened by wear, joint movement may be accompanied by crunching or crackling sounds called *crepitus.* OA affects especially the fingers, intervertebral joints, hips, and knees. As the articular cartilage wears away, exposed bone tissue often develops spurs that grow into the joint cavity, restrict movement, and cause pain. OA rarely occurs before age 40, but it affects about 85% of people older than 70, especially those who are overweight. It usually doesn't cripple, but in severe cases it can immobilize the hip.

*Rheumatoid arthritis (RA),* which is far more severe than osteoarthritis, results from an autoimmune attack against the joint tissues. It begins when the body produces antibodies to fight an infection. Failing to recognize the body's own tissues, a misguided antibody known as *rheumatoid factor* also attacks the synovial membranes. Inflammatory cells accumulate in the synovial fluid and produce enzymes that degrade the articular cartilage. The synovial membrane thickens and adheres to the articular cartilage, fluid accumulates in the joint capsule, and the capsule is invaded by fibrous connective tissue. As articular cartilage degenerates, the joint begins to ossify, and sometimes the bones become solidly fused and immobilized, a condition called *ankylosis*[32] **(fig. 9.31).** The disease tends to develop symmetrically—if the right wrist or hip develops RA, so does the left.

Rheumatoid arthritis is named for the fact that symptoms tend to flare up and subside (go into remission) periodically.[33] It affects women far more often than men, and because RA typically begins as early as age 30 to 40, it can cause decades of pain and disability. There is no cure, but joint damage can be slowed with hydrocortisone or other steroids. Because long-term use of steroids weakens the bone, however, aspirin is the treatment of first choice to control the inflammation. Physical therapy is also used to preserve the joint's range of motion and the patient's functional ability.

*Arthroplasty,*[34] a treatment of last resort, is the replacement of a diseased joint with an artificial device called a *joint prosthesis.*[35] Joint prostheses were first developed to treat injuries in World War II and the Korean War. Total hip replacement (THR), first performed in 1963 by English orthopedic surgeon Sir John Charnley, is now the most common orthopedic procedure for the elderly. The first knee replacements were performed in the 1970s. Joint prostheses are now available for finger, shoulder, and elbow joints, as well as the hip and knee. Arthroplasty is performed on over 250,000 patients per year in the United States, primarily to relieve pain and restore function in elderly people with OA or RA.

[31]*arthr* = joint; *itis* = inflammation

[32]*ankyl* = bent, crooked; *osis* = condition
[33]*rheumat* = tending to change
[34]*arthro* = joint; *plasty* = surgical repair
[35]*prosthe* = something added

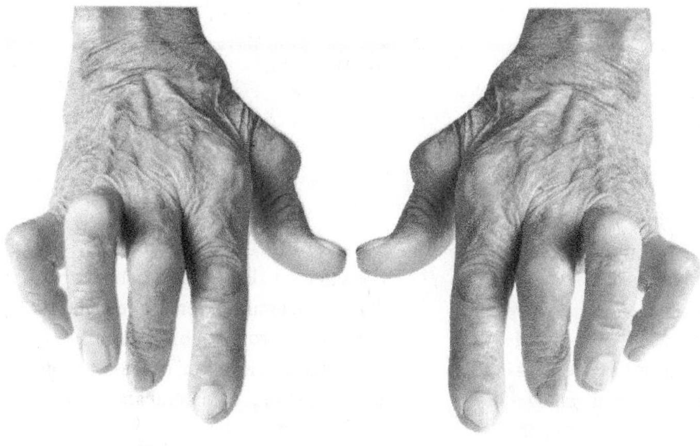

(a)

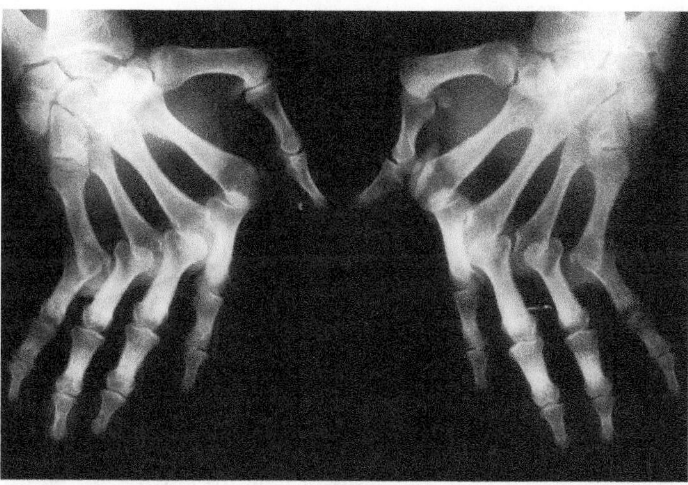

(b)

**FIGURE 9.31 Rheumatoid Arthritis (RA).** (a) A severe case with ankylosis of the joints. (b) X-ray of severe RA of the hands.

a: chaowalit407/iStock/Getty Images; b: Clinical Photography, Central Manchester University Hospitals NHS Foundation Trust, UK/Science Source

Arthroplasty presents ongoing challenges for biomedical engineering. An effective prosthesis must be strong, nontoxic, and corrosion-resistant. In addition, it must bond firmly to the patient's bones and enable a normal range of motion with a minimum of friction. The heads of long bones are usually replaced with prostheses made of very hard ceramics such as titanium carbide, cobalt–chromium, or other metal alloys. Joint sockets are made of polyethylene **(fig. 9.32).** Prostheses are bonded to the patient's bone with screws or bone cement.

Improvements in technology have resulted in long-lasting prostheses. Over 75% of artificial knees last 20 years, nearly 85% last 15 years, and over 90% last 10 years. The most common form of failure is detachment of the prosthesis from the bone. This problem has been reduced by using *porous-coated prostheses,* which become infiltrated by the patient's own bone and create a firmer bond. A prosthesis isn't as strong as a natural joint, however, and is not an option for many young, active patients.

Arthroplasty has been greatly improved by *computer-assisted design and manufacture (CAD/CAM).* A computer scans X-rays from the patient and presents several design possibilities for review. Once a design is selected, the computer generates a program to operate the machinery that produces the prosthesis. CAD/CAM has reduced the waiting period for a prosthesis from 12 weeks to about 2 weeks and has lowered the cost dramatically.

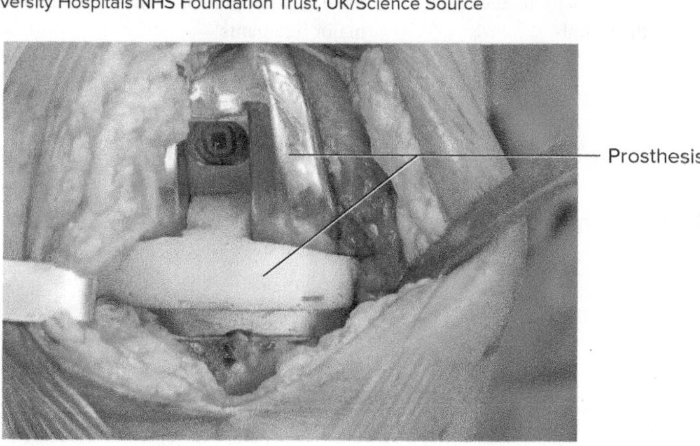


(a)

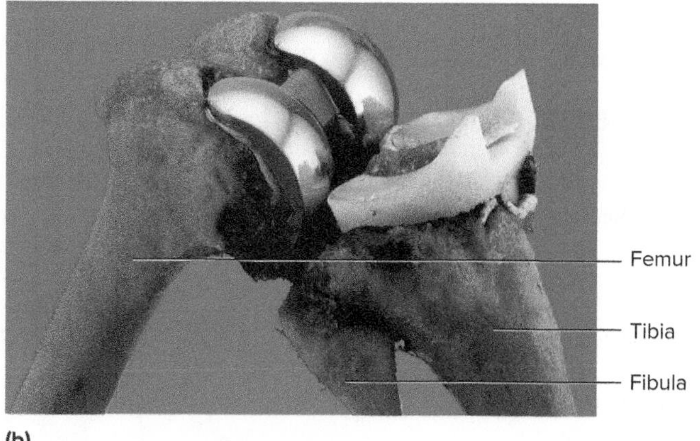


(b)

**FIGURE 9.32 Joint Prostheses.** (a) Knee replacement surgery. (b) Knee prostheses bonded to natural bone of the femur and tibia. Compare to the X-ray on the opening page of this chapter.

a: Samrith Na Lumpoon/Shutterstock; b: Ron Mensching/Medical Images RM

# STUDY GUIDE

## Assess Your Learning Outcomes

*To test your knowledge, discuss the following topics with a study partner or in writing, ideally from memory.*

### 9.1 Joints and Their Classification

1. The fundamental definition of *joint (articulation)* and why it cannot be defined as a point at which one bone moves relative to an adjacent bone
2. Relationships and differences between the sciences of arthrology, kinesiology, and biomechanics
3. The typical system for naming most joints after the bones they involve; examples of this
4. Basic criteria for classifying joints
5. Characteristics and examples of bony joints (synostoses)
6. Characteristics of fibrous joints (synarthroses) and each of their subclasses, with examples
7. Characteristics of cartilaginous joints (amphiarthroses) and each of their subclasses, with examples

### 9.2 Synovial Joints

1. The definition and anatomical features of a *synovial joint (diarthrosis)*, examples of this type, and why this type is of greatest interest for kinesiology
2. General anatomy of tendons, ligaments, bursae, and tendon sheaths, and their contributions to joint function
3. Three essential components of a lever
4. The meaning of *mechanical advantage* (MA); how the *MA* of a lever can be determined from measurements of its effort and resistance arms; and the respective advantages of levers in which the *MA* is greater than or less than 1.0
5. Comparison of first-, second-, and third-class levers, and anatomical examples of each
6. Variables that determine a joint's range of motion *(ROM)*, and the clinical relevance of *ROM*
7. Axes of rotation and degrees of freedom in joint movement, and how this relates to the classification of joints as monaxial, biaxial, or multiaxial
8. Six kinds of synovial joints; how each is classified as monaxial, biaxial, or multiaxial; imperfections in this classification; and examples of each type in the body
9. The concept of *zero position* and how it relates to the description of joint function
10. Examples of each of the following limb movements, including an ability to describe or demonstrate them: flexion, extension, hyperextension, abduction, adduction, hyperabduction, hyperadduction, circumduction, medial rotation, and lateral rotation
11. The same for supination, pronation, ulnar flexion, and radial flexion of the forearm and hand, and opposition, reposition, abduction, and adduction of the thumb
12. The same for flexion, extension, hyperextension, and lateral flexion of the spine, and right and left rotation of the trunk
13. The same for elevation, depression, protraction, retraction, and lateral and medial excursion of the mandible
14. The same for dorsiflexion, plantar flexion, inversion, eversion, pronation, and supination of the foot

### 9.3 Anatomy of Selected Diarthroses

1. Features of the jaw (temporomandibular) joint including the mandibular condyle, mandibular fossa, synovial cavity, articular disc, and principal ligaments
2. Features of the shoulder (glenohumeral) joint including the humeral head, glenoid cavity and labrum, five major ligaments and four bursae, and tendons of the biceps brachii and four rotator cuff muscles
3. Features of the elbow; the three joints that occur here; the olecranon bursa and four major ligaments
4. Features of the hip (coxal) joint including the femoral head, fovea capitis, acetabulum and labrum, and five principal ligaments
5. Features of the knee (tibiofemoral and patellofemoral joints), including the menisci, cruciate and other ligaments, and four major bursae around the patella
6. Features of the ankle (talocrural) joint, including the malleoli, calcaneal tendon, and major ligaments

## Testing Your Recall

*Answers in Appendix A*

1. Internal and external rotation of the humerus is made possible by a ______ joint.
   a. pivot
   b. condylar
   c. ball-and-socket
   d. saddle
   e. hinge
2. Which of the following is the least movable?
   a. a diarthrosis
   b. a synostosis
   c. a symphysis
   d. a synovial joint
   e. a condylar joint
3. Which of the following movements are unique to the foot?
   a. dorsiflexion and inversion
   b. elevation and depression
   c. circumduction and rotation
   d. abduction and adduction
   e. opposition and reposition

# STUDY GUIDE

4. Which of the following joints cannot be circumducted?
   a. carpometacarpal
   b. metacarpophalangeal
   c. glenohumeral
   d. coxal
   e. interphalangeal
5. Which of the following terms denotes a general condition that includes the other four?
   a. gout
   b. arthritis
   c. rheumatism
   d. osteoarthritis
   e. rheumatoid arthritis
6. In the adult, the ischium and pubis are united by
   a. a synchondrosis.
   b. a diarthrosis.
   c. a synostosis.
   d. an amphiarthrosis.
   e. a symphysis.
7. In a second-class lever, the effort
   a. is applied to the end opposite the fulcrum.
   b. is applied to the fulcrum itself.
   c. is applied between the fulcrum and resistance.
   d. always produces an *MA* less than 1.0.
   e. is applied on one side of the fulcrum to move a resistance on the other side.
8. Which of the following joints has anterior and posterior cruciate ligaments?
   a. the shoulder
   b. the elbow
   c. the hip
   d. the knee
   e. the ankle
9. To bend backward at the waist involves ______ of the vertebral column.
   a. rotation
   b. hyperextension
   c. dorsiflexion
   d. abduction
   e. flexion
10. The rotator cuff includes the tendons of all of the following muscles *except*
    a. the subscapularis.
    b. the supraspinatus.
    c. the infraspinatus.
    d. the biceps brachii.
    e. the teres minor.
11. The lubricant of a diarthrosis is called ______.
12. A fluid-filled sac that eases the movement of a tendon over a bone is called a/an ______.
13. A ______ joint allows one bone to swivel on another.
14. ______ is the science of movement.
15. The joint between a tooth and the mandible is called a/an ______.
16. In a ______ suture, the articulating bones have interlocking wavy margins, somewhat like a dovetail joint in carpentry.
17. In kicking a football, what type of action does the knee joint exhibit?
18. The angle through which a joint can move is called its ______.
19. The menisci of the knee are functionally similar to the ______ of the temporomandibular joint.
20. At the ankle, both the tibia and fibula articulate with what tarsal bone?

## Building Your Medical Vocabulary

*Answers in Appendix A*

*State a meaning of each word element, and give a medical term from this chapter that uses it or a slight variation of it.*

1. ab-
2. arthro-
3. -ate
4. cruci-
5. cruro-
6. -duc
7. kinesio-
8. men-
9. supin-
10. -trac

## What's Wrong with These Statements?

*Answers in Appendix A*

*Briefly explain why each of the following statements is false, or reword it to make it true.*

1. More people get rheumatoid arthritis than osteoarthritis.
2. A doctor who treats arthritis is called a kinesiologist.
3. Synovial joints are also known as synarthroses.
4. Menisci occur in the elbow and knee joints.
5. Reaching behind you to take something out of your hip pocket involves flexion of the shoulder.
6. The cruciate ligaments are in the feet.
7. The femur is held tightly in the acetabulum mainly by the round ligament.
8. The knuckles are amphiarthroses.
9. Synovial fluid is secreted by the bursae.
10. Like most ligaments, the periodontal ligaments attach one bone (the tooth) to another (the mandible or maxilla).

STUDY GUIDE

## Testing Your Comprehension

1. All second-class levers produce a mechanical advantage greater than 1.0 and all third-class levers produce a mechanical advantage less than 1.0. Explain why.
2. For each of the following joint movements, state what bone the axis of rotation passes through and which of the three anatomical planes contains the axis of rotation. You may find it helpful to produce some of these actions on an articulated laboratory skeleton so you can more easily visualize the axis of rotation. (a) Plantar flexion; (b) flexion of the hip; (c) adduction of the thigh; (d) flexion of the knee; (e) flexion of the first interphalangeal joint of the index finger. (Do not bend the fingers of a wired laboratory skeletal hand, because they can break off.)
3. In order of occurrence, list the joint actions (flexion, pronation, etc.) and the joints where they would occur as you (a) sit down at a table, (b) reach out and pick up an apple, (c) take a bite, and (d) chew it. Assume that you start in anatomical position.
4. The deltoid muscle inserts on the deltoid tuberosity of the humerus and abducts the arm. Imagine a person holding a weight in the hand and abducting the arm. On a laboratory skeleton, identify the fulcrum; measure the effort arm and resistance arm; determine the mechanical advantage of this movement; and determine which of the three lever types the upper limb acts as when performing this movement.
5. List the six types of synovial joints, and for each one, if possible, identify a joint in the upper limb and a joint in the lower limb that fall into each category. Which of these six joints has/have no examples in the lower limb?

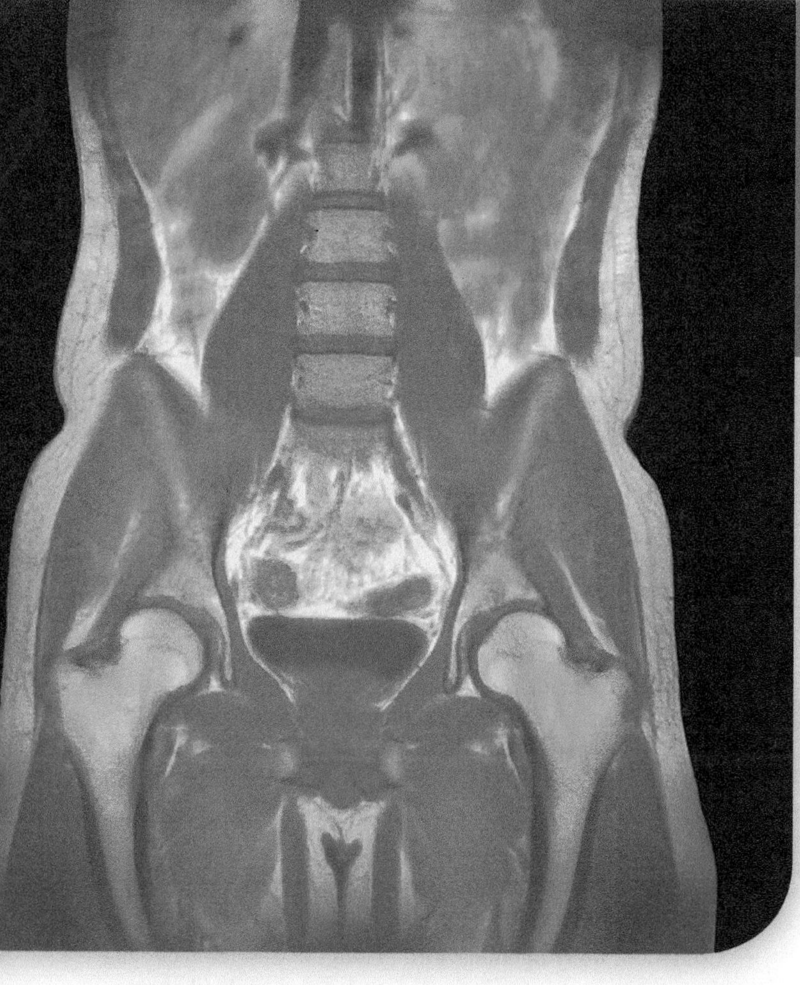

CHAPTER

# 10 THE MUSCULAR SYSTEM

Colorized MRI scan showing muscles of the lumbar, pelvic, and upper femoral regions
Simon Fraser/Science Source

## CHAPTER OUTLINE



## DEEPER INSIGHTS

**Module 6: Muscular System**

## BRUSHING UP

- Understanding of the skeletal muscles depends on a thorough knowledge of skeletal anatomy (chapter 8), including not just the bones but also their surface features (table 8.2), many of which are muscle attachments.
- This chapter describes the movements produced by muscles, called their *actions*, using the terminology of joint movements in section 9.2c.

Muscles constitute nearly half of the body's weight and occupy a place of central interest in several fields of health care and fitness. Physical and occupational therapists must be well acquainted with the muscular system to plan and carry out rehabilitation programs. Athletes and trainers, dancers and acrobats, and amateur fitness enthusiasts follow programs of resistance training to strengthen individual muscle groups through movement regimens based on knowledge of muscle, bone, and joint anatomy. Nurses employ their knowledge of the muscular system to give intramuscular injections correctly and to safely and effectively move patients who are physically incapacitated. Gerontological nurses are keenly aware of how deeply a person's muscular condition affects the quality of life in old age. The muscular system is highly important to biomedical disciplines even beyond the scope of the movement sciences. For example, it is the primary source of body heat in the moving individual, and loss of muscle mass can be a contributing factor in diabetes mellitus.

The muscular system is closely related to what we have covered in the preceding chapters. After this, we will examine the mechanisms of muscle contraction at the cellular and molecular levels in chapter 11, and chapter 12 will shed light on the relationship of the muscles to the nerves that control them.

## 10.1 Structural and Functional Organization of Muscles

### Expected Learning Outcomes

When you have completed this section, you should be able to

a. describe the various functions of muscular tissue;
b. describe the connective tissue components of a muscle and their relationship to the internal organization of a muscle and compartmentalization of muscle groups;
c. relate muscle fascicles to the shapes and relative strengths of muscles;
d. name the types of muscle–bone attachments and explain the shortcoming of calling their attachments *origins* and *insertions*;
e. distinguish between intrinsic and extrinsic muscles;
f. describe the ways muscles work in groups to aid, oppose, and moderate each other's actions;
g. describe in general terms the nerve and blood supply to skeletal muscles; and
h. explain how the Latin names of muscles aid in visualizing and remembering them.

The word ***muscle***[1] means "little mouse," and apparently was coined by one of the ancient Greek authorities who thought that skeletal muscles rippling under the skin resembled scurrying mice. As we saw in chapter 5, however, there are three kinds of muscle—skeletal, cardiac, and smooth. Despite their differences, all muscle is specialized for one fundamental purpose: to convert the chemical energy of ATP into the mechanical energy of motion. Muscle cells exert force on other tissues and organs, either to produce desirable movements or to prevent undesirable ones.

### 10.1a The Functions of Muscles

Collectively, the three types of muscle serve the following functions:

- **Movement.** Muscles enable us to move from place to place and to move individual body parts; they move body contents in the course of breathing, blood circulation, feeding and digestion, defecation, urination, and childbirth; and they serve various roles in communication—speech, writing, facial expressions, and other body language.
- **Stability.** Muscles maintain posture by preventing unwanted movements. Some are called *antigravity muscles* because, at least part of the time, they resist the pull of gravity and prevent us from falling or slumping over. Many muscles also stabilize the joints by maintaining tension on tendons and bones.
- **Control of body openings and passages.** Muscles encircling the mouth serve not only for speech but also for food intake and retention of food while chewing. In the eyelid and pupil, they regulate the admission of light to the eye. Internal muscular rings control the movement of food, bile, blood, and other materials within the body. Muscles encircling the urethra and anus control the elimination of waste. (Some of these muscles are called *sphincters,* but not all; this is clarified later.)
- **Heat production (thermogenesis).** The skeletal muscles produce 20% to 30% of the body's heat at rest and up to 85% during exercise. This body heat is vital to the functioning of enzymes and therefore to all metabolism.
- **Glycemic control.** This means the regulation of blood glucose concentration within its normal range. The skeletal muscles absorb, store, and use a large share of one's glucose and play a highly significant role in stabilizing its blood concentration. In old age, in obesity, and when muscles become deconditioned and weakened, people suffer an increased risk of type 2 diabetes mellitus because of the decline in this glucose-buffering function.

The rest of this chapter concerns only the skeletal muscles. The term **muscular system** refers only to these, not the other two types of muscle. The study of skeletal muscles is called **myology.**[2]

[1] *mus* = mouse; *cle* = little
[2] *myo* = muscle; *logy* = study of

There are about 600 muscles in the human muscular system, but fortunately you aren't expected to learn 600 names! Many have repetitious names, such as the right and left muscles of the same name and muscle series between ribs and vertebrae. This chapter describes fewer than one-third of the muscles.

### 10.1b Muscle Connective Tissues, Fascicles, and Compartments

A skeletal muscle consists of more than muscular tissue. It also includes connective tissue, nerves, and blood vessels. The connective tissue components, from the smallest to largest and from deep to superficial, are as follows **(fig. 10.1)**:

- **Endomysium**[3] (EN-doe-MIZ-ee-um). This is a thin sleeve of loose connective tissue that surrounds each muscle fiber. It creates room for blood capillaries and nerve fibers to reach every muscle fiber, ensuring that no muscle cell is without stimulation and nourishment. The endomysium also provides the extracellular chemical environment for the muscle fiber and its associated nerve ending. Excitation of a muscle fiber is based on the exchange of calcium, sodium, and potassium ions between the endomysial tissue fluid and the nerve and muscle fibers.

[3] *endo* = within; *mys* = muscle

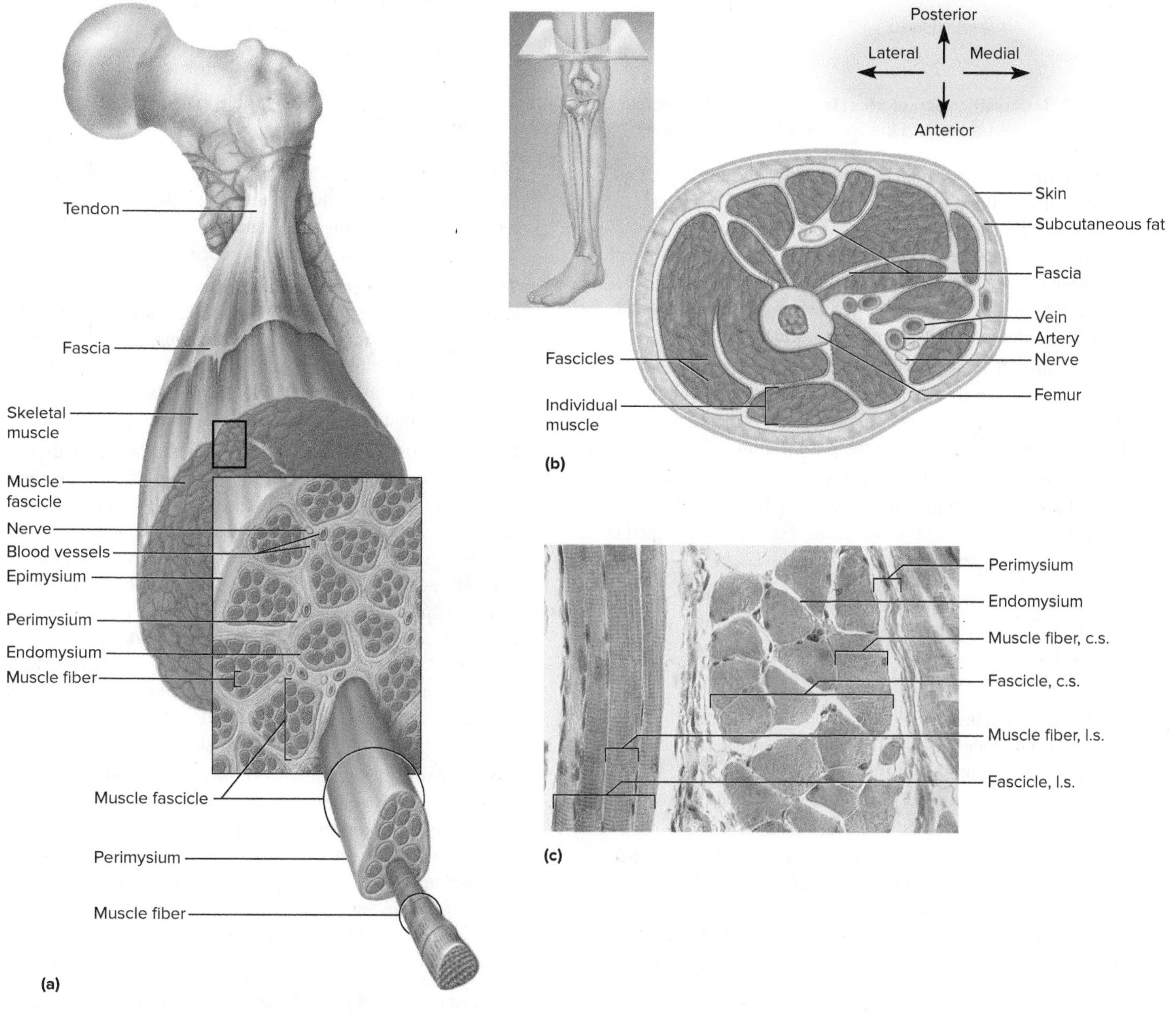

**FIGURE 10.1 Connective Tissues of a Muscle.** (a) The muscle–bone attachment and subdivisions of a skeletal muscle. (b) A cross section of the thigh showing the relationship of neighboring muscles to fasciae and bone. (c) Muscle fascicles in the tongue. Vertical fascicles passing between the superior and inferior surfaces of the tongue are seen alternating with cross-sectioned horizontal fascicles that pass from the rear to the tip of the tongue. A fibrous perimysium can be seen between the fascicles, and endomysium can be seen between the muscle fibers within each fascicle. (c.s. = cross section; l.s. = longitudinal section)

c: Victor Eroschenko

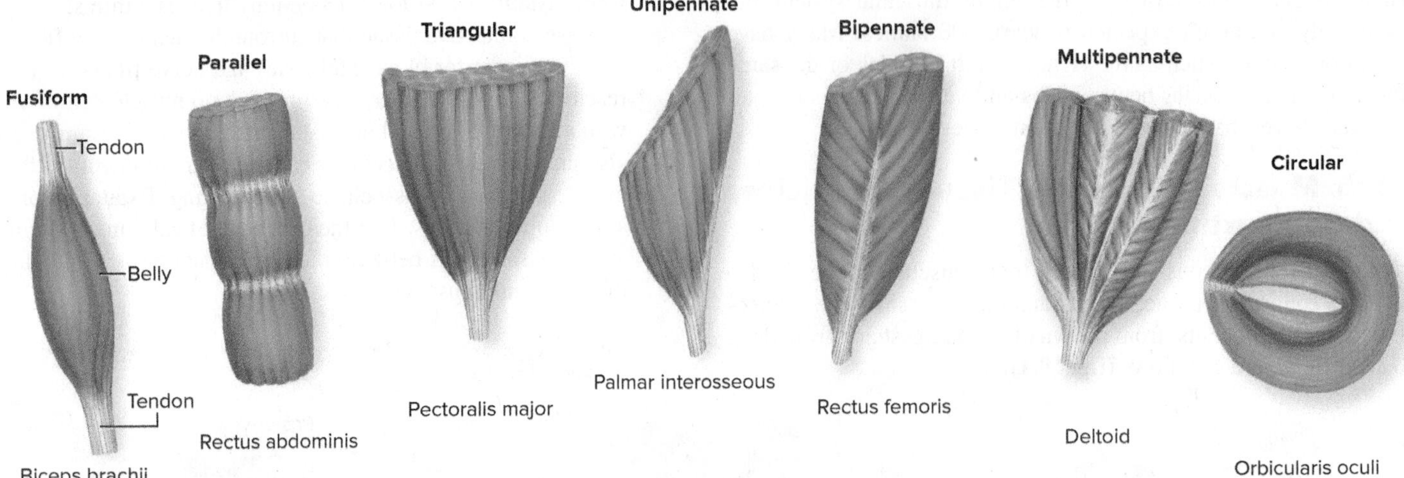


**FIGURE 10.2 Classification of Muscles According to Fascicle Orientation.** The fascicles are the grain visible in each illustration. Muscle types are named across the top and an example of each type across the bottom.

- **Perimysium.**[4] This is a thicker connective tissue sheath that wraps muscle fibers together in bundles called **fascicles**[5] (FASS-ih-culs). Fascicles are visible to the naked eye as parallel strands—the grain in a cut of meat; if you pull apart "fork-tender" roast beef, it separates along these fascicles. The perimysium carries the larger nerves and blood vessels as well as stretch receptors called muscle spindles.
- **Epimysium.**[6] This is a fibrous sheath that surrounds the entire muscle. On its outer surface, the epimysium grades into the fascia, and its inner surface issues projections between the fascicles to form the perimysium.
- **Fascia**[7] (FASH-ee-uh). This is a sheet of connective tissue that separates neighboring muscles or muscle groups from each other and from the subcutaneous tissue. Muscles are grouped in *compartments* separated from each other by fasciae.

The *fascicles* defined by the perimysium are oriented in a variety of ways that determine the strength of a muscle and the direction in which it pulls. According to fascicle orientation, muscles are classified as shown in **figure 10.2.**

- **Fusiform**[8] **muscles** are thick in the middle and tapered at each end. The *biceps brachii* of the arm and *gastrocnemius* of the calf are examples of this type. Muscle strength is proportional to the diameter of a muscle at its thickest point, and fusiform muscles are relatively strong.
- **Parallel muscles** have a fairly uniform width and parallel fascicles. Some of these are elongated straps, such as the *rectus abdominis* of the abdomen, *sartorius* of the thigh, and *zygomaticus major* of the face. Others are more squarish and are called *quadrilateral* (four-sided) muscles, such as the *masseter* of the jaw. Parallel muscles can span long distances, such as from hip to knee, and they shorten more than other muscle types. However, having fewer muscle fibers than a fusiform muscle of the same mass, they produce less force.
- **Triangular (convergent) muscles** are fan-shaped—broad at one end and narrower at the other. Examples include the *pectoralis major* in the chest and the *temporalis* on the side of the head. Despite their small localized insertions on a bone, these muscles are relatively strong because they contain a large number of fibers in the wider part of the muscle.
- **Pennate**[9] **muscles** are feather-shaped. Their fascicles insert obliquely on a tendon that runs the length of the muscle, like the shaft of a feather. There are three types of pennate muscles: *unipennate,* in which all fascicles approach the tendon from one side (for example, the *palmar interosseous muscles* of the hand and *semimembranosus* of the thigh); *bipennate,* in which fascicles approach the tendon from both sides (for example, the *rectus femoris* of the thigh); and *multipennate,* shaped like a bunch of feathers with their quills converging on a single point (for example, the *deltoid* of the shoulder). These muscles generate more force than the preceding types because they fit more muscle fibers into a given length of muscle.
- **Circular muscles (sphincters)** form rings around certain body openings. When they contract, they constrict the opening and tend to prevent the passage of material through it. Examples include the *orbicularis oculi* of the eyelids and the *external urethral* and *anal sphincters.* Smooth muscle can also form sphincters—for example, the *pyloric valve* at the passage from the stomach to the small intestine and some sphincters of the urinary tract and anal canal.

The fasciae are not components of the muscles themselves, but package groups of functionally related muscles into **muscle compartments (fig. 10.3)** and stand between the muscles and the overlying

[4]*peri* = around; *mys* = muscle
[5]*fasc* = bundle; *icle* = little
[6]*epi* = upon, above; *mys* = muscle
[7]*fascia* = band
[8]*fusi* = spindle; *form* = shape

[9]*penna* = feather; *ate* = characterized by

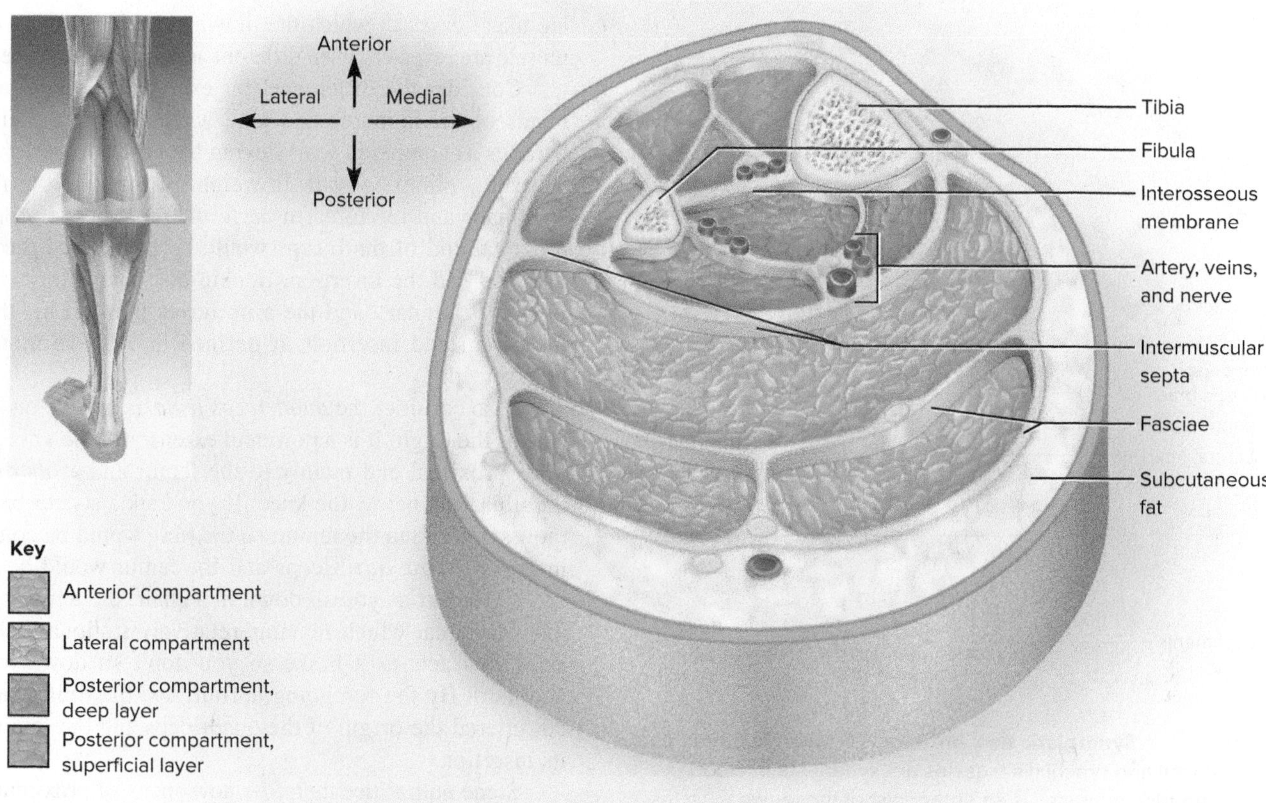


**FIGURE 10.3 Muscle Compartments.** A cross section of the left leg slightly above midcalf, oriented the same way as the reader's left leg.

hypodermis and skin. A compartment also contains the nerves and blood vessels that supply the muscle group. Such compartmentalization occurs in the thoracic and abdominal walls, pelvic floor, and limbs. Some of these fasciae are particularly thick and are called **intermuscular septa.** The tight binding of muscles by these fasciae contributes to a clinical problem described in Deeper Insight 10.1.

**DEEPER INSIGHT 10.1**

**CLINICAL APPLICATION**

***Compartment Syndrome***

Muscle compartments are very snugly contained in their fasciae. If a blood vessel in a compartment is damaged by overuse or contusion (a bruising injury), blood and tissue fluid accumulate in the compartment. The inelastic fascia prevents the compartment from expanding to relieve the pressure. Mounting pressure on the muscles, nerves, and blood vessels triggers a sequence of degenerative events called *compartment syndrome.* Blood flow to the compartment is obstructed by pressure on its arteries. If *ischemia* (poor blood flow) persists for more than 2 to 4 hours, nerves begin to die, and after 6 hours, so does muscle tissue. Nerves can regenerate after the pressure is relieved, but muscle necrosis is irreversible. The breakdown of muscle releases myoglobin into the blood. *Myoglobinuria,* the presence of myoglobin in the urine, gives the urine a dark color and is one of the key signs of compartment syndrome and some other degenerative muscle disorders. Compartment syndrome is treated by immobilizing and resting the limb and, if necessary, making an incision *(fasciotomy)* to relieve the pressure.

## 10.1c Muscle Attachments

Connective tissue components of a muscle emerge from it as collagenous fibers that continue into its tendon or other bone attachment, then into the periosteum and matrix of the bone, creating very strong structural continuity from muscle to bone. Some muscles insert not on bones but on the fascia or tendon of another muscle or on collagen fibers of the dermis. The distal tendon of the biceps brachii, for example, inserts partly on the fascia of the forearm. Many muscles of the face insert in the skin of the lips, eyelids, and other areas, enabling them to produce expressions such as a smile.

### Direct and Indirect Attachments

Muscles have two forms of attachment to bones—direct and indirect. In a **direct (fleshy) attachment,** such as in the *brachialis* and the lateral head of the *triceps brachii* in **figure 10.4,** there is so little separation between muscle and bone that to the naked eye, the red muscular tissue seems to emerge directly from the bone. At a microscopic level, however, the muscle fibers stop slightly short of the bone and the gap between muscle and bone is spanned by collagen fibers.

In an **indirect attachment,** the muscle ends visibly short of its bony destination, and the gap is bridged by a fibrous cord or band called a **tendon.** See, for example, the two ends of the biceps brachii in figure 10.4 and the photographs of tendons in figures 10.32b and 10.37. You can easily palpate tendons and feel their texture just above your heel (your *calcaneal* or *Achilles tendon*) and on the anterior side of your wrist (tendons of the *palmaris longus* and *flexor carpi radialis* muscles).

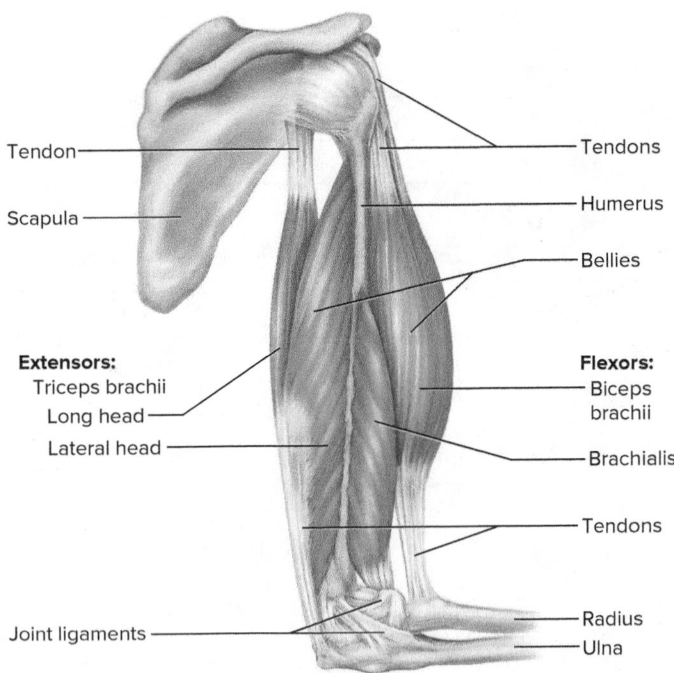


**FIGURE 10.4 Synergistic and Antagonistic Muscle Pairs.** The biceps brachii and brachialis muscles are synergists in elbow flexion. The triceps brachii is an antagonist of those two muscles and is the prime mover in elbow extension.

*Which of these muscles have direct attachments to the bones, and which have indirect attachments?*

In some cases, the tendon is a broad sheet called an **aponeurosis**[10] (AP-oh-new-RO-sis). This term originally referred to the tendon located beneath the scalp (hence the word root *neuro-*), but now it also refers to similar tendons associated with certain abdominal, lumbar, hand, and foot muscles. For example, the palmaris longus tendon passes through the wrist and then expands into a fanlike *palmar aponeurosis* beneath the skin of the palm (see fig. 10.29a).

In some places, groups of tendons from separate muscles pass under a band of connective tissue called a **retinaculum.**[11] One of these covers each surface of the wrist like a bracelet, for example. The tendons of several forearm muscles pass under them on their way to the hand (see figs. 5.13, 10.29a).

## Moving and Stationary Attachments

Since most muscles span at least one joint and attach to a different bone at each end, their contraction moves one bone relative to the other. Traditionally, the attachment at the stationary end has been called the **origin** of the muscle and the attachment at the moving end has been called the **insertion.** *Gray's Anatomy* and other current authorities, however, have largely abandoned the *origin* and *insertion* terms because they are imperfect and sometimes misleading. There are many cases in which the moving and nonmoving ends of the muscle are reversed when different actions are performed.

Consider the difference, for example, in the relative movements of the humerus and ulna when flexing the elbow to lift barbells as compared with flexing the elbow to perform chin-ups or scale a climbing wall. In weight lifting, the arm is relatively stationary and the forearm performs most of the motion, so the proximal end of the biceps would be considered the origin and its distal end the insertion. In chin-ups, by contrast, the forearm is more stationary and the arm moves more to lift the body, so the origin and insertion, if defined by relative motion, would be reversed.

Also consider the *quadriceps femoris* muscle on the anterior side of the thigh. It is a powerful extensor of the knee, connected at its proximal end mainly to the femur and at its distal end to the tibia, just below the knee. If you kick a soccer ball, the tibia moves more than the femur, so the tibia would be considered the insertion of the quadriceps and the femur would be considered its origin. But as you sit down in a chair, the femur moves more than the tibia, which remains relatively stationary. The quadriceps then acts as a brake so you don't sit down too abruptly and hard. By the foregoing definitions, the tibia would now be considered the origin of the quadriceps and the femur would be its insertion.

Some authorities therefore now speak of proximal and distal, medial and lateral, or superior and inferior muscle attachments, but no single system of naming applies throughout the body.

Even though *origin–insertion* terminology is becoming obsolete, it may still appear in some courses, board examinations, and other places. Therefore, for each muscle in tables 10.1 through 10.16, there are two bullet points (•) in the "Skeletal Attachments" column. The first bullet point denotes what has traditionally been called that muscle's origin, and the second one its insertion, enabling you to study the anatomy that way if your course so requires. These are aptly called skeletal attachments in the tables, because that applies to *nearly* all of them. Notwithstanding the table headers, though, be aware that a few of these muscles attach not to bone but to dermis, fasciae, or other soft connective tissues.

### 10.1d Functional Groups of Muscles

Consider the human hand. It requires subtle, finely controlled movement for such tasks as handwriting and keyboarding, but also powerful movements for such actions as climbing and tightly grasping tools. Muscles big enough to provide such power would be too bulky to fit within the hand itself, so they lie in the forearm and connect to the metacarpal bones and phalanges through long slender tendons that pass through the wrist. The more subtle movements are controlled by small muscles located entirely within the hand. Any muscle contained entirely within a region of interest is called an **intrinsic muscle.** A muscle that acts upon a designated organ or region such as the hand, but arises from another region such as the forearm, is called an **extrinsic muscle.** The intrinsic–extrinsic distinction applies not only to the hand but also to the muscles of the tongue, larynx, back, foot, and other regions. You will find several muscles classified this way in the tables in this chapter.

The effect produced by a muscle, whether it is to produce or prevent a movement, is called its **action.** Skeletal muscles seldom

[10] *apo* = upon, above; *neuro* = nervous system, brain
[11] *retinac* = retainer, bracelet; *cul* = little

act independently; instead, they function in groups whose combined actions produce the coordinated control of a joint. Muscles can be classified into four categories according to their actions, but it must be stressed that a particular muscle can act in a certain way during one joint action and in a different way during other actions of the same joint. Furthermore, the action of a given muscle depends on what other muscles are doing. For example, the *gastrocnemius* of the posterior calf usually flexes the knee, but if the *quadriceps* of the anterior thigh prevents knee flexion, the gastrocnemius flexes the ankle, causing plantar flexion. The following categories of muscle action are exemplified by muscles that act on the elbow (fig. 10.4):

1. The **prime mover (agonist)** is the muscle that produces most of the force during a particular joint action. In flexing the elbow, for example, the prime mover is the brachialis.
2. A **synergist**[12] (SIN-ur-jist) is a muscle that aids the prime mover. Two or more synergists acting on a joint can produce more power than a single larger muscle. The biceps brachii, for example, overlies the brachialis and works with it as a synergist to flex the elbow. The actions of a prime mover and its synergist aren't necessarily identical and redundant. If the prime mover worked alone at a joint, it could cause rotation or other undesirable movements of a bone. A synergist may stabilize a joint and restrict these movements, or modify the direction of a movement so that the action of the prime mover is more coordinated and specific.
3. An **antagonist**[13] is a muscle that opposes the prime mover. In some cases, it relaxes to give the prime mover almost complete control over an action. More often, however, the antagonist maintains some tension on a joint and thus limits the speed or range of the prime mover, preventing excessive movement, joint injury, or inappropriate actions. If you extend your arm to reach out and pick up a cup of tea, for example, your triceps brachii serves as the prime mover of elbow extension, and your brachialis acts as an antagonist to slow the extension and stop it at the appropriate point. If you extend your arm rapidly to throw a dart, however, the brachialis must be quite relaxed. The brachialis and triceps represent an **antagonistic pair** of muscles that act on opposite sides of a joint. We need antagonistic pairs at a joint because a muscle can only pull, not push—for example, a single muscle cannot flex *and* extend the elbow. Which member of the pair acts as the prime mover depends on the motion under consideration. In flexion of the elbow, the brachialis is the prime mover and the triceps is the antagonist; when the elbow is extended, their roles are reversed.
4. A **fixator** is a muscle that prevents a bone from moving. To *fix* a bone means to hold it steady, allowing another muscle attached to it to pull on something else. For example, consider again the flexion of the elbow by the biceps brachii. The biceps originates on the scapula, crosses both the shoulder and elbow joints, and inserts on the radius and forearm fascia. The scapula is loosely attached to the axial skeleton, so when the biceps contracts, it seems that it would pull the scapula laterally. However, there are fixator muscles (the *rhomboids*) that attach the scapula to the vertebral column (see fig. 10.18). They contract at the same time as the biceps, holding the scapula firmly in place and ensuring that the force generated by the biceps moves the radius rather than the scapula.

### 10.1e Innervation and Blood Supply

A skeletal muscle cannot contract unless it is stimulated by a nerve fiber. If its nerve is severed, the muscle is paralyzed. The nerve that supplies a given muscle is called its **innervation.** Knowing the innervation to each muscle enables clinicians to diagnose nerve, spinal cord, and brainstem injuries from their effects on muscle function, and to set realistic goals for rehabilitation. The innervations described in this chapter will be more meaningful after you have studied the peripheral nervous system (chapters 13 and 14), but a brief orientation will be helpful here. The muscles are innervated by nerve branches that arise from these two groups:

- **Spinal nerves** arise from the spinal cord, emerge through the intervertebral foramina, and supply branches to muscles below the neck. Spinal nerves are identified by letters and numbers that refer to the adjacent vertebrae—for example, T6 for the sixth thoracic nerve and S2 for the second sacral nerve. Immediately after emerging from an intervertebral foramen, each spinal nerve branches into a *posterior* and *anterior ramus.* You will note references to nerve numbers and rami in many of the muscle tables. The term *plexus* in some of the tables refers to weblike networks of spinal nerves adjacent to the vertebral column. All of the spinal nerves named here are illustrated, and most are also discussed, in chapter 13 (see the four tables starting at table 13.3).
- **Cranial nerves** arise from the base of the brain, emerge through the skull foramina, and innervate muscles of the head and neck. Cranial nerves are identified by roman numerals (CN I to CN XII) and by names given in table 14.1, although not all 12 of them innervate skeletal muscles.

The muscular system has a very heavy demand for energy, obtained from ATP, and thus it receives a generous flow of blood delivering oxygen and organic nutrients. Even at rest, it receives about one-quarter of all the blood pumped by the heart, or about 1.24 L/min. During exercise, its share may rise as high as three-quarters of the cardiac output, or about 11.6 L/min. Blood capillaries branch extensively through the endomysium to reach every muscle fiber, sometimes so intimately associated with the muscle fibers that the fibers have surface indentations to accommodate them. The capillaries of skeletal muscle undulate or coil when the muscle is contracted, allowing them enough slack to stretch out straight, without breaking, when the muscle lengthens. Chapter 20 describes some special physiological properties of muscle circulation and names the major arteries that supply the skeletal muscle groups.

### 10.1f Muscle Names and Learning Strategy

**Figures 10.5** and **10.6** show an overview of the major superficial muscles. Learning the names of these and other muscles may seem a forbidding task at first, especially when some of them have such

[12]*syn* = together; *erg* = work
[13]*ant* = against; *agonist* = actor, competitor

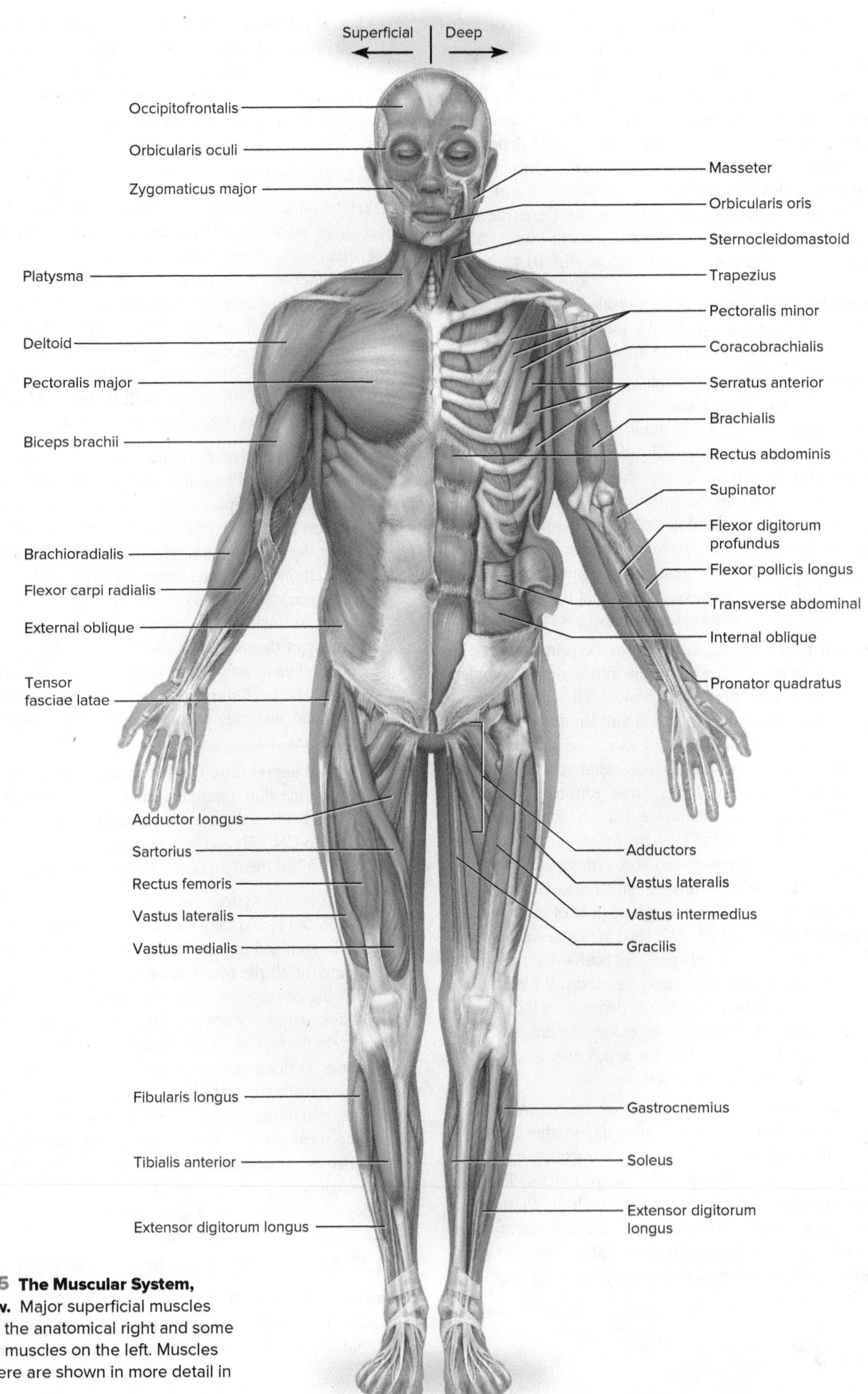


**FIGURE 10.5 The Muscular System, Anterior View.** Major superficial muscles are shown on the anatomical right and some of the deeper muscles on the left. Muscles not labeled here are shown in more detail in later figures.

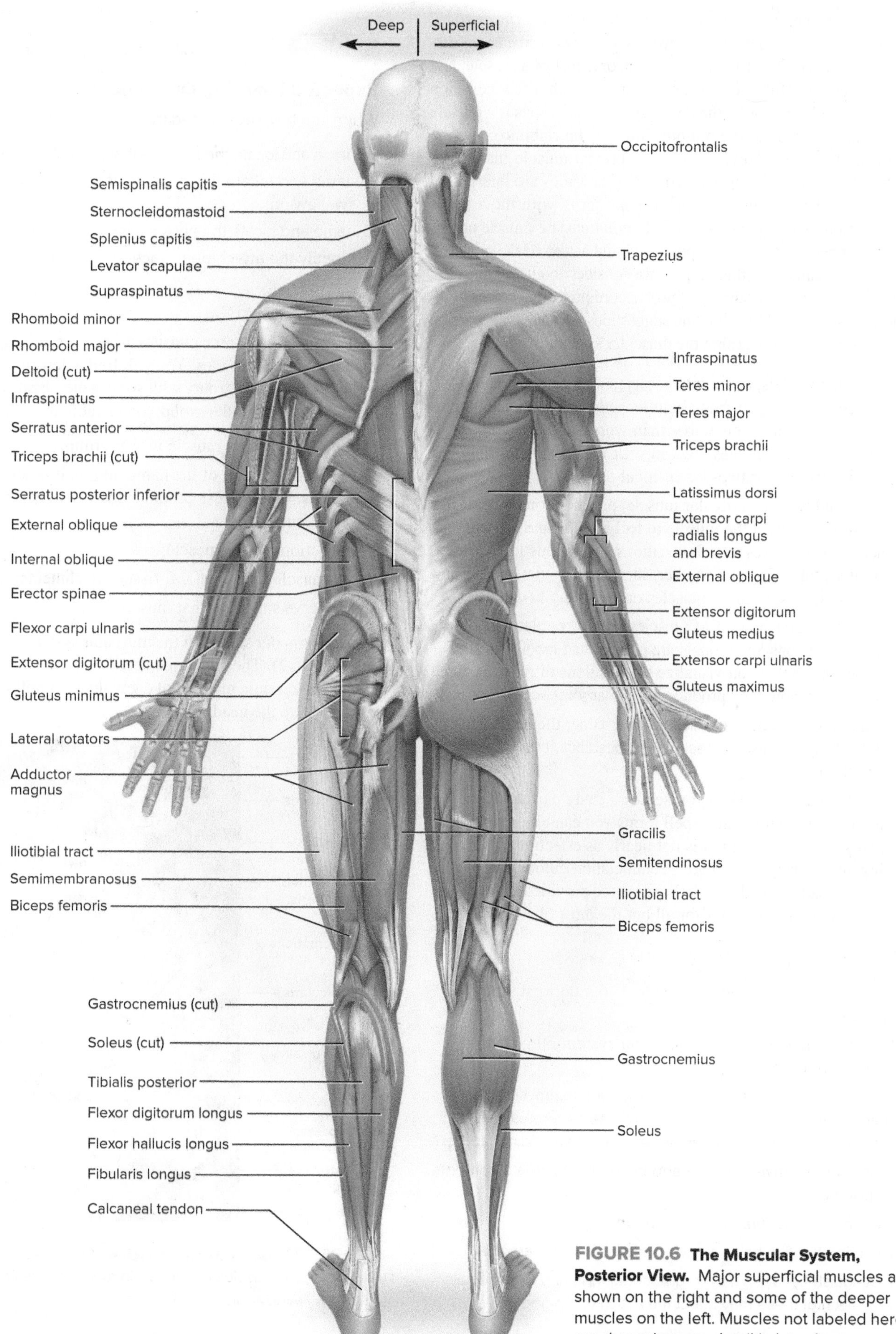


**FIGURE 10.6 The Muscular System, Posterior View.** Major superficial muscles are shown on the right and some of the deeper muscles on the left. Muscles not labeled here are shown in more detail in later figures.

long Latin names as *depressor labii inferioris* and *flexor digiti minimi brevis.* Such names, however, typically describe some distinctive aspects of the structure, location, or action of a muscle, and become very helpful once we grow familiar with a few common Latin words. For example, the depressor labii inferioris is a muscle that lowers (depresses) the bottom (inferior) lip (labium), and the flexor digiti minimi brevis is a short (brevis) muscle that flexes the smallest (minimi) finger (digit). Muscle names are interpreted in footnotes throughout the chapter. Familiarity with these terms and attention to the footnotes will help you translate muscle names and remember the location, appearance, and action of the muscles.

In the remainder of this chapter, we consider about 160 muscles; most courses cover considerably fewer according to the choices of individual instructors. The following suggestions may help you develop a rational strategy for learning the muscular system:

- Examine models, cadavers, dissected animals, or a photographic atlas as you read about these muscles. Visual images are often easier to remember than words, and direct observation of a muscle may stick in your memory better than descriptive text or two-dimensional drawings.
- When studying a particular muscle, palpate it on yourself if possible. Contract the muscle to feel it bulge and sense its action. This makes muscle locations and actions less abstract. Atlas B, following this chapter, shows where you can see and palpate several of these muscles on the living body.
- Locate the attachments of muscles on an articulated skeleton. Some skeletons and models are painted and labeled to show these. This helps you visualize the locations of muscles and understand how they produce particular joint actions.
- Study the derivation of each muscle name; the name usually describes the muscle's location, appearance, attachments, or action.
- Say the names aloud to yourself or a study partner. It is harder to remember and spell terms you cannot pronounce, and silent pronunciation is not nearly as effective as speaking and hearing the names. Pronunciation guides based on the leading medical dictionaries are provided in the following muscle tables for all but the most obvious cases.

**BEFORE YOU GO ON**

Answer the following questions to test your understanding of the preceding section:

1. List some functions of the muscular system other than movement of the body.
2. Describe the relationship of endomysium, perimysium, and epimysium to each other. Which of these separates one fascicle from another? Which separates one muscle from another?
3. Distinguish between direct and indirect muscle attachments to bones.
4. Define *belly, action,* and *innervation.*
5. Describe the five basic muscle shapes (fascicle arrangements).
6. Distinguish between a synergist, antagonist, and fixator. Explain how each of these may affect the action of a prime mover.

## 10.2 Muscles of the Head and Neck

**Expected Learning Outcomes**

When you have completed this section, you should be able to

a. name and locate the muscles that produce facial expressions;
b. name and locate the muscles used for chewing and swallowing;
c. name and locate the neck muscles that move the head; and
d. identify the attachments, action, and innervation of these muscles.

The rest of this chapter consists largely of tables of the body's principal skeletal muscles. You will find a description and illustrations of each muscle group, with some generalizations and special-interest points about the group, then a table that gives the details:

- the name of each muscle in that group;
- the pronunciation of the name, unless it is self-evident or repeats words whose pronunciation has been provided in a recent entry;
- the actions of the muscle;
- the muscle's bony or soft-tissue attachments; and
- the nerve supply to that muscle.

We begin our survey of the muscular system with the head and neck **(fig. 10.7).** The first three sections divide these into muscles of facial expression, muscles of chewing and swallowing, and muscles that move the head as a whole.

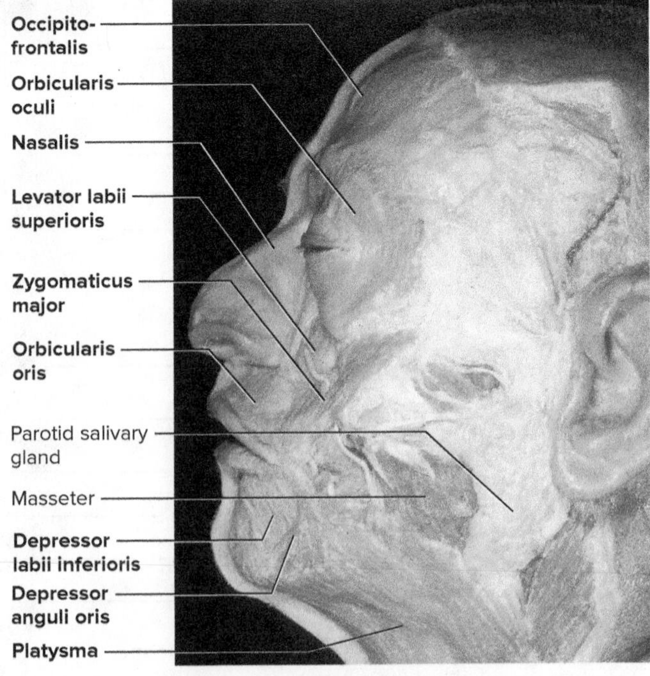


**FIGURE 10.7 Some Facial Muscles of the Cadaver.** Boldface labels indicate muscles employed in facial expression.

Rebecca Gray/McGraw-Hill Education

### 10.2a Muscles of Facial Expression

Humans have much more expressive faces than other mammals because of a complex array of muscles that insert in the dermis and subcutaneous tissues. These muscles tense the skin and produce such expressions as a pleasant smile, a flirtatious wink, a puzzled frown, or a threatening scowl **(fig. 10.8).** They add subtle shades of meaning to our spoken words. Facial muscles also contribute directly to speech, chewing, and other oral functions. All but one of them are innervated by the facial nerve (cranial nerve VII). This nerve is especially vulnerable to injury from lacerations and skull fractures, which can paralyze the muscles and cause parts of the face to sag. The only muscle not innervated by CN VII is the levator palpebrae superioris of the upper eyelid, innervated by the oculomotor nerve (CN III). **Table 10.1** groups these muscles into the following regions: the scalp; orbital and nasal regions (eye and nose); the oral region (encircling the mouth); and mental and buccal regions (chin and cheeks).

#### The Scalp

The **occipitofrontalis muscle** overlies the dome of the cranium. It is divided into a *frontal belly* in the forehead and *occipital belly* at the rear of the head **(fig. 10.9),** named for the underlying cranial bones. They are connected to each other by a broad aponeurosis, the **galea aponeurotica**[14] (GAY-lee-uh AP-oh-new-ROT-ih-cuh).

#### The Orbital and Nasal Regions

The **orbicularis oculi** is a sphincter of the eyelid that encircles and closes the eye. Deep to it, in the eyelid and orbit, is the **levator palpebrae superioris,** which opens the eye. Other muscles in this group move the eyelids and skin of the forehead and dilate the nostrils. Muscles within the orbit that move the eyeball itself are discussed in relation to vision in chapter 16.

[14] *galea* = helmet; *apo* = above; *neuro* = nervous system, brain

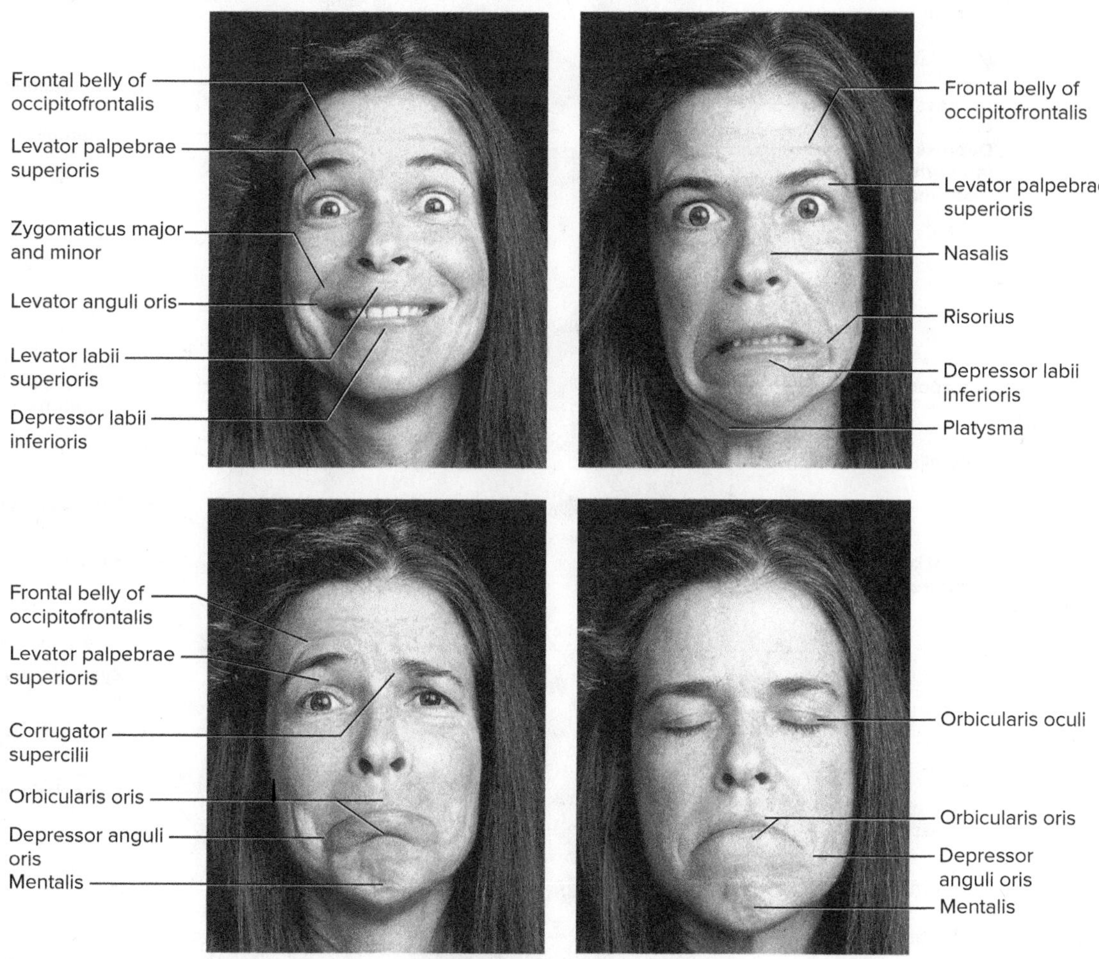


**FIGURE 10.8 Expressions Produced by Several of the Facial Muscles.** The ordinary actions of these muscles are usually more subtle than these demonstrations.

Joe DeGrandis/McGraw-Hill Education

? *Name an antagonist of each of these muscles: the depressor anguli oris, orbicularis oculi, and levator labii superioris.*

**FIGURE 10.9 Muscles of Facial Expression.** (a) Anterior view. (b) Lateral view. Boldface labels indicate muscles employed in facial expression. APR

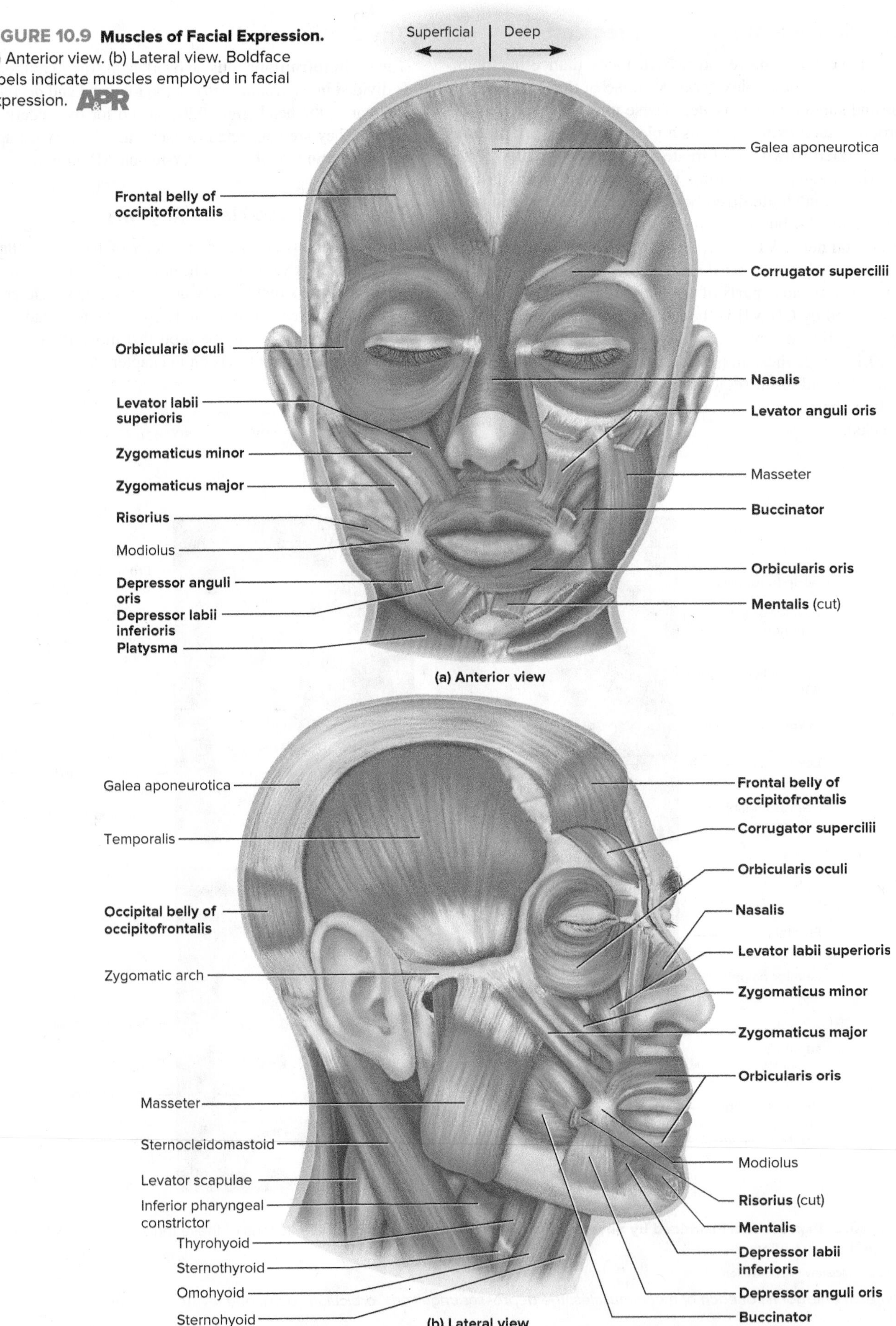

## The Oral Region

The mouth is the most expressive part of the face, and lip movements are necessary for intelligible speech; thus, it's not surprising that the muscles here are especially diverse. The **orbicularis oris** is a complex of muscles in the lips that encircles the mouth; until recently it was misinterpreted as a sphincter, or circular muscle, but it is actually composed of four independent quadrants that interlace and give only an appearance of circularity. Other muscles in this region approach the lips from all directions and thus draw the lips or angles (corners) of the mouth upward, laterally, and downward. Some of these arise from a complex cord called the **modiolus**[15] just lateral to each angle of the lips (fig. 10.9b). Named for the hub of a cartwheel, the modiolus is a point of convergence of several muscles of the lower face. You can palpate it by inserting one finger just inside the corner of your lips and pinching the corner between the finger and thumb, feeling for a thick knot of tissue.

## The Mental and Buccal Regions

Adjacent to the oral orifice are the *mental region* (chin) and *buccal region* (cheek). In addition to muscles already discussed that act on the lower lip, the mental region has a pair of small **mentalis muscles** extending from the upper margin of the mandible to the skin of the chin. In some people, they are especially thick and have a visible dimple between them called the mental cleft (see fig. 4.17). The **buccinator** is the muscle of the cheek. It has multiple functions in chewing, sucking, and blowing. If the cheeks are inflated with air, compression of the buccinators blows it out. Sucking is achieved by contracting the buccinators to draw the cheeks inward, then relaxing them. This action is especially important in nursing infants. To feel this action, hold your fingertips lightly against your cheeks as you make a kissing noise. You will notice relaxation of the buccinators at the moment air is sharply drawn in through the pursed lips. The **platysma** is a thin superficial muscle of the upper chest and lower face. It is relatively unimportant, but when men shave they tend to tense the platysma to make the concavity between the jaw and neck shallower and the skin tauter.

**TABLE 10.1 Muscles of Facial Expression**

| Name | Action | Skeletal Attachments | Innervation |
|---|---|---|---|
| **The Scalp** | | | |
| Occipitofrontalis, frontal belly (oc-SIP-ih-toe-frun-TAY-lis) | Elevates eyebrows in glancing upward and expressions of surprise or fright; draws scalp forward and wrinkles skin of forehead | • Galea aponeurotica<br>• Subcutaneous tissue of eyebrows | Facial nerve |
| Occipitofrontalis, occipital belly | Retracts scalp; fixes galea aponeurotica so frontal belly can act on eyebrows | • Superior nuchal line and temporal bone<br>• Galea aponeurotica | Facial nerve |
| **The Orbital and Nasal Regions** | | | |
| Orbicularis oculi[16] (or-BIC-you-LERR-is OC-you-lye) | Sphincter of the eyelids; closes eye in blinking, squinting, and sleep; aids in flow of tears across eye | • Lacrimal bone; adjacent regions of frontal bone and maxilla; medial angle of eyelids<br>• Upper and lower eyelids; skin around margin of orbit | Facial nerve |
| Levator palpebrae superioris[17] (leh-VAY-tur pal-PEE-bree soo-PEER-ee-OR-is) | Elevates upper eyelid; opens eye | • Lesser wing of sphenoid in posterior wall of orbit<br>• Upper eyelid | Oculomotor nerve |
| Corrugator supercilii[18] (COR-oo-GAY-tur SOO-per-SIL-ee-eye) | Draws eyebrows medially and downward in frowning and concentration; reduces glare of bright sunlight | • Medial end of supraorbital margin<br>• Skin of eyebrow | Facial nerve |
| Nasalis[19] (nay-ZAY-lis) | Widens nostrils; narrows internal air passage between vestibule and nasal cavity | • Maxilla just lateral to nose<br>• Bridge and alar cartilages of nose | Facial nerve |
| **The Oral Region** | | | |
| Orbicularis oris[20] (or-BIC-you-LERR-is OR-is) | Encircles mouth, closes lips, protrudes lips as in kissing; uniquely developed in humans for speech | • Modiolus of mouth<br>• Submucosa and dermis of lips | Facial nerve |

*(continued)*

[15] *modiolus* = hub
[16] *orb* = circle; *ocul* = eye
[17] *levator* = that which raises; *palpebr* = eyelid; *superior* = upper
[18] *corrug* = wrinkle; *supercilii* = of the eyebrow
[19] *nas* = of the nose
[20] *orb* = circle; *oris* = of the mouth

**TABLE 10.1 Muscles of Facial Expression (continued)**

| Name | Action | Skeletal Attachments | Innervation |
|---|---|---|---|
| **The Oral Region *(continued)*** | | | |
| Levator labii superioris[21] (leh-VAY-tur LAY-bee-eye soo-PEER-ee-OR-is) | Elevates and everts upper lip in sad, sneering, or serious expressions | • Zygomatic bone and maxilla near inferior margin of orbit<br>• Muscles of upper lip | Facial nerve |
| Levator anguli oris[22] (leh-VAY-tur ANG-you-lye OR-is) | Elevates angle of mouth as in smiling | • Maxilla just below infraorbital foramen<br>• Muscles at angle of mouth | Facial nerve |
| Zygomaticus[23] major (ZY-go-MAT-ih-cus) | Draws angle of mouth upward and laterally in laughing | • Zygomatic bone<br>• Superolateral angle of mouth | Facial nerve |
| Zygomaticus minor | Elevates upper lip, exposes upper teeth in smiling or sneering | • Zygomatic bone<br>• Muscles of upper lip | Facial nerve |
| Risorius[24] (rih-SOR-ee-us) | Draws angle of mouth laterally in expressions of laughing, horror, or disdain | • Zygomatic arch; fascia near ear<br>• Modiolus | Facial nerve |
| Depressor anguli oris[25] | Draws angle of mouth laterally and downward in opening mouth or sad expressions | • Inferior margin of mandibular body<br>• Modiolus | Facial nerve |
| Depressor labii inferioris[26] | Draws lower lip downward and laterally in chewing and expressions of melancholy or doubt | • Mandible near mental protuberance<br>• Skin and mucosa of lower lip | Facial nerve |
| **The Mental and Buccal Regions** | | | |
| Mentalis (men-TAY-lis) | Elevates and protrudes lower lip in drinking, pouting, and expressions of doubt or disdain; elevates and wrinkles skin of chin | • Mandible near inferior incisors<br>• Skin of chin at mental protuberance | Facial nerve |
| Buccinator[27] (BUC-sin-AY-tur) | Compresses cheek against teeth and gums; directs food between molars; retracts cheek from teeth when mouth is closing to prevent biting cheek; expels air and liquid from the mouth | • Alveolar processes on lateral surfaces of mandible and maxilla<br>• Orbicularis oris; submucosa of cheek and lips | Facial nerve |
| Platysma[28] (plah-TIZ-muh) | Draws lower lip and angle of mouth downward in expressions of horror or surprise; may aid in opening mouth widely; tenses skin of the chin and neck | • Fascia of deltoid and pectoralis major<br>• Mandible; skin and subcutaneous tissue of lower face | Facial nerve |

### 10.2b Muscles of Chewing and Swallowing

The muscles in this section are concerned primarily with the manipulation of food, including tongue movements, chewing, and swallowing.

#### Muscles of the Tongue

The tongue is a very agile organ. It pushes food between the molars for chewing and later forces it into the pharynx for swallowing. It is also, of course, crucial to articulate speech. Both intrinsic and extrinsic muscles are responsible for its complex movements. The *intrinsic muscles* consist of a variable number of vertical fascicles that extend from the superior to the inferior side of the tongue, transverse fascicles that extend from left to right, and longitudinal fascicles than extend from front to rear (see figs. 10.1c, 25.5b). **Table 10.2** describes the *extrinsic muscles* that connect the tongue to other structures in the head **(fig. 10.10).**

#### Muscles of Chewing

Four pairs of muscles produce the biting and cutting movements of the mandible: the **temporalis, masseter,** and two pairs of **pterygoid muscles (fig. 10.11).** Their actions include depression of the mandible for opening the mouth to receive food, elevation for biting off a piece of food or crushing it between the teeth; protraction so the incisors meet in cutting off a piece of food; retraction to draw the lower incisors behind the upper ones and make the rear teeth (premolars and molars) meet; and lateral and medial excursion, the side-to-side movements that grind food between the rear teeth (see fig. 9.20).

[21]*levat* = to raise; *labi* = lip; *superior* = upper
[22]*angul* = angle, corner; *oris* = of the mouth
[23]*zygo* = join, unite (refers to zygomatic bone)
[24]*risor* = laughter
[25]*depress* = to lower; *angul* = angle, corner; *oris* = of the mouth
[26]*labi* = lip; *inferior* = lower
[27]*buccinator* = trumpeter
[28]*platy* = flat

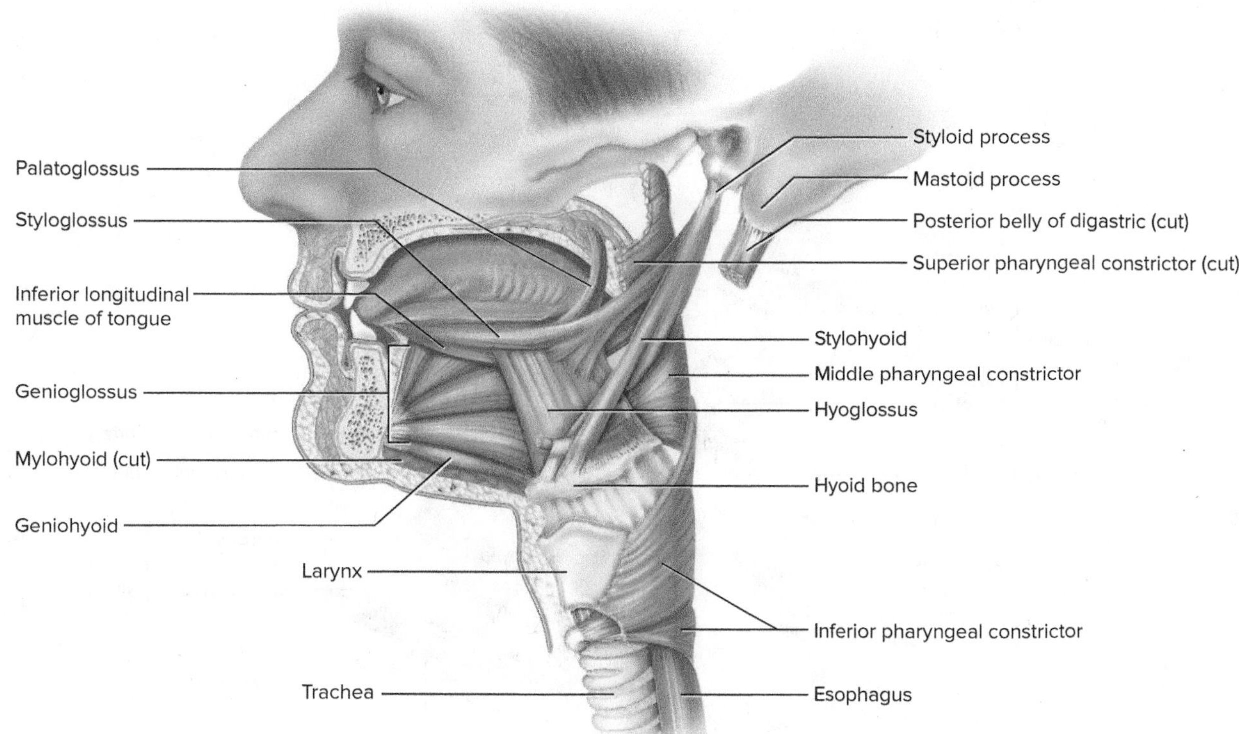


**FIGURE 10.10 Muscles of the Tongue and Pharynx.**

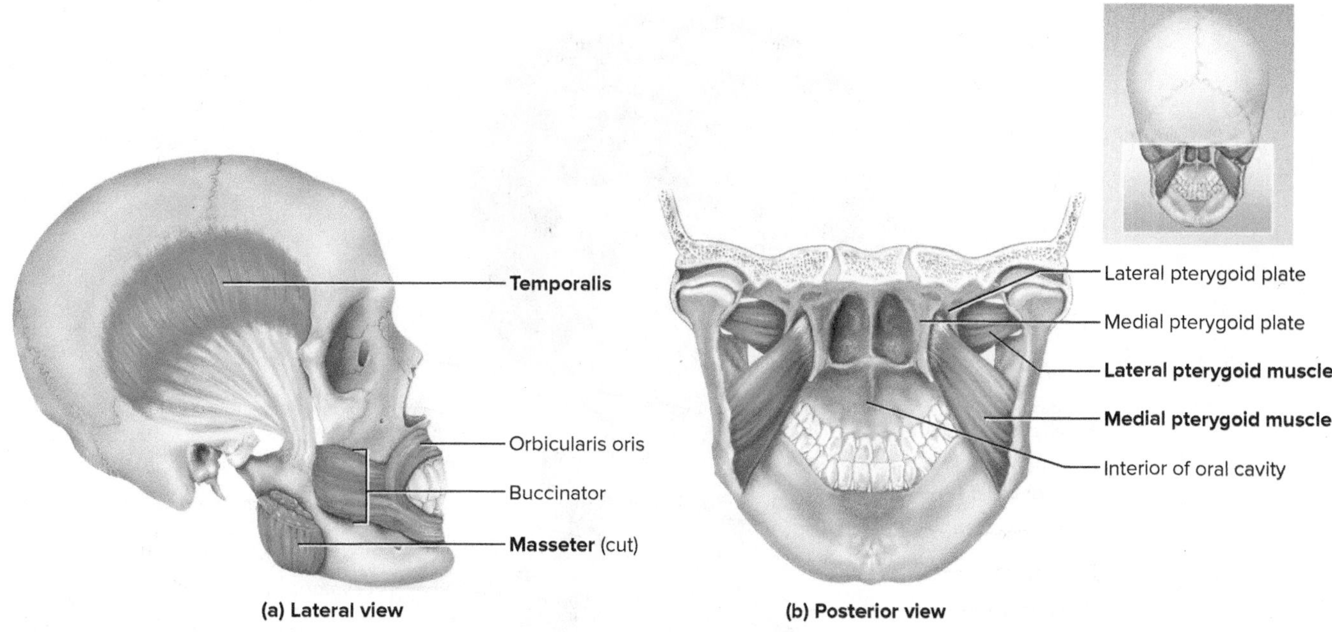


**FIGURE 10.11 Muscles of Chewing.** Boldface labels indicate muscles that act on the mandible in its chewing movements. (a) Right lateral view. In order to expose the insertion of the temporalis muscle on the mandible, part of the zygomatic arch and masseter muscle are removed. (b) View of the pterygoid muscles looking into the oral cavity from behind the skull.

## Suprahyoid Muscles

The hyoid bone, you will recall, is a slender U-shaped bone beneath the chin (see fig. 8.16). Eight pairs of *hyoid muscles* associated with this bone aid in chewing, swallowing, and speaking **(fig. 10.12).** Four of them, the *suprahyoid group,* are superior to the hyoid bone—the **digastric, geniohyoid, mylohyoid,** and **stylohyoid.** The digastric is an unusual muscle named for its two bellies. Its *posterior belly* arises from the *mastoid notch* of the cranium and slopes downward and forward. The *anterior belly* arises from a trench called the *digastric fossa* on the inner surface of the mandibular body. It slopes downward and backward. The two bellies meet at a constriction, the *intermediate tendon.* This

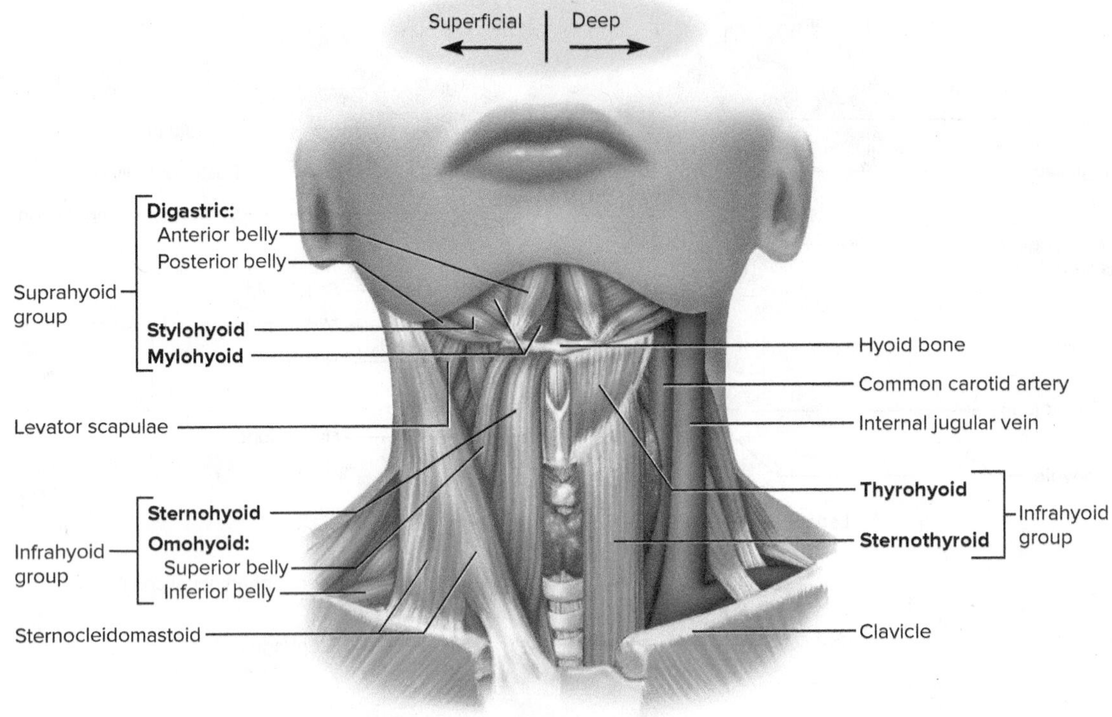


(a) Anterior view

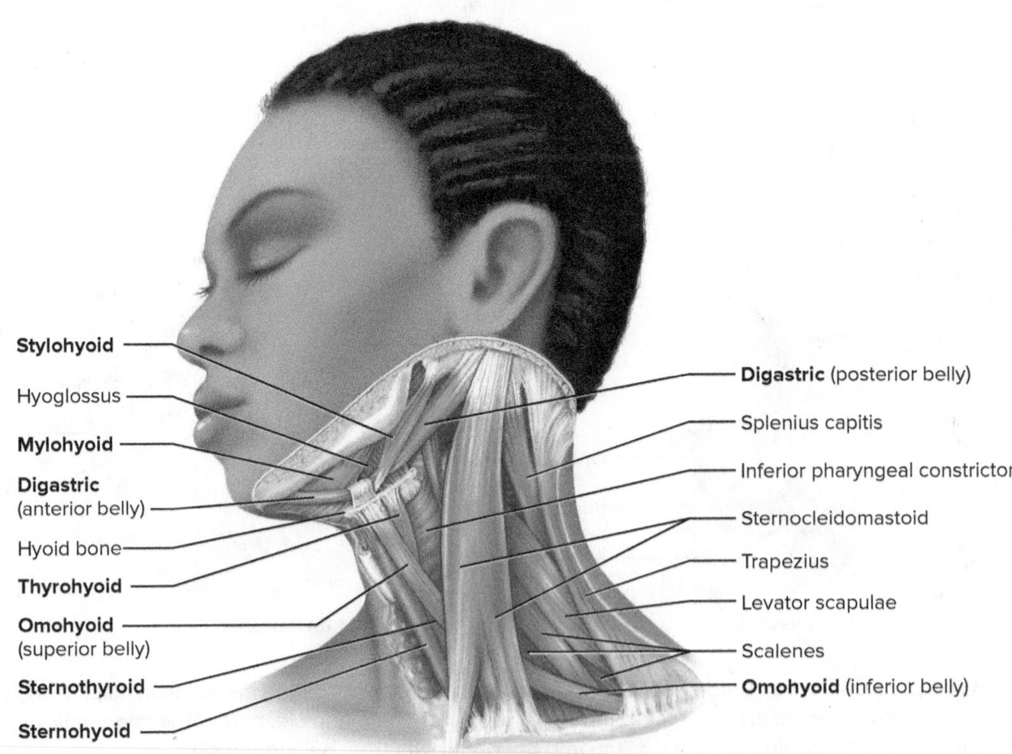


(b) Lateral view

**FIGURE 10.12 Muscles of the Neck.** (a) Anterior view. (b) Lateral view. Boldface labels indicate muscles of the suprahyoid and infrahyoid groups. Another muscle of the suprahyoid group, the geniohyoid, lies deep to the mylohyoid and can be seen in figure 10.10. APR

tendon passes through a connective tissue loop, the *fascial sling*, attached to the hyoid bone. Therefore, when the two bellies of the digastric contract, they elevate the hyoid; but if the hyoid is fixed from below, the digastric aids in wide opening of the mouth. The lateral pterygoids are more important in mouth opening, however, with the digastrics coming into play only in extreme opening, as in yawning or taking a large bite from an apple.

## Infrahyoid Muscles

The *infrahyoid muscles* are inferior to the hyoid bone. By fixing the hyoid from below, they enable the suprahyoid muscles to open the mouth. The **omohyoid** is unusual in that it arises from the shoulder, passes under the sternocleidomastoid muscle, then ascends to the hyoid bone. Like the digastric, it has two bellies—superior and inferior. The **thyrohyoid,** named for the hyoid bone and the large shield-shaped thyroid cartilage of the larynx, helps prevent choking. It elevates the larynx during swallowing so its superior opening is sealed by a flap of tissue, the epiglottis. You can feel this effect by holding a fingertip on your "Adam's apple" (anterior prominence of the thyroid cartilage) and feeling it bob up as you swallow.

The infrahyoid muscles are also regarded as extrinsic muscles of the larynx, since they act on it from outside. The intrinsic muscles of the larynx are described in relation to breathing and speech in chapter 22. The *ansa cervicalis*[29] in table 10.2 is a loop

**TABLE 10.2 Muscles of Chewing and Swallowing**

| Name | Action | Skeletal Attachments | Innervation |
|---|---|---|---|
| **Extrinsic Muscles of the Tongue** | | | |
| Genioglossus[30] (JEE-nee-oh-GLOSS-us) | Unilateral action draws tongue to one side; bilateral action depresses midline of tongue or protrudes tongue | • Superior mental spine on posterior surface of mental protuberance<br>• Inferior surface of tongue from root to apex | Hypoglossal nerve |
| Hyoglossus[31] (HI-oh-GLOSS-us) | Depresses tongue | • Body and greater horn of hyoid bone<br>• Lateral and inferior surfaces of tongue | Hypoglossal nerve |
| Styloglossus[32] (STY-lo-GLOSS-us) | Draws tongue upward and posteriorly | • Styloid process of temporal bone and ligament from styloid process to mandible<br>• Superolateral surface of tongue | Hypoglossal nerve |
| Palatoglossus[33] (PAL-a-toe-GLOSS-us) | Elevates root of tongue and closes oral cavity off from pharynx; forms palatoglossal arch at rear of oral cavity | • Soft palate<br>• Lateral surface of tongue | Accessory and vagus nerves |
| **Muscles of Chewing** | | | |
| Temporalis[34] (TEM-po-RAY-liss) | Elevation, retraction, and lateral and medial excursion of the mandible | • Temporal lines and temporal fossa of cranium<br>• Coronoid process and anterior border of mandibular ramus | Trigeminal nerve |
| Masseter[35] (ma-SEE-tur) | Elevation of the mandible, with smaller roles in protraction, retraction, and lateral and medial excursion | • Zygomatic arch<br>• Lateral surface of mandibular ramus and angle | Trigeminal nerve |
| Medial pterygoid[36] (TERR-ih-goyd) | Elevation, protraction, and lateral and medial excursion of the mandible | • Medial surface of lateral pterygoid plate; palatine bone; lateral surface of maxilla near molar teeth<br>• Medial surface of mandibular ramus and angle | Trigeminal nerve |
| Lateral pterygoid | Depression (in wide opening of the mouth), protraction, and lateral and medial excursion of the mandible | • Lateral surfaces of lateral pterygoid plate; greater wing of sphenoid<br>• Neck of mandible (just below condyle); articular disc and capsule of temporomandibular joint | Trigeminal nerve |

*(continued)*

[29]*ansa* = handle; *cervic* = neck; *alis* = of, belonging to
[30]*genio* = chin; *gloss* = tongue
[31]*hyo* = hyoid bone; *gloss* = tongue
[32]*stylo* = styloid process; *gloss* = tongue
[33]*palato* = palate; *gloss* = tongue
[34]*temporalis* = of the temporal region of the head
[35]*masset* = chew
[36]*pteryg* = wing; *oid* = resembling (refers to pterygoid plate of sphenoid bone)

**TABLE 10.2 Muscles of Chewing and Swallowing (continued)**

| Name | Action | Skeletal Attachments | Innervation |
|---|---|---|---|
| **Suprahyoid Muscles** | | | |
| Digastric[37] | Depresses mandible when hyoid is fixed; opens mouth widely, as when ingesting food or yawning; elevates hyoid when mandible is fixed | • Mastoid notch of temporal bone; digastric fossa of mandible<br>• Hyoid bone via fascial sling | Posterior belly: facial nerve<br>Anterior belly: trigeminal nerve |
| Geniohyoid[38] (JEE-nee-oh-HY-oyd) | Depresses mandible when hyoid is fixed; elevates and protracts hyoid when mandible is fixed | • Inferior mental spine of mandible<br>• Hyoid bone | Spinal nerve C1 via hypoglossal nerve |
| Mylohyoid[39] | Spans mandible from side to side and forms floor of mouth; elevates floor of mouth in initial stage of swallowing | • Mylohyoid line near inferior margin<br>• Hyoid bone | Trigeminal nerve |
| Stylohyoid | Elevates and retracts hyoid, elongating floor of mouth; roles in speech, chewing, and swallowing are not yet clearly understood | • Styloid process of temporal bone<br>• Hyoid bone | Facial nerve |
| **Infrahyoid Muscles** | | | |
| Omohyoid[40] | Depresses hyoid after it has been elevated | • Superior border of scapula<br>• Hyoid bone | Ansa cervicalis |
| Sternohyoid[41] | Depresses hyoid after it has been elevated | • Manubrium of sternum; medial end of clavicle<br>• Hyoid bone | Ansa cervicalis |
| Thyrohyoid[42] | Depresses hyoid; with hyoid fixed, elevates larynx as in singing high notes | • Thyroid cartilage of larynx<br>• Hyoid bone | Spinal nerve C1 via hypoglossal nerve |
| Sternothyroid | Depresses larynx after it has been elevated in swallowing and vocalization; aids in singing low notes | • Manubrium of sternum; costal cartilage<br>• Thyroid cartilage of larynx | Ansa cervicalis |
| **Pharyngeal Muscles** | | | |
| Superior, middle, and inferior pharyngeal constrictors | During swallowing, contract in order from *superior* to *middle* to *inferior constrictor* to drive food into esophagus | • Medial pterygoid plate; mandible; hyoid; stylohyoid ligament; cartilages of larynx<br>• Posteromedial seam of pharynx; basilar part of occipital bone | Glossopharyngeal and vagus nerves |

of nerve on the side of the neck that innervates three of the infrahyoid muscles; it is formed by certain nerve fibers from cervical nerves 1 to 3 (see fig. 13.15).

### Pharyngeal Muscles

Three pairs of **pharyngeal constrictors** encircle the pharynx on its posterior and lateral sides, forming a muscular funnel (see fig. 10.10). In swallowing, they push food from the pharynx into the esophagus.

## 10.2c Muscles Acting on the Head and Neck

Muscles that move the head arise from the vertebral column, thoracic cage, and pectoral girdle and end on the cranial bones **(table 10.3).** Their actions include flexion (tipping the head forward), extension (holding the head erect), hyperextension (as in looking upward), lateral flexion (tilting the head to one side), and rotation (turning the head to look left or right). Flexion, extension, and hyperextension involve simultaneous action of the right and left muscles of a pair; the other actions require the muscle

[37] *di* = two; *gastr* = bellies
[38] *genio* = chin
[39] *mylo* = mill, molar tooth
[40] *omo* = shoulder
[41] *sterno* = chest, sternum
[42] *thyro* = shield, thyroid cartilage

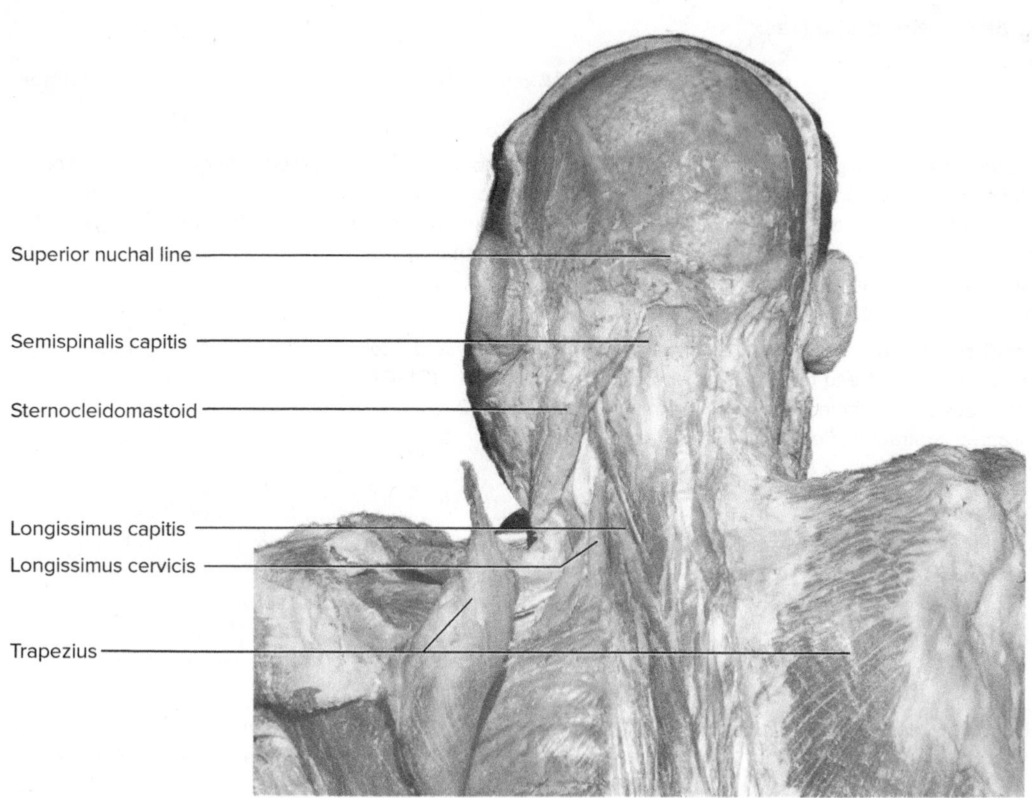


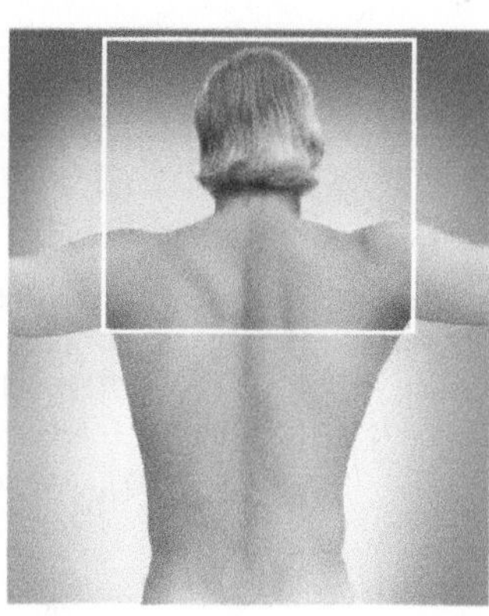

**FIGURE 10.13 Muscles of the Shoulder and Nuchal Regions of the Cadaver.**
Rebecca Gray/Don Kincaid/McGraw-Hill Education

on one side to contract more strongly than its mate. Many head actions result from a combination of these movements—for example, looking up over the shoulder involves a combination of rotation and hyperextension.

Depending on its skeletal attachments, a muscle may cause a *contralateral* movement of the head (toward the opposite side, as when contraction of a muscle on the left turns the face toward the right) or an *ipsilateral* movement (toward the same side as the muscle, as when contraction of a muscle on the left tilts the head to the left).

## Flexors of the Neck

The prime mover of neck flexion is the **sternocleidomastoid,** a thick muscular cord that extends from the upper chest (sternum and clavicle) to the mastoid process behind the ear (fig. 10.12). This is most easily seen when the head is rotated to one side and slightly extended. To visualize the action of a single sternocleidomastoid, place the index finger of your left hand on your left mastoid process and the index finger of your right hand on your suprasternal notch. Now contract your left sternocleidomastoid to bring your two fingertips as close together as possible. You will see that this tilts your face upward and to the right.

The three **scalenes**[43] on the side of the neck are named for their staircase-like arrangement. Their actions are similar so they are considered collectively in the table.

## Extensors of the Neck

The extensors are located mainly in the nuchal region (back of the neck; **fig. 10.13**) and therefore tend to hold the head erect or draw it back. The **trapezius** is the largest and most superficial of these. It extends from the nuchal region over the shoulders and halfway down the back. It is named for the fact that the right and left trapezii together form a diamond or trapezoidal shape (see fig. 10.6). The *splenius* is a deeper, elongated muscle with **splenius capitis** and **splenius cervicis** regions in the head and neck, respectively. It is nicknamed the "bandage muscle" because of the way it wraps around still deeper neck muscles. One of those deeper muscles is the *semispinalis,* another elongated muscle with head, neck, and thoracic regions. Only the **semispinalis capitis** and **cervicis** are tabulated here; the *semispinalis thoracis* doesn't act on the neck, but is included in table 10.6.

### ▶▶▶APPLY WHAT YOU KNOW

*Of the muscles you have studied so far, name three that you would consider intrinsic muscles of the head and three that you would classify as extrinsic. Explain your reason for each.*

[43] *scal* = staircase

**TABLE 10.3 Muscles Acting on the Head and Neck**

| Name | Action | Skeletal Attachments | Innervation |
|---|---|---|---|
| **Flexors of the Neck** | | | |
| Sternocleidomastoid[44] (STIR-no-CLY-do-MAST-oyd) | Unilateral action tilts head slightly upward and toward the opposite side, as in looking over one's contralateral shoulder. The most common action is probably rotating the head to the left or right. Bilateral action draws the head straight forward and down, as when eating or reading. Aids in deep breathing when head is fixed. | • Manubrium of sternum; medial one-third of clavicle<br>• Mastoid process; lateral half of superior nuchal line | Accessory nerve; spinal nerves C2–C4 |
| Anterior, middle, and posterior scalenes (SCAY-leens) | Unilateral contraction causes ipsilateral flexion or contralateral rotation (tilts head toward same shoulder, or rotates face away), depending on action of other muscles. Bilateral contraction flexes neck. If spine is fixed, scalenes elevate ribs 1–2 and aid in breathing. | • Transverse processes of all cervical vertebrae (C1–C7)<br>• Ribs 1–2 | Anterior rami of spinal nerves C3–C8 |
| **Extensors of the Neck** | | | |
| Trapezius[45] (tra-PEE-zee-us) | Extends and laterally flexes neck. See also roles in scapular movement in table 10.8. | • External occipital protuberance; medial one-third of superior nuchal line; nuchal ligament; spinous processes of vertebrae C7–T12<br>• Acromion and spine of scapula; lateral one-third of clavicle | Accessory nerve |
| Splenius capitis[46] and splenius cervicis[47] (SPLEE-nee-us CAP-ih-tiss, SIR-vih-sis) | Acting unilaterally, produce ipsilateral flexion and slight rotation of head; extend head when acting bilaterally | • Inferior half of nuchal ligament; spinous processes of vertebrae C7–T6<br>• Mastoid process and occipital bone just inferior to superior nuchal line; cervical vertebrae C1–C2 or C3 | Posterior rami of middle cervical nerves |
| Semispinalis capitis and semispinalis cervicis (SEM-ee-spy-NAY-lis) | Extend and contralaterally rotate head | • Articular processes of vertebrae C4–C7; transverse processes of T1–T6<br>• Occipital bone between nuchal lines; spinous processes of vertebrae C2–C5 | Posterior rami of cervical and thoracic nerves |

**BEFORE YOU GO ON**

Answer the following questions to test your understanding of the preceding section:

7. Name two muscles that elevate the upper lip and two that depress the lower lip.
8. Name the four paired muscles of mastication and state where they insert on the mandible.
9. Distinguish between the functions of the suprahyoid and infrahyoid muscles.
10. List the muscles of neck extension and flexion.

## 10.3 Muscles of the Trunk

### Expected Learning Outcomes

When you have completed this section, you should be able to

a. name and locate the muscles of respiration and explain how they affect airflow and abdominal pressure;
b. name and locate the muscles of the abdominal wall, back, and pelvic floor; and
c. identify the skeletal attachments, action, and innervation of these muscles.

In this section, we will examine muscles of the trunk of the body in four functional groups concerned with respiration, support of the abdominal wall, movement of the vertebral column, and support of the pelvic floor. In the illustrations, you will note some major muscles that are not discussed in the associated tables—for example, the pectoralis major and serratus anterior. Although they are *located* in the trunk, they *act upon* the limbs and limb girdles, and are further discussed in sections 10.4 and 10.5.

[44] *sterno* = chest, sternum; *cleido* = hammer, clavicle; *masto* = breastlike, mastoid process
[45] *trapez* = table, trapezoid
[46] *splenius* = bandage; *capitis* = of the head
[47] *cervicis* = of the neck

## 10.3a Muscles of Respiration

We breathe primarily by means of muscles that enclose the thoracic cavity—the diaphragm, external intercostal, internal intercostal, and innermost intercostal muscles **(fig. 10.14, table 10.4).**

The **diaphragm** is a muscular dome between the thoracic and abdominal cavities, bulging upward against the base of the lungs. It has openings for passage of the esophagus, major blood and lymphatic vessels, and nerves between the two cavities. Its fibers converge from the margins toward a fibrous **central tendon.** When the diaphragm contracts, it flattens slightly and enlarges the thoracic cavity, causing air intake (inspiration); when it relaxes, it rises and shrinks the thoracic cavity, expelling air (expiration).

Three layers of muscle lie between the ribs: the external, internal, and innermost intercostal muscles. The 11 pairs of **external intercostal muscles** constitute the most superficial layer. They extend from the rib tubercle posteriorly almost to the beginning of the costal cartilage anteriorly. Each one slopes downward and anteriorly from one rib to the next inferior one.

The 11 pairs of **internal intercostal muscles** lie deep to the external intercostals and extend from the margin of the sternum to the angles of the ribs. They are thickest in the region between the costal cartilages and grow thinner in the region where they overlap the internal intercostals. Their fibers slope downward and posteriorly from each rib to the one below, at nearly right angles to the external intercostals. Each is divided into an *intercartilaginous part* between the costal cartilages and an *interosseous part* between the bony part of the ribs. The two parts differ in their respiratory roles.

The **innermost intercostal muscles** vary in number, as they are sometimes absent from the upper thoracic cage. Their fibers run in the same direction as the internal intercostals, and they are presumed to serve the same function. The internal and innermost intercostals are separated by a fascia that allows passage for intercostal nerves and blood vessels (see fig. 13.14b).

The primary function of the intercostal muscles is to stiffen the thoracic cage during respiration so it doesn't cave inward when the diaphragm descends. However, they also contribute to enlargement and contraction of the thoracic cage and thus add to the air volume that ventilates the lungs.

Many other muscles of the chest and abdomen contribute significantly to breathing: the sternocleidomastoid and scalenes of the neck; pectoralis major and serratus anterior of the chest; latissimus dorsi of the lower back; internal and external obliques and transverse abdominal muscle; and even some of the anal muscles. The respiratory actions of all these muscles are described in section 22.2a.

**▶▶▶APPLY WHAT YOU KNOW**

*A young thoracic surgery resident performing an operation for esophageal cancer accidentally severs the patient's left phrenic nerve. Predict the effect of this accident on the patient's respiration.*

**▶▶▶APPLY WHAT YOU KNOW**

*Carl and Carla are enjoying a platter of barbecued ribs. What muscles are they eating? What is the tough fibrous membrane between the meat and the bone?*

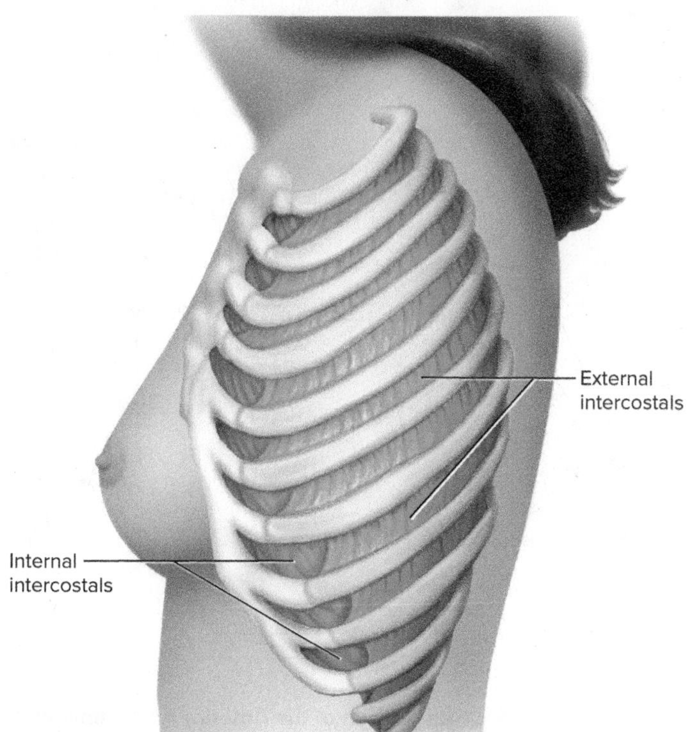


**(a) Lateral view of intercostal muscles**

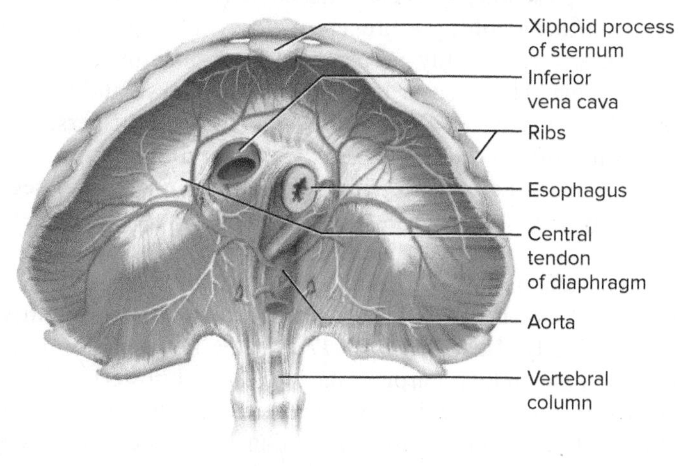


**(b) Inferior view of diaphragm**

**FIGURE 10.14 Muscles of Respiration.** (a) Lateral view of the intercostal muscles. (b) Inferior view of the diaphragm. APR

**TABLE 10.4 Muscles of Respiration**

| Name | Action | Skeletal Attachments | Innervation |
|---|---|---|---|
| Diaphragm[48] (DY-ah-fram) | Prime mover of inspiration (responsible for about two-thirds of air intake); contracts in preparation for sneezing, coughing, crying, laughing, and weight lifting; contraction compresses abdominal viscera and aids in childbirth and expulsion of urine and feces. | • Xiphoid process of sternum; ribs and costal cartilages 7–12; lumbar vertebrae<br>• Central tendon of diaphragm | Phrenic nerves |
| External intercostals[49] (IN-tur-COSS-tulz) | When scalenes fix rib 1, external intercostals elevate and protract ribs 2–12, expanding the thoracic cavity and creating a partial vacuum causing inflow of air; exercise a braking action during expiration so that expiration is not overly abrupt. | • Inferior margins of ribs 1–11<br>• Superior margin of next lower rib | Intercostal nerves |
| Internal intercostals | In inspiration, the intercartilaginous part aids in elevating the ribs and expanding the thoracic cavity; in expiration, the interosseous part depresses and retracts the ribs, compressing the thoracic cavity and expelling air; the latter occurs only in forceful expiration, not in relaxed breathing. | • Superior margins and costal cartilages of ribs 2–12; margin of sternum<br>• Inferior margin of next higher rib | Intercostal nerves |
| Innermost intercostals | Presumed to have the same action as the internal intercostals | • Superomedial surface of ribs 2–12; may be absent from upper ribs<br>• Medial edge of costal groove of next higher rib | Intercostal nerves |

## 10.3b Muscles of the Abdominal Wall

Unlike the thoracic cavity, the abdominal cavity has little skeletal support. It is enclosed, however, in layers of broad flat muscles whose fibers run in different directions, strengthening the abdominal wall on the same principle as the alternating layers of wood fibers in plywood **(table 10.5)**.

Three layers of muscle enclose the lumbar region and extend about halfway across the anterior abdomen **(fig. 10.15)**. The most superficial layer is the **external oblique muscle.** Its fibers pass downward and anteriorly. The next deeper layer is the **internal oblique muscle,** whose fibers pass upward and anteriorly, roughly perpendicular to those of the external oblique. The deepest layer is the **transverse abdominal muscle (transversus abdominis),** with horizontal fibers.

Anteriorly, a pair of vertical **rectus abdominis muscles** extends from sternum to pubis. These are divided into segments by three transverse *tendinous intersections,* giving them an appearance that body builders nickname the "six pack."

The tendons of the oblique and transverse muscles are *aponeuroses*—broad fibrous sheets that continue medially and inferiorly **(figs. 10.16, 10.17)**. At the rectus abdominis, they diverge and pass around its anterior and posterior sides, enclosing the muscle in a vertical sleeve called the rectus sheath. They meet again at a median line called the **linea alba**[50] between the rectus muscles. Another line, the **linea semilunaris,**[51] marks the lateral boundary where the rectus sheath meets the aponeurosis. The aponeurosis of the external

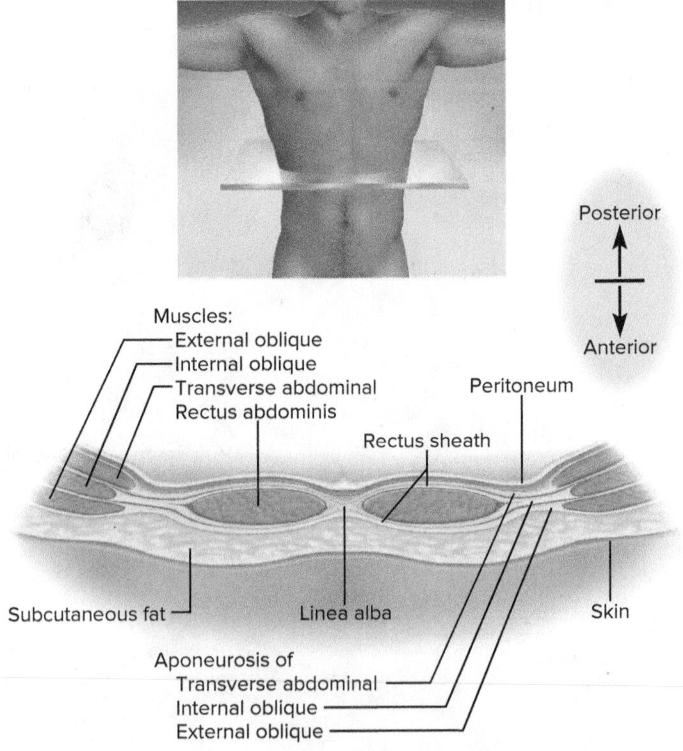


**FIGURE 10.15 Cross Section of the Anterior Abdominal Wall.**

[48]*dia* = across; *phragm* = partition
[49]*inter* = between; *costa* = rib
[50]*linea* = line; *alba* = white
[51]*linea* = line; *semilunar* = half-moon

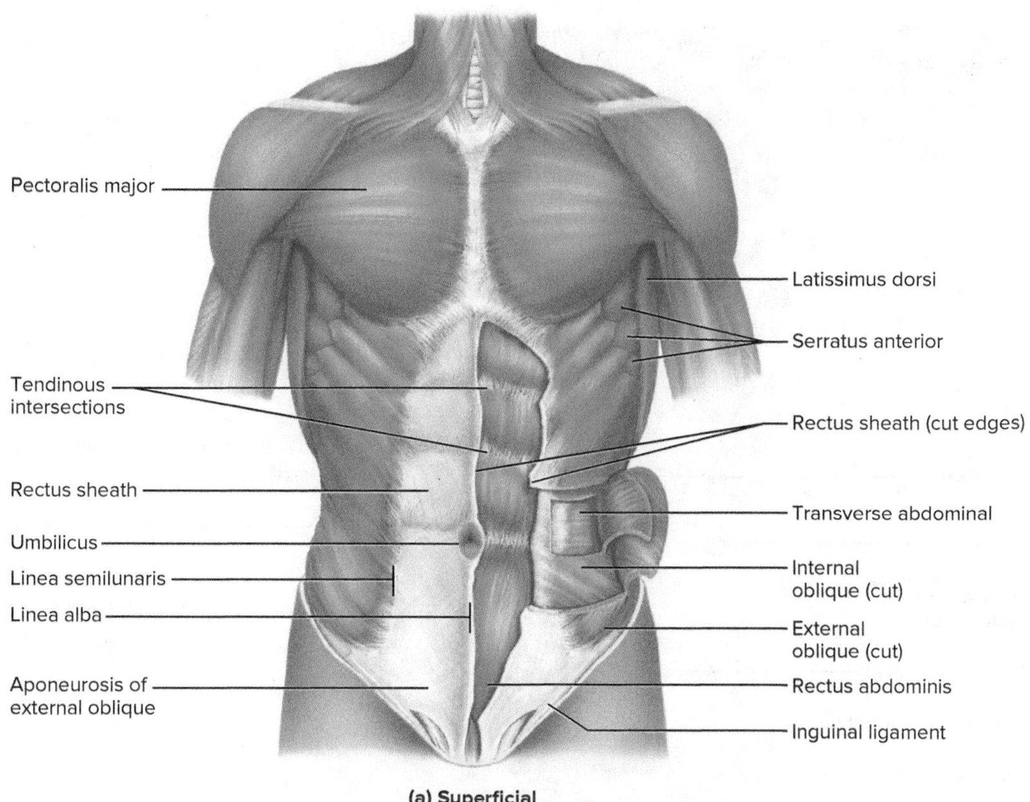


**(a) Superficial**

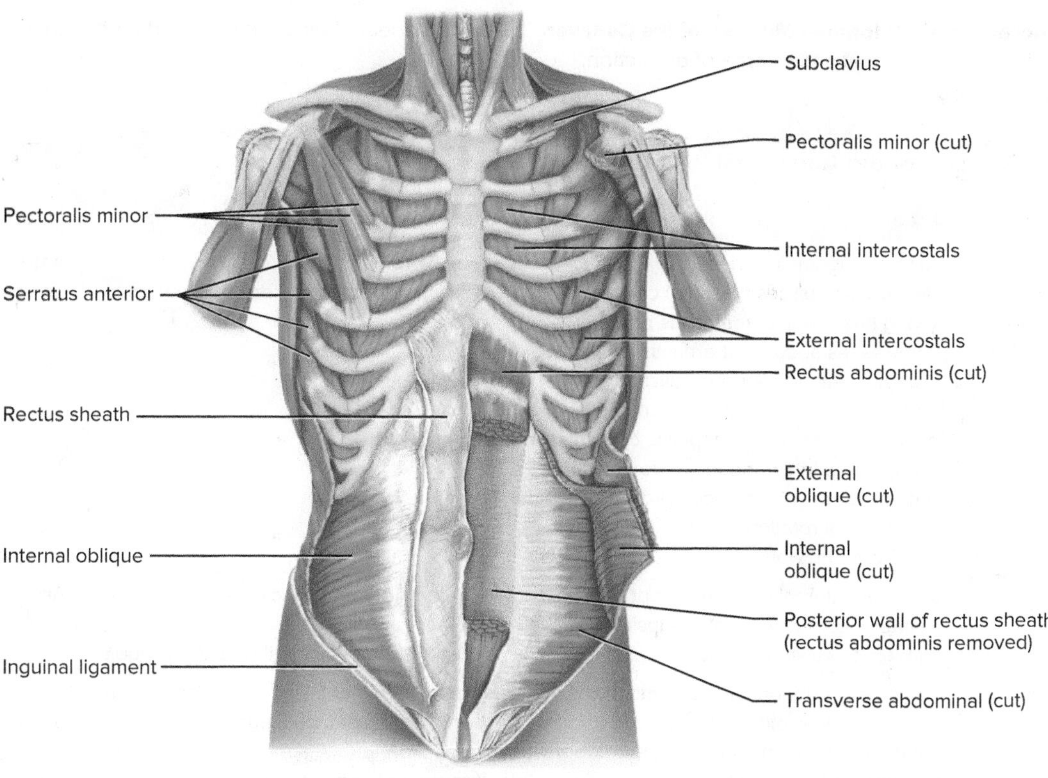


**(b) Deep**

**FIGURE 10.16 Thoracic and Abdominal Muscles.** (a) Superficial muscles. The left rectus sheath is cut away to expose the rectus abdominis muscle. (b) Deep muscles. On the anatomical right, the external oblique has been removed to expose the internal oblique and the pectoralis major has been removed to expose the pectoralis minor. On the anatomical left, the internal oblique has been cut to expose the transverse abdominal and the middle of the rectus abdominis has been cut out to expose the posterior rectus sheath. APR

*Name at least three muscles that lie deep to the pectoralis major.*

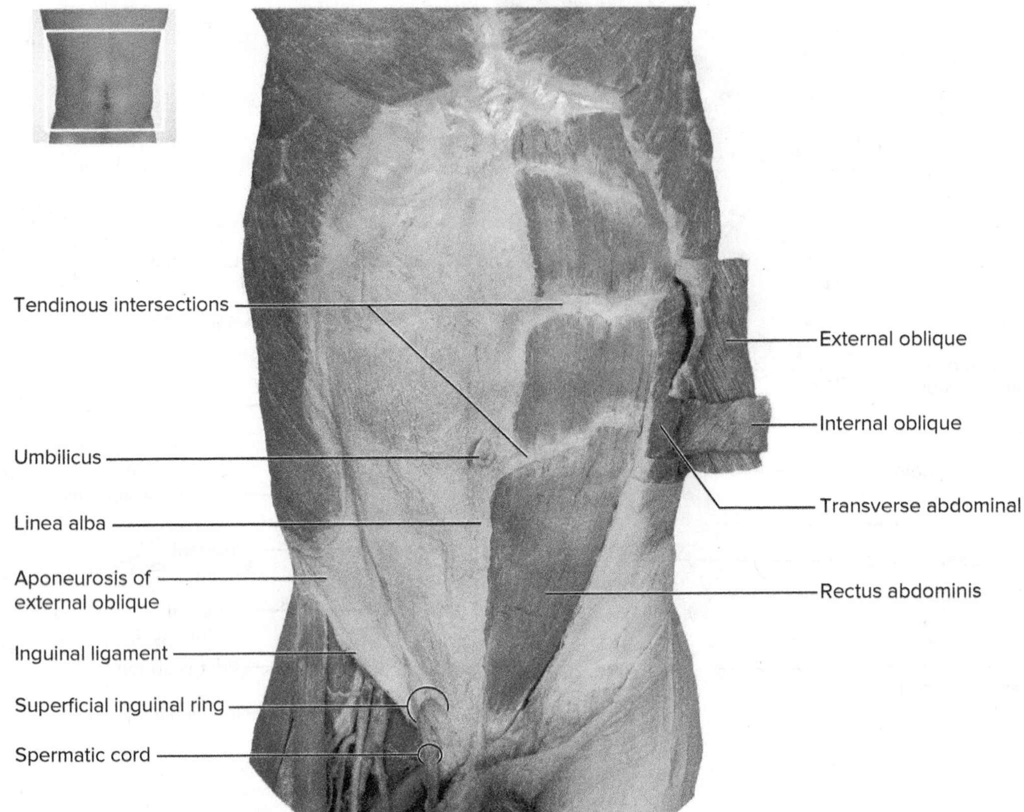


**FIGURE 10.17 Thoracic and Abdominal Muscles of the Cadaver.** The rectus sheath has been removed on the anatomical left to expose the left rectus abdominis muscle. Inset shows area of dissection.

Christine Eckel/McGraw-Hill Education

**TABLE 10.5 Muscles of the Abdominal Wall**

| Name | Action | Skeletal Attachments | Innervation |
|---|---|---|---|
| External oblique | Supports abdominal viscera against pull of gravity; stabilizes vertebral column during heavy lifting; maintains posture; compresses abdominal organs, thus aiding in deep breathing, loud vocalizations such as singing and public speaking, and in expulsion of abdominopelvic contents during childbirth, urination, defecation, and vomiting; unilateral contraction causes contralateral rotation of the spine, as in twisting at the waist. | • Ribs 5–12<br>• Anterior half of iliac crest; symphysis and superior margin of pubis | Anterior rami of spinal nerves T7–T12 |
| Internal oblique | Same as external oblique except that unilateral contraction causes ipsilateral rotation of waist | • Inguinal ligament; iliac crest; thoracolumbar fascia<br>• Ribs 10–12; costal cartilages 7–10; pubis | Anterior rami of spinal nerves T7–L1 |
| Transverse abdominal | Compresses abdominal contents, with same effects as external oblique, but does not contribute to movements of vertebral column | • Inguinal ligament; iliac crest; thoracolumbar fascia; costal cartilages 7–12<br>• Linea alba; pubis; aponeurosis of internal oblique | Anterior rami of spinal nerves T7–L1 |
| Rectus[52] abdominis (REC-tus ab-DOM-ih-nis) | Flexes waist, as in bending forward or doing sit-ups; stabilizes pelvic region during walking; and compresses abdominal viscera | • Pubic symphysis and superior margin of pubis<br>• Xiphoid process; costal cartilages 5–7 | Anterior rami of spinal nerves T6–T12 |

[52]*rectus* = straight

oblique also forms a cordlike **inguinal ligament** at its inferior margin. This extends obliquely from the anterior superior spine of the ilium to the pubis. The linea alba, linea semilunaris, and inguinal ligament are externally visible on a person with good muscle definition (see atlas B, fig. B.8). Weak points in the abdominal wall can be sites of inguinal and umbilical hernias (see Deeper Insight 10.3).

**APPLY WHAT YOU KNOW**

*Alice works out at a fitness center three times a week doing weight lifting and abdominal crunches. Martha prefers to sit on the sofa eating potato chips and watching TV. Both become pregnant. Other things being equal, give one reason related to table 10.5 why Alice may have an easier time with her childbirth than Martha will.*

### 10.3c Muscles of the Back

Muscles of the back **(table 10.6)** primarily extend, rotate, and laterally flex the vertebral column. The most prominent superficial back muscles are the *latissimus dorsi* and *trapezius* **(fig. 10.18),** but they are concerned with upper limb movements and covered in tables 10.8 and 10.9. Deep to these are the **serratus posterior superior** and **inferior** (figs. 10.18, **10.19**). They extend from the

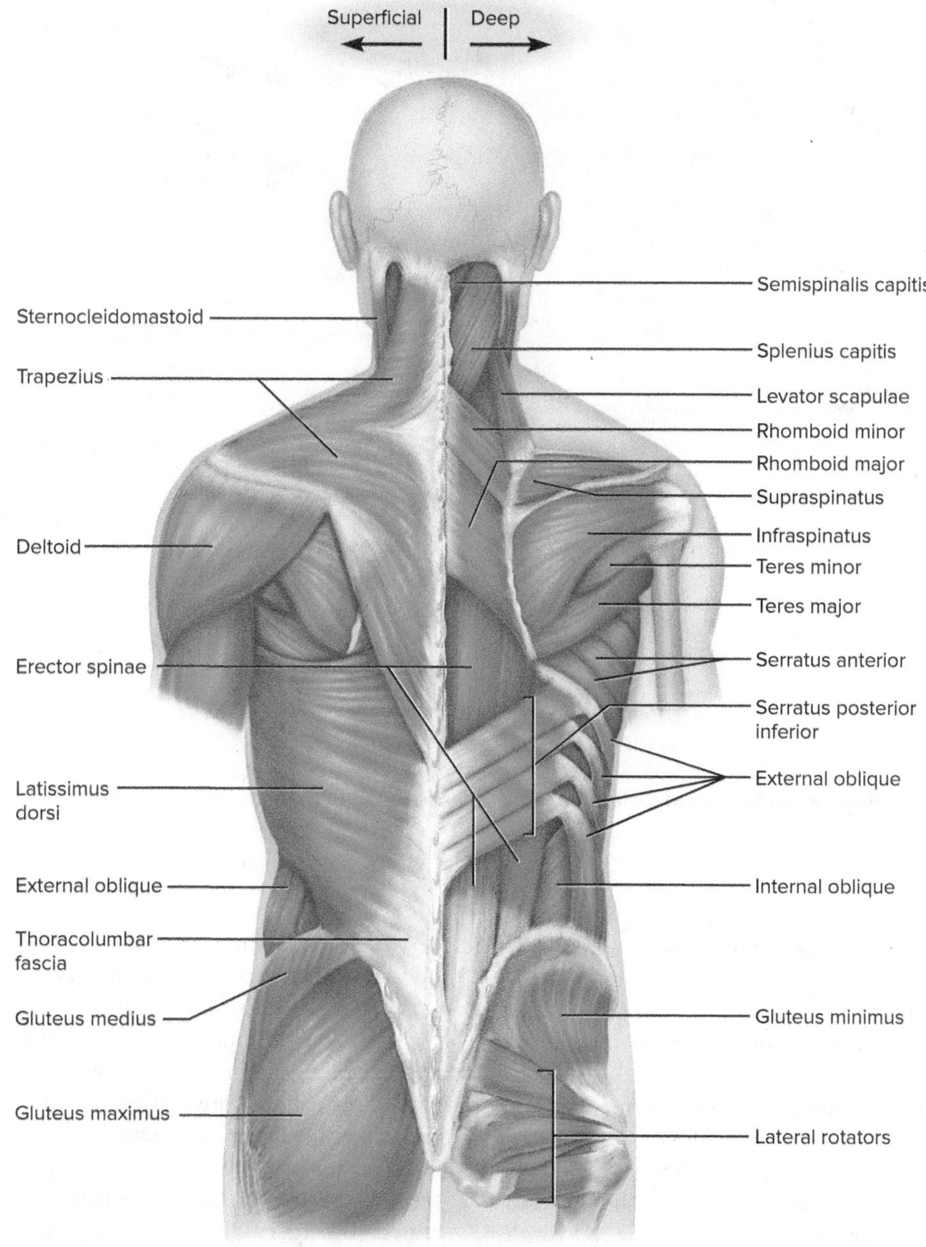


**FIGURE 10.18 Neck, Back, and Gluteal Muscles.** The most superficial muscles are shown on the left and the next deeper layer on the right. APR

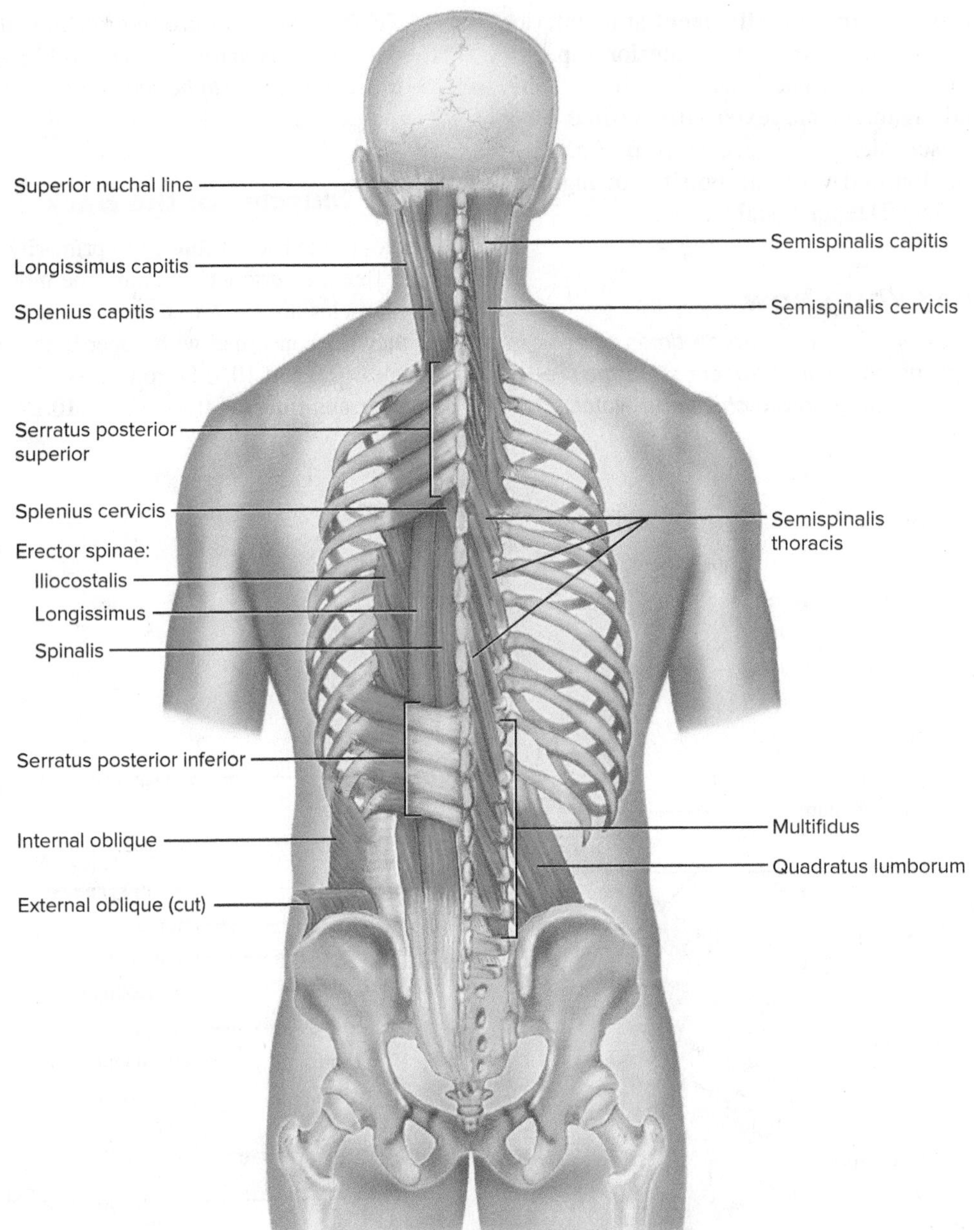


**FIGURE 10.19 Muscles Acting on the Vertebral Column.** These are deeper than the muscles in figure 10.18, and those on the right are deeper than those on the left.

vertebrae to the ribs. They aid in deep breathing and are further discussed in chapter 22.

Deep to these is a prominent muscle, the **erector spinae,** which runs vertically for the entire length of the back from the cranium to the sacrum **(fig. 10.20).** It is a thick muscle, easily palpated on each side of the vertebral column in the lumbar region. (Pork chops and T-bone steaks are cut from the erector spinae muscles of animals.) As it ascends, it divides in the upper lumbar region into three parallel columns. The most lateral of these is the **iliocostalis,** which from inferior to superior is divided into the *iliocostalis lumborum, iliocostalis thoracis,* and *iliocostalis cervicis* (lumbar, thoracic, and cervical regions).

The next column medially is the **longissimus,** divided from inferior to superior into the *longissimus thoracis, longissimus cervicis,* and *longissimus capitis* (thoracic, cervical, and cephalic regions). The most medial column is the **spinalis,** divided into *spinalis thoracis, spinalis cervicis,* and *spinalis capitis.* The functions of all three columns are sufficiently similar that we will treat them collectively as the erector spinae.

The major deep muscles are the **semispinalis thoracis** in the thoracic region and **quadratus lumborum** in the lumbar region (fig. 10.19). The erector spinae and quadratus lumborum are enclosed in a fibrous sheath called the **thoracolumbar fascia** (fig. 10.18), which is the origin of some of the abdominal and

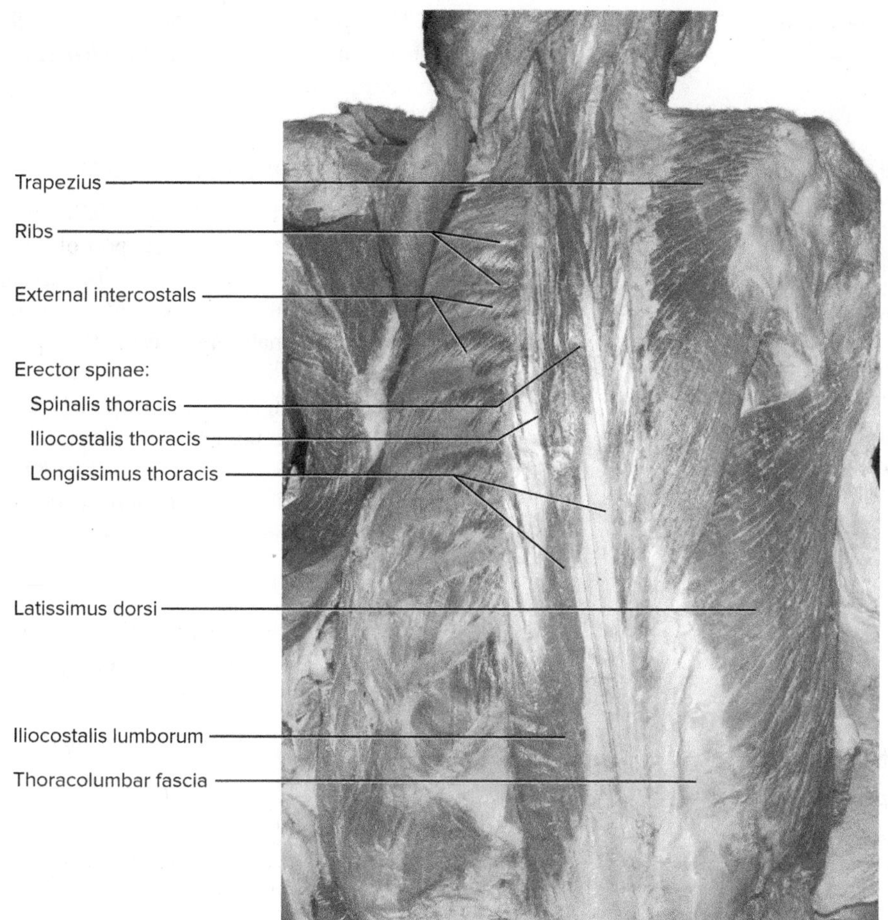


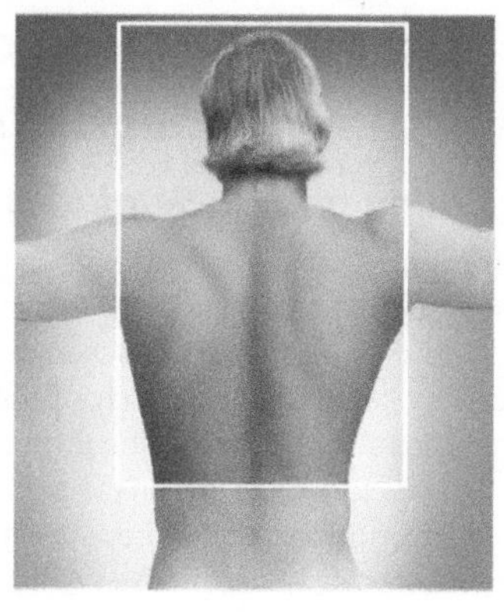

**FIGURE 10.20 Deep Back Muscles of the Cadaver.**
Rebecca Gray/Don Kincaid/McGraw-Hill Education

**TABLE 10.6 Muscles of the Back**

| Name | Action | Skeletal Attachments | Innervation |
|---|---|---|---|
| Erector spinae (eh-REC-tur SPY-nee) | Aids in sitting and standing erect; straightens back after one bends at waist, and is employed in arching the back; unilateral contraction flexes waist laterally; the longissimus capitis also produces ipsilateral rotation of the head. | • Nuchal ligament; ribs 3–12; thoracic and lumbar vertebrae; median and lateral sacral crests; thoracolumbar fascia<br>• Mastoid process; cervical and thoracic vertebrae; all ribs | Posterior rami of cervical to lumbar spinal nerves |
| Semispinalis thoracis (SEM-ee-spy-NAY-liss tho-RA-sis) | Extension and contralateral rotation of vertebral column | • Vertebrae T6–T10<br>• Vertebrae C6–T4 | Posterior rami of cervical and thoracic spinal nerves |
| Quadratus lumborum[53] (quad-RAY-tus lum-BORE-um) | Unilateral contraction causes ipsilateral flexion of lumbar spine; bilateral contraction extends lumbar spine. Aids respiration by fixing rib 12 and stabilizing attachments of diaphragm. | • Iliac crest; iliolumbar ligament<br>• Rib 12; vertebrae L1–L4 | Anterior rami of spinal nerves T12–L4 |
| Multifidus[54] (mul-TIFF-ih-dus) | Stabilizes adjacent vertebrae, maintains posture, controls vertebral movement when erector spinae acts on spine | • Vertebrae C4–L5; posterior superior iliac spine; sacrum; aponeurosis of erector spinae<br>• Laminae and spinous processes of vertebrae superior to origins | Posterior rami of cervical to lumbar spinal nerves |

[53] *quadrat* = four-sided; *lumborum* = of the lumbar region

[54] *multi* = many; *fid* = branched, sectioned

## DEEPER INSIGHT 10.2
## CLINICAL APPLICATION

### *Heavy Lifting and Back Injuries*

When you are fully bent over forward, as in touching your toes, the erector spinae is fully stretched. Because of the *length–tension relationship* explained in section 11.4e, muscles that are stretched to such extremes cannot contract very effectively. Standing up from such a position is therefore initiated by the hamstring muscles on the back of the thigh and the gluteus maximus of the buttocks. The erector spinae joins in the action when it is partially contracted.

Standing too suddenly or improperly lifting a heavy weight, however, can strain the erector spinae, cause painful muscle spasms, tear tendons and ligaments of the lower back, and rupture intervertebral discs. The lumbar muscles are adapted for maintaining posture, not for lifting. This is why it is important, in heavy lifting, to crouch and use the powerful extensor muscles of the thighs and buttocks to lift the load.

lumbar muscles. The **multifidus** is a collective name for a series of tiny muscles that connect adjacent vertebrae to each other from the cervical to lumbar region.

## 10.3d Muscles of the Pelvic Floor

The floor of the pelvic cavity (**fig. 10.21; table 10.7**) is a strong multilayered muscular sheet important for the support of the abdominal and pelvic viscera—especially in light of the bipedal stance of humans, since the abdominal wall no longer forms a supportive floor as it does in quadrupedal mammals. Weakness in the pelvic floor can result in urinary or fecal incontinence or the prolapse (dropping) of internal organs between the thighs. The muscles and skeletal landmarks here are also of special importance in obstetrics.

Viewed from within the pelvic cavity, its floor is formed mainly by an extensive muscle called the *levator ani*. Inferior to

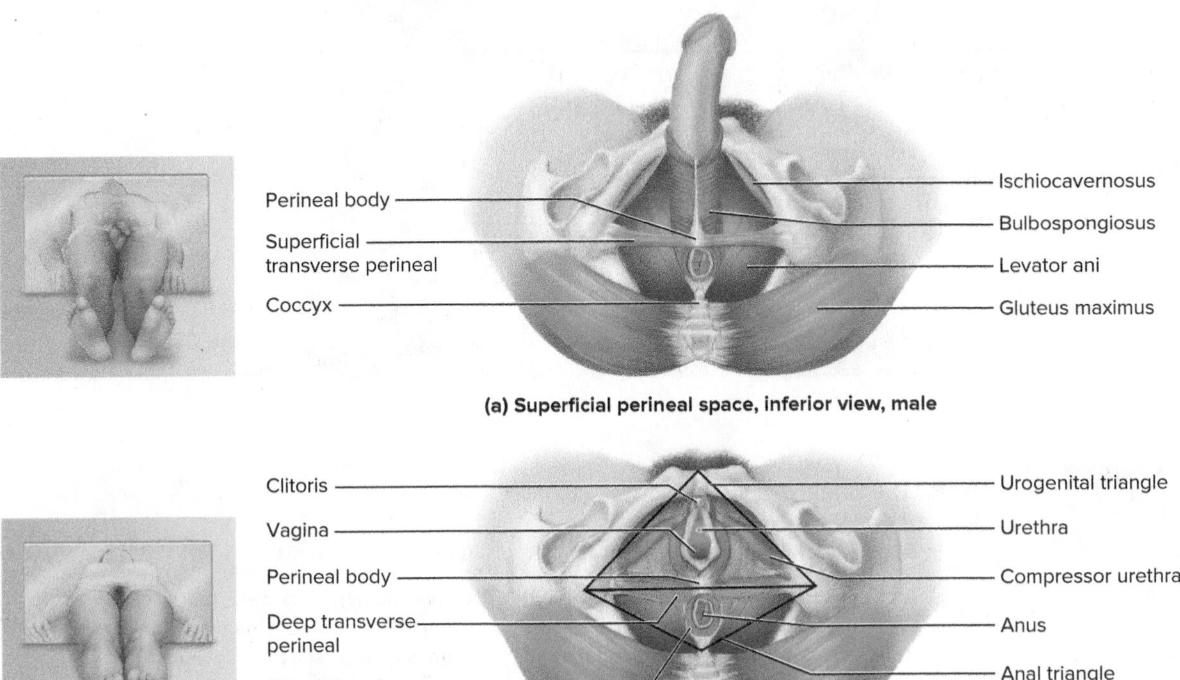


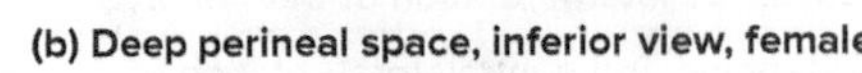


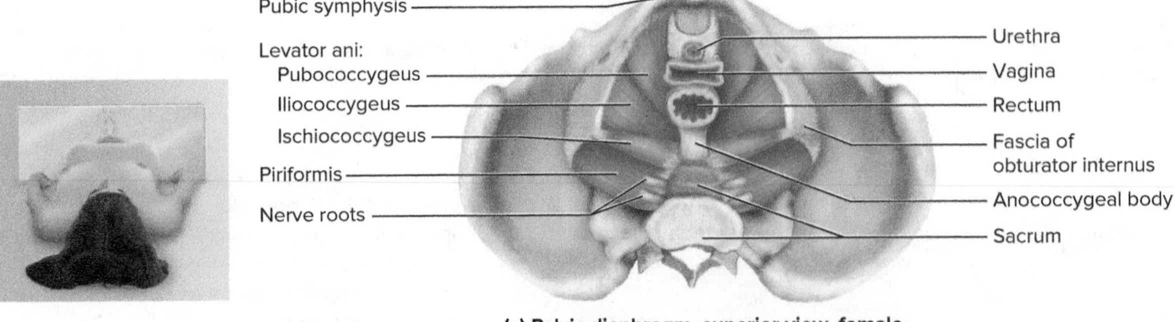


**FIGURE 10.21 Muscles of the Pelvic Floor.** (a) The superficial perineal space, male, viewed from below (the inferior aspect). (b) The deep perineal space, female, viewed from the same perspective. Other than the vaginal canal, the sexes are nearly identical at this level, including the urogenital and anal triangles. The root of the penis does not extend to this level. (c) The pelvic diaphragm, female, viewed from above (from within the pelvic cavity).

**TABLE 10.7 Muscles of the Pelvic Floor**

| Name | Action | Skeletal Attachments | Innervation |
|---|---|---|---|
| **Superficial Perineal Space** | | | |
| Ischiocavernosus[55] (ISS-kee-oh-CAV-er-NO-sus) | Maintains erection of the penis or clitoris by compressing deep structures of the organ and forcing blood forward into its body | • Ramus and tuberosity of ischium<br>• Ensheaths internal structures of penis and clitoris | Pudendal nerve |
| Bulbospongiosus[56] (BUL-bo-SPUN-jee-OH-sus) | Expels residual urine from urethra after bladder has emptied. Aids in erection of penis or clitoris. In male, spasmodic contractions expel semen during ejaculation. In female, contractions constrict vaginal orifice and expel secretions of greater vestibular glands. | • Perineal body and median raphe<br>• Male: ensheaths root of penis Female: pubic symphysis | Pudendal nerve |
| **Deep Perineal Space** | | | |
| Deep transverse perineal | Anchors perineal body, which supports other pelvic muscles; supports vaginal and urethral canals | • Ischiopubic rami<br>• Perineal body | Pudendal nerve |
| Compressor urethrae (yu-REE-three) | Aids in urine retention; found in females only | • Ischiopubic rami<br>• Right and left compressor urethrae meet each other inferior to external urethral sphincter | Pudendal nerve; spinal nerves S2–S4; pelvic splanchnic nerve |
| **Anal Triangle** | | | |
| External anal sphincter | Retains feces in rectum until voluntarily voided | • Coccyx, perineal body<br>• Encircles anal canal and orifice | Pudendal nerve; spinal nerves S2–S4; pelvic splanchnic nerve |
| **Pelvic Diaphragm** | | | |
| Levator ani[57] (leh-VAY-tur AY-nye) | Compresses anal canal and reinforces external anal and urethral sphincters; supports uterus and other pelvic viscera; aids in falling away of the feces; vertical movements affect pressure differences between abdominal and thoracic cavities and thus aid in deep breathing. | • Inner surface of lesser pelvis from pubis through margin of obturator internus to spine of ischium<br>• Coccyx via anococcygeal body; walls of urethra, vagina, and anal canal | Pudendal nerve; spinal nerves S2–S3 |

this is the **perineum** (PERR-ih-NEE-um), a diamond-shaped area between the thighs bordered by four bony landmarks: the pubic symphysis anteriorly, the coccyx posteriorly, and the ischial tuberosities laterally. The pelvic floor and perineum are penetrated by the anal canal, urethra, and vagina. The anterior half of the perineum is the **urogenital triangle** and the posterior half is the **anal triangle.**

The urogenital triangle is divided into two muscle compartments separated by a strong fibrous **perineal membrane.** The muscle compartment between this membrane and the skin is called *superficial perineal space,* and the compartment between the perineal membrane and levator ani is the *deep perineal space.* We will examine these structures beginning inferiorly, just beneath the skin, and progressing superiorly to the pelvic floor.

## The Superficial Perineal Space

The **superficial perineal space** (fig. 10.21a) contains three pairs of muscles: the *ischiocavernosus, bulbospongiosus,* and *superficial transverse perineal muscle.* In females, this space also contains the clitoris; various glands and erectile tissues of the genitalia (see fig. 28.8); and adipose tissue, which extends into and fattens the mons pubis and labia majora. In males, it contains the root of the penis.

The **ischiocavernosus** muscles converge like a V from the ischial tuberosities toward the penis or clitoris. In males, the **bulbospongiosus (bulbocavernosus)** muscles form a sheath around the root of the penis, and in females they enclose the vagina like a pair of parentheses. *Cavernosus* in these names refers to the spongy, cavernous structure of tissues in the penis and clitoris.

The **superficial transverse perineal muscles** extend from the ischial tuberosities to a strong median fibromuscular anchorage, the **perineal body,** and a median seam called the **perineal raphe** (RAY-fee) that extends anteriorly from the perineal body. These muscles may help to anchor the perineal body, but they are weakly developed and not always present, therefore not included in table 10.7. The other two muscle pairs of this layer serve primarily sexual functions.

[55]*ischio* = ischium of hip bone; *cavernosus* = corpus cavernosum of the penis or clitoris
[56]*bulbo* = bulb of the penis; *spongiosus* = corpus spongiosum of the penis
[57]*levator* = that which elevates; *ani* = of the anus

## DEEPER INSIGHT 10.3
### CLINICAL APPLICATION

### *Hernias*

A hernia is any condition in which the viscera protrude through a weak point in the muscular wall of the abdominopelvic cavity. The most common type to require treatment is an *inguinal hernia* **(fig. 10.22).** In the male fetus, each testis descends from the pelvic cavity into the scrotum by way of a passage called the *inguinal canal* through the muscles of the groin. A long pouch of peritoneum descends with the testis, but usually disappears by birth. Hernias occur in infants and children when this pouch persists, allowing a loop of intestine to enter it and appear near or in the scrotum *(indirect hernia).* Adult hernias may appear similar but are often due to a weakening of the inguinal canal *(direct hernia).* This can result from repetitive stress such as lifting weights. When the diaphragm and abdominal muscles contract, pressure in the abdominal cavity can soar to 1,500 pounds per square inch—more than 100 times the normal pressure and quite sufficient to produce an inguinal hernia, or "rupture." Inguinal hernias in women occur through the pelvic floor and other nearby sites.

Two other sites of hernia are the diaphragm and navel. A *hiatal hernia* is a condition in which part of the stomach protrudes through the diaphragm into the thoracic cavity. This is most common in overweight people over 40. It may cause heartburn due to the regurgitation of stomach acid into the esophagus, but most cases go undetected. In an *umbilical hernia,* abdominal viscera protrude through the navel.

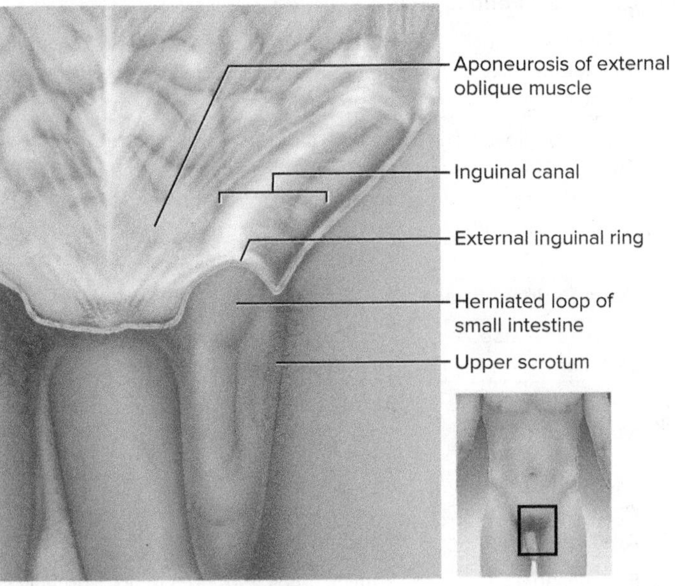


**FIGURE 10.22 Inguinal Hernia.** A loop of small intestine has protruded through the inguinal canal into a space beneath the skin.

## The Deep Perineal Space

The **deep perineal space** (fig. 10.21b) contains a pair of **deep transverse perineal muscles** and, in females only, the **compressor urethrae muscles.** The deep transverse perineal muscles anchor the perineal body on the median plane; the perineal body, in turn, anchors other pelvic muscles. The female external urethral sphincter, long thought to be part of the deep perineal space, is now regarded as part of the urethra itself and not part of the pelvic floor musculature.

## The Anal Triangle

The **anal triangle** contains the **external anal sphincter** and **anococcygeal ligament** (fig. 10.21b). The external anal sphincter is a tubular muscle surrounding the lower anal canal. The anococcygeal ligament is the median insertion of the levator ani muscles, and the ligament, in turn, inserts on the coccyx. It is therefore a major anchorage for the structures that compose the pelvic floor.

## The Pelvic Diaphragm

The **pelvic diaphragm** (fig. 10.21c) is deep to the foregoing structures (uppermost in the pelvic floor) and is composed mainly of the right and left **levator ani** muscles. (The piriformis, also illustrated, is primarily a lower limb muscle.) The levator ani spans most of the pelvic outlet and forms the floor of the lesser (true) pelvis. It is divided into three portions that are sometimes regarded as separate muscles—the *ischiococcygeus* (or *coccygeus*), *iliococcygeus,* and *pubococcygeus.* The left and right levator ani muscles converge on the anococcygeal ligament, through which they are indirectly anchored to the coccyx.

**BEFORE YOU GO ON**

Answer the following questions to test your understanding of the preceding section:

11. Which muscles are used more often, the external intercostals or internal intercostals? Explain.
12. Explain how pulmonary ventilation affects abdominal pressure and vice versa.
13. Name a major superficial muscle and two major deep muscles of the back.
14. Define *perineum, urogenital triangle,* and *anal triangle.*
15. Name one muscle in the superficial perineal space, one in the urogenital diaphragm, and one in the pelvic diaphragm. State the function of each.

## 10.4 Muscles Acting on the Shoulder and Upper Limb

### Expected Learning Outcomes

When you have completed this section, you should be able to

a. name and locate the muscles that act on the pectoral girdle, shoulder, elbow, wrist, and hand;
b. relate the actions of these muscles to the joint movements described in chapter 9; and
c. describe the skeletal attachments, action, and innervation of these muscles.

The upper and lower limbs have numerous muscles that serve primarily for movement of the body and manipulation of objects. These muscles are organized into distinct compartments separated from each other by the interosseous membranes of the forearm and leg (see figs. 8.34, 8.40) and by intermuscular septa. In the ensuing tables, you will find muscles of the upper limb divided into anterior and posterior compartments, and those of the lower limb divided into anterior, posterior, medial, and lateral compartments. In most limb regions, the muscle groups are further subdivided by thinner fasciae into superficial and deep layers.

The upper limb is used for a broad range of both powerful and subtle actions, ranging from climbing, grasping, and throwing to writing, playing musical instruments, and manipulating small objects. It therefore has an especially complex array of muscles, but the muscles fall into logical groups that make their functional relationships and names easier to understand. The next five tables group these into muscles that act on the scapula, those that act on the humerus and shoulder joint, those that act on the forearm and elbow joint, extrinsic (forearm) muscles that act on the wrist and hand, and intrinsic (hand) muscles that act on the fingers.

### 10.4a Muscles Acting on the Shoulder

Muscles that act on the pectoral girdle **(table 10.8)** extend from the axial skeleton to the clavicle and scapula. The scapula is only loosely attached to the thoracic cage and is capable of considerable movement **(fig. 10.23)**—rotation (as in raising and lowering the apex of the shoulder), elevation and depression (as in shrugging and lowering the shoulders), and

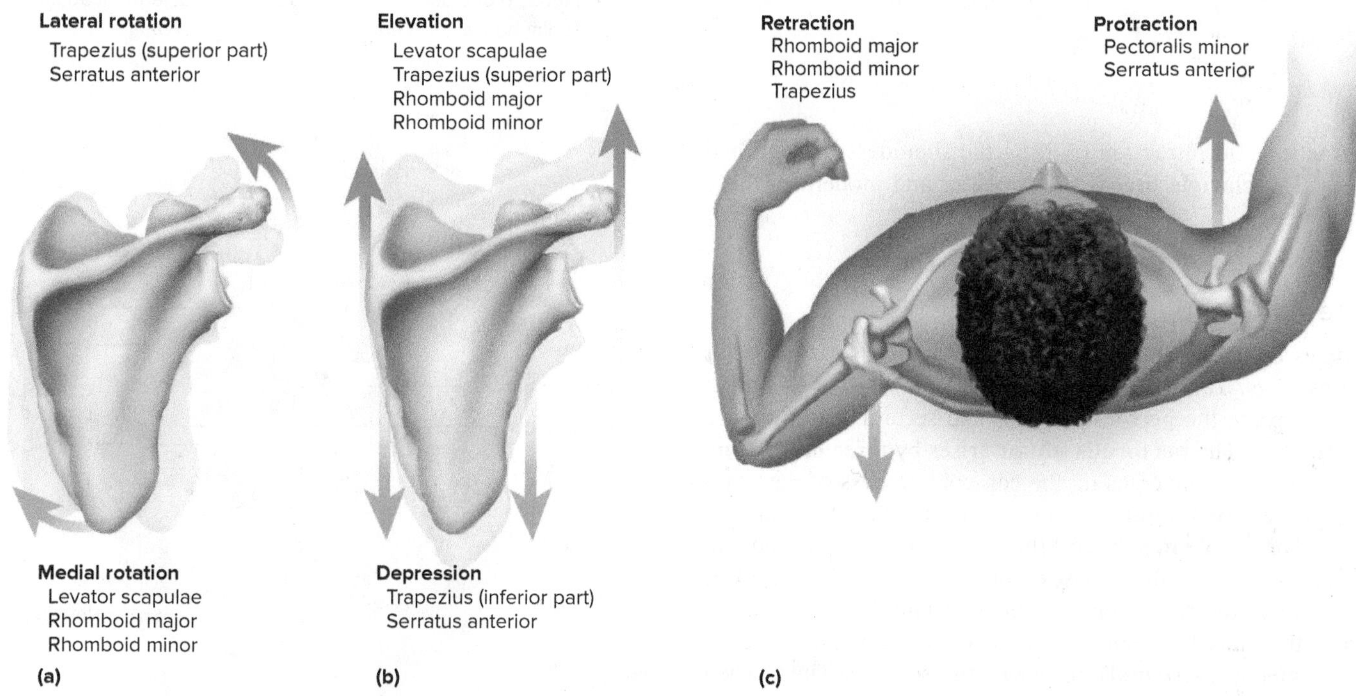


**FIGURE 10.23 Actions of Some Thoracic Muscles on the Scapula.** (a) Lateral and medial rotation. (b) Elevation and depression. (c) Retraction and protraction. Note that an individual muscle can contribute to multiple actions, depending on which fibers contract and what synergists act with it.

**TABLE 10.8 Muscles Acting on the Shoulder**

| Name | Action | Skeletal Attachments | Innervation |
|---|---|---|---|
| **Anterior Group** | | | |
| Pectoralis minor (PECK-toe-RAY-liss) | With serratus anterior, draws scapula laterally and forward around chest wall; with other muscles, rotates scapula and depresses apex of shoulder, as in reaching down to pick up a suitcase | • Ribs 3–5 and overlying fascia<br>• Coracoid process of scapula | Medial and lateral pectoral nerves |
| Serratus[58] anterior (serr-AY-tus) | With pectoralis minor, draws scapula laterally and forward around chest wall; protracts scapula, and is the prime mover in all forward-reaching and pushing actions; aids in rotating scapula to elevate apex of shoulder; fixes scapula during abduction of arm | • All or nearly all ribs<br>• Medial border of scapula | Long thoracic nerve |
| **Posterior Group** | | | |
| Trapezius (tra-PEE-zee-us) | Stabilizes scapula and shoulder during arm movements; elevates and depresses apex of shoulder; acts with other muscles to rotate and retract scapula (see also roles in head and neck movements in table 10.3) | • External occipital protuberance; medial one-third of superior nuchal line; nuchal ligament; spinous processes of vertebrae C7–T12<br>• Acromion and spine of scapula; lateral one-third of clavicle | Accessory nerve |
| Levator scapulae (leh-VAY-tur SCAP-you-lee) | Elevates scapula if cervical vertebrae are fixed; flexes neck laterally if scapula is fixed; retracts scapula and braces shoulder; rotates scapula and depresses apex of shoulder | • Transverse processes of vertebrae C1–C4<br>• Superior angle to medial border of scapula | Spinal nerves C3–C4, and C5 via posterior scapular nerve |
| Rhomboid minor (ROM-boyd) | Retracts scapula and braces shoulder; fixes scapula during arm movements | • Spinous processes of vertebrae C7–T1; nuchal ligament<br>• Medial border of scapula | Posterior scapular nerve |
| Rhomboid major | Same as rhomboid minor | • Spinous processes of vertebrae T2–T5<br>• Medial border of scapula | Posterior scapular nerve |

protraction and retraction (pulling the shoulders forward and back). The clavicle braces the shoulder and moderates these movements.

## Anterior Group

Muscles of the pectoral girdle fall into anterior and posterior groups **(figs. 10.24, 10.25).** The major muscles of the anterior group are the pectoralis minor and serratus anterior (see fig. 10.16b). The **pectoralis minor** arises by three heads from ribs 3 to 5 and converges on the coracoid process of the scapula. The **serratus anterior** is nicknamed the "boxer's muscle" because of its role in powerful thrusting movements of the arm such as a boxer's jab. It arises from separate heads on all or nearly all of the ribs, wraps laterally around the chest, passes across the back between the rib cage and scapula, and ends on the medial (vertebral) border of the scapula. Thus, when it contracts, the scapula glides laterally and slightly forward around the ribs.

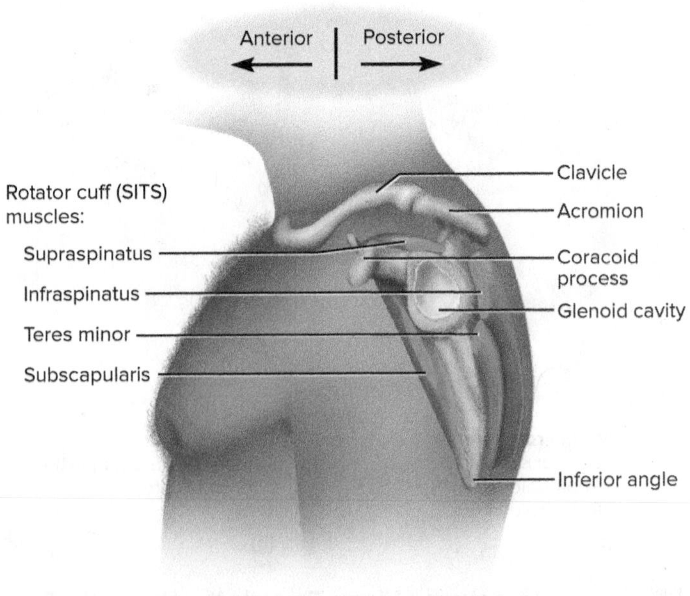

**FIGURE 10.24 Rotator Cuff Muscles in Relation to the Scapula (Lateral View).** For posterior and anterior views of these muscles, see figure 10.25, b and d.

[58]*serrate* = scalloped, zigzag

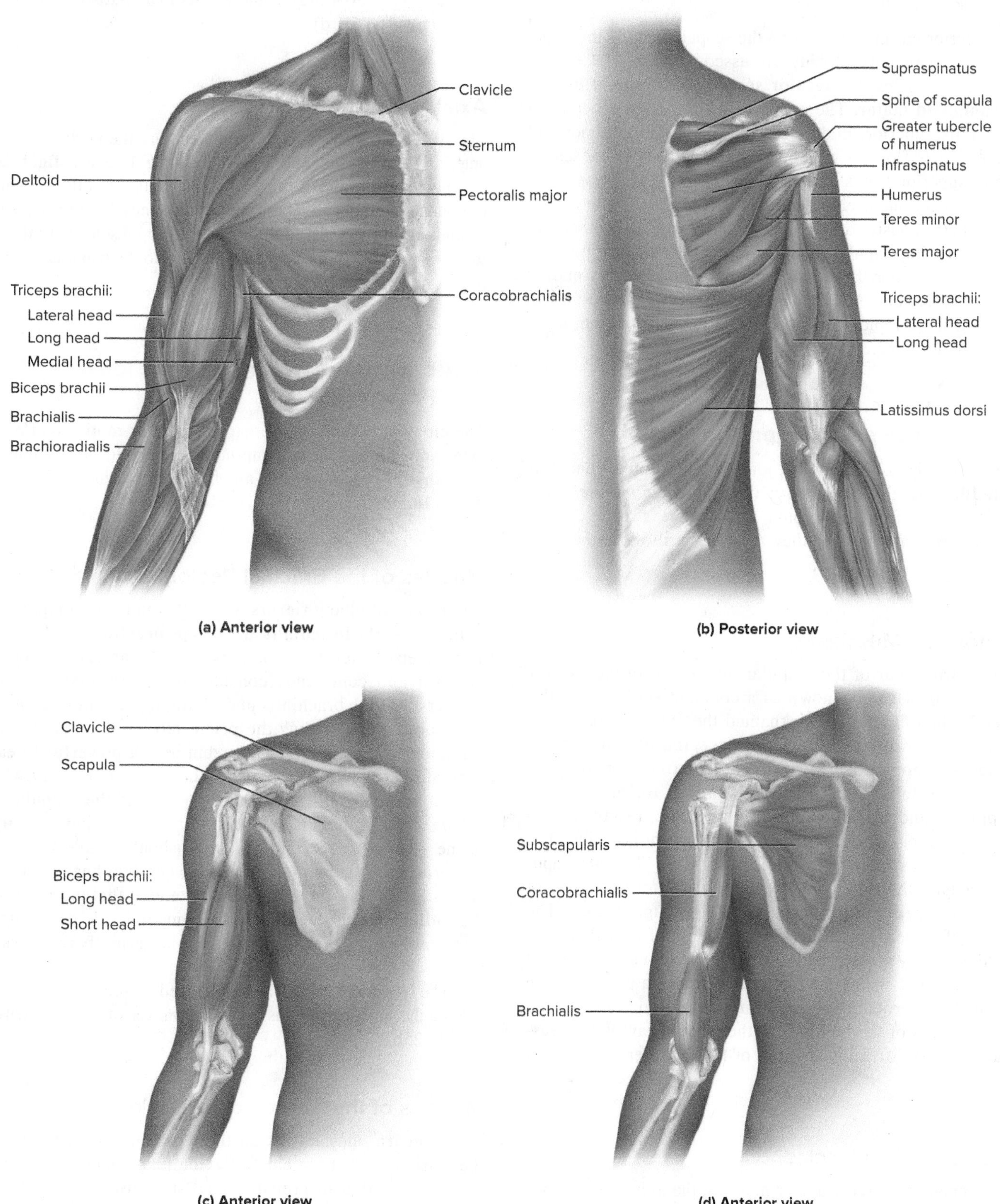


**FIGURE 10.25 Pectoral and Brachial Muscles.** (a) Superficial muscles, anterior view. (b) Superficial muscles, posterior view. (c) The biceps brachii, the superficial flexor of the elbow. (d) The brachialis, the deep flexor of the elbow, and the coracobrachialis and subscapularis, which act on the humerus. APR

### Posterior Group

The posterior muscles that act on the scapula include the large, superficial **trapezius,** already discussed (see table 10.3), and three deep muscles: the **levator scapulae, rhomboid minor,** and **rhomboid major.** The action of the trapezius depends on whether its superior, middle, or inferior fibers contract and whether it acts alone or with other muscles. The levator scapulae and superior fibers of the trapezius rotate the scapula in opposite directions if either of them acts alone. If both act together, their opposite rotational effects balance each other and they elevate the scapula and shoulder, as when you lift a suitcase from the floor. Depression of the scapula occurs mainly by gravitational pull, but the trapezius and serratus anterior can depress it more rapidly and forcefully, as in swimming, hammering, and rowing.

## 10.4b Muscles Acting on the Arm

Nine muscles cross the shoulder joint and insert on the humerus **(table 10.9).** Seven of them are considered *scapular muscles* because they arise from the scapula, and the other two are considered *axial muscles* because they arise primarily from the axial skeleton.

### Rotator Cuff Muscles

Tendons from four of the scapular muscles form the **rotator cuff** (fig. 10.24), well known as a common site of musculoskeletal injury. These are nicknamed the "SITS muscles" for the first letters of their names—**supraspinatus, infraspinatus, teres minor,** and **subscapularis.** The first three of these lie on the posterior side of the scapula (fig. 10.25b). The supraspinatus and infraspinatus occupy the supraspinous and infraspinous fossae, above and below the scapular spine. The teres minor lies inferior to the infraspinatus. The subscapularis occupies the subscapular fossa on the anterior surface of the scapula, between the scapula and ribs (fig. 10.25d). The tendons of these muscles merge with the joint capsule of the shoulder as they cross it en route to the humerus. They insert on the proximal end of the humerus, forming a partial sleeve around it. The rotator cuff reinforces the joint capsule and holds the head of the humerus in the glenoid cavity. It is easily damaged by strenuous actions of the shoulder (see Deeper Insight 10.4).

### Other Scapular Muscles

Of the remaining three scapular muscles, the most conspicuous is the **deltoid,** the thick triangular muscle that caps the shoulder (fig. 10.25a). Intramuscular drug injections are often given here. Its anterior, lateral, and posterior fibers act like three different muscles. The **teres major** and **coracobrachialis** complete this group (fig. 10.25b, d).

### Axial Muscles

The two axial muscles, both prominent, are the pectoralis major anteriorly and latissimus dorsi posteriorly (fig. 10.25a, b; **fig. 10.26**). The **pectoralis major** is the thick, fleshy muscle of the mammary region and the **latissimus dorsi** is a broad muscle of the back that extends from the waist to the axilla. These muscles bear the primary responsibility for attaching the arm to the trunk and are the prime movers of the shoulder joint.

## 10.4c Muscles Acting on the Elbow and Forearm

The elbow and forearm are capable of four motions—flexion, extension, pronation, and supination—carried out by muscles in both the brachium and antebrachium (arm and forearm) **(table 10.10).**

### Muscles of the Brachial Region

The principal elbow flexors are in the anterior compartment of the arm—the **brachialis** and **biceps brachii** (fig. 10.25c, d). The biceps brachii appears as a large anterior bulge on the arm and commands considerable interest among body builders, but the brachialis underlying it generates about 50% more power and is thus the prime mover of elbow flexion. The biceps is not only a flexor but also a powerful forearm supinator. It is named for its two heads: a *short head* whose tendon arises from the coracoid process of the scapula, and a *long head* whose tendon arises from the superior margin of the glenoid cavity, loops over the shoulder, and braces the humerus against the glenoid cavity. The two heads converge close to the elbow on a single distal tendon that terminates on the radius and on the fascia of the medial side of the upper forearm. Note that *biceps* is the singular term; there is no such word as *bicep.*

The **triceps brachii** is a three-headed muscle on the posterior side of the humerus, and is the prime mover of elbow extension (fig. 10.25b).

### Muscles of the Antebrachial Region

Most forearm muscles act on the wrist and hand, but two of them are synergists in elbow flexion and extension and three of them function in pronation and supination. The **brachioradialis** is the large fleshy mass of the lateral (radial) side of the forearm just distal to the elbow (fig. 10.25a; also see fig. 10.29a). It extends from the distal end of the humerus to the

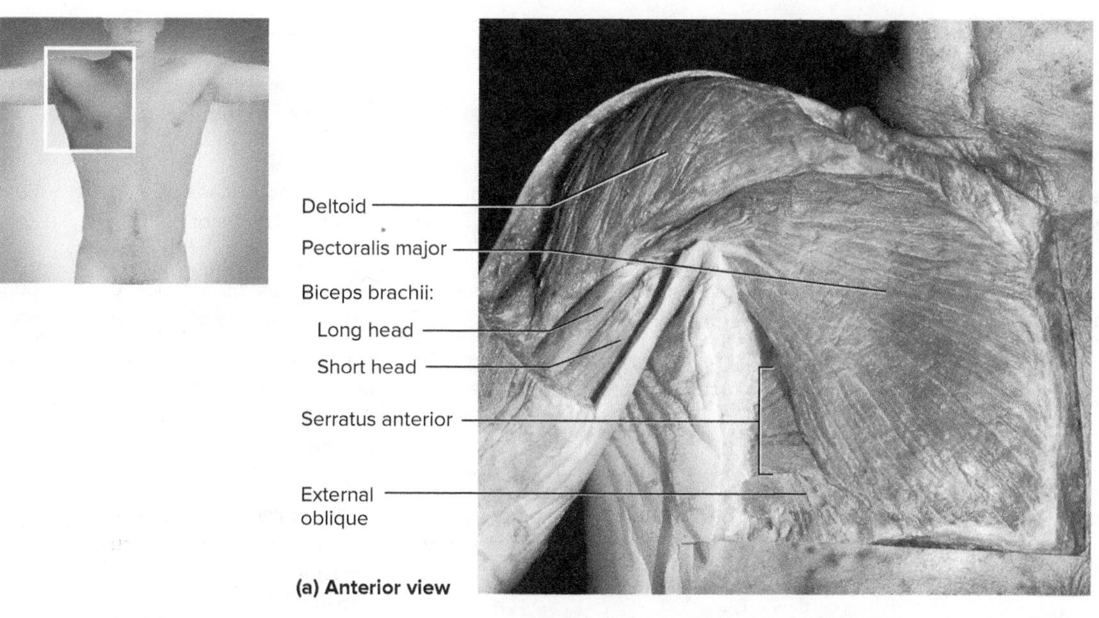


(a) Anterior view

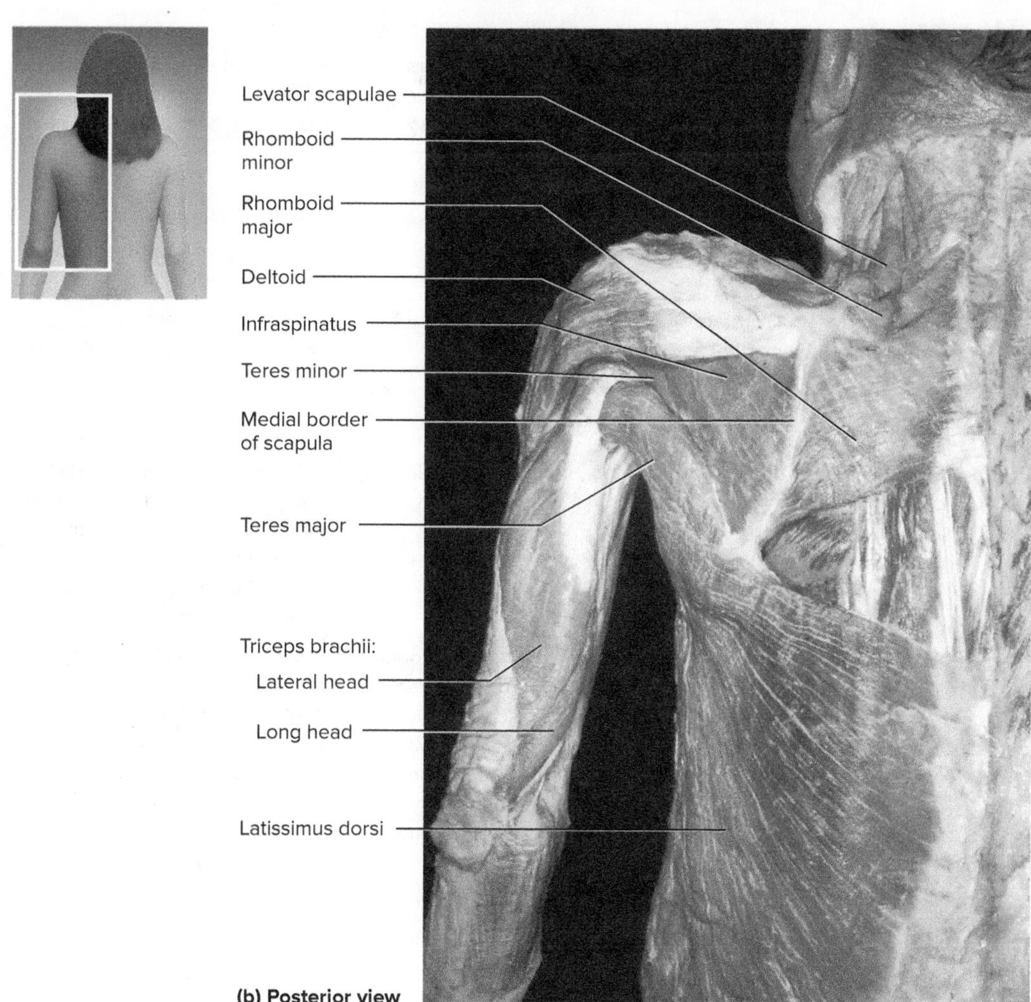


(b) Posterior view

FIGURE 10.26 **Pectoral, Brachial, and Upper Back Muscles of the Cadaver.** (a) Anterior view. (b) Posterior view.

a–b: Rebecca Gray/McGraw-Hill Education

**TABLE 10.9 Muscles Acting on the Arm**

| Name | Action | Skeletal Attachments | Innervation |
|---|---|---|---|
| **Rotator Cuff Muscles** | | | |
| Supraspinatus[59] (SOO-pra-spy-NAY-tus) | Aids deltoid in abduction of arm; resists downward slippage of humeral head when arm is relaxed or when carrying weight | • Supraspinous fossa of scapula<br>• Greater tubercle of humerus | Suprascapular nerve |
| Infraspinatus[60] (IN-fra-spy-NAY-tus) | Modulates action of deltoid, preventing humeral head from sliding upward; rotates humerus laterally | • Infraspinous fossa of scapula<br>• Greater tubercle of humerus | Suprascapular nerve |
| Teres minor (TERR-eez) | Modulates action of deltoid, preventing humeral head from sliding upward as arm is abducted; rotates humerus laterally | • Lateral border and adjacent posterior surface of scapula<br>• Greater tubercle of humerus; posterior surface of joint capsule | Axillary nerve |
| Subscapularis[61] (SUB-SCAP-you-LERR-iss) | Modulates action of deltoid, preventing humeral head from sliding upward as arm is abducted; rotates humerus medially | • Subscapular fossa of scapula<br>• Lesser tubercle of humerus; anterior surface of joint capsule | Upper and lower subscapular nerves |
| **Other Scapular Muscles** | | | |
| Deltoid | Anterior fibers flex and medially rotate arm; lateral fibers abduct arm; posterior fibers extend and laterally rotate arm; involved in arm swinging during such actions as walking or bowling, and in adjustment of hand height for various manual tasks | • Acromion and spine of scapula; clavicle<br>• Deltoid tuberosity of humerus | Axillary nerve |
| Teres major (TERR-eez) | Extends and medially rotates humerus; contributes to arm swinging | • Inferior angle of scapula<br>• Medial lip of intertubercular sulcus of humerus | Lower subscapular nerve |
| Coracobrachialis (COR-uh-co-BRAY-kee-AY-lis) | Flexes and medially rotates arm; resists deviation of arm from frontal plane during abduction | • Coracoid process<br>• Medial aspect of humeral shaft | Musculocutaneous nerve |
| **Axial Muscles** | | | |
| Pectoralis major (PECK-toe-RAY-liss) | Flexes, adducts, and medially rotates humerus, as in climbing or hugging; aids in deep inspiration | • Medial half of clavicle; lateral margin of sternum; costal cartilages 1–7; aponeurosis of external oblique<br>• Lateral lip of intertubercular sulcus of humerus | Medial and lateral pectoral nerves |
| Latissimus dorsi[62] (la-TISS-ih-mus DOR-sye) | Adducts and medially rotates humerus; extends the shoulder joint as in pulling on the oars of a rowboat; produces backward swing of arm in such actions as walking and bowling; with hands grasping overhead objects, pulls body forward and upward, as in climbing; aids in deep inspiration, sudden expiration such as sneezing and coughing, and prolonged forceful expiration as in singing or blowing a sustained note on a wind instrument | • Vertebrae T7–L5; lower three or four ribs; iliac crest; thoracolumbar fascia<br>• Floor of intertubercular sulcus of humerus | Thoracodorsal nerve |

**▶▶▶APPLY WHAT YOU KNOW**

*Perform an action as if lifting a cup to your mouth to take a sip of tea. Describe the contribution of your deltoid to this action, using the terminology of joint movement in section 9.2c.*

[59] *supra* = above; *spin* = spine of scapula
[60] *infra* = below, under; *spin* = spine of scapula
[61] *sub* = below, under
[62] *latissimus* = broadest; *dorsi* = of the back

## DEEPER INSIGHT 10.4
### CLINICAL APPLICATION

### *Rotator Cuff Injury*

Rotator cuff injury is a tear in the tendon of any of the SITS (rotator cuff) muscles, most often the supraspinatus. Such injuries are caused by strenuous circumduction of the arm, shoulder dislocation, hard falls or blows to the shoulder, or repetitive use of the arm in a position above the horizontal. They are common among baseball pitchers and third basemen, bowlers, swimmers, and weight lifters, and in racquet sports. Recurrent inflammation of a SITS tendon can cause a tendon to degenerate and then to rupture in response to moderate stress. Injury causes pain and makes the shoulder joint unstable and subject to dislocation.

distal end of the radius. With the latter attachment so far from the fulcrum of the elbow, it does not generate as much force as the brachialis and biceps; it is effective mainly when those muscles have already partially flexed the elbow. The **anconeus** is a weak synergist of elbow extension on the posterior side of the elbow (see fig. 10.30).

Pronation and supination are important forearm movements for such purposes as eating, manipulating and inspecting objects in the hands, and generating force in twisting movements of the hand (see fig. 9.18). The prime mover of pronation is the **pronator quadratus** near the wrist; the **pronator teres** near the elbow is a synergist. Supination is usually achieved by the **supinator** of the upper forearm, with the biceps brachii aiding when additional speed or power is required **(fig. 10.27).**

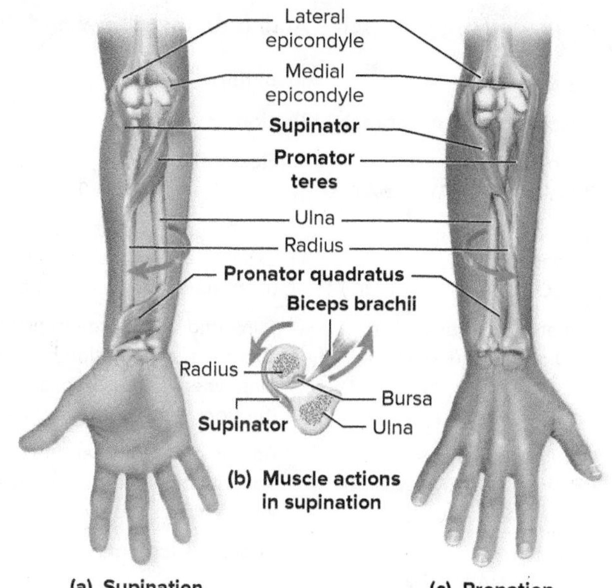


**FIGURE 10.27 Actions of the Rotator Muscles on the Forearm.** (a) Supination. (b) Cross section just distal to the elbow, showing the synergistic action of the biceps brachii and supinator. (c) Pronation.

 *What do the names of the pronator teres and pronator quadratus muscles indicate about their shapes?*

## 10.4d Muscles Acting on the Wrist and Hand

The hand is acted upon by extrinsic muscles in the forearm **(table 10.11)** and intrinsic muscles in the hand itself. The bellies of the extrinsic muscles, along with the brachioradialis,

**TABLE 10.10 Muscles Acting on the Elbow and Forearm**

| Name | Action | Skeletal Attachments | Innervation |
|---|---|---|---|
| **Muscles of the Brachial Region** | | | |
| Brachialis (BRAY-kee-AY-lis) | Prime mover of elbow flexion | • Anterior surface of distal half of humerus<br>• Coronoid process and tuberosity of ulna | Musculocutaneous nerve; radial nerve |
| Biceps brachii (BY-seps BRAY-kee-eye) | Rapid or forceful supination of forearm; synergist in elbow flexion; slight shoulder flexion; tendon of long head stabilizes shoulder by holding humeral head against glenoid cavity | • Long head: superior margin of glenoid cavity<br>Short head: coracoid process<br>• Tuberosity of radius; fascia of forearm | Musculocutaneous nerve |
| Triceps brachii (TRI-seps BRAY-kee-eye) | Extends elbow; long head extends and adducts humerus | • Long head: inferior margin of glenoid cavity and joint capsule<br>Lateral head: posterior surface of proximal end of humerus<br>Medial head: posterior surface of entire humeral shaft<br>• Olecranon; fascia of forearm | Radial nerve |

(continued)

**TABLE 10.10 Muscles Acting on the Elbow and Forearm (continued)**

| Name | Action | Skeletal Attachments | Innervation |
|---|---|---|---|
| **Muscles of the Antebrachial Region** | | | |
| Brachioradialis (BRAY-kee-oh-RAY-dee-AY-lis) | Flexes elbow | • Lateral supracondylar ridge of humerus<br>• Lateral surface of radius near styloid process | Radial nerve |
| Anconeus[63] (an-CO-nee-us) | Extends elbow; may help to control ulnar movement during pronation | • Lateral epicondyle of humerus<br>• Olecranon and posterior surface of ulna | Radial nerve |
| Pronator quadratus (PRO-nay-tur quad-RAY-tus) | Prime mover of forearm pronation; also resists separation of radius and ulna when force is applied to forearm through wrist, as in doing push-ups | • Anterior surface of distal ulna<br>• Anterior surface of distal radius | Median nerve |
| Pronator teres (PRO-nay-tur TERR-eez) | Assists pronator quadratus in pronation, but only in rapid or forceful action; weakly flexes elbow | • Humeral shaft near medial epicondyle; coronoid process of ulna<br>• Lateral surface of radial shaft | Median nerve |
| Supinator (SOO-pih-NAY-tur) | Supinates forearm | • Lateral epicondyle of humerus; supinator crest and fossa of ulna just distal to radial notch; anular and radial collateral ligaments of elbow<br>• Proximal one-third of radius | Radial nerve |

form the fleshy roundness of the upper forearm; their tendons extend into the wrist and hand. Their actions are mainly flexion and extension of the wrist and digits, but also include radial and ulnar flexion, finger abduction and adduction, and thumb opposition. These muscles are numerous and complex, but their names often describe their location, appearance, and function.

Many of them act on the **metacarpophalangeal joints** between the metacarpal bones of the hand and the proximal phalanges of the fingers, and the **interphalangeal joints** between the proximal and middle or the middle and distal phalanges of the fingers (or between the proximal and distal phalanges in the thumb, which has no middle phalanx). The metacarpophalangeal joints form the knuckles at the bases of the fingers, and the interphalangeal joints form the second and third knuckles. Some tendons cross multiple joints before inserting on a middle or distal phalanx, and can flex or extend all the joints they cross.

Fasciae divide the forearm muscles into anterior and posterior compartments and each compartment into superficial and deep layers **(fig. 10.28).** The muscles in these four groups are described in the following sections.

### The Anterior (Flexor) Compartment, Superficial Layer

Most muscles of the anterior compartment are wrist and finger flexors that arise from a common tendon on the humerus **(fig. 10.29).** The two prominent tendons you can palpate at the wrist belong to the **palmaris longus** on the medial side and the **flexor carpi radialis** on the lateral side (see fig. B.19a). The latter is an important landmark for finding the radial artery, where the pulse is usually taken. The palmaris longus is absent on one or both sides (most commonly the left) in about 14% of people. To see if you have one, flex your wrist and touch the tips of your thumb and little finger together. If present, the palmaris longus tendon will stand up prominently on the wrist.

Most tendons of these flexor muscles pass under a fibrous, braceletlike ligament called the **flexor retinaculum** on the anterior side of the wrist (see fig. 5.13); the palmaris longus tendon, unlike the rest, passes over it. The retinaculum prevents the tendons from standing up like taut bowstrings when the flexors contract. The **carpal tunnel** is a tight space between the flexor retinaculum and carpal bones. The flexor tendons passing through the tunnel are enclosed in tendon sheaths that enable them to slide back and forth quite easily, although continual repetitive motion of these tendons can cause the painful inflammation known as *carpal tunnel syndrome* (see Deeper Insight 10.5).

### The Anterior (Flexor) Compartment, Deep Layer

Two anterior flexors constitute the deep layer—the **flexor digitorum profundus,** which flexes fingers II–V, and the **flexor pollicis longus,** which flexes only the thumb (fig. 10.29c). The latter is one of several muscles serving exclusively for thumb movements, attesting to the supreme importance of the thumb for hand function.

### The Posterior (Extensor) Compartment, Superficial Layer

Superficial muscles of the posterior compartment are mostly wrist and finger extensors, and share a single tendon arising from the humerus **(fig. 10.30a).** The first of these, the **extensor digitorum,**

[63]*anconeus* = elbow

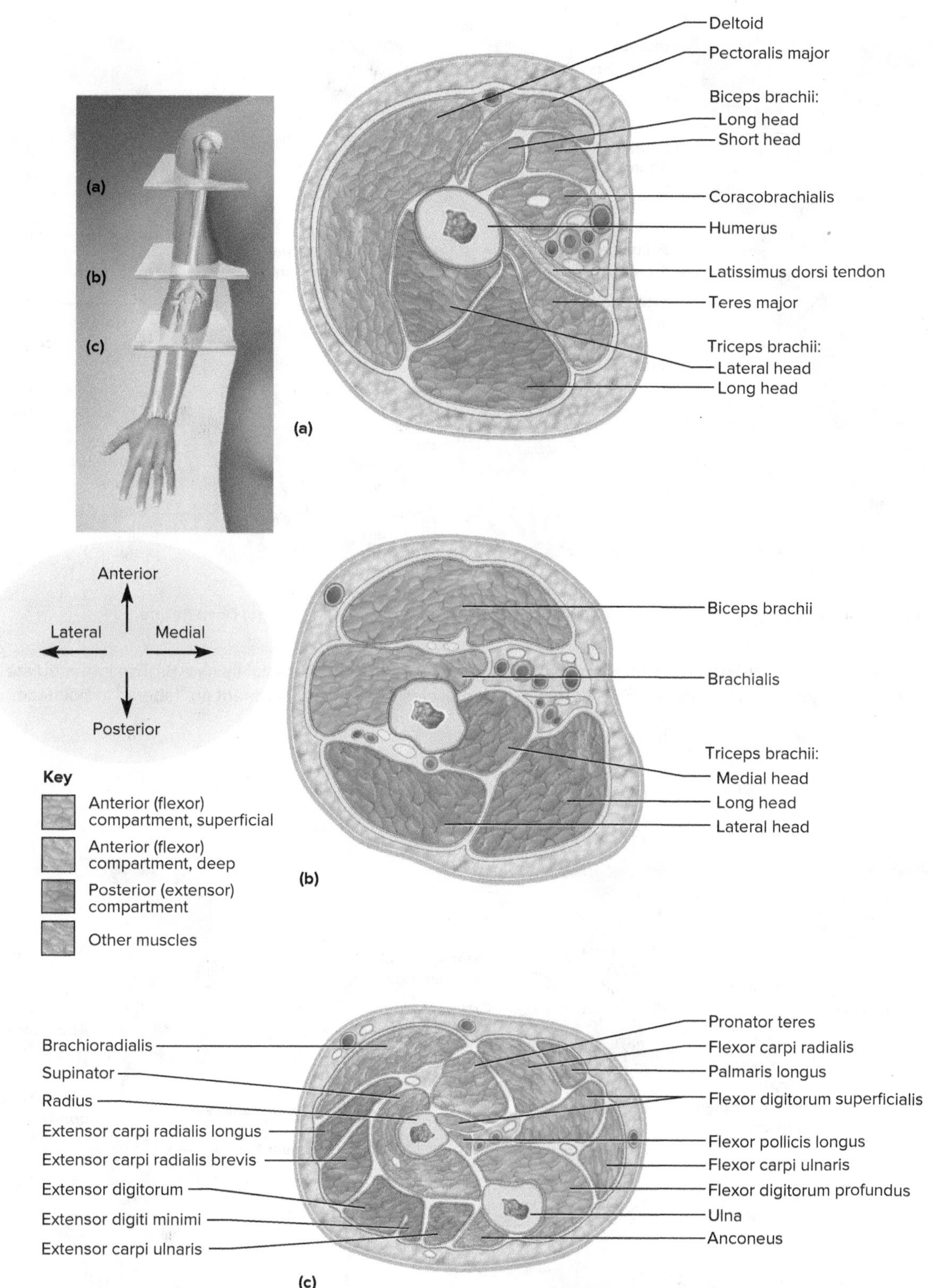


**FIGURE 10.28 Serial Cross Sections Through the Upper Limb.** Each section is taken at the correspondingly lettered level in the figure at the left and is pictured with the posterior muscle compartment facing the bottom of the page, as if viewing a person's right limb extended toward you with the palm up. (a) Superior arm at axilla. (b) Inferior arm. (c) Superior forearm.

? *Why are the extensor pollicis longus and extensor indicis not seen in part (c)?*

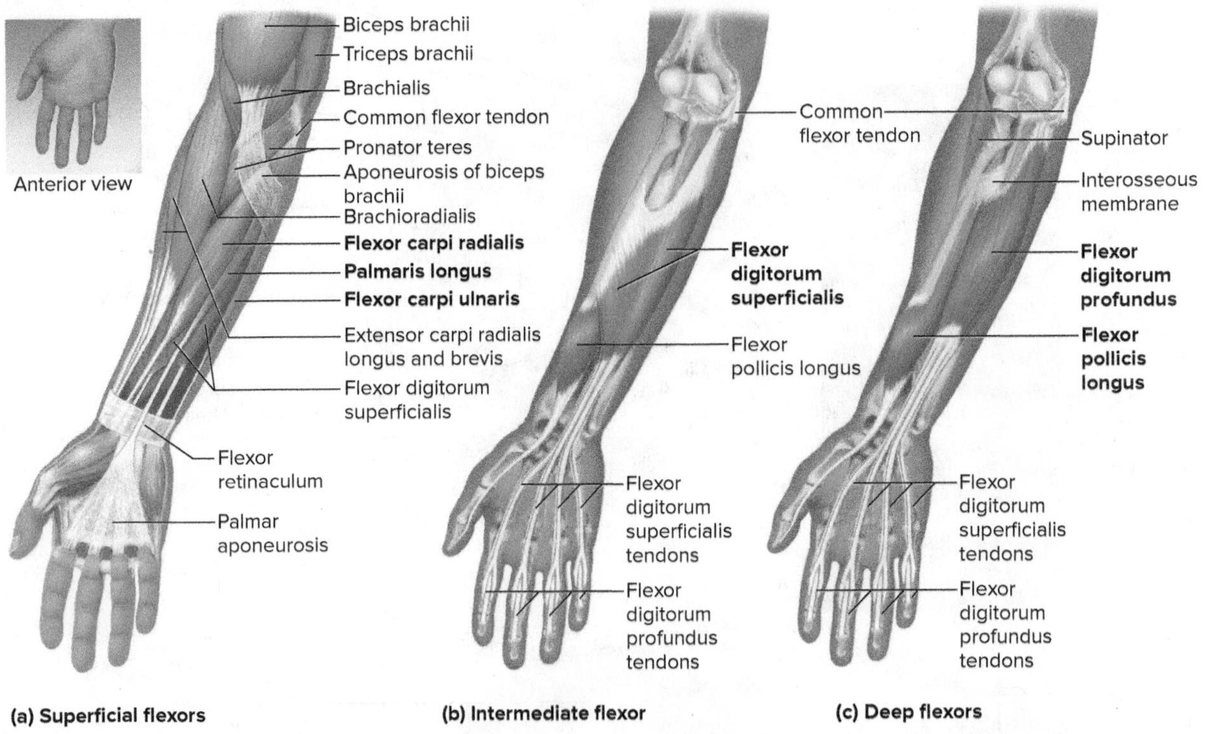


**FIGURE 10.29 Flexors of the Wrist and Hand.** Anterior views of the forearm. (a) Superficial flexors. (b) The intermediate flexor digitorum superficialis, deep to the muscles in part (a). (c) Deep flexors. Flexor muscles of each compartment are labeled in boldface. APR

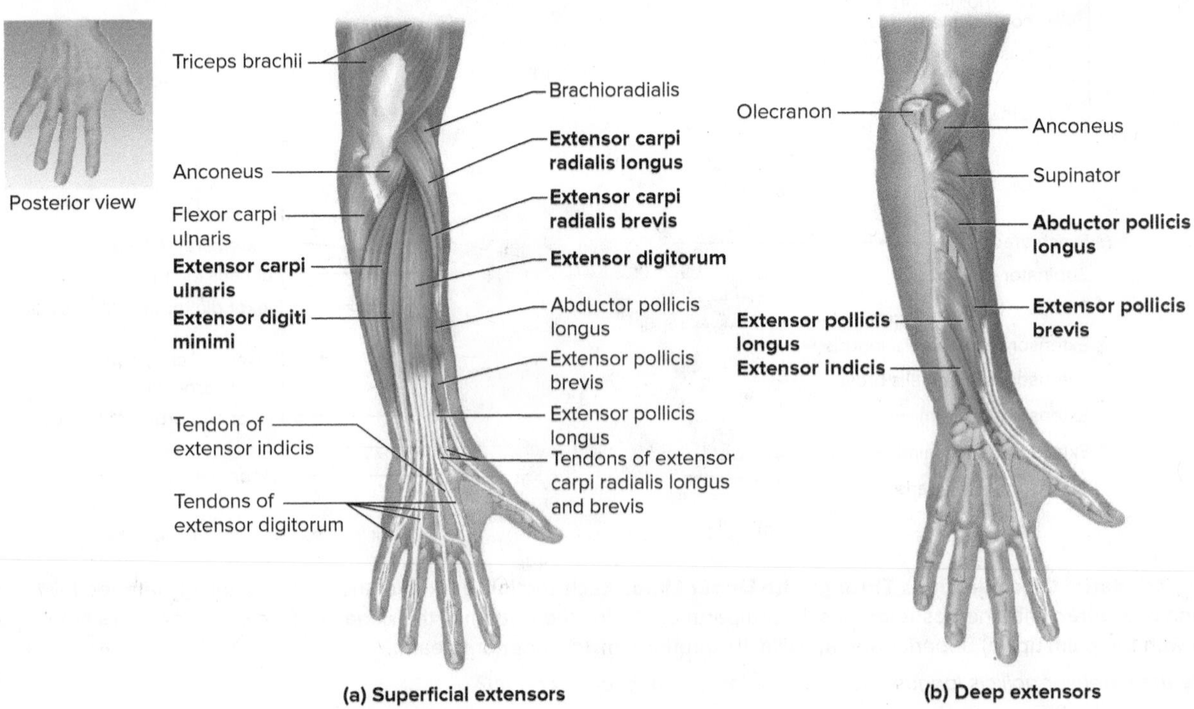


**FIGURE 10.30 Extensors of the Wrist and Hand.** Posterior views of the forearm. Extensor muscles of each compartment are labeled in boldface. (a) Superficial extensors. (b) Deep extensors. APR

has four distal tendons that can easily be seen and palpated on the back of the hand when the fingers are strongly extended (see fig. B.19b). It serves digits II through V, and the other muscles in this group each serve a single digit. These superficial extensors are tabulated as follows and in the table from lateral to medial.

## The Posterior (Extensor) Compartment, Deep Layer

The deep muscles that follow serve only the thumb and index finger **(fig. 10.30b)**. By strongly abducting and extending the thumb into a hitchhiker's position, you may see a deep dorsolateral pit at the base of the thumb, with a taut tendon on each side of it (see fig. B.19b). This depression is called the *anatomical snuffbox* because it was once fashionable to place a pinch of snuff here and inhale it. It is bordered laterally by the tendons of the **abductor pollicis longus** and **extensor pollicis brevis,** and medially by the tendon of the **extensor pollicis longus.** Dedication of so many muscles to the thumb alone (to which *pollicis* refers) attests to the supreme importance of the thumb for so much of the hand's functionality; try to imagine how much less you could do with your hands without the thumbs and these muscles.

**TABLE 10.11 Muscles Acting on the Wrist and Hand**

| Name | Action | Skeletal Attachments | Innervation |
|---|---|---|---|
| **The Anterior (Flexor) Compartment, Superficial Layer** | | | |
| Flexor carpi radialis[64] (FLEX-ur CAR-pye RAY-dee-AY-lis) | Flexes wrist anteriorly; aids in radial flexion of wrist | • Medial epicondyle of humerus<br>• Base of metacarpals II–III | Median nerve |
| Flexor carpi ulnaris[65] (ul-NAY-ris) | Flexes wrist anteriorly; aids in ulnar flexion of wrist | • Medial epicondyle of humerus; medial margin of olecranon; posterior surface of ulna<br>• Metacarpal V; pisiform; hamate | Ulnar nerve |
| Flexor digitorum superficialis[66] (DIDJ-ih-TOE-rum SOO-per-FISH-ee-AY-lis) | Flexes wrist, metacarpophalangeal, and interphalangeal joints depending on action of other muscles | • Medial epicondyle of humerus; ulnar collateral ligament; coronoid process; superior half of radius<br>• Middle phalanges II–V | Median nerve |
| Palmaris longus (pal-MERR-iss) | Anchors skin and fascia of palmar region; resists shearing forces when stress is applied to skin by such actions as climbing and tool use. Weakly developed and sometimes absent. | • Medial epicondyle of humerus<br>• Flexor retinaculum, palmar aponeurosis | Median nerve |
| **Anterior (Flexor) Compartment, Deep Layer** | | | |
| Flexor digitorum profundus[67] | Flexes wrist, metacarpophalangeal, and interphalangeal joints; sole flexor of the distal interphalangeal joints | • Proximal three-quarters of ulna; coronoid process; interosseous membrane<br>• Distal phalanges II–V | Median nerve; ulnar nerve |
| Flexor pollicis[68] longus (PAHL-ih-sis) | Flexes phalanges of thumb | • Radius; interosseous membrane<br>• Distal phalanx I | Median nerve |

*(continued)*

[64]*carpi* = of the wrist; *radialis* = of the radius
[65]*ulnaris* = of the ulna
[66]*digitorum* = of the digits; *superficialis* = shallow, near the surface
[67]*profundus* = deep
[68]*pollicis* = of the thumb

**TABLE 10.11 Muscles Acting on the Wrist and Hand (continued)**

| Name | Action | Skeletal Attachments | Innervation |
|---|---|---|---|
| **Posterior (Extensor) Compartment, Superficial Layer** | | | |
| Extensor carpi radialis longus | Extends wrist; aids in radial flexion of wrist | • Lateral supracondylar ridge of humerus<br>• Base of metacarpal II | Radial nerve |
| Extensor carpi radialis brevis (BREV-iss) | Extends wrist; aids in radial flexion of wrist | • Lateral epicondyle of humerus<br>• Base of metacarpal III | Radial nerve |
| Extensor digitorum | Extends wrist, metacarpophalangeal, and interphalangeal joints; tends to spread digits apart when extending metacarpophalangeal joints | • Lateral epicondyle of humerus<br>• Dorsal surfaces of phalanges II–V | Radial nerve |
| Extensor digiti minimi[69] (DIDJ-ih-ty MIN-ih-my) | Extends wrist and all joints of little finger | • Lateral epicondyle of humerus<br>• Proximal phalanx V | Radial nerve |
| Extensor carpi ulnaris | Extends and fixes wrist when fist is clenched or hand grips an object; aids in ulnar flexion of wrist | • Lateral epicondyle of humerus; posterior surface of ulnar shaft<br>• Base of metacarpal V | Radial nerve |
| **Posterior (Extensor) Compartment, Deep Layer** | | | |
| Abductor pollicis longus | Abducts thumb in frontal (palmar) plane (radial abduction); extends thumb at carpometacarpal joint | • Posterior surfaces of radius and ulna; interosseous membrane<br>• Trapezium; base of metacarpal I | Radial nerve |
| Extensor pollicis brevis | Extends metacarpal I and proximal phalanx of thumb | • Shaft of radius; interosseous membrane<br>• Proximal phalanx I | Radial nerve |
| Extensor pollicis longus | Extends distal phalanx I; aids in extending proximal phalanx I and metacarpal I; adducts and laterally rotates thumb | • Posterior surface of ulna; interosseous membrane<br>• Distal phalanx I | Radial nerve |
| Extensor indicis (IN-dih-sis) | Extends wrist and index finger | • Posterior surface of ulna; interosseous membrane<br>• Middle and distal phalanges of index finger | Radial nerve |

## 10.4e Intrinsic Muscles of the Hand

The intrinsic muscles of the hand **(table 10.12)** assist the flexors and extensors in the forearm and make finger movements more precise. They are divided into three groups: the *thenar group* at the base of the thumb, the *hypothenar group* at the base of the little finger, and the *midpalmar group* between these **(fig. 10.32).**

### The Thenar Group

The **thenar group** of muscles forms the thick fleshy mass *(thenar eminence)* at the base of the thumb, and the **adductor pollicis** forms the web between the thumb and palm. All are concerned with thumb movements. The adductor pollicis has an oblique head that extends from the capitate bone of the wrist to the ulnar side of the base of the thumb, and a transverse head that extends from metacarpal III to the same termination as the oblique head.

### The Hypothenar Group

The **hypothenar group** forms the fleshy mass *(hypothenar eminence)* at the base of the little finger. All of these muscles are concerned with movement of that digit.

### The Midpalmar Group

The **midpalmar group** occupies the hollow of the palm. It has 11 small muscles divided into three groups—four **dorsal interosseous,** three **palmar interosseous,** and four **lumbrical muscles.**

[69] *digit* = finger; *minim* = smallest

## DEEPER INSIGHT 10.5
### CLINICAL APPLICATION

### *Carpal Tunnel Syndrome*

Prolonged, repetitive motions of the wrist and fingers can cause tissues in the carpal tunnel to become inflamed, swollen, or fibrotic. Since the carpal tunnel cannot expand, swelling puts pressure on the median nerve of the wrist, which passes through the carpal tunnel with the flexor tendons **(fig. 10.31).** This pressure causes tingling and muscular weakness in the palm and medial side of the hand and pain that may radiate to the arm and shoulder. This condition, called *carpal tunnel syndrome,* is common among keyboard operators, pianists, meat cutters, and others who spend long hours making repetitive wrist motions. Carpal tunnel syndrome is treated with aspirin and other anti-inflammatory drugs, immobilization of the wrist, and sometimes dividing the flexor retinaculum with a longitudinal incision to relieve pressure on the nerve.

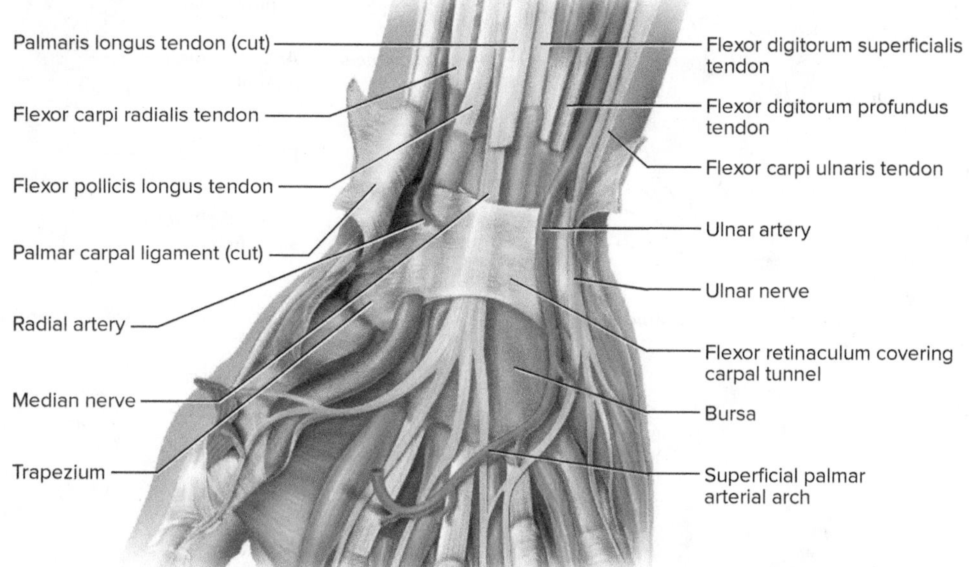


**(a) Anterior view**

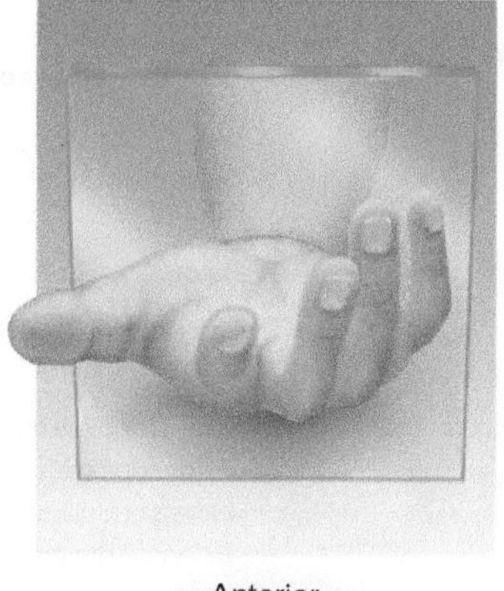

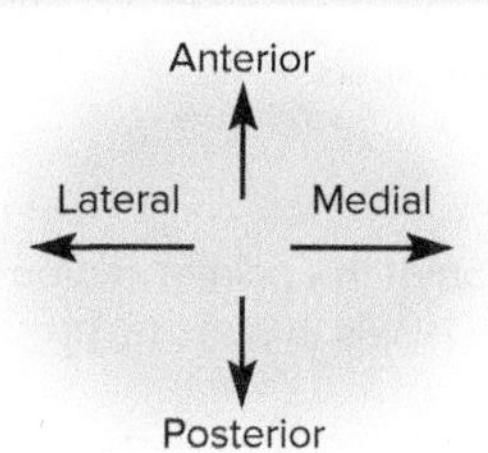


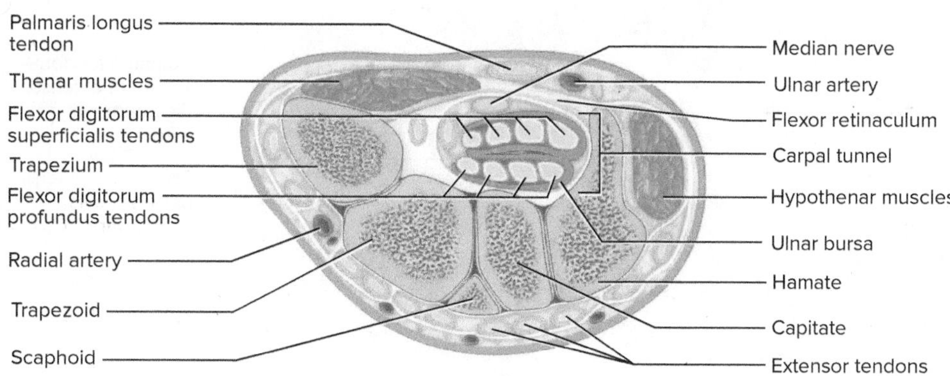


**(b) Cross section**

**FIGURE 10.31 The Carpal Tunnel.** (a) Dissection of the wrist (anterior view) showing the tendons, nerve, and bursae that pass under the flexor retinaculum. APR (b) Cross section of the wrist, viewed as if from the distal end of a person's right forearm extended toward you with the palm up. Note how the flexor tendons and median nerve are confined in the tight space between the carpal bones and flexor retinaculum. That tight packing and repetitive sliding of the flexor tendons through the tunnel contribute to carpal tunnel syndrome.

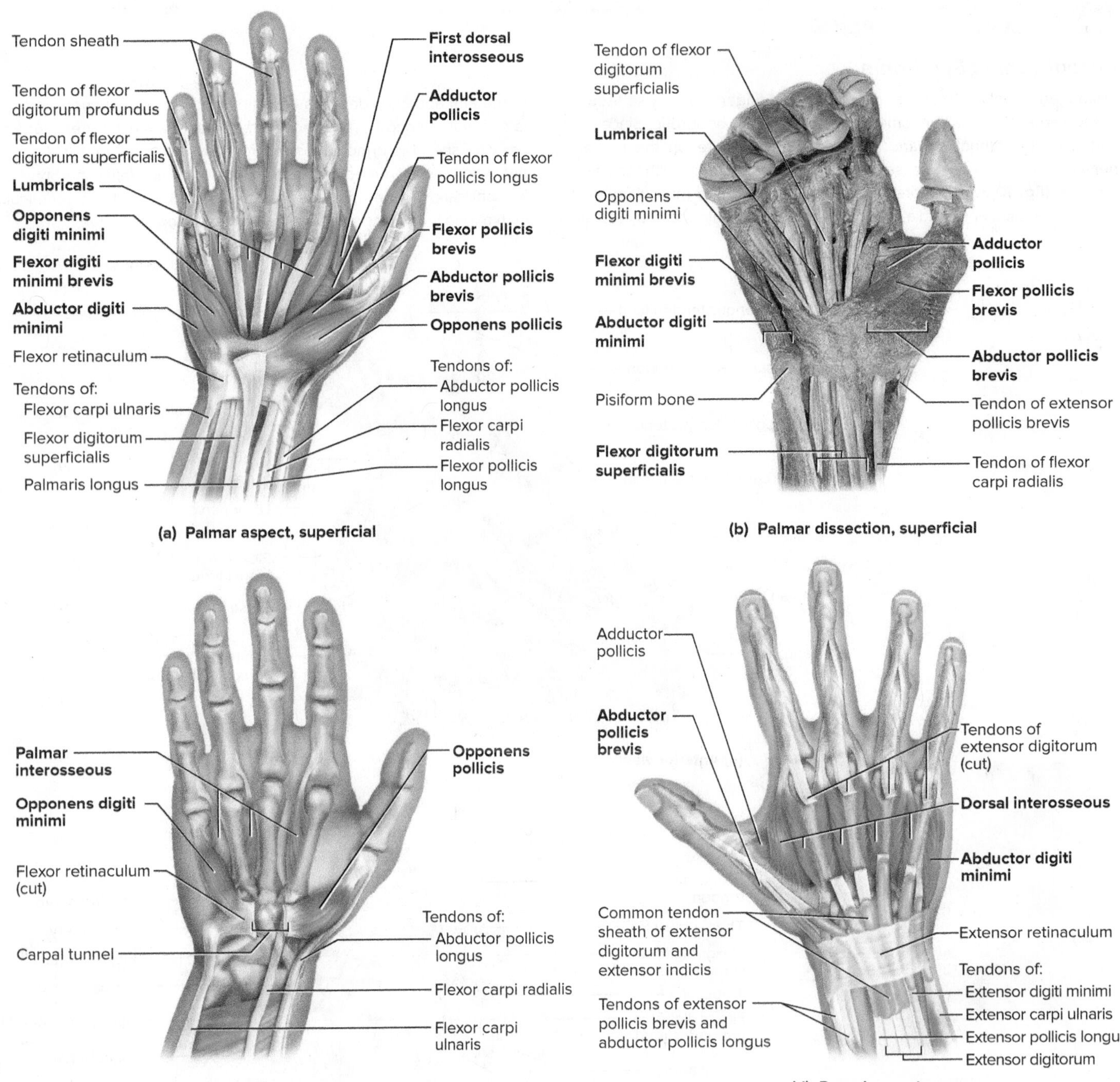


**FIGURE 10.32 Intrinsic Muscles of the Hand.** (a) Superficial muscles of the palmar aspect. (b) Dissection of the palmar region of the cadaver hand. (c) Deep muscles of the palmar aspect. (d) Muscles of the dorsal aspect. The boldface labels in parts (a), (c), and (d) indicate the muscles that belong to the respective layers. APR

**TABLE 10.12 Intrinsic Muscles of the Hand**

| Name | Action | Skeletal Attachments | Innervation |
|---|---|---|---|
| **Thenar Group** | | | |
| Adductor pollicis | Draws thumb toward palm as in gripping a tool | • Capitate; bases of metacarpals II–III; anterior ligaments of wrist; tendon sheath of flexor carpi radialis<br>• Medial surface of proximal phalanx I | Ulnar nerve |
| Abductor pollicis brevis | Abducts thumb in sagittal plane | • Mainly flexor retinaculum; also scaphoid, trapezium, and abductor pollicis longus tendon<br>• Lateral surface of proximal phalanx I | Median nerve |
| Flexor pollicis brevis | Flexes metacarpophalangeal joint of thumb | • Trapezium; trapezoid; capitate; anterior ligaments of wrist; flexor retinaculum<br>• Proximal phalanx I | Median nerve; ulnar nerve |
| Opponens pollicis (op-PO-nenz) | Flexes metacarpal I to oppose thumb to fingertips | • Trapezium; flexor retinaculum<br>• Metacarpal I | Median nerve |
| **Hypothenar Group** | | | |
| Abductor digiti minimi | Abducts little finger, as in spreading fingers apart | • Pisiform; tendon of flexor carpi ulnaris<br>• Medial surface of proximal phalanx V | Ulnar nerve |
| Flexor digiti minimi brevis | Flexes little finger at metacarpophalangeal joint | • Hamulus of hamate bone; flexor retinaculum<br>• Medial surface of proximal phalanx V | Ulnar nerve |
| Opponens digiti minimi | Flexes metacarpal V at carpometacarpal joint when little finger is moved into opposition with tip of thumb; deepens palm of hand | • Hamulus of hamate bone; flexor retinaculum<br>• Medial surface of metacarpal V | Ulnar nerve |
| **Midpalmar Group** | | | |
| Four dorsal interosseous[70] muscles (IN-tur-OSS-ee-us) | Abduct fingers; strongly flex metacarpophalangeal joints but extend interphalangeal joints, depending on action of other muscles; important in grip strength | • Each with two heads arising from facing surfaces of adjacent metacarpals<br>• Proximal phalanges II–IV | Ulnar nerve |
| Three palmar interosseous muscles | Adduct fingers; other actions same as for dorsal interosseous muscles | • Metacarpals I, II, IV, V<br>• Proximal phalanges II, IV, V | Ulnar nerve |
| Four lumbrical[71] muscles (LUM-brih-cul) | Extend interphalangeal joints; contribute to ability to pinch objects between fleshy pulp of thumb and finger, instead of these digits meeting by the edges of their nails | • Tendons of flexor digitorum profundus<br>• Proximal phalanges II–V | Median nerve; ulnar nerve |

**BEFORE YOU GO ON**

Answer the following questions to test your understanding of the preceding section:

**16.** Name a muscle that inserts on the scapula and plays a significant role in each of the following actions:
   a. pushing a stalled car,
   b. paddling a canoe,
   c. squaring the shoulders in military attention,
   d. lifting the shoulder to carry a heavy box on it, and
   e. lowering the shoulder to lift a suitcase.

**17.** Describe three contrasting actions of the deltoid muscle.

**18.** Name the four rotator cuff muscles and describe the scapular surfaces against which they lie.

**19.** Name the prime movers of elbow flexion and extension.

**20.** Identify three functions of the biceps brachii.

**21.** Name three extrinsic muscles and two intrinsic muscles that flex the phalanges.

[70] *inter* = between; *osse* = bones
[71] *lumbrical* = resembling an earthworm

## 10.5 Muscles Acting on the Hip and Lower Limb

**Expected Learning Outcomes**

When you have completed this section, you should be able to

a. name and locate the muscles that act on the hip, knee, ankle, and toe joints;
b. relate the actions of these muscles to the joint movements described in chapter 9; and
c. describe the skeletal attachments, action, and innervation of these muscles.

The largest muscles are found in the lower limb. Unlike those of the upper limb, they are adapted less for precision than for the strength needed to stand, maintain balance, walk, and run. Several of them cross and act upon two or more joints, such as the hip and knee. To avoid confusion in this discussion, remember that in the anatomical sense the word *leg* refers only to that part of the limb between the knee and ankle. The *foot* includes the tarsal region, metatarsal region, and toes. The next four tables group the muscles of the lower limb into those that act on the thigh and hip joint, those that act on the leg and knee joint, extrinsic (leg) muscles that act on the foot and ankle joint, and intrinsic (foot) muscles that act on the arches and toes.

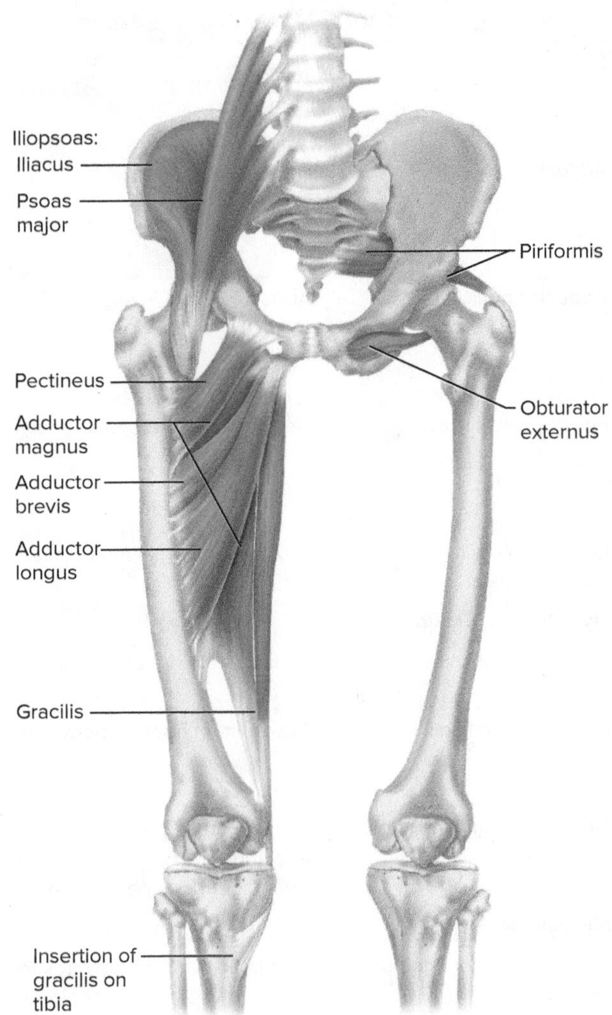


**FIGURE 10.33 Muscles That Act on the Hip and Femur (Anterior View).** APR

### 10.5a Muscles Acting on the Hip and Thigh

The hip joint and thigh are acted on by muscles arising from both the pelvic girdle and the femur **(table 10.13).**

#### Anterior Muscles of the Hip

Most muscles that act on the femur originate on the hip bone. The two principal anterior muscles are the **iliacus,** which fills most of the broad iliac fossa of the pelvis, and the **psoas major,** a thick rounded muscle that arises mainly from the lumbar vertebrae **(fig. 10.33).** Collectively, they are called the **iliopsoas** and share a common tendon to the femur.

#### Lateral and Posterior Muscles of the Hip

On the lateral and posterior sides of the hip are the **tensor fasciae latae** and three gluteal muscles. The **fascia lata** is a fibrous sheath that encircles the thigh like a subcutaneous stocking and tightly binds its muscles. On the lateral surface, it combines with the tendons of the gluteus maximus and tensor fasciae latae to form the **iliotibial tract,** which extends from the iliac crest to the lateral condyle of the tibia (see fig. 10.34; table 10.14). The tensor fasciae latae tautens the iliotibial tract and braces the knee, especially when the opposite foot is lifted.

The gluteal muscles are the **gluteus maximus, gluteus medius,** and **gluteus minimus (fig. 10.34).** The gluteus maximus is the largest of these and forms most of the lean mass of the buttock. It is an extensor of the hip joint that produces the backswing of the leg in walking and provides most of the lift when you climb stairs. It generates its maximum force when the thigh is flexed at a 45° angle to the trunk. This is the advantage in starting a foot race from a crouched position. The gluteus medius is deep and lateral to the gluteus maximus. Its name refers to its size, not its position. The gluteus minimus is the smallest and deepest of the three.

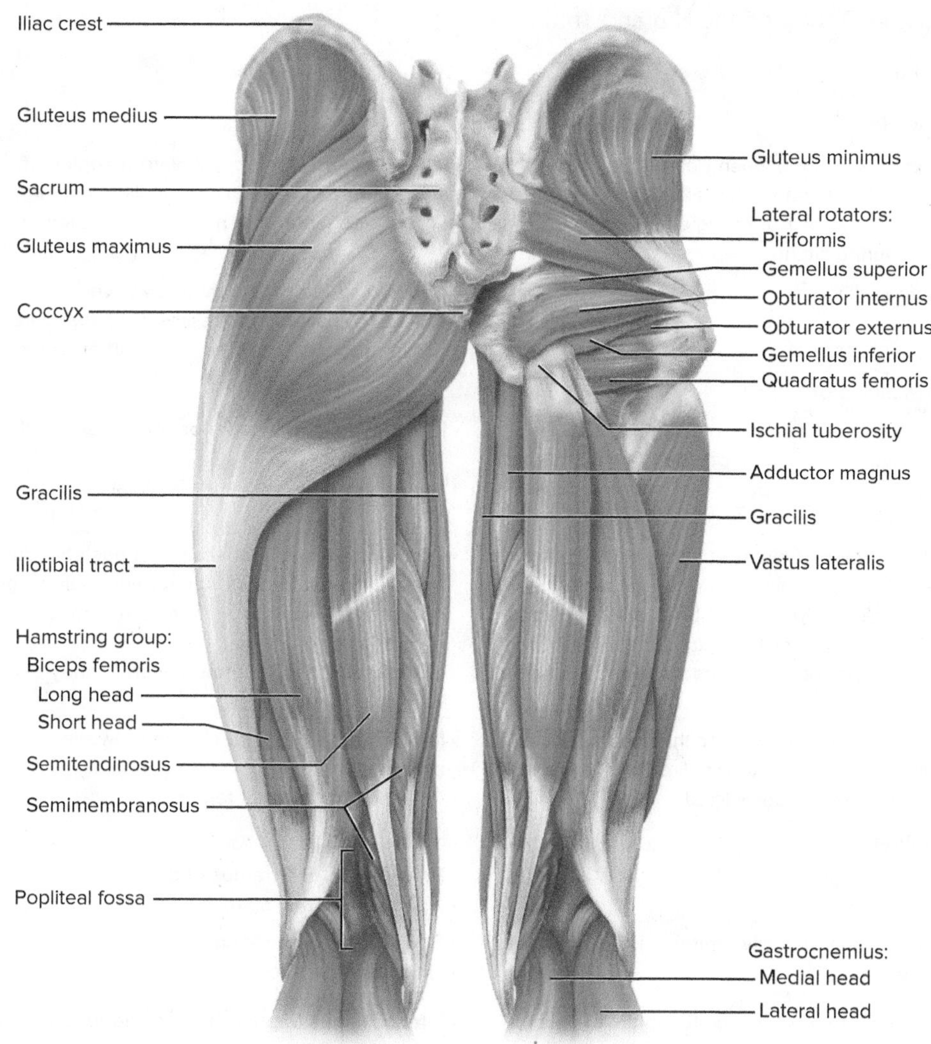


**FIGURE 10.34 Posterior Gluteal and Thigh Muscles.** The left side shows the superficial muscles. On the right, the gluteus medius and maximus are removed to show the deeper gluteus minimus, lateral rotator group, and hamstring origins. The oblique white tendinous band across the semitendinosus is not always present. APR

*Describe two everyday movements of the body that employ the power of the gluteus maximus.*

## Medial (Adductor) Compartment of the Thigh

Fasciae divide the thigh into three compartments: the anterior (extensor) compartment, posterior (flexor) compartment, and medial (adductor) compartment (see fig. 10.41). Muscles of the anterior and posterior compartments function mainly as extensors and flexors of the knee, respectively, and are treated in table 10.14. The five muscles of the medial compartment act primarily as adductors of the thigh (see fig. 10.33), but some of them cross both the hip and knee joints and have additional actions as follows.

## Lateral Rotators

Inferior to the gluteus minimus and deep to the other two gluteal muscles are six muscles called the **lateral rotators,** named for their action on the femur (fig. 10.34). Their action is most clearly visualized when you cross your legs to rest an ankle on your knee, causing your femur to rotate and the knee to point laterally. Thus, they oppose medial rotation by the gluteus medius and minimus. Most of them also abduct or adduct the femur. The abductors are important in walking because when one lifts a foot from the ground, they shift the body weight to the other leg and prevent falling.

**TABLE 10.13 Muscles Acting on the Hip and Thigh**

| Name | Action | Skeletal Attachments | Innervation |
|---|---|---|---|
| **Anterior Muscles of the Hip** | | | |
| Iliacus[72] (ih-LY-uh-cus) | Flexes thigh at hip when trunk is fixed; flexes trunk at hip when thigh is fixed, as in bending forward in a chair or sitting up in bed; balances trunk during sitting | • Iliac crest and fossa; superolateral region of sacrum; anterior sacroiliac and iliolumbar ligaments<br>• Lesser trochanter and nearby shaft of femur | Femoral nerve |
| Psoas[73] major (SO-ass) | Same as iliacus | • Bodies and intervertebral discs of vertebrae T12–L5; transverse processes of lumbar vertebrae<br>• Lesser trochanter and nearby shaft of femur | Anterior rami of lumbar spinal nerves |
| **Lateral and Posterior Muscles of the Hip** | | | |
| Tensor fasciae latae[74] (TEN-sur FASH-ee-ee LAY-tee) | Extends knee, laterally rotates tibia, aids in abduction and medial rotation of femur; during standing, steadies pelvis on femoral head and steadies femoral condyles on tibia | • Iliac crest; anterior superior spine; deep surface of fascia lata<br>• Lateral condyle of tibia via iliotibial tract | Superior gluteal nerve |
| Gluteus maximus[75] | Extends thigh at hip as in stair climbing (rising to next step) or running and walking (backswing of limb); abducts thigh; elevates trunk after stooping; prevents trunk from pitching forward during walking and running; helps stabilize femur on tibia | • Posterior gluteal line of ilium, on posterior surface from iliac crest to posterior superior spine; coccyx; posterior surface of lower sacrum; aponeurosis of erector spinae<br>• Gluteal tuberosity of femur; lateral condyle of tibia via iliotibial tract | Inferior gluteal nerve |
| Gluteus medius and gluteus minimus | Abduct and medially rotate thigh; during walking, shift weight of trunk toward limb with foot on the ground as other foot is lifted | • Most of lateral surface of ilium between crest and acetabulum<br>• Greater trochanter of femur | Superior gluteal nerve |
| **Medial (Adductor) Compartment of the Thigh** | | | |
| Adductor brevis | Adducts thigh | • Body and inferior ramus of pubis<br>• Linea aspera and spiral line of femur | Obturator nerve |
| Adductor longus | Adducts and medially rotates thigh; flexes thigh at hip | • Body and inferior ramus of pubis<br>• Linea aspera of femur | Obturator nerve |
| Adductor magnus | Adducts and medially rotates thigh; extends thigh at hip | • Inferior ramus of pubis; ramus and tuberosity of ischium<br>• Linea aspera, gluteal tuberosity, and medial supracondylar line of femur | Obturator nerve; tibial nerve |
| Gracilis[76] (GRASS-ih-lis) | Flexes and medially rotates tibia at knee | • Body and inferior ramus of pubis; ramus of ischium<br>• Medial surface of tibia just below condyle | Obturator nerve |
| Pectineus[77] (pec-TIN-ee-us) | Flexes and adducts thigh | • Superior ramus of pubis<br>• Spiral line of femur | Femoral nerve |
| **Lateral Rotators** | | | |
| Gemellus[78] superior (jeh-MEL-us) | Laterally rotates extended thigh; abducts flexed thigh; sometimes absent | • Ischial spine<br>• Greater trochanter of femur | Nerve to obturator internus |
| Gemellus inferior | Same actions as gemellus superior | • Ischial tuberosity<br>• Greater trochanter of femur | Nerve to quadratus femoris |
| Obturator[79] externus (OB-too-RAY-tur) | Not well understood; thought to laterally rotate thigh in climbing | • External surface of obturator membrane; rami of pubis and ischium<br>• Femur between head and greater trochanter | Obturator nerve |

[72] *ili* = loin, flank
[73] *psoa* = loin
[74] *fasc* = band; *lat* = broad
[75] *glut* = buttock; *maxim* = largest
[76] *gracil* = slender
[77] *pectin* = comb
[78] *gemellus* = twin
[79] *obtur* = to close, stop up

| TABLE 10.13 | Muscles Acting on the Hip and Thigh (continued) | | |
|---|---|---|---|
| **Name** | **Action** | **Skeletal Attachments** | **Innervation** |
| **Lateral Rotators** *(continued)* | | | |
| Obturator internus | Not well understood; thought to laterally rotate extended thigh and abduct flexed thigh | • Ramus of ischium; inferior ramus of pubis; anteromedial surface of lesser pelvis<br>• Greater trochanter of femur | Nerve to obturator internus |
| Piriformis[80] (PIR-ih-FOR-mis) | Laterally rotates extended thigh; abducts flexed thigh | • Anterior surface of sacrum; gluteal surface of ilium; capsule of sacroiliac joint<br>• Greater trochanter of femur | Spinal nerves L5–S2 |
| Quadratus femoris[81] (quad-RAY-tus FEM-oh-ris) | Laterally rotates thigh | • Ischial tuberosity<br>• Intertrochanteric crest of femur | Nerve to quadratus femoris |

## 10.5b Muscles Acting on the Knee and Leg

The following muscles **(table 10.14)** form most of the mass of the thigh and produce their most obvious actions on the knee joint. Some of them, however, cross both the hip and knee joints and produce actions at both, moving the femur, tibia, and fibula.

### Anterior (Extensor) Compartment of the Thigh

The anterior compartment of the thigh contains the large **quadriceps femoris,** the prime mover of knee extension and the most powerful muscle of the body **(figs. 10.35, 10.36).** As the name *quadriceps* implies, it has four heads: the **rectus femoris, vastus lateralis, vastus medialis,** and **vastus intermedius.** All four converge on a single **quadriceps (patellar) tendon,** which extends to the patella, then continues as the **patellar ligament** and inserts on the tibial tuberosity. (Remember that a tendon usually extends from muscle to bone, and a ligament from bone to bone.) The patellar ligament is struck with a rubber reflex hammer to test the knee-jerk reflex. The quadriceps extends the knee when you stand up, take a step, or kick a ball. One head, the rectus femoris, contributes to running by acting with the iliopsoas to flex the hip in each airborne phase of the leg's cycle of motion. The rectus femoris also flexes the hip in such actions as high kicks, stair climbing, or simply drawing the leg forward during a stride.

Crossing the quadriceps from the lateral side of the hip to the medial side of the knee is the narrow, straplike **sartorius,** the longest muscle of the body. It flexes the hip and knee joints and laterally rotates the thigh, as in crossing the legs. It is colloquially called the "tailor's muscle" after the cross-legged posture of a tailor supporting his work on the raised knee.

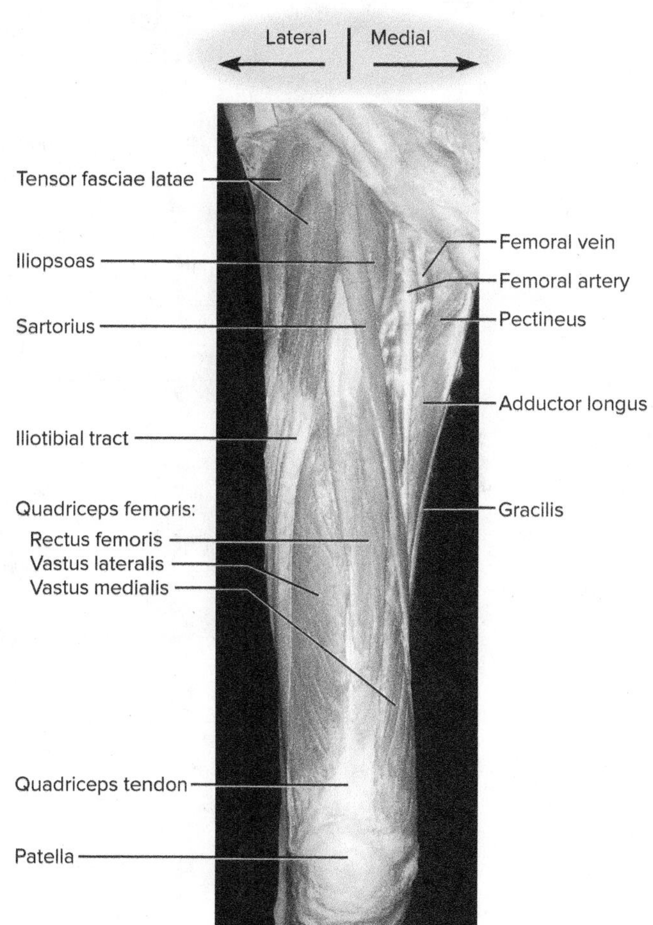


**FIGURE 10.35 Superficial Anterior Thigh Muscles of the Cadaver.** Right thigh.

Rebecca Gray/McGraw-Hill Education

### Posterior (Flexor) Compartment of the Thigh

The posterior compartment contains three muscles colloquially known as the **hamstring muscles;** from lateral to medial, they are the **biceps femoris, semitendinosus,** and **semimembranosus** (see fig. 10.34). The pit at the back of the knee, known anatomically as the **popliteal fossa,** is colloquially called the *ham.* The tendons of these muscles can be felt as prominent cords on both sides of the fossa—the biceps tendon on the lateral side and the

[80]*piri* = pear; *form* = shaped
[81]*quadrat* = four-sided; *femoris* = of the thigh or femur

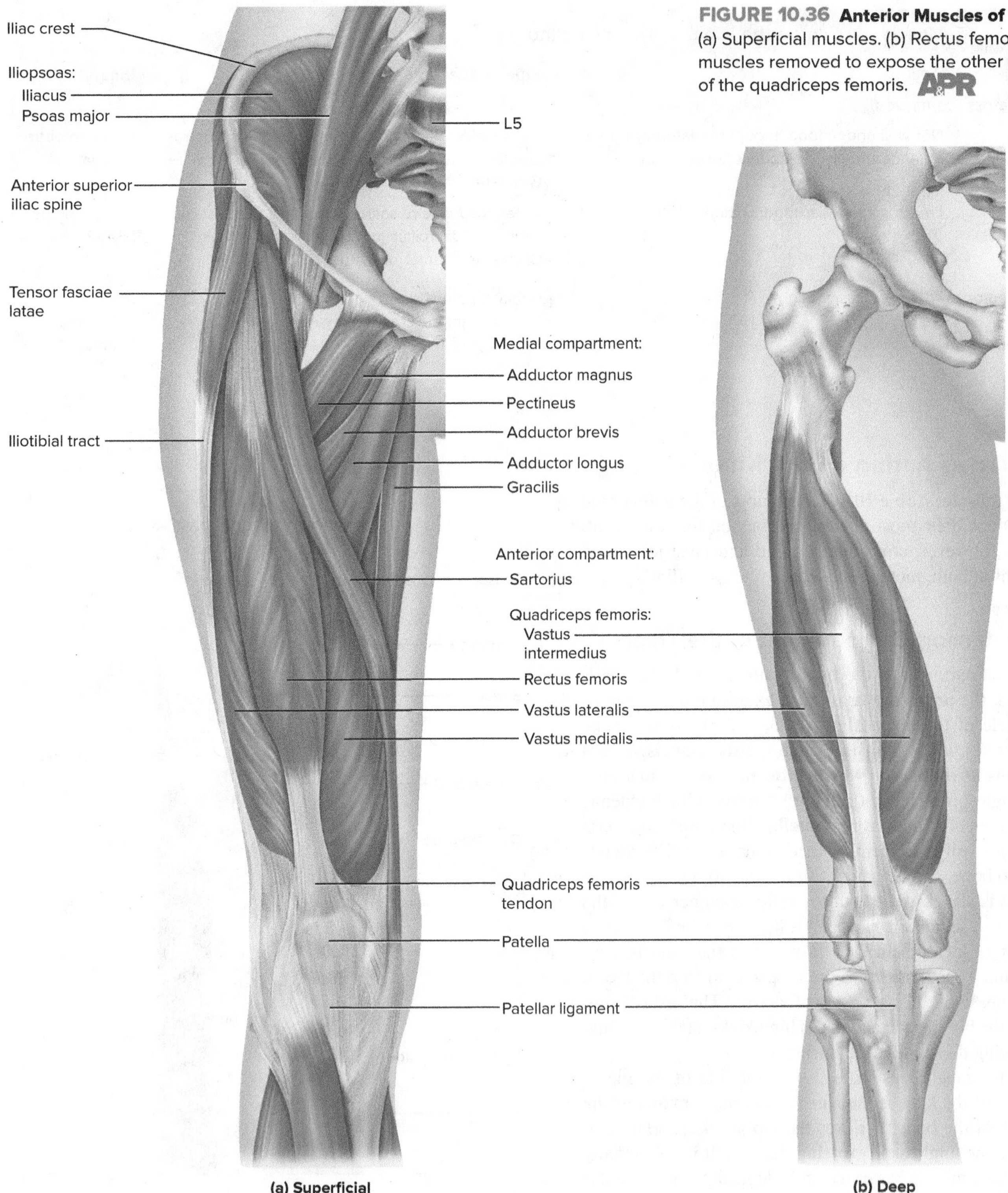


**FIGURE 10.36 Anterior Muscles of the Thigh.** (a) Superficial muscles. (b) Rectus femoris and other muscles removed to expose the other three heads of the quadriceps femoris. APR

semimembranosus and semitendinosus tendons on the medial side. When wolves attack large prey, they instinctively attempt to sever the hamstring tendons, because this renders the prey helpless. The hamstrings flex the knee, and aided by the gluteus maximus, they extend the hip during walking and running. The semitendinosus is named for its unusually long tendon. This muscle also is usually bisected by a transverse or oblique tendinous band. The semimembranosus is named for the flat shape of its superior attachment.

## Posterior Compartment of the Leg

Most muscles in the posterior compartment of the leg act on the ankle and foot and are reviewed in table 10.15, but the **popliteus** acts on the knee (see figs. 10.39, 10.40).

**TABLE 10.14 Muscles Acting on the Knee and Leg**

| Name | Action | Skeletal Attachments | Innervation |
|---|---|---|---|
| **Anterior (Extensor) Compartment of the Thigh** | | | |
| Quadriceps femoris (QUAD-rih-seps FEM-oh-ris) | Extends the knee, in addition to the actions of individual heads noted subsequently | • Varies; see individual heads<br>• Patella; tibial tuberosity; lateral and medial condyles of tibia | Femoral nerve |
| Rectus femoris | Extends knee; flexes thigh at hip; flexes trunk on hip if thigh is fixed | • Ilium at anterior inferior spine and superior margin of acetabulum; capsule of hip joint<br>• See quadriceps femoris | Femoral nerve |
| Vastus[82] lateralis | Extends knee; retains patella in groove on femur during knee movements | • Femur at greater trochanter and intertrochanteric line, gluteal tuberosity, and linea aspera<br>• See quadriceps femoris | Femoral nerve |
| Vastus medialis | Same as vastus lateralis | • Femur at intertrochanteric line, spiral line, linea aspera, and medial supracondylar line<br>• See quadriceps femoris | Femoral nerve |
| Vastus intermedius | Extends knee | • Anterior and lateral surfaces of femoral shaft<br>• See quadriceps femoris | Femoral nerve |
| Sartorius[83] | Aids in knee and hip flexion, as in sitting or climbing; abducts and laterally rotates thigh | • On and near anterior superior spine of ilium<br>• Medial surface of proximal end of tibia | Femoral nerve |
| **Posterior (Flexor) Compartment of the Thigh** | | | |
| Biceps femoris | Flexes knee; extends hip; elevates trunk from stooping posture; laterally rotates tibia on femur when knee is flexed; laterally rotates femur when hip is extended; counteracts forward bending at hips | • Long head: ischial tuberosity<br>Short head: linea aspera and lateral supracondylar line of femur<br>• Head of fibula | Tibial nerve; common fibular nerve |
| Semitendinosus[84] (SEM-ee-TEN-din-OH-sus) | Flexes knee; medially rotates tibia on femur when knee is flexed; medially rotates femur when hip is extended; counteracts forward bending at hips | • Ischial tuberosity<br>• Medial surface of upper tibia | Tibial nerve |
| Semimembranosus[85] (SEM-ee-MEM-bran-OH-sus) | Same as semitendinosus | • Ischial tuberosity<br>• Medial condyle and nearby margin of tibia; intercondylar line and lateral condyle of femur; ligament of popliteal region | Tibial nerve |
| **Posterior Compartment of the Leg** | | | |
| Popliteus[86] (pop-LIT-ee-us) | Rotates tibia medially on femur if femur is fixed (as in sitting down), or rotates femur laterally on tibia if tibia is fixed (as in standing up); unlocks knee to allow flexion; may prevent forward dislocation of femur during crouching | • Lateral condyle of femur; lateral meniscus and joint capsule<br>• Posterior surface of upper tibia | Tibial nerve |

[82]*vastus* = large, extensive
[83]*sartor* = tailor
[84]*semi* = half; *tendinosus* = tendinous
[85]*semi* = half; *membranosus* = membranous
[86]*poplit* = ham (pit) of the knee

## 10.5c Muscles Acting on the Ankle and Foot

The fleshy mass of the leg is formed by a group of crural muscles **(table 10.15),** which act on the foot **(fig. 10.37).** These muscles are tightly bound by fasciae that compress them and aid in the return of blood from the legs. The fasciae separate the crural muscles into anterior, lateral, and posterior compartments (see fig. 10.41b).

### Anterior (Extensor) Compartment of the Leg

Muscles of the anterior compartment dorsiflex the ankle and prevent the toes from scuffing the ground during walking. From lateral to medial, these muscles are the **fibularis tertius, extensor digitorum longus** (extensor of toes II–V), **extensor hallucis longus** (extensor of the great toe), and **tibialis anterior (fig. 10.38).** Their tendons are held tightly against the ankle and kept from bowing by two **extensor retinacula** similar to the one at the wrist.

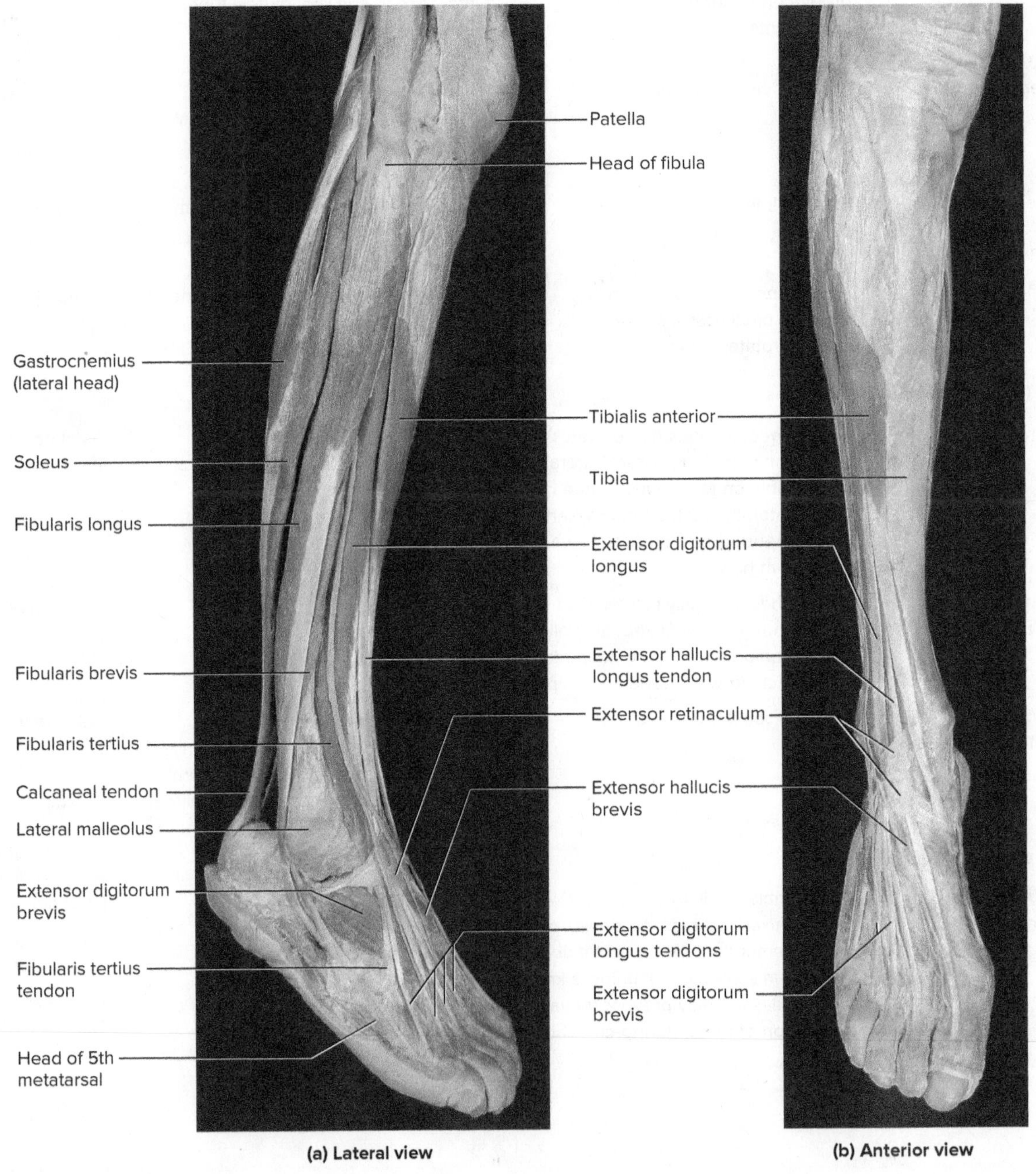


**FIGURE 10.37 Superficial Crural Muscles of the Cadaver.** Right leg. (a) Lateral view. (b) Anterior view.

a, b: Christine Eckel/McGraw-Hill Education

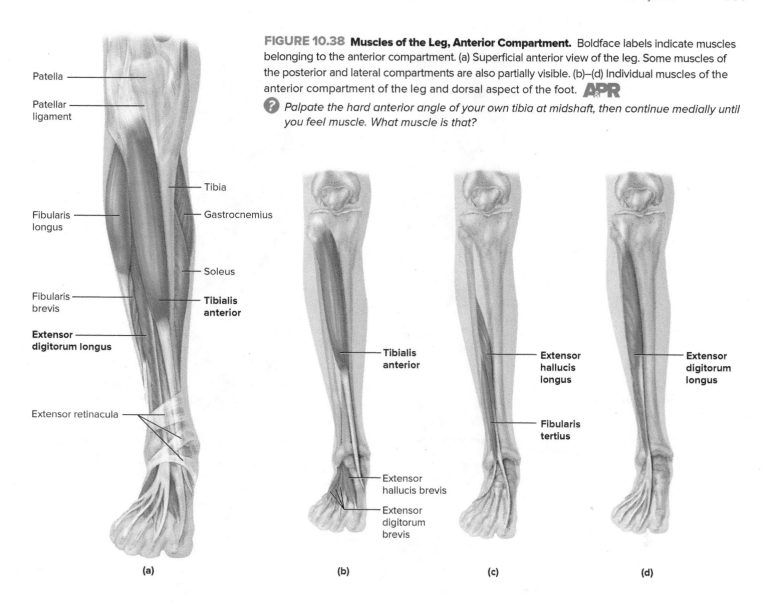

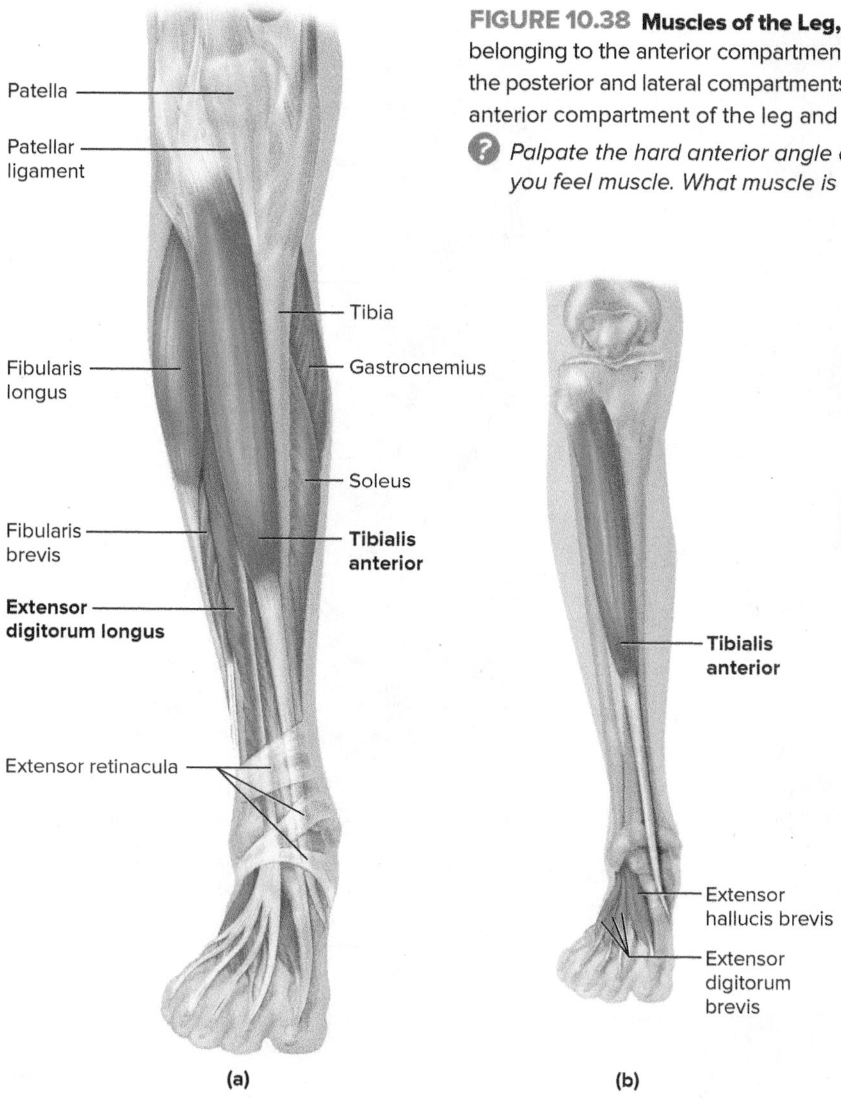

**FIGURE 10.38 Muscles of the Leg, Anterior Compartment.** Boldface labels indicate muscles belonging to the anterior compartment. (a) Superficial anterior view of the leg. Some muscles of the posterior and lateral compartments are also partially visible. (b)–(d) Individual muscles of the anterior compartment of the leg and dorsal aspect of the foot. APR

? *Palpate the hard anterior angle of your own tibia at midshaft, then continue medially until you feel muscle. What muscle is that?*

Inflammation of these tendons is one of the causes of *shinsplints* (see Deeper Insight 10.6).

## Posterior (Flexor) Compartment of the Leg, Superficial Group

The posterior compartment has superficial and deep muscle groups **(fig. 10.39).** The three muscles of the superficial group are plantar flexors: the **gastrocnemius, soleus,** and **plantaris.** The first two of these, collectively known as the **triceps surae,**[87] insert on the calcaneus by way of the **calcaneal (Achilles) tendon.** This is the strongest tendon of the body but is nevertheless a common site of sports injuries resulting from sudden stress (see Deeper Insight 10.7). The *plantaris,* a weak synergist of the triceps surae, is a relatively unimportant muscle and is absent from many people; it is not tabulated here. Surgeons often use the plantaris tendon for tendon grafts needed in other parts of the body.

[87]*tri* = three; *ceps* = heads; *surae* = of the calf

## DEEPER INSIGHT 10.6

### CLINICAL APPLICATION

#### *Shinsplints*

*Shinsplints* is a general term embracing several kinds of injury with pain in the crural region: tendinitis of the tibialis posterior muscle, inflammation of the tibial periosteum, and anterior compartment syndrome. Shinsplints can result from unaccustomed jogging, walking on snowshoes, or any vigorous activity of the legs after a period of relative inactivity.

## Posterior (Flexor) Compartment of the Leg, Deep Group

There are four muscles in the deep group **(fig. 10.40).** The **flexor digitorum longus, flexor hallucis longus,** and **tibialis posterior** are plantar flexors. The fourth muscle, the *popliteus,* is described in table 10.14 because it acts on the knee rather than on the foot.

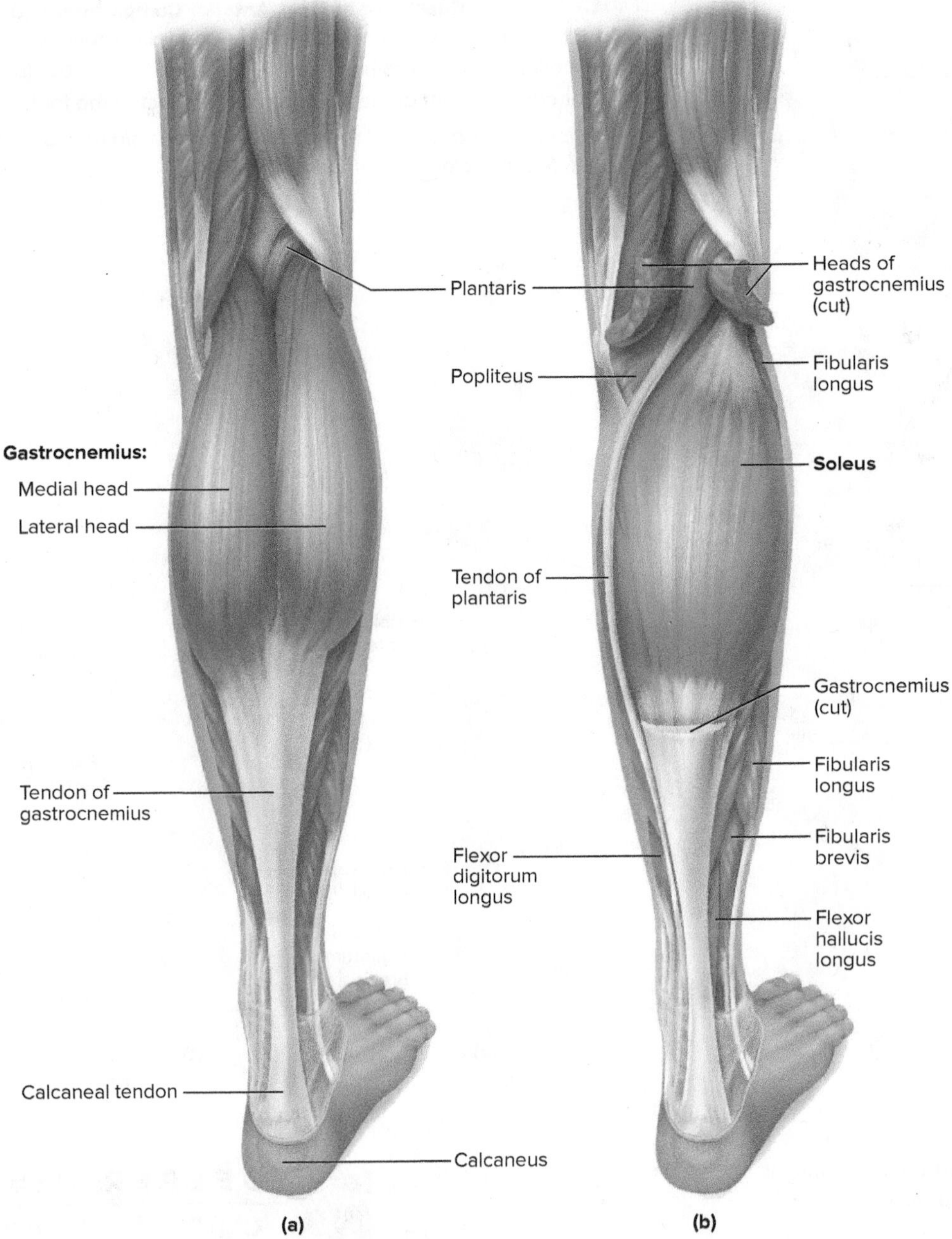

FIGURE 10.39 **Superficial Muscles of the Leg, Posterior Compartment.** (a) The gastrocnemius. (b) The soleus, deep to the gastrocnemius and sharing the calcaneal tendon with it. APR

## DEEPER INSIGHT 10.7

## CLINICAL APPLICATION

### *Calcaneal Tendon Rupture*

Calcaneal tendon rupture is a common injury experienced in amateur, strenuous sports such as basketball and tennis. When pushing off strongly from the ground as in a basketball jump shot, the tendon may rupture with a loud pop, described by some as sounding like a gunshot. The rupture causes pain just above the heel and inability to stand or walk on the affected leg. Two visible signs of a ruptured tendon are a large knot, the contracted triceps surae, in the upper calf; and abnormal dorsiflexion of the foot, caused by the action of the tibialis anterior suddenly unfettered by the opposing action of the triceps. Calcaneal tendon rupture is most common in overweight men, 30 to 40 years old, who are not in great physical condition but partake in an unaccustomed game such as pickup basketball or backyard football. A ruptured tendon can often heal on its own with rest and proper care, but may require surgical repair, especially in young physically active people not inclined to rest it for months.

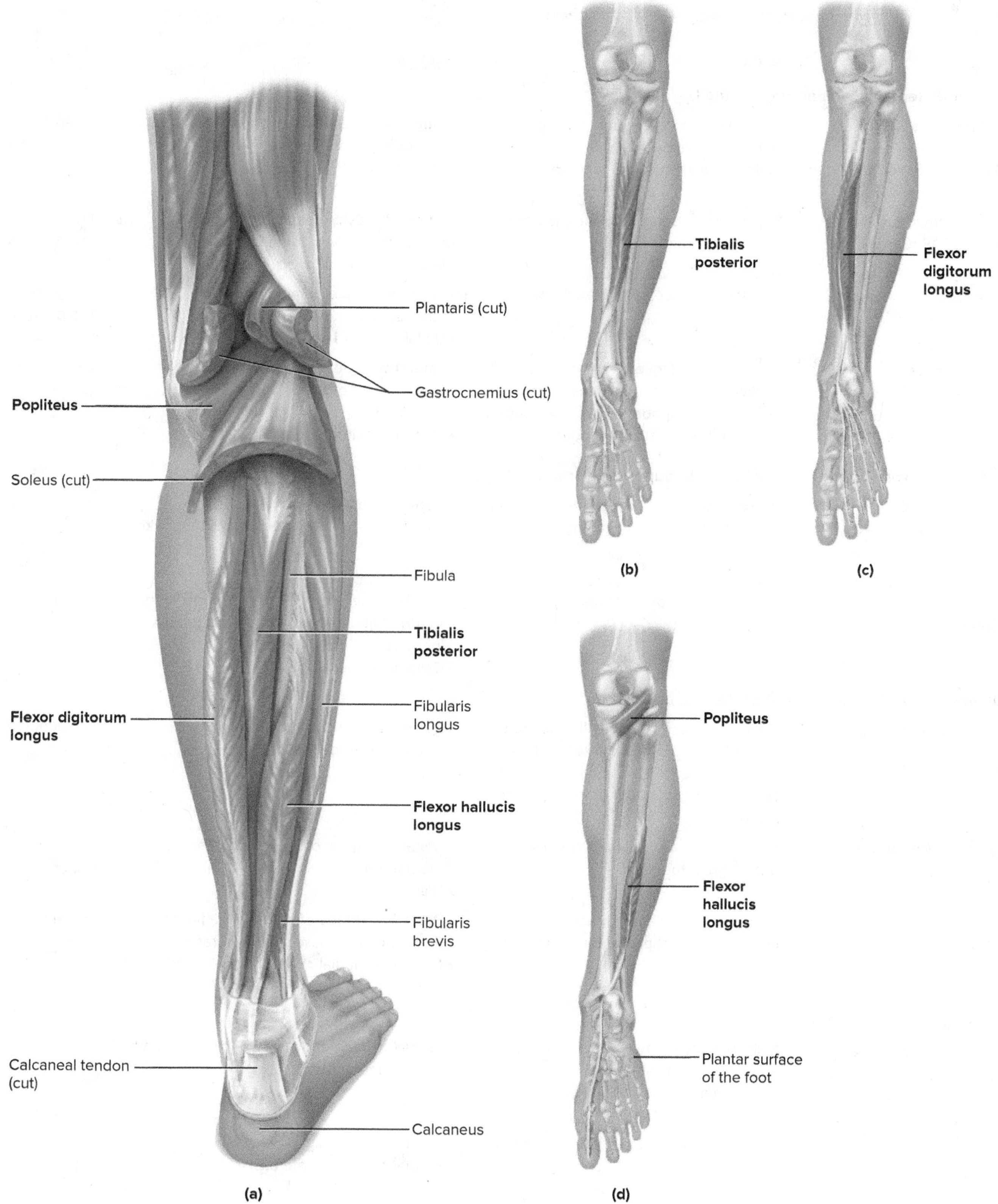


**FIGURE 10.40 Deep Muscles of the Leg, Posterior and Lateral Compartments.** (a) Muscles deep to the soleus. (b)–(d) Exposure of some individual deep muscles with the foot plantar flexed (sole facing viewer). APR

**TABLE 10.15 Muscles Acting on the Ankle and Foot**

| Name | Action | Skeletal Attachments | Innervation |
|---|---|---|---|
| **Anterior (Extensor) Compartment of the Leg** | | | |
| Fibularis (peroneus[88]) tertius[89] (FIB-you-LERR-iss TUR-she-us) | Dorsiflexes and everts foot during walking; helps toes clear the ground during forward swing of leg | • Medial surface of lower one-third of fibula; interosseous membrane<br>• Metatarsal V | Deep fibular (peroneal) nerve |
| Extensor digitorum longus (DIDJ-ih-TOE-rum) | Extends toes; dorsiflexes foot; tautens plantar aponeurosis | • Lateral condyle of tibia; shaft of fibula; interosseous membrane<br>• Middle and distal phalanges II–V | Deep fibular (peroneal) nerve |
| Extensor hallucis longus (ha-LOO-sis) | Extends great toe; dorsiflexes foot | • Anterior surface of middle of fibula, interosseous membrane<br>• Distal phalanx I | Deep fibular (peroneal) nerve |
| Tibialis[90] anterior (TIB-ee-AY-lis) | Dorsiflexes and inverts foot; resists backward tipping of body (as when standing on a moving boat deck); helps support medial longitudinal arch of foot | • Lateral condyle and lateral margin of proximal half of tibia; interosseous membrane<br>• Medial cuneiform, metatarsal I | Deep fibular (peroneal) nerve |
| **Posterior (Flexor) Compartment of the Leg, Superficial Group** | | | |
| Gastrocnemius[91] (GAS-trock-NEE-me-us) | Plantar flexes foot, flexes knee; active in walking, running, and jumping | • Condyles, popliteal surface, and lateral supracondylar line of femur; capsule of knee joint<br>• Calcaneus | Tibial nerve |
| Soleus[92] (SO-lee-us) | Plantar flexes foot; steadies leg on ankle during standing | • Posterior surface of head and proximal one-fourth of fibula; middle one-third of tibia; interosseous membrane<br>• Calcaneus | Tibial nerve |
| **Posterior (Flexor) Compartment of the Leg, Deep Group** | | | |
| Flexor digitorum longus | Flexes phalanges of digits II–V as foot is raised from ground; stabilizes metatarsal heads and keeps distal pads of toes in contact with ground in toe-off and tiptoe movements | • Posterior surface of tibial shaft<br>• Distal phalanges II–V | Tibial nerve |
| Flexor hallucis longus | Same actions as flexor digitorum longus, but for great toe (digit I) | • Distal two-thirds of fibula and interosseous membrane<br>• Distal phalanx I | Tibial nerve |
| Tibialis posterior | Inverts foot; may assist in strong plantar flexion or control pronation of foot during walking | • Posterior surface of proximal half of tibia, fibula, and interosseous membrane<br>• Navicular, medial cuneiform, metatarsals II–IV | Tibial nerve |
| **Lateral (Fibular) Compartment of the Leg** | | | |
| Fibularis (peroneus) brevis | Maintains concavity of sole during toe-off and tiptoeing; may evert foot and limit inversion and help steady leg on foot | • Lateral surface of distal two-thirds of fibula<br>• Base of metatarsal V | Superficial fibular (peroneal) nerve |
| Fibularis (peroneus) longus | Maintains concavity of sole during toe-off and tiptoeing; everts and plantar flexes foot | • Head and lateral surface of proximal two-thirds of fibula<br>• Medial cuneiform, metatarsal I | Superficial fibular (peroneal) nerve |

[88] *perone* = pinlike (fibula)
[89] *fibularis* = of the fibula; *tert* = third
[90] *tibialis* = of the tibia
[91] *gastro* = belly; *cnem* = leg
[92] Named for its resemblance to a flatfish (sole)

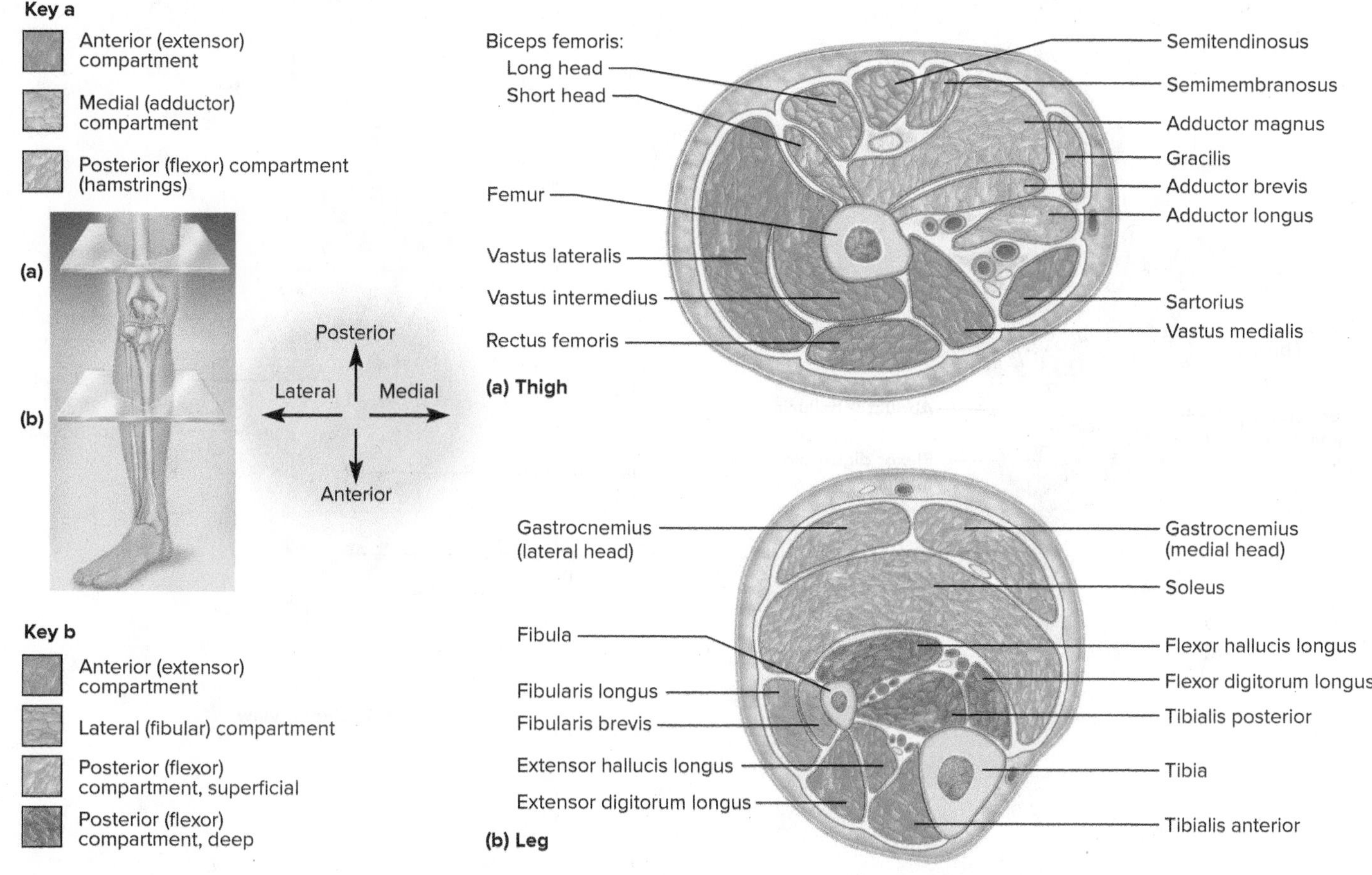


**FIGURE 10.41 Serial Cross Sections Through the Lower Limb.** Cross sections of the femur (a) and leg (b) are taken at the correspondingly lettered levels in the figure at the left.

### Lateral (Fibular) Compartment of the Leg

The lateral compartment includes the **fibularis brevis** and **fibularis longus** (see figs. 10.37a, 10.38a; **fig. 10.41**). They plantar flex and evert the foot. Plantar flexion is important not only in standing on tiptoes but in providing lift and forward thrust each time you take a step.

**▶▶▶ APPLY WHAT YOU KNOW**

*Suppose you tilt your foot upward to trim or paint your toenails. Identify as many muscles as you know that can contribute to this action.*

**▶▶▶ APPLY WHAT YOU KNOW**

*Suppose you are playing Frisbee and your Frisbee lands on the roof of your house. You have to climb a ladder to get it. Identify as many muscles as you can that would aid you in ascending from one rung of the ladder to the next.*

## 10.5d Intrinsic Muscles of the Foot

The intrinsic muscles of the foot **(table 10.16)** help to support the arches and act on the toes in ways that aid locomotion. Several of them are similar in name and location to the intrinsic muscles of the hand.

### Dorsal (Superior) Aspect of the Foot

Only one of the intrinsic muscles, the **extensor digitorum brevis,** is on the dorsal (superior) side of the foot. The medial slip of this muscle, serving the great toe, is sometimes called the *extensor hallucis brevis*.

### Ventral Layer 1 (Most Superficial)

All remaining intrinsic muscles are on the ventral (inferior) aspect of the foot or between the metatarsal bones. They are grouped in four layers **(fig. 10.42).** Dissecting into the foot from the plantar surface, one first encounters a tough fibrous sheet, the **plantar aponeurosis,** between the skin and muscles. It diverges like a fan from the calcaneus to the bases of all the toes, and is a common site of painful inflammation (see Deeper Insight 10.8). Several ventral muscles arise from this aponeurosis. The ventral muscles include the stout **flexor digitorum brevis** on the midline of the foot, with four tendons that supply all digits except the great toe. It is flanked by the **abductor digiti minimi** laterally and the **abductor hallucis** medially.

### Ventral Layer 2

The next deeper layer consists of the thick **quadratus plantae (flexor accessorius)** in the middle of the foot and the four **lumbrical muscles** located between the metatarsals.

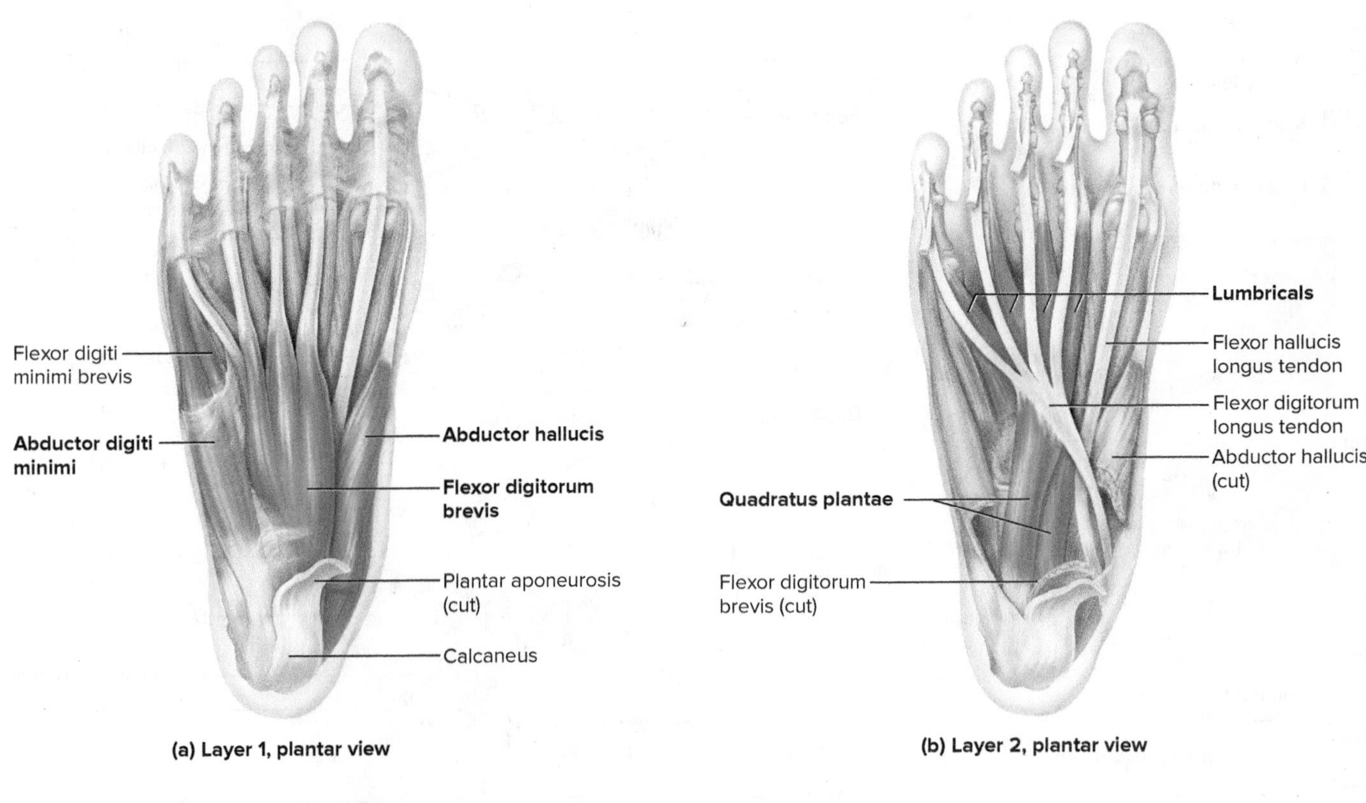


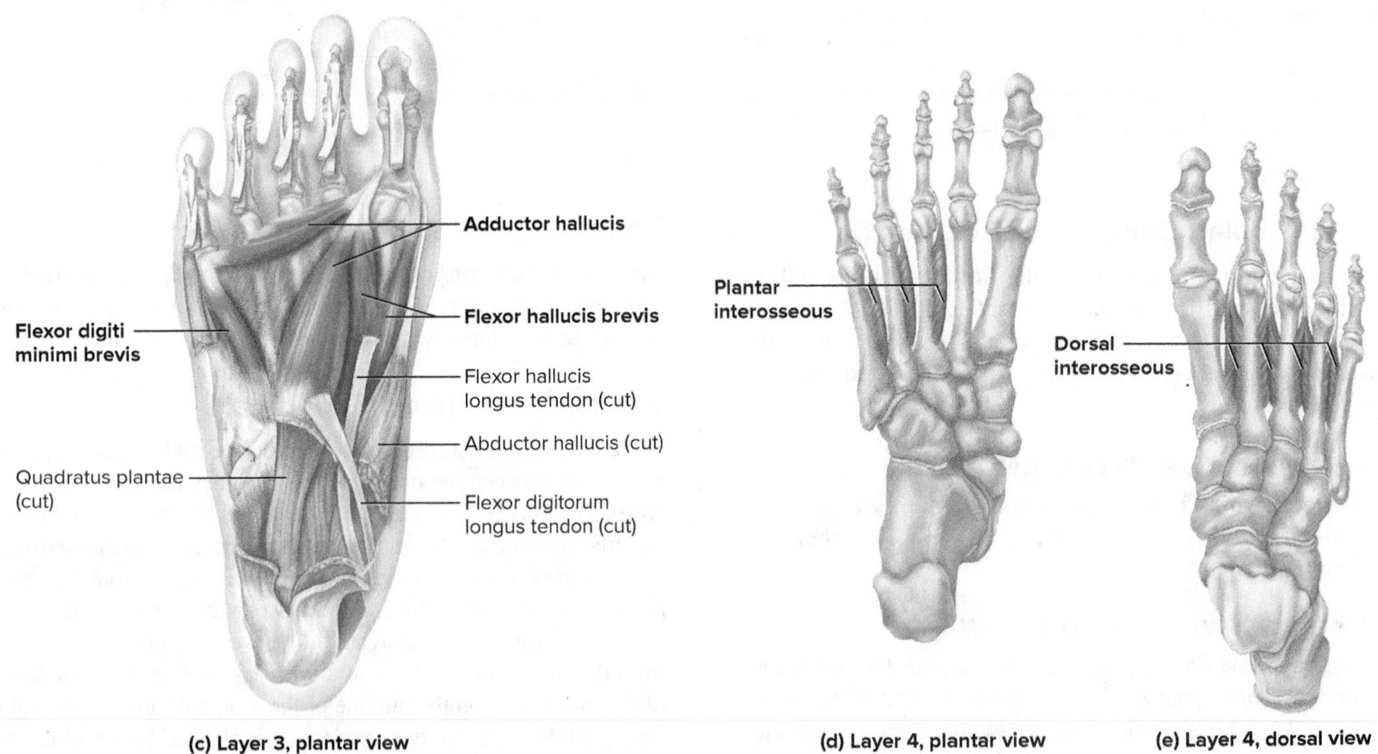


**FIGURE 10.42 Intrinsic Muscles of the Foot.** (a)–(d) First through fourth layers, respectively, in ventral (plantar) views. (e) Fourth layer, dorsal view. The muscles belonging to each layer are shown in color and with boldface labels. APR

## DEEPER INSIGHT 10.8

### CLINICAL APPLICATION

### *Plantar Fasciitis*

*Plantar fasciitis* (FASH-ee-EYE-tis) is inflammation of the plantar aponeurosis, typically felt as a recurring pain in the heel and medial aspect of the foot. The pain is often most severe when one begins to walk after prolonged sitting or when rising from bed. It usually subsides in 5 to 10 minutes, but occurs again after the next period of rest. Dorsiflexion of the foot often intensifies the pain. Plantar fasciitis typically results from excessive or unaccustomed running and high-impact aerobics, especially in persons who don't wear properly supportive athletic footwear.

**TABLE 10.16 Intrinsic Muscles of the Foot**

| Name | Action | Skeletal Attachments | Innervation |
|---|---|---|---|
| **Dorsal (Superior) Aspect of Foot** | | | |
| Extensor digitorum brevis | Extends proximal phalanx I and all phalanges of digits II–IV | • Calcaneus; inferior extensor retinaculum of ankle<br>• Proximal phalanx I, tendons of extensor digitorum longus to middle and distal phalanges II–IV | Deep fibular (peroneal) nerve |
| **Ventral Layer 1 (Most Superficial)** | | | |
| Flexor digitorum brevis | Flexes digits II–IV; supports arches of foot | • Calcaneus; plantar aponeurosis<br>• Middle phalanges II–V | Medial plantar nerve |
| Abductor digiti minimi[93] | Abducts and flexes little toe; supports arches of foot | • Calcaneus; plantar aponeurosis<br>• Proximal phalanx V | Lateral plantar nerve |
| Abductor hallucis | Abducts great toe; supports arches of foot | • Calcaneus; plantar aponeurosis; flexor retinaculum<br>• Proximal phalanx I | Medial plantar nerve |
| **Ventral Layer 2** | | | |
| Quadratus plantae[94] (quad-RAY-tus PLAN-tee) | Same as flexor digitorum longus (table 10.15); flexion of digits II–V and associated locomotor functions | • Two heads on the medial and lateral sides of calcaneus<br>• Distal phalanges II–V via flexor digitorum longus tendons | Lateral plantar nerve |
| Four lumbrical muscles (LUM-brih-cul) | Flex toes II–V | • Tendon of flexor digitorum longus<br>• Proximal phalanges II–V | Lateral and medial plantar nerves |
| **Ventral Layer 3** | | | |
| Flexor digiti minimi brevis | Flexes little toe | • Metatarsal V, sheath of fibularis longus<br>• Proximal phalanx V | Lateral plantar nerve |
| Flexor hallucis brevis | Flexes great toe | • Cuboid; lateral cuneiform; tibialis posterior tendon<br>• Proximal phalanx I | Medial plantar nerve |
| Adductor hallucis | Adducts great toe | • Metatarsals II–IV; fibularis longus tendon; ligaments at bases of digits III–V<br>• Proximal phalanx I | Lateral plantar nerve |
| **Ventral Layer 4 (Deepest)** | | | |
| Four dorsal interosseous muscles | Abduct toes II–IV | • Each with two heads arising from facing surfaces of two adjacent metatarsals<br>• Proximal phalanges II–IV | Lateral plantar nerve |
| Three plantar interosseous muscles | Adduct toes III–V | • Medial aspect of metatarsals III–V<br>• Proximal phalanges III–V | Lateral plantar nerve |

[93]*digit* = toe; *minim* = smallest

[94]*quadrat* = four-sided; *plantae* = of the plantar region

## Ventral Layer 3

The muscles of this layer serve only the great and little toes. They are the **flexor digiti minimi brevis, flexor hallucis brevis,** and **adductor hallucis.** The adductor hallucis has an oblique head that extends diagonally from the midplantar region to the base of the great toe, and a transverse head that passes across the bases of digits II–IV and meets the long head at the base of the great toe.

## Ventral Layer 4 (Deepest)

This layer consists only of the small interosseous muscles located between the metatarsal bones—four dorsal and three plantar. Each **dorsal interosseous muscle** is bipennate and originates on two adjacent metatarsals. The **plantar interosseous muscles** are unipennate and originate on only one metatarsal each.

**▶▶▶APPLY WHAT YOU KNOW**

*Not everyone has the same muscles. From the information provided in this chapter, identify at least three muscles that are lacking in some people.*

**BEFORE YOU GO ON**

Answer the following questions to test your understanding of the preceding section:

**22.** In the middle of a stride, you have one foot on the ground and you are about to swing the other leg forward. What muscles produce the movements of that leg?

**23.** Name the muscles that cross both the hip and knee joints and produce actions at both.

**24.** List the major actions of the muscles of the anterior, medial, and posterior compartments of the thigh.

**25.** Describe the roles of plantar flexion and dorsiflexion in walking. What muscles produce these actions?

## DEEPER INSIGHT 10.9

### CLINICAL APPLICATION

### *Common Athletic Injuries*

Although the muscular system is subject to fewer diseases than most organ systems, it is particularly vulnerable to injuries resulting from sudden and intense stress placed on muscles and tendons. Each year, thousands of athletes from the high-school to professional level sustain some type of injury to their muscles, as do the increasing numbers of people who have taken up running and other forms of physical conditioning. Overzealous exertion without proper conditioning and warm-up is frequently the cause. This chapter has already described several examples: compartment syndrome, rotator cuff injury, shinsplints, calcaneal tendon rupture, and plantar fasciitis. A few more are described here.

**Baseball finger**—tears in the extensor tendons of the fingers resulting from the impact of a baseball with the extended fingertip.

**Blocker's arm**—abnormal calcification in the lateral margin of the forearm as a result of repeated impact with opposing players.

**Charley horse**—any painful tear, stiffness, and blood clotting in a muscle. A charley horse of the quadriceps femoris is often caused by football tackles.

**Pitcher's arm**—inflammation at the proximal attachment of the flexor carpi muscles resulting from hard wrist flexion in releasing a baseball.

**Pulled groin**—strain in the adductor muscles of the thigh; common in gymnasts and dancers who perform splits and high kicks.

**Pulled hamstrings**—strained hamstring muscles or a partial tear in their tendons, often with a hematoma (blood clot) in the fascia lata. This condition is frequently caused by repetitive kicking (as in football and soccer) or long, hard running.

**Tennis elbow**—inflammation at the proximal attachment of the extensor carpi muscles on the lateral epicondyle of the humerus. It occurs when these muscles are repeatedly tensed during backhand strokes and then strained by sudden impact with the tennis ball. Any activity that requires rotary movements of the forearm and a firm grip of the hand (for example, using a screwdriver) can cause the symptoms of tennis elbow.

Most athletic injuries can be prevented by proper conditioning. A person who suddenly takes up vigorous exercise may not have sufficient muscle and bone mass to withstand the stresses such exercise entails. These must be developed gradually. Stretching exercises keep ligaments and joint capsules supple and therefore reduce injuries. Warm-up exercises promote more efficient and less injurious musculoskeletal function in several ways. Most of all, moderation is important, as most injuries simply result from overuse of the muscles. "No pain, no gain" is a risky misconception.

Muscular injuries can be treated initially with "RICE": rest, ice, compression, and elevation. Rest prevents further injury and allows repair processes to occur; ice reduces swelling; compression with an elastic bandage helps to prevent fluid accumulation and swelling; and elevation of an injured limb promotes drainage of blood from the affected area and limits further swelling. If these measures are not enough, anti-inflammatory drugs may be employed, including corticosteroids as well as aspirin and other nonsteroidal agents. Serious injuries, such as compartment syndrome, require emergency attention by a physician.

# STUDY GUIDE

## Assess Your Learning Outcomes

*To test your knowledge, discuss the following topics with a study partner or in writing, ideally from memory.*

### 10.1 Structural and Functional Organization of Muscles

1. Which muscles are included in the muscular system and which ones are not; the name of the science that specializes in the muscular system
2. Functions of the muscular system
3. The relationship of muscle structure to the endomysium, perimysium, and epimysium; what constitutes a fascicle of skeletal muscle and how it relates to these connective tissues; and the relationship of a fascia to a muscle
4. Classification of muscles according to the orientation of their fascicles
5. Muscle compartments, interosseous membranes, and intermuscular septa
6. Direct, indirect, moving, and stationary muscle attachments
7. The flaw in *origin–insertion* terminology of muscle attachments
8. The action of a muscle; how it relates to the classification of muscles as *prime movers, synergists, antagonists,* or *fixators;* why these terms are not fixed for a given muscle but differ from one joint movement to another, and examples to illustrate this point
9. Intrinsic versus extrinsic muscles, with examples
10. The nerve and blood supplies to muscles
11. Features to which the Latin names of muscles commonly refer, with examples

### 10.2 Muscles of the Head and Neck

*Know the locations, actions, skeletal attachments, and innervations of the named muscles in each of the following groups, and be able to recognize them on laboratory specimens or models to the extent required in your course.*

1. The occipitofrontalis muscle of the scalp, eyebrows, and forehead (table 10.1)
2. The orbicularis oculi, levator palpebrae superioris, and corrugator supercilii muscles, which move the eyelid and other tissues around the eye (table 10.1)
3. The nasalis muscle, which flares and compresses the nostrils (table 10.1)
4. The orbicularis oris, levator labii superioris, levator anguli oris, zygomaticus major and minor, risorius, depressor anguli oris, depressor labii inferioris, and mentalis muscles, which act on the lips (table 10.1)
5. The buccinator muscles of the cheeks (table 10.1)
6. The platysma, which acts upon the mandible and the skin of the neck (table 10.1)
7. The intrinsic muscles of the tongue in general, and specific extrinsic muscles: the genioglossus, hyoglossus, styloglossus, and palatoglossus muscles (table 10.2)
8. The temporalis, masseter, medial pterygoid, and lateral pterygoid muscles of biting and chewing (table 10.2)
9. The suprahyoid group: the digastric, geniohyoid, mylohyoid, and stylohyoid muscles (table 10.2)
10. The infrahyoid group: the omohyoid, sternohyoid, thyrohyoid, and sternothyroid muscles (table 10.2)
11. The superior, middle, and inferior pharyngeal constrictor muscles of the throat (table 10.2)
12. The sternocleidomastoid and three scalene muscles, which flex the neck, and the trapezius, splenius capitis, and semispinalis capitis muscles, which extend it (table 10.3)

### 10.3 Muscles of the Trunk

*For the following muscles, know the same information as for section 10.2.*

1. The diaphragm and the external intercostal, internal intercostal, and innermost intercostal muscles of respiration (table 10.4)
2. The external oblique, internal oblique, transverse abdominal, and rectus abdominis muscles of the anterior and lateral abdominal wall (table 10.5)
3. The superficial erector spinae muscle (and its subdivisions) and the deep semispinalis thoracis, quadratus lumborum, and multifidus muscles of the back (table 10.6)
4. The perineum, its two triangles, and their skeletal landmarks (table 10.7)
5. The ischiocavernosus and bulbospongiosus muscles of the superficial perineal space of the pelvic floor (table 10.7)
6. The deep transverse perineal muscle, and in females, the compressor urethrae of the deep perineal space of the pelvic floor, and the external anal sphincter of the anal triangle (table 10.7)
7. The levator ani muscle of the pelvic diaphragm, the deepest compartment of the pelvic floor (table 10.7)

### 10.4 Muscles Acting on the Shoulder and Upper Limb

*For the following muscles, know the same information as for section 10.2.*

1. The pectoralis minor, serratus anterior, trapezius, levator scapulae, rhomboid major, and rhomboid minor muscles of scapular movement (table 10.8)
2. Muscles that act on the humerus, including the pectoralis major, latissimus dorsi, deltoid, teres major, coracobrachialis, and four rotator cuff (SITS) muscles—the supraspinatus, infraspinatus, teres minor, and subscapularis (table 10.9)
3. The brachialis, biceps brachii, triceps brachii, brachioradialis, anconeus, pronator quadratus, pronator teres, and supinator muscles of forearm movement (table 10.10)
4. The relationship of the flexor retinaculum, extensor retinaculum, and carpal tunnel to the tendons of the forearm muscles
5. The palmaris longus, flexor carpi radialis, flexor carpi ulnaris, and flexor digitorum superficialis muscles of the superficial anterior compartment of the forearm, and the flexor digitorum profundus and flexor pollicis longus muscles of the deep anterior compartment (table 10.11)
6. The extensor carpi radialis longus, extensor carpi radialis brevis, extensor digitorum, extensor digiti minimi, and extensor carpi ulnaris muscles of the superficial posterior compartment (table 10.11)
7. The abductor pollicis longus, extensor pollicis brevis, extensor pollicis longus, and extensor indicis muscles of the deep posterior compartment (table 10.11)
8. The thenar group of intrinsic hand muscles: adductor pollicis, abductor pollicis brevis, flexor pollicis brevis, and opponens pollicis (table 10.12)
9. The hypothenar group of intrinsic hand muscles: abductor digiti minimi, flexor digiti minimi brevis, and opponens digiti minimi (table 10.12)
10. The midpalmar group of intrinsic hand muscles: four dorsal interosseous muscles, three palmar interosseous muscles, and four lumbrical muscles (table 10.12)

# STUDY GUIDE

**10.5 Muscles Acting on the Hip and Lower Limb**

*For the following muscles, know the same information as for section 10.2.*

1. The iliopsoas muscle of the hip, and its two subdivisions, the iliacus and psoas major (table 10.13)
2. The tensor fasciae latae, gluteus maximus, gluteus medius, and gluteus minimus muscles of the hip and buttock, and the relationship of the first two to the fascia lata and iliotibial tract (table 10.13)
3. The lateral rotators: gemellus superior, gemellus inferior, obturator externus, obturator internus, piriformis, and quadratus femoris muscles (table 10.13)
4. The compartments of the thigh muscles: anterior (extensor), medial (adductor), and posterior (flexor) compartments
5. Muscles of the medial compartment of the thigh: adductor brevis, adductor longus, adductor magnus, gracilis, and pectineus (table 10.13)
6. Muscles of the anterior compartment of the thigh: sartorius and quadriceps femoris, and the four heads of the quadriceps (table 10.14)
7. The hamstring muscles of the posterior compartment of the thigh: biceps femoris, semitendinosus, and semimembranosus (table 10.14)
8. The compartments of the leg muscles: anterior, posterior, and lateral (table 10.15)
9. Muscles of the anterior compartment of the leg: fibularis tertius, extensor digitorum longus, extensor hallucis longus, and tibialis anterior muscles of the anterior compartment (table 10.15)
10. Muscles of the superficial posterior compartment of the leg: popliteus and triceps surae (gastrocnemius and soleus), and the relationship of the triceps surae to the calcaneal tendon and calcaneus (table 10.15)
11. Muscles of the deep posterior compartment of the leg: flexor digitorum longus, flexor hallucis longus, and tibialis posterior muscles of the deep posterior compartment
12. Muscles of the lateral compartment of the leg: fibularis brevis and fibularis longus (table 10.15)
13. The extensor digitorum brevis of the dorsal aspect of the foot (table 10.16)
14. The four muscle compartments (layers) of the ventral aspect of the foot, and the muscles in each: the flexor digitorum brevis, abductor digiti minimi, and abductor hallucis (layer 1); the quadratus plantae and four lumbrical muscles (layer 2); the flexor digiti minimi brevis, flexor hallucis brevis, and adductor hallucis (layer 3); and the four dorsal interosseous muscles and three plantar interosseous muscles (layer 4) (table 10.16)

## ▶ Testing Your Recall

*Answers in Appendix A*

1. Which of the following muscles does *not* contribute to the rotator cuff?
   a. teres minor
   b. teres major
   c. subscapularis
   d. infraspinatus
   e. supraspinatus

2. Make a fist, then straighten your fingers. The muscles that performed the latter action have tendons that pass through
   a. the flexor retinaculum.
   b. the extensor retinaculum.
   c. the carpal tunnel.
   d. the rotator cuff.
   e. the plantar region of the wrist.

3. Which of these is *not* a suprahyoid muscle?
   a. genioglossus
   b. geniohyoid
   c. stylohyoid
   d. mylohyoid
   e. digastric

4. Which of these muscles is an extensor of the neck?
   a. external oblique
   b. sternocleidomastoid
   c. splenius capitis
   d. iliocostalis
   e. latissimus dorsi

5. Which of these muscles of the pelvic floor is the deepest?
   a. superficial transverse perineal
   b. bulbospongiosus
   c. ischiocavernosus
   d. deep transverse perineal
   e. levator ani

6. Which of these actions is *not* performed by the trapezius?
   a. extension of the neck
   b. depression of the scapula
   c. elevation of the scapula
   d. rotation of the scapula
   e. adduction of the humerus

7. Both the hands and feet are acted upon by a muscle or muscles called
   a. the extensor digitorum.
   b. the abductor digiti minimi.
   c. the flexor digitorum profundus.
   d. the abductor hallucis.
   e. the flexor digitorum longus.

8. Which of the following muscles does *not* extend the hip joint?
   a. quadriceps femoris
   b. gluteus maximus
   c. biceps femoris
   d. semitendinosus
   e. semimembranosus

9. Both the gastrocnemius and ______ muscles insert on the heel by way of the calcaneal tendon.
   a. semimembranosus
   b. tibialis posterior
   c. tibialis anterior
   d. soleus
   e. plantaris

10. Which of the following muscles raises the upper lip?
    a. levator palpebrae superioris
    b. orbicularis oris
    c. zygomaticus minor
    d. masseter
    e. mentalis

11. What muscle is the prime mover in sucking through a soda straw or spitting out a mouthful of liquid?

12. A bundle of muscle fibers surrounded by perimysium is called a/an ______.

13. The ______ is the muscle that generates the most force in a given joint movement.

14. The three large muscles on the posterior side of the thigh are commonly known as the ______ muscles.

## STUDY GUIDE

15. Connective tissue bands called _____ prevent flexor tendons of the forearm and leg from rising like bowstrings.
16. The anterior half of the perineum is a region called the _____.
17. The abdominal aponeuroses converge on a median fibrous band on the abdomen called the _____.
18. A muscle that works with another to produce the same or similar movement is called a/an _____.
19. A muscle somewhat like a feather, with fibers obliquely approaching its tendon from both sides, is called a/an _____ muscle.
20. A circular muscle that closes a body opening is called a/an _____.

### Building Your Medical Vocabulary

*Answers in Appendix A*

*State a meaning of each word element, and give a medical term from this chapter that uses it or a slight variation of it.*

1. capito-
2. ergo-
3. fasc-
4. labio-
5. lumbo-
6. mus-
7. mys-
8. omo-
9. penn-
10. tert-

### What's Wrong with These Statements?

*Answers in Appendix A*

*Briefly explain why each of the following statements is false, or reword it to make it true.*

1. Each skeletal muscle fiber is enclosed in a perimysium that separates it from adjacent fibers.
2. The orbicularis oris is a sphincter.
3. The biceps brachii is a bipennate muscle.
4. A synergist is a muscle whose action is opposite that of an agonist.
5. Each skeletal muscle is innervated by at least one spinal nerve.
6. One must contract the internal intercostal muscles in order to exhale.
7. In climbing stairs, the hamstrings provide much of the thrust that lifts the body to each higher step.
8. Severing the large trigeminal nerve would paralyze more facial muscles than severing the facial nerve.
9. The following intrinsic hand muscles are listed in order from strongest to weakest: abductor digiti minimi, adductor pollicis, dorsal interosseous.
10. The tibialis anterior and tibialis posterior are synergists.

### Testing Your Comprehension

1. Radical mastectomy, once a common treatment for breast cancer, involved removal of the pectoralis major along with the breast. What functional impairments would result from this? What synergists could a physical therapist train a patient to use to recover some lost function?
2. Removal of cancerous lymph nodes from the neck sometimes requires removal of the sternocleidomastoid on that side. How would this affect a patient's range of head movement?
3. Bicycles are designed so the rider leans forward at about a 45° angle rather than sitting upright. Aside from issues of wind resistance, explain the advantage of this in terms of musculoskeletal anatomy of the hip region.
4. Women who wear high heels most of the time may suffer painful "high heel syndrome" when they go barefoot or wear flat shoes. What muscle(s) and tendon(s) are involved? Explain.
5. A student moving out of a dormitory crouches, in correct fashion, to lift a heavy box of books. What prime movers are involved as he straightens his legs to lift the box?

ATLAS

# B

# REGIONAL AND SURFACE ANATOMY

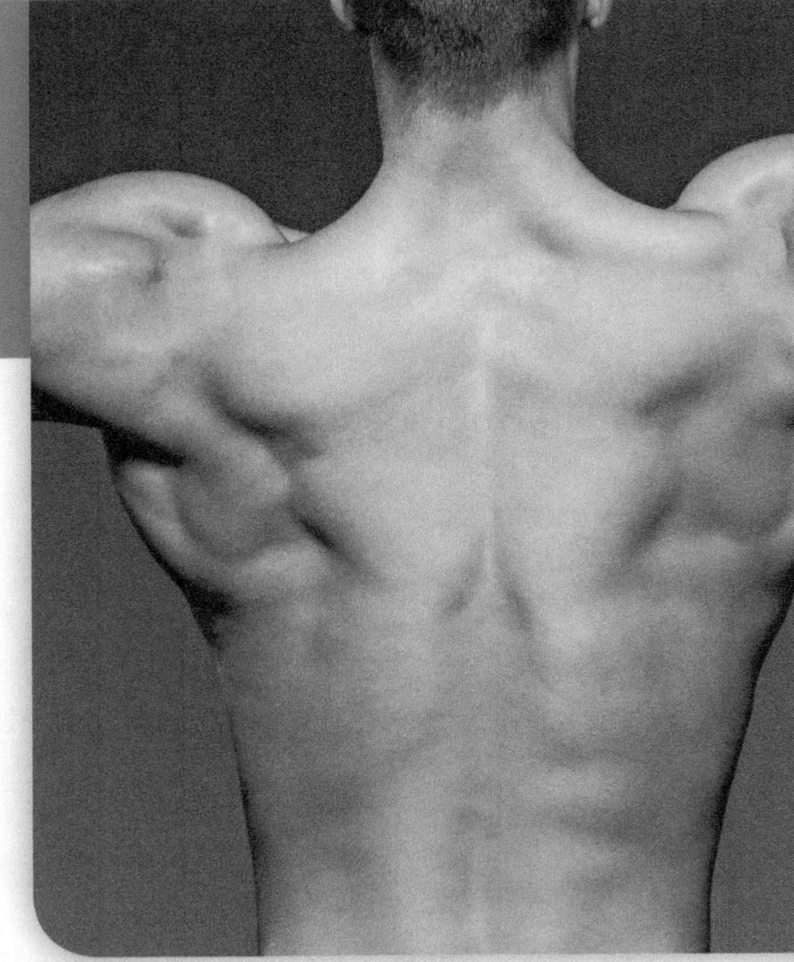

How many muscles can you identify from their surface appearance?

Y Photo Studio/Shutterstock

## ATLAS OUTLINE

**Module 6: Muscular System**

## B.1 Regional Anatomy

On the whole, this book takes a systems approach to anatomy, examining the structure and function of each organ system, one at a time, regardless of which body regions it may traverse. Physicians and surgeons, however, think and act in terms of regional anatomy. If a patient presents with pain in the lower right quadrant (see atlas A, fig. A.4a), the source may be the appendix, an ovary, or an inguinal muscle, among other possibilities. The question is to think not of an entire organ system (the esophagus is probably irrelevant to that quadrant), but of what organs are present in that region and what possibilities must be considered as the cause of the pain. This atlas presents several views of the body region by region so that you can see some of the spatial relationships that exist among the organ systems considered in their separate chapters.

## B.2 The Importance of Surface Anatomy

In the study of human anatomy, it is easy to become so preoccupied with internal structure that we forget the importance of what we can see and feel externally. Yet external anatomy and appearance are major concerns in giving a physical examination and in many aspects of patient care. A knowledge of the body's surface landmarks is essential to one's competence in physical therapy, cardiopulmonary resuscitation, surgery, making X-rays and electrocardiograms, giving injections, drawing blood, listening to heart and respiratory sounds, measuring the pulse and blood pressure, and finding pressure points to stop arterial bleeding, among other procedures. A misguided attempt to perform some of these procedures while disregarding or misunderstanding external anatomy can be very harmful and even fatal to a patient.

Having just studied skeletal and muscular anatomy in the preceding chapters, this is an opportune time for you to study the body surface. Much of what we see there reflects the underlying structure of the superficial bones and muscles. A broad photographic overview of surface anatomy is given in atlas A (see fig. A.3), where it is necessary for providing a vocabulary for reference in subsequent chapters. This atlas shows this surface anatomy in closer detail so you can relate it to the musculoskeletal anatomy of the three preceding chapters.

## B.3 Learning Strategy

To make the most profitable use of this atlas, refer back to earlier chapters as you study these illustrations. Relate drawings of the clavicle in figure 8.31 to the photograph in figure B.1, for example. Study the shape of the scapula in figure 8.32 and see how much of it you can trace on the photographs in figure B.9. See if you can relate the tendons visible on the hand (see fig. B.19) to the muscles of the forearm illustrated in figures 10.29 and 10.30, and the external markings of the pelvic girdle (see fig. B.15) to bone structure in section 8.5a.

For learning surface anatomy, there is a resource available to you that is far more valuable than any laboratory model or textbook illustration—your own body. For the best understanding of human structure, compare the art and photographs in this book with your body or with structures visible on a study partner. In addition to bones and muscles, you can palpate a number of superficial arteries, veins, tendons, ligaments, and cartilages, among other structures. By palpating regions such as the shoulder, elbow, or ankle, you can develop a mental image of the subsurface structures better than the image you can obtain by looking at two-dimensional textbook images. And the more you can study with other people, the more you will appreciate the variations in human structure and be able to apply your knowledge to your future patients or clients, who will not look quite like any textbook diagram or photograph you have ever seen. Through comparisons of art, photography, and the living body, you will get a much deeper understanding of the body than if you were to study this atlas in isolation from the earlier chapters.

At the end of this atlas, you can test your knowledge of externally visible muscle anatomy. The two photographs in figure B.25 have 30 numbered muscles and a list of 26 names, some of which are shown more than once in the photographs and some of which are not shown at all. Identify the muscles to your best ability without looking back at the previous illustrations, and then check your answers in appendix A.

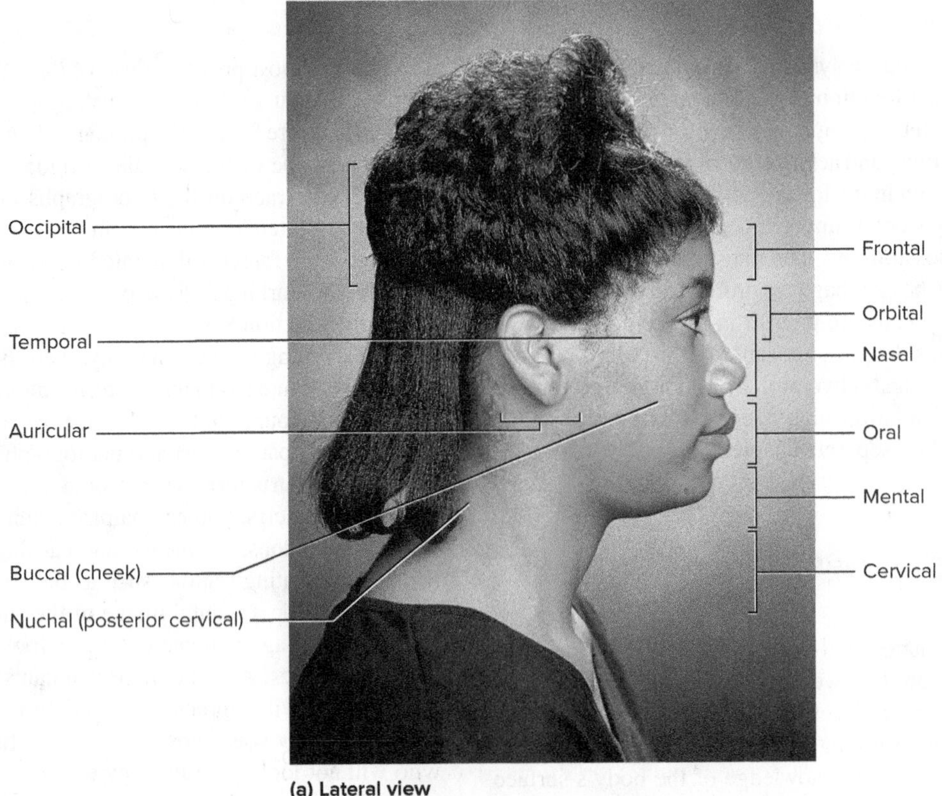


(a) Lateral view

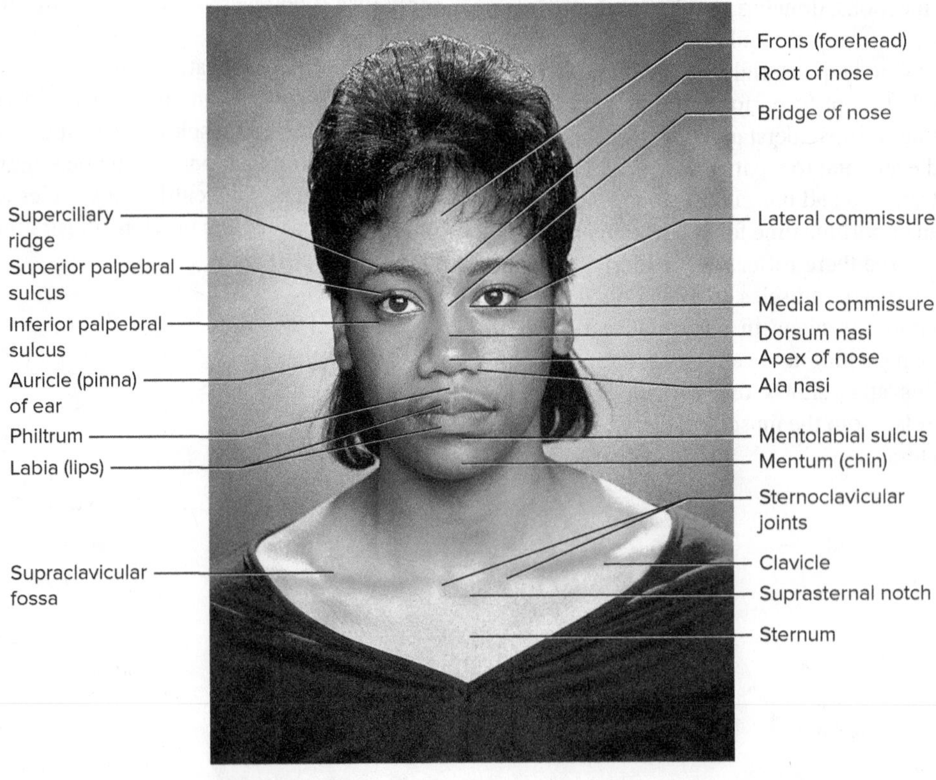


(b) Anterior view

**FIGURE B.1 The Head and Neck.** (a) Anatomical regions of the head. (b) Features of the facial region and upper thorax.

a–b: Joe DeGrandis/McGraw-Hill Education

*What muscle underlies the region of the philtrum? What muscle forms the slope of the shoulder?*

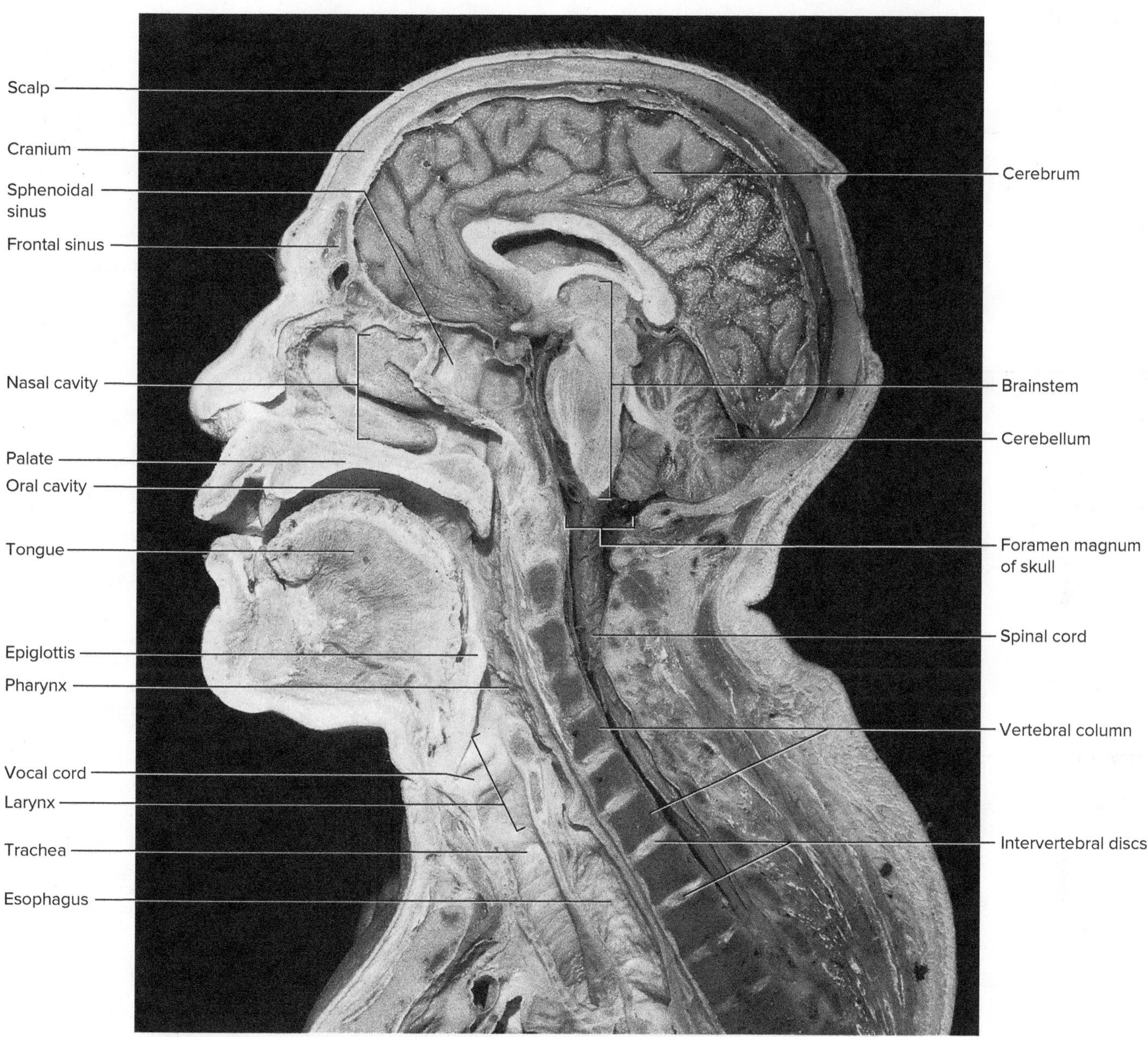


**FIGURE B.2** **Median Section of the Head.** Shows contents of the cranial, nasal, and oral cavities.

Rebecca Gray/McGraw-Hill Education

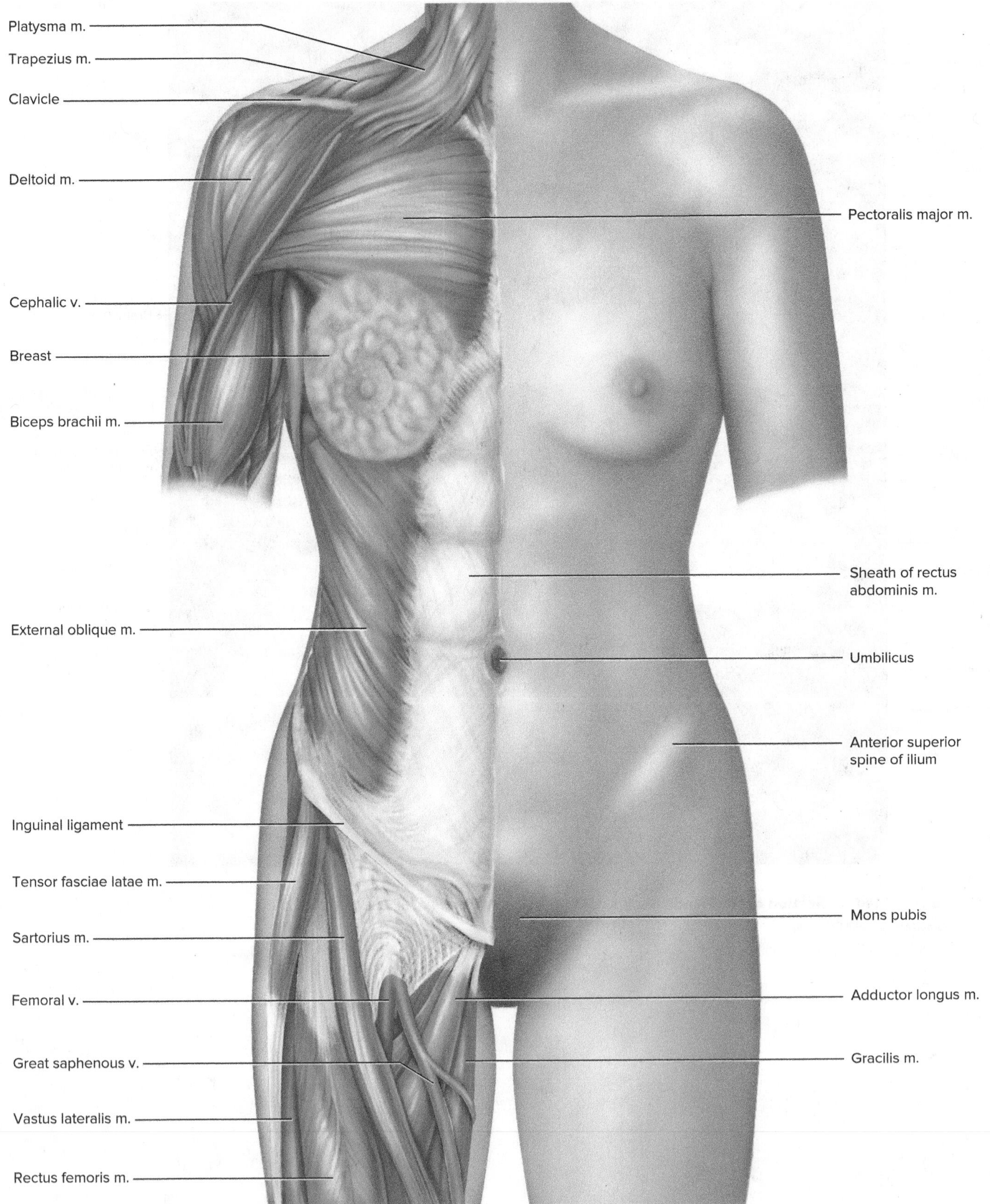


**FIGURE B.3 Superficial Anatomy of the Trunk (Female).** Surface anatomy is shown on the anatomical left, and structures immediately deep to the skin on the right.

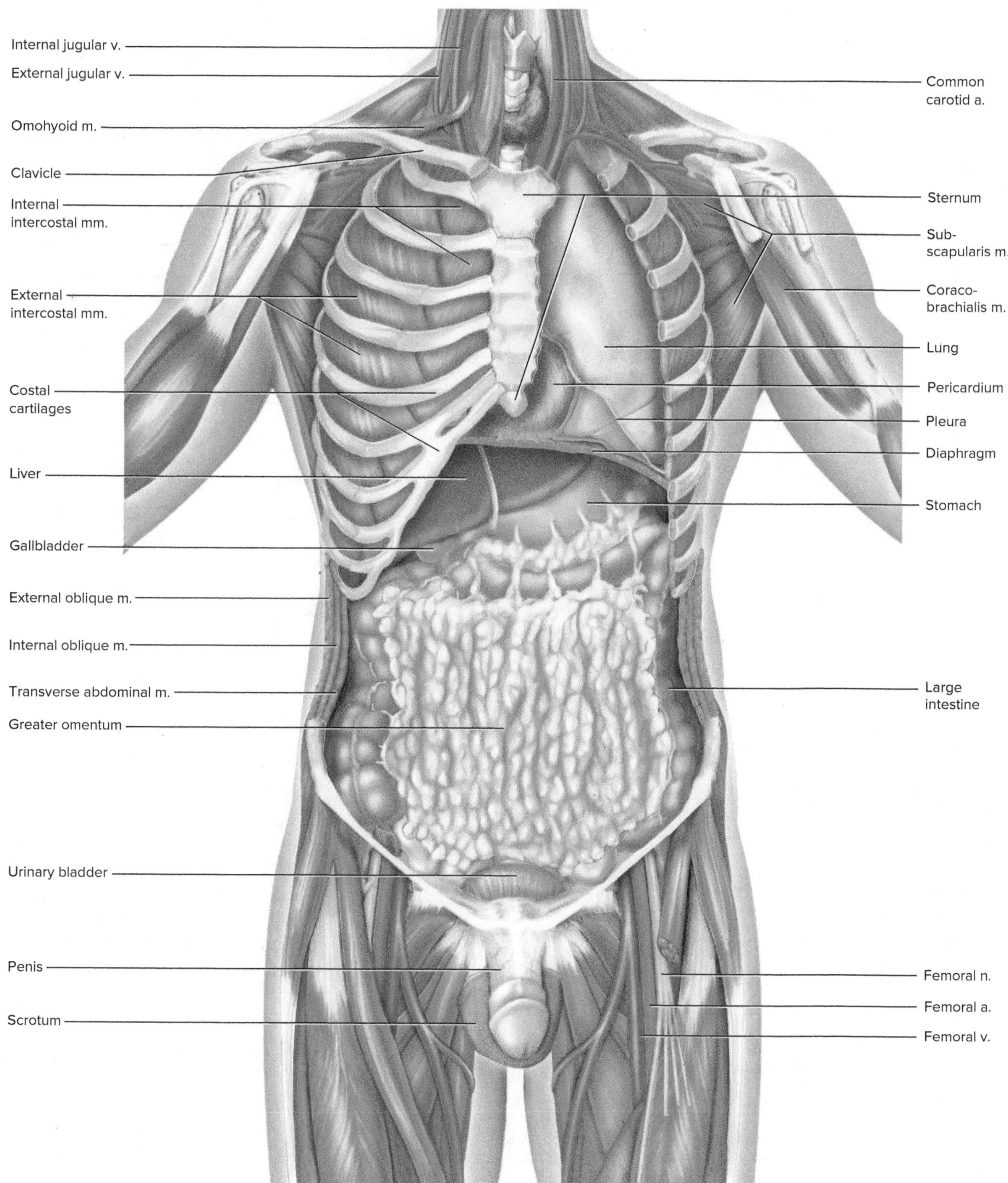


**FIGURE B.4 Anatomy at the Level of the Rib Cage and Greater Omentum (Male).** The anterior body wall is removed, and the ribs, intercostal muscles, and pleura are removed from the anatomical left.

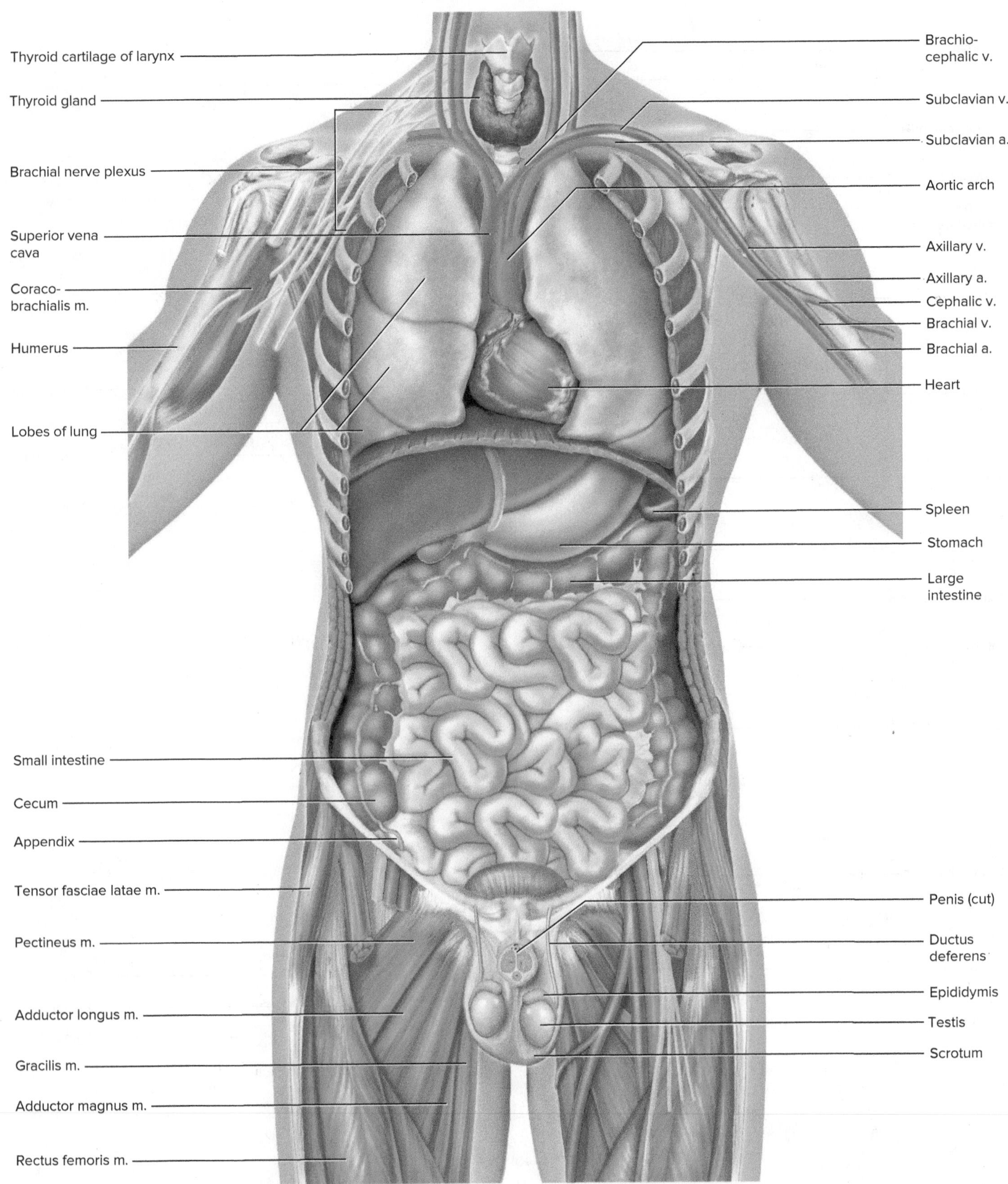


**FIGURE B.5 Anatomy at the Level of the Lungs and Intestines (Male).** The sternum, ribs, and greater omentum are removed.

*Name several viscera that are protected by the rib cage.*

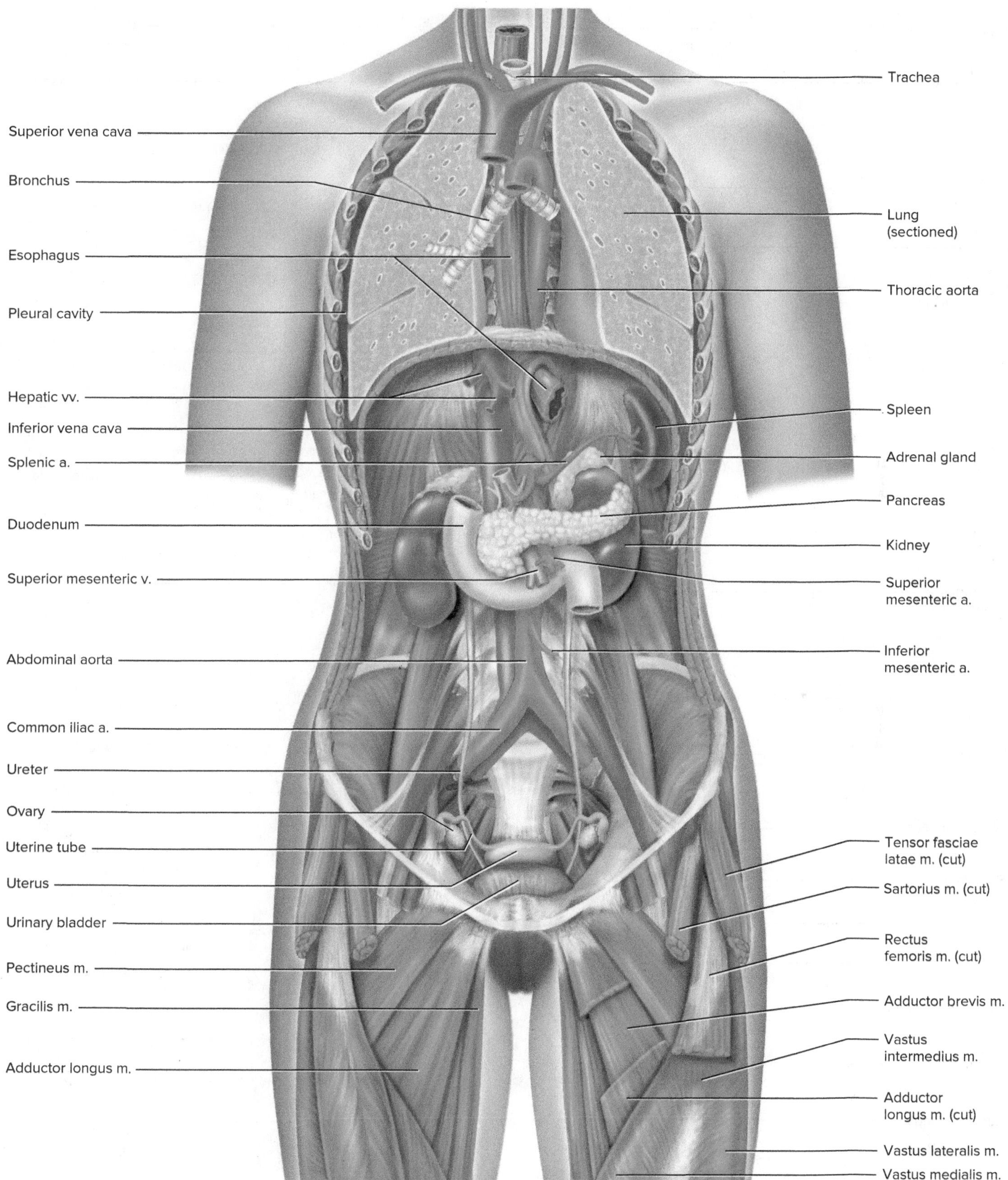


**FIGURE B.6 Anatomy at the Level of the Retroperitoneal Viscera (Female).** The heart is removed, the lungs are frontally sectioned, and the viscera of the peritoneal cavity and the peritoneum itself are removed.

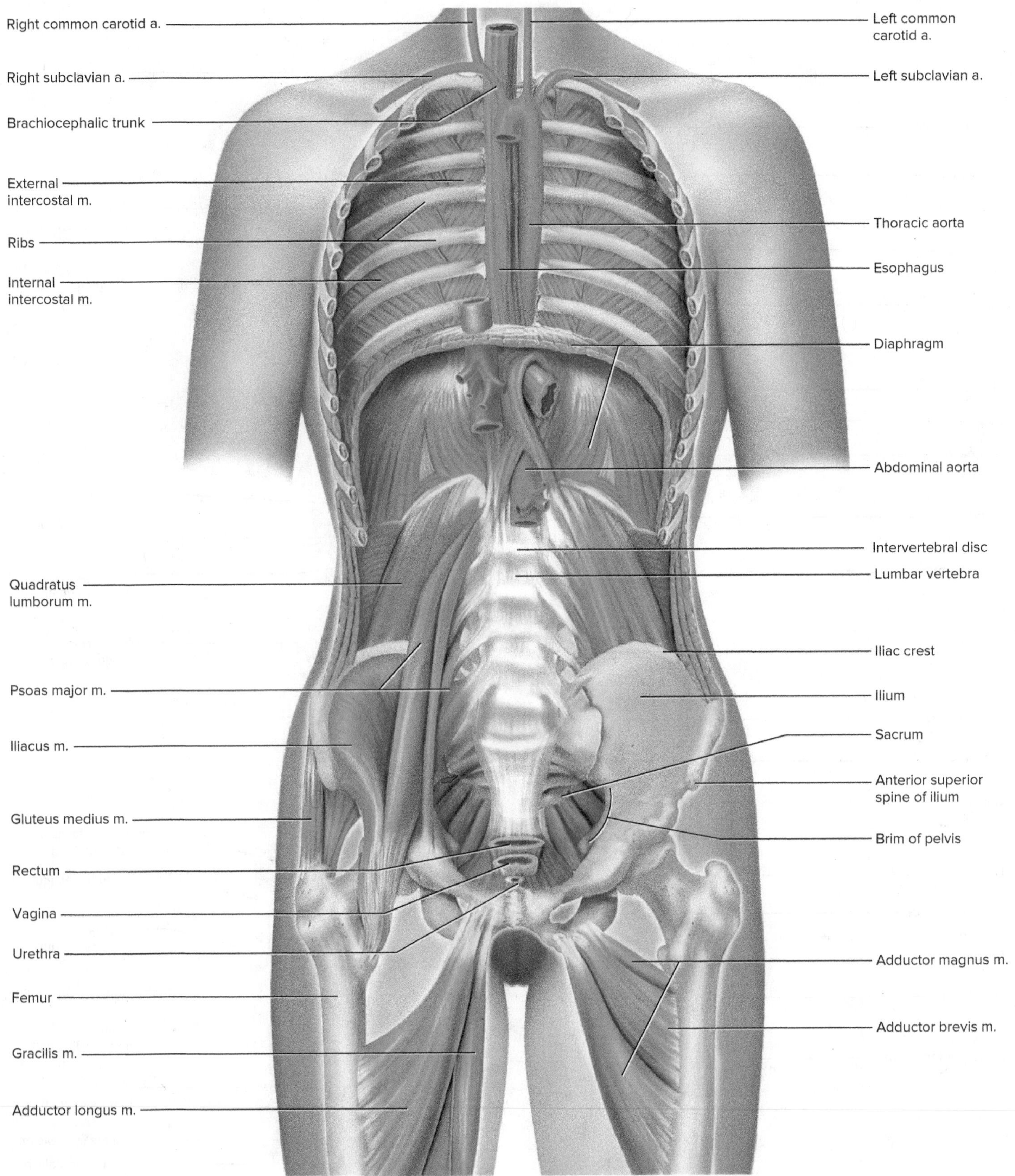


**FIGURE B.7 Anatomy at the Level of the Posterior Body Wall (Female).** The lungs and retroperitoneal viscera are removed.

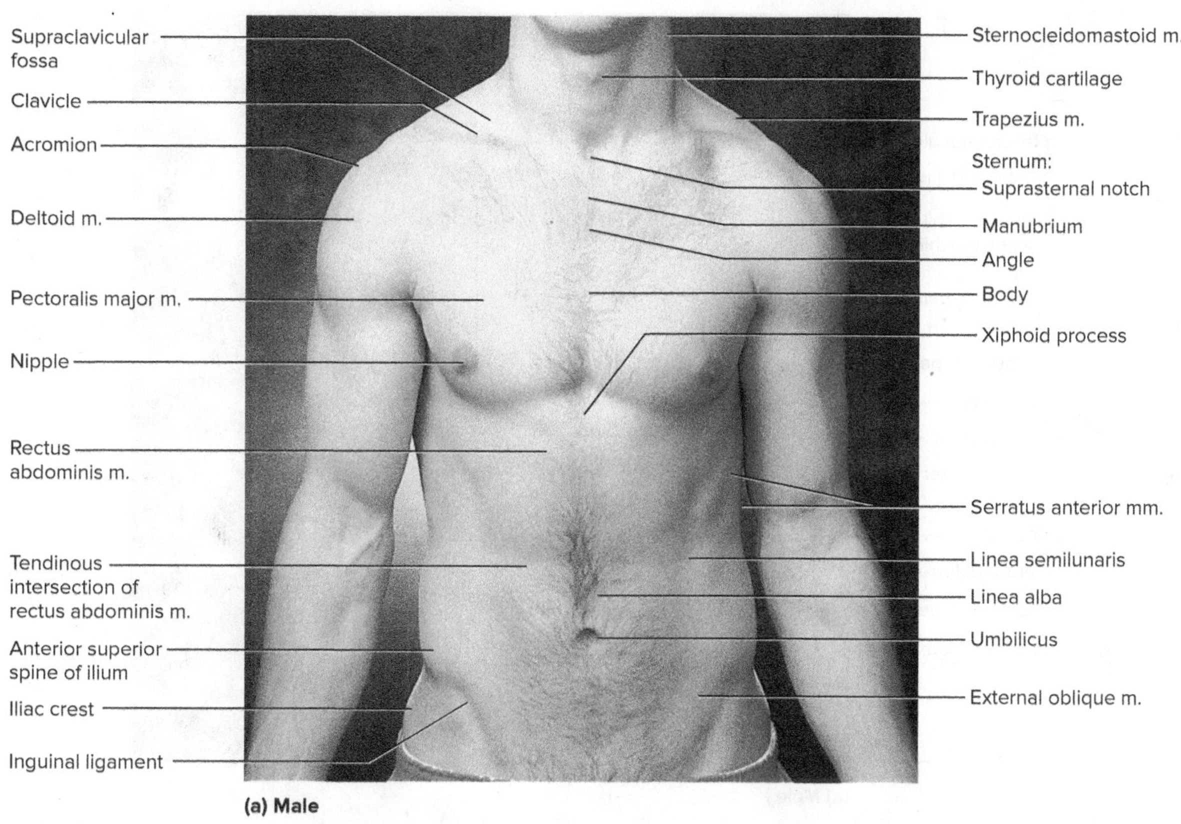


**(a) Male**

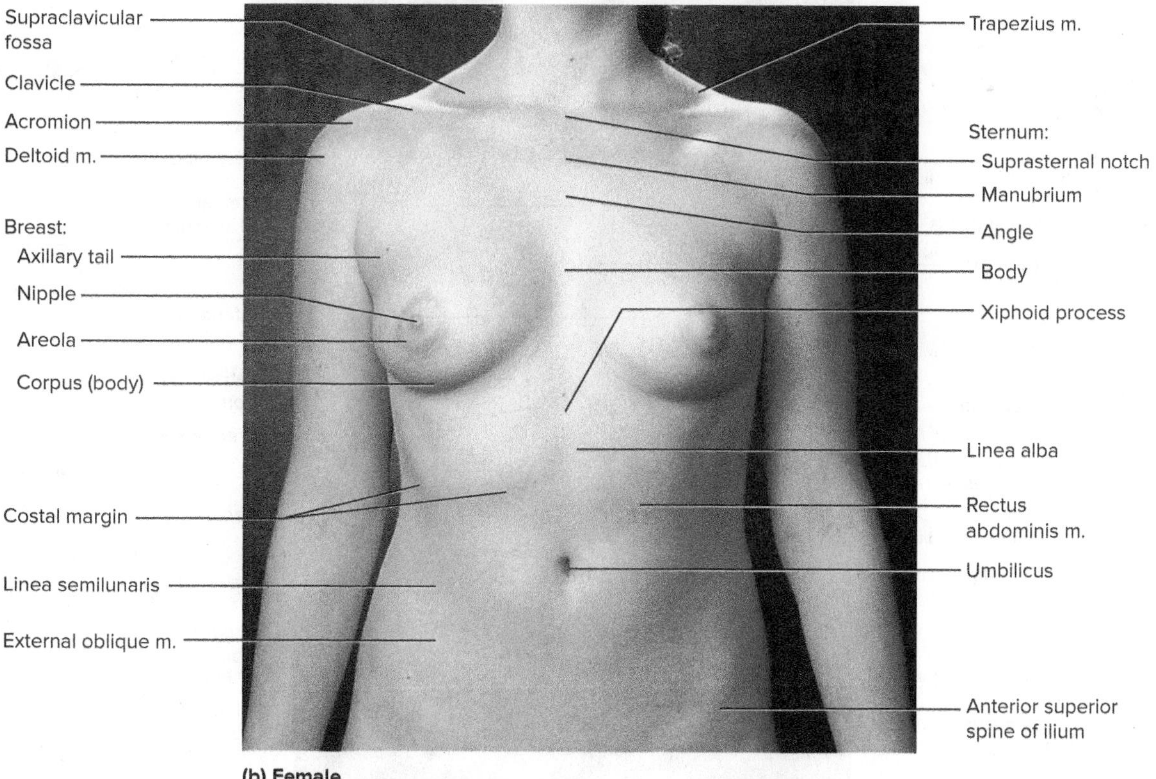


**(b) Female**

**FIGURE B.8 The Thorax and Abdomen (Anterior View).** (a) Male. (b) Female. All of the features labeled are common to both sexes, though some are labeled only on the photograph that shows them best.

a–b: Joe DeGrandis/McGraw-Hill Education

*The V-shaped tendons on each side of the suprasternal notch in part (a) belong to what muscles?*

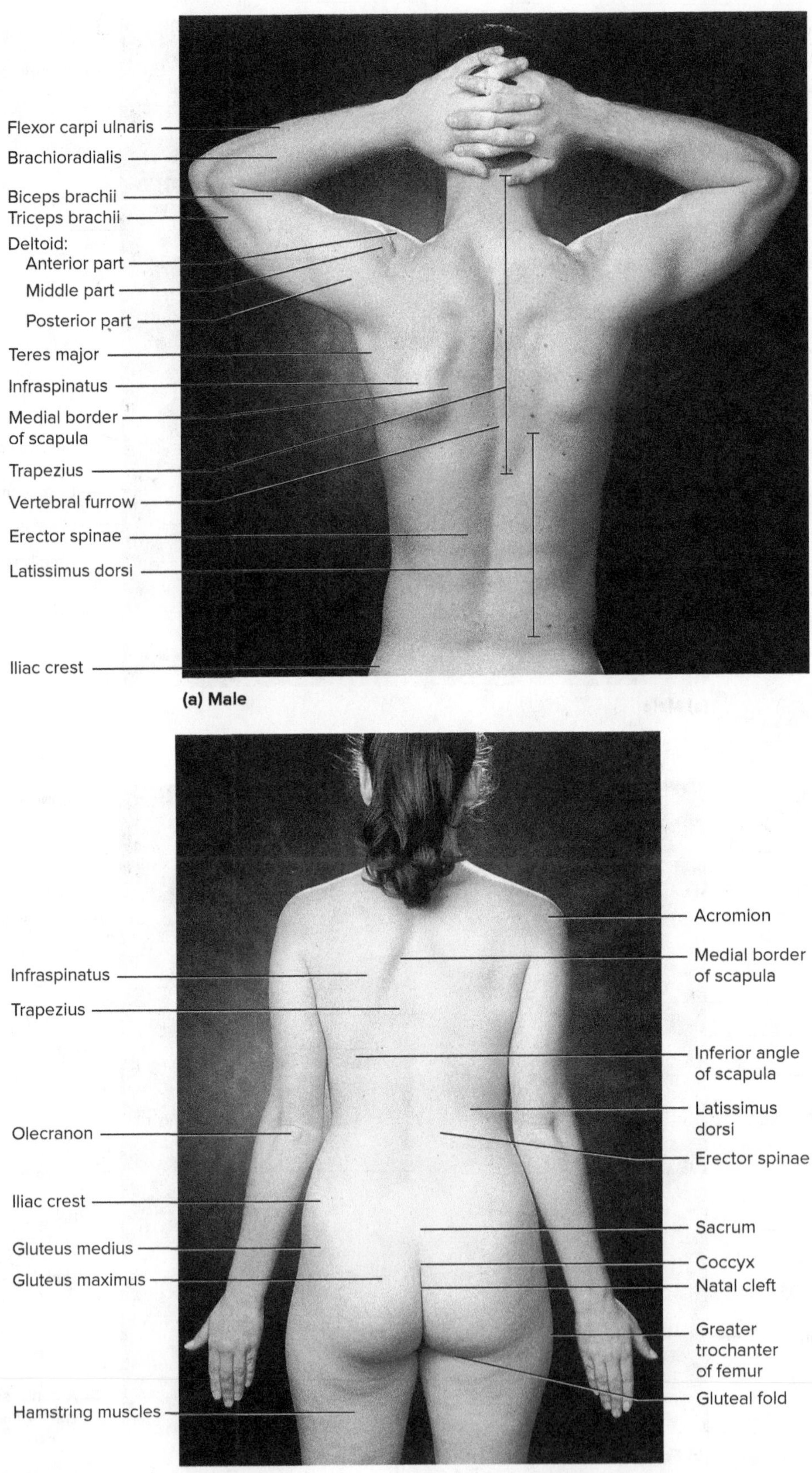


**FIGURE B.9 The Back and Gluteal Region.** (a) Male. (b) Female. All of the features labeled are common to both sexes, though some are labeled only on the photograph that shows them best.

a–b: Joe DeGrandis/McGraw-Hill Education

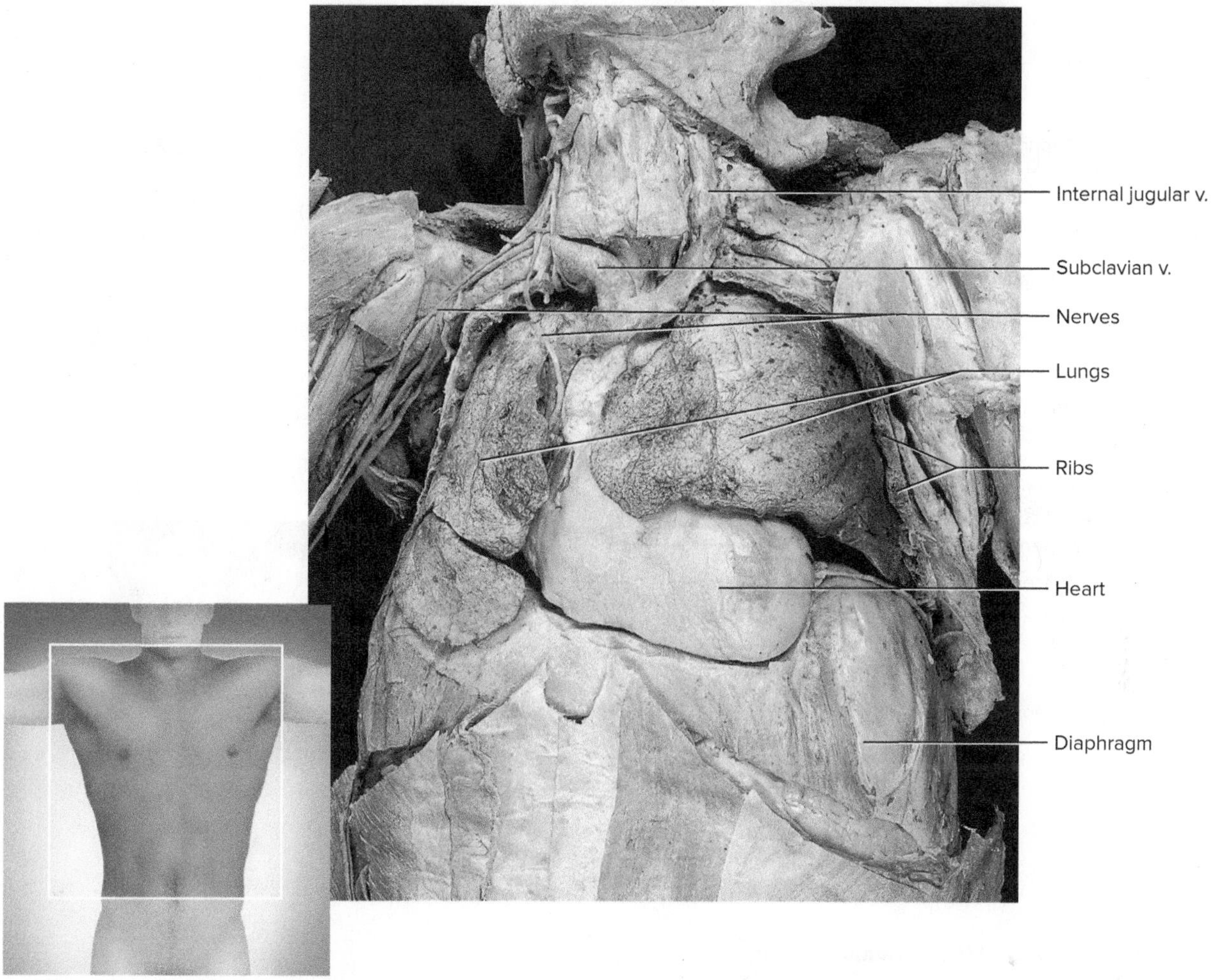

**FIGURE B.10 Frontal View of the Thoracic Cavity.**
Rebecca Gray/McGraw-Hill Education

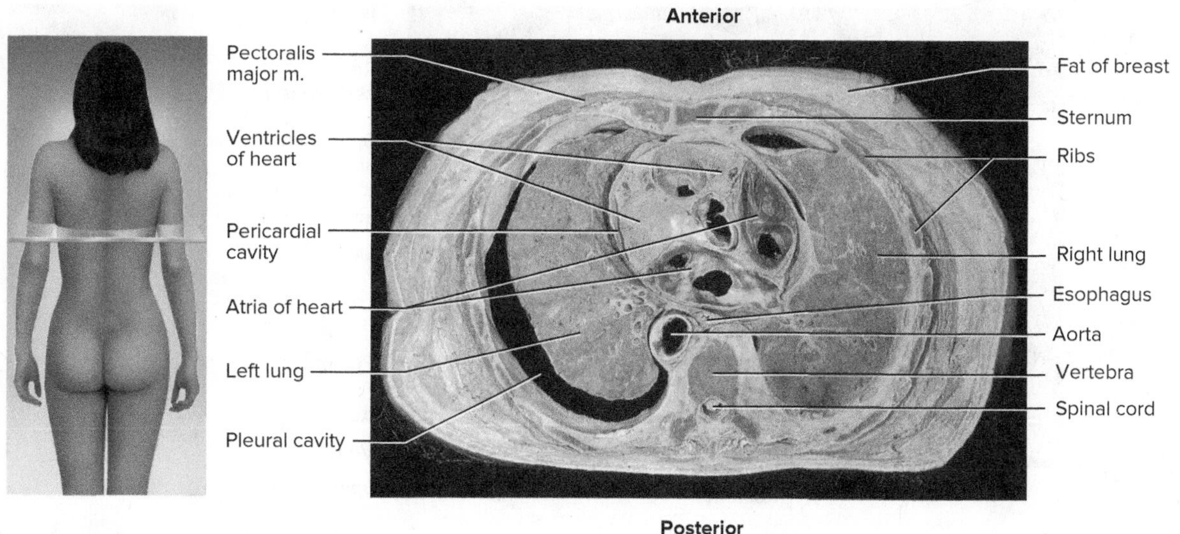


**FIGURE B.11 Transverse Section of the Thorax.** Section taken at the level shown by the inset and oriented the same as the reader's body.
Rebecca Gray/Don Kincaid/McGraw-Hill Education

? *In this section, which term best describes the position of the aorta relative to the heart: posterior, lateral, inferior, or proximal?*

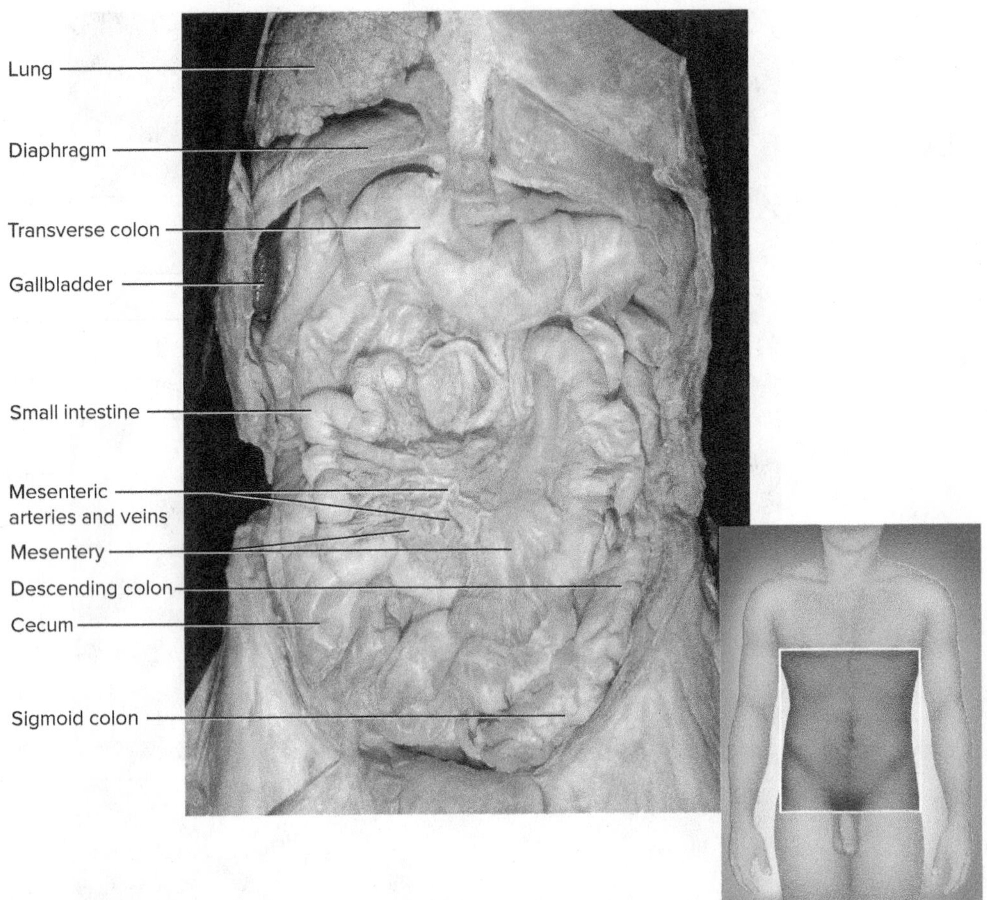


**FIGURE B.12 Frontal View of the Abdominal Cavity.**

Rebecca Gray/Don Kincaid/McGraw-Hill Education

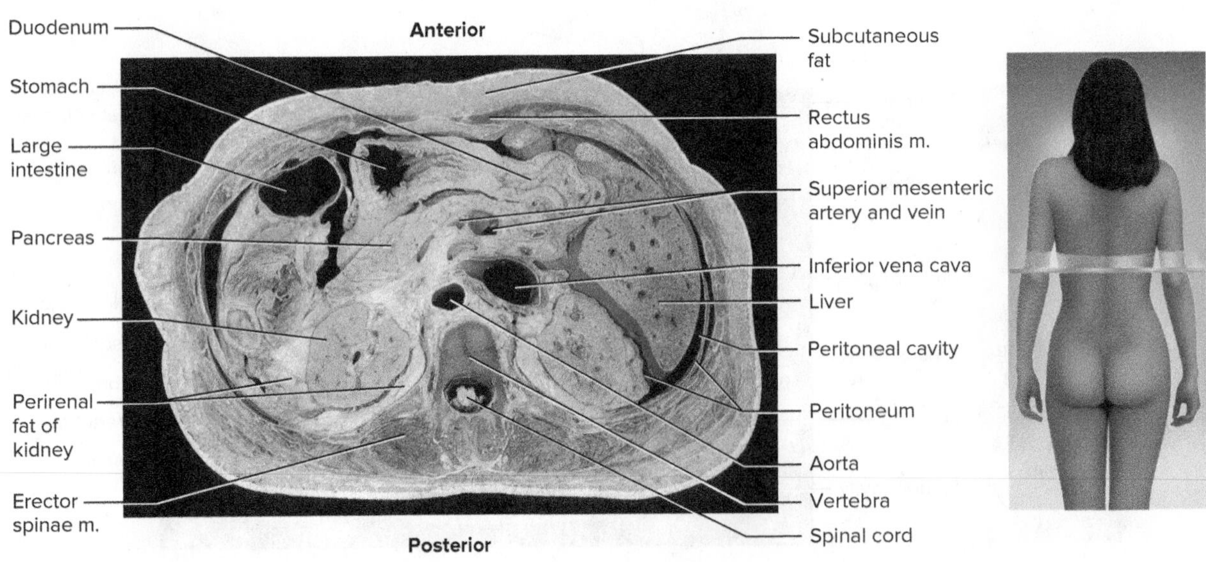


**FIGURE B.13 Transverse Section of the Abdomen.** Section taken at the level shown by the inset and oriented the same as the reader's body.

Rebecca Gray/Don Kincaid/McGraw-Hill Education

*What tissue in this photograph is immediately superficial to the rectus abdominis muscle?*

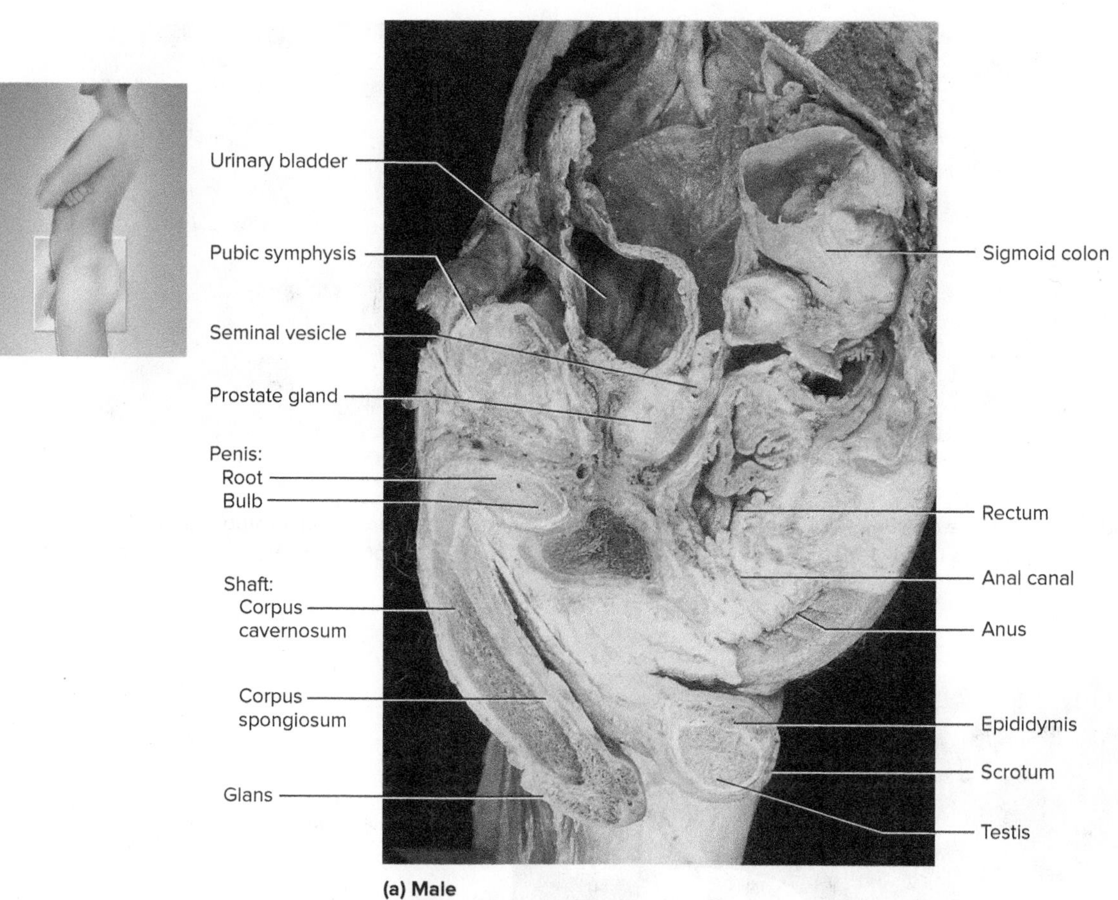


(a) Male

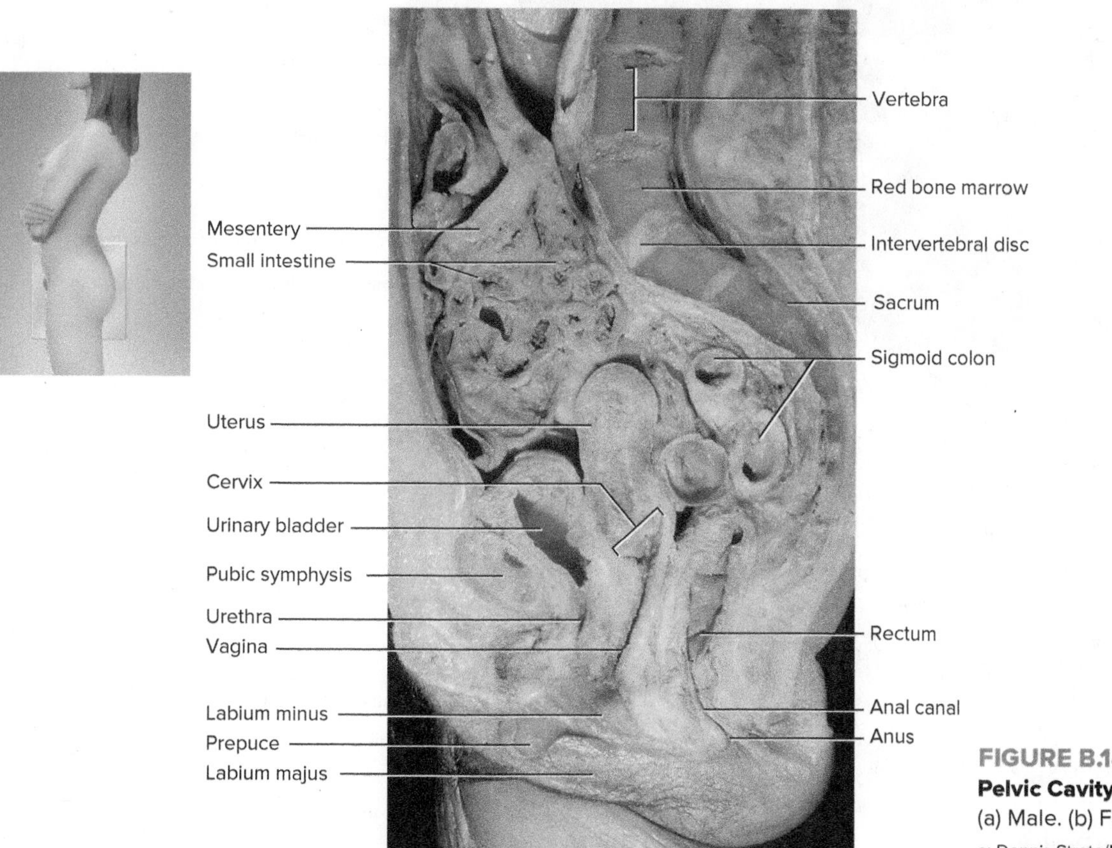


(b) Female

**FIGURE B.14 Median Sections of the Pelvic Cavity (Left Lateral Views).** (a) Male. (b) Female.

a: Dennis Strete/McGraw-Hill Education; b: Rebecca Gray/Don Kincaid/McGraw-Hill Education

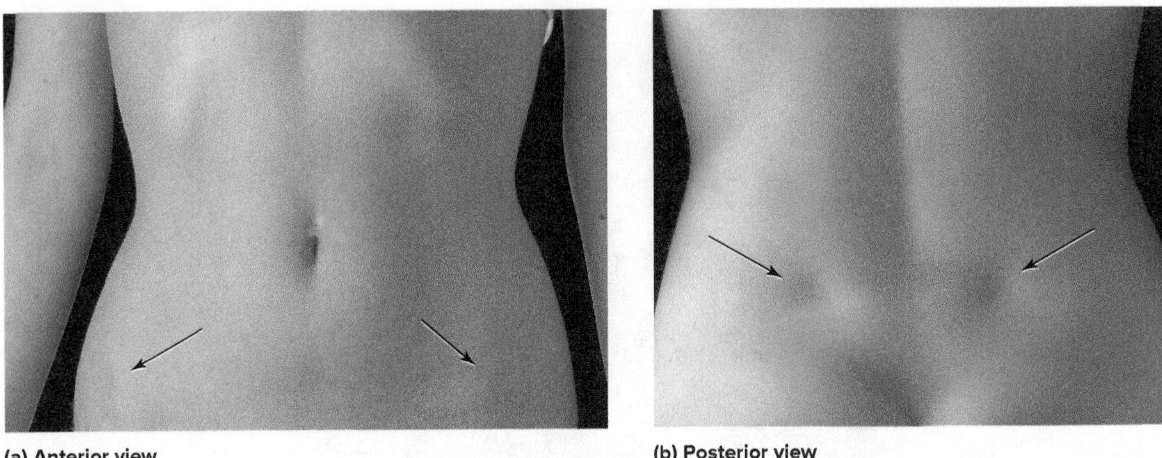


**FIGURE B.15 Pelvic Landmarks.** (a) The anterior superior spines of the ilium are marked by anterolateral protuberances (arrows) at about the location where the front pockets usually open on a pair of pants. (b) The posterior superior spines are marked in some people by dimples in the sacral region (arrows).

a–b: Joe DeGrandis/McGraw-Hill Education

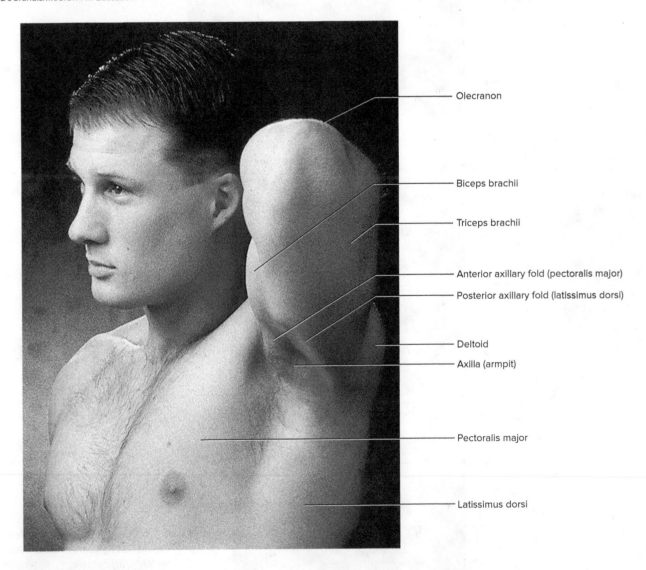

Olecranon
Biceps brachii
Triceps brachii
Anterior axillary fold (pectoralis major)
Posterior axillary fold (latissimus dorsi)
Deltoid
Axilla (armpit)
Pectoralis major
Latissimus dorsi

**FIGURE B.16 The Axillary Region.**

Joe DeGrandis/McGraw-Hill Education

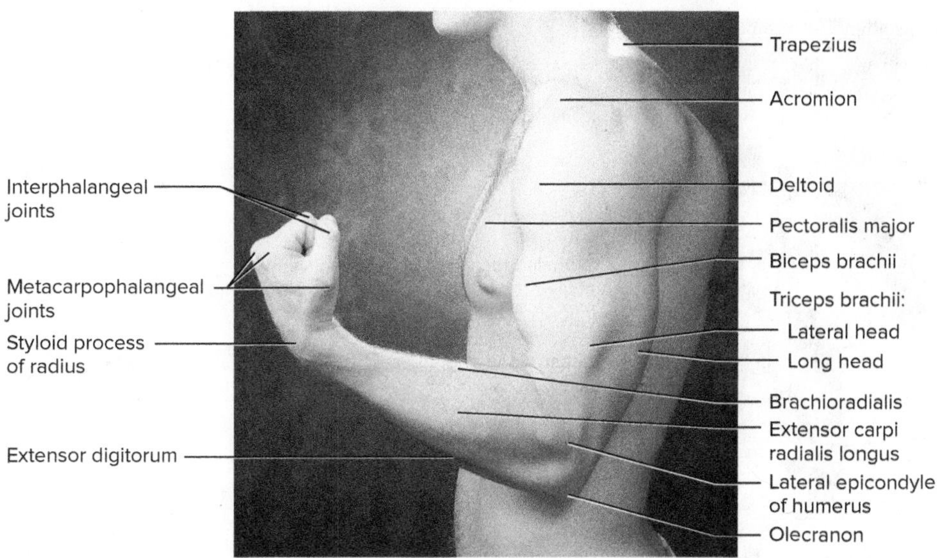

**FIGURE B.17 The Upper Limb (Left Lateral View).**

Joe DeGrandis/McGraw-Hill Education

**(a) Anterior view**

**(b) Posterior view**

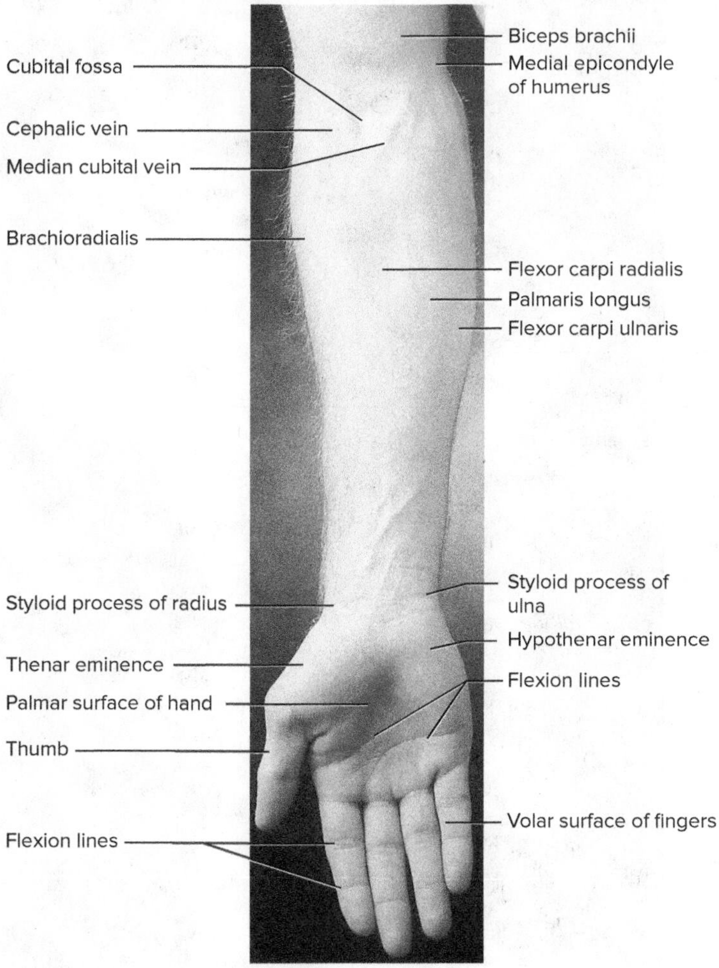

**FIGURE B.18 The Antebrachium (Forearm).** (a) Anterior view. (b) Posterior view.

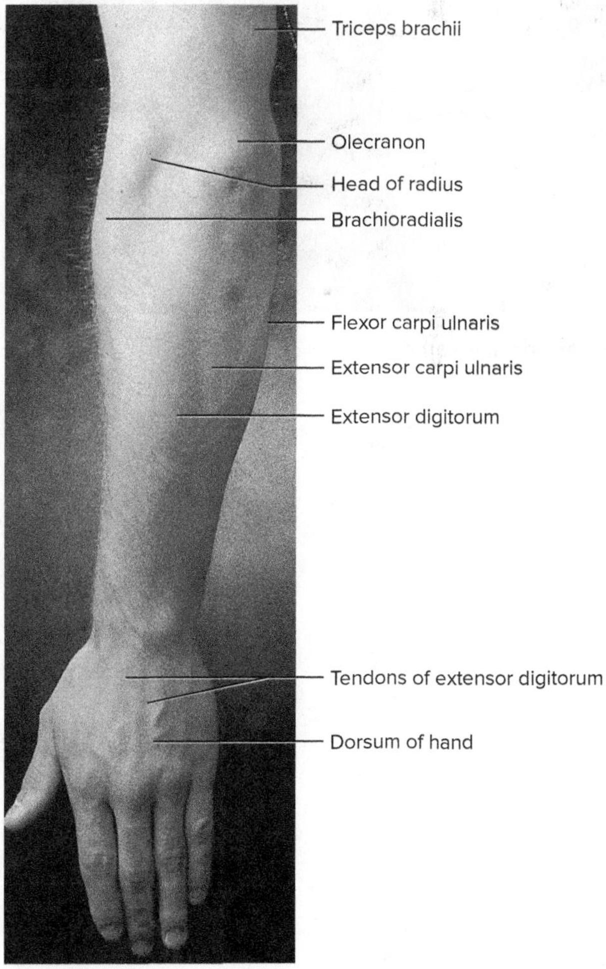

**a–b:** Joe DeGrandis/McGraw-Hill Education

*Only two tendons of the extensor digitorum are labeled, but how many tendons does this muscle have in all?*

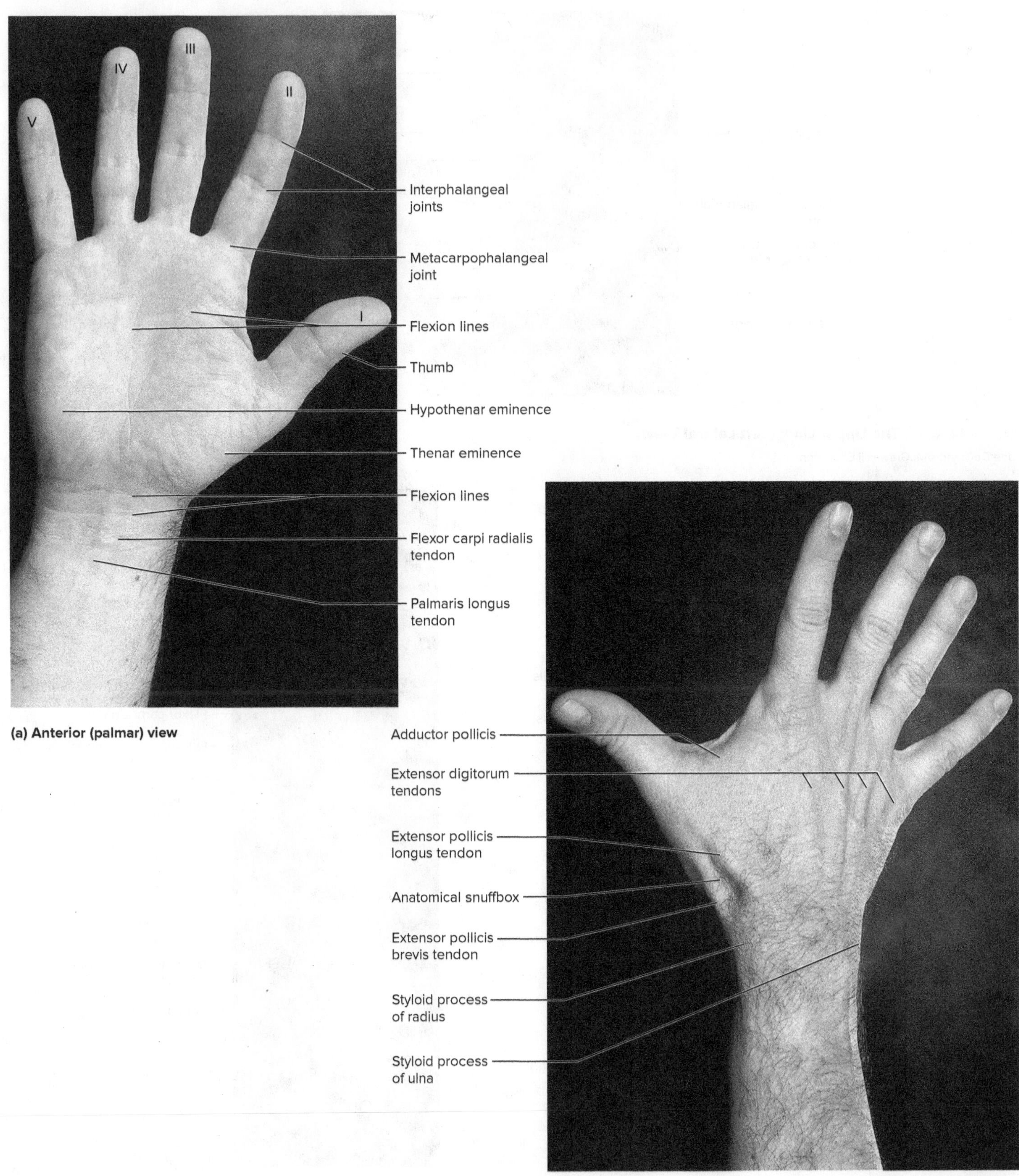


**(a) Anterior (palmar) view**

**(b) Posterior (dorsal) view**

**FIGURE B.19 The Wrist and Hand.** (a) Anterior (palmar) view. (b) Posterior (dorsal) view.

a–b: Joe DeGrandis/McGraw-Hill Education

*Mark the spot on one or both photographs where a saddle joint can be found.*

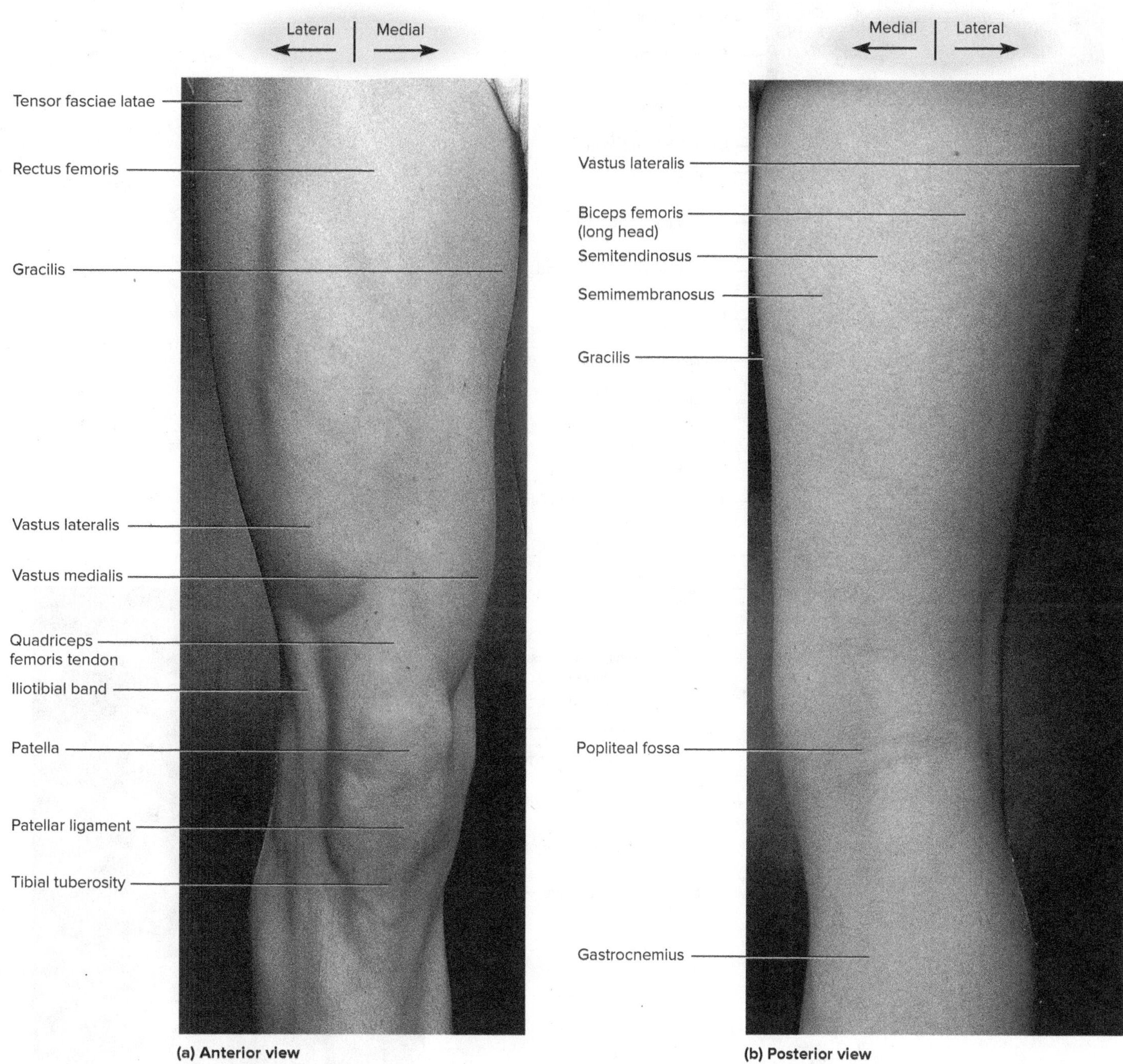


**FIGURE B.20 The Thigh and Knee.** (a) Anterior view. (b) Posterior view. Locations of posterior thigh muscles are indicated, but the boundaries of the individual muscles are rarely visible on a living person.

a–b: Joe DeGrandis/McGraw-Hill Education

? *Mark the spot on part (a) where the vastus intermedius would be found.*

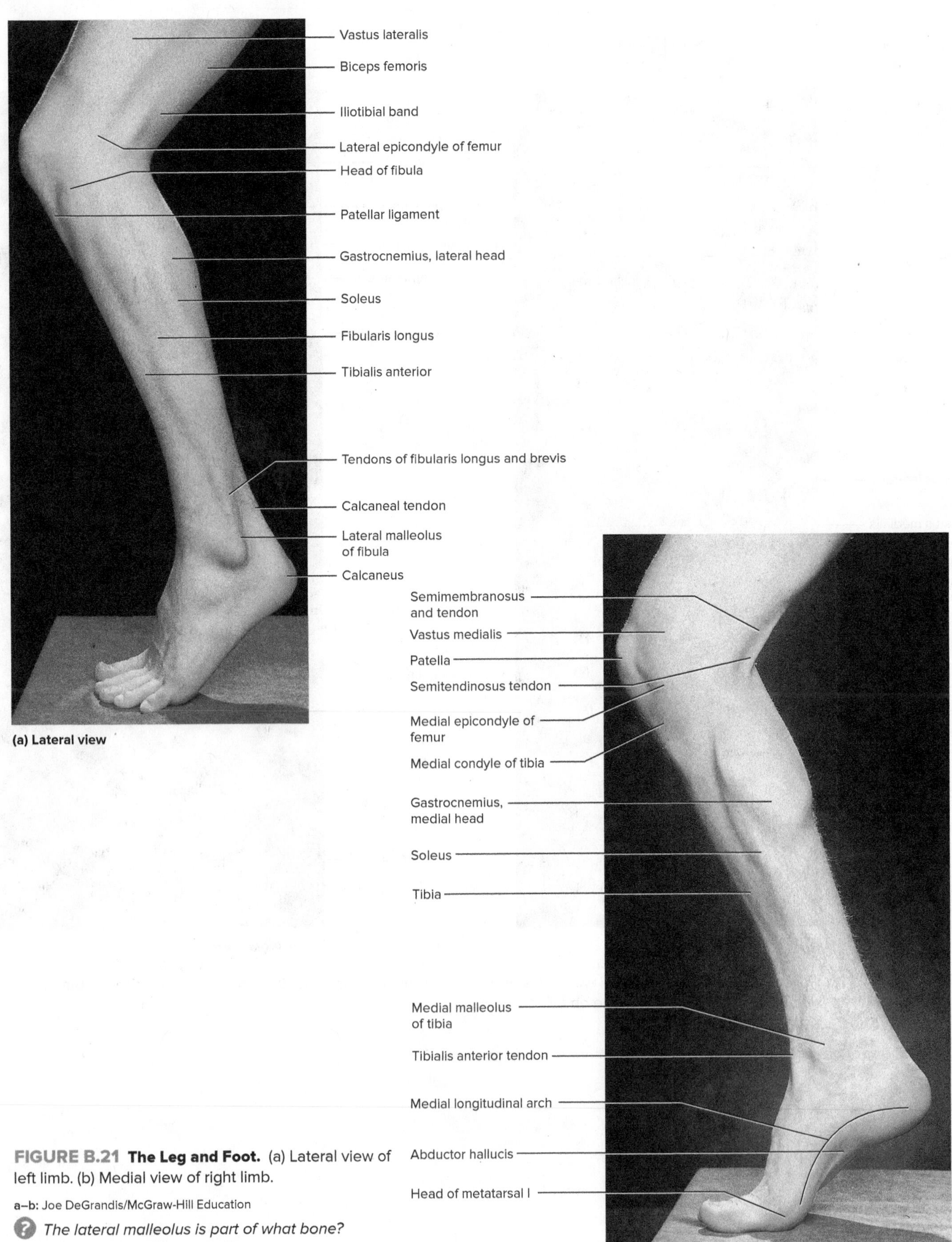


**FIGURE B.21 The Leg and Foot.** (a) Lateral view of left limb. (b) Medial view of right limb.

a–b: Joe DeGrandis/McGraw-Hill Education

*The lateral malleolus is part of what bone?*

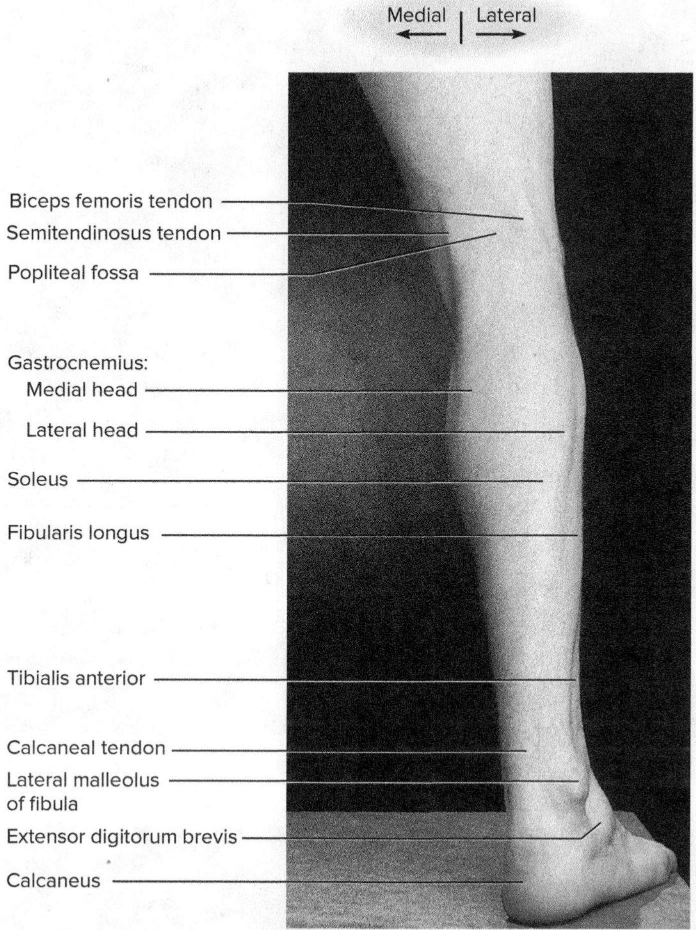


**FIGURE B.22 The Leg and Foot, Posterior View.**

Joe DeGrandis/McGraw-Hill Education

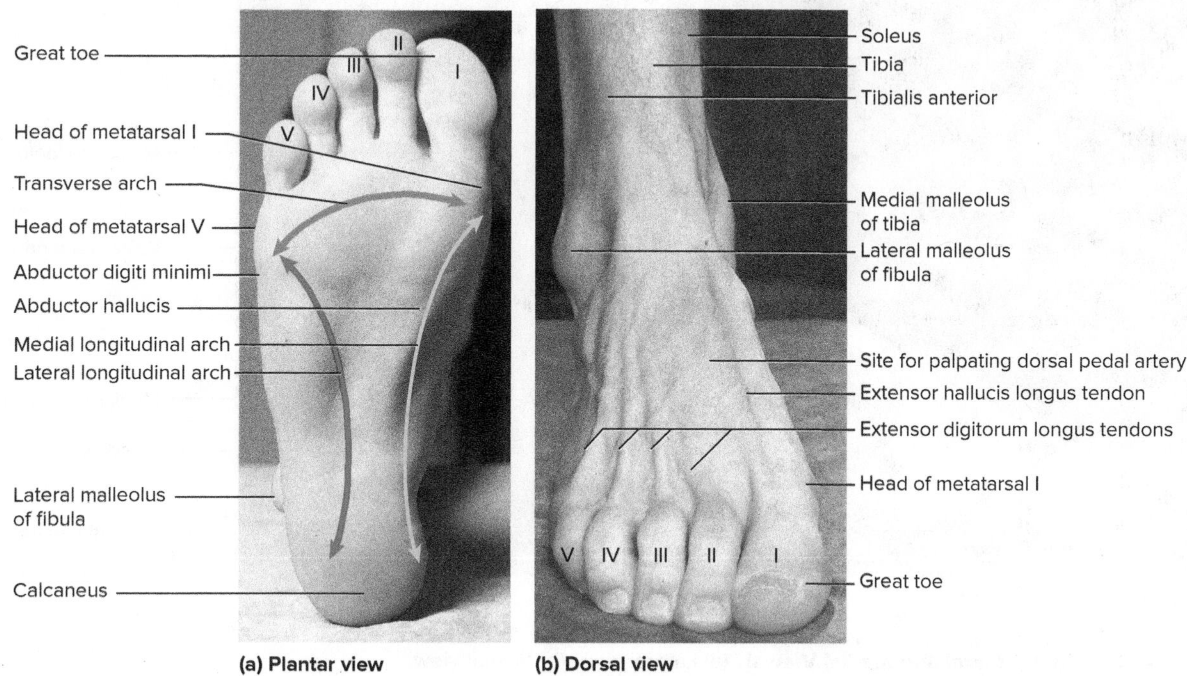


**FIGURE B.23 The Foot (Plantar and Dorsal Views).** (a) Plantar view. (b) Dorsal view. Compare the arches in part (a) to the skeletal anatomy in figure 8.43.

a–b: Joe DeGrandis/McGraw-Hill Education

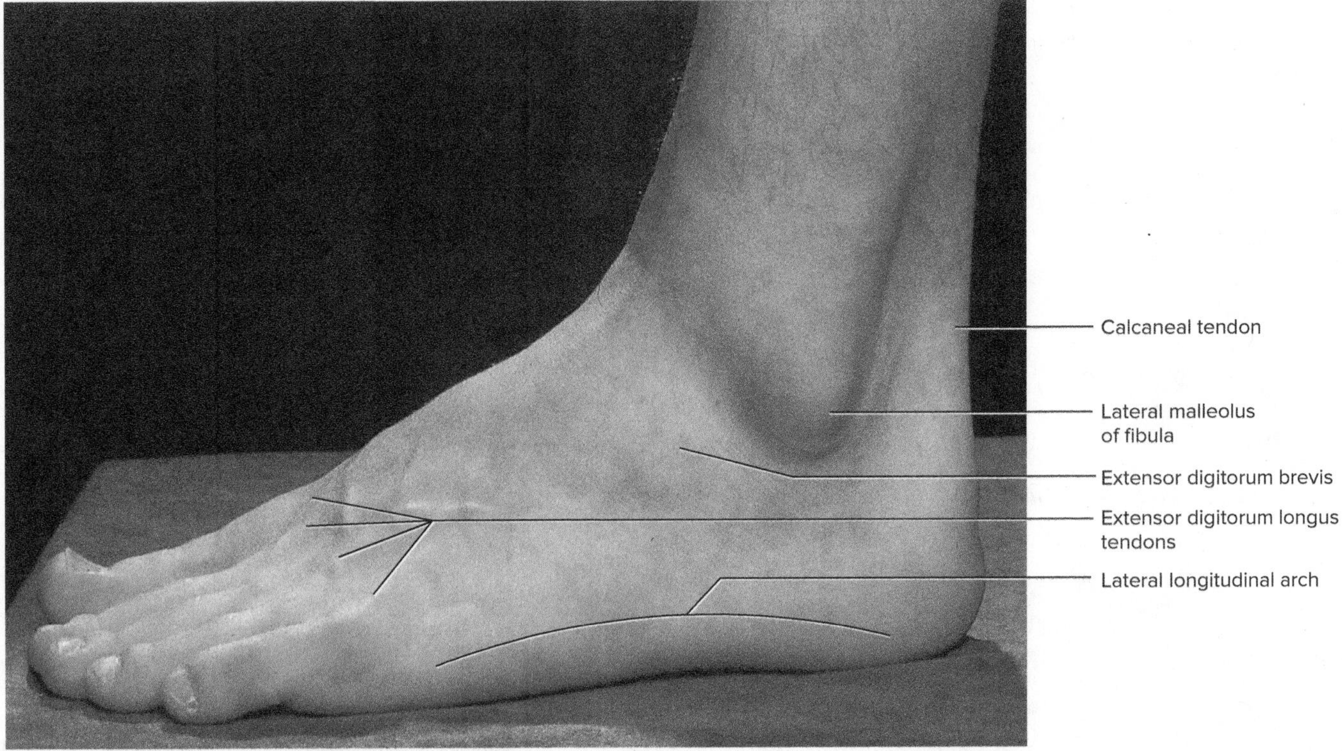


(a) Lateral view

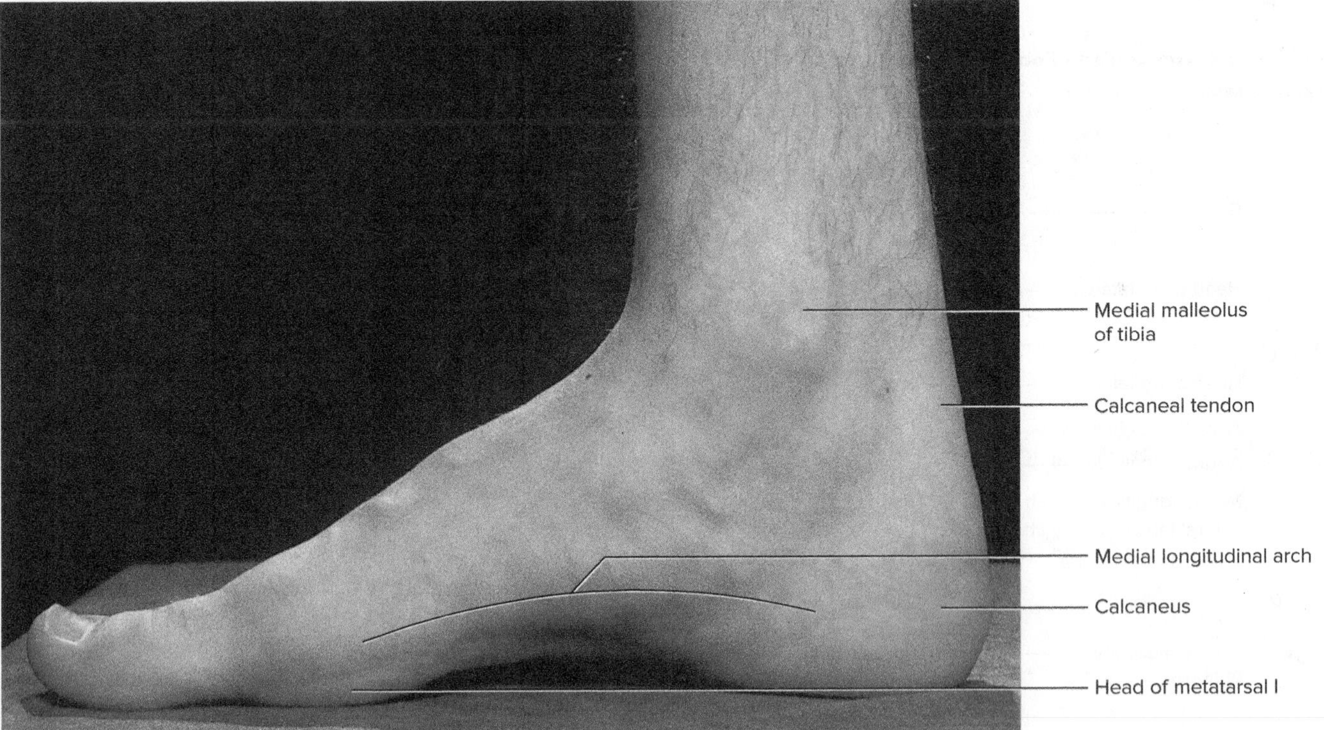


(b) Medial view

**FIGURE B.24 The Foot (Lateral and Medial Views).** (a) Lateral view. (b) Medial view.

a–b: Joe DeGrandis/McGraw-Hill Education

*Indicate the position of middle phalanx I on each photograph.*

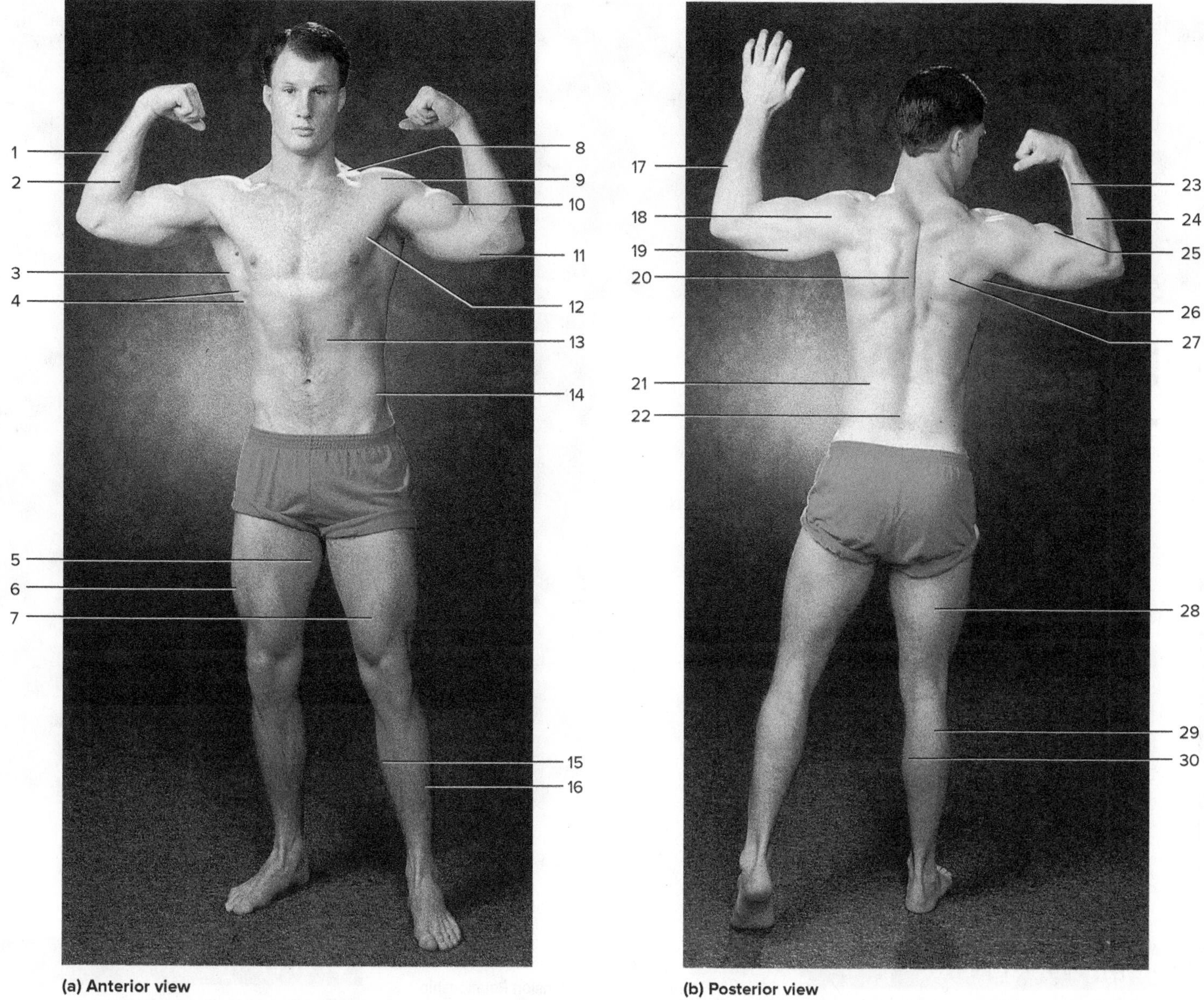


**(a) Anterior view**

**(b) Posterior view**

**FIGURE B.25 Test of Muscle Recognition.** To test your knowledge of muscle anatomy, match the 30 labeled muscles on these photographs to the following alphabetical list of muscles. Answer as many as possible without referring back to the previous illustrations. Some of these names will be used more than once since the same muscle may be shown from different perspectives, and some of these names will not be used at all. The answers are in appendix A.

a–b: Joe DeGrandis/McGraw-Hill Education

Throughout these illustrations, the following abbreviations apply: a. = artery; m. = muscle; n. = nerve; v. = vein. Double letters such as mm. or vv. represent the plurals.

a. biceps brachii
b. brachioradialis
c. deltoid
d. erector spinae
e. external oblique
f. flexor carpi ulnaris
g. gastrocnemius
h. gracilis
i. hamstrings
j. infraspinatus
k. latissimus dorsi
l. pectineus
m. pectoralis major
n. rectus abdominis
o. rectus femoris
p. serratus anterior
q. soleus
r. splenius capitis
s. sternocleidomastoid
t. subscapularis
u. teres major
v. tibialis anterior
w. trapezius
x. triceps brachii
y. vastus lateralis
z. vastus medialis

CHAPTER

# 11

# MUSCULAR TISSUE

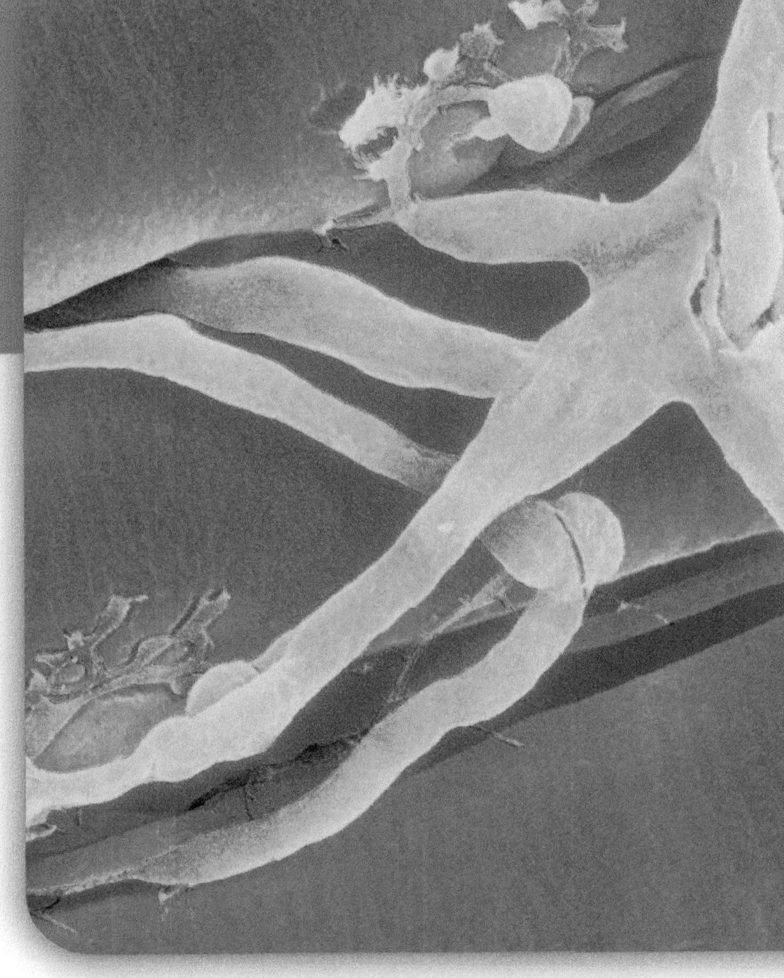

**Neuromuscular junctions (SEM)**

Dr. Donald Fawcett/Science Source

## CHAPTER OUTLINE



## DEEPER INSIGHTS

**Module 6: Muscular System**

**BRUSHING UP**

- You should be familiar with the organization of a typical skeletal muscle and its associated connective tissues (see section 10.1 b).
- You should know the basic neuron structure introduced in table 5.10 to understand the nerve–muscle relationship in this chapter.
- The stimulation of a muscle fiber by a neuron is based on principles of plasma membrane proteins as receptors and as ligand- and voltage-gated ion channels (see "Membrane Proteins" in section 3.2a).
- Section 1.6e, "Gradients and Flow," provides a core concept (especially electrochemical gradients) for understanding muscle excitation and the activation of contraction.
- The differences between aerobic respiration and anaerobic fermentation (see fig. 2.31) are central to understanding exercise physiology and the energy metabolism of muscle.
- Familiarity with desmosomes and gap junctions (see section 5.5a) will enhance your appreciation of the fundamental properties of cardiac and smooth muscle.

Movement is a fundamental characteristic of all living organisms, from bacteria to humans. Even plants and other seemingly immobile organisms move cellular components from place to place. Across the entire spectrum of life, the molecular mechanisms of movement are very similar, involving motor proteins such as myosin and dynein. But in animals, movement has developed to the highest degree, with the evolution of **muscle cells** specialized for this function. A muscle cell is essentially a device for converting the chemical energy of ATP into the mechanical energy of movement.

The three types of muscular tissue—skeletal, cardiac, and smooth—are described and compared in table 5.11. Cardiac and smooth muscle are further described in this chapter, and cardiac muscle is discussed most extensively in chapter 19. Most of the present chapter, however, concerns skeletal muscle, the type that holds the body erect against the pull of gravity and produces its outwardly visible movements.

This chapter treats the structure, contraction, and metabolism of skeletal muscle at the molecular, cellular, and tissue levels of organization. Understanding muscle at these levels provides an indispensable basis for understanding such aspects of motor performance as quickness, strength, endurance, and fatigue. Such factors have obvious relevance to athletic performance, and they become very important when a lack of physical conditioning, old age, or injury interferes with a person's ability to carry out everyday tasks or meet the extra demands for speed or strength that we all occasionally encounter.

## 11.1 Types and Characteristics of Muscular Tissue

**Expected Learning Outcomes**

When you have completed this section, you should be able to

a. describe the physiological properties that all muscle types have in common;
b. list the defining characteristics of skeletal muscle; and
c. discuss the elastic functions of the connective tissue components of a muscle.

### 11.1a Universal Characteristics of Muscle

The functions of the muscular system were detailed in the preceding chapter: movement, stability, communication, control of body openings and passages, heat production, and glycemic control. To carry out those functions, all muscle cells have the following characteristics.

- **Excitability (responsiveness).** Excitability is a property of all living cells, but muscle and nerve cells have developed this property to the highest degree. When stimulated by chemical signals, stretch, and other stimuli, muscle cells respond with electrical changes across the plasma membrane.
- **Conductivity.** Stimulation of a muscle cell produces more than a local effect. Local electrical excitation sets off a wave of excitation that travels rapidly along the cell and initiates processes leading to contraction.
- **Contractility.** Muscle cells are unique in their ability to shorten substantially when stimulated. This enables them to pull on bones and other organs to create movement.
- **Extensibility.** In order to contract, a muscle cell must also be extensible—able to stretch again between contractions. Most cells rupture if they are stretched even a little, but skeletal muscle cells can stretch to as much as three times their contracted length.
- **Elasticity.** When a muscle cell is stretched and then released, it recoils to a shorter length. If it were not for this elastic recoil, resting muscles would be too slack or flabby. Owing to a *length–tension relationship* to be described in this chapter, they wouldn't contract very strongly when stimulated.

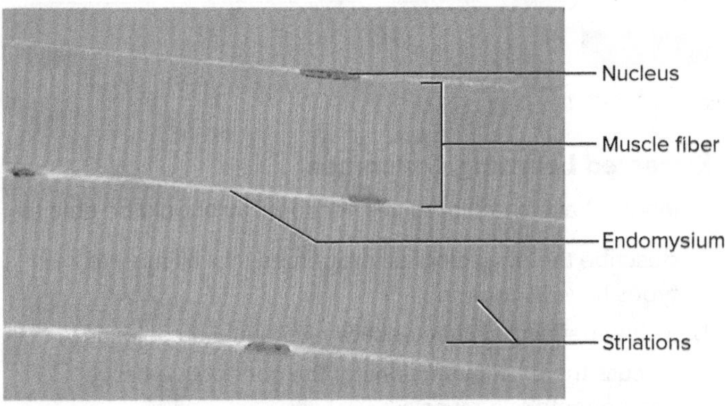


**FIGURE 11.1 Skeletal Muscle Fibers.** 
Ed Reschke

*What tissue characteristics evident in this photo distinguish this from cardiac and smooth muscle?*

## 11.1b Skeletal Muscle

**Skeletal muscle** may be defined as voluntary striated muscle that is usually attached to one or more bones. A skeletal muscle exhibits alternating light and dark transverse bands, or **striations (fig. 11.1),** that reflect an overlapping arrangement of their internal contractile proteins. Skeletal muscle is called **voluntary** because it is usually subject to conscious control. The other types of muscle are **involuntary** (not usually under conscious control), and they are never attached to bones.

A typical skeletal muscle cell is about 100 μm in diameter and 3 cm (30,000 μm) long; some are as thick as 500 μm and as long as 30 cm. Because of their extraordinary length, skeletal muscle cells are usually called **muscle fibers** or **myofibers.**

Recall that a skeletal muscle is composed not only of muscular tissue, but also of fibrous connective tissue: the *endomysium* that surrounds each muscle fiber, the *perimysium* that bundles muscle fibers together into fascicles, and the *epimysium* that encloses the entire muscle (see fig. 10.1). These connective tissues are continuous with the collagen fibers of tendons and those, in turn, with the collagen of the bone matrix. Thus, when a muscle fiber contracts, it pulls on these collagen fibers and typically moves a bone.

Collagen is neither excitable nor contractile, but it is somewhat extensible and elastic. When a muscle lengthens, for example during extension of a joint, its collagenous components resist excessive stretching and protect the muscle from injury. When a muscle relaxes, elastic recoil of the collagen may help to return the muscle to its resting length and keep it from becoming too flaccid. Some authorities contend that recoil of the tendons and other collagenous tissues contributes significantly to the power output and efficiency of a muscle. When you are running, for example, recoil of the calcaneal tendon may help to lift the heel and produce some of the thrust as your toes push off from the ground. (Such recoil contributes significantly to the long, efficient leaps of a kangaroo.) Others feel that the elasticity of these components is negligible in humans and that the recoil is produced entirely by certain intracellular proteins of the muscle fibers themselves.

**BEFORE YOU GO ON**

Answer the following questions to test your understanding of the preceding section:

1. Define *responsiveness, conductivity, contractility, extensibility,* and *elasticity*. State why each of these properties is necessary for muscle function.
2. How is skeletal muscle different from the other types of muscle?
3. Name and define the three layers of collagenous connective tissue in a skeletal muscle.

# 11.2 Skeletal Muscle Cells

**Expected Learning Outcomes**

When you have completed this section, you should be able to

a. describe the structural components of a muscle fiber;
b. relate the striations of a muscle fiber to the overlapping arrangement of its protein filaments; and
c. name the major proteins of a muscle fiber and state the function of each.

## 11.2a The Muscle Fiber

In order to understand muscle function, you must know how the organelles and macromolecules of a muscle fiber are arranged. Perhaps more than any other cell, a muscle fiber exemplifies the adage, Form follows function. It has a complex, tightly organized internal structure in which even the spatial arrangement of protein molecules is closely tied to its contractile function.

The plasma membrane of a muscle fiber is called the **sarcolemma,**[1] and its cytoplasm is called the **sarcoplasm.** The sarcoplasm is occupied mainly by long protein cords called **myofibrils** about 1 μm in diameter **(fig. 11.2).** It also contains an abundance of **glycogen,** a starchlike carbohydrate that provides energy for the cell during heightened levels of exercise, and the red oxygen-binding pigment **myoglobin,** which provides some of the oxygen needed for muscular activity.

Muscle fibers have multiple flattened or sausage-shaped nuclei pressed against the inside of the sarcolemma. This unusual multinuclear condition results from the embryonic development of a muscle fiber—several stem cells called **myoblasts**[2] fuse to produce each fiber, with each myoblast contributing one nucleus. Some myoblasts remain as unspecialized **satellite cells** between the muscle fiber and endomysium. These play an important role in the regeneration of damaged skeletal muscle.

[1]*sarco* = flesh, muscle; *lemma* = husk
[2]*myo* = muscle; *blast* = precursor

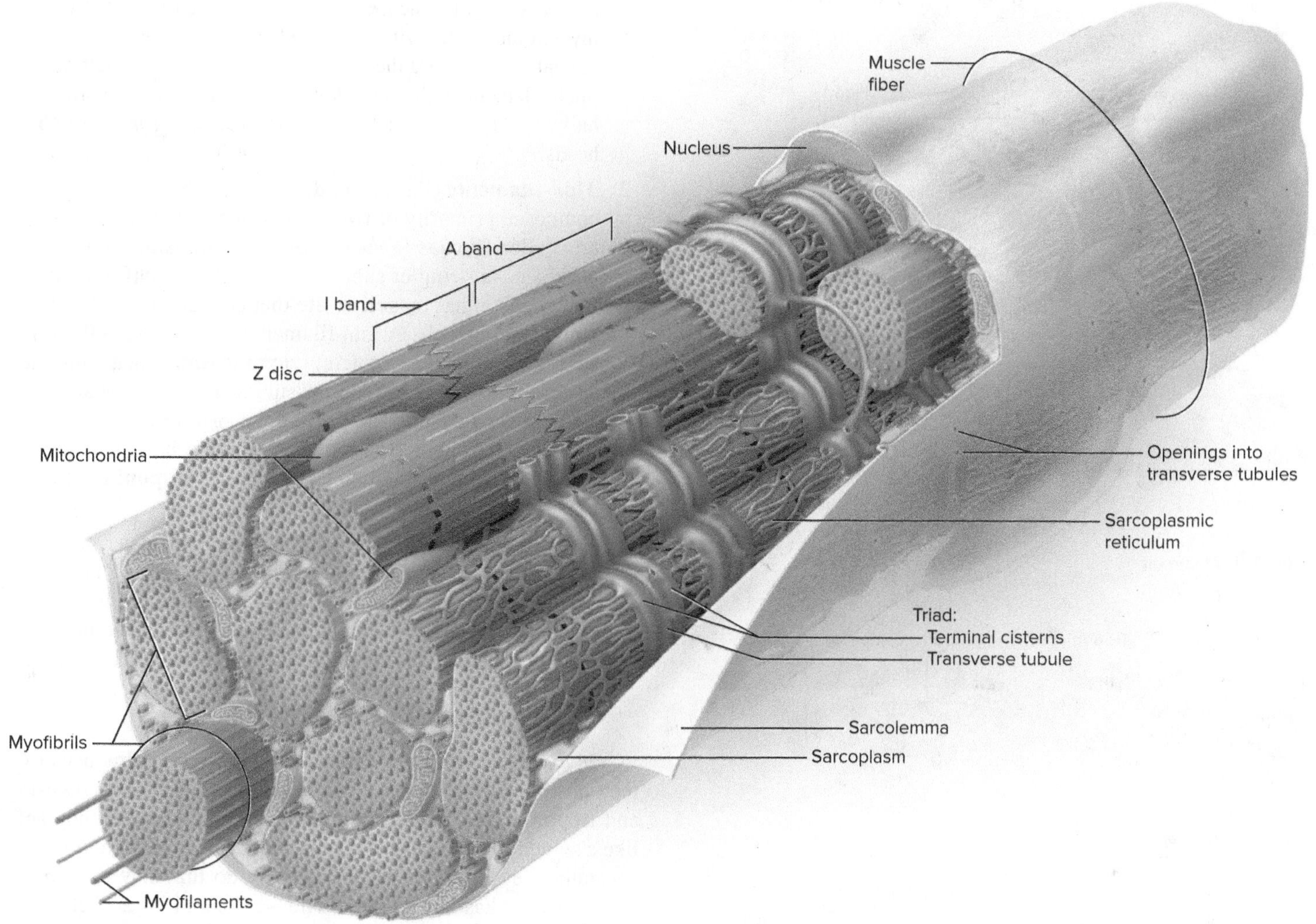


**FIGURE 11.2 Structure of a Skeletal Muscle Fiber.** This is a single cell containing 11 myofibrils (9 shown at the left end and 2 cut off at midfiber). A few myofilaments are shown projecting from the myofibril at the left. Most muscle fibers have from several dozen to a thousand or more myofibrils. Myofibril fine structure is shown in figure 11.3.

*After reading a little farther in this chapter, explain why it is important for the transverse tubule to be so closely associated with the terminal cisterns.*

Most other organelles of the cell, such as mitochondria, are packed into the spaces between the myofibrils. The smooth endoplasmic reticulum, here called the **sarcoplasmic reticulum (SR),** forms a network around each myofibril (the blue web in fig. 11.2). It periodically exhibits dilated end sacs called **terminal cisterns,** which cross the muscle fiber from one side to the other. The sarcolemma has tubular infoldings called **transverse (T) tubules,** which penetrate through the cell and emerge on the other side. Each T tubule is closely associated with two terminal cisterns running alongside it, one on each side. The T tubule and the two cisterns associated with it constitute a *triad.*

Muscle has a high demand for ATP and therefore possesses an exceptionally large number of mitochondria wedged in between the myofibils. Muscle contraction also requires a lot of calcium ions ($Ca^{2+}$), as you will see, but this presents a problem. A high concentration of $Ca^{2+}$ in the cytosol is lethal—it can react with phosphate ions to precipitate as calcium phosphate crystals, and can trigger cell death by apoptosis. Therefore, at rest, a muscle cell stores its $Ca^{2+}$ in the sarcoplasmic reticulum, safely bound to a protein called **calsequestrin.**[3] In a resting muscle fiber, $Ca^{2+}$ is about 10,000 times as concentrated in the SR as it is in the cytosol. When the cell is stimulated, ion gates in the SR membrane open and $Ca^{2+}$ floods into the cytosol to activate contraction. The T tubule signals the SR when to release these calcium bursts.

## 11.2b Myofilaments

Let's return to the myofibrils just mentioned—the long protein cords that fill most of the muscle cell—and look at their structure at a finer, molecular level. It is here that the key to muscle contraction lies. Each myofibril is a bundle of parallel proteins called **muscle filaments** or **myofilaments** (see the left end of fig. 11.2). There are three kinds of myofilaments:

1. **Thick filaments (fig. 11.3a, b)** are about 15 nm in diameter. Each is made of several hundred molecules of a motor

[3]*cal* = calcium; *sequestr* = to set apart or separate; *in* = protein

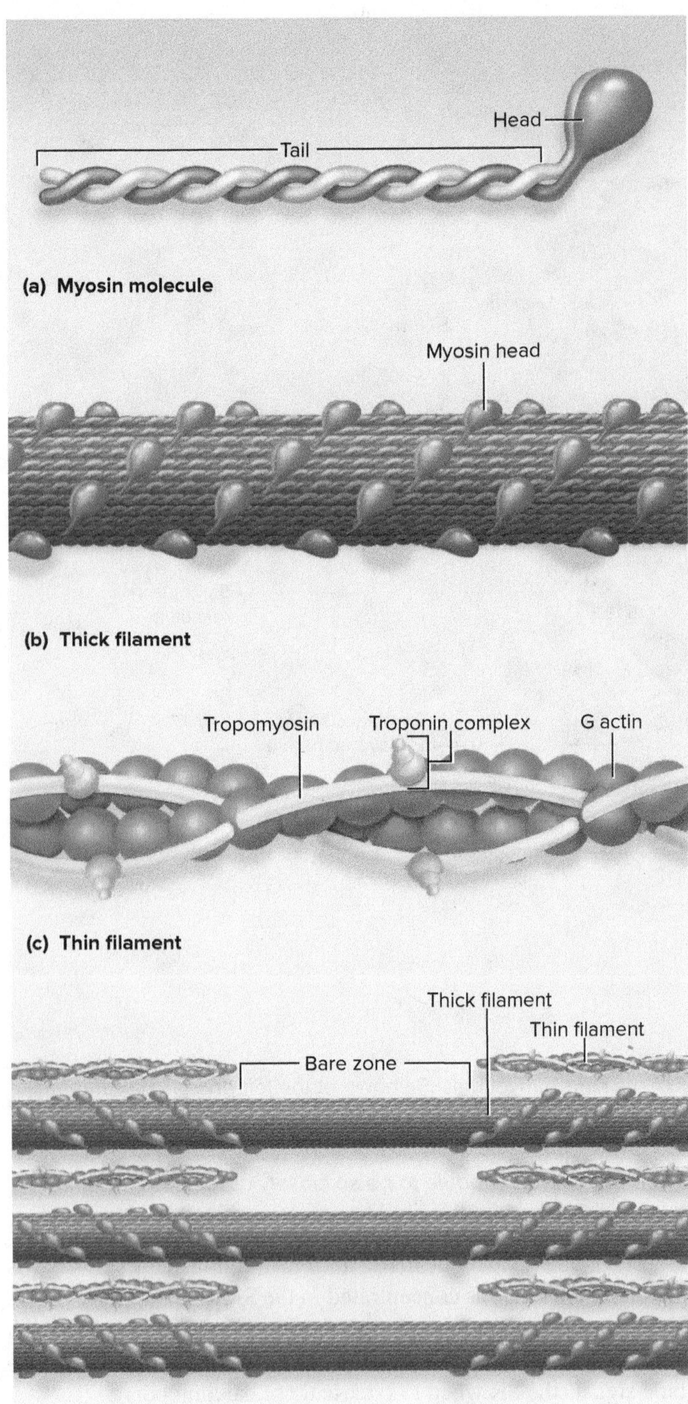


**FIGURE 11.3 Molecular Structure of Thick and Thin Filaments.** (a) A single myosin molecule composed of two intertwined proteins. (b) A thick filament composed of a bundle of myosin molecules. (c) A thin filament composed of actin, tropomyosin, and troponin. (d) A region of overlap between the thick and thin filaments.

protein called **myosin.** A myosin molecule is shaped like a golf club, with two chains intertwined to form a shaft-like *tail* and a double globular *head* projecting from it at an angle. A thick filament consists of a bundle of 200 to 500 myosin molecules with their heads directed outward in a helical array around the bundle. The heads on one half of the thick filament angle to the left, and the heads on the other half angle to the right; in the middle is a *bare zone* with no heads.

2. **Thin filaments (fig. 11.3c, d),** 7 nm in diameter, are composed primarily of two intertwined strands of a protein called **fibrous (F) actin.** Each F actin is like a bead necklace—a string of subunits called **globular (G) actin.** Each G actin has an **active site** that can bind to the head of a myosin molecule. A thin filament also has 40 to 60 molecules of yet another protein, **tropomyosin.** When a muscle fiber is relaxed, each tropomyosin blocks the active sites of six or seven G actins and prevents myosin from binding to them. Each tropomyosin molecule, in turn, has a smaller, three-part calcium-binding protein called **troponin** bound to it.
3. **Elastic filaments** (see fig. 11.5b), 1 nm in diameter, are made of a huge springy protein called **titin.**[4] They run through the core of each thick filament and anchor it to structures called the *Z disc* at one end and *M line* at the other. Titin stabilizes the thick filament, centers it between the thin filaments, prevents overstretching, and recoils like a spring after a muscle is stretched.

Myosin and actin are called **contractile proteins** because they do the work of shortening the muscle fiber. Tropomyosin and troponin are called **regulatory proteins** because they act like a switch to determine when the fiber can contract and when it cannot. Several clues as to how they do this may be apparent from what has already been said—calcium ions are released into the sarcoplasm to activate contraction; calcium binds to troponin; troponin is also bound to tropomyosin; and tropomyosin blocks the active sites of actin, so that myosin cannot bind to it when the muscle is not stimulated. Perhaps you are already forming some idea of the contraction mechanism to be explained shortly.

At least seven other accessory proteins occur in the thick and thin filaments or are associated with them. Among other functions, they anchor the myofilaments, regulate their length, and keep them aligned with each other for optimal contractile effectiveness. The most clinically important of these is **dystrophin,** an enormous protein located between the sarcolemma and the outermost myofilaments. It links actin filaments to a peripheral protein on the inner face of the sarcolemma. Through a series of linking proteins **(fig. 11.4),** this leads ultimately to the fibrous endomysium surrounding the muscle fiber. Therefore, when the thin filaments move, dystrophin transfers the force to the basal lamina, endomysium, and ultimately to the tendon. Genetic defects in dystrophin are responsible for the disabling disease *muscular dystrophy* (see Deeper Insight 11.4).

[4] *tit* = giant; *in* = protein

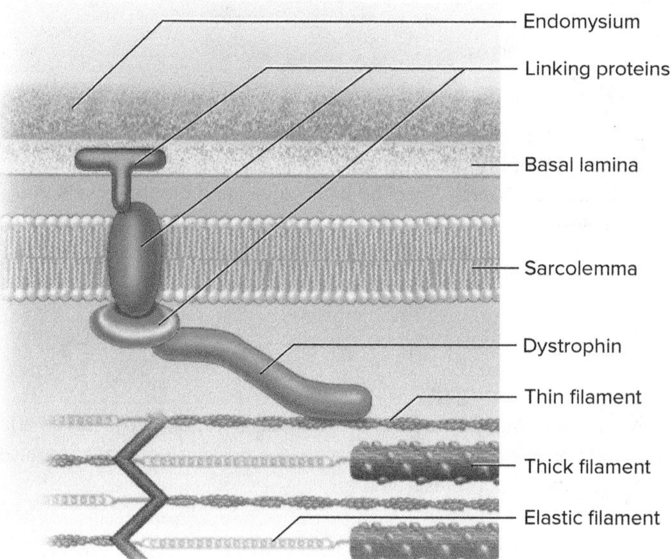


**FIGURE 11.4 Dystrophin.** Dystrophin ultimately transfers the force of moving actin filaments to tissues leading to the tendon of a muscle.

## 11.2c Striations

Myosin and actin are not unique to muscle; they occur in nearly all cells, where they function in cellular motility, mitosis, and transport of intracellular materials. In skeletal and cardiac muscle they are especially abundant, however, and are organized in a precise array that accounts for the striations of these muscle types (**figs. 11.5,** 11.3d).

Striated muscle has dark **A bands** alternating with lighter **I bands.** (*A* stands for *anisotropic* and *I* for *isotropic,* which refer to the way these bands affect polarized light. To help remember which band is which, think "dArk" and "lIght.") Each A band consists of thick filaments lying side by side. Part of the A band, where thick and thin filaments overlap, is especially dark. In this region, each thick filament is surrounded by a hexagonal array of thin filaments. In the middle of the A band, there is a lighter region called the **H band,**[5] into which the thin filaments do not reach. In the middle of the H band, the thick filaments are linked to each other through a dark, transverse protein complex called the **M line.**[6]

Each light I band is bisected by a dark narrow **Z disc**[7] **(Z line),** which provides anchorage for the thin and elastic filaments. Each segment of a myofibril from one Z disc to the next is called a **sarcomere**[8] (SAR-co-meer), the functional contractile unit of the muscle

[5]*H* = *helle* = bright (German)
[6]*M* = *Mittel* = middle (German)
[7]*Z* = *Zwichenscheibe* = between disc (German)
[8]*sarco* = muscle; *mere* = part, segment

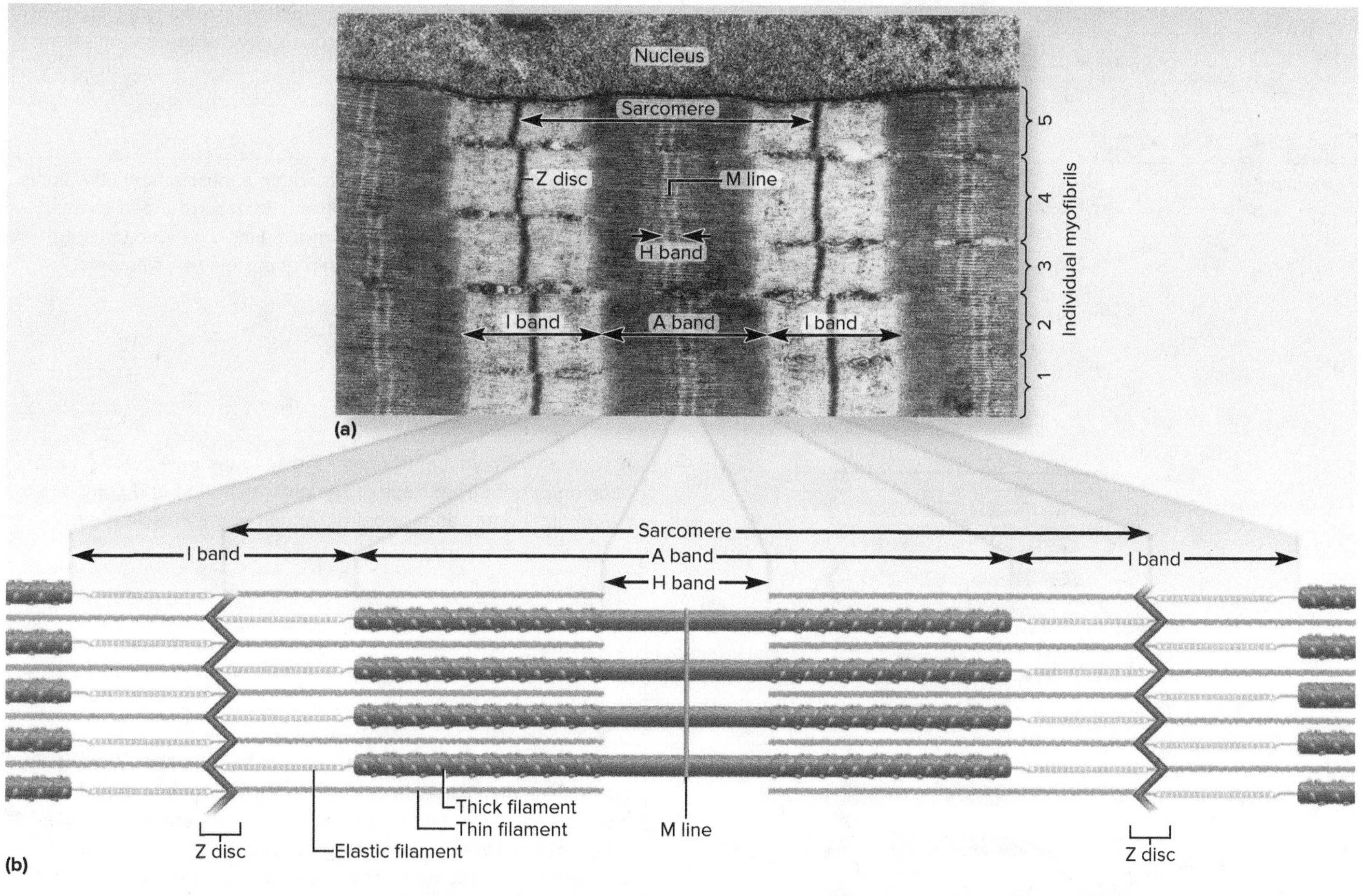

**FIGURE 11.5 Muscle Striations and Their Molecular Basis.** (a) Five myofibrils of a single muscle fiber, showing the striations in the relaxed state (TEM). (b) The overlapping pattern of thick and thin filaments that accounts for the striations seen in part (a). APR

a: Don W. Fawcett/Science Source

## TABLE 11.1 The Structural Hierarchy of a Skeletal Muscle

| Structural Level | Description |
|---|---|
| Muscle 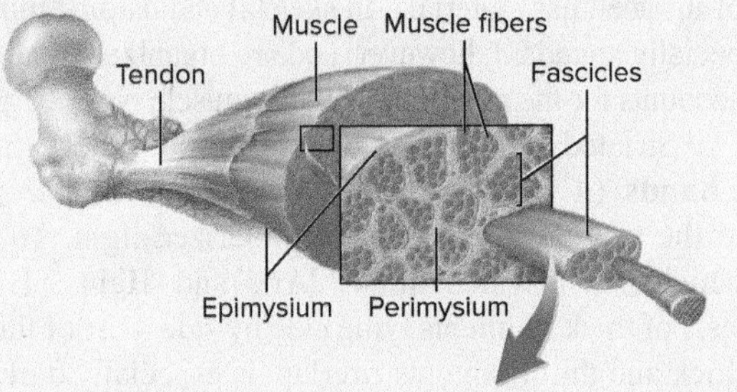 | A contractile organ, usually attached to bones by way of tendons. Composed of bundles (fascicles) of tightly packed, long, parallel cells (muscle fibers). Supplied with nerves and blood vessels and enclosed in a fibrous epimysium that separates it from neighboring muscles. |
| Fascicle 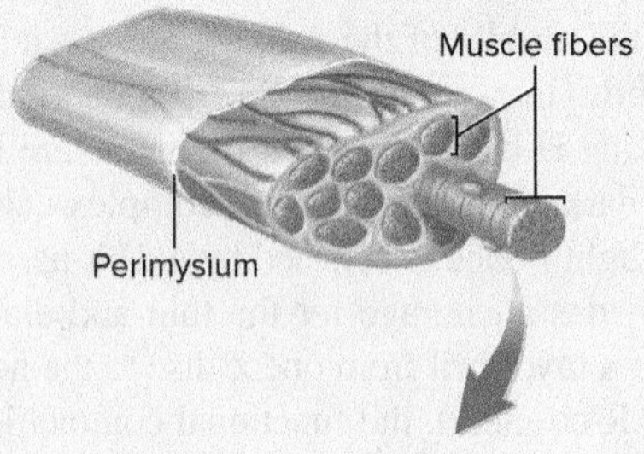 | A bundle of muscle fibers within a muscle. Supplied by nerves and blood vessels and enclosed in a fibrous perimysium that separates it from neighboring fascicles. |
| Muscle Fiber 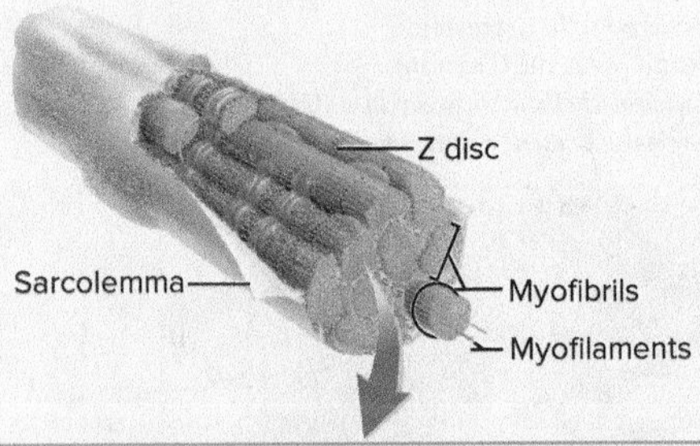 | A single muscle cell. Slender, elongated, threadlike, enclosed in a specialized plasma membrane (sarcolemma). Contains densely packed bundles (myofibrils) of contractile protein myofilaments, multiple nuclei immediately beneath the sarcolemma, and an extensive network of specialized smooth endoplasmic reticulum (sarcoplasmic reticulum). Enclosed in a thin fibrous sleeve called endomysium. |
| Myofibril 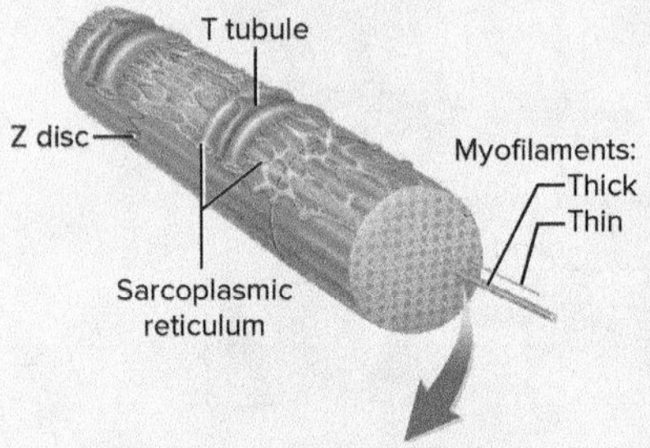 | A bundle of protein myofilaments within a muscle fiber; myofibrils collectively fill most of the cytoplasm. Each surrounded by sarcoplasmic reticulum and mitochondria. Has a banded (striated) appearance due to orderly overlap of protein myofilaments. |
| Sarcomere 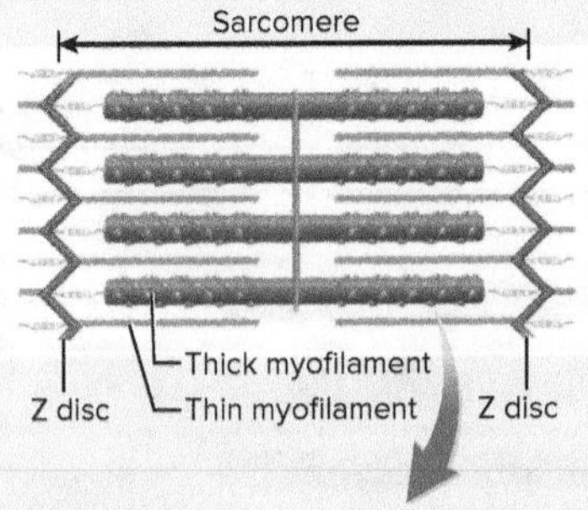 | A segment of myofibril from one Z disc to the next in the fiber's striation pattern. Hundreds of sarcomeres end to end compose a myofibril. The functional, contractile unit of the muscle fiber. |
| Myofilaments 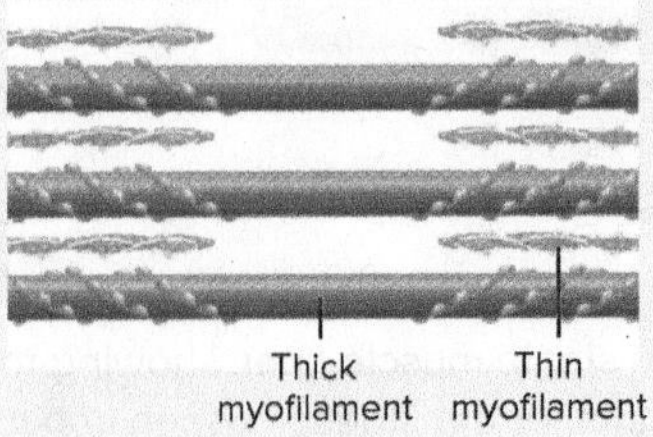 | Fibrous protein strands that carry out the contraction process. Two types: thick myofilaments composed mainly of myosin, and thin myofilaments composed mainly of actin. Thick and thin myofilaments slide over each other to shorten each sarcomere. Shortening of end-to-end sarcomeres shortens the entire muscle. |

fiber. A muscle shortens because its individual sarcomeres shorten and pull the Z discs closer to each other, and dystrophin and the linking proteins pull on the extracellular proteins of the muscle. As the Z discs are pulled closer together, they pull on the sarcolemma to achieve overall shortening of the cell.

**Table 11.1** reviews the organization of skeletal muscle at successive structural levels from the whole muscle to the myofilaments.

**BEFORE YOU GO ON**

Answer the following questions to test your understanding of the preceding section:

4. What special terms are given to the plasma membrane, cytoplasm, and smooth ER of a muscle cell?
5. What is the difference between a myofilament and a myofibril?
6. List five proteins of the myofilaments and describe their physical arrangement.
7. Sketch the overlapping pattern of myofilaments to show how they account for the A bands, I bands, H bands, and Z discs.

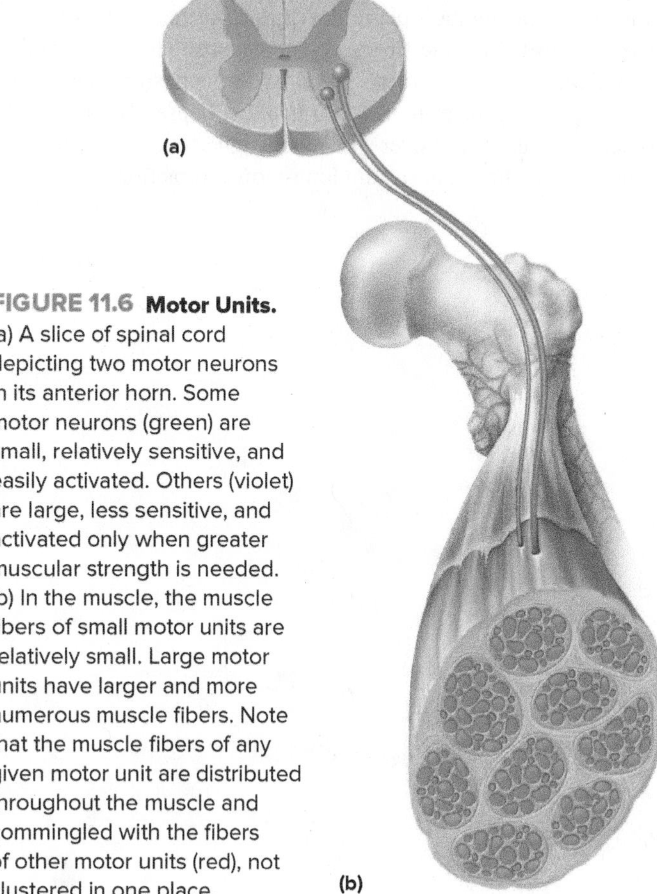


FIGURE 11.6 **Motor Units.** (a) A slice of spinal cord depicting two motor neurons in its anterior horn. Some motor neurons (green) are small, relatively sensitive, and easily activated. Others (violet) are large, less sensitive, and activated only when greater muscular strength is needed. (b) In the muscle, the muscle fibers of small motor units are relatively small. Large motor units have larger and more numerous muscle fibers. Note that the muscle fibers of any given motor unit are distributed throughout the muscle and commingled with the fibers of other motor units (red), not clustered in one place.

## 11.3 The Nerve–Muscle Relationship

**Expected Learning Outcomes**

When you have completed this section, you should be able to

a. explain what a motor unit is and how it relates to muscle contraction;
b. describe the structure of the junction where a nerve fiber meets a muscle fiber; and
c. explain why a cell has an electrical charge difference across its plasma membrane and, in general terms, how this relates to muscle contraction.

Skeletal muscle cannot contract unless it is stimulated by a nerve (or with electrodes). If its nerve connections are severed or poisoned, a muscle is paralyzed. If the connection is not restored, the paralyzed muscle wastes away in a shrinkage called *denervation atrophy.* Thus, muscle contraction cannot be understood without first understanding the relationship between nerve and muscle cells.

### 11.3a Motor Neurons and Motor Units

Skeletal muscles are served by nerve cells called *somatic motor neurons,* whose cell bodies are in the brainstem and spinal cord. Their axons, called **somatic motor fibers,** lead to the muscles. Each nerve fiber branches out to multiple muscle fibers, but each muscle fiber is supplied by only one motor neuron.

When a nerve signal approaches the end of an axon, it spreads out over all of its terminal branches and stimulates all muscle fibers supplied by them. Thus, these muscle fibers contract in unison; there is no way to stimulate some but not all of them. Since they behave as a single functional unit, one nerve fiber and all the muscle fibers innervated by it are called a **motor unit (fig. 11.6).** The muscle fibers of a motor unit are not clustered together but dispersed throughout a muscle. Therefore, when stimulated, they cause a weak contraction over a wide area—not just a local twitch in one small region. Effective muscle contraction usually requires the activation of many motor units at once.

On average, about 200 muscle fibers are innervated by each motor neuron, but motor units can be much smaller or larger than this to serve different purposes. Where fine control is needed, we have *small motor units.* These typically are supplied by small, relatively sensitive neurons. Where strength is more important than fine control, we have *large motor units.* These are innervated by less sensitive neurons with larger cell bodies, activated when strength is needed for a demanding task.

Consider a hand or eye muscle that requires fine motor control. Here, 1,000 muscle fibers may be innervated by 200 to 300 motor neurons with small motor units of only 3 to 5 muscle fibers each. Turning a few motor units on or off would produce small, subtle changes in muscle action. Then consider a powerful thigh or calf muscle such as the quadriceps femoris or gastrocnemius. Here, every 1,000 muscle fibers may be controlled by only 1 or 2 neurons with large motor units of 500 to 1,000 muscle fibers each. Turning a few motor units on or off would produce relatively large changes in muscle action, with large increments in strength but little fine control or subtlety.

In addition to adjustments in strength and control, another advantage of having multiple motor units in each muscle is that they work in shifts. Muscle fibers fatigue when subjected to continual stimulation. If all the fibers in one of your postural muscles fatigued at once, for example, you could collapse. To prevent this, other motor units take over while the fatigued ones recover, and the muscle as a whole can sustain long-term contraction.

### 11.3b The Neuromuscular Junction

The point where a nerve fiber meets any target cell is called a **synapse** (SIN-aps). When the target cell is a muscle fiber, the synapse is also called a **neuromuscular junction (NMJ)** or **motor end plate (fig. 11.7).** Each terminal branch of the nerve fiber within the NMJ forms a separate synapse with the muscle fiber. The sarcolemma of the NMJ is irregularly indented, a little like a handprint

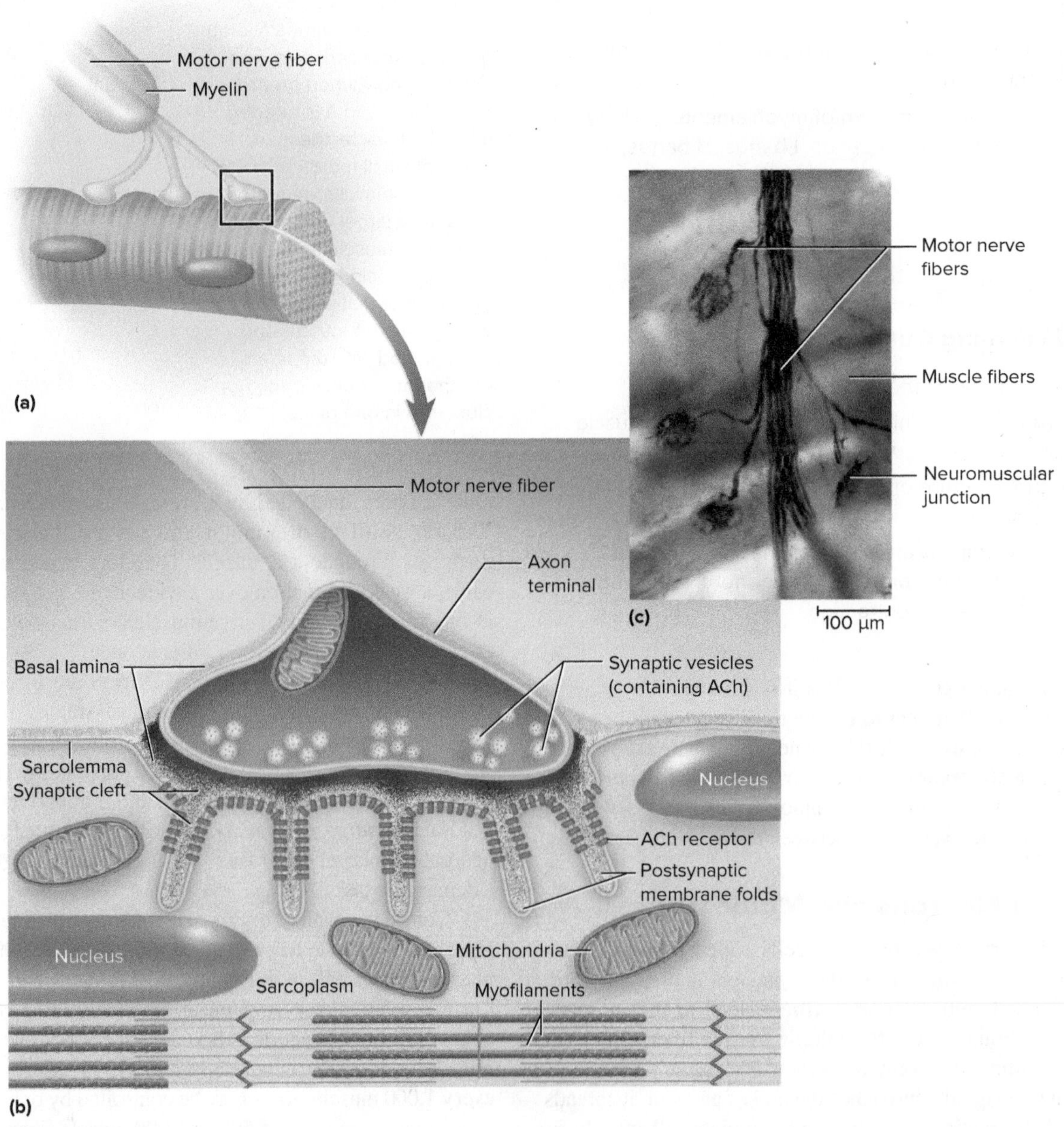


**FIGURE 11.7 Innervation of Skeletal Muscle.** (a) Motor nerve ending on a muscle fiber. (b) Detail of the neuromuscular junction. (c) Light micrograph (LM) of neuromuscular junctions (compare the SEM photo on the opening page of this chapter). APR

c: Al Telser/McGraw-Hill Education

pressed into soft clay. If you imagine the nerve fiber to be like your forearm, branching out at the end like your fingers, the individual synapses would be like the dents where your fingertips press into the clay. Thus, one nerve fiber stimulates the muscle fiber at several nearby points within the NMJ.

At each synapse, the nerve fiber ends in a bulbous swelling called the **axon terminal.** The terminal doesn't directly touch the muscle fiber but is separated from it by a narrow space called the **synaptic cleft,** about 60 to 100 nm wide (scarcely wider than the thickness of one plasma membrane).

The axon terminal contains spheroidal organelles called **synaptic vesicles,** which are filled with a chemical, **acetylcholine (ACh)** (ASS-eh-till-CO-leen)—one of many *neurotransmitters* to be introduced in the next chapter. The electrical signal (nerve impulse) traveling down a nerve fiber cannot cross the synaptic cleft like a spark jumping between two electrodes—rather, it causes the synaptic vesicles to undergo exocytosis, releasing ACh into the cleft. ACh thus functions as a chemical messenger from the nerve cell to the muscle cell.

To respond to ACh, each synapse has about 50 million **ACh receptors**—proteins incorporated into the sarcolemma across from the axon terminals. To maximize the number of ACh receptors and thus its sensitivity to the neurotransmitter, the sarcolemma in this area has infoldings about 1 μm deep, called **postsynaptic membrane folds (junctional folds),** which increase the surface area of ACh-sensitive membrane. The muscle nuclei beneath the folds are specifically dedicated to the synthesis of ACh receptors and other proteins of the local sarcolemma. A deficiency of ACh receptors leads to muscle weakness in the disease *myasthenia gravis* (see Deeper Insight 11.4).

The entire NMJ is enclosed in a **basal lamina,** a mat of collagen and glycoprotein that separates the muscle fiber and nerve ending from the surrounding connective tissue. The basal lamina also passes through the synaptic cleft and virtually fills it. Both the sarcolemma and that part of the basal lamina in the cleft contain **acetylcholinesterase (AChE)** (ASS-eh-till-CO-lin-ESS-ter-ase). This is an enzyme that breaks down ACh after the ACh has stimulated the muscle cell; thus, it is important in turning off muscle contraction and allowing the muscle to relax (see Deeper Insight 11.1).

### 11.3c Electrically Excitable Cells

Muscle and nerve cells are regarded as *electrically excitable cells* because their plasma membranes exhibit voltage changes in response to stimulation. The study of the electrical activity of cells, called **electrophysiology,** is a key to understanding nerve activity, muscle contraction, the heartbeat and electrocardiogram, and other physiological phenomena. The details of electrophysiology are presented in section 12.4, but a few fundamental principles must be introduced here so you can understand muscle excitation.

The electrical activity of cells hinges on differences in the concentration of ions in the intracellular fluid (ICF) and extracellular fluid (ECF) adjacent to the plasma membrane. The ICF contains a greater concentration of negative anions than the ECF does—especially negatively charged proteins, nucleic acids, and phosphates, which are trapped in the cell and give its interior a net negative charge. That is, the membrane is **polarized,** like a little battery. Also contained in the ICF is a great excess of potassium ions ($K^+$), whereas the ECF contains a great excess of sodium ions ($Na^+$). The electrical events that initiate muscle contraction are driven by the movements of these two cations through the membrane when a muscle or nerve cell is excited.

## DEEPER INSIGHT 11.1
### CLINICAL APPLICATION

### *Neuromuscular Toxins and Paralysis*

Toxins that interfere with synaptic function can paralyze the muscles. Organophosphate pesticides such as malathion are *cholinesterase inhibitors* that bind to AChE and prevent it from degrading ACh. Depending on the dose, this can prolong the action of ACh and produce *spastic paralysis,* a state in which the muscles contract and cannot relax; clinically, this is called a *cholinergic crisis.* It poses a danger of suffocation if it affects the laryngeal and respiratory muscles. Another example of spastic paralysis is *tetanus (lockjaw),* caused by the toxin of a soil bacterium, *Clostridium tetani.* In the spinal cord, a neurotransmitter called glycine normally stops motor neurons from producing unwanted muscle contractions. The tetanus toxin blocks glycine release and thus causes overstimulation and spastic paralysis of the muscles.

*Flaccid paralysis* is a state in which the muscles are limp and cannot contract. This too can cause respiratory arrest if it affects the thoracic muscles. Among the causes of flaccid paralysis are poisons such as curare (cue-RAH-ree), which competes with ACh for receptor sites but doesn't stimulate the muscle. Curare is extracted from certain plants and used by some South American natives to poison blowgun darts. It has been used to treat muscle spasms in some neurological disorders and to relax abdominal muscles for surgery, but other muscle relaxants have now replaced curare for most purposes.

Another cause of flaccid paralysis is *botulism,* a type of food poisoning caused by a neuromuscular toxin secreted by the bacterium *Clostridium botulinum.* Botulinum toxin blocks ACh release. Purified botulinum toxin is marketed as Botox Cosmetic. It is injected in small doses into specific facial muscles. Wrinkles gradually disappear as muscle paralysis sets in over the next few hours. The effect lasts about 4 months until the muscles retighten and the wrinkles return. Botox treatment has become the fastest-growing cosmetic medical procedure in the United States, as its usage has expanded to other conditions and many people go for cosmetic treatment every few months. It has had some undesirable consequences, however, as it is sometimes administered by unqualified practitioners. Even some qualified physicians use it for treatments not yet approved by the FDA, and some host festive "Botox parties" for treatment of patients in assembly-line fashion.

A difference in electrical charge from one point to another is called an *electrical potential,* or *voltage.* It typically measures 12 volts (V) for a car battery and 1.5 V for a flashlight battery, for example. On the sarcolemma of a muscle cell, the voltage is much smaller, about –90 millivolts (mV), but critically important to life. (The negative sign refers to the relatively negative charge on the intracellular side of the membrane.) This voltage is called the **resting membrane potential (RMP).** It is maintained by the sodium–potassium pump, as explained in section 12.4b.

When a nerve or muscle cell is stimulated, dramatic things happen electrically, as we shall soon see in the excitation of muscle. Ion channels in the plasma membrane open and $Na^+$ instantly flows into the cell, driven both by its concentration difference across the membrane and by its attraction to the negative charge of the cell interior—that is, it flows down an **electrochemical gradient.** These $Na^+$ cations override the negative charge just inside the membrane, so the inside of the membrane briefly becomes positive. This is called **depolarization** of the membrane. Immediately, $Na^+$ channels close and $K^+$ channels open. $K^+$ rushes out of the cell, partly because it is repelled by the positive sodium charge and partly because it is more concentrated in the ICF than in the ECF—that is, it flows down its own electrochemical gradient in the direction opposite from the sodium movement. The loss of $K^+$ ions from the cell turns the inside of the membrane negative again **(repolarization).** This quick up-and-down voltage shift, from the negative RMP to a positive value and then back to the RMP again, is called an **action potential.** The RMP is a stable voltage seen in a "waiting" cell, whereas the action potential is a quickly fluctuating voltage seen in an active, stimulated cell.

Action potentials have a way of perpetuating themselves—an action potential at one point on a plasma membrane causes another one to happen immediately in front of it, which triggers another one a little farther along, and so forth. A wave of action potentials spreading along a nerve fiber like this is called a *nerve impulse* or *nerve signal.* Such signals also travel along the sarcolemma of a muscle fiber. Next we will see how this leads to muscle contraction.

**BEFORE YOU GO ON**

Answer the following questions to test your understanding of the preceding section:

8. What differences would you expect to see between a motor unit where muscular strength is more important than fine control and another motor unit where fine control is more important?
9. State the functions of the axon terminal and its synaptic vesicles.
10. Distinguish between acetylcholine, an acetylcholine receptor, and acetylcholinesterase. State where each is found and describe the function it serves.
11. What accounts for the resting membrane potential seen in unstimulated nerve and muscle cells?
12. What is the difference between a resting membrane potential and an action potential?

## 11.4 Behavior of Skeletal Muscle Fibers

**Expected Learning Outcomes**

When you have completed this section, you should be able to

a. explain how a nerve fiber stimulates a skeletal muscle fiber;
b. explain how stimulation of a muscle fiber activates its contractile mechanism;
c. explain the mechanism of muscle contraction;
d. explain how a muscle fiber relaxes; and
e. explain why the force of a muscle contraction depends on the muscle's length prior to stimulation.

The process of muscle contraction and relaxation has four major phases: (1) excitation, (2) excitation–contraction coupling, (3) contraction, and (4) relaxation. Each phase occurs in several smaller steps, which we now examine in detail.

### 11.4a Excitation

**Excitation** is the process in which action potentials in the nerve fiber lead to action potentials in the muscle fiber. The steps in excitation are shown in **figure 11.8.** Follow these carefully as you read the following description to ensure understanding of the process.

1. A nerve signal arrives at the axon terminal and opens voltage-gated calcium channels. Calcium ions enter the terminal.
2. Calcium stimulates the synaptic vesicles to release acetylcholine (ACh) into the synaptic cleft. One action potential causes exocytosis of about 60 vesicles, and each vesicle releases about 10,000 molecules of ACh.
3. ACh diffuses across the synaptic cleft and binds to receptors on the sarcolemma.
4. These receptors are ligand-gated ion channels. Two ACh molecules must bind to each receptor to open the channel. When it opens, $Na^+$ flows quickly into the cell and $K^+$ flows out. The voltage on the sarcolemma quickly rises to a less negative value as $Na^+$ enters the cell, then falls back to the RMP as $K^+$ exits. This rapid up-and-down fluctuation in voltage at the motor end plate is called the **end-plate potential (EPP).**
5. Areas of sarcolemma next to the end plate have voltage-gated ion channels that open in response to the EPP. Some of these are specific for $Na^+$ and admit it to the cell, while others are specific for $K^+$ and allow it to leave. These ion movements create an *action potential.* The muscle fiber is now excited.

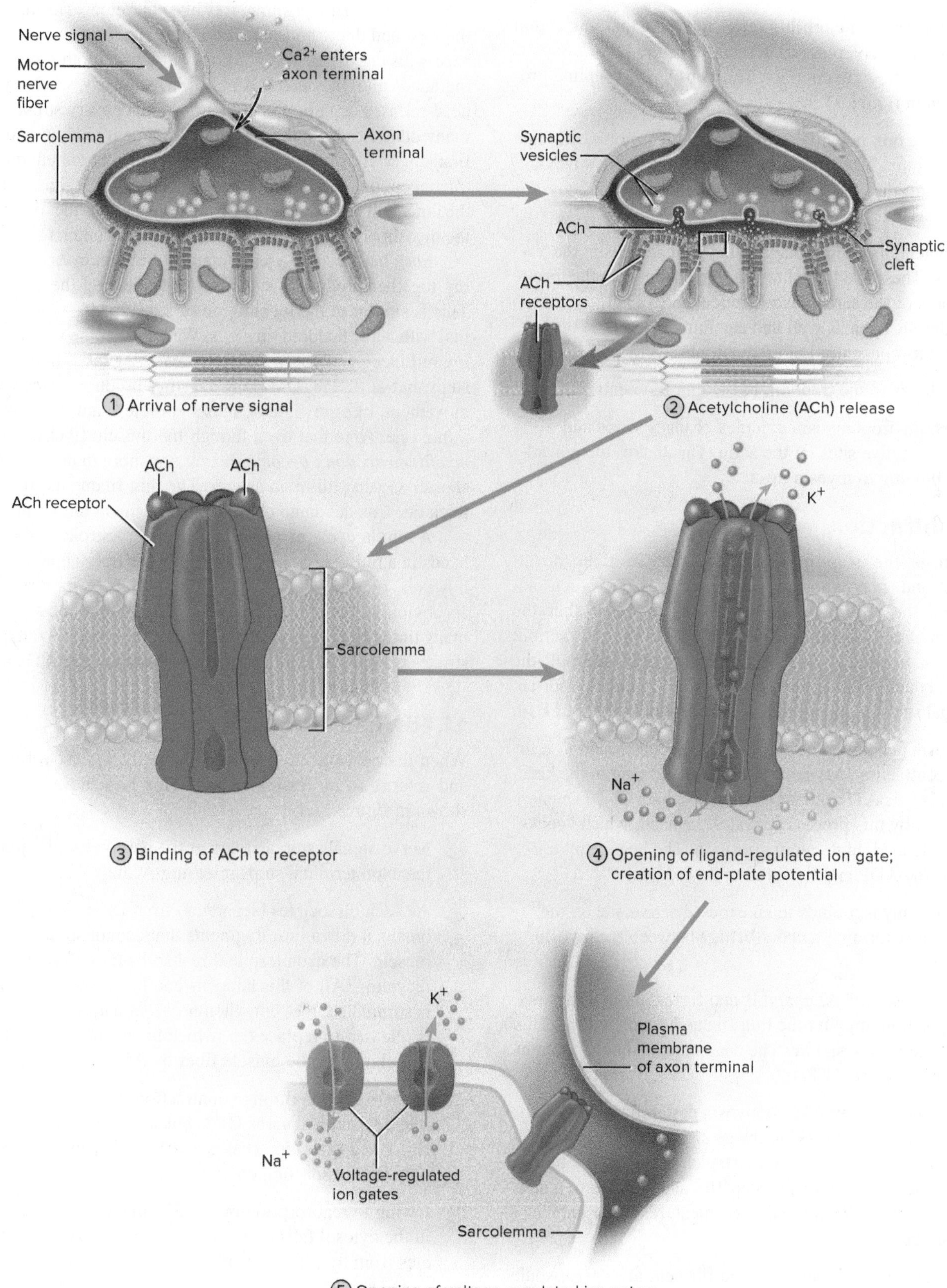


**FIGURE 11.8 Excitation of a Muscle Fiber.** These events link action potentials in a nerve fiber to the generation of action potentials in the muscle fiber. See the corresponding numbered steps in the text for explanation.

### 11.4b Excitation–Contraction Coupling

**Excitation–contraction coupling** refers to events that link action potentials on the sarcolemma to activation of the myofilaments, thereby preparing them to contract. The steps in the coupling process are shown in **figure 11.9.**

⑥ A wave of action potentials spreads from the motor end plate in all directions, like ripples on a pond. When this wave of excitation reaches the T tubules, it continues down them into the cell interior.

⑦ Action potentials open voltage-gated ion channels in the T tubules. These are linked to calcium channels in the terminal cisterns of the sarcoplasmic reticulum (SR). Thus, channels in the SR open as well and calcium diffuses out of the SR, down its concentration gradient into the cytosol.

⑧ Calcium binds to the troponin of the thin filaments.

⑨ The troponin–tropomyosin complex changes shape and exposes the active sites on the actin. This makes them available for binding to myosin heads.

### 11.4c Contraction

**Contraction** is the step in which the muscle fiber develops tension and may shorten. The mechanism of contraction is called the **sliding filament theory.** It holds that the myofilaments don't become any shorter during contraction; rather, the thin filaments slide over the thick ones and pull the Z discs behind them, causing each sarcomere as a whole to shorten. The individual steps in this mechanism are shown in **figure 11.10.**

⑩ The myosin head must have an ATP molecule bound to it to initiate contraction. **Myosin ATPase,** an enzyme in the head, hydrolyzes this ATP into ADP and phosphate ($P_i$). The energy released by this process activates the head, which "cocks" into an extended, high-energy position. The head temporarily keeps the ADP and $P_i$ bound to it.

⑪ The cocked myosin binds to an exposed active site on the thin filament, forming a **cross-bridge** between the myosin and actin.

⑫ Myosin releases the ADP and $P_i$ and flexes into a bent, low-energy position, tugging the thin filament along with it. This is called the **power stroke.** The head remains bound to actin until it binds a new ATP.

⑬ The binding of a new ATP to myosin destabilizes the myosin–actin bond, breaking the cross-bridge. The myosin head now undergoes a **recovery stroke.** It hydrolyzes the new ATP, recocks (returns to step 10), and attaches to a new active site farther down the thin filament, ready for another power stroke.

It may seem as if releasing the thin filament at step 13 would simply allow it to slide back to its previous position, so nothing would have been accomplished. Think of the sliding filament mechanism, however, as being similar to the way you would pull in a boat anchor hand over hand. When the myosin head cocks, it is like your hand reaching out to grasp the anchor rope. When it flexes back into the low-energy position, it is like your elbow flexing to pull on the rope and draw the anchor up a little bit. When you let go of the rope with one hand, you hold onto it with the other one, alternating hands until the anchor is pulled in. Similarly, when one myosin head releases actin in preparation for the recovery stroke, there are many other heads on the same thick filament holding onto the thin filament so it doesn't slide back. At any given moment during contraction, about half of the heads are bound to the thin filament and the other half are extending forward to grasp it farther down. That is, the myosin heads don't all stroke at once but contract sequentially.

Each head acts in a jerky manner, but hundreds of them working together produce a smooth, steady pull on the thin filament. This is similar to the locomotion of a millipede—a wormlike animal with a few hundred tiny legs. Watch an online video of a crawling millipede and you will see that each leg takes individual jerky steps, but all the legs working together produce a smooth gliding movement, like the glide of a thick muscle filament walking along a thin one. Note that even though the muscle fiber contracts, the *myofilaments don't become shorter* any more than a rope becomes shorter as you pull in an anchor. The thin filaments slide over the thick ones, as the name of the sliding filament theory implies.

A single cycle of power and recovery strokes by all myosin heads in a muscle fiber would shorten the fiber about 1%. A fiber, however, may shorten by as much as 40% of its resting length, so obviously the cycle of power and recovery must be repeated many times by each myosin head. Each head carries out about five strokes per second, and each stroke consumes one ATP.

### 11.4d Relaxation

When the nerve fiber stops stimulating it, a muscle fiber relaxes and returns to its resting length. This is achieved by the steps shown in **figure 11.11.**

⑭ Nerve signals stop arriving at the neuromuscular junction, so the axon terminal stops releasing ACh.

⑮ As ACh dissociates (separates) from its receptor, AChE breaks it down into fragments that cannot stimulate the muscle. The axon terminal reabsorbs these fragments for recycling. All of this happens continually while the muscle is stimulated, too, but when nerve signals stop, no more ACh is released to replace that which breaks down. Therefore, stimulation of the muscle fiber by ACh ceases.

⑯ From excitation through contraction, the SR simultaneously releases and reabsorbs $Ca^{2+}$; but when the nerve fiber stops firing and excitation ceases, $Ca^{2+}$ release also ceases and only its reabsorption continues.

⑰ Owing to reabsorption by the SR, the level of free calcium in the cytosol falls dramatically. Now, when calcium dissociates from troponin, it is not replaced.

⑱ Tropomyosin moves back into the position where it blocks the active sites of the actin filament. Myosin can no longer bind to actin, and the muscle fiber ceases to produce or maintain tension.

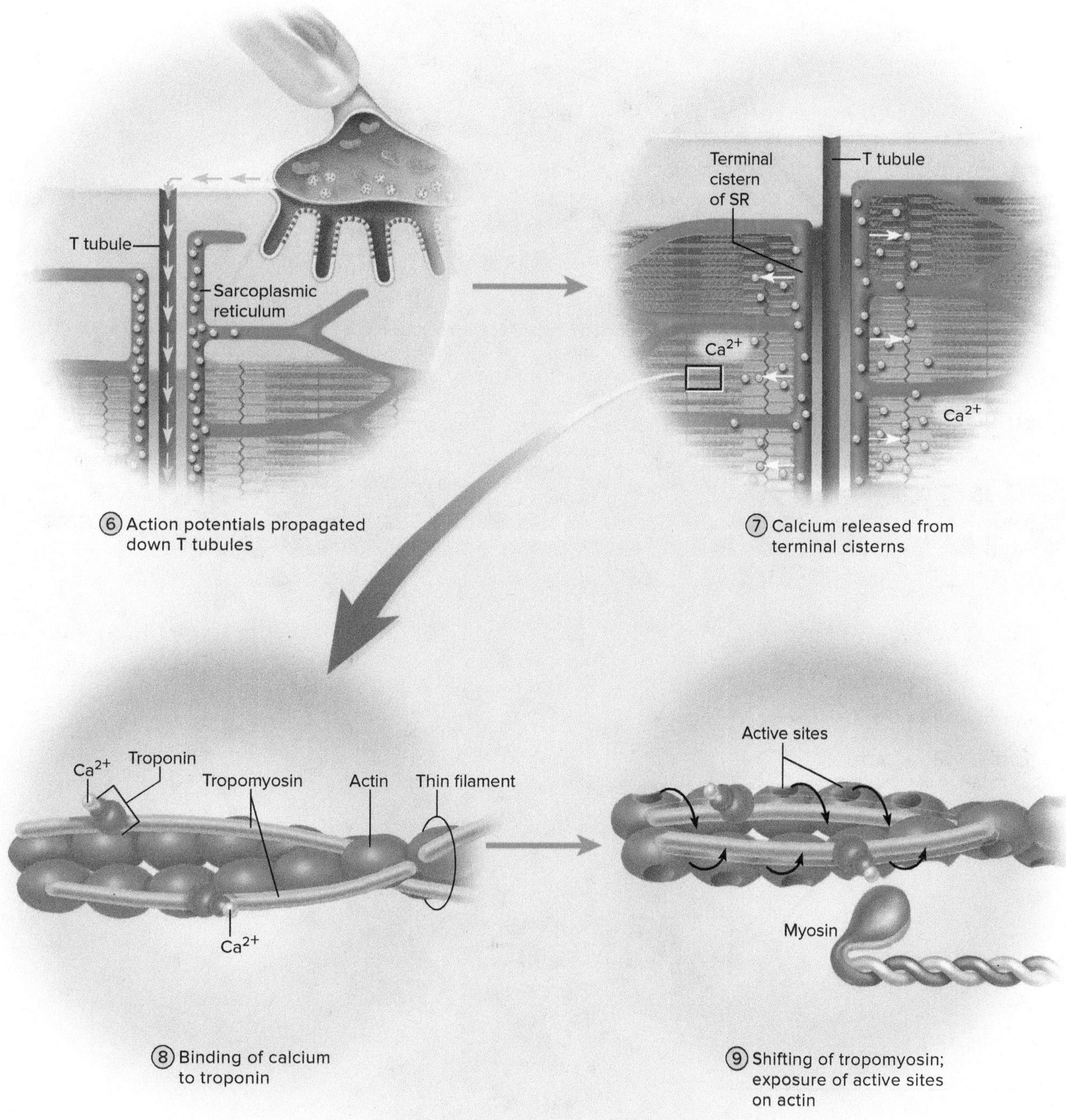


**FIGURE 11.9 Excitation–Contraction Coupling.** These events link action potentials in the muscle fiber to the release and binding of calcium ions. See the corresponding numbered steps in the text for explanation. The numbers in this figure begin where figure 11.8 ended.

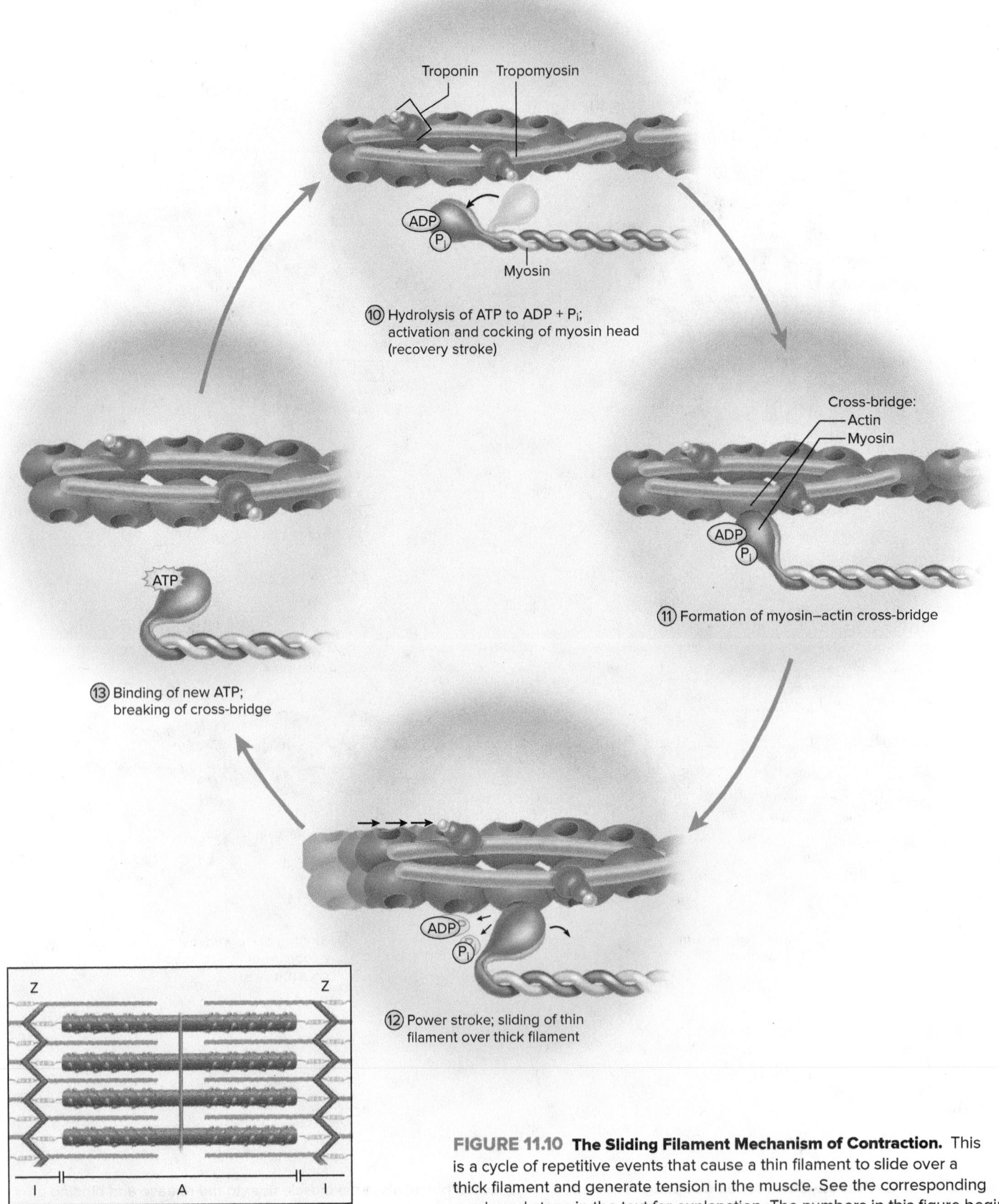


**FIGURE 11.10 The Sliding Filament Mechanism of Contraction.** This is a cycle of repetitive events that cause a thin filament to slide over a thick filament and generate tension in the muscle. See the corresponding numbered steps in the text for explanation. The numbers in this figure begin where figure 11.9 ended. Lower left: diagram of a contracting sarcomere.

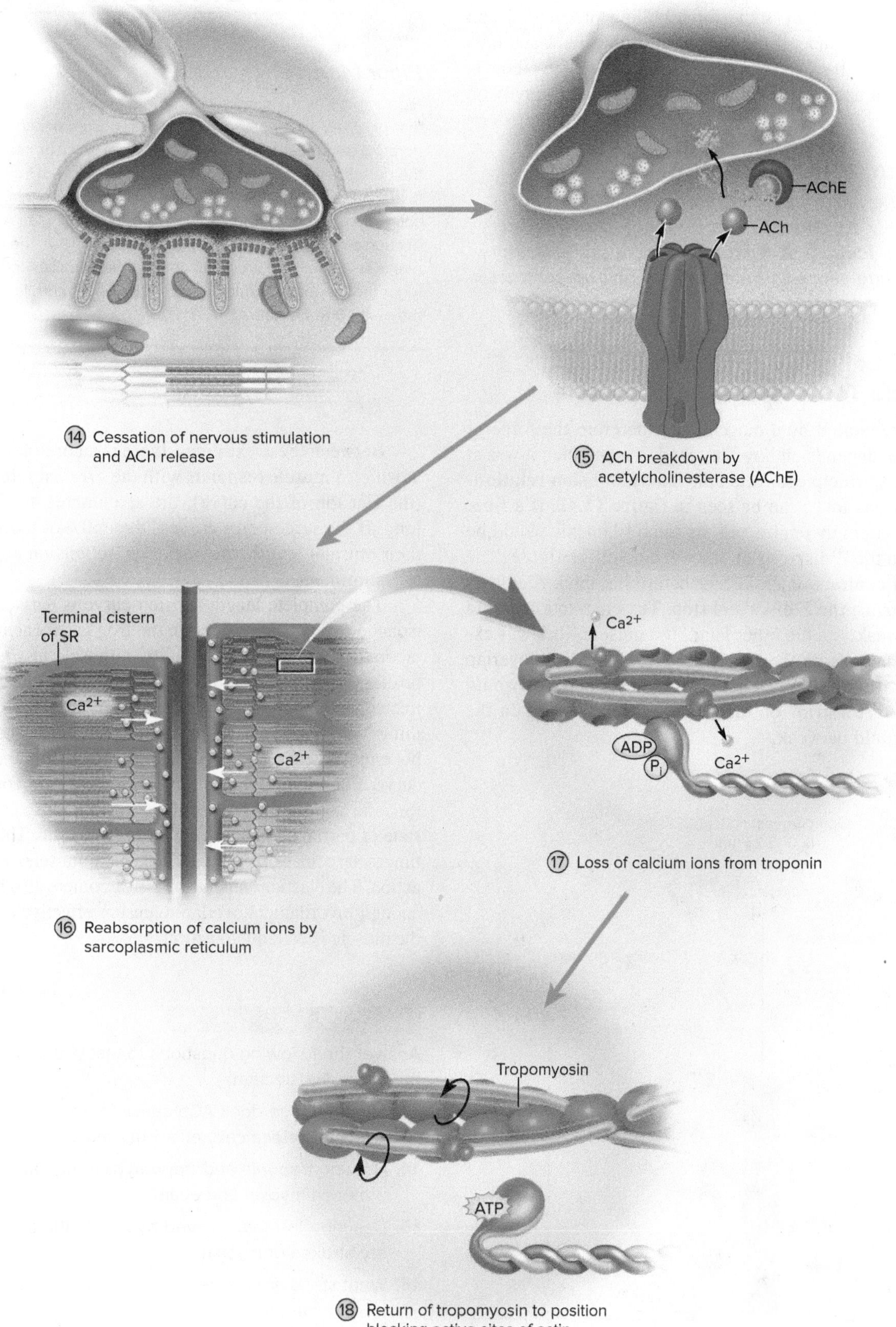


**FIGURE 11.11 Relaxation of a Muscle Fiber.** These events lead from the cessation of a nerve signal to the release of thin filaments by myosin. See the corresponding numbered steps in the text for explanation. The numbers in this figure begin where figure 11.10 ended.

Relaxation alone doesn't return a muscle to its resting length. That must be achieved by some force pulling the muscle and stretching it. For example, if the biceps flexes the elbow and then relaxes, it stretches back to its resting length only if the elbow is extended by contraction of the triceps or by the pull of gravity on the forearm.

**APPLY WHAT YOU KNOW**

*One of the most important properties of proteins is their ability to change shape repeatedly (see section 2.4e). Identify at least two muscle proteins that must change shape in order for a muscle to contract and relax.*

## 11.4e The Length–Tension Relationship and Muscle Tone

The tension generated by a muscle, and therefore the force of its contraction, depends on how stretched or contracted it was at the outset. This principle is called the **length–tension relationship.** The reasons for it can be seen in **figure 11.12.** If a fiber was already extremely contracted, its thick filaments would be rather close to the Z discs, as on the left side of the figure. The fiber couldn't contract much farther before the thick filaments would butt against the Z discs and stop. The contraction would be brief and weak. On the other hand, if a muscle fiber was extremely stretched, as on the right, there would be little overlap between the thick and thin filaments. The myosin heads would be unable to "get a grip" on the thin filaments, and again the contraction would be weak.

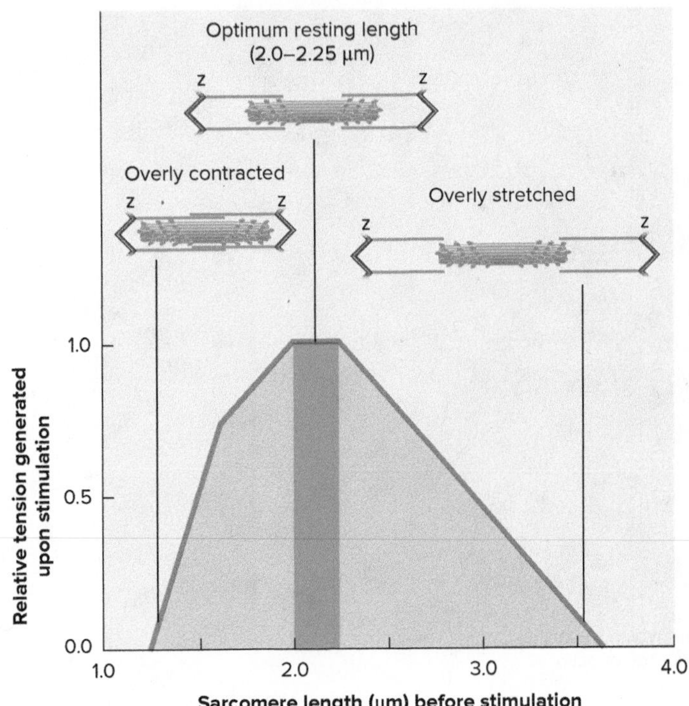


**FIGURE 11.12 The Length–Tension Relationship.**

### DEEPER INSIGHT 11.2
### CLINICAL APPLICATION

**Rigor Mortis**

*Rigor mortis*[9] is the hardening of the muscles and stiffening of the body that begins 3 to 4 hours after death. It occurs partly because the deteriorating sarcoplasmic reticulum releases calcium into the cytosol, and the deteriorating sarcolemma admits more calcium from the extracellular fluid. The calcium activates myosin–actin cross-bridging. Once bound to actin, myosin cannot release it without first binding an ATP molecule, and of course no ATP is available in a dead body. Thus, the thick and thin filaments remain rigidly cross-linked until the myofilaments begin to decay. Rigor mortis peaks about 12 hours after death and then diminishes over the next 48 to 60 hours.

Between these extremes, there is an optimum resting length at which a muscle responds with the greatest force. In this range (the flat top of the curve), the sarcomeres are 2.0 to 2.25 μm long. If the sarcomeres are less than 60% or more than 175% of their optimal length, they develop no tension at all in response to a stimulus.

The complete length–tension curve is derived from muscles isolated from an animal (often the frog gastrocnemius muscle) for laboratory stimulation. In reality, a muscle *in situ* (in its natural position in the living body) is never as extremely stretched or contracted as the far right and left sides of the figure depict. For one thing, the attachments of muscles to the bones and limitations on bone movement restrict muscle contraction to the midrange of the curve. For another, the central nervous system continually monitors and adjusts the length of the resting muscles, maintaining a state of partial contraction called **muscle tone.** This maintains optimum sarcomere length and makes the muscles ideally ready for action. The elastic filaments of the sarcomere also help to maintain enough myofilament overlap to ensure effective contraction when the muscle is called into action.

**BEFORE YOU GO ON**

Answer the following questions to test your understanding of the preceding section:

13. What change does ACh cause in an ACh receptor? How does this electrically affect the muscle fiber?
14. How do troponin and tropomyosin regulate the interaction between myosin and actin?
15. Describe the roles played by ATP in the power and recovery strokes of myosin.
16. What steps are necessary for a contracted muscle to return to its resting length?

[9]*rigor* = rigidity; *mortis* = of death

## 11.5 Behavior of Whole Muscles

**Expected Learning Outcomes**

When you have completed this section, you should be able to

a. describe the stages of a muscle twitch;
b. explain how successive muscle twitches can add up to produce stronger muscle contractions;
c. distinguish between isometric and isotonic contraction; and
d. distinguish between concentric and eccentric contraction.

Now you know how an individual muscle cell shortens. Our next objective is to move up to the organ grade of structure and consider how this relates to the action of the muscle as a whole.

### 11.5a Threshold, Latent Period, and Twitch

The timing and strength of a muscle's contraction can be shown in a chart called a **myogram (fig. 11.13).** A weak (subthreshold) electrical stimulus to a muscle produces no reaction. By gradually increasing the voltage and stimulating the muscle again, one can determine the **threshold,** or minimum voltage necessary to generate an action potential in the muscle fiber. At threshold or higher, a single stimulus causes a quick cycle of contraction and relaxation called a **twitch.**

There is a delay, or **latent period,** of about 2 milliseconds (ms) between the onset of the stimulus and onset of the twitch. This is the time required for excitation, excitation–contraction coupling, and tensing of the elastic components of the muscle. The force generated during this time is called *internal tension.* It isn't visible on the myogram because it causes no shortening of the muscle. On the left side, the myogram is therefore flat.

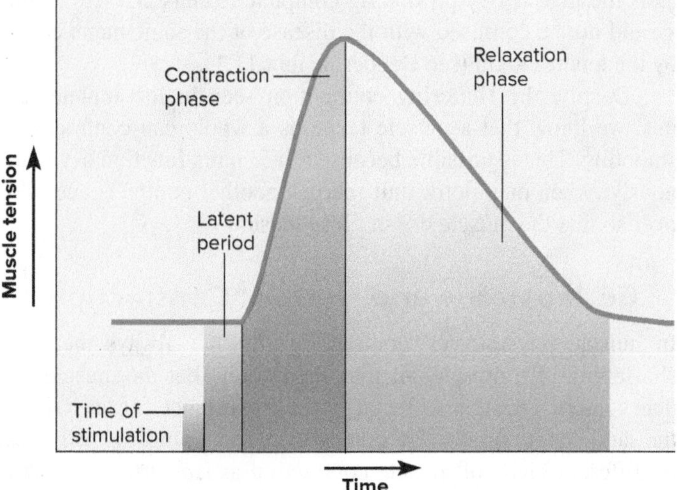


**FIGURE 11.13 Idealized Myogram of a Muscle Twitch.**

 *What role does ATP play during the relaxation phase?*

**DEEPER INSIGHT 11.3**
**MEDICAL HISTORY**

***Galvani, Volta, and Animal Electricity***

The invention of modern dry cells can be traced to studies of frog muscle by Italian anatomist Luigi Galvani (1737–98). He suspended isolated frog legs from a copper hook and noticed that they twitched when touched with an iron scalpel. He attributed this to "animal electricity" in the legs. The physicist Alessandro Volta (1745–1827) investigated Galvani's discovery further. He concluded that when two different metals (such as the copper hook and iron scalpel) are separated by an electrolyte solution (a frog's tissue fluids), a chemical reaction occurs that produces an electrical current. This current had stimulated the muscle in the legs of Galvani's frogs and caused the twitch. Based on this principle, Volta invented the first simple voltaic cell, the forerunner of today's dry cells and automobile batteries. The frog gastrocnemius muscle and its attached sciatic nerve, typically removed from the body and attached to laboratory stimulating and recording equipment, have remained a popular preparation for muscle research and teaching muscle physiology for centuries since Galvani's and Volta's time, even today.

Once the elastic components are taut, the muscle begins to produce *external tension* and move a resisting object, or load, such as a bone or body limb. This is called the **contraction phase** of the twitch. By analogy, imagine lifting a weight suspended from a rubber band. At first, internal tension would only stretch the rubber band. Then, as the rubber band became taut, external tension would lift the weight.

The contraction phase is short-lived, because the sarcoplasmic reticulum quickly reabsorbs $Ca^{2+}$ before the muscle develops maximal force. As the $Ca^{2+}$ level in the cytoplasm falls, myosin releases the thin filaments and muscle tension declines. This is seen in the myogram as the **relaxation phase.** As shown by the asymmetry of the myogram, the muscle contracts more quickly than it relaxes. The entire twitch lasts from about 7 to 100 ms, so a muscle could theoretically complete about 10 to 140 twitches per second (if only the math mattered).

### 11.5b Contraction Strength of Twitches

We have seen that a subthreshold stimulus induces no muscle contraction at all, but at threshold intensity, a twitch is produced. Increasing the stimulus voltage still more, however, produces twitches no stronger than those at threshold. Superficially, the muscle fiber seems to be giving its maximum response once the stimulus intensity is at threshold or higher. However, even for a constant voltage, twitches vary in strength. This is so for a variety of reasons:

- Twitch strength depends on how stretched the muscle was just before it was stimulated, as we have just seen in the length–tension relationship.
- Twitches become weaker as a muscle fatigues, as discussed later in this chapter.
- Twitches vary with the temperature of the muscle; a warmed-up muscle contracts more strongly because enzymes such as the myosin heads work more quickly.

- Twitch strength varies with the muscle's state of hydration, which affects the spacing between thick and thin filaments and therefore the ability to form myosin–actin cross-bridges.
- Twitch strength varies with stimulus frequency; stimuli arriving close together produce stronger twitches than stimuli arriving at longer time intervals, as we will see shortly.

It should not be surprising that twitches vary in strength. Indeed, an individual twitch isn't strong enough to do any useful work. Muscles must contract with variable strength for different tasks, such as lifting a glass of champagne compared with lifting barbells at the gym.

Let us examine more closely the contrasting effects of stimulus *intensity* versus stimulus *frequency* on contraction strength. Suppose we apply a stimulating electrode to a motor nerve that supplies a muscle, such as a laboratory preparation of a frog sciatic nerve connected to its gastrocnemius muscle. Subthreshold stimulus voltages produce no response **(fig. 11.14).** At threshold, we see a weak twitch (at *3* in the bottom row of the figure), and if we continue to raise the voltage, we see stronger twitches. The reason for this is that higher voltages excite more and more nerve fibers in the motor nerve (middle row of the figure), and thus stimulate more and more motor units to contract. The process of bringing more motor units into play is called **recruitment,** or **multiple motor unit (MMU) summation.** This is seen not just in artificial stimulation, but is part of the way the nervous system behaves naturally to produce varying muscle contractions. The neuromuscular system behaves according to the **size principle**—smaller, less powerful motor units with smaller, slower nerve fibers are activated first. This is sufficient for delicate tasks and refined movements, but if more power is needed, then larger motor units with larger, faster nerve fibers are subsequently activated.

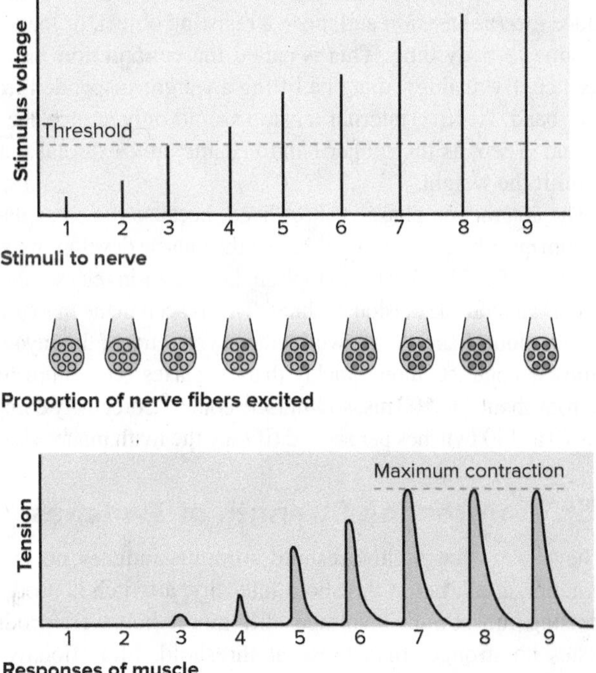


**FIGURE 11.14 The Relationship Between Stimulus Intensity (Voltage) and Muscle Tension.** Top row: Nine stimuli of increasing strengths. The first two are subthreshold stimuli. Middle row: Cross section of a motor nerve with seven nerve fibers. The colored nerve fibers are the excited ones; note that none are excited by the subthreshold stimuli above. Bottom row: Graph of muscle tension. Subthreshold stimuli (1–2) produce no muscle contraction. When stimuli reach or exceed threshold (3–7), they excite more and more nerve fibers and motor units; thus, they produce stronger and stronger contractions. This is multiple motor unit summation (recruitment). Once all of the nerve fibers are stimulated (7–9), further increases in stimulus strength produce no further increase in muscle tension.

But even when stimulus intensity (voltage) remains constant, twitch strength can vary with stimulus frequency. High-frequency stimulation produces stronger twitches than low-frequency stimulation. In **figure 11.15a,** we see that when a muscle is stimulated at low frequency, say 5 to 10 stimuli/s, it produces an identical twitch for each stimulus and fully recovers between twitches.

At higher stimulus frequencies, say 20 to 40 stimuli/s, each new stimulus arrives before the previous twitch is over. Each new twitch "rides piggyback" on the previous one and generates higher tension **(fig. 11.15b).** This phenomenon goes by two names: **temporal**[10] **summation,** because it results from two stimuli arriving close together in time, or **wave summation,** because it results from one wave of contraction added to another. Wave upon wave, each twitch reaches a higher level of tension than the one before, and the muscle relaxes only partially between stimuli. This effect produces a state of sustained fluttering contraction called **incomplete tetanus.**

In the laboratory, an isolated muscle can be stimulated at such high frequency that the twitches fuse into a single, nonfluctuating contraction called **complete (fused) tetanus (fig. 11.15c).** This doesn't happen in the body, however, because motor neurons don't fire that fast. Indeed, there is an inhibitory mechanism in the spinal cord that prevents them from doing so. Complete tetanus is injurious to muscle and associated soft tissues, so spinal inhibition protects the muscles by preventing complete tetanus. Muscle tetanus should not be confused with the disease of the same name caused by the tetanus toxin (see Deeper Insight 11.1).

Despite the fluttering contraction seen in incomplete tetanus, we know that a muscle taken as a whole can contract very smoothly. This is possible because motor units function asynchronously; when one motor unit relaxes, another contracts and takes over so that the muscle doesn't lose tension.

## 11.5c Isometric and Isotonic Contraction

In muscle physiology, "contraction" doesn't always mean the shortening of a muscle—it may mean only that the muscle produces internal tension while an external resistance causes it to stay the same length or even become longer. Thus, physiologists speak of different kinds of muscle contraction as *isometric* versus *isotonic* and *concentric* versus *eccentric* **(fig. 11.16).**

[10]*tempor* = time; *al* = pertaining to

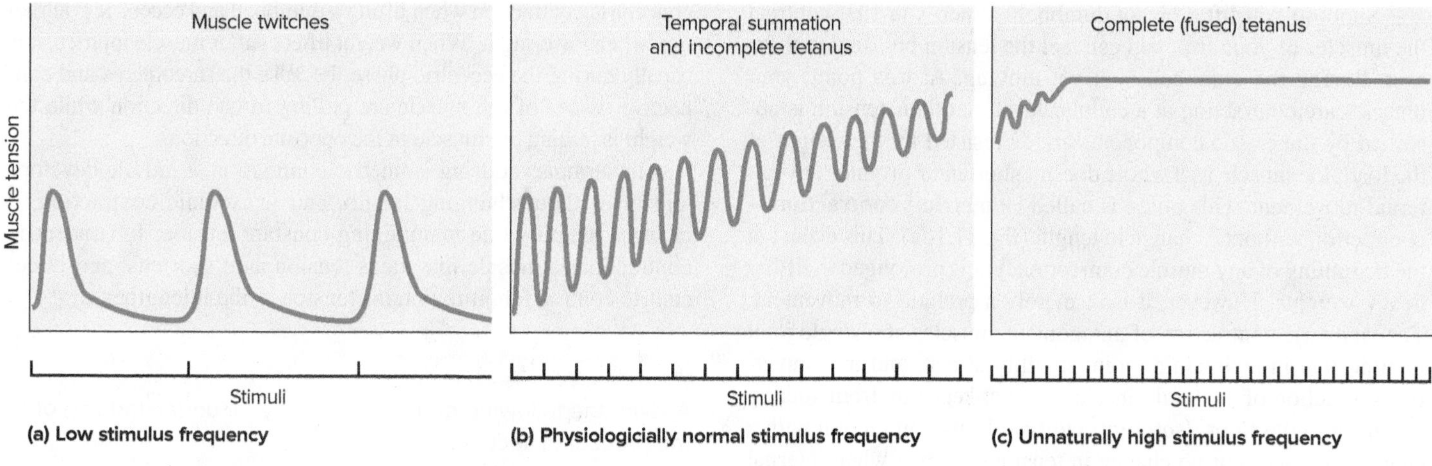


**FIGURE 11.15 The Relationship Between Stimulus Frequency and Muscle Tension.** (a) Twitch. At an unnaturally low stimulus frequency, as in laboratory preparations, the muscle relaxes completely between stimuli and shows twitches of uniform strength. (b) At a stimulus frequency within normal physiological range, the muscle doesn't have time to relax completely between twitches and the force of each twitch builds on the previous one, creating the state of incomplete tetanus. In this state, a muscle can attain three to four times as much tension, or force, as a single twitch produces. (c) At an unnaturally high stimulus frequency, attained only in laboratory preparations, the muscle can't relax at all between twitches, and twitches fuse into a state of complete tetanus.

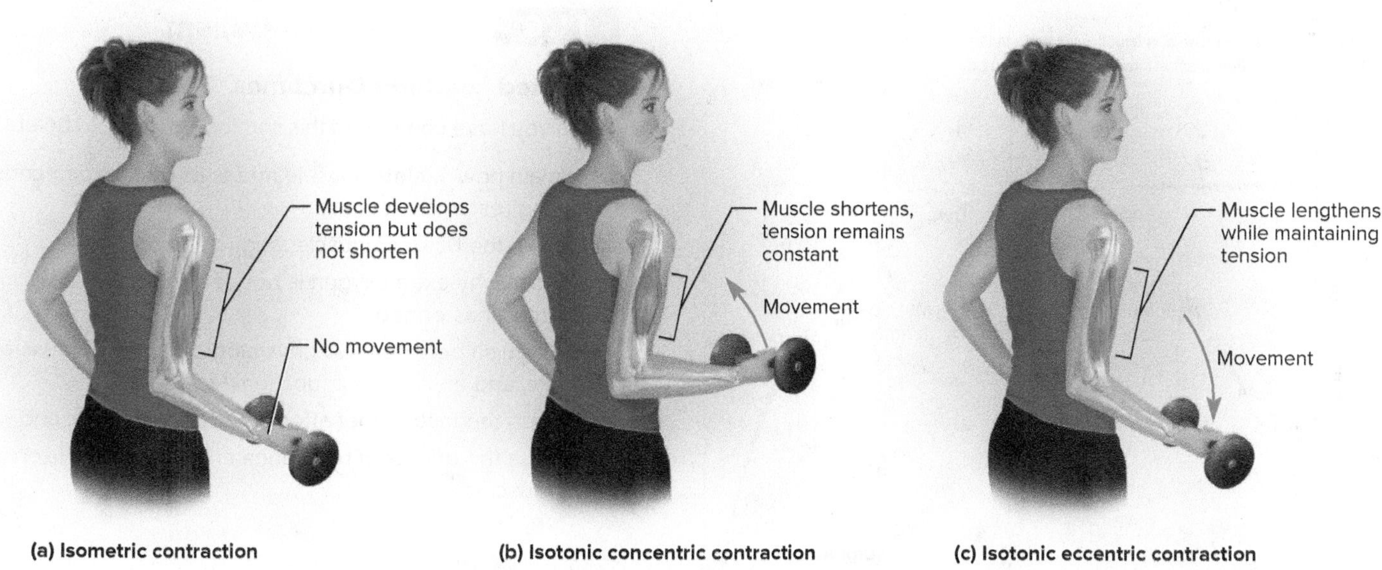


**FIGURE 11.16 Isometric and Isotonic Contraction.** (a) Isometric contraction, in which a muscle develops tension but doesn't shorten. (b) Isotonic concentric contraction, in which the muscle shortens while maintaining a constant degree of tension. (c) Isotonic eccentric contraction, in which the muscle maintains tension while it lengthens, allowing a muscle to relax without going suddenly limp.

? *Name a muscle that undergoes eccentric contraction as you sit down in a chair.*

Suppose you lift a heavy dumbbell. When you first contract the muscles of your arm, you can feel the tension building in them even though the dumbbell isn't yet moving. At this point, your muscles are contracting at a cellular level, but their tension is absorbed by the elastic components and is resisted by the weight of the load; the muscle as a whole doesn't shorten or produce any external movement. This phase is called **isometric**[11] **contraction**—contraction without a change in length (fig. 11.16a). This occurs at the beginning of any muscle contraction, but is prolonged in lifting heavy weights. However, it isn't merely a prelude to movement. The isometric contraction of antagonistic muscles at a single joint is important in maintaining joint stability at rest, and the isometric contraction of postural muscles is what keeps us from sinking in a heap to the floor. **Isotonic**[12] **contraction**—contraction with a change in length but no change in tension—begins when internal tension builds to the point that it overcomes the resistance. The muscle now shortens, moves the load, and maintains essentially the same tension from then on (fig. 11.16b). Isometric and isotonic contraction are both phases of normal muscular action **(fig. 11.17).**

There are two forms of isotonic contraction: concentric and eccentric. In **concentric contraction,** a muscle shortens as it maintains tension—for example, when the biceps contracts and flexes the elbow. In **eccentric contraction,** a muscle lengthens as it maintains tension. If you set that dumbbell down again (fig. 11.16c), your biceps lengthens as you extend your elbow, but it maintains tension to act as a brake and keep you from simply dropping the weight. A weight lifter uses concentric contraction when lifting a dumbbell and eccentric contraction when lowering it. When weight lifters suffer muscle injuries, it is usually during the eccentric phase, because the sarcomeres and connective tissues of the muscle are pulling in one direction while the weight is pulling the muscle in the opposite direction.

In summary, during isometric contraction, a muscle develops tension without changing length, and in isotonic contraction, it changes length while maintaining constant tension. In concentric contraction, a muscle maintains tension as it shortens, and in eccentric contraction, it maintains tension while it lengthens.

[11] *iso* = same, uniform; *metr* = length; *ic* = pertaining to
[12] *iso* = same, uniform; *ton* = tension; *ic* = pertaining to

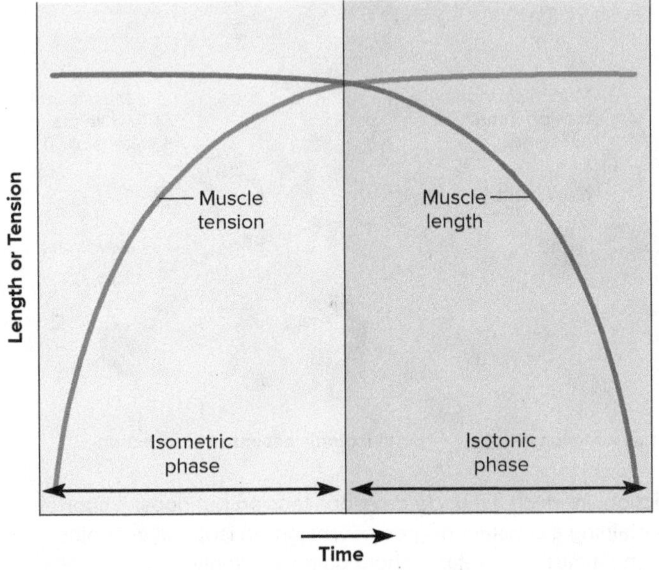


**FIGURE 11.17 Isometric and Isotonic Phases of Contraction.** At the beginning of a contraction (isometric phase), muscle tension rises but the length remains constant (the muscle does not shorten). When tension overcomes the resistance of the load, the tension levels off and the muscle begins to shorten and move the load (isotonic phase).

? *How would you extend this graph in order to show eccentric contraction?*

**BEFORE YOU GO ON**

Answer the following questions to test your understanding of the preceding section:

17. State three or more reasons why muscle twitch strength can vary even when stimulus intensity remains constant.
18. Explain the role of tetanus in normal muscle action.
19. Describe an everyday activity not involving the arms in which your muscles would switch from isometric to isotonic contraction.
20. Describe an everyday activity not involving the arms that would involve concentric contraction and one that would involve eccentric contraction.

## 11.6 Muscle Metabolism

**Expected Learning Outcomes**

When you have completed this section, you should be able to

a. explain how skeletal muscle meets its energy demands during rest and exercise;
b. explain the basis of muscle fatigue and soreness;
c. discuss why extra oxygen is needed even after an exercise has ended;
d. distinguish between two physiological types of muscle fibers, and explain their functional roles;
e. discuss the factors that affect muscular strength; and
f. discuss the effects of resistance and endurance exercises on muscles.

### 11.6a ATP Sources

All muscle contraction depends on ATP; no other energy source can serve in its place. The supply of ATP depends, in turn, on the availability of oxygen and organic fuels such as glucose and fatty acids. To understand how muscle manages its ATP budget, you must be acquainted with the two main pathways of ATP synthesis: *anaerobic fermentation* and *aerobic respiration* (see fig. 2.31). Each of these has advantages and disadvantages. Anaerobic fermentation enables a cell to produce ATP without the need for oxygen, but the ATP yield is very limited and the process generates

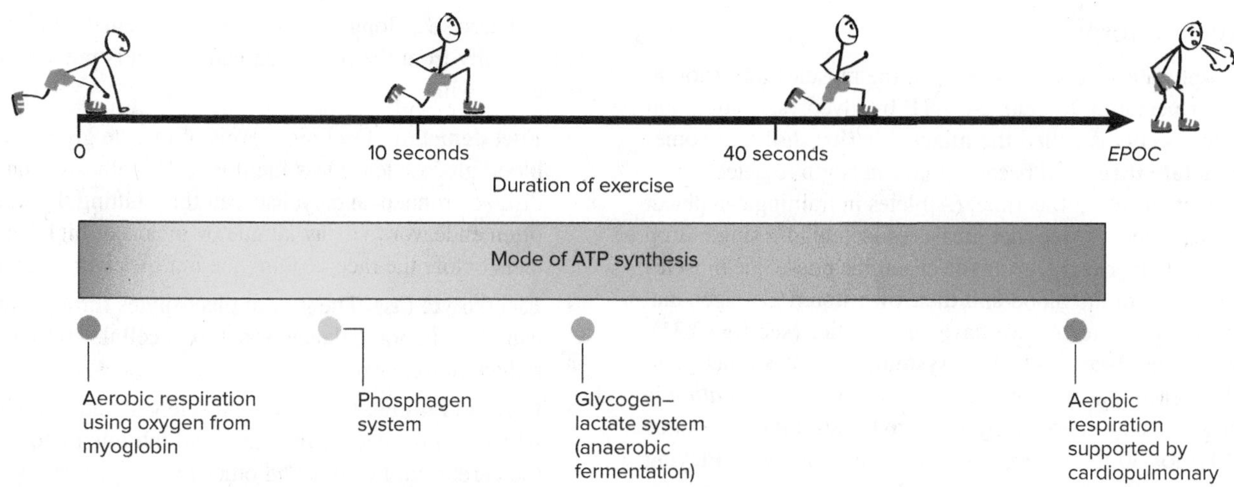


**FIGURE 11.18 Modes of ATP Synthesis During Exercise.**

a toxic by-product, lactate (lactic acid), which must be removed from the muscle and disposed of by the liver. By contrast, aerobic respiration produces far more ATP and no lactate, but it requires a continual supply of oxygen. Although aerobic respiration is best known as a pathway for glucose oxidation, it is also used to extract energy from other organic compounds. In a resting muscle, most ATP is generated by the aerobic respiration of fatty acids.

During the course of exercise, different mechanisms of ATP synthesis are used depending on the exercise duration. We will view these from the standpoint of immediate, short-term, and long-term energy, but it must be stressed that muscle doesn't make sudden shifts from one mechanism to another like an automobile transmission shifting gears. Rather, these mechanisms blend and overlap as the exercise continues **(fig. 11.18).**

## Immediate Energy

In a short, intense exercise such as a 100 m dash, the myoglobin in a muscle fiber supplies oxygen for a limited amount of aerobic respiration at the outset, but this oxygen supply is quickly depleted. Until the respiratory and cardiovascular systems catch up with the heightened oxygen demand, the muscle meets most of its ATP needs by borrowing phosphate groups ($P_i$) from other molecules and transferring them to ADP. Two enzyme systems control these phosphate transfers **(fig. 11.19):**

1. **Myokinase** (MY-oh-KY-nase) transfers $P_i$ from one ADP to another, converting the latter to ATP that myosin can use.
2. **Creatine kinase** (CREE-uh-tin KY-nase) obtains $P_i$ from a phosphate-storage molecule, **creatine phosphate (CP),** and donates it to ADP to make ATP. This is a fast-acting system that helps to maintain the ATP level while other ATP-generating mechanisms are being activated.

ATP and CP, collectively called the **phosphagen system,** provide nearly all the energy used for short bursts of intense activity. Muscle contains about 5 millimoles of ATP and 15 millimoles of CP per kilogram of tissue. Perhaps surprisingly, at the outset of an intense exercise, the amount of ATP in the muscle fibers changes very little, but the amount of CP drops rapidly. The total supply of ATP + CP is enough to power about 1 minute of brisk walking or 6 seconds of sprinting or fast swimming. The phosphagen system is especially important in activities requiring short bursts of maximal effort, such as football, baseball, and weight lifting.

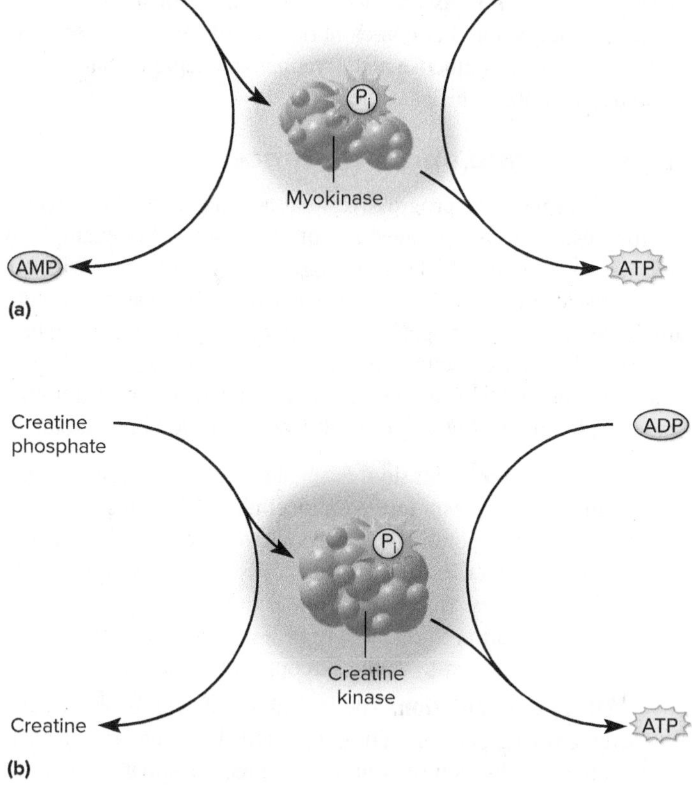


**FIGURE 11.19 The Phosphagen System.** (a) Myokinase, which obtains phosphates from ADP. (b) Creatine kinase, which obtains phosphates from creatine phosphate.

### Short-Term Energy

As the phosphagen system is exhausted, the muscles transition to anaerobic fermentation to generate ATP by glycolysis. The point at which this occurs is called the **anaerobic threshold,** or sometimes the **lactate threshold** because one can begin to detect a rise in blood lactate levels at this time. (Athletes in training can detect this with a handheld device that measures lactate in a single drop of blood from a pinprick.) During the anaerobic phase, the muscles obtain glucose from the blood and their own stored glycogen and metabolize it to lactate. As we have seen earlier (see fig. 2.31), this pathway, the **glycogen–lactate system,** generates a net yield of 2 ATP for each glucose consumed. (*Anaerobic fermentation* is its final step, the conversion of pyruvate to lactate.) It can produce enough ATP for 30 to 40 seconds of maximum activity. Playing basketball or running completely around a baseball diamond, for example, depends heavily on this energy-transfer system.

### Long-Term Energy

After 40 seconds or so, the respiratory and cardiovascular systems "catch up" and deliver oxygen to the muscles fast enough for aerobic respiration to once again meet most of the ATP demand. Aerobic respiration produces much more ATP than glycolysis does—typically another 30 ATP per glucose. Thus it is a very efficient means of meeting the ATP demands of prolonged exercise. One's rate of oxygen consumption rises for 3 to 4 minutes and then levels off at a *steady state* in which aerobic ATP production keeps pace with the demand. In exercises lasting more than 10 minutes, over 90% of the ATP is produced aerobically. For up to 30 minutes, the energy for this comes about equally from glucose and fatty acids; then, as glucose and glycogen are depleted, fatty acids become the more significant fuel.

## 11.6b Fatigue and Endurance

Muscle **fatigue** is the progressive weakness and loss of contractility that results from prolonged use of the muscles. For example, if you hold a heavy book at arm's length for a minute, you will feel your muscles growing weaker and soon you'll be unable to hold it up. Repeatedly squeezing a rubber ball, pushing a video game button, or trying to take lecture notes from a fast-talking professor produces fatigue in the hand muscles. In high-intensity, short-duration exercise, fatigue is thought to result from the following factors:

- **Potassium accumulation.** Each action potential releases $K^+$ from the sarcoplasm to the extracellular fluid. This lowers the membrane potential (hyperpolarizes the cell) and makes the muscle fiber less excitable. This is especially significant in the T tubules, where the low volume of ECF enables the $K^+$ concentration to rise to a high level and interfere with the release of calcium from the sarcoplasmic reticulum.
- **ADP/$P_i$ accumulation.** The hydrolysis of ATP generates an ever-growing pool of ADP + $P_i$. ADP slows the cross-bridge cycling mechanism of contraction. Free phosphate ($P_i$) inhibits calcium release from the sarcoplasmic reticulum, calcium sensitivity of the contractile mechanism, and force production by the myofibrils. It is now thought to be a major contributor to muscle fatigue.

In exercise of long duration but low intensity, fatigue may result partially from the preceding causes, but is predominantly due to the following:

- **Fuel depletion.** Declining levels of muscle glycogen and blood glucose leave less fuel for ATP synthesis. Long-distance runners and cyclists call this "hitting the wall," and often endeavor to delay fatigue by means of high-carbohydrate diets before the race, loading the muscles with extra glycogen.
- **Electrolyte loss.** The loss of electrolytes through sweating can alter the ion balance of the extracellular fluid enough to reduce muscle excitability.
- **Central fatigue.** Exercising muscle generates ammonia, which is absorbed by the brain and inhibits motor neurons of the cerebrum. For this and other reasons not yet well understood, the central nervous system produces less signal output to the skeletal muscles. This is where psychological factors come into play, such as the will to complete a marathon.

Some former hypotheses on muscle fatigue have been discredited by more recent research. ATP depletion per se is no longer thought to cause fatigue; the ATP level in fatigued muscle is almost as great as in rested muscle. It was also long thought that the lactate from anaerobic fermentation contributed to fatigue by lowering the pH in the muscle fiber. Alterations in protein conformation by low pH could interfere with many processes required for contraction, such as $Ca^{2+}$ binding by troponin, cross-bridge formation, and ATP hydrolysis by myosin, among others. Evidence has now shown, however, that lactate is removed to the liver about as fast as the muscles produce it, so it doesn't accumulate in the muscle tissue and probably has little or nothing to do with fatigue.

The ability to maintain high-intensity exercise for more than 4 or 5 minutes is determined in large part by one's **maximum oxygen uptake ($Vo_2$max)**—the point at which the rate of oxygen consumption reaches a plateau and increases no further with an added workload. $Vo_2$max is proportional to body size; it peaks around age 20; it is usually greater in males than in females; and it can be twice as great in a trained endurance athlete as in an untrained person. A typical sedentary adult uses a maximum of about 35 milliliters of oxygen per minute per kilogram of body weight. Such a person weighing 73 kg (160 lb) and exercising at maximum intensity could therefore "burn" oxygen at about 2.6 L/min., which sets a limit to his rate of ATP production. Elite endurance athletes can have a $Vo_2$max of about 70 mL/min./kg (5.2 L/min. for the same body weight).

## 11.6c Excess Postexercise Oxygen Consumption

You have probably noticed that you breathe heavily not only during strenuous exercise but also for several minutes afterward (fig. 11.18). This is to meet a metabolic demand called **excess postexercise oxygen consumption (EPOC),** also known by an older popularized term, **oxygen debt.** EPOC is the difference between the elevated rate of oxygen consumption at the end of an exercise and the normal rate at rest. It occurs in part because oxygen is needed to regenerate ATP aerobically, and that ATP goes in part to regenerate creatine phosphate. A small amount of oxygen serves to reoxygenate the muscle myoglobin, and the liver consumes oxygen in disposing of the lactate generated by exercise. In addition, exercise raises the body temperature and overall metabolic rate, which in itself consumes more oxygen.

ATP and CP are replenished in the early minutes of heaviest postexercise breathing, and oxygen consumption remains elevated for as much as an hour more as the liver uses it to oxidize lactate. EPOC can be as much as six times one's basal oxygen consumption, indicating that anaerobic mechanisms of ATP production during exercise allow six times as much physical exertion as would have been possible without those mechanisms.

### 11.6d Physiological Classes of Muscle Fibers

Not all muscle fibers are alike or adapted for the same tasks. For example, the weight-bearing and postural muscles of the back and lower limbs react slowly to stimulation and take up to 100 ms to reach peak tension. By contrast, muscles that control eye and hand movements react quickly to stimulation and reach peak tension in as little as 7.5 ms. The predominant fibers that compose these muscles are therefore called *slow-twitch* and *fast-twitch* fibers, respectively. We can find reasons for their differences in response time by looking at their cellular structure and biochemistry **(table 11.2).** The different fiber types can be identified in tissue sections with special histochemical staining **(fig. 11.20).**

**Slow-twitch fibers** are also called **slow oxidative (SO)** or **type I fibers.** They are well adapted for endurance and fatigue resistance, so they are particularly important in muscles that support the body and maintain posture, such as the erector spinae and quadratus lumborum of the back. Their fatigue resistance stems from their *oxidative* mode of ATP production—that is, aerobic respiration. Oxidative metabolism, of course, requires a liberal supply of oxygen and the means to use it efficiently. Therefore, these fibers are surrounded by a dense network of blood capillaries, they are rich in mitochondria, and they have a high concentration of myoglobin, the red pigment that facilitates diffusion of oxygen from the blood into the muscle fiber. Slow-twitch fibers are also relatively thin, which minimizes the distance that oxygen must diffuse to even the deepest mitochondria. The slowness of these muscles is due to a sarcoplasmic reticulum that is relatively slow to release and reabsorb calcium, and a form of myosin ATPase that is relatively slow in its ATP hydrolysis and cross-bridge cycling. The high myoglobin concentration of these fibers gives them a relatively bright red color, so they are also called **red fibers.**

**TABLE 11.2 Classification of Skeletal Muscle Fibers**

| | Fiber Type | |
|---|---|---|
| **Property** | **Slow-Twitch (Slow Oxidative)** | **Fast-Twitch (Fast Glycolytic)** |
| Twitch duration | As long as 100 ms | As short as 7.5 ms |
| Motor unit size | Smaller | Larger |
| Motor neurons | Smaller, more excitable | Larger, less excitable |
| Motor unit strength | Weaker | Stronger |
| Relative diameter | Smaller | Larger |
| ATP synthesis | Aerobic | Anaerobic |
| Fatigue resistance | Good | Poor |
| ATP hydrolysis | Slow | Fast |
| Glycolysis | Moderate | Fast |
| Myoglobin content | Abundant | Low |
| Glycogen content | Low | Abundant |
| Mitochondria | Abundant and large | Fewer and smaller |
| Capillaries | Abundant | Fewer |
| Color | Red | White, pale |
| **Representative muscles in which fiber type is predominant** | Soleus<br>Erector spinae<br>Quadratus lumborum | Gastrocnemius<br>Biceps brachii<br>Muscles of eye movement |

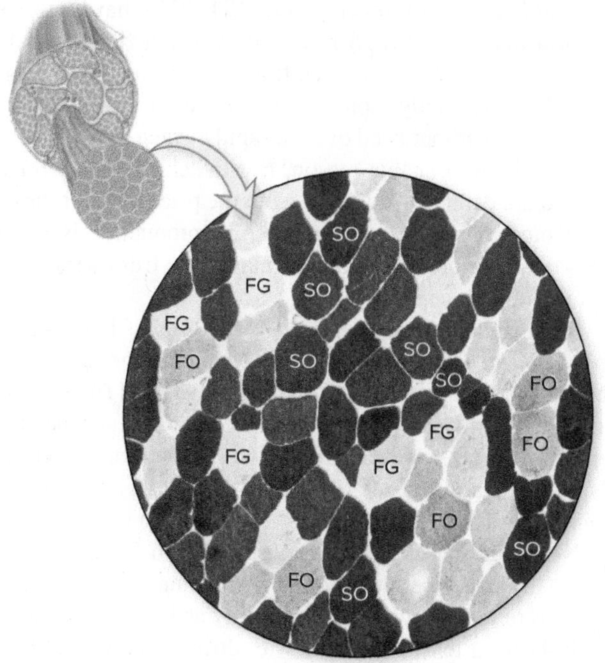


**FIGURE 11.20 Skeletal Muscle Fiber Types.** (FG, fast glycolytic fibers; SO, slow oxidative fibers; FO, fast oxidative fibers)
G W Willis/Getty Images

**Fast-twitch fibers** are also called **fast glycolytic (FG)** or **type II fibers.** They are well adapted for quick responses, so they are particularly important in the aforesaid eye and hand muscles, and in large muscles such as the gastrocnemius and biceps brachii, which we employ in such actions as jumping and elbow flexion. Their quickness stems from an especially extensive sarcoplasmic reticulum with fast release and reabsorption of calcium, and a form of myosin with very quick ATP hydrolysis and cross-bridge cycling. For energy, they depend primarily on glycolysis and anaerobic fermentation, which produces ATP more quickly (yet less efficiently) than aerobic respiration. To support this, they contain a high concentration of glycogen. They also have a high concentration of creatine phosphate, which, you will recall, aids in rapidly regenerating ATP. They have fewer mitochondria than slow-twitch fibers. Fast-twitch fibers are thicker than slow-twitch, because thick fibers are stronger and they have no need for especially rapid oxygen delivery to the deepest cytoplasm. Also, without need of such rapid oxygen uptake, they have less myoglobin. For this reason, fast-twitch fibers are relatively pale and are called **white fibers.** But the price paid for these fast-twitch mechanisms and anaerobic ATP production is that these fibers fatigue more easily, as you may know from writer's cramp or doing rapid biceps curls.

Some authorities recognize two subtypes of FG fibers called types IIA and IIB. Type IIB is the common type just described, whereas IIA (**intermediate** or **fast oxidative [FO] fibers**) combine fast-twitch responses with aerobic fatigue-resistant metabolism. Type IIA fibers, however, are known mainly from other species of mammals and are relatively rare in humans except in some endurance-trained athletes.

Nearly all muscles are composed of both SO and FG fibers, but usually one type or the other predominates according to the functions of that muscle—quick motility and reflexes, or sustained weight-bearing tension. People with different types and levels of physical activity differ in the proportion of one fiber type to another even in the same muscle, such as the *quadriceps femoris* of the anterior thigh (**table 11.3**). It is thought that people are born with a genetic predisposition for a certain ratio of fiber types. Those who go into competitive sports discover the sports at which they can excel and gravitate toward those for which heredity has best equipped them. One person might be a "born sprinter" and another a "born marathoner."

In humans, small motor units are composed of relatively small SO muscle fibers and supplied by small but easily excited motor neurons. These motor units are not as strong as large ones but produce more precise movements. Large motor units are composed of larger FG fibers; supplied by larger, less excitable neurons; and produce more power but less fine control. In the *size principle* discussed earlier (section 11.5b), the nervous system recruits small SO motor units first, then larger FG motor units only if more strength is needed for a particular task.

Muscles composed mainly of SO fibers are called *red muscles,* and those composed mainly of FG fibers are called *white muscles* because of the color difference stemming from their difference in myoglobin content. Anyone who eats chicken or turkey may be unwittingly familiar with this distinction. The thighs are dark meat composed of SO fibers adapted to long periods of standing, and the breast is white meat composed of FG fibers adapted for short bursts of power when the birds take flight. Duck breast, however, is dark meat (red muscle) adapted for long-distance flight, because unlike chickens and turkeys, domestic ducks are descended from migratory ancestors.

We saw in chapter 10 that sometimes two or more muscles act across the same joint and seem to have the same function. We have already seen some reasons why such muscles are not as redundant as they seem. Another reason is that they may differ in the proportion of SO to FG fibers. For example, the gastrocnemius and soleus muscles of the calf both insert on the calcaneus, so they exert the same pull on the heel. The gastrocnemius, however, is a white, predominantly FG muscle adapted for quick, powerful movements such as jumping, whereas the soleus is a red, SO muscle that does most of the work in standing and in endurance exercises such as jogging and skiing.

**TABLE 11.3 Proportion of Slow Oxidative (SO) and Fast Glycolytic (FG) Fibers in the Quadriceps Femoris Muscle of Male Athletes**

| Sample Population | SO | FG |
|---|---|---|
| Marathon runners | 82% | 18% |
| Swimmers | 74 | 26 |
| Average males | 45 | 55 |
| Sprinters and jumpers | 37 | 63 |

### 11.6e Muscular Strength and Conditioning

We have far more muscular strength than we normally use. The gluteus maximus can generate 1,200 kg of tension, and all the muscles collectively can produce a total tension of 22,000 kg (nearly 25 tons). Indeed, the muscles can generate more tension than the bones and tendons can withstand—a fact that accounts for many injuries to the patellar and calcaneal tendons. Muscular strength depends on a variety of anatomical and physiological factors:

- **Muscle size.** The strength of a muscle depends primarily on its size; thicker muscles can form more myosin–actin cross-bridges and therefore generate more tension. A muscle can exert a tension of about 3 to 4 $kg/cm^2$ of cross-sectional area. This is why weight lifting increases both size and strength of a muscle.
- **Fascicle arrangement** (see fig. 10.2). Pennate muscles such as the rectus femoris are stronger than parallel muscles such as the sartorius, which in turn are stronger than circular muscles such as the orbicularis oculi.
- **Size of active motor units.** Large motor units produce stronger contractions than small ones.
- **Multiple motor unit summation.** When a stronger muscle contraction is desired, the nervous system activates more and larger motor units. Getting "psyched up" for athletic competition is partly a matter of multiple motor unit (MMU) summation.
- **Temporal summation.** Nerve impulses usually arrive at a muscle in a series of closely spaced action potentials. Because of the temporal summation described earlier, the greater the frequency of stimulation, the stronger the muscle contraction.
- **The length–tension relationship.** As noted earlier, a muscle resting at optimum length is prepared to contract more forcefully than a muscle that is excessively contracted or stretched. This is affected by one's posture, such as a runner's crouch, just before the onset of muscular effort.

- **Fatigue.** Rested muscles contract more strongly than fatigued ones.

As fitness trainers and exercise enthusiasts know, there are two kinds of exercise with different effects on muscles—resistance and endurance exercise. **Resistance exercise,** such as weight lifting, is the contraction of muscles against a load that resists movement. A few minutes of resistance exercise at a time, a few times each week, is enough to stimulate muscle growth. Growth results primarily from cellular enlargement, not cellular division. The muscle fibers synthesize more myofilaments and the myofibrils grow thicker. Myofibrils split longitudinally when they reach a certain size, so a well-conditioned muscle has more myofibrils than a poorly conditioned one. Muscle fibers themselves are incapable of mitosis, but there is some evidence that as they enlarge, they too may split longitudinally. A small part of muscle growth may therefore result from an increase in the number of fibers, but most of it results from the enlargement of fibers that have existed since puberty.

**Endurance (aerobic) exercise,** such as jogging or swimming, improves the fatigue resistance of the muscles by enhancing the delivery and use of oxygen. Slow-twitch fibers, especially, produce more mitochondria and glycogen and acquire a greater density of blood capillaries as a result of conditioning. Endurance exercise also improves skeletal strength; increases the red blood cell count and the oxygen transport capacity of the blood; and enhances the function of the cardiovascular, respiratory, and nervous systems.

Endurance training doesn't significantly increase muscular strength, and resistance training doesn't improve endurance. Optimal performance and musculoskeletal health require **cross-training,** which incorporates elements of both types. If muscles aren't kept sufficiently active, they become *deconditioned*—weaker and more easily fatigued.

**▶▶▶APPLY WHAT YOU KNOW**

*Is a weight lifter's muscle growth mainly the result of hypertrophy or hyperplasia?*

**BEFORE YOU GO ON**

Answer the following questions to test your understanding of the preceding section:

**21.** From which two molecules can ADP borrow a phosphate group to become ATP? What is the enzyme that catalyzes each transfer?

**22.** In a long period of intense exercise, why does muscle generate ATP anaerobically at first and then switch to aerobic respiration?

**23.** List four causes of muscle fatigue.

**24.** List three causes of excess postexercise oxygen consumption.

**25.** What properties of fast glycolytic and slow oxidative fibers adapt them for different physiological purposes?

## 11.7 Cardiac and Smooth Muscle

**Expected Learning Outcomes**

When you have completed this section, you should be able to

a. describe the structural and physiological differences between cardiac muscle and skeletal muscle;

b. explain why these differences are important to cardiac function;

c. describe the structural and physiological differences between smooth muscle and skeletal muscle; and

d. relate the unique properties of smooth muscle to its locations and functions.

Cardiac and smooth muscle have special structural and physiological properties in common with each other, but different from those of skeletal muscle **(table 11.4).** These are related to their distinctive functions.

Any of the three types of muscle cells can be called **myocytes.** This term is preferable to *muscle fiber* for smooth and cardiac muscle because these two types of cells don't have the long fibrous shape of skeletal muscle cells. They are relatively short, and in further contrast to skeletal muscle fibers, they have only one or two nuclei. Cardiac muscle cells are also called **cardiomyocytes.**

Cardiac and smooth muscle are *involuntary* muscle tissues, not usually subject to our conscious control. They receive no innervation from somatic motor neurons, but cardiac muscle and some smooth muscle receive nerves from the sympathetic and parasympathetic divisions of the autonomic nervous system (see chapter 15).

### 11.7a Cardiac Muscle APR

Cardiac muscle is limited to the heart, where its function is to pump blood. Knowing that, we can predict the properties that it must have: (1) It must contract with a regular rhythm; (2) it must function in sleep and wakefulness, without fail or need of conscious attention; (3) it must be highly resistant to fatigue; (4) the cardiomyocytes of a given heart chamber must contract in unison so that the chamber can effectively expel blood; and (5) each contraction must last long enough to expel blood from the chamber. These functional necessities are the key to understanding how cardiac muscle differs structurally and physiologically from skeletal muscle (table 11.4).

Cardiac muscle is striated like skeletal muscle, but cardiomyocytes are shorter and thicker. They have one or two nuclei near the middle of the cell. Each cell is enclosed in an endomysium, but there is no perimysium or epimysium as in skeletal muscle. Cardiomyocytes branch slightly so each is joined end to end with several others. These intercellular connections, called **intercalated discs** (in-TUR-kuh-LAY-ted), appear as thick dark lines in stained tissue sections. An intercalated disc

**TABLE 11.4 Comparison of Skeletal, Cardiac, and Smooth Muscle**

| Feature | Skeletal Muscle | Cardiac Muscle | Smooth Muscle |
|---|---|---|---|
| Location | Associated with skeletal system | Heart | Walls of viscera and blood vessels, iris of eye, arrector muscle of hair follicles |
| Cell shape | Long threadlike fibers | Short, slightly branched cells | Short fusiform cells |
| Cell length | 100 μm–30 cm | 50–120 μm | 30–200 μm |
| Cell width | 10–500 μm | 10–20 μm | 5–10 μm |
| Striations | Present | Present | Absent |
| Nuclei | Multiple nuclei, adjacent to sarcolemma | Usually one nucleus, near middle of cell | One nucleus, near middle of cell |
| Connective tissues | Endomysium, perimysium, epimysium | Endomysium only | Endomysium only |
| Sarcoplasmic reticulum | Abundant | Present | Scanty |
| T tubules | Present, narrow | Present, wide | Absent |
| Gap junctions | Absent | Present in intercalated discs | Present in unitary smooth muscle |
| Autorhythmicity | Absent | Present | Present in unitary smooth muscle |
| Thin filament attachment | Z discs | Z discs | Dense bodies |
| Regulatory proteins | Tropomyosin, troponin | Tropomyosin, troponin | Calmodulin, myosin light-chain kinase |
| $Ca^{2+}$ source | Sarcoplasmic reticulum | Sarcoplasmic reticulum and extracellular fluid | Mainly extracellular fluid |
| $Ca^{2+}$ receptor | Troponin of thin filament | Troponin of thin filament | Calmodulin of thick filament |
| Innervation and control | Somatic motor fibers (voluntary) | Autonomic fibers (involuntary) | Autonomic fibers (involuntary) |
| Nervous stimulation required? | Yes | No | No |
| Effect of nervous stimulation | Excitatory only | Excitatory or inhibitory | Excitatory or inhibitory |
| Mode of tissue repair | Limited regeneration, mostly fibrosis | Limited regeneration, mostly fibrosis | Relatively good capacity for regeneration |

has electrical *gap junctions* that allow each cardiomyocyte to directly stimulate its neighbors, and mechanical junctions that keep the cardiomyocytes from pulling apart when the heart contracts. The sarcoplasmic reticulum is less developed than in skeletal muscle, but the T tubules are larger and admit $Ca^{2+}$ from the extracellular fluid. Damaged cardiac muscle is repaired by fibrosis. Cardiac muscle has no satellite cells, and even though mitosis has been detected in cardiomyocytes following heart attacks, it does not produce a significant amount of regenerated functional muscle.

Unlike skeletal muscle, cardiac muscle can contract without the need of nervous stimulation. The heart has a built-in **pacemaker** that rhythmically sets off a wave of electrical excitation, which travels through the muscle and triggers the contraction of the heart chambers. The heart is said to be **autorhythmic**[13] because of this ability to contract rhythmically and independently. Stimulation by the autonomic nervous system, however, can increase or decrease the heart rate and contraction strength. Cardiac muscle does not exhibit quick twitches like skeletal muscle. Rather, it maintains tension for about 200 to 250 ms, giving the heart time to expel blood.

Cardiac muscle uses aerobic respiration almost exclusively. It is very rich in myoglobin and glycogen, and it has especially large mitochondria that fill about 25% of the cell, compared with smaller mitochondria occupying about 2% of a skeletal muscle fiber. Cardiac muscle is very adaptable with respect to the fuel used, but very vulnerable to interruptions in oxygen supply. Because it makes little use of anaerobic fermentation, cardiac muscle is highly resistant to fatigue.

### 11.7b Smooth Muscle APR

**Smooth muscle** is named for the fact that it has no striations, for a reason to be described shortly. Its myocytes are relatively small,

[13] *auto* = self

allowing for fine control of such tissues and organs as a single hair, the iris of the eye, and the tiniest arteries; yet, in the pregnant uterus, the myocytes become quite large and contribute to the powerful contractions of childbirth.

Smooth muscle isn't always innervated, but when it is, the nerve supply is autonomic, like that of the heart. Autonomic nerve fibers usually don't form precisely localized neuromuscular junctions with the myocytes. Rather, a nerve fiber has as many as 20,000 periodic swellings called **varicosities** along its length **(fig. 11.21).** Each varicosity contains synaptic vesicles from which it releases neurotransmitters—usually norepinephrine from the sympathetic fibers and acetylcholine from the parasympathetic fibers. The myocyte has no motor end plate, but instead has receptors for these neurotransmitters distributed over its surface. The varicosities simply release a flood of neurotransmitter into the tissue, and each myocyte may respond to more than one nerve fiber.

Whether innervated or not, smooth muscle responds to a wide variety of stimuli and often without any electrical excitation of the sarcolemma. It is much slower than skeletal and cardiac muscle to contract and relax, but it can remain contracted for a long time without fatigue and with minimal energy expenditure.

Smooth muscle doesn't usually form organs in itself, but forms layers in the walls of larger organs such as the stomach, intestines, uterus, and urinary bladder. In such cases, the muscle layer is quite variable in complexity. It can consist of as little as one cell in small arteries. The esophagus and intestines have an outer layer of longitudinal smooth muscle adjacent to a deeper, inner layer of circular muscle **(fig. 11.22).** When the longitudinal layer contracts, it shortens and dilates the organ; when the circular layer contracts, it constricts and lengthens the organ. In the stomach, urinary bladder, and uterus, smooth muscle forms three or more layers with bundles of myocytes running in multiple directions.

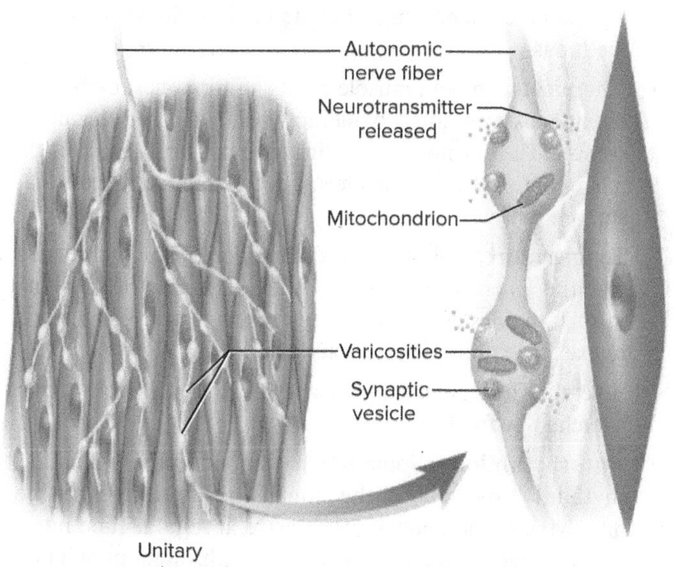


**FIGURE 11.21 Varicosities of an Autonomic Nerve Fiber in Unitary Smooth Muscle.**

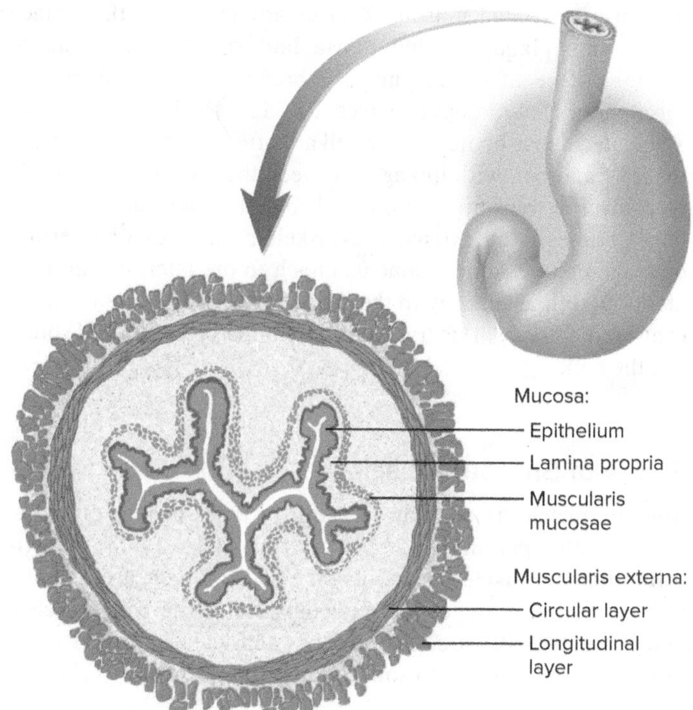


**FIGURE 11.22 Layers of Visceral Muscle in a Cross Section of the Esophagus.**

Smooth muscle can propel the contents of an organ, such as driving food through the digestive tract, voiding urine and feces, and expelling the infant in childbirth. By dilating or constricting the blood vessels and airway, it can modify the speed of air and blood flow, maintain blood pressure, and reroute blood from one pathway to another.

Unlike skeletal and cardiac muscle, smooth muscle is capable of not only hypertrophy (cellular growth) but also mitosis and hyperplasia (cell division). Thus, an organ such as the pregnant uterus grows by the addition of new myocytes as well as enlargement of existing ones. Injured smooth muscle regenerates well by mitosis.

## Myocyte Structure

Smooth muscle myocytes have a fusiform shape, typically about 5 to 10 μm wide at the middle, tapering to a point at each end, and usually ranging from 30 to 200 μm long—but up to 500 μm long in the pregnant uterus. They are enclosed in endomysium but have no perimysium, fascicles, or epimysium. There is only one nucleus, located near the middle of the cell. The sarcoplasmic reticulum is scanty and there are no T tubules. Thick and thin filaments are present, but there are no striations, sarcomeres, or myofibrils because the myofilaments are not bundled and aligned with each other the way they are in striated muscle. Z discs are absent. In their place are protein plaques called **dense bodies,** some adhering to the inner face of the plasma membrane and others dispersed throughout the sarcoplasm (see fig. 11.24). The membrane-associated dense bodies of one cell are often directly across from those of another, with linkages between them so that contractile force can be transmitted from cell to cell. Associated with the dense bodies is an extensive cytoskeletal network of intermediate filaments. Actin filaments attach to the intermediate filaments as well as directly to the dense bodies, so their movement (powered by myosin) is transferred to the sarcolemma and shortens the cell.

## Types of Smooth Muscle

Smooth muscle tissue shows a range of types between two extremes called *multiunit* and *unitary* types **(fig. 11.23). Multiunit smooth muscle** occurs in some of the largest arteries and pulmonary air passages, arrector muscles of the hair follicles, and eye muscles that control the iris and lens. Its innervation, although autonomic, is to some degree similar to that of skeletal muscle—the terminal branches of a nerve fiber synapse with individual myocytes and form a motor unit. Each varicosity is associated with a particular myocyte, and each myocyte responds independently of all the others—hence the name *multiunit.* Multiunit smooth muscle does not, however, generate action potentials. It contracts in response to variable (graded) electrical changes in the sarcolemma or even in the absence of electrical excitation.

**Unitary (single-unit) smooth muscle** is more common. It occurs in most blood vessels and in the digestive, respiratory, urinary, and reproductive tracts—therefore, it is also called **visceral muscle.** This type forms the aforementioned layers in many of the hollow viscera. The names *unitary* and *single-unit* refer to the fact that the myocytes of this type of muscle are electrically coupled to each other by gap junctions. This allows them to directly stimulate each other, so numerous cells contract as a unit, almost as if they were a single cell. In this muscle type, the nerve varicosities are not associated with a specific myocyte, but stimulate several of them at once when they release neurotransmitter.

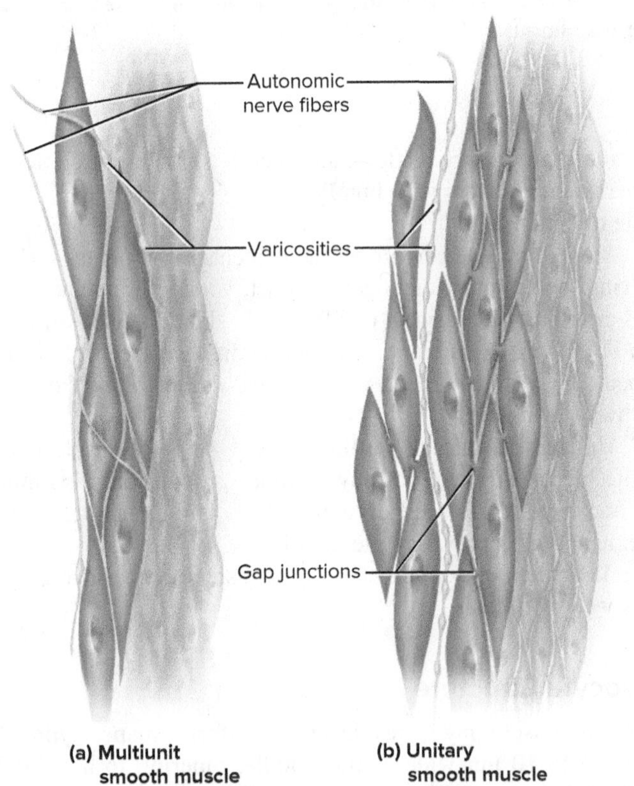


**FIGURE 11.23 Multiunit and Unitary Smooth Muscle.**
(a) Multiunit smooth muscle, in which each muscle cell receives its own nerve supply and contracts independently. (b) Unitary smooth muscle, in which a nerve fiber passes through the tissue without synapsing with any specific muscle cell, and muscle cells are coupled by electrical gap junctions.

## Excitation of Smooth Muscle

Whereas skeletal muscle contracts only in response to excitatory stimulation by a somatic motor fiber, smooth muscle can be stimulated in a multitude of ways. Some stimuli excite the myocyte and others inhibit it. Some produce action potentials in the sarcolemma, particularly in unitary smooth muscle, whereas others stimulate the myocyte by nonelectrical means. Some smooth muscle has no nerve supply at all. Modes of smooth muscle stimulation and some examples include

- **Autonomic nerve fibers and neurotransmitters.** For example, parasympathetic nerves secrete acetylcholine and stimulate gastrointestinal motility; sympathetic nerves secrete norepinephrine and dilate the bronchioles of the lungs.
- **Chemicals.** Smooth muscle reacts to hormones, carbon dioxide, oxygen, nitric oxide, low pH, and other chemical stimuli. The hormone oxytocin, for example, stimulates the labor contractions of the uterus, and histamine relaxes the smooth muscle of arteries.
- **Temperature.** Cold induces contraction of smooth muscle resulting in erection of the hairs and tautening of the skin in such regions as the areola and scrotum, whereas warmth relaxes smooth muscle in arteries of the skin.
- **Stretch.** The stomach and urinary bladder contract when stretched by food or urine.
- **Autorhythmicity.** Some unitary smooth muscle is autorhythmic, especially in the stomach and intestines. Some myocytes spontaneously depolarize at regular time intervals and set off waves of contraction throughout an entire layer of muscle. The rhythm is much slower than in cardiac muscle.

Regardless of how a myocyte is stimulated, however, the immediate trigger for contraction is the same as in skeletal and cardiac muscle—calcium ions. In some cases, the $Ca^{2+}$ comes from the sarcoplasmic reticulum (SR), as it does in skeletal muscle. With a relatively sparse SR, however, smooth muscle usually gets most of its $Ca^{2+}$ from the extracellular fluid by way of gated calcium channels in the sarcolemma. Compensating for the paucity of SR, the sarcolemma has numerous little pockets called **caveolae** (CAV-ee-OH-lee) where its calcium channels are concentrated. Calcium is 10,000 times as concentrated in the ECF as in the cytosol, so if these channels are opened, it diffuses quickly into the cell. Because smooth muscle cells are relatively small, the incoming $Ca^{2+}$ quickly reaches all of the myofilaments.

What opens these gated channels? Some are mechanically gated and open in response to physical distortion such as stretch. This is the case in organs that periodically fill and empty, such as the stomach and urinary bladder. Some are voltage-gated and open in response to electrical depolarization of the sarcolemma. Still others are ligand-gated and open in response to chemicals originating outside the cell or from the cytosol. Acetylcholine and norepinephrine, for example, bind to surface receptors and activate the formation of second messengers within the smooth muscle cell. This leads to a series of intracellular events that open the surface calcium channels from within.

**APPLY WHAT YOU KNOW**

*How is smooth muscle contraction affected by the drugs called calcium channel blockers? (See Deeper Insight 3.1.)*

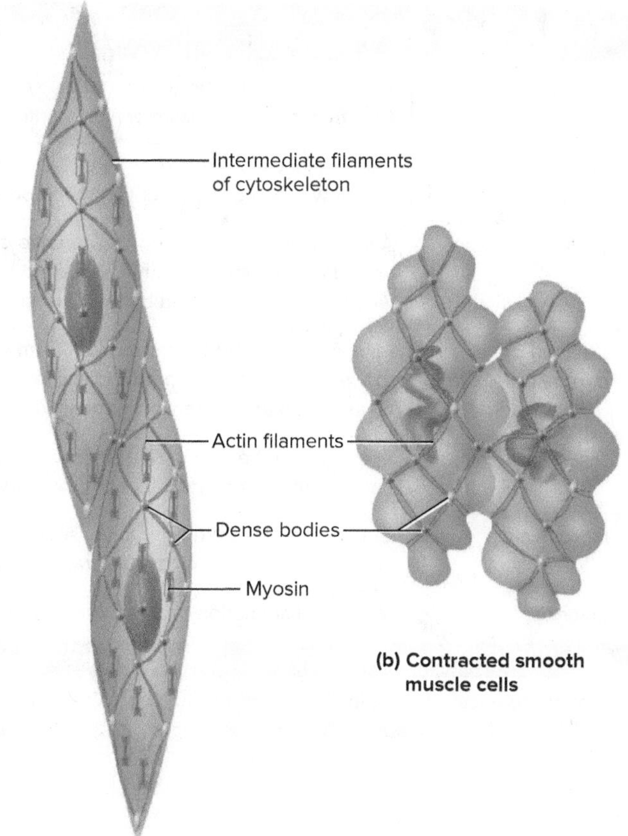


**FIGURE 11.24 Smooth Muscle Contraction.** (a) Relaxed cells. (b) Contracted cells.

## Contraction and Relaxation

Calcium ions are the immediate trigger for contraction, but unlike skeletal and cardiac muscle, smooth muscle has no troponin to bind it. Calcium binds instead to a similar protein called **calmodulin**[14] (cal-MOD-you-lin), associated with myosin. Calmodulin then activates an enzyme called **myosin light-chain kinase,** which adds a phosphate group to a small regulatory protein on the myosin head. This activates the myosin ATPase, enabling it to bind to actin and hydrolyze ATP. The myosin then produces repetitive power and recovery strokes like those of skeletal muscle.

As thick filaments pull on the thin ones, the thin filaments pull on the dense bodies and membrane plaques. Through the dense bodies and cytoskeleton, force is transferred to the plasma membrane and the entire cell shortens. When a smooth muscle cell contracts, it puckers and twists somewhat like wringing out a wet towel **(fig. 11.24).**

In skeletal muscle, there is typically a 2 ms latent period between stimulation and the onset of contraction. In smooth muscle, by contrast, the latent period is 50 to 100 ms long. Tension peaks about 500 ms (0.5 second) after the stimulus and then declines over a period of 1 to 2 seconds. The effect of all this is that compared with skeletal muscle, smooth muscle is very slow to contract and relax. It is slow to contract because its myosin ATPase is a slow enzyme. It is slow to relax because the pumps that remove $Ca^{2+}$ from the cytosol are also slow. As the $Ca^{2+}$ level falls, myosin releases its phosphate group and is no longer able to hydrolyze ATP and execute power strokes. However, it doesn't necessarily detach from actin immediately. It has a **latch-bridge mechanism** that enables it to remain attached to actin for a prolonged time without consuming more ATP.

Smooth muscle often exhibits tetanus and is very resistant to fatigue. It makes most of its ATP aerobically, but its ATP requirement is small and it has relatively few mitochondria. Skeletal muscle requires 10 to 300 times as much ATP as smooth muscle to maintain the same amount of tension. The fatigue resistance and latch-bridge mechanism of smooth muscle are important in enabling it to maintain a state of continual tonic contraction called **smooth muscle tone.** Muscle tone keeps the arteries in a state of partial constriction called *vasomotor tone.* A widespread loss of muscle tone in the arteries can cause a dangerous drop in blood pressure. Smooth muscle tone also keeps the intestines partially contracted. The intestines are much

[14]acronym for *calcium modulating protein*

| TABLE 11.5 | Some Disorders of the Muscular System |
|---|---|
| Contracture | Abnormal muscle shortening not caused by nervous stimulation. Can result from failure of the calcium pump to remove $Ca^{2+}$ from the sarcoplasm or from contraction of scar tissue, as in burn patients. |
| Cramps | Painful muscle spasms caused by rapid firing of motor neurons; triggered by heavy exercise, cold, dehydration, electrolyte loss, low blood glucose, or lack of blood flow. |
| Crush syndrome | A shocklike state following the massive crushing of muscles; associated with high and potentially fatal fever, cardiac irregularities resulting from $K^+$ released from the muscle, and kidney failure resulting from blockage of the renal tubules with myoglobin released by the traumatized muscle. Myoglobinuria (myoglobin in the urine) is a common sign. |
| Delayed-onset muscle soreness | Pain, stiffness, and tenderness felt from several hours to a day after strenuous exercise. Associated with microtrauma to the muscles; with disrupted Z discs, myofibrils, and plasma membranes; and with elevated levels of myoglobin, creatine kinase, and lactate dehydrogenase in the blood. |
| Disuse atrophy | Reduction in the size of muscle fibers as a result of nerve damage or muscular inactivity, for example in limbs in a cast and in patients confined to a bed or wheelchair. Muscle strength can be lost at a rate of 3% per day of bed rest. |
| Fibromyalgia | Chronic pain of unknown cause, seeming to come from the muscles and bones but actually arising from abnormal processing of pain signals by the brain. Occurring twice as often in women as in men, especially between ages 30 and 50. |
| Myositis | Muscle inflammation and weakness resulting from infection or autoimmune disease. |

***You can find other muscle disorders described in the following places:***

*Compartment syndrome* in Deeper Insight 10.1; *back injuries* in Deeper Insight 10.2; *hernia* in Deeper Insight 10.3; *common athletic injuries* in Deeper Insight 10.9; *paralysis* in Deeper Insights 11.1 and 13.5; and *muscular dystrophy* and *myasthenia gravis* in Deeper Insight 11.4.

longer in a cadaver than they are in a living person because of the loss of muscle tone at death.

## Response to Stretch

Stretch alone sometimes causes smooth muscle to contract by opening mechanically gated calcium channels in the sarcolemma. Distension of the esophagus with food or the colon with feces, for example, evokes a wave of contraction called **peristalsis** (PERR-ih-STAL-sis) that propels the contents along the organ.

Smooth muscle exhibits a reaction called the **stress–relaxation** (or **receptive-relaxation**) **response.** When stretched, it briefly contracts and resists, but then relaxes. The significance of this response is apparent in the urinary bladder. If the stretched bladder contracted and didn't soon relax, it would expel urine almost as soon as it began to fill, thus failing to store the urine until an opportune time.

Remember that skeletal muscle cannot contract very forcefully if it is overstretched. Smooth muscle, however, is less limited by the length–tension relationship. It contracts forcefully even when greatly stretched, so hollow organs such as the stomach and bladder can fill and then expel their contents efficiently. Skeletal muscle must be within 30% of optimum length in order to contract strongly when stimulated. Smooth muscle, by contrast, can be anywhere from half to twice its resting length and still contract powerfully. There are three reasons for this: (1) There are no Z discs, so thick filaments cannot butt against them and stop the contraction; (2) since the thick and thin filaments are not arranged in orderly sarcomeres, stretching of the muscle doesn't cause a situation in which there is too little overlap for cross-bridges to form; and (3) the thick filaments of smooth muscle have myosin heads along their entire length (there is no bare zone), so cross-bridges can form anywhere, not just at the ends. Smooth muscle also exhibits **plasticity**—the ability to adjust its tension to the degree of stretch. Thus, a hollow organ such as the bladder can be greatly stretched yet not become flabby when it is empty.

The muscular system suffers fewer diseases than any other organ system, but several of its more common dysfunctions are listed in **table 11.5.** The effects of aging on the muscular system are described in section 29.4a.

**BEFORE YOU GO ON**

Answer the following questions to test your understanding of the preceding section:

**26.** Explain why intercalated discs are important to cardiac muscle function.

**27.** Explain why it is important for cardiac muscle to have longer-lasting contractions than skeletal muscle.

**28.** How do unitary and multiunit smooth muscle differ in innervation and contractile behavior?

**29.** How does smooth muscle differ from skeletal muscle with respect to its source of calcium and its calcium receptor?

**30.** Explain why the stress–relaxation response is an important factor in smooth muscle function.

## DEEPER INSIGHT 11.4
### CLINICAL APPLICATION

### *Muscular Dystrophy and Myasthenia Gravis*

*Muscular dystrophy*[15] is a collective term for several hereditary diseases in which the muscles degenerate, weaken, and are gradually replaced by fat and fibrous scar tissue. The most common form of the disease is *Duchenne*[16] *muscular dystrophy (DMD),* a sex-linked recessive trait affecting about 1 out of every 3,500 live-born boys.

DMD is not evident at birth, but begins to exhibit its effects as a child shows difficulty keeping up with other children, falls frequently, and finds it hard to stand again. It is typically diagnosed between the ages of 2 and 10 years. It affects the muscles of the hips first; then the legs; and then progresses to the abdominal, spinal, and respiratory muscles as well as cardiac muscle. The muscles shorten as they atrophy, causing postural abnormalities such as scoliosis. Persons with DMD are usually wheelchair-dependent by the age of 10 or 12, and seldom live past the age of 20. For obscure reasons, they also frequently suffer a progressive decline in mental ability. Death usually results from respiratory insufficiency, pulmonary infection, or heart failure. DMD is incurable, but is treated with exercise to slow the atrophy of the muscles and with braces to reinforce the weakened hips and maintain posture.

The underlying cause of DMD is a mutation in the gene for the muscle protein dystrophin (see fig. 11.4)—a large gene highly vulnerable to mutation. Without dystrophin, there is no coupling between the thin myofilaments and the sarcolemma. The sarcomeres move independently of the sarcolemma, creating tears in the membrane. The torn membrane admits excess $Ca^{2+}$ into the cell, which activates intracellular proteases (protein-digesting enzymes). These enzymes degrade the contractile proteins of the muscle, leading to weakness and cellular necrosis. Dying muscle fibers are replaced with scar tissue, which blocks blood circulation in the muscle and thereby contributes to still further necrosis. Muscle degeneration accelerates in a fatal spiral of positive feedback.

Genetic screening can identify heterozygous carriers of DMD, allowing for counseling of prospective parents on the risk of having a child with the disease. However, about one out of three cases arises by a new spontaneous mutation and therefore cannot be predicted by genetic testing.

*Myasthenia gravis*[17] *(MG)* (MY-ass-THEE-nee-uh GRAV-is) usually occurs in women between the ages of 20 and 40. It is an autoimmune disease in which antibodies attack the neuromuscular junctions and bind ACh receptors together in clusters. The muscle fiber then removes the clusters from the sarcolemma by endocytosis. As a result, the muscle fibers become less and less sensitive to ACh. The effects often appear first in the facial muscles and commonly include drooping eyelids (*ptosis,* **fig. 11.25**) and double vision (due to *strabismus,* inability to fixate on the same point with both eyes). The initial symptoms are often followed by difficulty in swallowing, weakness of the limbs, and poor physical endurance. Some people with MG die quickly as a result of respiratory failure, but others have normal life spans. One method of assessing the progress of the disease is to use *bungarotoxin,* a protein from cobra venom that binds to ACh receptors. The amount that binds is proportional to the number of receptors that are still functional. The muscle of an MG patient sometimes binds less than one-third as much bungarotoxin as normal muscle does.

Myasthenia gravis is often treated with cholinesterase inhibitors. These drugs retard the breakdown of ACh in the neuromuscular junction and enable it to stimulate the muscle longer. Immunosuppressive agents such as prednisone and azathioprine (Imuran) may be used to suppress the production of the antibodies that destroy ACh receptors. Since certain immune cells are stimulated by hormones from the thymus, removal of the thymus *(thymectomy)* helps to dampen the overactive immune response that causes myasthenia gravis. Also, a technique called *plasmapheresis* may be used to remove harmful antibodies from the blood plasma.

[15] *dys* = bad, abnormal; *trophy* = growth
[16] Guillaume B. A. Duchenne (1806–75), French physician

[17] *my* = muscle; *asthen* = weakness; *grav* = severe

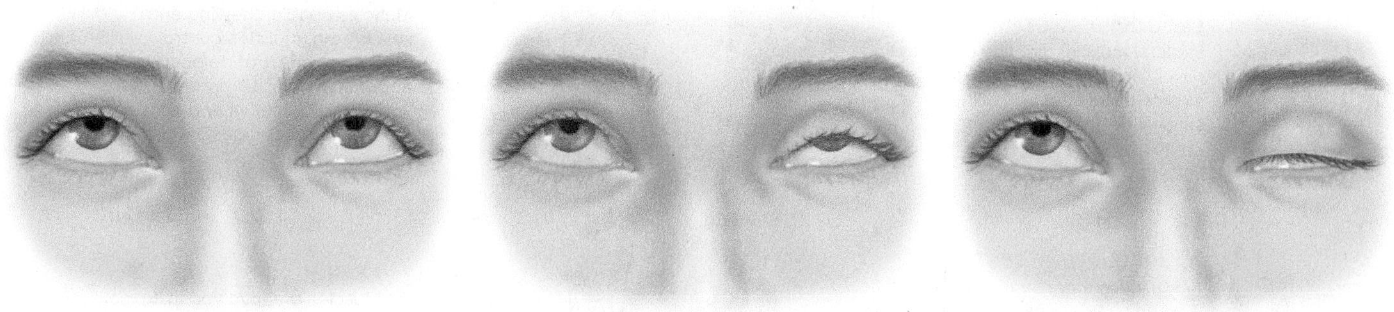


**FIGURE 11.25 Test of Myasthenia Gravis.** The subject is told to gaze upward. Within 60 to 90 seconds, there is obvious sagging (ptosis) of one eyelid due to inability to sustain stimulation of the orbicularis oculi muscle.

# CONNECTIVE ISSUES

## Effects of the **MUSCULAR SYSTEM** on Other Organ Systems

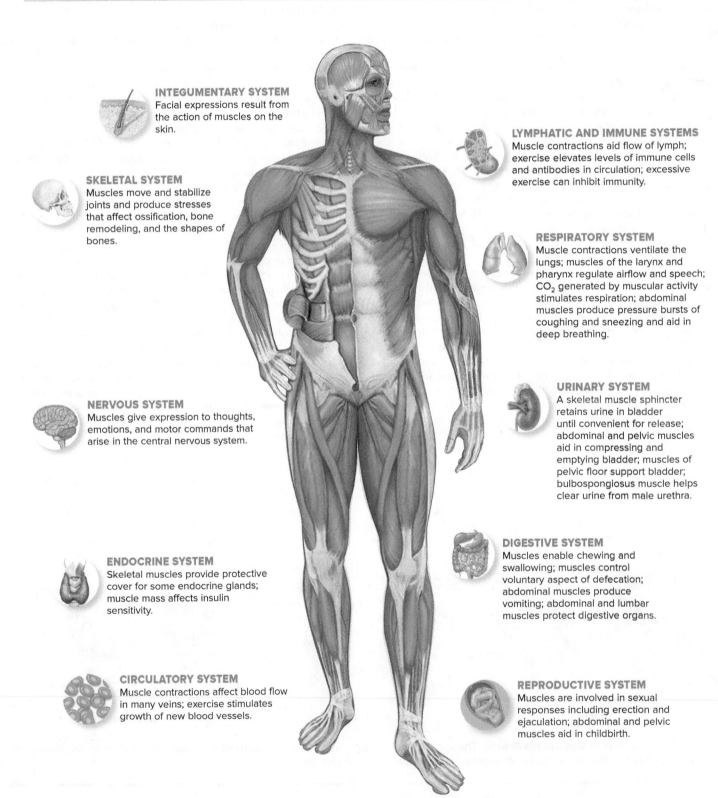

**INTEGUMENTARY SYSTEM**
Facial expressions result from the action of muscles on the skin.

**SKELETAL SYSTEM**
Muscles move and stabilize joints and produce stresses that affect ossification, bone remodeling, and the shapes of bones.

**NERVOUS SYSTEM**
Muscles give expression to thoughts, emotions, and motor commands that arise in the central nervous system.

**ENDOCRINE SYSTEM**
Skeletal muscles provide protective cover for some endocrine glands; muscle mass affects insulin sensitivity.

**CIRCULATORY SYSTEM**
Muscle contractions affect blood flow in many veins; exercise stimulates growth of new blood vessels.

**LYMPHATIC AND IMMUNE SYSTEMS**
Muscle contractions aid flow of lymph; exercise elevates levels of immune cells and antibodies in circulation; excessive exercise can inhibit immunity.

**RESPIRATORY SYSTEM**
Muscle contractions ventilate the lungs; muscles of the larynx and pharynx regulate airflow and speech; $CO_2$ generated by muscular activity stimulates respiration; abdominal muscles produce pressure bursts of coughing and sneezing and aid in deep breathing.

**URINARY SYSTEM**
A skeletal muscle sphincter retains urine in bladder until convenient for release; abdominal and pelvic muscles aid in compressing and emptying bladder; muscles of pelvic floor support bladder; bulbospongiosus muscle helps clear urine from male urethra.

**DIGESTIVE SYSTEM**
Muscles enable chewing and swallowing; muscles control voluntary aspect of defecation; abdominal muscles produce vomiting; abdominal and lumbar muscles protect digestive organs.

**REPRODUCTIVE SYSTEM**
Muscles are involved in sexual responses including erection and ejaculation; abdominal and pelvic muscles aid in childbirth.

# STUDY GUIDE

## Assess Your Learning Outcomes

*To test your knowledge, discuss the following topics with a study partner or in writing, ideally from memory.*

### 11.1 Types and Characteristics of Muscular Tissue

1. Five physiological properties of all muscular tissue and their relevance to muscle function
2. Distinguishing characteristics of skeletal muscle
3. Dimensions of a typical skeletal muscle fiber and of the longest fibers
4. Connective tissues associated with a muscle fiber and their relationship to muscle–bone attachments

### 11.2 Skeletal Muscle Cells

1. The sarcolemma and sarcoplasm, and the roles of glycogen and myoglobin in the sarcoplasm
2. The role of myoblasts in the development of a muscle fiber, and how they give rise to the multinuclear condition of the muscle fiber and to the satellite cells external to the fiber
3. Structure and function of the sarcoplasmic reticulum and transverse tubules
4. Types of myofilaments that constitute a myofibril
5. Composition and molecular organization of a thick filament, and the structure of a myosin molecule
6. Composition of a thin filament; the organization of its actin, tropomyosin, and troponin; and the active sites of its actin monomers
7. Composition of elastic filaments and their relationship to the thick filaments and Z discs
8. The position and function of dystrophin in the muscle fiber
9. Names of the striations of skeletal and cardiac muscle and how they relate to the overlapping arrangement of thick and thin filaments
10. The definition of *sarcomere*

### 11.3 The Nerve–Muscle Relationship

1. Motor units; the meanings of *large* and *small motor units;* and the respective advantages of the two types
2. Structure of a neuromuscular junction and function of each of its components
3. The source, role, and fate of acetylcholine (ACh) in the neuromuscular junction
4. The role of acetylcholinesterase in neuromuscular function
5. How a nerve or muscle cell generates a resting membrane potential (RMP); the typical voltage of this potential in a skeletal muscle fiber
6. How an action potential differs from the RMP, and the effects of an action potential on a nerve or muscle cell

### 11.4 Behavior of Skeletal Muscle Fibers

1. Excitation of a muscle fiber; how a nerve signal leads to a traveling wave of electrical excitation in a muscle fiber
2. Excitation–contraction coupling; how electrical excitation of a muscle fiber leads to exposure of the active sites on the actin of a thin myofilament
3. The sliding filament mechanism of contraction; how exposure of the active sites leads to repetitive binding of myosin to actin and sliding of the thin filaments over the thick filaments
4. Muscle relaxation; how the cessation of the nerve signal leads to blockage of the active sites so myosin can no longer bind to them and maintain muscle tension
5. The roles of calcium, troponin, tropomyosin, and ATP in these processes
6. The length–tension relationship in muscle; why muscle would contract weakly if it was overcontracted or overstretched just prior to stimulation; and how this principle relates to the function of muscle tone

### 11.5 Behavior of Whole Muscles

1. Terms for the minimum stimulus intensity needed to make a muscle contract, and for the delay between stimulation and contraction
2. The phases of a muscle twitch
3. Reasons why muscle twitches vary in strength (tension)
4. How recruitment and tetanus are produced and how they affect muscle tension
5. Differences between isometric and isotonic contraction, and between the concentric and eccentric forms of isotonic contraction

### 11.6 Muscle Metabolism

1. Why a muscle cannot contract without ATP
2. Differences between aerobic respiration and anaerobic fermentation with respect to muscle function
3. The use of myoglobin and aerobic respiration to generate ATP at the outset of exercise
4. Two ways in which the phosphagen system generates ATP for continued exercise
5. How anaerobic fermentation generates ATP after the phosphagen system is depleted
6. Why a muscle is able to switch back to aerobic respiration to generate ATP after 40 seconds or so of exercise
7. Causes of muscle fatigue
8. $Vo_2$max, why it partially determines one's ability to maintain high-intensity exercise, and why it differs from one person to another
9. Why exercise is followed by a prolonged state of elevated oxygen consumption, and the name of that state
10. Differences between slow oxidative and fast glycolytic muscle fibers; the respective advantages of each; how they relate to the power and recruitment of motor units; and examples of muscles in which each type predominates
11. Factors that determine the strength of a muscle
12. Examples of resistance exercise and endurance exercise, and the effects of each on muscle performance

### 11.7 Cardiac and Smooth Muscle

1. Reasons why cardiac muscle must differ physiologically from skeletal muscle
2. Structural differences between cardiomyocytes and skeletal muscle fibers
3. The autorhythmicity of the heart and its ability to contract without nervous stimulation
4. The unusual fatigue resistance of cardiac muscle; structural and biochemical properties that account for it
5. Functional differences between smooth muscle and the two forms of striated muscle
6. How the innervation of smooth muscle differs from that of skeletal muscle
7. Variations in the complexity and anatomical organization of smooth muscle
8. Various functions of smooth muscle
9. Two modes of growth of smooth muscle tissue
10. The structure of smooth muscle cells and what takes the place of the absent Z discs and T tubules
11. Differences between multiunit and unitary smooth muscle, and the nerve–muscle relationship of each

# STUDY GUIDE

12. Various modes of stimulation of smooth muscle
13. How excitation–contraction coupling in smooth muscle differs from that in skeletal muscle; the roles of calmodulin and myosin light-chain kinase in smooth muscle contraction
14. The nature and effect of the latch-bridge mechanism in smooth muscle
15. The role of smooth muscle in peristalsis
16. Benefits of the stress–relaxation response of smooth muscle, and of its absence of a length–tension relationship

## ▶ Testing Your Recall

*Answers in Appendix A*

1. To make a muscle contract more strongly, the nervous system can activate more motor units. This process is called
   a. recruitment.
   b. summation.
   c. incomplete tetanus.
   d. twitch.
   e. concentric contraction.

2. The functional unit of a muscle fiber is the ______, a segment from one Z disc to the next.
   a. myofibril
   b. I band
   c. sarcomere
   d. neuromuscular junction
   e. striation

3. Before a skeletal muscle fiber can contract, ATP must bind to
   a. a Z disc.
   b. the myosin head.
   c. tropomyosin.
   d. troponin.
   e. actin.

4. Before a skeletal muscle fiber can contract, $Ca^{2+}$ must bind to
   a. calsequestrin.
   b. calmodulin.
   c. the myosin head.
   d. troponin.
   e. actin.

5. Which of the following muscle proteins is *not* intracellular?
   a. actin
   b. myosin
   c. collagen
   d. troponin
   e. dystrophin

6. Smooth muscle cells have ______, whereas skeletal muscle fibers do not.
   a. sarcoplasmic reticulum
   b. tropomyosin
   c. calmodulin
   d. Z discs
   e. myosin ATPase

7. ACh receptors are found mainly in
   a. synaptic vesicles.
   b. terminal cisterns.
   c. thick filaments.
   d. thin filaments.
   e. junctional folds.

8. Unitary smooth muscle cells can stimulate each other because they have
   a. a latch-bridge.
   b. diffuse junctions.
   c. gap junctions.
   d. tight junctions.
   e. cross-bridges.

9. A person with a high $Vo_2max$
   a. needs less oxygen than someone with a low $Vo_2max$.
   b. has stronger muscles than someone with a low $Vo_2max$.
   c. is less likely to show muscle tetanus than someone with a low $Vo_2max$.
   d. has fewer muscle mitochondria than someone with a low $Vo_2max$.
   e. experiences less muscle fatigue during exercise than someone with a low $Vo_2max$.

10. Slow oxidative fibers have all of the following *except*
    a. an abundance of myoglobin.
    b. an abundance of glycogen.
    c. high fatigue resistance.
    d. a red color.
    e. a high capacity to synthesize ATP aerobically.

11. The minimum stimulus intensity that will make a muscle contract is called ______.

12. Red muscles consist mainly of slow ______, or type I, muscle fibers.

13. Parts of the sarcoplasmic reticulum called ______ lie on each side of a T tubule.

14. Thick filaments consist mainly of the protein ______.

15. The neurotransmitter that stimulates skeletal muscle is ______.

16. Muscle contains an oxygen-binding pigment called ______.

17. The ______ of skeletal muscle play the same role as dense bodies in smooth muscle.

18. In autonomic nerve fibers that stimulate unitary smooth muscle, the neurotransmitter is contained in swellings called ______.

19. A state of continual partial muscle contraction is called ______.

20. ______ is an increase in muscle tension without a change in length.

## ▶ Building Your Medical Vocabulary

*Answers in Appendix A*

*State a meaning of each word element, and give a medical term from this chapter that uses it or a slight variation of it.*

1. astheno-
2. auto-
3. dys-
4. iso-
5. metri-
6. myo-
7. sarco-
8. temporo-
9. tono-
10. -trophy

# STUDY GUIDE

## What's Wrong with These Statements?

Answers in Appendix A

*Briefly explain why each of the following statements is false, or reword it to make it true.*

1. Each motor neuron supplies one muscle fiber.
2. Somatic motor neurons excite skeletal muscle but inhibit cardiac muscle.
3. Fast glycolytic muscle fibers are relatively resistant to fatigue.
4. Thin myofilaments are found only in the I bands of striated muscle.
5. Thin myofilaments shorten when a muscle contracts.
6. Smooth muscle lacks striations because it does not have thick and thin myofilaments.
7. A muscle must contract to the point of complete tetanus if it is to move a load.
8. If no ATP were available to a muscle fiber, it could still be excited but it could not contract.
9. For the first 30 seconds of an intense exercise, muscle gets most of its energy from lactate.
10. Like cardiac muscle, all smooth muscle is autorhythmic.

## Testing Your Comprehension

1. Without ATP, relaxed muscle cannot contract and a contracted muscle cannot relax. Explain why.
2. Smooth muscle controls the curvature of the lens of the eye and the diameter of the pupil, but it would serve poorly for controlling eye movements as in tracking a flying bird or reading a page of print. Explain why.
3. Why would skeletal muscle be unsuitable for the wall of the urinary bladder? Explain how this illustrates the complementarity of form and function at a cellular and molecular level.
4. As skeletal muscle contracts, one or more bands of the sarcomere become narrower and disappear, and one or more of them remain the same width. Which bands will change—A, H, or I—and why?
5. Polio is a muscle-paralyzing disease caused by infection with poliovirus. This virus, however, never infects muscular tissue. (a) Explain how it could paralyze the muscles without invading them. (b) Explain why it does not paralyze cardiac muscle and stop the heart.

CHAPTER 12

# NERVOUS TISSUE

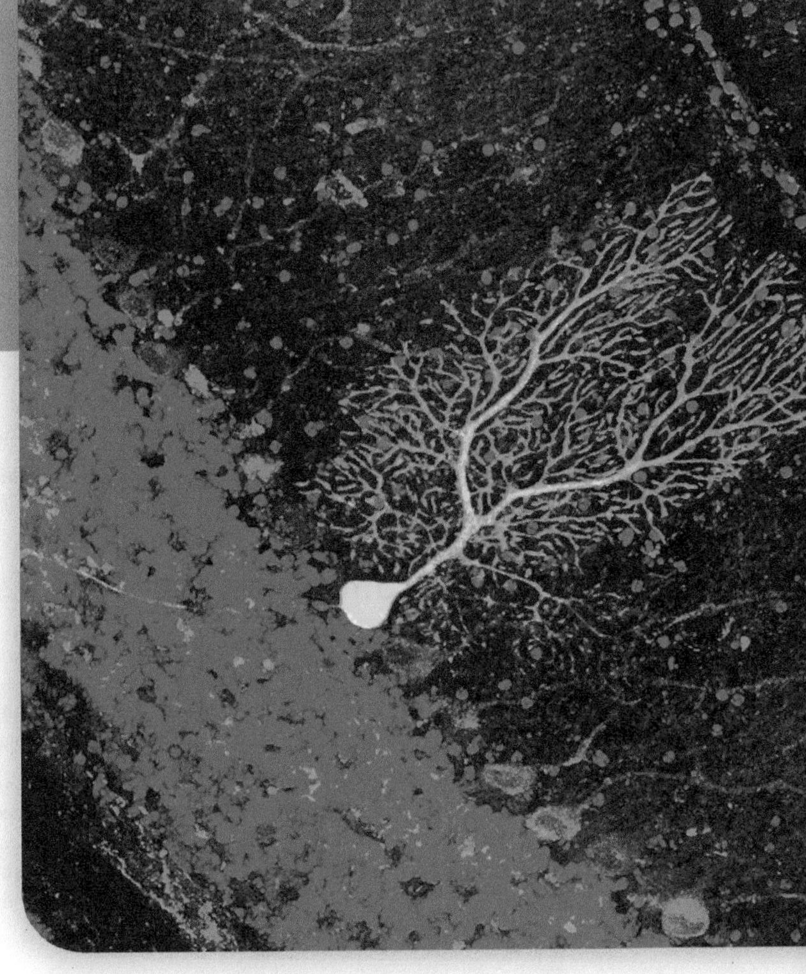

**A Purkinje cell, a neuron from the cerebellum of the brain**
SPL/Science Source

## CHAPTER OUTLINE



## DEEPER INSIGHTS

**Module 7: Nervous System**

## BRUSHING UP

- This chapter explains the electrophysiology of neurons, and must assume you are familiar with concentration and electrochemical gradients (see section 1.6e).
- This topic also assumes familiarity with "Membrane Proteins" in section 3.2a—especially receptors, enzymes, ligand- and voltage-gated ion channels, leak channels, and the sodium–potassium pump.

The nervous system is one of great complexity and mystery, and will absorb our attention for the next five chapters. It is the foundation of all our conscious experience, personality, and behavior. It profoundly intrigues biologists, physicians, psychologists, and even philosophers. Its scientific study, called **neurobiology,** is regarded by many as the ultimate challenge facing the behavioral and life sciences. We will begin at the simplest organizational level—the nerve cells *(neurons)* and cells called *neuroglia* that support their function in various ways. We will then progress to the organ level to examine the spinal cord (chapter 13), brain (chapter 14), autonomic nervous system (chapter 15), and sense organs (chapter 16).

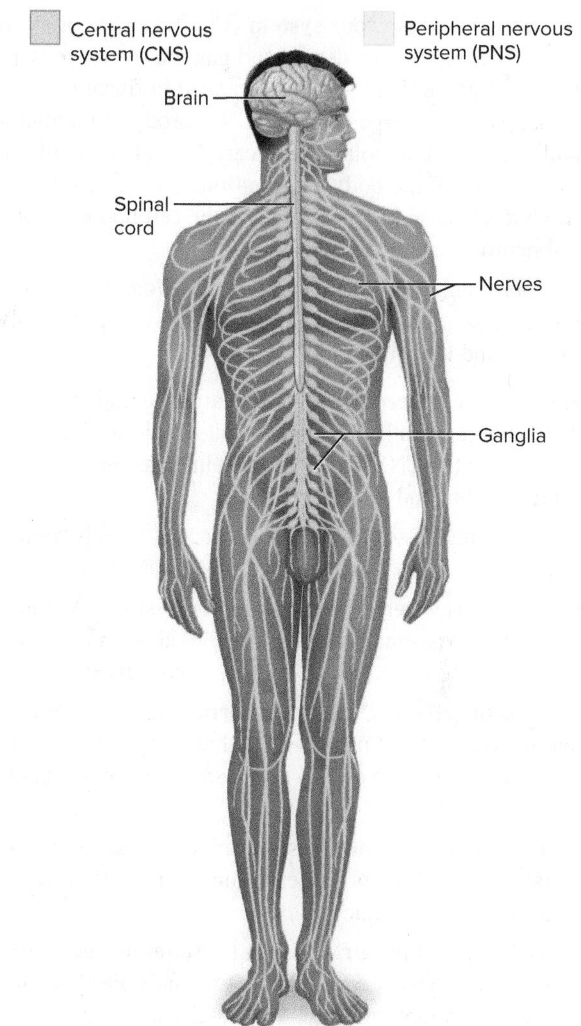


**FIGURE 12.1 The Nervous System.**

## 12.1 Overview of the Nervous System

### Expected Learning Outcomes

When you have completed this section, you should be able to

a. describe the overall function of the nervous system; and
b. describe its major anatomical and functional subdivisions.

If the body is to maintain homeostasis and function effectively, its trillions of cells must work together in a coordinated fashion. If each cell behaved without regard to what others were doing, the result would be physiological chaos and death. We have two organ systems dedicated to maintaining internal coordination—the **endocrine system** (see chapter 17), which communicates by means of chemical messengers (hormones) secreted into the blood, and the **nervous system (fig. 12.1),** which employs electrical and chemical means to send messages very quickly from cell to cell.

The nervous system carries out its coordinating task in three basic steps: (1) It receives information about changes in the body and external environment and transmits messages to the *central nervous system (CNS).* (2) The CNS processes this information and determines what response, if any, is appropriate to the circumstances. (3) The CNS issues commands primarily to muscle and gland cells to carry out such responses.

The nervous system has two major anatomical subdivisions **(fig. 12.2):**

- The **central nervous system (CNS)** consists of the brain and spinal cord, which are enclosed and protected by the cranium and vertebral column.

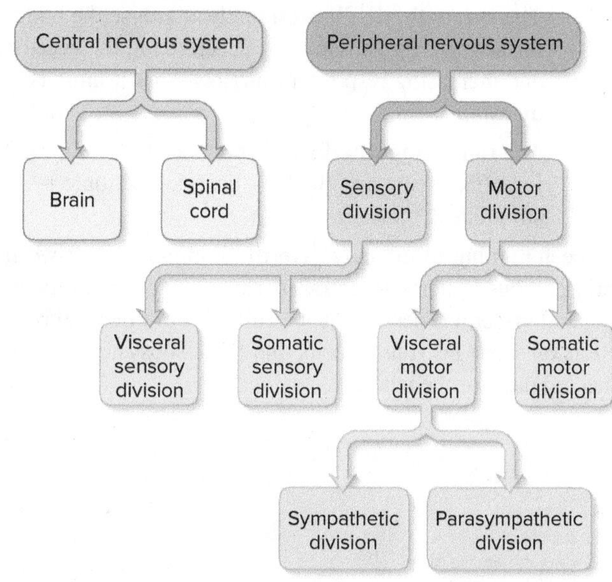


**FIGURE 12.2 Subdivisions of the Nervous System.**

- The **peripheral nervous system (PNS)** consists of all the rest; it is composed of nerves and ganglia. A **nerve** is a bundle of nerve fibers (axons) wrapped in fibrous connective tissue. Nerves emerge from the CNS through foramina of the skull and vertebral column and carry signals to and from other organs of the body. A **ganglion**[1] (plural, *ganglia*) is a knotlike swelling in a nerve where the cell bodies of peripheral neurons are concentrated.

The peripheral nervous system is functionally divided into *sensory* and *motor* divisions, and each of these is further divided into *somatic* and *visceral* subdivisions.

- The **sensory (afferent[2]) division** carries signals from various **receptors** (sense organs and simple sensory nerve endings) to the CNS. This pathway informs the CNS of stimuli within and around the body.
  - The **somatic[3] sensory division** carries signals from receptors in the skin, muscles, bones, and joints.
  - The **visceral sensory division** carries signals mainly from the viscera of the thoracic and abdominal cavities, such as the heart, lungs, stomach, and urinary bladder.
- The **motor (efferent[4]) division** carries signals from the CNS mainly to gland and muscle cells that carry out the body's responses. Cells and organs that respond to these signals are called **effectors.**
  - The **somatic motor division** carries signals to the skeletal muscles. This produces voluntary muscle contractions as well as automatic reflexes.
  - The **visceral motor division (autonomic[5] nervous system, ANS)** carries signals to glands, cardiac muscle, and smooth muscle. We usually have no voluntary control over these effectors, and the ANS operates at an unconscious level. The responses of the ANS and its effectors are *visceral reflexes*. The ANS has two further divisions:
    - The **sympathetic division** tends to arouse the body for action—for example, by accelerating the heartbeat and increasing respiratory airflow—but it inhibits digestion.
    - The **parasympathetic division** tends to have a calming effect—slowing the heartbeat, for example—but it stimulates digestion.

The foregoing terms may give the impression that we have several nervous systems—central, peripheral, sensory, motor, somatic, and visceral. These are just terms of convenience, however. There is only one nervous system, and these subsystems are interconnected parts of the whole.

[1]*gangli* = knot
[2]*af* = *ad* = toward; *fer* = to carry
[3]*somat* = body; *ic* = pertaining to
[4]*ef* = *ex* = out, away; *fer* = to carry
[5]*auto* = self; *nom* = law, governance

**BEFORE YOU GO ON**

Answer the following questions to test your understanding of the preceding section:

1. What is a receptor? Give two examples of effectors.
2. Distinguish between the central and peripheral nervous systems, and between visceral and somatic divisions of the sensory and motor systems.
3. What is another name for the visceral motor nervous system? What are its two subdivisions? What are their functions?

## 12.2 Properties of Neurons

**Expected Learning Outcomes**

When you have completed this section, you should be able to

a. describe three functional properties found in all neurons;
b. define the three most basic functional categories of neurons;
c. identify the parts of a neuron; and
d. explain how neurons transport materials between the cell body and tips of the axon.

### 12.2a Universal Properties

The communicative role of the nervous system is carried out by **nerve cells,** or **neurons.** These cells have three fundamental physiological properties that enable them to communicate with other cells:

1. **Excitability.** All cells are excitable—that is, they respond to environmental changes **(stimuli).** Neurons exhibit this property to the highest degree.
2. **Conductivity.** Neurons respond to stimuli by producing electrical signals that are quickly conducted to other cells at distant locations.
3. **Secretion.** When the signal reaches the end of a nerve fiber, the neuron secretes a *neurotransmitter* that crosses the gap and stimulates the next cell.

**APPLY WHAT YOU KNOW**

*What basic physiological properties do a nerve cell and a muscle cell have in common? Name a physiological property of each that the other one lacks.*

### 12.2b Functional Classes

There are three general classes of neurons **(fig. 12.3)** corresponding to the three major aspects of nervous system function listed earlier:

1. **Sensory (afferent) neurons** are specialized to detect stimuli such as light, heat, pressure, and chemicals, and transmit information about them to the CNS. Such neurons begin in almost

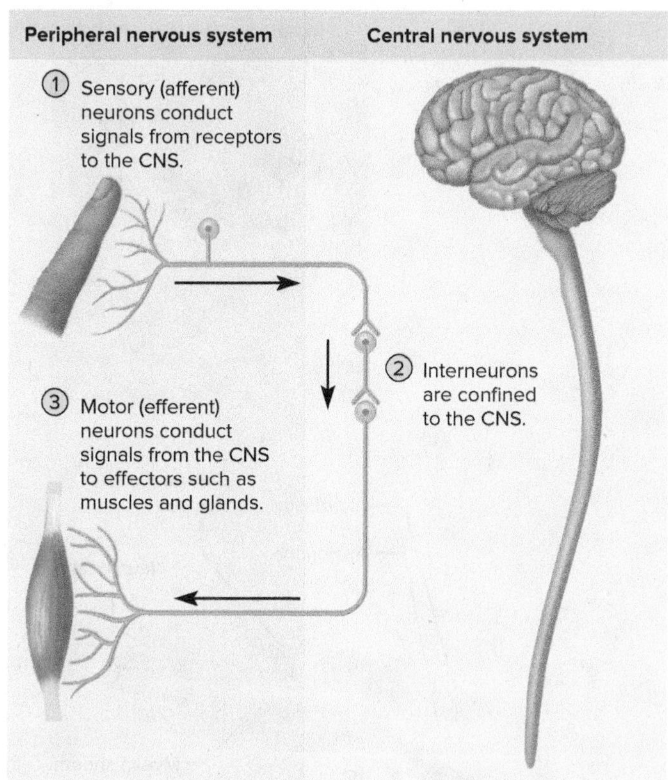
Peripheral nervous system
Central nervous system
① Sensory (afferent) neurons conduct signals from receptors to the CNS.
② Interneurons are confined to the CNS.
③ Motor (efferent) neurons conduct signals from the CNS to effectors such as muscles and glands.

**FIGURE 12.3 The Three Functional Classes of Neurons.** All neurons can be classified as sensory, motor, or interneurons depending on their location and the direction of signal conduction.

every organ of the body and end in the CNS; the word *afferent* refers to signal conduction *toward* the CNS. Some receptors, such as those for pain and smell, are themselves neurons. In other cases, such as taste and hearing, the receptor is a separate cell that communicates directly with a sensory neuron.

② **Interneurons** lie entirely within the CNS. They receive signals from many other neurons and carry out the integrative function of the nervous system—that is, they process, store, and retrieve information and "make decisions" that determine how the body responds to stimuli. About 90% of our neurons are interneurons. The word *interneuron* refers to the fact that they lie *between,* and interconnect, the incoming sensory pathways and the outgoing motor pathways of the CNS.

③ **Motor (efferent) neurons** send signals predominantly to muscle and gland cells, the effectors. They are called *motor* neurons because most of them lead to muscle cells, and *efferent* neurons to signify signal conduction *away from* the CNS.

### 12.2c Structure of a Neuron

There are several varieties of neurons, but a good starting point for discussion is a motor neuron of the spinal cord **(fig. 12.4).** The control center of the neuron is the **neurosoma,**[6] also called the **soma, cell body,** or **perikaryon.**[7] It has a centrally located nucleus with a large nucleolus. The cytoplasm contains mitochondria, lysosomes, a Golgi complex, numerous inclusions, and an extensive rough endoplasmic reticulum and cytoskeleton. The cytoskeleton consists of a dense mesh of microtubules and **neurofibrils** (bundles of actin filaments), which compartmentalize the rough ER into dark-staining regions called **chromatophilic**[8] **substance** (fig. 12.4e). This is unique to neurons and a helpful clue to identifying them in tissue sections with mixed cell types. Mature neurons have no centrioles and cannot undergo any further mitosis after adolescence. Consequently, neurons that die are usually irreplaceable; surviving neurons cannot multiply to replace those lost. However, neurons are unusually long-lived cells, capable of functioning for over a hundred years.

The major inclusions in the neurosoma are glycogen granules, lipid droplets, melanin, and a golden brown pigment called *lipofuscin*[9] (LIP-oh-FEW-sin), produced when lysosomes degrade worn-out organelles and other products. Lipofuscin accumulates with age and pushes the nucleus to one side of the cell. Lipofuscin granules are also called "wear-and-tear granules" because they are most abundant in old neurons. They are also associated with certain degenerative diseases such as macular degeneration of the eye and amyotrophic lateral sclerosis (ALS).

The somas of most neurons give rise to a few thick processes that branch into a vast number of **dendrites**[10]—named for their striking resemblance to the bare branches of a tree in winter. Dendrites are the primary site for receiving signals from other neurons. Some neurons have only one dendrite and some have thousands. The more dendrites a neuron has, the more information it can receive and incorporate into its decision making. As tangled as the dendrites may seem, they provide exquisitely precise pathways for the reception and processing of neural information.

On one side of the neurosoma is a mound called the **axon hillock,** from which the **axon (nerve fiber)** originates. The axon is cylindrical and relatively unbranched for most of its length, although it may give rise to a few branches called *axon collaterals* near the soma, and most axons branch extensively at their distal end. An axon is specialized for rapid conduction of nerve signals to points remote from the soma. Its cytoplasm is called the **axoplasm** and its membrane the **axolemma.**[11] A neuron never has more than one axon, and some neurons have none.

Somas range from 5 to 135 μm in diameter, and axons from 1 to 20 μm in diameter and from a few millimeters to more than a meter long. (In the great blue whale, one nerve cell can be more than 30 m, or 100 ft, long.) The dimensions of a human neuron are more impressive when we scale them up to the size of familiar objects. If the soma of a spinal motor neuron were the size of a tennis ball, its dendrites would form a dense bushy mass that could

[6] *soma* = body

[7] *peri* = around, surrounding; *karyo* = nucleus
[8] *chromato* = color; *philic* = loving, attracting
[9] *lipo* = fat, lipid; *fusc* = dusky, brown
[10] *dendr* = tree, branch; *ite* = little
[11] *axo* = axis, axon; *lemma* = husk, peel, sheath

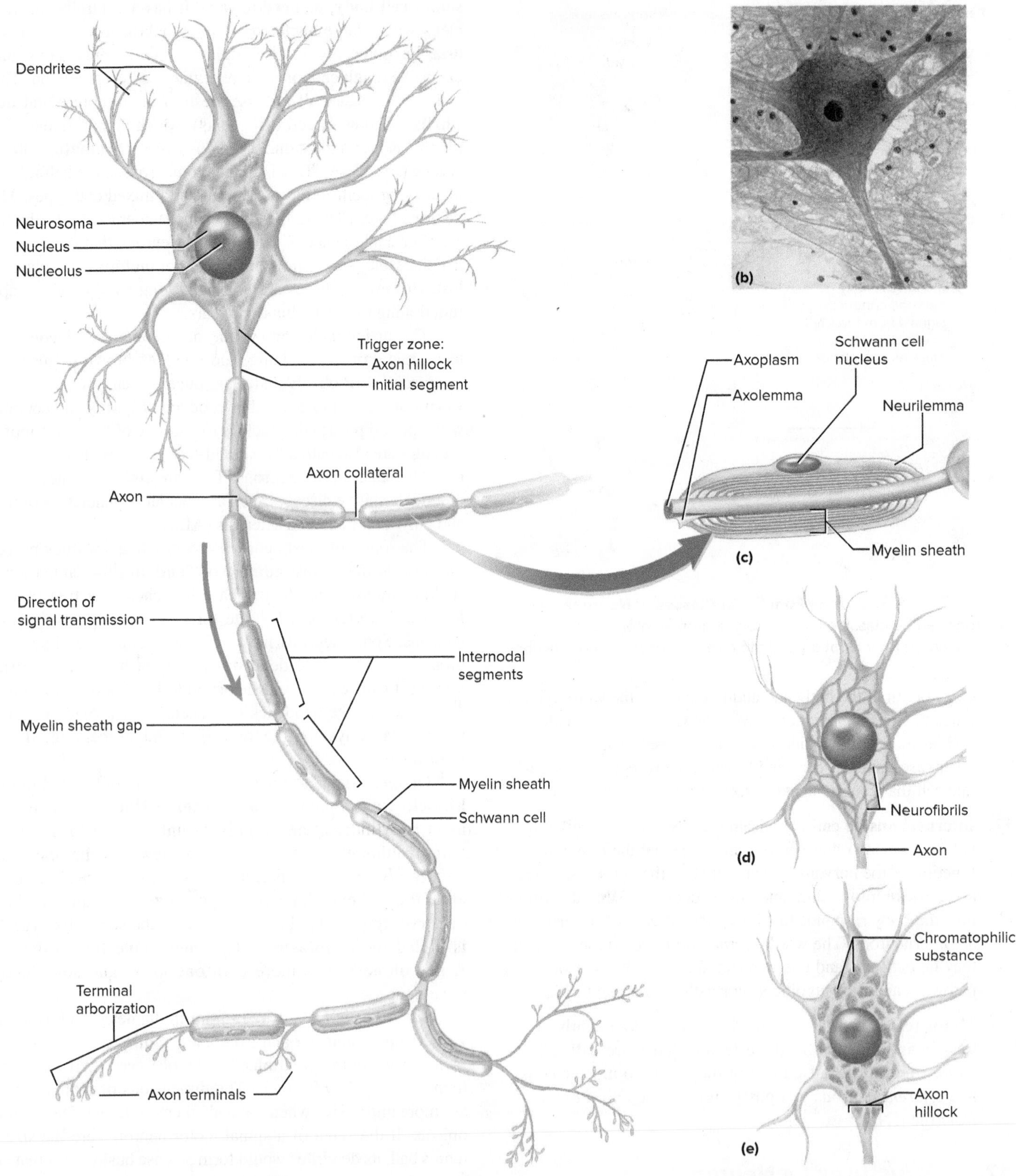


**FIGURE 12.4 General Structure of a Neuron.** (a) Structure of a multipolar neuron such as a spinal motor neuron. (b) Photograph of this neuron type. (c) Detail of the myelin sheath. (d) Neurofibrils of the neurosoma. (e) Chromatophilic substance, stained masses of rough ER separated by the bundles of neurofibrils shown in part (d). See section 12.3b for description of the myelin sheath.

b: Ed Reschke

fill a 30-seat classroom from floor to ceiling. Its axon would be up to a mile long but a little narrower than a garden hose. This is quite a point to ponder. The neuron must assemble molecules and organelles in its "tennis ball" soma and deliver them through its "mile-long garden hose" to the end of the axon. How it achieves this remarkable feat is explained shortly.

At the distal end, an axon usually has a **terminal arborization**[12]—an extensive complex of fine branches. Each branch ends in a bulbous **axon terminal (terminal button),** which forms a junction **(synapse**[13]**)** with the next cell. It contains **synaptic vesicles** full of neurotransmitter. In most autonomic neurons, however, the axon has numerous beads called **varicosities** along its length (see fig. 11.21). Each varicosity contains synaptic vesicles and secretes neurotransmitter.

Not all neurons fit the preceding description. Neurons are classified structurally according to the number of processes extending from the soma **(fig. 12.5):**

- **Multipolar neurons** are those, like the preceding, that have one axon and multiple dendrites. This is the most common type and includes most neurons of the brain and spinal cord.
- **Bipolar neurons** have one axon and one dendrite. Examples include olfactory cells of the nose, certain neurons of the retina, and sensory neurons of the ear.
- **Unipolar neurons** have only a single process leading away from the soma. They are represented by the neurons that carry signals to the spinal cord for such senses as touch and pain. They are also called *pseudounipolar* because they start out as bipolar neurons in the embryo, but their two processes fuse into one as the neuron matures. A short distance away from the soma, the process branches like a T into a *peripheral fiber* and a *central fiber.* The peripheral fiber begins with a sensory ending often far away from the soma—in the skin, for example. Its signals travel toward the soma, but bypass it and continue along the central fiber for a short remaining distance to the spinal cord. The dendrites are considered to be only the short receptive endings. The rest of the process, both peripheral and central, is the axon, defined by the presence of myelin and the ability to generate action potentials.
- **Anaxonic neurons** have multiple dendrites but no axon. They communicate locally through their dendrites and do not produce action potentials. Some anaxonic neurons are found in the brain, retina, and adrenal medulla. In the retina, they help in visual processes such as the perception of contrast.

## 12.2d Axonal Transport

All of the proteins needed by a neuron must be made in the soma, where the protein-synthesizing organelles such as the nucleus,

[12]*arbor* = tree

[13]*syn* = together; *aps* = to touch, join

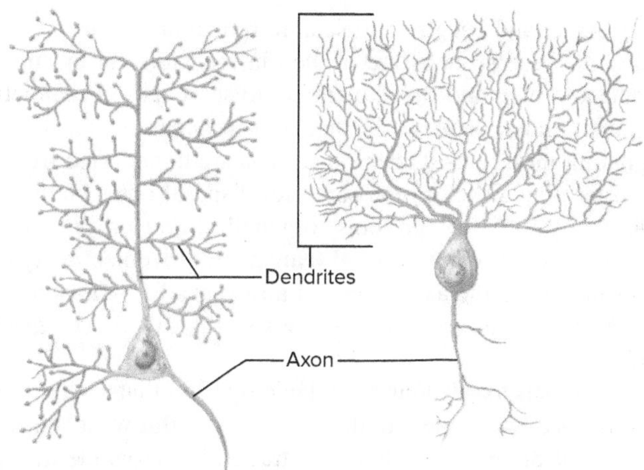


**(a) Multipolar neurons**

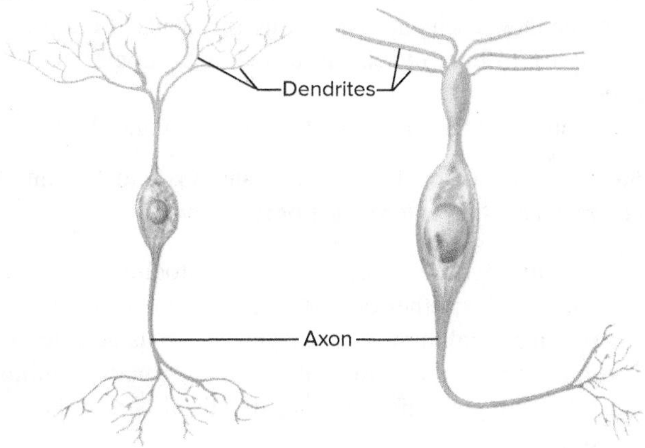


**(b) Bipolar neurons**

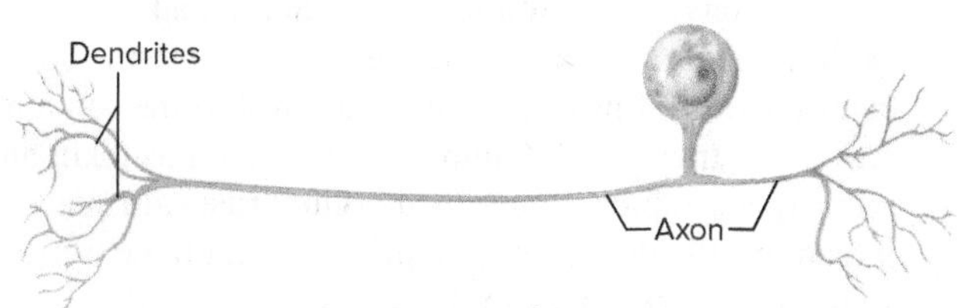


**(c) Unipolar neuron**

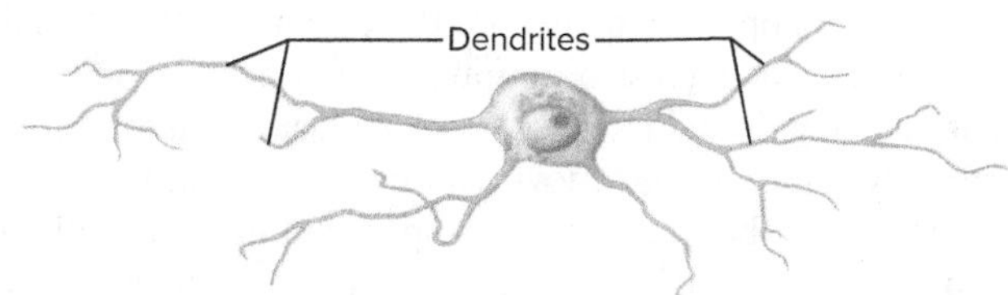


**(d) Anaxonic neuron**

**FIGURE 12.5 Variation in Neuron Structure.** (a) Two multipolar neurons of the brain—a pyramidal cell *(left)* and a Purkinje cell. (b) Two bipolar neurons—a bipolar cell of the retina *(left)* and an olfactory neuron. (c) A unipolar neuron of the type involved in the senses of touch and pain. (d) An anaxonic neuron—an amacrine cell of the retina.

ribosomes, and rough endoplasmic reticulum are located. Yet many of these proteins are needed in the axon, for example to repair and maintain the axolemma, to serve as ion channels in the membrane, or to act in the axon terminal as enzymes and signaling molecules. Other substances are transported from the axon terminals back to the soma for disposal or recycling. The two-way passage of proteins, organelles, and other materials along an axon is called **axonal transport.** Movement away from the soma down the axon is called **anterograde**[14] **transport** and movement up the axon toward the soma is called **retrograde**[15] **transport.**

Materials travel along axonal microtubules that act like monorail tracks to guide them to their destination. But what is the "engine" that drives them along the tracks? Anterograde transport employs a motor protein called *kinesin*[16] and retrograde transport uses one called *dynein*[17] (the same protein responsible for the motility of cilia and flagella). These proteins carry materials "on their backs" while they reach out, like the myosin heads of muscle (see section 11.4c), to bind repeatedly to the microtubules and walk along them.

There are two types of axonal transport: fast and slow.

1. **Fast axonal transport** occurs at a rate of 200 to 400 mm/day and may be either anterograde or retrograde:

   - *Fast anterograde transport* moves mitochondria; synaptic vesicles; other organelles; components of the axolemma; calcium ions; enzymes such as acetylcholinesterase; and small molecules such as glucose, amino acids, and nucleotides toward the distal end of the axon.
   - *Fast retrograde transport* returns used synaptic vesicles and other materials to the soma and informs the soma of conditions at the axon terminals. Some pathogens exploit this process to invade the nervous system. They enter the distal tips of an axon and travel to the soma by retrograde transport. Examples include tetanus toxin and the herpes simplex, rabies, and polio viruses. In such infections, the delay between infection and the onset of symptoms corresponds to the time needed for the pathogens to reach the somas.

2. **Slow axonal transport** is an anterograde process that works in a stop-and-go fashion. If we compare fast axonal transport to an express train traveling nonstop to its destination, slow axonal transport is like a local train that stops at every station. When moving, it goes just as fast as the express train, but the frequent stops result in an overall progress of only 0.2 to 0.5 mm/day. It moves enzymes and cytoskeletal components down the axon, renews worn-out axoplasmic components in mature neurons, and supplies new axoplasm for developing or regenerating neurons. Damaged nerves regenerate at a speed governed by slow axonal transport.

[14]*antero* = forward; *grad* = to walk, to step
[15]*retro* = back; *grad* = to walk, to step
[16]*kines* = motion; *in* = protein
[17]*dyne* = force; *in* = protein

**▶▶▶APPLY WHAT YOU KNOW**

*The axon of a neuron has a dense cytoskeleton. Considering the functions of the cytoskeleton discussed in section 3.4a, give two reasons why this is so important to neuron structure and function.*

**BEFORE YOU GO ON**

Answer the following questions to test your understanding of the preceding section:

4. Sketch a multipolar neuron and label its neurosoma, dendrites, axon, terminal arborization, axon terminals, and myelin sheath.
5. Explain the differences between a sensory neuron, motor neuron, and interneuron.
6. What is the functional difference between a dendrite and an axon?
7. How do proteins and other chemicals synthesized in the soma get to the axon terminals? By what process can a virus that invades a peripheral nerve fiber get to the soma of that neuron?

## 12.3 Supportive Cells

**Expected Learning Outcomes**

When you have completed this section, you should be able to

a. name the six types of cells that aid neurons, and state their respective functions;
b. describe the myelin sheath that is found around certain nerve fibers, and explain its importance;
c. describe the relationship of unmyelinated nerve fibers to their supportive cells; and
d. explain how damaged nerve fibers regenerate.

There are about a trillion ($10^{12}$) neurons in the nervous system—10 times as many neurons in your body as there are stars in our galaxy! Because they branch so extensively, they make up about 50% of the volume of the nervous tissue. Yet they are outnumbered at least 10 to 1 by cells called **neuroglia** (noo-ROG-lee-uh), or **glial cells** (GLEE-ul). Glial cells protect the neurons and help them function. The word *glia,* which means "glue," implies one of their roles—to bind neurons together and provide a supportive framework for the nervous tissue. In the fetus, they form a scaffold that guides young migrating neurons to their destinations. Wherever a mature neuron is not in synaptic contact with another cell, it is covered with glial cells. This prevents neurons from contacting each other except at points specialized for signal transmission, thus giving precision to their conduction pathways.

### 12.3a Types of Neuroglia

There are six kinds of neuroglia, each with a unique function **(table 12.1).** The first four types occur only in the central nervous system **(fig. 12.6):**

1. **Oligodendrocytes**[18] (OL-ih-go-DEN-dro-sites) somewhat resemble an octopus; they have a bulbous body with as many as 15 arms. Each arm reaches out to a nerve fiber and spirals around it like electrical tape wrapped repeatedly around a wire. This wrapping, called the *myelin sheath,* insulates the nerve fiber from the extracellular fluid and speeds up signal conduction in the nerve fiber.
2. **Ependymal**[19] **cells** (ep-EN-dih-mul) resemble a cuboidal epithelium lining the internal cavities of the brain and spinal cord. Unlike true epithelial cells, however, they have no basement membrane and they exhibit rootlike processes that penetrate into the underlying tissue. Ependymal cells produce *cerebrospinal fluid (CSF),* a liquid that bathes the CNS and fills its internal cavities. They have patches of cilia on their apical surfaces that help to circulate the CSF. Ependymal cells and CSF are considered in more detail in section 14.2b.
3. **Microglia** are small macrophages that develop from white blood cells called monocytes. They wander through the CNS, putting out fingerlike extensions to constantly probe the tissue for cellular debris or other problems. They are thought to perform a complete checkup on the brain tissue

[18]*oligo* = few; *dendro* = branches; *cyte* = cell
[19]*ependyma* = upper garment

**TABLE 12.1 Types of Glial Cells**

| Types | Functions |
|---|---|
| **Neuroglia of CNS** | |
| Oligodendrocytes | Form myelin in brain and spinal cord |
| Ependymal cells | Line cavities of brain and spinal cord; secrete and circulate cerebrospinal fluid |
| Microglia | Phagocytize and destroy microorganisms, foreign matter, and dead nervous tissue |
| Astrocytes | Cover brain surface and nonsynaptic regions of neurons; form supportive framework in CNS; induce formation of blood–brain barrier; nourish neurons; produce growth factors that stimulate neurons; promote the formation of synapses and neural circuitry; communicate electrically with neurons and may influence synaptic signaling; remove $K^+$ and some neurotransmitters from ECF of brain and spinal cord; help to regulate composition of ECF; form scar tissue to replace damaged nervous tissue |
| **Neuroglia of PNS** | |
| Schwann cells | Form neurilemma around all PNS nerve fibers and myelin around most of them; aid in regeneration of damaged nerve fibers |
| Satellite cells | Surround somas of neurons in the ganglia; provide electrical insulation and regulate chemical environment of neurons |

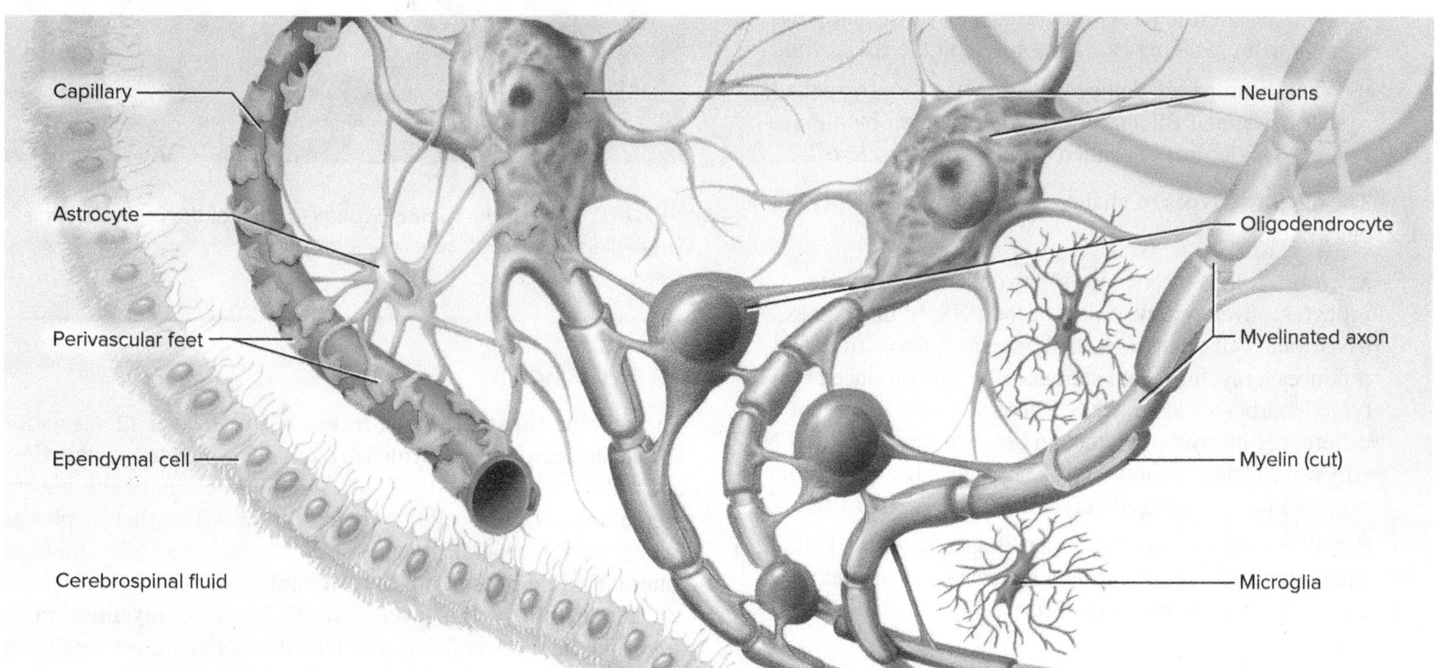


**FIGURE 12.6 Neuroglia of the Central Nervous System.**

several times a day, phagocytizing dead tissue, microorganisms, and other foreign matter. They become concentrated in areas damaged by infection, trauma, or stroke. Pathologists look for clusters of microglia in brain tissue as a clue to sites of injury. Microglia also aid in synaptic remodeling, changing the connections between neurons.

4. **Astrocytes**[20] are the most abundant glial cells in the CNS and constitute over 90% of the tissue in some areas of the brain. They cover the entire brain surface and most nonsynaptic regions of the neurons in the gray matter. They are named for their many-branched, somewhat starlike shape. They have the most diverse functions of any glia:

   - They form a supportive framework for the nervous tissue.
   - They have extensions called *perivascular feet,* which contact the blood capillaries and stimulate them to form a tight, protective seal called the blood–brain barrier (see section 14.2c).
   - They monitor neuron activity, stimulate dilation and constriction of blood vessels, and thus regulate blood flow in the brain tissue to meet changing needs for oxygen and nutrients.
   - They convert blood glucose to lactate and supply this to the neurons for nourishment.
   - They secrete *nerve growth factors* that regulate nerve development (see Deeper Insight 12.3).
   - They promote synapse formation and fine-tune neural circuitry.
   - They communicate electrically with neurons and influence synaptic signaling between them.
   - They regulate the composition of the tissue fluid. When neurons transmit signals, they release neurotransmitters and potassium ions. Astrocytes absorb these and prevent them from reaching excessive levels in the tissue fluid.
   - When neurons are damaged, astrocytes form hardened scar tissue and fill space formerly occupied by the neurons. This process is called *astrocytosis* or *sclerosis.*

The other two types of glial cells occur only in the peripheral nervous system:

5. **Schwann**[21] **cells** (pronounced "shwon"), or **neurilemmocytes,** envelop nerve fibers of the PNS. In most cases, a Schwann cell winds repeatedly around a nerve fiber and produces a myelin sheath similar to the one produced by oligodendrocytes in the CNS. There are some important differences in myelin production between the CNS and PNS, which we consider shortly. Schwann cells also assist in the regeneration of damaged nerve fibers (see section 12.3e).
6. **Satellite cells** surround the somas in ganglia of the PNS. They provide insulation around the soma and regulate the chemical environment of the neurons.

[20]*astro* = star; *cyte* = cell

[21]Theodor Schwann (1810–82), German histologist

### DEEPER INSIGHT 12.1
### CLINICAL APPLICATION

#### *Glial Cells and Brain Tumors*

A tumor consists of a mass of rapidly dividing cells. Mature neurons, however, have little or no capacity for mitosis and seldom form tumors. Some brain tumors arise from the meninges (protective membranes of the CNS) or arise by metastasis from tumors elsewhere, such as malignant melanoma and colon cancer. Most adult brain tumors, however, are composed of glial cells, which are mitotically active throughout life. Such tumors are called *gliomas*[22] **(fig. 12.7).** Gliomas usually grow rapidly and are highly malignant. Because of the blood–brain barrier, brain tumors usually do not yield to chemotherapy and must be treated with radiation or surgery.

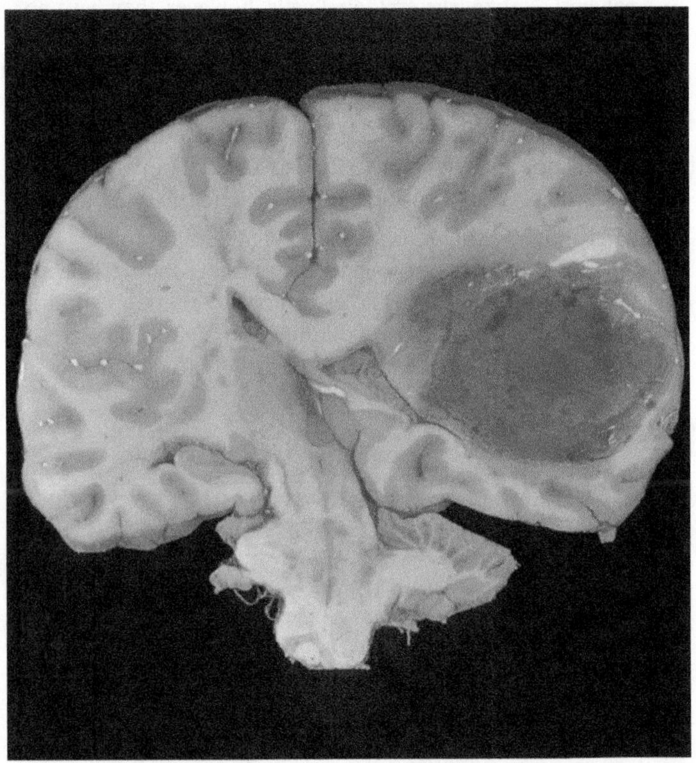

**FIGURE 12.7 Brain Tumor.** Frontal section of the brain showing a large glioma in the left cerebral hemisphere.

CNRI/Science Source

## 12.3b Myelin

The **myelin sheath** (MY-eh-lin) is a spiral layer of insulation around a nerve fiber, formed by oligodendrocytes in the CNS and Schwann cells in the PNS. Since it consists of the plasma membranes of glial cells, its composition is like that of plasma membranes in general. It is about 20% protein and 80% lipid, the latter including phospholipids, glycolipids, and cholesterol.

Production of the myelin sheath is called **myelination.** It begins in the fourteenth week of fetal development, yet hardly any

[22]*glia* = glial cells; *oma* = tumor

myelin exists in the brain at the time of birth. Myelination proceeds rapidly in infancy and isn't completed until late adolescence. Since myelin has such a high lipid content, dietary fat is important to early nervous system development. It is best not to give children under 2 years old the sort of low-fat diets (skimmed milk, etc.) that may be beneficial to an adult.

In the PNS, a Schwann cell spirals repeatedly around a single nerve fiber, laying down up to 100 compact layers of its own membrane with almost no cytoplasm between the membranes **(fig. 12.8a).** These layers constitute the myelin sheath. The Schwann cell spirals outward as it wraps the nerve fiber, finally ending with a thick outermost coil called the **neurilemma**[23] (noor-ih-LEM-ah). Here, the bulging body of the Schwann cell contains its nucleus and most of its cytoplasm. External to the neurilemma is a basal lamina and then a thin sleeve of fibrous connective tissue called the *endoneurium.* To visualize this myelination process, imagine that you wrap an almost-empty tube of toothpaste tightly around a pencil. The pencil represents the axon, and the spiral layers of toothpaste tube represent the myelin. The toothpaste, like the cytoplasm of the cell, would be forced to one end of the tube and form a bulge on the external surface of the wrapping, like the body of the Schwann cell.

In the CNS, each oligodendrocyte reaches out to myelinate several nerve fibers in its immediate vicinity **(fig. 12.8b).** Since it is anchored to multiple nerve fibers, it can't migrate around any one of them like a Schwann cell does. It must push newer layers of myelin under the older ones, so myelination spirals inward toward the nerve fiber. Nerve fibers of the CNS have no neurilemma or endoneurium. The contrasting modes of myelination are called *centrifugal myelination* ("away from the center") in the PNS and *centripetal myelination* ("toward the center") in the CNS.

In both the PNS and CNS, a nerve fiber is much longer than the reach of a single glial cell, so it requires many Schwann cells or oligodendrocytes to cover one nerve fiber. Consequently, the myelin sheath is segmented. Each gap between segments is called a **myelin sheath gap** or **node of Ranvier**[24] (RON-vee-AY) (*node* for short); the myelin-covered segments from each node to the next are called **internodal segments** (see fig. 12.4a). These segments are about 0.2 to 1.0 mm long. The short section of nerve fiber between the axon hillock and the first glial cell is called the **initial segment.** Since the axon hillock and initial segment play an important role in initiating a nerve signal, they are collectively called the **trigger zone.**

## 12.3c Unmyelinated Nerve Fibers

Many nerve fibers in the CNS and PNS are unmyelinated. In the PNS, however, even the unmyelinated fibers are enveloped in Schwann cells. In this case, one Schwann cell harbors from 1 to 12 small nerve fibers in grooves in its surface **(fig. 12.9).** The Schwann cell's plasma membrane doesn't spiral repeatedly around the fiber as it does in a myelin sheath, but folds once around each fiber and may somewhat overlap itself along the edges. This wrapping is the neurilemma. Most nerve fibers travel through individual channels in the Schwann cell, but small fibers are sometimes bundled together within a single channel, as on the right side of this figure. A basal lamina surrounds the entire Schwann cell along with its nerve fibers.

## 12.3d Conduction Speed of Nerve Fibers

The speed at which a nerve signal travels along a nerve fiber depends on two factors: the diameter of the fiber and the presence or absence of myelin. Signal conduction occurs along the surface of a fiber, not deep within its axoplasm. Large fibers have more surface area and conduct signals more rapidly than small fibers. Myelin further speeds signal conduction by a mechanism to be explained in section 12.4f. Nerve signals travel about 0.5 to 2.0 m/s in small unmyelinated fibers (2–4 μm in diameter); 3 to 15 m/s in myelinated fibers of the same size; and as fast as 120 m/s in large myelinated fibers (up to 20 μm in diameter). One may wonder why all of our nerve fibers aren't large, myelinated, and fast; but if this were so, our nervous system would be impossibly bulky or limited to far fewer fibers. Large nerve fibers require large somas and a large expenditure of energy to maintain them. The evolution of myelin allowed for the subsequent evolution of more complex and responsive nervous systems with smaller, more energy-efficient neurons. Slow unmyelinated fibers are quite sufficient for processes in which quick responses aren't

### DEEPER INSIGHT 12.2
### CLINICAL APPLICATION

#### *Diseases of the Myelin Sheath*

Multiple sclerosis and Tay–Sachs disease are degenerative disorders of the myelin sheath. In *multiple sclerosis*[25] *(MS),* the oligodendrocytes and myelin sheaths of the CNS deteriorate and are replaced by hardened scar tissue, especially between the ages of 20 and 40. Nerve conduction is disrupted, with effects that depend on what part of the CNS is involved—double vision, blindness, speech defects, neurosis, tremors, or numbness, for example. Patients experience variable cycles of milder and worse symptoms until they eventually become bedridden. The cause of MS remains uncertain; most hypotheses suggest that it is an autoimmune disorder triggered by a virus in genetically susceptible individuals. There is no cure. There is conflicting evidence of how much it shortens a person's life expectancy, if at all. A few die within 1 year of diagnosis, but many people live with MS for 25 or 30 years.

*Tay–Sachs*[26] disease is a hereditary disorder seen mainly in infants of Eastern European Jewish ancestry. It results from the abnormal accumulation of a glycolipid called $GM_2$ (ganglioside) in the myelin sheath. $GM_2$ is normally decomposed by a lysosomal enzyme, but this enzyme is lacking from people who are homozygous recessive for the Tay–Sachs allele. As $GM_2$ accumulates, it disrupts the conduction of nerve signals and the victim typically suffers blindness, loss of coordination, and dementia. Signs begin to appear before the child is a year old, and most victims die by the age of 3 or 4 years. Asymptomatic adult carriers can be identified by a blood test and advised by genetic counselors on the risk of their children having the disease.

[23]*neuri* = nerve; *lemma* = husk, peel, sheath

[24]L. A. Ranvier (1835–1922), French histologist and pathologist

[25]*scler* = hard, tough; *osis* = condition

[26]Warren Tay (1843–1927), English physician; Bernard Sachs (1858–1944), American neurologist

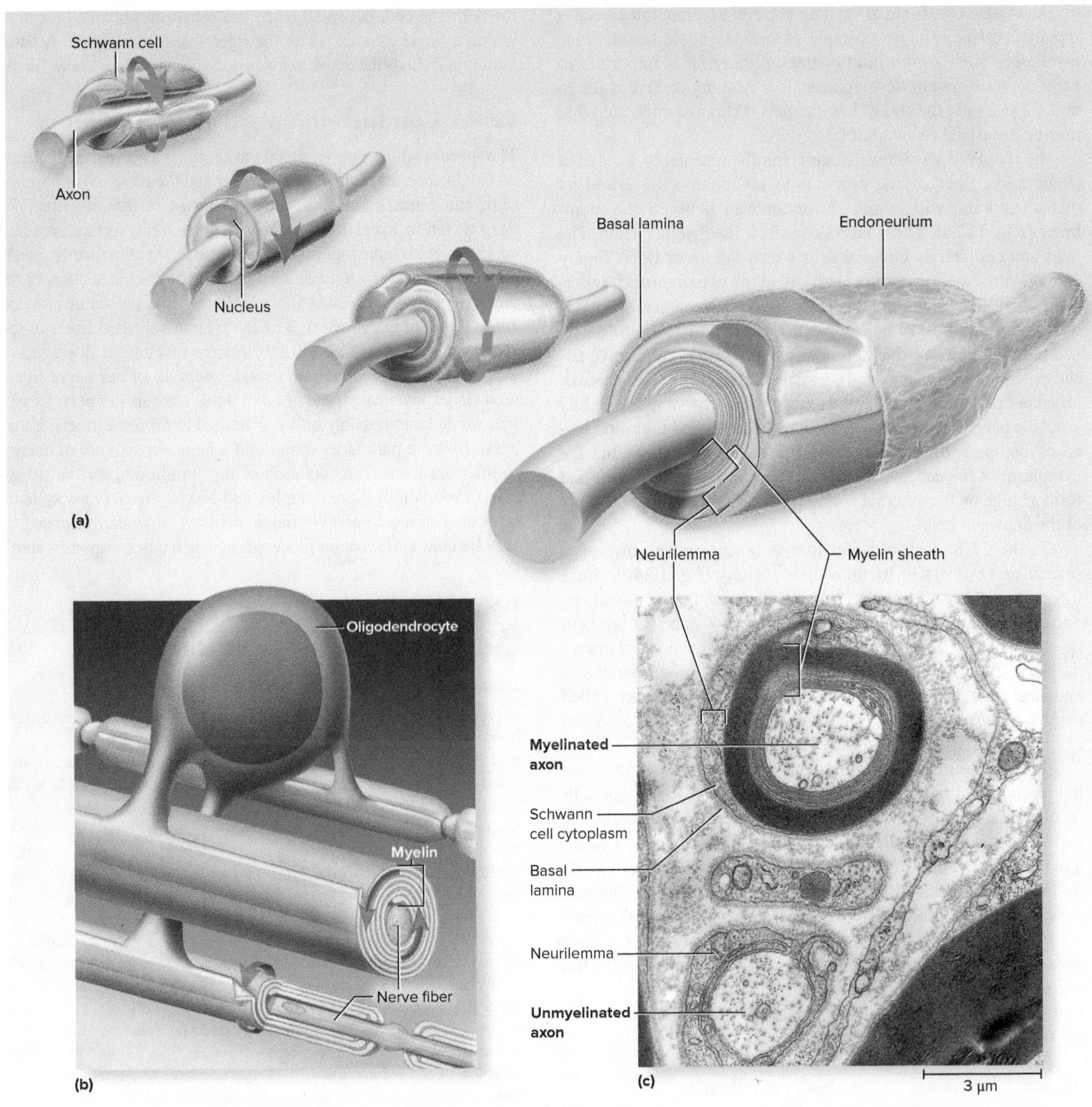


**FIGURE 12.8 Myelination.** (a) A Schwann cell of the PNS, wrapping repeatedly around an axon to form the multilayered myelin sheath. The myelin spirals outward away from the axon as it is laid down. (b) An oligodendrocyte of the CNS wrapping around the axons of multiple neurons. Here, the myelin spirals inward toward the axon as it is laid down. (c) A myelinated axon (top) and unmyelinated axon (bottom) (TEM).

c: Dr. Dennis Emery, Iowa State University/McGraw-Hill Education

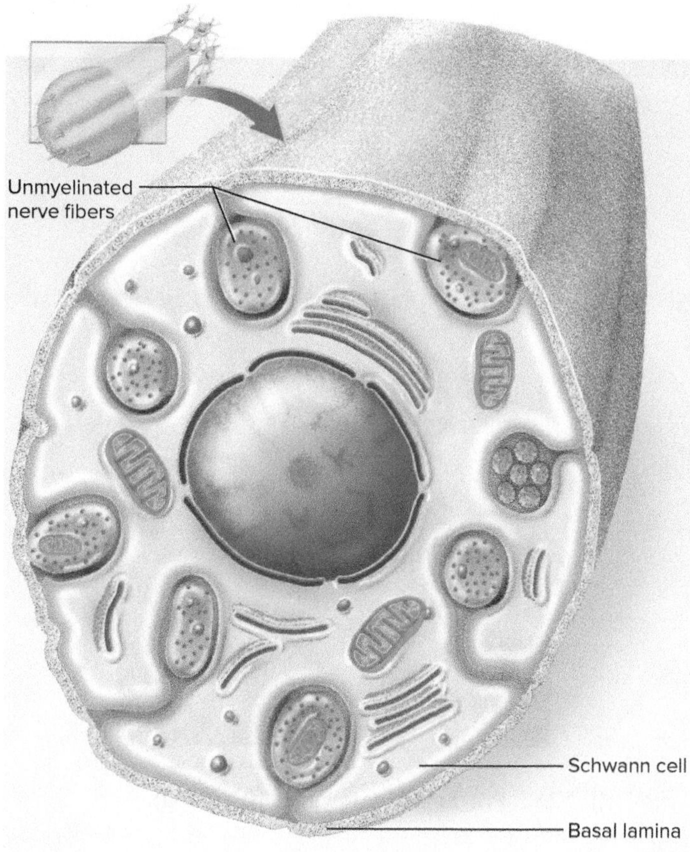


**FIGURE 12.9 Unmyelinated Nerve Fibers.**

*What is the functional disadvantage of an unmyelinated nerve fiber? What is its anatomical advantage?*

particularly important, such as secreting stomach acid or dilating the pupil. Fast myelinated fibers are employed where speed is more important, as in motor commands to the skeletal muscles and sensory signals for vision and balance.

## 12.3e Nerve Regeneration

Nerve fibers of the PNS are vulnerable to cuts, crushing injuries, and other trauma. A damaged peripheral nerve fiber may regenerate, however, if its soma is intact and at least some neurilemma remains. **Figure 12.10** shows the process of regeneration, taking as its example a somatic motor neuron:

1. In the normal nerve fiber, note the size of the soma and the size of the muscle fibers for comparison to later stages.
2. When a nerve fiber is cut, the fiber distal to the injury can't survive because it is incapable of protein synthesis. Protein-synthesizing organelles are mostly in the soma. As the distal fiber degenerates, so do its Schwann cells, which depend on it for their maintenance. Macrophages clean up tissue debris at the point of injury and beyond.
3. The soma exhibits a number of abnormalities of its own, probably because it is cut off from the supply of nerve growth factors from the neuron's target cells (see

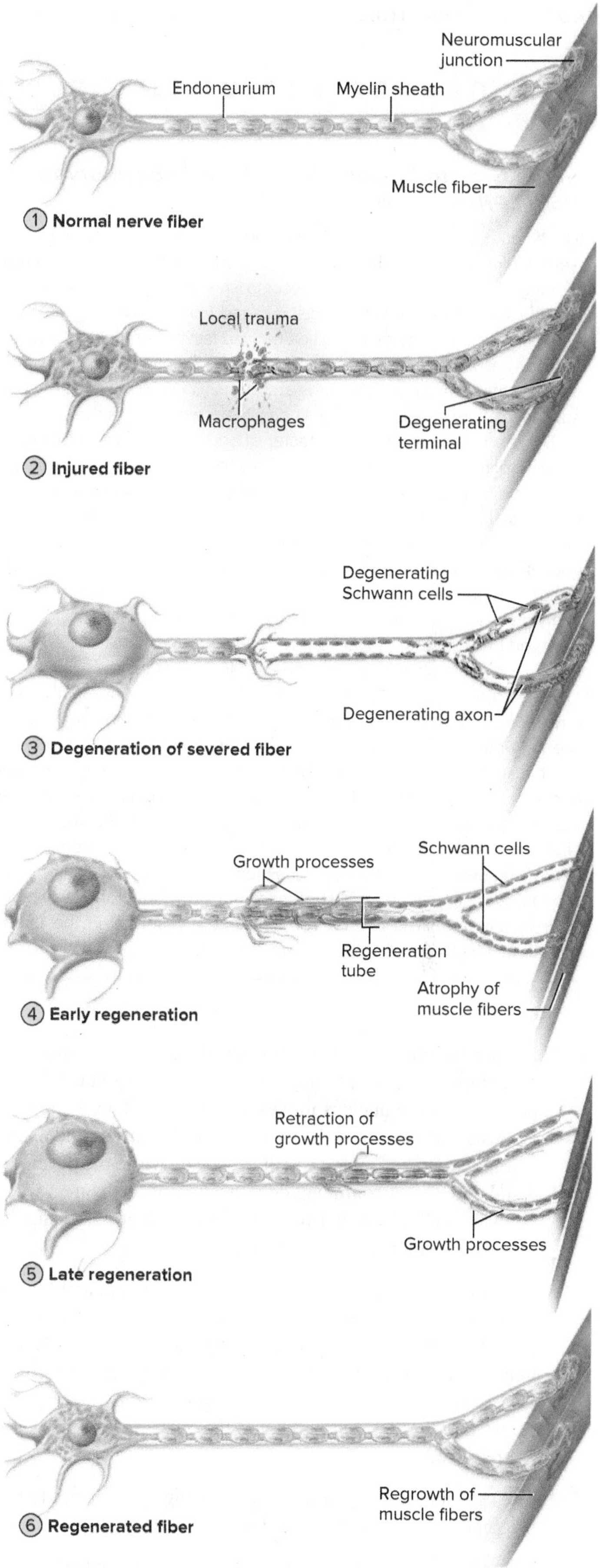

**FIGURE 12.10 Regeneration of a Damaged Nerve Fiber.** See numbered steps in text for explanation. Nerve fibers of the PNS can regenerate if the neurosoma is intact.

## DEEPER INSIGHT 12.3
### MEDICAL HISTORY

### *Nerve Growth Factor—From Home Laboratory to Nobel Prize*

It is remarkable what odds can be overcome by self-confident persistence. Neurobiologist Rita Levi-Montalcini **(fig. 12.11)** affords a striking example. Although born of a cultured and accomplished Italian Jewish family, she and her twin sister Paola were discouraged from considering a college education or career by their tradition-minded father. Determined to attend university anyway, they hired their own tutor to prepare them. Rita graduated summa cum laude in medicine and surgery in 1930 and embarked on advanced study in neurology. Paola became a renowned artist.

But then arose the sinister specter of anti-Semitism, as fascist dictator Mussolini barred Jews from professional careers. Rita despaired of pursuing medicine or research until a college friend reminded her of how much Cajal had achieved under very primitive conditions. That inspired her to set up a little laboratory in her bedroom, where she studied nervous system development in chick embryos. She had read of work by Viktor Hamburger in St. Louis, who believed that limb tissues secrete a chemical that attracts nerves to grow into them. Levi-Montalcini, however, believed that nerves grow into the limbs without such attractants, but die if they fail to receive a substance needed to sustain them.

Fleeing first from Allied bombing and then Hitler's invasion of Italy, Levi-Montalcini had to abandon her work as the family went underground until the end of the war. At war's end, Hamburger invited her to join him in America, where they found her hypothesis to be correct. She and Stanley Cohen isolated the nerve-sustaining substance and named it *nerve growth factor (NGF)*, for which they shared a 1986 Nobel Prize. NGF is a protein secreted by muscle and glial cells. It prevents apoptosis in growing neurons and thus enables them to establish connections with their target cells. It was the first of many cell growth factors discovered, and launched what is today a vibrant field of research in the use of growth factors to stimulate tissue development and repair.

**FIGURE 12.11 Rita Levi-Montalcini (1909–2012).**
Olycom/SIPA/Newscom

Rita and Paola created the Levi-Montalcini Foundation to support the career development of young people and especially the scientific education of women in Africa. Rita also served as an honored member of the Italian Senate from 2001 until 2012, when she died at the age of 103.

Deeper Insight 12.3). The soma swells, the endoplasmic reticulum breaks up (so the chromatophilic substance disperses), and the nucleus moves off center. Not all damaged neurons survive; some die at this stage. But often, the axon stump sprouts multiple growth processes while the severed distal end shows continued degeneration of its axon and Schwann cells. Muscle fibers deprived of their nerve supply exhibit a shrinkage called *denervation atrophy*.

4. Near the injury, Schwann cells, the basal lamina, and the neurilemma form a **regeneration tube.** The Schwann cells produce cell-adhesion molecules and nerve growth factors that enable a neuron to regrow to its original destination. When one growth process finds its way into the tube, it grows rapidly (3–5 mm/day), and the other growth processes are retracted.

5. The regeneration tube guides the growing sprout back to the original target cells, reestablishing synaptic contact.

6. When contact is established, the soma shrinks and returns to its original appearance, and the reinnervated muscle fibers regrow.

Regeneration isn't perfect. Some nerve fibers connect to the wrong muscle fibers or never find a muscle fiber at all, and some damaged neurons simply die. Nerve injury is therefore often followed by some degree of functional deficit. Even when regeneration is achieved, the slow rate of axon regrowth means that some nerve function may take as long as 2 years to recover.

Schwann cells and endoneurium are required for nerve fiber regeneration. Both of these are lacking from the CNS, so damaged CNS nerve fibers cannot regenerate at all. However, since the CNS is encased in bone, it suffers less trauma than the peripheral nerves.

#### BEFORE YOU GO ON

Answer the following questions to test your understanding of the preceding section:

8. How is a glial cell different from a neuron? List the six types of glial cells and discuss their functions.
9. How is myelin produced? How does myelin production in the CNS differ from that in the PNS?
10. How can a severed peripheral nerve fiber find its way back to the cells it originally innervated?

## 12.4 Electrophysiology of Neurons

**Expected Learning Outcomes**

When you have completed this section, you should be able to

a. explain why a cell has an electrical charge difference (voltage) across its membrane;
b. explain how stimulation of a neuron causes a local electrical response in its membrane;
c. explain how local responses generate a nerve signal; and
d. explain how the nerve signal is conducted down an axon.

The nervous system has intrigued scientists and philosophers since ancient times. Galen, the preeminent physician of ancient Rome, thought that the brain pumped a vapor called *psychic pneuma* through hollow nerves and squirted it into the muscles to make them contract. The French philosopher René Descartes still argued for this theory in the seventeenth century. It finally fell out of favor in the eighteenth century, when Luigi Galvani discovered the role of electricity in muscle contraction (see Deeper Insight 11.3). Further progress had to await improvements in microscope technology and histological staining methods. Italian histologist Camillo Golgi (1843–1926) developed an important method for staining neurons with silver. This enabled Spanish histologist Santiago Ramón y Cajal (1852–1934), with tremendous skill and patience, to trace the course of nerve fibers over long distances through serial tissue sections. He demonstrated that the nervous pathway was not a continuous "wire" or tube, but a series of cells separated by the gaps we now call synapses. Golgi and Cajal, even though they intensely disliked each other, shared the 1906 Nobel Prize for Physiology or Medicine for these important discoveries.

Cajal's theory suggested another direction for research: How do neurons communicate? Two key issues in neurophysiology are (1) How does a neuron generate an electrical signal? and (2) How does it transmit a meaningful message to the next cell? These are the questions to which this section and the next are addressed.

### 12.4a Electrical Potentials and Currents

Neural communication, like muscle excitation, is based on electrophysiology—cellular mechanisms for producing electrical potentials and currents. An **electrical potential** is a difference in the concentration of charged particles between one point and another. It is a form of potential energy that, under the right circumstances, can produce a current. An electrical **current** is a flow of charged particles from one point to another. A new flashlight battery, for example, typically has a potential, or charge, of 1.5 volts (V). If a lightbulb and the two poles of the battery are connected by a wire, electrons flow through the wire from one pole to the other, creating a current that lights the bulb. As long as the battery has a potential (voltage), we say it is **polarized.**

Living cells are also polarized. The charge difference across the plasma membrane is called the **resting membrane potential (RMP).** It is much less than the potential of a flashlight battery—typically about –70 millivolts (mV) in an unstimulated, "resting" neuron. The negative value means there are more negatively charged particles on the inside of the membrane than on the outside.

We don't have free electrons in the body as we do in an electrical circuit. Electrical currents in the body are created, instead, by the flow of ions such as $Na^+$ and $K^+$ through gated channels in the plasma membrane. Gated channels can be opened and closed by various stimuli, as we have seen earlier (see "Membrane Proteins" in section 3.2a and "Electrically Excitable Cells," section 11.3c). This enables cells to turn electrical currents on and off.

### 12.4b The Resting Membrane Potential

The reason a cell has a resting membrane potential is that electrolytes are unequally distributed between the extracellular fluid (ECF) on the outside of the plasma membrane and the intracellular fluid (ICF) on the inside. The RMP results from the combined effect of three factors: (1) the diffusion of ions down their concentration gradients through the membrane; (2) selective permeability of the membrane, allowing some ions to pass more easily than others; and (3) the electrical attraction of cations and anions to each other.

Potassium ions ($K^+$) have the greatest influence on the RMP because the plasma membrane is more permeable to $K^+$ than to any other ion. Imagine a hypothetical cell in which all the $K^+$ starts out in the ICF, with none in the ECF. Also in the ICF are a number of cytoplasmic anions that cannot escape from the cell because of their size or charge—phosphates, sulfates, small organic acids, proteins, ATP, and RNA. Potassium ions diffuse freely through leak channels in the plasma membrane, down their concentration gradient and out of the cell, leaving these cytoplasmic anions behind **(fig. 12.12).** As a result, the ICF grows more and more negatively charged. But as the ICF becomes more negative, it

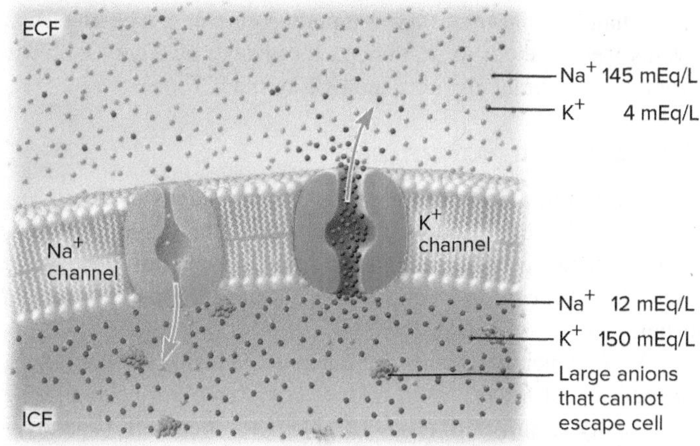


**FIGURE 12.12 Ionic Basis of the Resting Membrane Potential.** Note that sodium ions are much more concentrated in the extracellular fluid (ECF) than in the intracellular fluid (ICF), while potassium ions are more concentrated in the ICF. Large anions unable to penetrate the plasma membrane give the cytoplasm a negative charge relative to the ECF.

exerts a stronger attraction for the positive potassium ions and attracts some of them back into the cell. Eventually an *equilibrium* is reached in which $K^+$ is moving out of the cell (down its concentration gradient) and into the cell (by electrical attraction) at equal rates. There is no further *net* diffusion of $K^+$. At the point of equilibrium, $K^+$ is about 40 times as concentrated in the ICF as in the ECF.

If $K^+$ were the only ion affecting the RMP, it would give the membrane a potential of about –90 mV. However, sodium ions ($Na^+$) also enter the picture. Sodium is about 12 times as concentrated in the ECF as in the ICF. The resting plasma membrane is much less permeable to $Na^+$ than to $K^+$, but $Na^+$ does diffuse down its concentration gradient into the cell, attracted by the negative charge in the ICF. This sodium leak is only a trickle, but it is enough to cancel some of the negative charge and reduce the voltage across the membrane.

Sodium leaks into the cell and potassium leaks out, but the sodium–potassium ($Na^+$–$K^+$) pump continually compensates for this leakage. It pumps 3 $Na^+$ out of the cell for every 2 $K^+$ it brings in, consuming 1 ATP for each exchange cycle (see fig. 3.19). By removing more cations from the cell than it brings in, it contributes about –3 mV to the RMP. The resting membrane potential of –70 mV is the net effect of all these ion movements—$K^+$ diffusion out of the cell, $Na^+$ diffusion inward, and the $Na^+$–$K^+$ pump continually offsetting this ion leakage.

The $Na^+$–$K^+$ pump accounts for about 70% of the energy (ATP) requirement of the nervous system. Every signal generated by a neuron slightly upsets the distribution of $Na^+$ and $K^+$, so the pump must work continually to restore equilibrium. This is why nervous tissue has one of the highest rates of ATP consumption of any tissue in the body, and why it demands so much glucose and oxygen. Although a neuron is said to be resting when it is not producing signals, it is highly active maintaining its RMP and "waiting," as it were, for something to happen.

The uneven distribution of $Na^+$ and $K^+$ on the two sides of the plasma membrane pertains only to a very thin film of ions immediately adjacent to the membrane surfaces. The electrical events we are about to examine don't involve ions very far away from the membrane in either the ECF or the ICF.

### 12.4c Local Potentials

Stimulation of a neuron causes local disturbances in membrane potential. Typically (but with exceptions), the response begins at a dendrite, spreads through the soma, travels down the axon, and ends at the axon terminal. We consider the process in that order.

Various neurons can be stimulated by chemicals, light, heat, or mechanical forces. We'll take as our example a neuron being chemically stimulated **(fig. 12.13)**. The chemical (ligand)—perhaps a pain signal from a damaged tissue or odor molecule in a breath of air—binds to receptors on the neuron. This opens ligand-gated sodium channels that allow $Na^+$ to flow into the cell. The $Na^+$ inflow cancels some of the internal negative charge, so the voltage across the membrane at that point drifts toward zero. Any such case in which the voltage shifts to a less negative value is called **depolarization.**

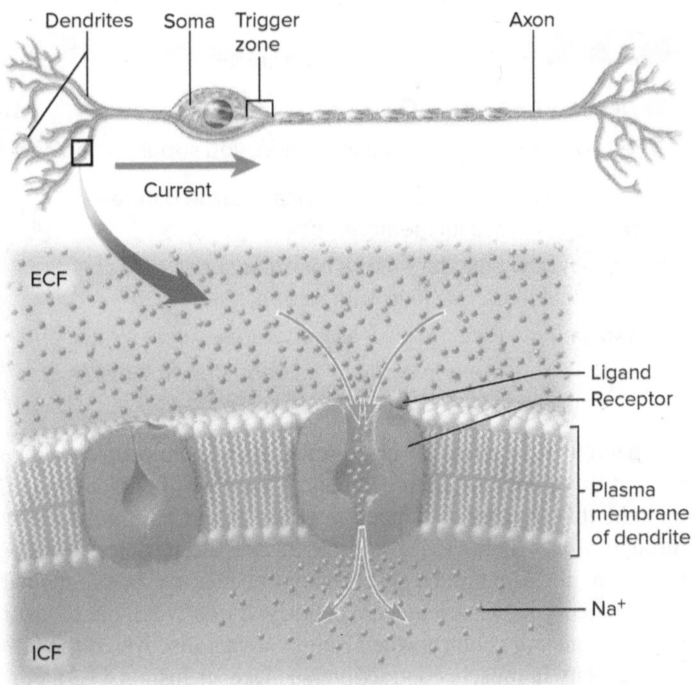


**FIGURE 12.13 Excitation of a Neuron by a Chemical Stimulus.**

The incoming $Na^+$ diffuses for short distances along the inside of the plasma membrane, creating a wave of excitation that spreads out from the point of stimulation, like ripples spreading across a pond when you drop a stone into it. This short-range change in voltage is called a **local potential.** There are four characteristics that distinguish local potentials from the action potentials we will study in the next section **(table 12.2)**. You will appreciate these distinctions more fully after you have studied action potentials.

1. Local potentials are **graded,** meaning they vary in magnitude (voltage) according to the strength of the stimulus. An intense or prolonged stimulus opens more gated ion channels than a weaker stimulus, and they stay open longer. Thus, more $Na^+$ enters the cell and the voltage changes more than it does with a weaker stimulus.
2. Local potentials are **decremental,** meaning they get weaker as they spread from the point of origin. They decline in strength partly because the $Na^+$ leaks back out of the cell through channels along its path, and partly because as $Na^+$ spreads out under the plasma membrane and depolarizes it, $K^+$ flows out and reverses the effect of the $Na^+$ inflow. Therefore, the voltage shift caused by $Na^+$ diminishes rapidly with distance. This prevents local potentials from having long-distance effects.
3. Local potentials are **reversible,** meaning that if stimulation ceases, cation diffusion out of the cell quickly returns the membrane voltage to its resting potential.
4. Local potentials can be either **excitatory** or **inhibitory.** So far, we have considered only excitatory local potentials, which depolarize a cell and make a neuron more likely to

**TABLE 12.2 Comparison of Local Potentials and Action Potentials**

| Local Potential | Action Potential |
|---|---|
| Produced by gated channels on the dendrites and soma | Produced by voltage-gated channels on the trigger zone and axon |
| May be a positive (depolarizing) or negative (hyperpolarizing) voltage change | Always begins with depolarization |
| Graded; proportional to stimulus strength | All or none; either does not occur at all or exhibits the same peak voltage regardless of stimulus strength |
| Reversible; returns to RMP if stimulation ceases before threshold is reached | Irreversible; goes to completion once it begins |
| Local; has effects for only a short distance from point of origin | Self-propagating; has effects a great distance from point of origin |
| Decremental; signal grows weaker with distance | Nondecremental; signal maintains same strength regardless of distance |

produce an action potential. Acetylcholine usually has this effect. Other neurotransmitters, such as glycine, cause an opposite effect—they **hyperpolarize** a cell, or make the membrane more negative. This inhibits a neuron, making it less sensitive and less likely to produce an action potential. A balance between excitatory and inhibitory potentials is very important to information processing in the nervous system (see section 12.6b).

## 12.4d Action Potentials

An **action potential** is a more dramatic change produced by voltage-gated ion channels in the plasma membrane. Action potentials occur only where there is a high enough density of voltage-gated channels. Most of the soma has only 50 to 75 channels per square micrometer ($\mu m^2$), not dense enough to generate action potentials. The trigger zone, however, has 350 to 500 channels/$\mu m^2$. If an excitatory local potential spreads all the way to the trigger zone and is still strong enough when it arrives, it can open these channels and generate an action potential.

The action potential is a rapid up-and-down shift in voltage. **Figure 12.14a** shows an action potential numbered to correspond to the following description.

① When the local current arrives at the axon hillock, it depolarizes the membrane at that point. This appears as a steadily rising local potential.

② For anything more to happen, this local potential must rise to a critical voltage called the **threshold** (typically about –55 mV), the minimum needed to open voltage-gated channels.

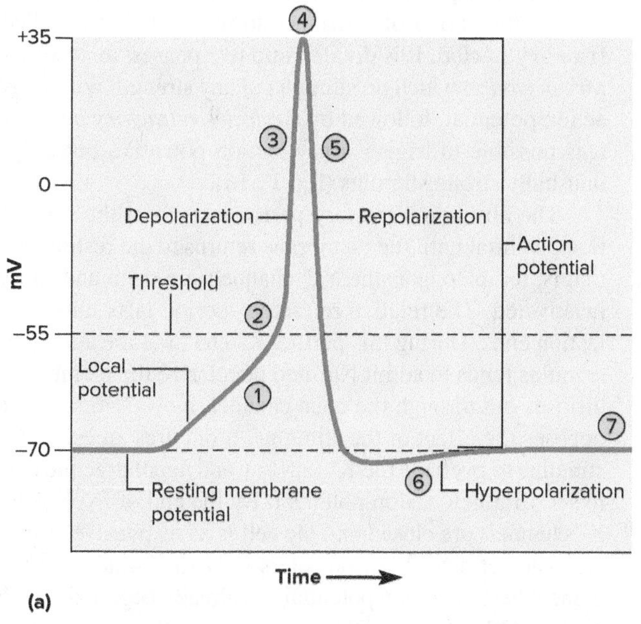


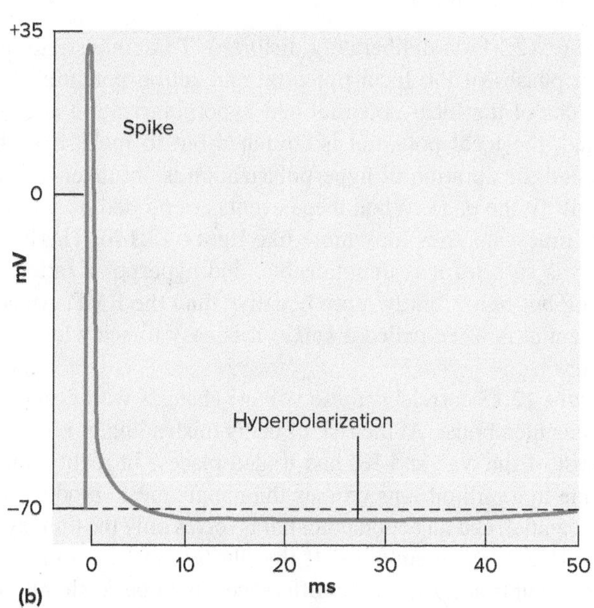


**FIGURE 12.14 An Action Potential.** (a) Diagrammed with a distorted timescale to make details of the action potential visible. Numbers correspond to stages discussed in the text. (b) On a more accurate timescale, the local potential is so brief it is imperceptible, the action potential appears as a spike, and the hyperpolarization is very prolonged.

3. The neuron now "fires," or produces an action potential. At threshold, voltage-gated $Na^+$ channels open quickly, while gated $K^+$ channels open more slowly. The initial effect on membrane potential is therefore due to $Na^+$. Initially, only a few $Na^+$ channels open, but as $Na^+$ enters the cell, it further depolarizes the membrane. This stimulates still more voltage-gated $Na^+$ channels to open and admit even more $Na^+$, a positive feedback loop that causes the membrane voltage to rise even more rapidly.
4. As the rising potential passes 0 mV, $Na^+$ channels are *inactivated* and begin closing. By the time they all close and $Na^+$ inflow ceases, the voltage peaks at approximately +35 mV. (The peak is as low as 0 mV in some neurons and as high as 50 mV in others.) The membrane is now positive on the inside and negative on the outside—its polarity is reversed compared to the RMP.
5. By the time the voltage peaks, the slow $K^+$ channels are fully open. Potassium ions, repelled by the positive ICF, now exit the cell. Their outflow **repolarizes** the membrane—that is, it shifts the voltage back into the negative numbers. The action potential consists of the up-and-down voltage shifts that occur from the time the threshold is reached to the time the voltage returns to the RMP.
6. Potassium channels stay open longer than $Na^+$ channels, so slightly more $K^+$ leaves the cell than the amount of $Na^+$ that entered. Therefore, the membrane voltage drops to 1 or 2 mV more negative than the original RMP, producing a negative overshoot called *hyperpolarization.*
7. As you can see, $Na^+$ and $K^+$ switch places across the membrane during an action potential. During hyperpolarization, the membrane voltage gradually returns to the RMP because of $Na^+$ diffusion into the cell.

Figure 12.14a is deliberately distorted. To demonstrate the different phases of the local potential and action potential, the magnitudes of the local potential and hyperpolarization are exaggerated, the local potential is stretched out to make it seem longer, and the duration of hyperpolarization is shrunken so the graph will fit the page. When these events are plotted on a more realistic timescale, they look more like **figure 12.14b.** The local potential is so brief it is unnoticeable, and hyperpolarization is very long but only slightly more negative than the RMP. An action potential is often called a *spike;* it is easy to see why from this figure.

**Figure 12.15** correlates these voltage changes with events in the plasma membrane. At the risk of being misleading, it is drawn as if most of the $Na^+$ and $K^+$ had traded places. In reality, only about one in a million ions crosses the membrane to produce an action potential, and an action potential involves only the thin layer of ions close to the membrane. If the illustration tried to represent these points accurately, the difference would be so slight you couldn't see it. Even after thousands of action potentials, the cytosol still has a higher concentration of $K^+$ and a lower concentration of $Na^+$ than the ECF does.

Earlier we saw that local potentials are graded, decremental, and reversible. We can now contrast this with action potentials.

- Action potentials follow an **all-or-none law.** If a stimulus depolarizes the neuron to threshold, the neuron fires at its maximum voltage (such as +35 mV); if threshold is not reached, the neuron doesn't fire at all. Above threshold, stronger stimuli don't produce stronger action potentials. Thus, action potentials are not graded (proportional to stimulus strength) like local potentials are.
- Action potentials are **nondecremental.** They don't get weaker with distance. The last action potential at the end of a nerve fiber is just as strong as the first one in the trigger zone, no matter how far away—even in a pain fiber that extends from your toes to your brainstem.
- Action potentials are **irreversible.** If a neuron reaches threshold, the action potential goes to completion; it can't be stopped once it begins.

In some respects, we can compare the firing of a neuron to the firing of a gun. As the trigger is squeezed, a gun either fires with maximum force or doesn't fire at all (analogous to the all-or-none law). You can't fire a fast bullet by squeezing the trigger hard or a slow bullet by squeezing it gently—once the trigger is pulled to its "threshold," the bullet always leaves the muzzle at the same velocity. And, like an action potential, the firing of a gun is irreversible once the threshold is reached; neither a bullet nor an action potential can be called back. Table 12.2 further contrasts a local potential with an action potential, including some characteristics of action potentials explained in the following sections.

### 12.4e The Refractory Period

During an action potential and for a few milliseconds after, it is difficult or impossible to stimulate that region of a neuron to fire again. This period of resistance to restimulation is called the **refractory period.** It is divided into two phases: an *absolute refractory period* in which no stimulus of any strength will trigger a new action potential, followed by a *relative refractory period* in which it is possible to trigger a new action potential, but only with an unusually strong stimulus **(fig. 12.16).**

The absolute refractory period lasts from the start of the action potential until the membrane returns to the resting potential—that is, for as long as the $Na^+$ channels are open and subsequently inactivated. The relative refractory period lasts until hyperpolarization ends. During this period, $K^+$ channels are still open. A new stimulus tends to admit $Na^+$ and depolarize the membrane, but $K^+$ diffuses out through the open channels as $Na^+$ comes in, and thus opposes the effect of the stimulus. It requires an especially strong stimulus to override the $K^+$ outflow and depolarize the cell enough to set off a new action potential. By the end of hyperpolarization, $K^+$ channels are closed and the cell is as responsive as ever.

The refractory period refers only to a small patch of membrane where an action potential has already begun, not to the entire neuron. Other parts of the neuron can still be stimulated while a small area of it is refractory, and even this area quickly recovers once the nerve signal has passed.

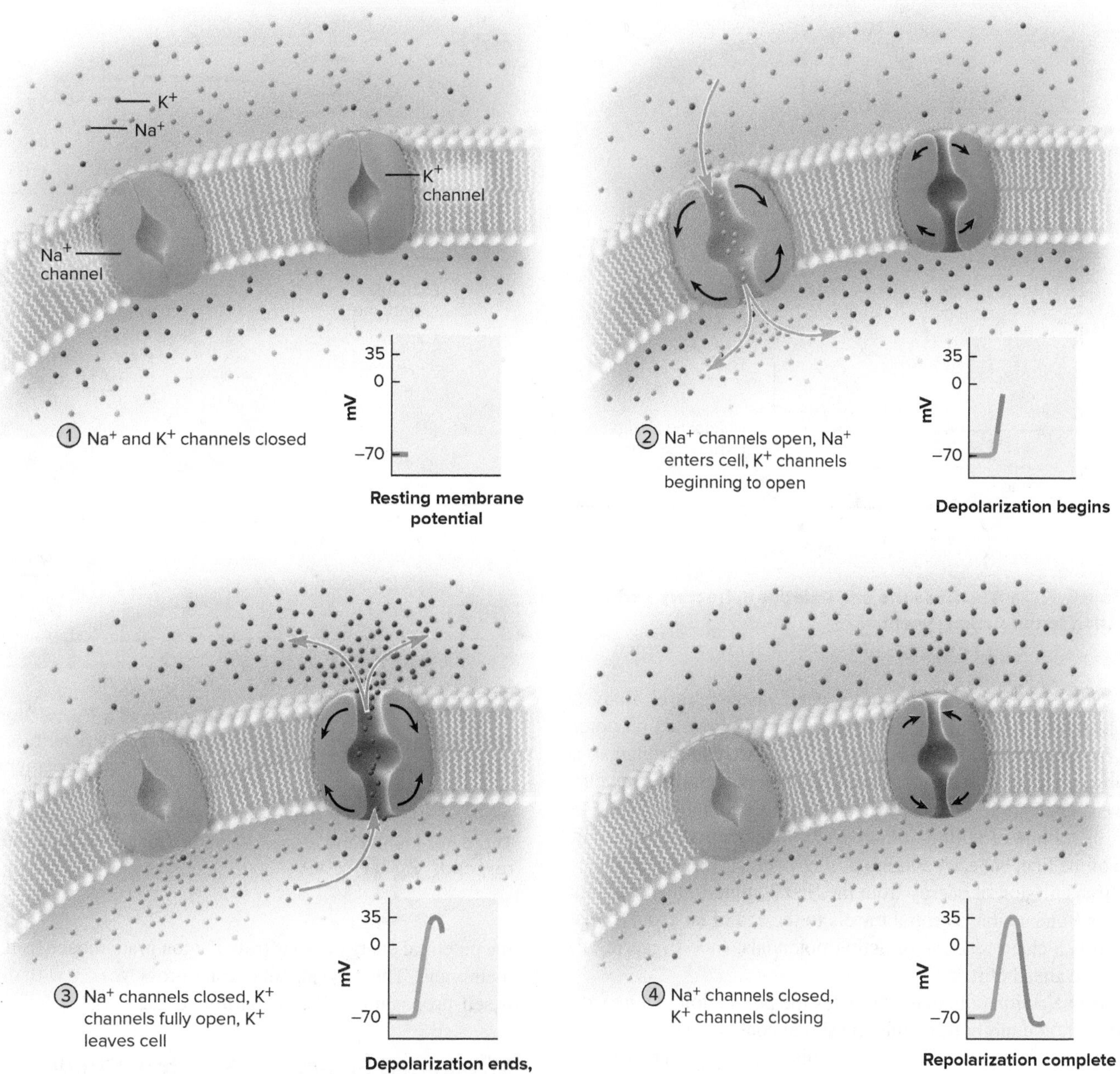
K+
Na+
K+ channel
Na+ channel
35
0
mV
–70
① Na+ and K+ channels closed
Resting membrane potential
② Na+ channels open, Na+ enters cell, K+ channels beginning to open
Depolarization begins
③ Na+ channels closed, K+ channels fully open, K+ leaves cell
Depolarization ends, repolarization begins
④ Na+ channels closed, K+ channels closing
Repolarization complete

**FIGURE 12.15 Actions of the Sodium and Potassium Channels During an Action Potential.** The red part of each graph shows the point in the action potential where the events of steps 1 through 4 occur. APR

## 12.4f Signal Conduction in Nerve Fibers

If a neuron is to communicate with another cell, a signal has to travel to the end of the axon. We now examine how this is achieved.

### Unmyelinated Fibers and Continuous Conduction

Unmyelinated fibers present a relatively simple case of signal conduction, easy to understand based on what we have already covered **(fig. 12.17)**. An unmyelinated fiber has voltage-gated channels along its entire length. When an action potential occurs at the trigger zone, $Na^+$ enters the axon and diffuses for a short distance just beneath the plasma membrane. The resulting depolarization excites voltage-gated channels immediately distal to the action potential. Sodium and potassium channels open and close just as they did at the trigger zone, and a new action potential is produced. By repetition, this excites the membrane immediately distal to that. This chain reaction continues until the traveling signal reaches the end of the axon. Because this produces an uninterrupted wave of electrical excitation all along the fiber, this mechanism is called **continuous conduction.**

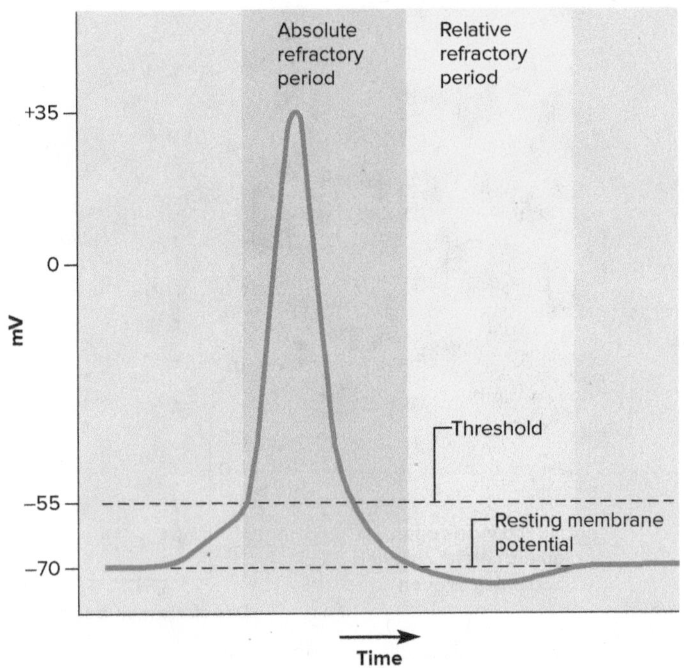


**FIGURE 12.16 The Absolute and Relative Refractory Periods in Relation to the Action Potential.**

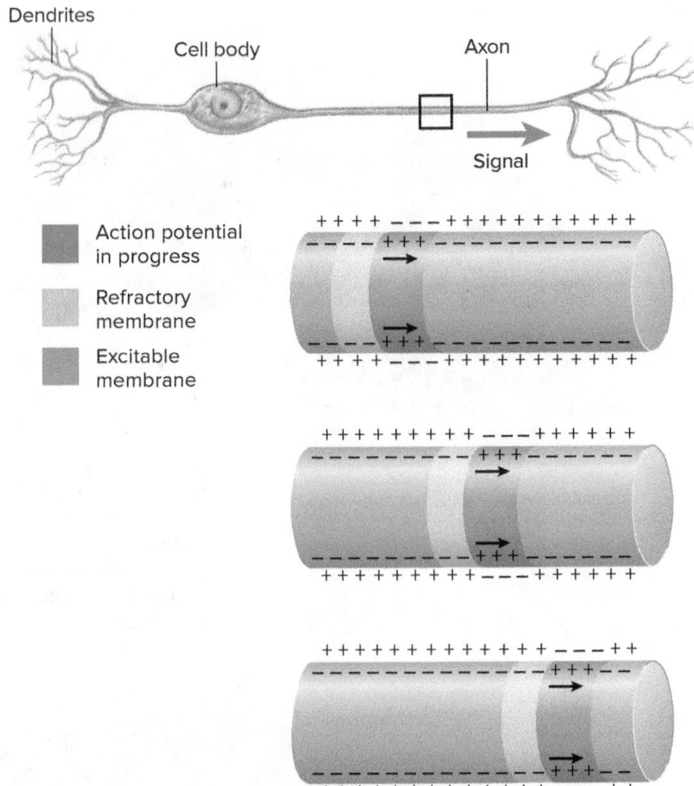


**FIGURE 12.17 Continuous Conduction of a Nerve Signal in an Unmyelinated Fiber.** Note that the membrane polarity is reversed in the region of the action potential (red). A region of membrane in its refractory period (yellow) trails the action potential and prevents the nerve signal from going backward toward the soma. The other membrane areas (green) are fully polarized and ready to respond. APR

Note that an action potential itself doesn't travel along an axon; rather, it stimulates the production of a new action potential in the membrane just ahead of it. Thus, we can distinguish an action potential from a nerve signal. The **nerve signal** is a traveling wave of excitation produced by self-propagating action potentials. It is like a line of falling dominoes. No one domino travels to the end of the line, but each domino pushes over the next one and there is a transmission of energy from the first domino to the last. Similarly, no one action potential travels to the end of an axon; a nerve signal is a chain reaction of action potentials, each triggering the next one ahead of it.

If one action potential stimulates the production of a new one next to it, you might think that the signal could also start traveling backward and return to the soma. This does not occur, however, because the membrane immediately behind the nerve signal is still in its refractory period and cannot be restimulated. Only the membrane ahead is sensitive to stimulation. The refractory period thus ensures that nerve signals are conducted in the proper direction, from the soma to the axon terminals.

A traveling nerve signal is an electrical current, but it isn't the same as a current traveling through a wire. A current in a wire travels millions of meters per second and is decremental—it gets weaker with distance. A nerve signal is much slower (not more than 2 m/s in unmyelinated fibers), but as already noted, it is nondecremental. To clarify this concept, we can compare the nerve signal to a burning fuse on a firecracker. When a fuse is lit, the heat ignites powder immediately in front of this point, and this repeats itself in a self-propagating fashion until the end of the fuse is reached. At the end, the fuse burns just as hotly as it did at the beginning. In a fuse, the combustible powder is the source of potential energy that keeps the process going in a nondecremental fashion. In an axon, the potential energy comes from the ion gradient across the plasma membrane. Thus, the signal doesn't grow weaker with distance; it is self-propagating, like the burning of a fuse.

## Myelinated Fibers and Saltatory Conduction

Myelinated fibers conduct signals in a very different manner called **saltatory**[27] **conduction**—meaning "leaping" or "jumping." These fibers cannot conduct a signal in continuous mode, like a burning fuse, because voltage-gated ion channels are too scarce in the myelin-covered internodal segments—fewer than 25/μm$^2$ in these regions compared with 2,000 to 12,000/μm$^2$ at the myelin sheath gaps (nodes of Ranvier). There would be little point in having ion channels in the internodal segments anyway—myelin insulates the fiber from the ECF in these segments, and $Na^+$ from the ECF couldn't flow into the cell even if more channels were present. Therefore, no action potentials can occur in the internodal segments, and the nerve signal requires some other way of traversing the distance from one node to the next.

[27]from *saltare* = to leap, to dance

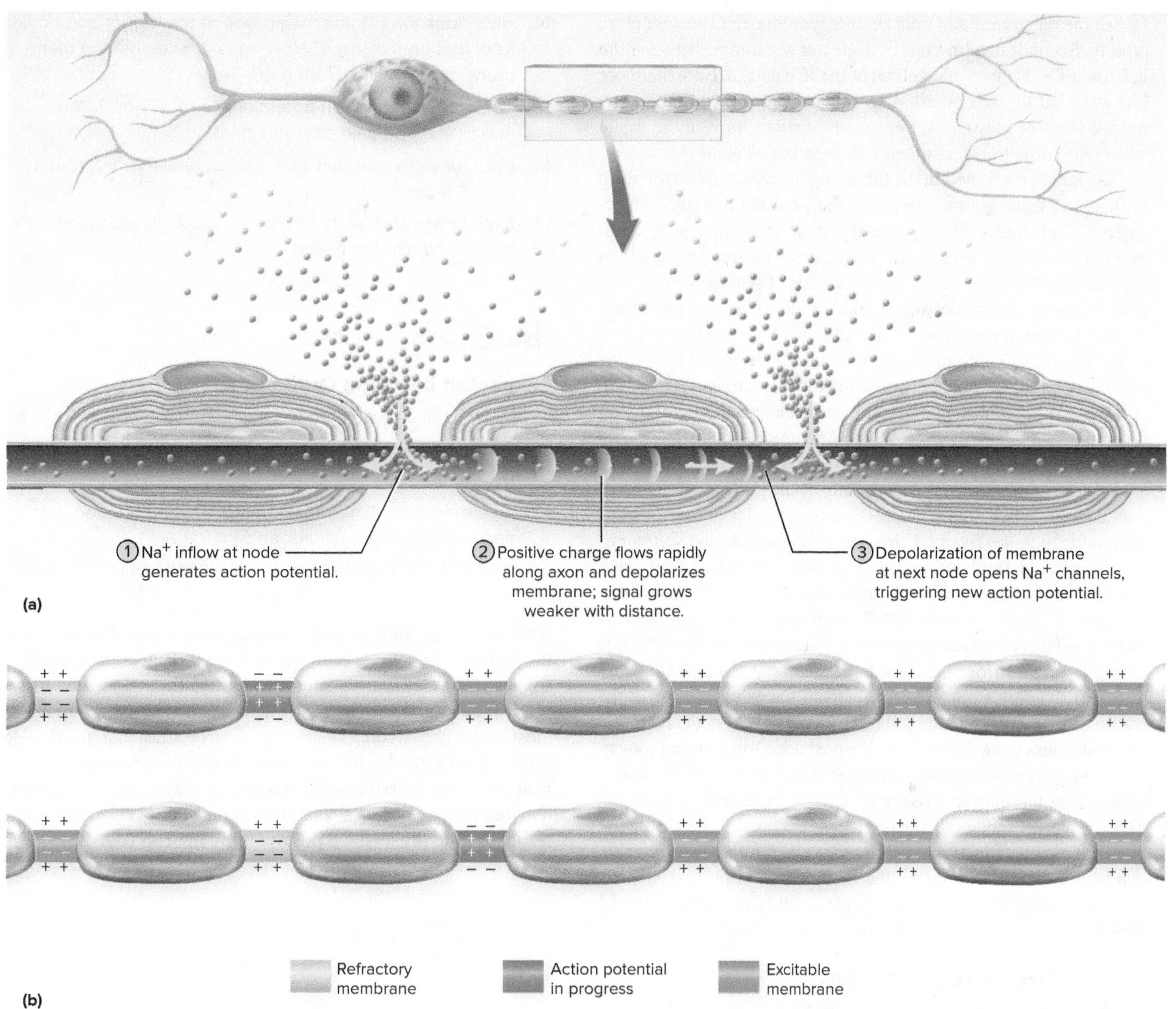

① Na⁺ inflow at node generates action potential.
② Positive charge flows rapidly along axon and depolarizes membrane; signal grows weaker with distance.
③ Depolarization of membrane at next node opens Na⁺ channels, triggering new action potential.
(a)
Refractory membrane
Action potential in progress
Excitable membrane
(b)

**FIGURE 12.18 Saltatory Conduction of a Nerve Signal in a Myelinated Fiber.** (a) Sodium inflow at myelin sheath gaps, regenerating the flow of positive charges at each gap. (b) Action potentials can occur only at myelin sheath gaps, so the nerve signal appears as if it were jumping from gap to gap. The membrane (yellow) behind each action potential is temporarily in the refractive state, whereas the membrane (green) ahead of it is fully excitable and ready for action.

When $Na^+$ enters the axon at a node, it diffuses for a short distance along the inner face of the membrane **(fig. 12.18a).** Each sodium ion has an electrical field around it. When one $Na^+$ moves toward another, its field repels the other ion, which moves slightly and repels another, and so forth—like two magnets that repel each other if you try to push their north poles together. No one ion moves very far, but this energy transfer travels down the axon much faster and farther than any of the individual ions. The signal grows weaker with distance, however, partly because the axoplasm resists the movement of the ions and partly because $Na^+$ leaks back out of the axon along the way. Therefore, with distance, there is a lower and lower concentration of $Na^+$ to relay the charge. Furthermore, with a surplus of positive charges on the inner face of the axolemma and a surplus of negative charges on the outer face, these cations and anions are attracted to each other through the membrane—like the opposite poles of two magnets attracting each other through a sheet of paper. This results in a "storage" (called *capacitance*) of unmoving or sluggishly moving charges on the membrane.

Myelin speeds up signal conduction in two ways. First of all, by wrapping tightly around the axon, it seals the nerve fiber and greatly increases its resistance to the leakage of $Na^+$ out of the axon. Sodium ions therefore maintain a higher density on the inner face of the membrane and transfer energy from one to another more rapidly. Second, myelin creates a greater separation between the ICF and ECF. Cations and anions of the ICF and ECF are therefore less attracted to each other—like two magnets now separated by a thick sheet of plastic. $Na^+$ ions can therefore move more freely within the axon, transferring energy from one to another.

A signal propagated in the foregoing manner can't travel much farther than 1 mm before it becomes too weak to open any voltage-gated $Na^+$ channels. But fortunately, there is another node (gap) every millimeter or less along the axon, where the axolemma is exposed to ECF and there is an abundance of voltage-gated channels. When the internodal signal reaches this point, it is just strong enough to open these channels, admit more $Na^+$, and create a new action potential. This action potential has the same strength as the one at the previous node, so each node boosts the signal back to its original strength (+35 mV). However, the generation of action potentials is a relatively time-consuming process that slows down the nerve signal at the nodes.

Since action potentials occur only at the nodes, this mode of conduction creates a false impression that the nerve signal jumps from node to node **(fig. 12.18b)**—hence the expression *saltatory*.

You could think of saltatory conduction by analogy to a crowded subway car. The doors open (like the $Na^+$ gates at a node), 20 more people get on (like $Na^+$ flowing into the axon), and everyone has to push to the rear of the car to make room for them. No one passenger moves from the door to the rear, but the crowding and transfer of energy from person to person forces even those at the rear to move a little, like the sodium ions at the next node. Events at one node thus create excitation at the next node some distance away.

In summary, saltatory conduction is based on a process that is very fast in the internodal segments (transfer of energy from ion to ion), but decremental. In the nodes, conduction is slower but nondecremental. Since most of the axon is covered with myelin, conduction occurs mainly by the fast internodal process. This is why myelinated fibers conduct signals much faster (up to 120 m/s) than unmyelinated ones (up to 2 m/s).

**APPLY WHAT YOU KNOW**

*You are about to have a dental procedure and the dentist "numbs you up" with an injection of lidocaine (Xylocaine). This is a local anesthetic that prevents voltage-gated $Na^+$ channels from opening. Explain why this mechanism would block the conduction of pain signals from your teeth to your brain.*

**BEFORE YOU GO ON**

Answer the following questions to test your understanding of the preceding section:

11. What causes $K^+$ to diffuse out of a resting cell? What attracts it into the cell?
12. What happens to $Na^+$ when a neuron is stimulated on its dendrite? Why does the movement of $Na^+$ raise the voltage on the plasma membrane?
13. What does it mean to say a local potential is graded, decremental, and reversible?
14. How does the plasma membrane at the trigger zone differ from that on the soma? How does it resemble the membrane at a myelin sheath gap?
15. What makes an action potential rise to +35 mV? What makes it drop again after this peak?
16. List four ways in which an action potential is different from a local potential.
17. Explain why myelinated fibers conduct signals much faster than unmyelinated fibers.

## 12.5 Synapses

**Expected Learning Outcomes**

When you have completed this section, you should be able to

a. explain how messages are transmitted from one neuron to another;
b. give examples of neurotransmitters and neuromodulators and describe their actions; and
c. explain how stimulation of a postsynaptic cell is stopped.

All good things must come to an end; a nerve signal soon reaches the end of an axon and can go no farther. But in most cases, it triggers the release of a neurotransmitter that stimulates a new wave of electrical activity in the next cell across the synapse. The most thoroughly studied synapse is the neuromuscular junction described in chapter 11, but here we consider synapses between two neurons. Signals arrive at the synapse by way of the **presynaptic neuron,** which releases a neurotransmitter. The next neuron, which responds to it, is called the **postsynaptic neuron (fig. 12.19a).**

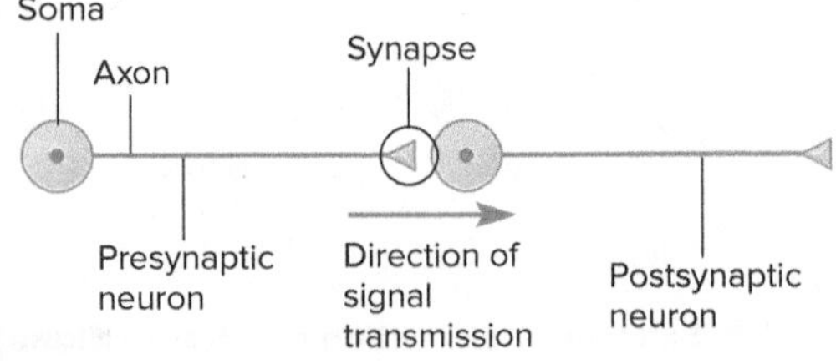


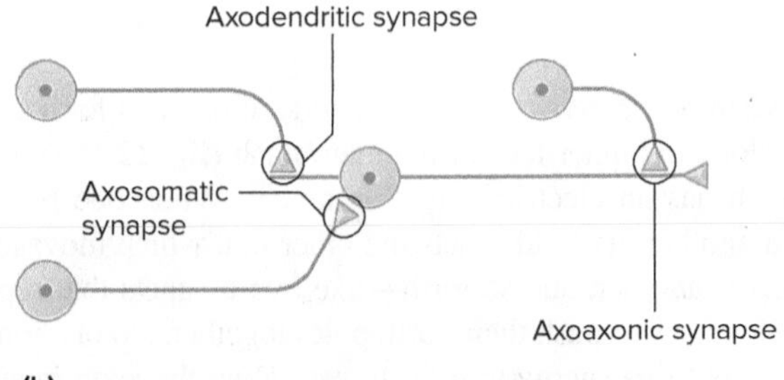


**FIGURE 12.19 Synaptic Relationships Between Neurons.** (a) Pre- and postsynaptic neurons. (b) Types of synapses defined by the site of contact on the postsynaptic neuron.

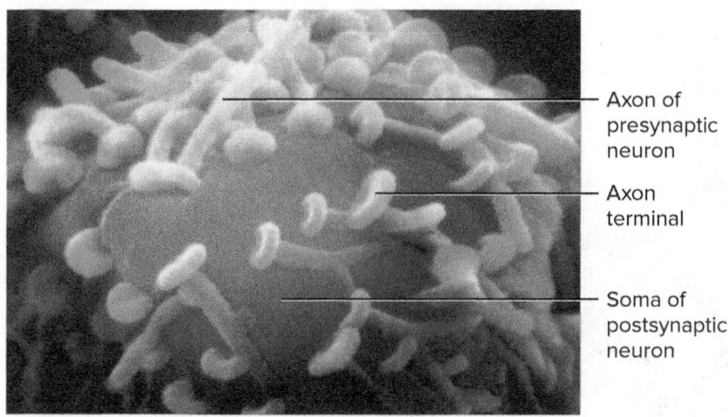


**FIGURE 12.20 Axon Terminals Synapsing with the Soma of a Neuron in a Marine Slug, *Aplysia* (SEM).**
Omikron/Science Source/Getty Images

The presynaptic neuron may synapse with a dendrite, the soma, or the axon of a postsynaptic neuron, forming an *axodendritic, axosomatic,* or *axoaxonic synapse,* respectively **(fig. 12.19b).** A neuron can have an enormous number of synapses **(fig. 12.20).** For example, a spinal motor neuron is covered with about 10,000 axon terminals from other neurons—8,000 ending on its dendrites and another 2,000 on the soma. In a part of the brain called the cerebellum, one neuron can have as many as 100,000 synapses.

## 12.5a The Discovery of Neurotransmitters

In the early twentieth century, biologists assumed that synaptic communication was electrical—a logical hypothesis given that neurons seemed to touch each other and signals were transmitted so quickly from one to the next. Cajal's careful histological examinations, however, revealed a 20 to 40 nm gap between neurons—the **synaptic cleft**—casting doubt on the possibility of electrical transmission. Cajal was rudely criticized for such a "preposterous" idea, but he was eventually proved correct.

In 1921, German pharmacologist Otto Loewi conclusively demonstrated that neurons communicate by releasing chemicals. The *vagus nerves* supply the heart, among other organs, and slow it down. Loewi opened two frogs and flooded the hearts with saline to keep them moist. He stimulated the vagus nerve of one frog, and its heart rate dropped as expected. He then removed saline from that heart and squirted it onto the heart of the second frog. The solution alone reduced that frog's heart rate. Evidently it contained something released by the vagus nerve of the first frog. Loewi had discovered what we now call acetylcholine—the first known neurotransmitter.

**▶▶▶APPLY WHAT YOU KNOW**

*As described, does the previous experiment conclusively prove that the second frog's heart slowed as a result of something released by the vagus nerves? If you were Loewi, what control experiment would you do to rule out alternative hypotheses?*

Following Loewi's work, the idea of electrical communication between cells fell into disrepute. Now, however, we realize that some neurons, neuroglia, and cardiac and unitary smooth muscle do indeed have **electrical synapses,** where adjacent cells are joined by gap junctions and ions diffuse directly from one cell into the next. These junctions have the advantage of quick transmission because there is no delay for the release and binding of neurotransmitter. They are important in synchronizing the activity of local suites of neurons in certain regions of the brain. Their disadvantage, however, is that they cannot integrate information and make decisions. The ability to do that is a property of **chemical synapses,** in which neurons communicate by neurotransmitters. Chemical synapses are also the site of learning and memory, the target of many prescription drugs, and the site of action of drugs of addiction, among other things.

## 12.5b Structure of a Chemical Synapse

The axon terminal **(fig. 12.21)** contains synaptic vesicles, many of which are "docked" at release sites on the plasma membrane, ready to release neurotransmitter on demand. A reserve pool of synaptic vesicles is located a little farther away from the membrane, tethered to the cytoskeleton.

The postsynaptic neuron lacks these conspicuous specializations. At this end, the neuron has no synaptic vesicles and cannot release neurotransmitter. Its membrane does, however, have neurotransmitter receptors and ligand-gated ion channels.

## 12.5c Neurotransmitters and Related Messengers

More than 100 neurotransmitters have been identified since Loewi's time. Neurotransmitters can be defined as molecules that are synthesized by a neuron, released when a nerve signal reaches an axon terminal or varicosity of the nerve fiber, and have a specific effect on a receiving cell's physiology. Most of them are small organic molecules that are released by exocytosis and bind to specific receptors on the receiving cell, but there are exceptions. Some of the best-known neurotransmitters are listed in **table 12.3.** Parts of the brain referred to in this table will become familiar as you study chapter 14, and you may wish to refer back to this table then to enhance your understanding of brain function. Most neurotransmitters fall into the following categories **(fig. 12.22).**

1. **Acetylcholine** is in a class by itself. It is formed from acetic acid (acetate) and choline.
2. **Amino acid** neurotransmitters include glycine, glutamate, aspartate, and γ-aminobutyric acid (GABA).
3. **Monoamines (biogenic amines)** are synthesized from amino acids by removal of the —COOH group. They retain the $—NH_2$ (amino group), hence their name. Some monoamine neurotransmitters are epinephrine, norepinephrine, dopamine, serotonin (5-hydroxytryptamine, or 5-HT), and histamine. The first three of these are in a subclass called **catecholamines** (CAT-eh-COAL-uh-meens).
4. **Purines** serving as neurotransmitters include adenosine and ATP (adenosine triphosphate).

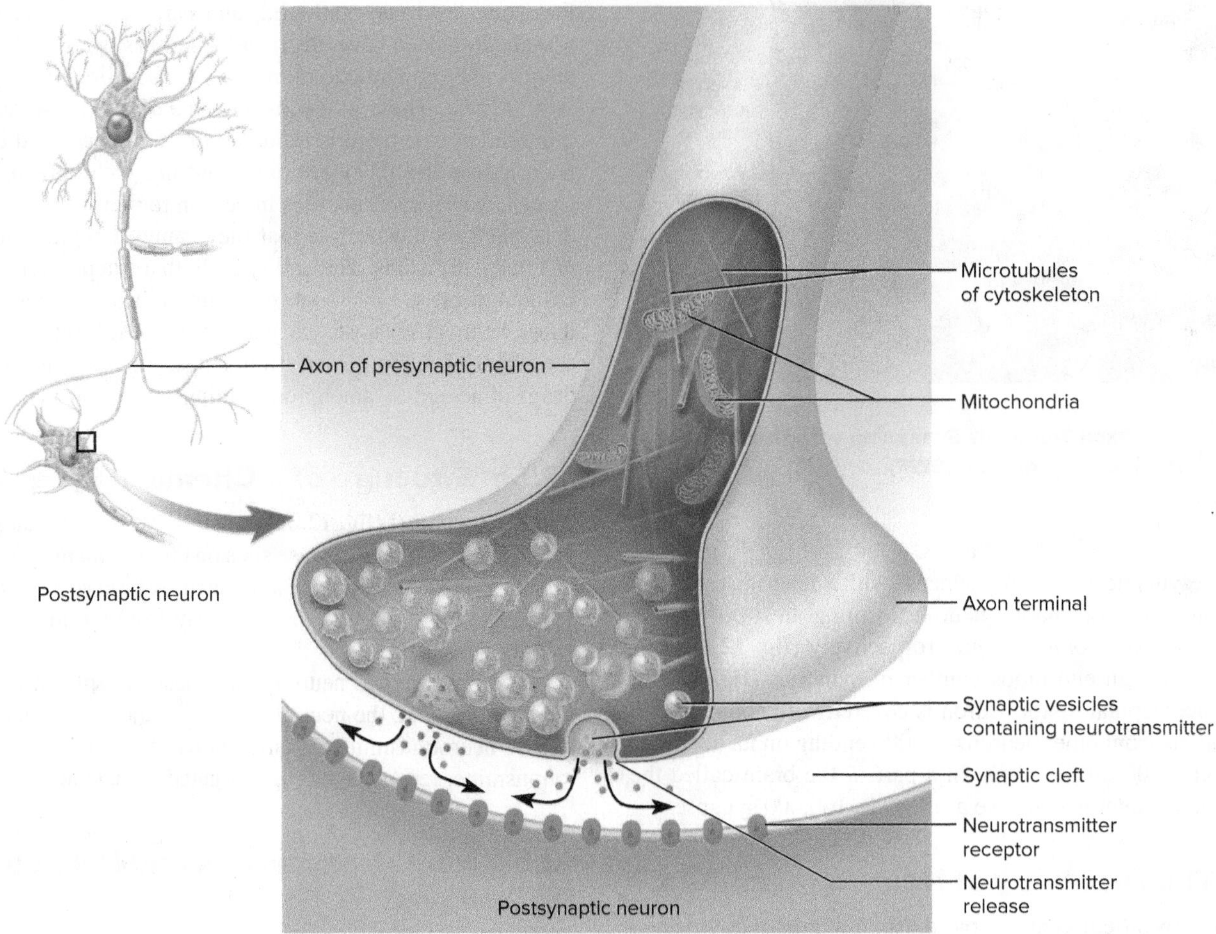


**FIGURE 12.21 Structure of a Chemical Synapse.**

5. **Gases,** specifically nitric oxide (NO) and carbon monoxide (CO), are inorganic exceptions to the usual definition of neurotransmitters. They are synthesized as needed rather than stored in synaptic vesicles; they simply diffuse out of the axon terminal rather than being released by exocytosis; and they diffuse into the postsynaptic neuron rather than bind to a surface receptor.
6. **Neuropeptides** are chains of 2 to 40 amino acids. Some examples are cholecystokinin (CCK) and the endorphins. Neuropeptides are stored in *secretory granules (dense-core vesicles)* that are about 100 nm in diameter, twice as large as typical synaptic vesicles. Some neuropeptides also function as hormones or as *neuromodulators* (see section 12.5f). Some are produced not only by neurons but also by the digestive tract; thus, they are known as *gut–brain peptides.* Some of these cause cravings for specific nutrients such as fat, protein, or carbohydrates (see section 26.1b) and may be associated with certain eating disorders.

**APPLY WHAT YOU KNOW**

*Unlike other neurotransmitters, neuropeptides can be synthesized only in the soma and must be transported to the axon terminals. Why is their synthesis limited to the soma?*

We will see, especially in chapter 15, that a given neurotransmitter does not have the same effect everywhere in the body. There are multiple receptor types in the body for a particular neurotransmitter—over 14 receptor types for serotonin, for example—and it is the receptor that governs what effect a neurotransmitter has on its target cell. Most human and other mammalian neurons can secrete two or more neurotransmitters and can switch from one to another under different circumstances.

## 12.5d Synaptic Transmission

Some neurotransmitters are excitatory, some are inhibitory, and for some the effect depends on what kind of receptor the postsynaptic cell has. Some open ligand-gated ion channels and others act through second messengers. Bearing this diversity in mind, we will examine three kinds of synapses with different modes of action.

### An Excitatory Cholinergic Synapse

A **cholinergic**[28] (CO-lin-UR-jic) synapse employs acetylcholine (ACh) as its neurotransmitter. ACh excites some postsynaptic cells (such as skeletal muscle) and inhibits others (such as

[28] *cholin* = acetylcholine; *erg* = work, action

**TABLE 12.3 Neurotransmitters (Selected Examples)**

| Name | Locations and Actions |
|---|---|
| **Acetylcholine (ACh)** | Neuromuscular junctions, most synapses of autonomic nervous system, retina, and many parts of the brain; excites skeletal muscle, inhibits cardiac muscle, and has excitatory or inhibitory effects on smooth muscle and glands depending on location |
| **Amino Acids** | |
| Glutamate | Cerebral cortex and brainstem; accounts for about 75% of all excitatory synaptic transmission in the brain; involved in learning and memory |
| Aspartate | Spinal cord; effects similar to those of glutamate |
| Glycine | Inhibitory neurons of the brain, spinal cord, and retina; most common inhibitory neurotransmitter in the spinal cord |
| GABA | Thalamus, hypothalamus, cerebellum, occipital lobes of cerebrum, and retina; the most common inhibitory neurotransmitter in the brain |
| **Monoamines** | |
| Norepinephrine | Sympathetic nervous system, cerebral cortex, hypothalamus, brainstem, cerebellum, and spinal cord; involved in dreaming, waking, and mood; excites cardiac muscle; can excite or inhibit smooth muscle and glands depending on location |
| Epinephrine | Hypothalamus, thalamus, spinal cord, and adrenal medulla; effects similar to those of norepinephrine |
| Dopamine | Hypothalamus, limbic system, cerebral cortex, and retina; highly concentrated in substantia nigra of midbrain; involved in elevation of mood and control of skeletal muscles |
| Serotonin | Hypothalamus, limbic system, cerebellum, retina, and spinal cord; also secreted by blood platelets and intestinal cells; involved in sleepiness, alertness, thermoregulation, and mood |
| Histamine | Hypothalamus; also a potent vasodilator released by mast cells of connective tissue and basophils of the blood |
| **Neuropeptides** | |
| Substance P | Basal nuclei, midbrain, hypothalamus, cerebral cortex, small intestine, and pain-receptor neurons; mediates pain transmission |
| Enkephalins | Hypothalamus, limbic system, pituitary, pain pathways of spinal cord, and nerve endings of digestive tract; act as analgesics (pain relievers) by inhibiting substance P; inhibit intestinal motility; modulate immune responses |
| β-endorphin | Digestive tract, spinal cord, and many parts of the brain; also secreted as a hormone by the pituitary; suppresses pain; secretion rises sharply during labor and delivery and in response to other pain situations |
| Cholecystokinin | Cerebral cortex and small intestine; suppresses appetite |

**Acetylcholine**

$H_3C-N^+(CH_3)_2-CH_2-CH_2-O-C(=O)-CH_3$

**Amino acids**

$HO(O=)C-CH_2-CH_2-CH_2-NH_2$ GABA

$HO(O=)C-CH_2-NH_2$ Glycine

$HO(O=)C-CH(NH_2)-CH_2-C(=O)OH$ Aspartic acid

$HO(O=)C-CH(NH_2)-CH_2-CH_2-C(=O)OH$ Glutamic acid

**Monoamines**

**Catecholamines**

$(HO)_2C_6H_3-CH(OH)-CH_2-NH-CH_3$ Epinephrine

$(HO)_2C_6H_3-CH(OH)-CH_2-NH_2$ Norepinephrine

$(HO)_2C_6H_3-CH_2-CH_2-NH_2$ Dopamine

HO–(indole)–$CH_2-CH_2-NH_2$ Serotonin

(imidazole)–$CH_2-CH_2-NH_2$ Histamine

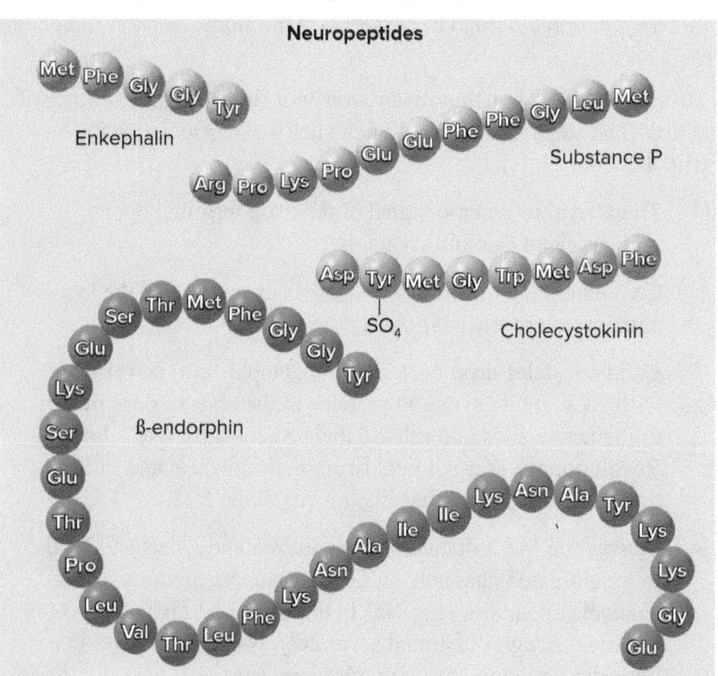


**FIGURE 12.22 Classification of Some Neurotransmitters.** The neuropeptides are chains of amino acids, each identified by its three-letter code. Appendix D explains the codes.

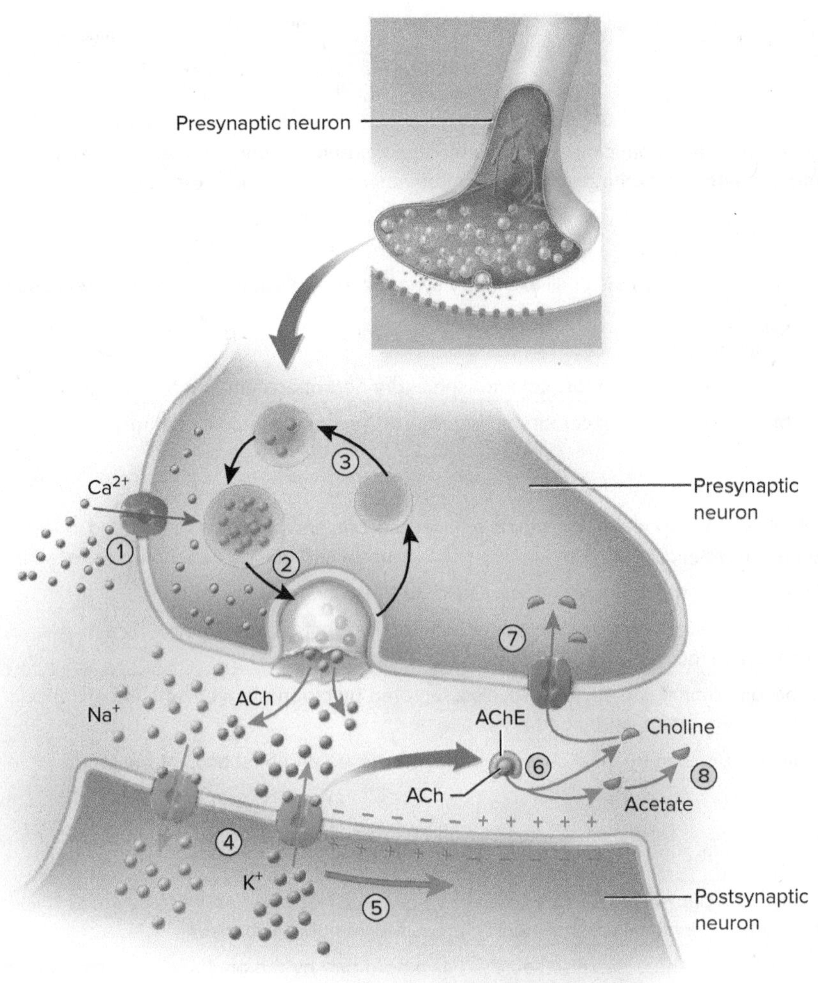


**FIGURE 12.23 Transmission at a Cholinergic Synapse.** Acetylcholine directly opens ion channels in the plasma membrane of the postsynaptic neuron. Numbered steps 1 through 5 correspond to the description in the adjacent text. Steps 6 through 8 pertain to cessation of the signal (section 12.5e). APR

cardiac muscle), but this discussion will describe an excitatory action. The steps in transmission at such a synapse are as follows **(fig. 12.23):**

(1) The arrival of a nerve signal at the axon terminal opens voltage-gated calcium channels.

(2) $Ca^{2+}$ enters the terminal and triggers exocytosis of the synaptic vesicles, releasing ACh.

(3) Empty vesicles drop back into the cytoplasm to be refilled with ACh, while synaptic vesicles in the reserve pool move to the active sites and release their ACh—a bit like a line of Revolutionary War soldiers firing their muskets and falling back to reload as another line moves to the fore.

(4) Meanwhile, ACh diffuses across the synaptic cleft and binds to ligand-gated channels on the postsynaptic neuron. These channels open, allowing $Na^+$ to enter the cell and $K^+$ to leave. Although illustrated separately, $Na^+$ and $K^+$ pass in opposite directions through the same gates.

(5) As $Na^+$ enters, it spreads out along the inside of the plasma membrane and depolarizes it, producing a local voltage shift called the **postsynaptic potential.** Like other local potentials, if this is strong and persistent enough (that is, if enough current makes it to the axon hillock), it opens voltage-gated ion channels in the trigger zone and causes the postsynaptic neuron to fire.

Steps 6 through 8 in figure 12.23 concern the mechanism for halting transmission and are explained shortly (see section 12.5e).

## An Inhibitory GABA-ergic Synapse

Synapses that employ γ-aminobutyric acid (GABA) as their neurotransmitter are called **GABA-ergic synapses.** Amino acid neurotransmitters such as GABA work by the same mechanism as ACh; they bind to ion channels and cause immediate changes in membrane potential. The release of GABA and binding to its receptor are similar to the preceding case. The GABA receptor, however, is a chloride channel. When it opens, $Cl^-$ enters the cell and makes the inside even more negative than the resting membrane potential. The neuron is therefore inhibited, or less likely to fire.

## An Excitatory Adrenergic Synapse

An **adrenergic synapse** employs the neurotransmitter norepinephrine (NE), also called noradrenaline. NE, other monoamines, and neuropeptides act through second-messenger systems such as cyclic AMP (cAMP). The receptor is not an ion channel but a transmembrane protein associated with a G protein on the inner face of the membrane. **Figure 12.24** shows some ways in which an adrenergic synapse can function, numbered to correspond to the following:

(1) The unstimulated NE receptor is bound to a G protein.

(2) Binding of NE to the receptor causes the G protein to dissociate from it.

(3) The G protein binds to adenylate cyclase and activates this enzyme, which converts ATP to cAMP.

(4) Cyclic AMP can induce several alternative effects in the cell.

(5) One effect is to produce an internal chemical that binds to a ligand-gated ion channel from the inside, opening the channel and depolarizing the cell.

(6) Another is to activate preexisting cytoplasmic enzymes, which can lead to diverse metabolic changes (for example, inducing a liver cell to break down glycogen and release glucose into the blood).

(7) Yet another is for cAMP to induce genetic transcription, so that the cell produces new enzymes leading to diverse metabolic effects.

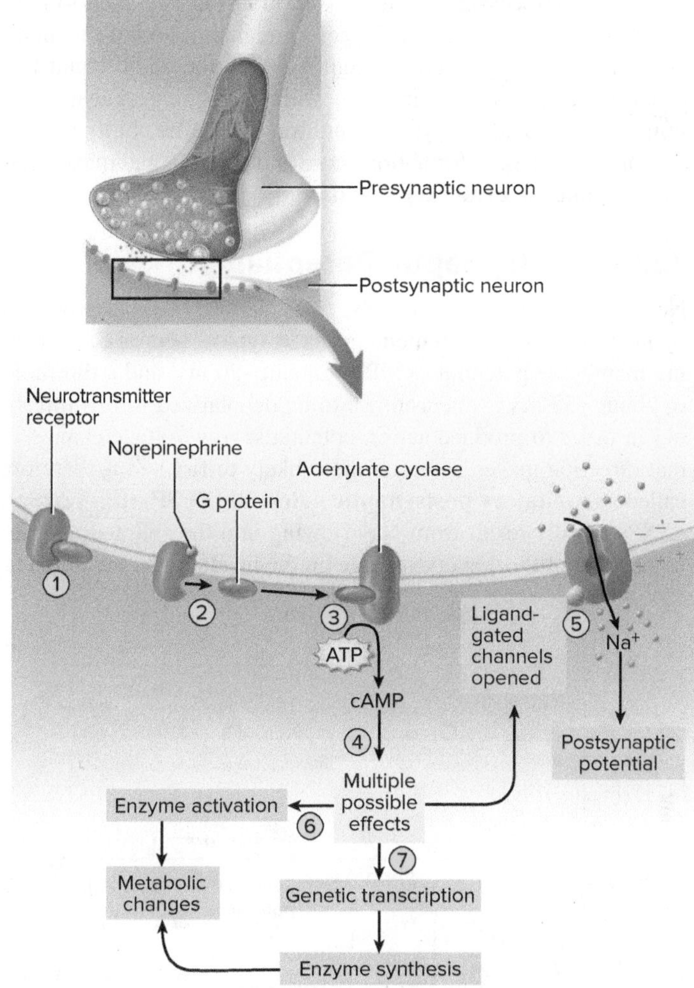


**FIGURE 12.24 Transmission at an Adrenergic Synapse.** Numbered steps correspond to the description in nearby text.

Although slower to respond than cholinergic and GABA-ergic synapses, adrenergic synapses do have an advantage—**signal amplification.** A single NE molecule binding to a receptor can induce the formation of many cAMPs, each of those can activate many enzyme molecules or induce the transcription of a gene to generate numerous mRNA molecules, and each of those can result in the production of a vast number of enzyme molecules and metabolic products such as glucose molecules.

As complex as synaptic events may seem, they typically require only 0.5 ms or so—an interval called **synaptic delay.** This is the time from the arrival of a signal at the axon terminal of a presynaptic cell to the beginning of an action potential in the postsynaptic cell.

## 12.5e Cessation of the Signal

It is important not only to stimulate a postsynaptic cell but also to turn off the stimulus in due time. Otherwise the postsynaptic neuron could continue firing indefinitely, causing a breakdown in physiological coordination. But a neurotransmitter molecule binds to its receptor for only 1 ms or so, then dissociates from it. If the presynaptic cell continues to release neurotransmitter, one molecule is quickly replaced by another and the postsynaptic cell is restimulated. This immediately suggests a way of stopping synaptic transmission—stop adding new neurotransmitter and get rid of that which is already there. The first step is achieved simply by the cessation of signals in the presynaptic nerve fiber. The second can be achieved in the following ways, pictured as steps 6 to 8 in figure 12.23:

(6) **Neurotransmitter degradation.** An enzyme in the synaptic cleft breaks the neurotransmitter down into fragments that have no stimulatory effect on the postsynaptic cell. Depicted here is acetylcholinesterase (AChE) breaking ACh down into choline and acetate.

(7) **Reuptake.** A neurotransmitter or its breakdown products are reabsorbed by transport proteins in the axon terminal, removing them from the synapse and ending their stimulatory effect. Choline from ACh is recycled to make new ACh. Amino acid and monoamine neurotransmitters are similarly reabsorbed, then broken down within the axon terminal by an enzyme called **monoamine oxidase (MAO).** Some antidepressant drugs work by inhibiting MAO (see Deeper Insight 15.2). Some cases of autism, attention-deficit/hyperactivity disorder (ADHD), parkinsonism, and depression stem from mutations that render some of these transport proteins nonfunctional.

(8) **Diffusion.** Neurotransmitters or their breakdown products simply diffuse away from the synapse into the nearby extracellular fluid. As shown in figure 12.23, this is what happens to the acetate component of ACh, but in other cases, the neurotransmitter escapes the synapse intact. In the CNS, astrocytes absorb stray neurotransmitters and return them to the presynaptic neurons. In ganglia of the PNS, it seems that the satellite cells that surround neurons perform this role; this is an area of current scientific investigation.

## 12.5f Neuromodulators

Neurons sometimes secrete chemical signals that have long-term effects on entire groups of neurons instead of brief, quick effects at an individual synapse. Some call these **neuromodulators** to distinguish them from neurotransmitters; others use the term *neurotransmitter* broadly to include these. Neuromodulators adjust, or *modulate,* the activity of neuron groups in various ways: increasing the release of neurotransmitters by presynaptic neurons; adjusting the sensitivity of postsynaptic neurons to neurotransmitters; or altering the rate of neurotransmitter reuptake or breakdown to prolong their effects.

The simplest neuromodulator is the gas **nitric oxide (NO).** NO diffuses readily into a postsynaptic cell and activates second-messenger pathways with such effects as relaxing smooth muscle. This has the effect of dilating small arteries and increasing blood flow to a tissue; this is the basis for the action of drugs for erectile dysfunction (see Deeper Insight 27.4). The neuropeptides are neuromodulators; among these are the **enkephalins** and **endorphins,** which inhibit spinal neurons from transmitting pain signals to the brain (see section 16.2d). Other neuromodulators include hormones and some neurotransmitters such as dopamine, serotonin, and histamine. The last point may seem confusing, but the terms *neurotransmitter, hormone,* and *neuromodulator* define not so much the chemical itself, but the role it plays in a given context. One chemical can play two or more of these roles in different places and circumstances.

**BEFORE YOU GO ON**

Answer the following questions to test your understanding of the preceding section:

**18.** Concisely describe five steps that occur between the arrival of an action potential at the axon terminal and the beginning of a new action potential in the postsynaptic neuron.

**19.** Contrast the actions of acetylcholine, GABA, and norepinephrine at their respective synapses.

**20.** Describe three mechanisms that stop synaptic transmission.

**21.** What is the function of neuromodulators? Compare and contrast neuromodulators and neurotransmitters.

## 12.6 Neural Integration

**Expected Learning Outcomes**

When you have completed this section, you should be able to

a. explain how a neuron "decides" whether or not to generate action potentials;

b. explain how the nervous system translates complex information into a simple code;

c. explain how neurons work together in groups to process information and produce effective output; and

d. describe how memory works at the cellular and molecular levels.

Synaptic delay slows the transmission of nerve signals; the more synapses there are in a neural pathway, the longer it takes information to get from its origin to its destination. You may wonder, therefore, why we have synapses—why a nervous pathway is not, indeed, a continuous "wire" as biologists believed before Cajal. The presence of synapses is not due to limitations on axon length—after all, one nerve fiber can reach from your toes to your brainstem. (In the neck of the giraffe, the *recurrent laryngeal nerve* has nerve fibers 4.6 m, or 15 ft, long. Nerve fibers from the hind foot to the brainstem are even longer by far.) We also have seen that cells communicate much more quickly through gap junctions than through chemical synapses. So why have chemical synapses at all?

What we value most about our nervous system is its ability to process information, store it, and make decisions—and chemical synapses are the decision-making devices of the system. The more synapses a neuron has, the greater its information-processing capability. At this moment, you are using certain *pyramidal cells* of the cerebral cortex (see fig. 12.5a) to read and comprehend this passage. Each pyramidal cell has about 40,000 synaptic contacts with other neurons. The cerebral cortex alone (the main information-processing tissue of your brain) is estimated to have 100 trillion ($10^{14}$) synapses. To get some impression of this number, imagine trying to count them. Even if you could count two synapses per second, day and night without stopping, and you were immortal, it would take you 1.6 million years. The ability of your neurons to process information, store and recall it, and make decisions is called **neural integration.**

### 12.6a Postsynaptic Potentials

Neural integration is based on the postsynaptic potentials produced by neurotransmitters. Remember that a typical neuron has a resting membrane potential (RMP) of about –70 mV and a threshold of about –55 mV. A neuron has to be depolarized to this threshold in order to produce action potentials. Any voltage change in that direction makes a neuron more likely to fire and is therefore called an **excitatory postsynaptic potential (EPSP) (fig. 12.25a).** EPSPs usually result from $Na^+$ flowing into the cell and neutralizing some of the negative charge on the inside of the membrane.

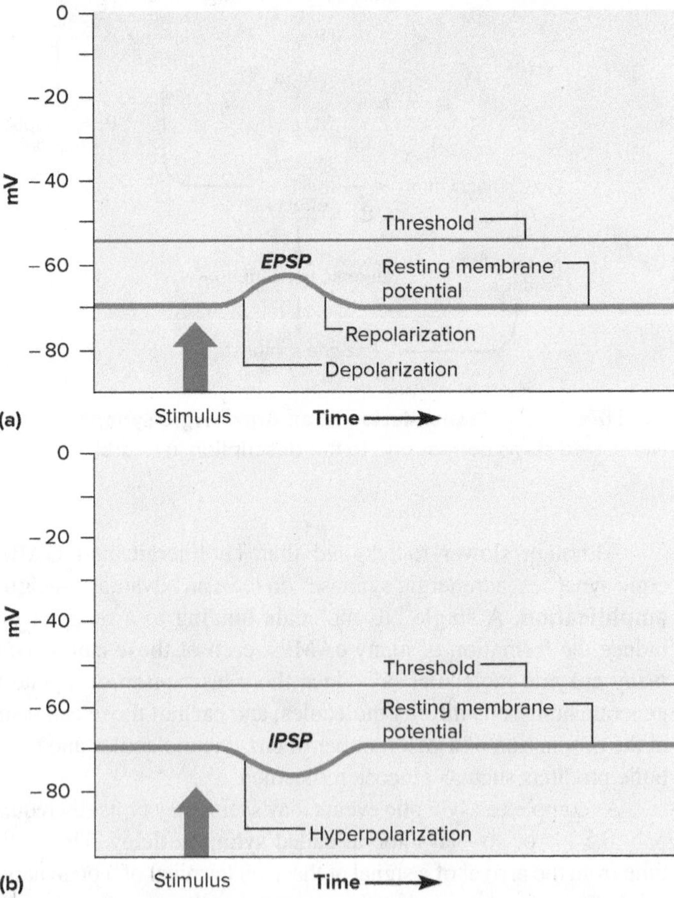


**FIGURE 12.25 Postsynaptic Potentials.** (a) An excitatory postsynaptic potential (EPSP), which shifts the membrane voltage closer to threshold and makes the cell more likely to fire. (b) An inhibitory postsynaptic potential (IPSP), which shifts the membrane voltage farther away from threshold and makes the cell less likely to fire. The sizes of these postsynaptic potentials are greatly exaggerated here for clarity; compare figure 12.27.

? *Why is a single EPSP insufficient to make a neuron fire?*

In other cases, a neurotransmitter hyperpolarizes the postsynaptic cell and makes it more negative than the RMP. Since this makes the postsynaptic cell less likely to fire, it is called an **inhibitory postsynaptic potential (IPSP) (fig. 12.25b).** Some IPSPs are produced by a neurotransmitter opening ligand-gated chloride channels, causing $Cl^-$ to flow into the cell and make the cytosol more negative. A less common way is to open selective $K^+$ channels, increasing $K^+$ diffusion out of the cell.

We must recognize that because of ion leakage through their membranes, all neurons fire at a certain background rate even when they are not being stimulated. EPSPs and IPSPs don't determine whether or not a neuron fires, but only change the rate of firing by stimulating or inhibiting the production of more action potentials.

Glutamate and aspartate are excitatory brain neurotransmitters that produce EPSPs. Glycine and GABA produce IPSPs and are therefore inhibitory. Acetylcholine (ACh) and norepinephrine are excitatory to some cells and inhibitory to others, depending on the type of receptors present. For example, ACh excites skeletal muscle but inhibits cardiac muscle because of different types of ACh receptors.

## 12.6b Summation, Facilitation, and Inhibition

One neuron may receive input from thousands of other neurons. Some incoming nerve fibers may produce EPSPs while others produce IPSPs. The neuron's response depends on whether the *net* input is excitatory or inhibitory. If EPSPs override the IPSPs, threshold may be reached and set off an action potential; if IPSPs prevail, they inhibit the neuron from firing. **Summation** is the process of adding up postsynaptic potentials and responding to their net effect. It occurs in the trigger zone.

Suppose, for example, you're working in the kitchen and accidentally touch a hot pot. EPSPs in your motor neurons might cause you to jerk your hand back quickly and avoid being burned. Yet a moment later, you might nonchalantly sip a cup of hot tea. Since you are expecting it to be hot, you don't jerk it away from your lips. You have learned that it won't injure you, so at some level of the nervous system, IPSPs prevail and inhibit the motor response.

It is fundamentally a balance between EPSPs and IPSPs that enables the nervous system to make decisions. A postsynaptic neuron is like a little cellular democracy acting on the "majority vote" of hundreds or thousands of presynaptic cells. In the tea example, some presynaptic neurons send messages that signify "Hot! Danger!" in the form of EPSPs that may activate a hand-withdrawal reflex, while at the same time, others produce IPSPs that signify "Safe" and suppress the reflex. Whether you jerk your hand away depends on whether the EPSPs override the IPSPs or vice versa.

Weak stimulation of a postsynaptic neuron may generate an EPSP, but it fades before reaching threshold. A typical EPSP is a voltage change of only 0.5 mV and lasts only 15 to 20 ms. If a neuron has an RMP of –70 mV and a threshold of –55 mV, it needs at least 30 EPSPs to reach threshold and fire. There are two ways in which EPSPs can add up to do this, and both may occur simultaneously.

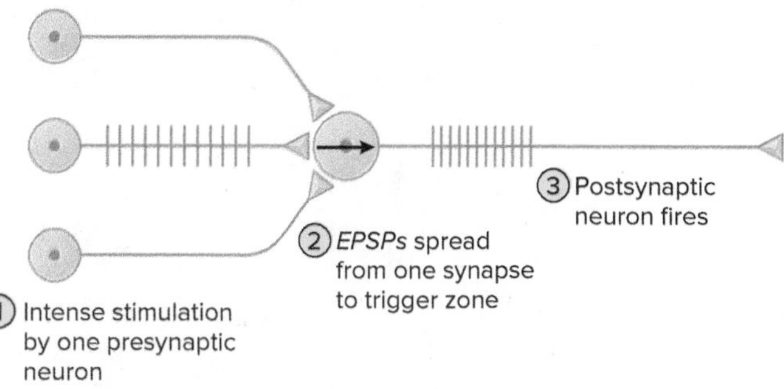

① Intense stimulation by one presynaptic neuron
② EPSPs spread from one synapse to trigger zone
③ Postsynaptic neuron fires
(a) Temporal summation

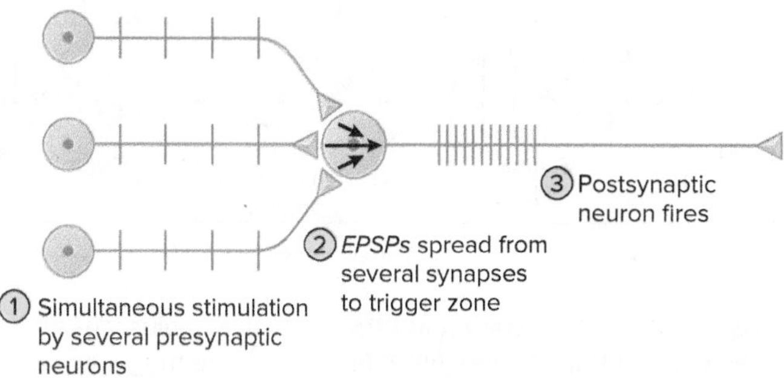

① Simultaneous stimulation by several presynaptic neurons
② EPSPs spread from several synapses to trigger zone
③ Postsynaptic neuron fires
(b) Spatial summation

**FIGURE 12.26 Temporal and Spatial Summation.** Vertical lines on the nerve fibers indicate relative firing frequency. Arrows within the postsynaptic neuron indicate the path of local graded potentials. (a) Temporal summation resulting from rapid firing of a single presynaptic neuron. (b) Spatial summation as an additive effect of multiple presynaptic neurons firing at moderate rates.

1. **Temporal summation (fig. 12.26a).** This occurs when a single synapse generates EPSPs so quickly that each is generated before the previous one fades. This allows the EPSPs to add up over time to a threshold voltage that triggers an action potential **(fig. 12.27).** Temporal summation can occur if even one presynaptic neuron stimulates the postsynaptic neuron at a fast enough rate.
2. **Spatial summation (fig. 12.26b).** This occurs when EPSPs from several synapses add up to threshold at the axon hillock. Any one synapse may generate only a weak signal, but several synapses acting together can bring the hillock to threshold. The presynaptic neurons collaborate to induce the postsynaptic neuron to fire.

Neurons routinely work in groups to modify each other's actions. **Presynaptic facilitation** is a process in which one neuron enhances the effect of another. **Figure 12.28** depicts such an interaction between three neurons we will call neuron F for a facilitating neuron, S for a stimulating neuron, and R for a responding neuron. Neuron F forms an axoaxonic synapse with the axon terminal of neuron S. When neuron F is quiescent, neuron S shows only a low level of activity, releasing some neurotransmitter but not necessarily enough to excite neuron R to threshold. But if circumstances call for enhancing information transmission across synapse S-R, neuron F can release a neurotransmitter

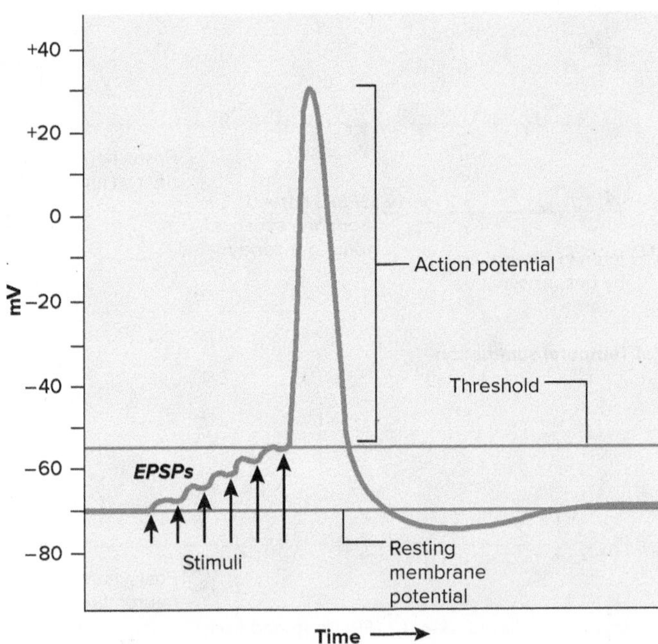


**FIGURE 12.27 Summation of EPSPs.** Each stimulus (arrow) produces one EPSP. If enough EPSPs arrive at the trigger zone faster than they fade, they can build on each other to bring the neuron to threshold and trigger an action potential.

such as serotonin. Serotonin makes voltage-gated calcium channels in the axon terminal of S remain open longer. Increased calcium inflow increases neurotransmitter release by S, which now excites neuron R. The facilitating neuron F thus accentuates synaptic transmission.

The spatial summation seen in figure 12.26b is another way of facilitating the firing of a postsynaptic neuron. One neuron acting alone may be unable to induce a postsynaptic neuron to fire, but when they collaborate, their combined "effort" does induce firing in the postsynaptic cell.

**Presynaptic inhibition** is the opposite of facilitation, a mechanism in which one presynaptic neuron suppresses another one. This mechanism is used to reduce or halt unwanted synaptic transmission. In **figure 12.29,** we see another three neurons in which the facilitating neuron is replaced by an inhibitory neuron, I. When neuron I is silent, neuron S releases its neurotransmitter and triggers a response in R. But when there is a need to block transmission across this pathway, neuron I releases the inhibitory neurotransmitter GABA. GABA prevents the voltage-gated calcium channels of neuron S from opening. Consequently, neuron S releases less neurotransmitter or none, and fails to stimulate neuron R.

## 12.6c Neural Coding

The nervous system must interpret and pass along both quantitative and qualitative information about its environment—whether a light is dim or bright, red or green; whether a taste is mild or intense, salty or sour; whether a sound is loud or soft, high-pitched or low. Considering the complexity of information to be communicated about conditions in and around the body, it seems a marvel that it can be done in the form of something as simple as action potentials—particularly since all the action potentials of a given neuron are identical. Yet when we considered the genetic code in chapter 4, we saw that complex messages can indeed be expressed in simple codes. The way in which the nervous system converts information to a meaningful pattern of action potentials is called **neural coding** (or *sensory coding* when it occurs in the sense organs).

The most important mechanism for transmitting qualitative information is the **labeled line code.** This code is based on the

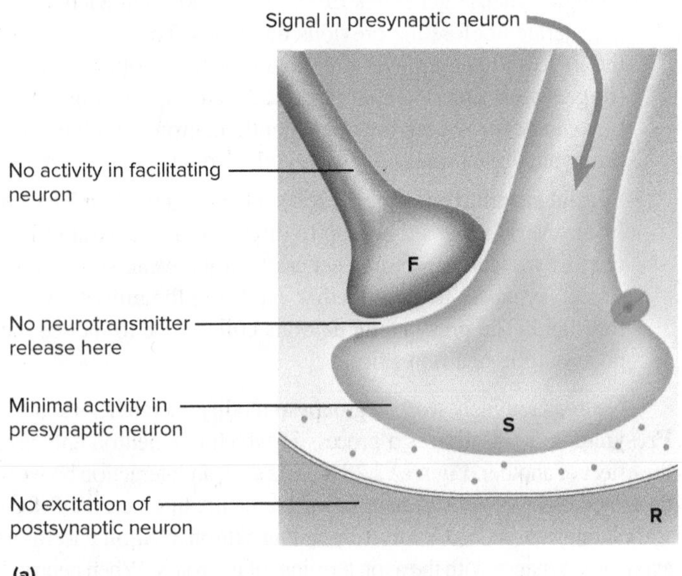


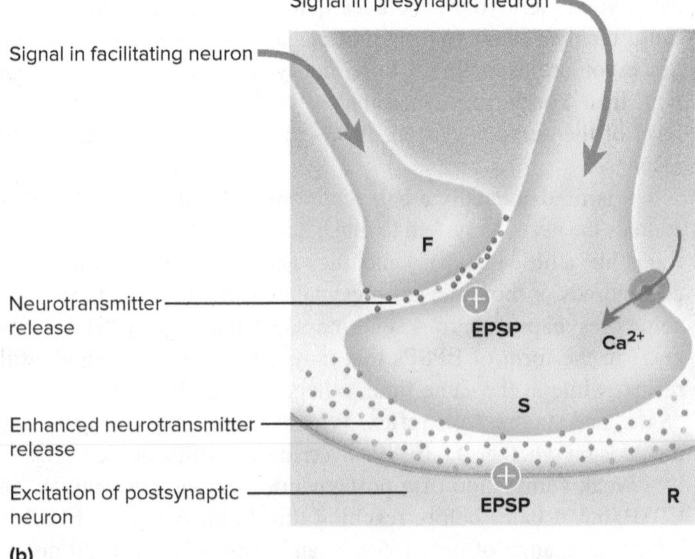


**FIGURE 12.28 Presynaptic Facilitation.** F, facilitating neuron; S, stimulating neuron; R, responding postsynaptic neuron; +, excitation (EPSP). (a) Inactivity of neuron R owing to absence of stimulation by neuron F. (b) Activity in neuron R owing to stimulation (facilitation) of the S-R synapse by neuron F.

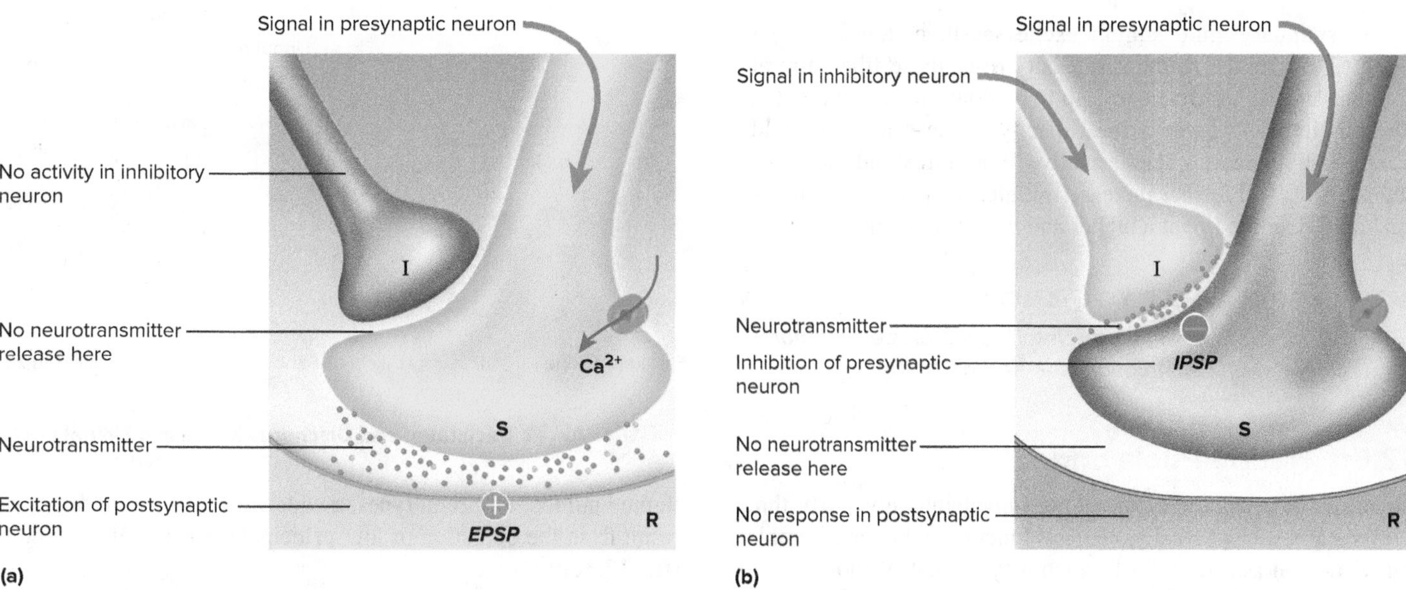


**FIGURE 12.29 Presynaptic Inhibition.** S, stimulating neuron; I, inhibitory neuron; R, responding postsynaptic neuron; +, excitation (EPSP); –, inhibition (IPSP). (a) Activity in the S-R synapse in the absence of inhibition by neuron I. (b) Activity of neuron I inhibiting synaptic transmission between S and R.

fact that each nerve fiber to the brain leads from a receptor that specifically recognizes a particular stimulus type. Nerve fibers in the optic nerve, for example, carry signals only from light receptors in the eye; these fibers never carry information about taste or sound. The brain therefore interprets any signals in those fibers in terms of light—even if the signals result from artificial stimulation of the nerve. This effect is seen when you rub your eyelids and see flashes of light as the pressure on the eyeball mechanically stimulates optic nerve fibers. Electrical stimulation of the auditory nerve can enable deaf people to hear sounds of different frequencies, even when receptors in the inner ear are nonfunctional. Thus, each nerve fiber to the brain is a line of communication "labeled," or recognized by the brain, as representing a particular stimulus quality—the color of a light, the pitch of a sound, or the salty or sour quality of a taste, for example.

Quantitative information—information about the intensity of a stimulus—is encoded in two ways. One depends on the fact that different neurons have different thresholds of excitation. A weak stimulus excites sensitive neurons with the lowest thresholds, while a strong stimulus excites less sensitive high-threshold neurons. Bringing additional neurons into play as the stimulus becomes stronger is called **recruitment.** It enables the nervous system to judge stimulus strength by which neurons, and how many of them, are firing.

Another way of encoding stimulus strength depends on the fact that the more strongly a neuron is stimulated, the more frequently it fires. A weak stimulus may cause a neuron to generate 6 action potentials per second, and a strong stimulus, 600 per second. Thus, the central nervous system can judge stimulus strength from the firing frequency of afferent neurons **(fig. 12.30).**

There is a limit to how often a neuron can fire, set by its absolute refractory period. Think of an electronic camera flash by analogy. If you take a photograph and your flash unit takes 10 seconds to recharge, then you can't take more than six photos per minute. Similarly, if a nerve fiber takes 1 ms to repolarize after it has fired, then it can't fire more than 1,000 times per second. Refractory periods may be as short as 0.5 ms, which sets a theoretical limit to firing frequency of 2,000 action potentials per second. The highest frequencies actually observed, however, are 500 to 1,000 per second.

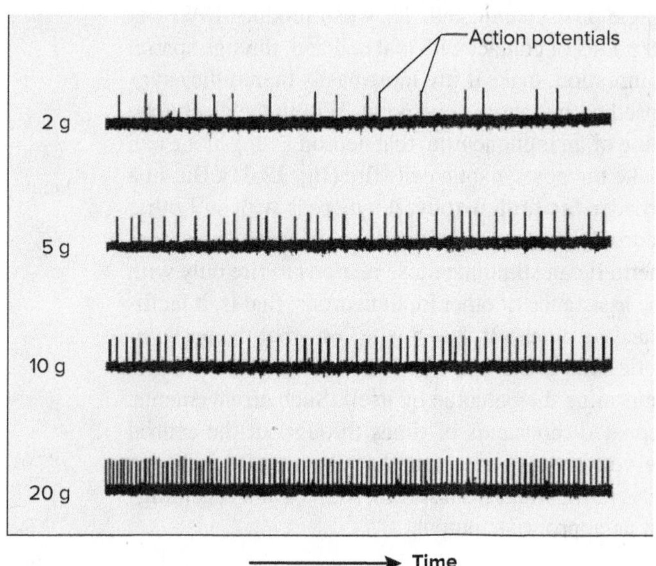


**FIGURE 12.30 An Example of Neural Coding.** This figure is based on recordings made from a sensory fiber of the frog sciatic nerve as the gastrocnemius muscle was stretched by suspending weights from it. As the stimulus strength (weight) and stretch increase, the firing frequency of the neuron increases. Firing frequency is a coded message that informs the CNS of stimulus intensity.

? *In what other way is the CNS informed of stimulus intensity?*

In summary, mild stimuli excite sensitive, low-threshold nerve fibers. As the stimulus intensity rises, these fibers fire at a higher and higher frequency, up to a certain maximum. If the stimulus intensity exceeds the capacity of these low-threshold fibers, it may recruit less sensitive, high-threshold fibers to begin firing. Still further increases in intensity cause these high-threshold fibers to fire at a higher and higher frequency.

**APPLY WHAT YOU KNOW**

*How is neural recruitment related to the process of multiple motor unit summation (see section 11.5b)?*

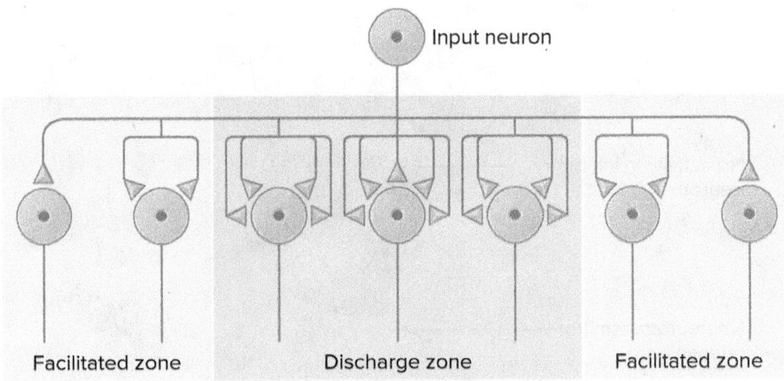


**FIGURE 12.31 Facilitated and Discharge Zones in a Neural Pool.**

## 12.6d Neural Pools and Circuits

So far, we have dealt with interactions involving only two or three neurons at a time. Actually, neurons function in larger ensembles called **neural pools,** each of which may consist of thousands of interneurons concerned with a particular body function—one to control the rhythm of your breathing, one to move your limbs rhythmically as you walk, one to regulate your sense of hunger, and another to interpret smells, for example. At this point, we explore a few ways in which neural pools collectively process information.

### Discharge and Facilitated Zones

Information arrives at a neural pool through one or more input neurons, which branch repeatedly and synapse with numerous interneurons in the pool. Some input neurons form multiple synapses with a single postsynaptic cell. They can produce EPSPs at all points of contact with that cell and, through spatial summation, make it fire more easily than if they synapsed with it at only one point. Within the **discharge zone** of an input neuron, that neuron acting alone can make the postsynaptic cells fire (**fig. 12.31**). But in a broader **facilitated zone,** it synapses with still other neurons in the pool, with fewer synapses on each of them. It can stimulate those neurons to fire only with the assistance of other input neurons; that is, it facilitates the others. It "has a vote" on what the postsynaptic cells in the facilitated zone will do, but it cannot determine the outcome by itself. Such arrangements, repeated thousands of times throughout the central nervous system, give neural pools great flexibility in integrating input from several sources and "deciding" on an appropriate output.

### Types of Neural Circuits

The functioning of a radio can be understood from a circuit diagram showing its components and their connections. Similarly, the functions of a neural pool are partly determined by its **neural circuit**—the pathways among its neurons. Just as a wide variety of electronic devices are constructed from a relatively limited number of circuit types, a wide variety of neural functions result from the operation of four principal kinds of neural circuits (**fig. 12.32**):

1. In a **diverging circuit,** an individual neuron sends signals to multiple downstream neurons, or one neural pool may send output to multiple downstream neural pools. Each of those neurons or neural pools may communicate with several more, so input from just one pathway may produce output through hundreds of others. Such a circuit allows signals from one motor neuron of the brain, for example, to ultimately stimulate thousands of muscle fibers.

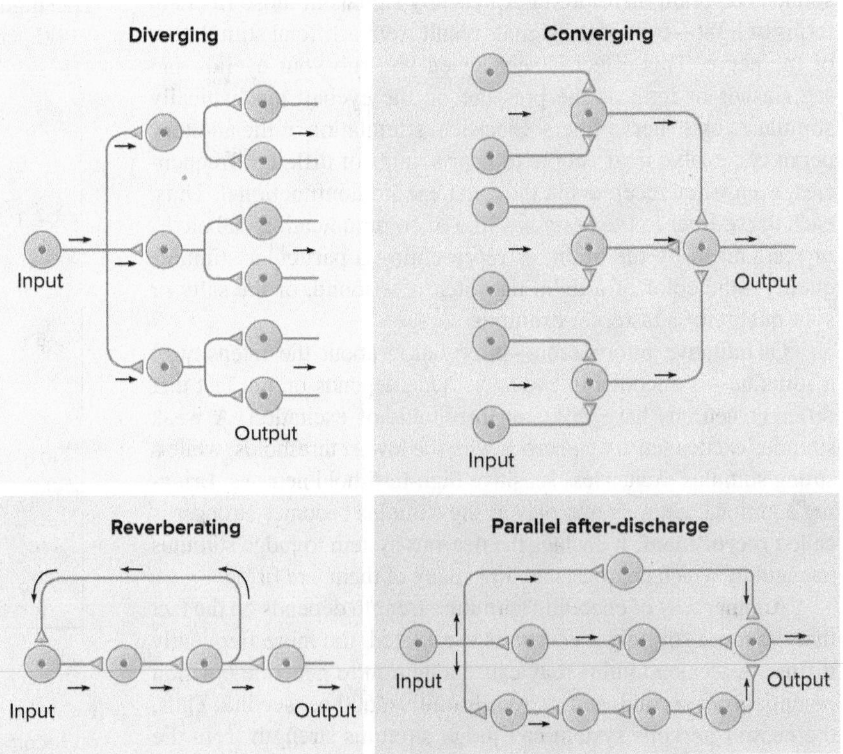


**FIGURE 12.32 Four Types of Neural Circuits.** Arrows indicate the direction of the nerve signal.

*Which of these four circuits is likely to fire the longest after a stimulus ceases? Why?*

2. A **converging circuit** is the opposite of a diverging circuit—input from many nerve fibers or neural pools is funneled to fewer and fewer intermediate or output pathways. For example, you have a brainstem respiratory center that receives converging information from other parts of your brain, blood chemistry sensors in your arteries, and stretch receptors in your lungs. The respiratory center can then produce an output that takes all of these factors into account and sets an appropriate pattern of breathing.
3. In a **reverberating circuit,** neurons stimulate each other in a linear sequence from input to output neurons, but some of the neurons late in the path send axon collaterals back to neurons earlier in the path and restimulate them. As an exceedingly simplified model of such a circuit, consider a path such as A ⟶ B ⟶ C ⟶ D, in which neuron C sends an axon collateral back to A. As a result, every time C fires it not only stimulates output neuron D, but also restimulates A and starts the process over. Such a circuit produces a prolonged or repetitive effect that lasts until one or more neurons in the circuit fail to fire, or an inhibitory signal from another source stops one of them from firing. A reverberating circuit sends repetitious signals to your diaphragm and intercostal muscles, for example, to make you inhale. Sustained output from the circuit ensures that the respiratory muscles contract for the 2 seconds or so that it normally takes to fill the lungs. When the circuit stops firing, you exhale; the next time it fires, you inhale again. Reverberating circuits may also be involved in short-term memory, as discussed in the next section, and they may play a role in the uncontrolled "storms" of neural activity that occur in epilepsy.
4. In a **parallel after-discharge** circuit, an input neuron diverges to stimulate several chains of neurons. Each chain has a different number of synapses, but eventually they all reconverge on one or a few output neurons. Since the chains differ in total synaptic delay, their signals arrive at the output neurons at different times, and the output neurons may go on firing for some time after input has ceased. Unlike a reverberating circuit, this type has no feedback loop. Once all the neurons in the circuit have fired, the output ceases. Continued firing after the stimulus stops is called *after-discharge.* It explains why you can stare at a lamp, then close your eyes and continue to see an image of it for a while. Such a circuit is also important in withdrawal reflexes, in which a brief pain produces a longer-lasting output to the limb muscles and causes you to draw back your hand or foot from danger.

### Serial and Parallel Processing

In relation to these circuit types, the nervous system handles information in two modes called serial and parallel processing. In **serial processing,** neurons and neural pools relay information along a pathway in a relatively simple linear fashion and can process only one flow of information at a time. For example, you can read your e-mail or listen to a class lecture, and the language recognition centers of your brain can process one linguistic input or the other; however, you can't do both simultaneously. To understand the e-mail, you have to stop paying attention to the lecture; to understand the lecture, you have to stop checking your e-mail. You may jump back and forth between one and the other, only half understanding each, but you can't simultaneously process the written message in an e-mail and the spoken language of the lecture. Each must be processed separately and serially.

In **parallel processing,** information is transmitted along diverging circuits through different pathways that act on it simultaneously, to different purposes. For example, when you're driving your car, your visual system (eye and brain) must simultaneously process information about color, shape, depth of field, and motion in the scene before your eyes. This requires complex parallel processing circuits from the retinas of your eyes through the visual centers at the rear of your brain. At the same time, you must process traffic sounds and signals from your body's own joint and motion sensors to know, for example, how hard you are pressing the gas or brake pedal. Efficient simultaneous processing of such information is crucial to your own ability to drive safely.

Serial and parallel processing certainly occur as well in innumerable unconscious processes much simpler than the foregoing examples. In chapter 13, you should be able to see how they apply to certain spinal reflexes.

## 12.6e Memory and Synaptic Plasticity

You may have wondered as you studied this chapter, How am I going to remember all of this? It seems fitting that we end this chapter with the subject of how memory works, for you now have the information necessary to understand its cellular and chemical basis.

The things we learn and remember aren't stored in individual "memory cells" in the brain. You don't have a neuron assigned to remember your phone number and another to remember your grandmother's face, for example. Instead, the physical basis of memory is a *pathway* through the brain called a **memory trace (engram[29]),** in which new synapses have formed or existing synapses have been modified to make transmission easier. In other words, synapses aren't fixed for life; in response to experience, they can be added, taken away, or modified to make transmission easier or harder. Indeed, synapses can be created or deleted in as little as 1 or 2 hours. The ability of synapses to change is called **synaptic plasticity.**

Think about when you learned as a child to tie your shoes. The procedure was very slow, confusing, and laborious at first, but eventually it became so easy you could do it with little thought—like a motor program playing out in your brain without requiring your conscious attention. It became easier to do because the synapses in a certain pathway were modified to allow signals to travel more easily across them than across "untrained" synapses thus creating your *motor memory* for the task. The process of making transmission easier is called **synaptic potentiation** (one form of synaptic plasticity).

Neuroscientists still argue about how to classify the various forms of memory, but three kinds often recognized are *immediate*

[29] *en* = inner; *gram* = mark, trace, record

*memory, short-term memory,* and *long-term memory.* We also know of different modes of synaptic potentiation that last from just a few seconds to a lifetime, and we can correlate these at least tentatively with different forms of memory.

## Immediate Memory

**Immediate memory** is the ability to hold something in mind for just a few seconds. By remembering what just happened, we get a feeling for the flow of events and a sense of the present. Immediate memory is indispensable to the ability to read; you must remember the earliest words of a sentence until you get to its end in order to extract any meaning from it. You couldn't make any sense of what you read if you forgot each word as soon as you moved on to the next one. Immediate memory may be based on reverberating circuits. Our impression of what just happened can thus echo in our minds for a few seconds as we experience the present moment and anticipate the next one.

## Short-Term Memory

**Short-term memory (STM)** lasts from a few seconds to a few hours. Information stored in STM may be quickly forgotten if you stop mentally reciting it, you are distracted, or you have to remember something new. **Working memory** is a form of STM that allows you to hold an idea in mind long enough to carry out an action such as calling a telephone number you just looked up, working out the steps of a mathematics problem, or searching for a lost set of keys while remembering where you've already looked. It is limited to a few bits of information such as the digits of a telephone number. Evidence suggests that working memory resides in a circuit of facilitated synapses that remain quiescent (consuming little energy) most of the time, but are reactivated by new stimulation.

Making it easier to transmit signals across a synapse is called **synaptic facilitation** (different from the facilitation of one neuron by another that we studied earlier in the chapter). Synaptic facilitation can be produced by *tetanic stimulation,* the rapid arrival of repetitive signals at a synapse. Each signal causes a certain amount of $Ca^{2+}$ to enter the axon terminal. If signals arrive rapidly, the neuron cannot pump out all the $Ca^{2+}$ admitted by one action potential before the next action potential occurs. More and more $Ca^{2+}$ accumulates in the terminal. Since $Ca^{2+}$ is what triggers the release of neurotransmitter, each new signal releases more neurotransmitter than the one before. With more neurotransmitter, the EPSPs in the postsynaptic cell become stronger and stronger, and that cell is more likely to fire.

Memories lasting for a few hours, such as remembering what someone said to you earlier in the day or remembering an upcoming appointment, may involve **posttetanic potentiation.** In this process, the $Ca^{2+}$ level in the axon terminal stays elevated for so long that another signal, coming well after the tetanic stimulation has ceased, releases an exceptionally large burst of neurotransmitter. That is, if a synapse has been heavily used in the recent past, a new stimulus can excite the postsynaptic cell more easily. Thus, your memory may need only a slight jog to recall something from several hours earlier.

## Long-Term Memory

**Long-term memory (LTM)** lasts up to a lifetime and is less limited than STM in the amount of information it can store. LTM allows you to memorize the lines of a play, the words of a favorite song, or (one hopes!) textbook information for an exam. On a still longer timescale, it enables you to remember your name, the route to your home, and your childhood experiences.

There are two forms of long-term memory: explicit and implicit. **Explicit** or **declarative memory** is the retention of events and facts that you can put into words—numbers, names, dates, and so forth. You must think to remember these things. **Implicit memory** is the memory of things that come reflexively or unconsciously, including *emotional memories* (such as the fear of being stung if a wasp lands on you) and *procedural memory,* the retention of motor skills—how to tie your shoes, play a musical instrument, or type on a keyboard. These forms of memory involve different regions of the brain but are probably similar at the cellular level.

Some LTM involves the physical remodeling of synapses or the formation of new ones through the growth and branching of axon terminals and dendrites. In the pyramidal cells of the brain, the dendrites are studded with knoblike *dendritic spines* that increase the area of synaptic contact (see fig. 12.5a). Studies on fish and other experimental animals have shown that social and sensory deprivation causes these spines to decline in number, while a richly stimulatory environment causes them to proliferate—an intriguing clue to the importance of a stimulating environment to infant and child development. In some cases of LTM, a new synapse grows beside the original one, giving the presynaptic cell twice as much input into the postsynaptic cell.

LTM can also be grounded in molecular changes called **long-term potentiation (LTP).** This involves *NMDA*[30] *receptors,* which are glutamate-binding receptors found on the dendritic spines of pyramidal cells. NMDA receptors are usually blocked by magnesium ions ($Mg^{2+}$), but when they bind glutamate *and* are simultaneously subjected to high-frequency stimulation, they expel the $Mg^{2+}$ and open to admit $Ca^{2+}$ into the dendrite. When $Ca^{2+}$ enters, it acts as a second messenger with multiple effects. A high $Ca^{2+}$ level activates enzymes called *protein kinases,* which phosphorylate (add phosphate to) proteins employed in building and strengthening synapses. The neuron also produces even more NMDA receptors, making it more sensitive to glutamate, and it may send signals such as nitric oxide (NO) back to the presynaptic cell to enhance its release of neurotransmitter.

You can see that in all of these ways, long-term potentiation can increase transmission across "experienced" synapses. Remodeling a synapse or installing more neurotransmitter receptors has longer-lasting effects than facilitation or posttetanic potentiation.

[30]*N-methyl-D-aspartate,* a chemical similar to glutamate

## How We Forget

Forgetting is arguably as important as remembering; we would likely be driven mad if we couldn't forget the myriad trivial things we encounter every day. People with a pathological inability to forget trivial information have great difficulty in reading comprehension and other functions that require us to distinguish what is important from what is not.

Immediate and short-term memories vanish simply as neural circuits cease to fire. Long-term memories can be erased by a process of **long-term depression (LTD).** Low-frequency stimulation of a synapse results in low levels of intracellular $Ca^{2+}$. This activates *protein phosphatases,* which dephosphorylate synaptic proteins such as actin microfilaments that support dendritic spines. These proteins are then degraded by *proteasomes* (see section 3.4b, fig. 3.31), which tear down dendritic spines and remove little-used synapses from the neural circuits.

The anatomical sites of memory in the brain are discussed in section 14.5d. Regardless of the sites, however, the cellular mechanisms are as described here.

**BEFORE YOU GO ON**

Answer the following questions to test your understanding of the preceding section:

22. Contrast the two types of summation at a synapse and explain how they function in synaptic decision making.
23. Describe how the nervous system communicates quantitative and qualitative information about stimuli.
24. List the four types of neural circuits and describe their similarities and differences. Discuss the unity of form and function in these four types—that is, explain why each type would not perform as it does if its neurons were connected differently.
25. Contrast serial and parallel processing and describe how each can be involved in your everyday mental experiences.
26. State the essence of how immediate, short-term, and long-term memory work.
27. Explain how long-term potentiation and long-term depression influence what you remember and forget.

## DEEPER INSIGHT 12.4

### CLINICAL APPLICATION

### *Alzheimer and Parkinson Diseases*

Alzheimer and Parkinson diseases are the two most common degenerative disorders of the brain. Both are associated with neurotransmitter deficiencies.

*Alzheimer*[31] *disease (AD)* may begin before the age of 50 with signs so slight and ambiguous that early diagnosis is difficult. One of its first signs is memory loss, especially for recent events. A person with AD may ask the same questions repeatedly, show a reduced attention span, and become disoriented and lost in previously familiar places. Family members often feel helpless and confused as they watch their loved one's personality gradually deteriorate beyond recognition. The AD patient may become moody, confused, paranoid, combative, or hallucinatory. The patient may eventually lose even the ability to read, write, talk, walk, and eat. Death typically ensues from pneumonia or other complications of confinement and immobility.

AD affects about 11% of the U.S. population over the age of 65; the incidence rises to 47% by age 85. It accounts for nearly half of all nursing home admissions and is a leading cause of death among the elderly. AD claims about 100,000 lives per year in the United States.

Diagnosis of AD can be confirmed by autopsy. There is atrophy of some of the gyri (folds) of the cerebral cortex and the hippocampus, an important center of memory. Nerve cells exhibit *neurofibrillary tangles*—dense masses of broken and twisted cytoskeleton **(fig. 12.33).** Alois Alzheimer first observed these in 1907 in the brain of a patient who had died of senile dementia. The more severe the signs of disease, the more neurofibrillary tangles are seen at autopsy. In the intercellular spaces, there are *senile plaques* consisting of aggregations of cells, altered nerve fibers, and a core of *β-amyloid protein*—the breakdown product of a glycoprotein of plasma membranes. Amyloid protein is rarely seen in elderly people without AD. Oxidative stress (free radical injury) is now widely believed to underlie the formation of amyloid protein and neurofibrillary tangles, and all the other aspects of AD pathology. This has led to interest in whether dietary antioxidants or antioxidant therapy can reduce the incidence or progression of AD.

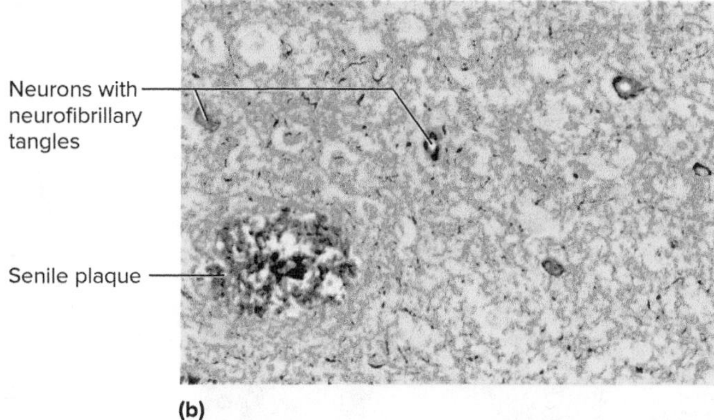


**FIGURE 12.33 Alzheimer Disease.** (a) Brain of a person who died of AD. Note the shrunken folds of cerebral tissue (gyri) and wide gaps (sulci) between them. (b) Cerebral tissue from a person with AD. Neurofibrillary tangles are present within the neurons, and a senile plaque is evident in the extracellular matrix.

a: ©Science Source; b: Simon Fraser/Science Source

[31]Alois Alzheimer (1864–1915), German neurologist

Intense biomedical research efforts are currently geared toward identifying the causes of AD and developing treatment strategies. Three genes on chromosomes 1, 14, and 21 have been implicated in various forms of early- and late-onset AD. Interestingly, persons with Down syndrome (trisomy-21), who have three copies of chromosome 21 instead of the usual two, tend to show early-onset Alzheimer disease. Nongenetic (environmental) factors also seem to be involved.

As for treatment, considerable attention now focuses on trying to halt β-amyloid formation or stimulate the immune system to clear β-amyloid from the brain tissue, but clinical trials in both of these approaches have been suspended until certain serious side effects can be resolved. AD patients show deficiencies of acetylcholine (ACh) and nerve growth factor (NGF). Some patients show improvement when treated with NGF or cholinesterase inhibitors, but results so far have been modest.

*Parkinson*[32] *disease (PD),* also called *paralysis agitans* or *parkinsonism,* is a progressive loss of motor function beginning in a person's 50s or 60s. It is due to degeneration of dopamine-releasing neurons in a portion of the brainstem called the *substantia nigra* **(fig. 12.34).** A gene has recently been identified for a hereditary form of PD, but most cases are nonhereditary and of little-known cause; some authorities suspect environmental neurotoxins.

Dopamine (DA) is an inhibitory neurotransmitter that normally prevents excessive activity in motor centers of the brain called the *basal nuclei.* Degeneration of dopamine-releasing neurons leads to an excessive ratio of ACh to DA, causing hyperactivity of the basal nuclei. As a result, a person with PD suffers involuntary muscle contractions. These take such forms as shaking of the hands (tremor) and compulsive "pill-rolling" motions of the thumb and fingers. In addition, the facial muscles may become rigid and produce a staring, expressionless face with a slightly open mouth. The patient's range of motion diminishes. He or she takes smaller steps and develops a slow, shuffling gait with a forward-bent posture and a tendency to fall forward. Speech becomes slurred and handwriting becomes cramped and eventually illegible. Tasks such as buttoning clothes and preparing food become increasingly laborious.

Patients cannot be expected to recover from PD, but its effects can be alleviated with drugs and physical therapy. Treatment with dopamine is ineffective because it can't cross the blood–brain barrier, but its precursor, levodopa (L-dopa), does cross the barrier and has been used to treat PD since the 1960s. L-dopa affords some relief, but it doesn't slow progression of the disease and it has undesirable side effects on the liver and heart. It is effective for only 5 to 10 years of treatment. A newer drug, deprenyl, is a monoamine oxidase (MAO) inhibitor that retards neural degeneration and slows the development of PD.

A surgical technique called *pallidotomy* has been used since the 1940s to quell severe tremors. It involves the destruction of a small portion of cerebral tissue in an area called the *globus pallidus.* Pallidotomy fell out of favor in the late 1960s when L-dopa came into common use. By the early 1990s, however, the limitations of L-dopa had become apparent, while MRI- and CT-guided methods had improved surgical precision and reduced the risks of brain surgery. Pallidotomy has thus made a comeback. Other surgical treatments for parkinsonism target brain areas called the *subthalamic nucleus* and the *ventral intermediate nucleus* of the thalamus, and involve either the destruction of tiny areas of tissue or the implantation of a stimulating electrode. Such procedures are generally used only in severe cases that are unresponsive to medication.

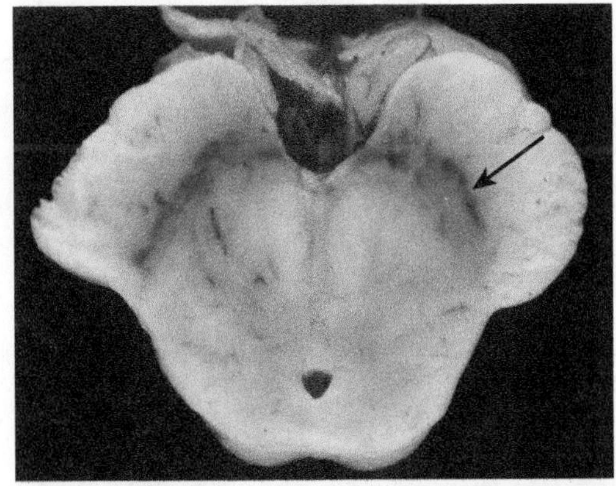

(a)

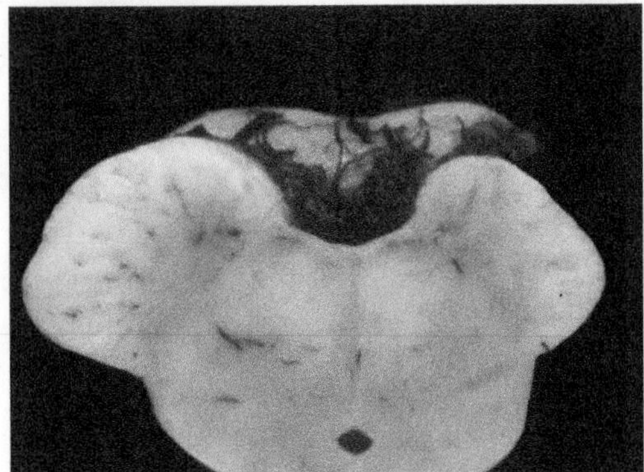

(b)

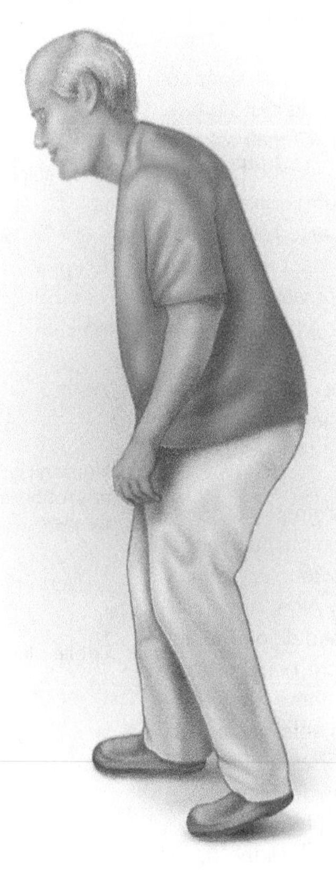

(c)

**FIGURE 12.34 Parkinson Disease (PD).** (a) Cross section of midbrain of a healthy person showing normal, dark band of substantia nigra at arrow. (b) Midbrain section of a PD patient showing absence of substantia nigra. (c) Dyskinesia, a difficulty in walking and forward-tilted stance characteristic of persons with PD.

a–b: ISM/Pr J.J. Hauw/Medical Images

[32]James Parkinson (1755–1824), British physician

# CONNECTIVE ISSUES

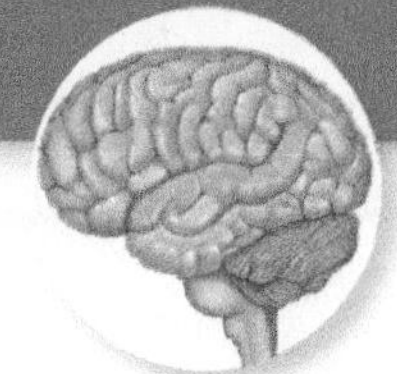

## Effects of the NERVOUS SYSTEM on Other Organ Systems

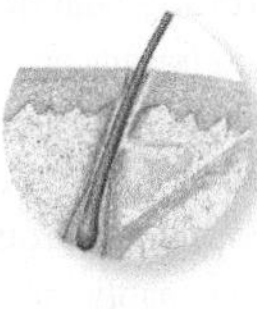

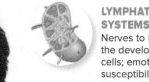

### INTEGUMENTARY SYSTEM

Cutaneous nerves regulate piloerection, sweating, cutaneous vasoconstriction and vasodilation, and heat loss through the body surface, and provide for cutaneous sensations such as touch, itch, tickle, pressure, heat, and cold.

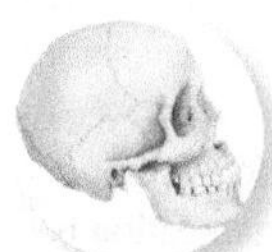

### SKELETAL SYSTEM

Nervous stimulation maintains the muscle tension that stimulates bone growth and remodeling; nerves in the bones respond to strains and fractures.

### MUSCULAR SYSTEM

Skeletal muscles cannot contract without nervous stimulation; the nervous system controls all body movements and muscle tone.

### ENDOCRINE SYSTEM

The hypothalamus controls the pituitary gland; the sympathetic nervous system controls the adrenal medulla; neuroendocrine cells are neurons that secrete hormones such as oxytocin; sensory and other nervous input influences the secretion of numerous other hormones.

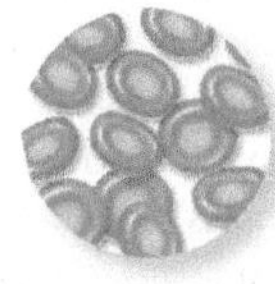

### CIRCULATORY SYSTEM

The nervous system regulates the rate and force of the heartbeat, regulates blood vessel diameters, monitors and controls blood pressure and blood gas concentrations, routes blood to organs where needed, and influences blood clotting.

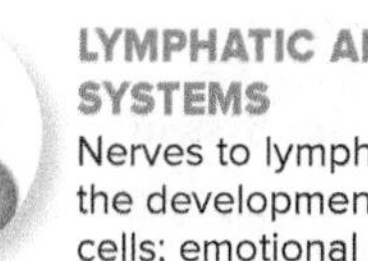

### LYMPHATIC AND IMMUNE SYSTEMS

Nerves to lymphatic organs influence the development and activity of immune cells; emotional states influence susceptibility to infection and other failures of immunity.

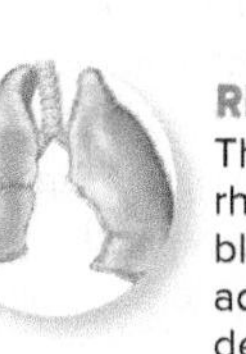

### RESPIRATORY SYSTEM

The brainstem regulates the rhythm of breathing, monitors blood pH and blood gases, and adjusts the respiratory rate and depth to control these within normal ranges.

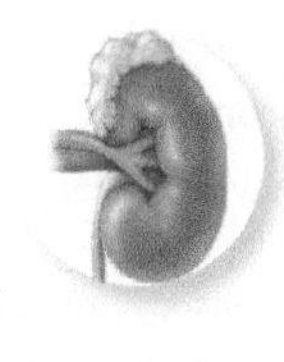

### URINARY SYSTEM

Sympathetic nerves modify the rate of urine production by the kidneys; nervous stimulation of urinary sphincters aids in urine retention in the bladder, and nervous reflexes control its emptying.

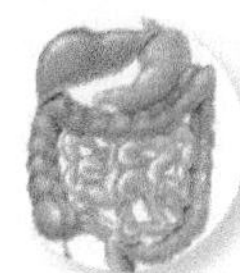

### DIGESTIVE SYSTEM

The nervous system regulates appetite, feeding behavior, digestive secretion and motility, and defecation.

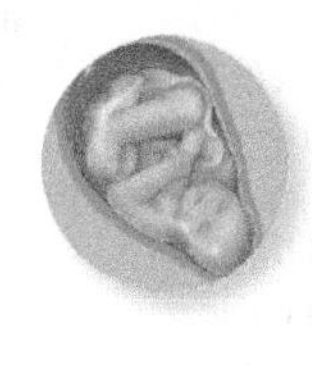

### REPRODUCTIVE SYSTEM

The nervous system regulates sex drive, arousal, and orgasm; the brain regulates the secretion of pituitary hormones that control spermatogenesis in males and the ovarian cycle in females; the nervous system controls various aspects of pregnancy and childbirth; the brain produces oxytocin, which is involved in labor contractions and lactation.

# STUDY GUIDE

## ▶ Assess Your Learning Outcomes

*To test your knowledge, discuss the following topics with a study partner or in writing, ideally from memory.*

### 12.1 Overview of the Nervous System

1. What the nervous and endocrine systems have in common
2. Three fundamental functions of the nervous system; the roles of receptors and effectors in carrying out these functions
3. Differences between the central nervous system (CNS) and peripheral nervous system (PNS); between the sensory and motor divisions of the PNS; and between the somatic and visceral subdivisions of both the sensory and motor divisions
4. The autonomic nervous system and its two divisions

### 12.2 Properties of Neurons

1. Three fundamental physiological properties of neurons
2. Differences between sensory (afferent) neurons, interneurons (association neurons), and motor (efferent) neurons
3. The parts of a generalized multipolar neuron, and their functions
4. Differences between multipolar, bipolar, unipolar, and anaxonic neurons; an example of each
5. Ways in which neurons transport substances between the neurosoma and the distal ends of the axon

### 12.3 Supportive Cells

1. Six kinds of neuroglia; the structure and functions of each; and which kinds are found in the CNS and which ones in the PNS
2. Structure of the myelin sheath, and how CNS and PNS glial cells produce it
3. How fiber diameter and the presence or absence of myelin affect the conduction speed of a nerve fiber
4. The regeneration of a damaged nerve fiber; the roles of Schwann cells, the basal lamina, and neurilemma in regeneration; and why CNS neurons cannot regenerate

### 12.4 Electrophysiology of Neurons

1. The meanings of *electrical potential* and *resting membrane potential* (RMP); the typical voltage of an RMP
2. What an electrical current is, and how sodium ions and gated membrane channels generate a current
3. How stimulation of a neuron generates a local potential; the physiological properties of a local potential
4. Special properties of the trigger zone and unmyelinated regions of a nerve fiber that enable these regions to generate action potentials
5. The mechanism of an action potential; how it relates to ion flows and the action of membrane channels; and what is meant by *depolarization* and *repolarization* of the plasma membrane during local and action potentials
6. The all-or-none law and how it applies to an action potential; other properties of action potentials in contrast to local potentials
7. The basis and significance of the refractory period that follows an action potential
8. How one action potential triggers another; how the continuous conduction seen in unmyelinated nerve fibers result from a chain reaction of action potentials; and what normally prevents the signal from traveling backward to the neurosoma
9. Saltatory conduction in a myelinated nerve fiber; differences in conduction mechanisms of the myelin sheath gaps and internodal segments; and why signals travel faster in myelinated fibers than in unmyelinated fibers of comparable size

### 12.5 Synapses

1. The structure and locations of synapses
2. The role of neurotransmitters in synaptic transmission
3. Categories of neurotransmitters and common examples of each
4. Why the same neurotransmitter can have different effects on different cells
5. Excitatory synapses; how acetylcholine and norepinephrine excite a postsynaptic neuron
6. Inhibitory synapses; how γ-aminobutyric acid (GABA) inhibits a postsynaptic neuron
7. How second-messenger systems function at synapses
8. Three ways in which synaptic transmission is ended
9. Neuromodulators, their chemical nature, and how they affect synaptic transmission

### 12.6 Neural Integration

1. Why synapses slow down nervous communication; the overriding benefit of synapses
2. The meaning of *excitatory* and *inhibitory postsynaptic potentials* (EPSPs and IPSPs)
3. Why the production of an EPSP or IPSP may depend on both the neurotransmitter released by the presynaptic neuron and the type of receptor on the postsynaptic neuron
4. How a postsynaptic neuron's decision to fire depends on the ratio of EPSPs to IPSPs
5. Temporal and spatial summation, where they occur, and how they determine whether a neuron fires
6. Mechanisms of presynaptic facilitation and inhibition, and how communication between two neurons can be strengthened or weakened by a third neuron employing one of these mechanisms
7. Mechanisms of neural coding; how a neuron communicates qualitative and quantitative information
8. Why the refractory period sets a limit to how frequently a neuron can fire
9. The meanings of *neural pool* and *neural circuit*
10. The difference between a neuron's discharge zone and facilitated zone, and how this relates to neurons working in groups
11. Diverging, converging, reverberating, and parallel after-discharge circuits of neurons; examples of their relevance to familiar body functions
12. The difference between serial and parallel processing of information and how they influence everyday body functions
13. The cellular basis of memory; what memory consists of in terms of neural pathways, and how it relates to synaptic plasticity and potentiation
14. Types of things remembered in immediate memory, short-term memory (STM), and long-term memory (LTM), and in the explicit and implicit forms of LTM
15. Neural mechanisms thought to be involved in these different forms of memory and in forgetting

# STUDY GUIDE

## Testing Your Recall

Answers in Appendix A

1. The integrative functions of the nervous system are performed mainly by
   a. afferent neurons.
   b. efferent neurons.
   c. neuroglia.
   d. sensory neurons.
   e. interneurons.

2. The highest density of voltage-gated ion channels is found in the _____ of a neuron.
   a. dendrites
   b. neurosoma
   c. myelin sheath gaps
   d. internodal segments
   e. axon terminals

3. The neurosoma of a mature neuron lacks
   a. a nucleus.
   b. endoplasmic reticulum.
   c. lipofuscin.
   d. centrioles.
   e. ribosomes.

4. The glial cells that fight infections in the CNS are
   a. microglia.
   b. satellite cells.
   c. ependymal cells.
   d. oligodendrocytes.
   e. astrocytes.

5. Posttetanic potentiation of a synapse increases the amount of _____ in the axon terminal.
   a. neurotransmitter
   b. neurotransmitter receptors
   c. calcium
   d. sodium
   e. NMDA

6. An IPSP is _____ of the postsynaptic neuron.
   a. a refractory period
   b. an action potential
   c. a depolarization
   d. a repolarization
   e. a hyperpolarization

7. Saltatory conduction occurs only
   a. at chemical synapses.
   b. in the initial segment of an axon.
   c. in both the initial segment and axon hillock.
   d. in myelinated nerve fibers.
   e. in unmyelinated nerve fibers.

8. Some neurotransmitters can have either excitatory or inhibitory effects depending on the type of
   a. receptors on the postsynaptic cell.
   b. synaptic vesicles in the axon.
   c. synaptic potentiation that occurs.
   d. postsynaptic potentials on the axon terminal.
   e. neuromodulator involved.

9. Differences in the volume of a sound are likely to be encoded by differences in _____ in nerve fibers from the inner ear.
   a. neurotransmitters
   b. signal conduction velocity
   c. types of postsynaptic potentials
   d. firing frequency
   e. voltage of the action potentials

10. Motor effects that depend on repetitive output from a neural pool are most likely to use
    a. parallel after-discharge circuits.
    b. reverberating circuits.
    c. facilitated circuits.
    d. diverging circuits.
    e. converging circuits.

11. Neurons that convey information to the CNS are called sensory, or _____, neurons.

12. To perform their role, neurons must have the properties of excitability, secretion, and _____.

13. The _____ is a period of time in which a neuron is producing an action potential and cannot respond to another stimulus of any strength.

14. Neurons receive incoming signals by way of specialized extensions of the cell called _____.

15. In the CNS, myelin is produced by glial cells called _____.

16. A myelinated nerve fiber can produce action potentials only in specialized regions called _____.

17. The trigger zone of a neuron consists of its _____ and _____.

18. The neurotransmitter secreted at an adrenergic synapse is _____.

19. A presynaptic nerve fiber cannot cause other neurons in its _____ to fire, but it can make them more sensitive to stimulation from other presynaptic fibers.

20. _____ are substances released along with a neurotransmitter that modify the neurotransmitter's effect.

## Building Your Medical Vocabulary

Answers in Appendix A

*State a meaning of each word element, and give a medical term from this chapter that uses it or a slight variation of it.*

1. antero-
2. -aps
3. astro-
4. dendro-
5. -fer
6. gangli-
7. -grad
8. neuro-
9. sclero-
10. somato-

# STUDY GUIDE

## What's Wrong with These Statements?

Answers in Appendix A

*Briefly explain why each of the following statements is false, or reword it to make it true.*

1. A neuron may have anywhere from one to several axons.
2. Astrocytes perform the same function in the brain as Schwann cells do in the peripheral nerves.
3. A resting neuron has a higher concentration of $Na^+$ in its cytoplasm than in the extracellular fluid surrounding it.
4. During an action potential, most of the $Na^+$ and $K^+$ exchange places across the plasma membrane.
5. Excitatory postsynaptic potentials lower the threshold of a neuron and thus make it easier to stimulate.
6. In theory, there is no upper limit to how often a neuron can fire if it is stimulated strongly enough.
7. A given neurotransmitter has the same effect no matter where in the body it is secreted.
8. Myelinated nerve fibers conduct signals more rapidly than unmyelinated ones because they have gaps in the myelin sheath.
9. Learning occurs by increasing the number of neurons in the brain tissue.
10. Dead neurons in the brain are quickly replaced by mitosis of surviving neurons.

## Testing Your Comprehension

1. Schizophrenia is sometimes treated with drugs such as chlorpromazine that inhibit dopamine receptors. A side effect is that patients begin to develop muscle tremors, speech impairment, and other disorders similar to Parkinson disease. Explain.
2. Hyperkalemia is an excess of potassium in the extracellular fluid. What effect would this have on the resting membrane potentials of the nervous system and on neural excitability?
3. Suppose a poison were to slow down the $Na^+$–$K^+$ pumps of nerve cells. How would this affect the resting membrane potentials of neurons? Would it make neurons more excitable than normal, or make them more difficult to stimulate? Explain.
4. The unity of form and function is an important concept in understanding synapses. Give two structural reasons why nerve signals cannot travel backward across a chemical synapse. What could be the consequences if signals did travel freely in both directions?
5. Positive feedback is usually harmful to the body, or even life-threatening, but there are a few cases where it is beneficial and necessary. Identify such a case in neuron electrophysiology. If necessary, review the defining characteristics of positive feedback in section 1.6d.

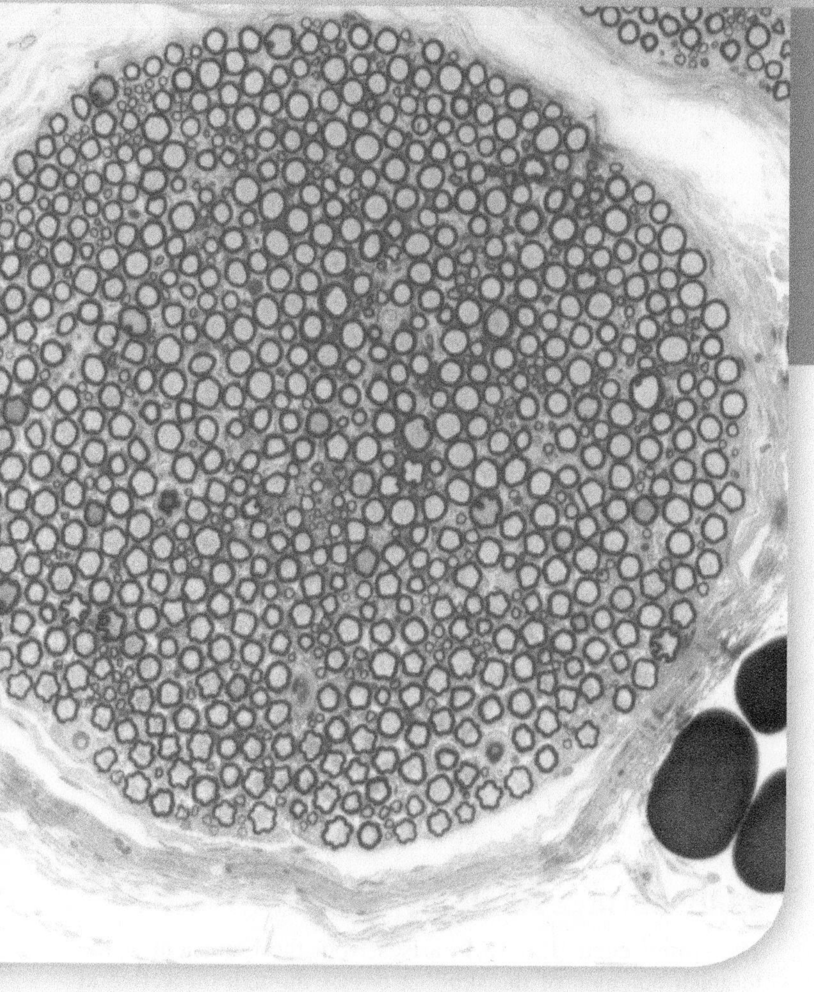

Cross section of the sciatic nerve, showing myelinated nerve fibers (large pale circles) and small unmyelinated fibers scattered among them
Science Photo Library/Alamy Stock Photo

CHAPTER 13

# THE SPINAL CORD, SPINAL NERVES, AND SOMATIC REFLEXES

## CHAPTER OUTLINE



## DEEPER INSIGHTS

**Module 7: Nervous System**

## BRUSHING UP

- This chapter assumes that you have a basic knowledge of neuron structure (see section 12.2c).
- Spinal cord anatomy is described here in terms that assume you are familiar with anatomy of the spinal (vertebral) column in section 8.3.
- To understand spinal reflexes, you must be familiar with the ways muscles work together at a joint, especially antagonistic muscles (see fig. 10.4 and the associated discussion).
- Understanding spinal reflexes also requires a knowledge of excitatory and inhibitory postsynaptic potentials (EPSPs and IPSPs) and the parallel after-discharge type of neural circuit (see sections 12.6a, 12.6d).

Every year in the United States, thousands of people become paralyzed by spinal cord injuries, with devastating effects on their quality of life. The treatment of such injuries is one of the most lively areas of medical research today. Therapists in this specialty must know spinal cord anatomy and function to understand their patients' functional deficits and prospects for improvement and to plan a regimen of treatment. Such knowledge is necessary, as well, for understanding paralysis resulting from strokes and other brain injuries. The spinal cord is the "information highway" that connects the brain with the lower body; it contains the neural routes that explain why a lesion to a specific part of the brain results in a functional loss in a specific locality in the lower body.

In this chapter, we will study not only the spinal cord but also the spinal nerves that arise from it with ladderlike regularity at intervals along its length. Thus, we will examine components of both the central and peripheral nervous systems, but these are so closely related, structurally and functionally, that it is appropriate to consider them together. Similarly, the brain and cranial nerves will be considered together in the following chapter. Chapters 13 and 14 therefore elevate our study of the nervous system from the cellular level (chapter 12) to the organ and system levels.

## 13.1 The Spinal Cord

### Expected Learning Outcomes

When you have completed this section, you should be able to

a. state the three principal functions of the spinal cord;
b. describe its gross and microscopic structure; and
c. trace the pathways followed by nerve signals traveling up and down the spinal cord.

### 13.1a Functions

The spinal cord serves four principal functions:

1. **Conduction.** It contains bundles of nerve fibers that conduct information up and down the cord, connecting different levels of the trunk with each other and with the brain. This enables sensory information to reach the brain, motor commands to reach the effectors, and input received at one level of the cord to affect output from another level.
2. **Neural integration.** Pools of spinal neurons receive input from multiple sources, integrate the information, and execute an appropriate output. For example, the spinal cord can integrate the stretch sensation from a full bladder with cerebral input concerning the appropriate time and place to urinate and execute control of the bladder accordingly.
3. **Locomotion.** Walking involves repetitive, coordinated contractions of several muscle groups in the limbs. Motor neurons in the brain initiate walking and determine its speed, distance, and direction, but the simple repetitive muscle contractions that put one foot in front of another, over and over, are coordinated by groups of neurons called **central pattern generators** in the cord. These neural circuits produce the sequence of outputs to the extensor and flexor muscles that cause alternating movements of the lower limbs.
4. **Reflexes.** Spinal reflexes play vital roles in posture, motor coordination, and protective responses to pain or injury.

### 13.1b Surface Anatomy

The **spinal cord (fig. 13.1)** arises from the brainstem at the foramen magnum of the skull. It passes through the vertebral canal as far as the inferior margin of the first lumbar vertebra (L1) or slightly beyond. In adults, it averages about 45 cm long and 1.8 cm thick (about as thick as one's little finger). Early in fetal development, the cord extends for the full length of the vertebral column. However, the vertebral column grows faster than the spinal cord, so the cord extends only to L3 by the time of birth and to L1 in an adult. Thus, it occupies only the upper two-thirds of the vertebral canal; the lower one-third is described shortly.

The cord gives rise to 31 pairs of *spinal nerves.* Although the spinal cord is not visibly segmented, the part supplied by each pair of nerves is called a *segment.* The cord exhibits longitudinal grooves on its anterior and posterior sides—the *anterior median fissure* and *posterior median sulcus,* respectively **(fig. 13.2).**

The spinal cord is divided into **cervical, thoracic, lumbar,** and **sacral regions.** It may seem odd that it has a sacral region when the cord itself ends well above the sacrum. These regions, however, are named for the level of the vertebral column from which the spinal nerves emerge, not for the vertebrae that contain the cord itself.

In two areas, the cord is a little thicker than elsewhere. In the inferior cervical region, a **cervical enlargement** gives rise to nerves of the upper limbs. In the lumbosacral region, there is a similar **lumbosacral enlargement** that issues nerves to the pelvic

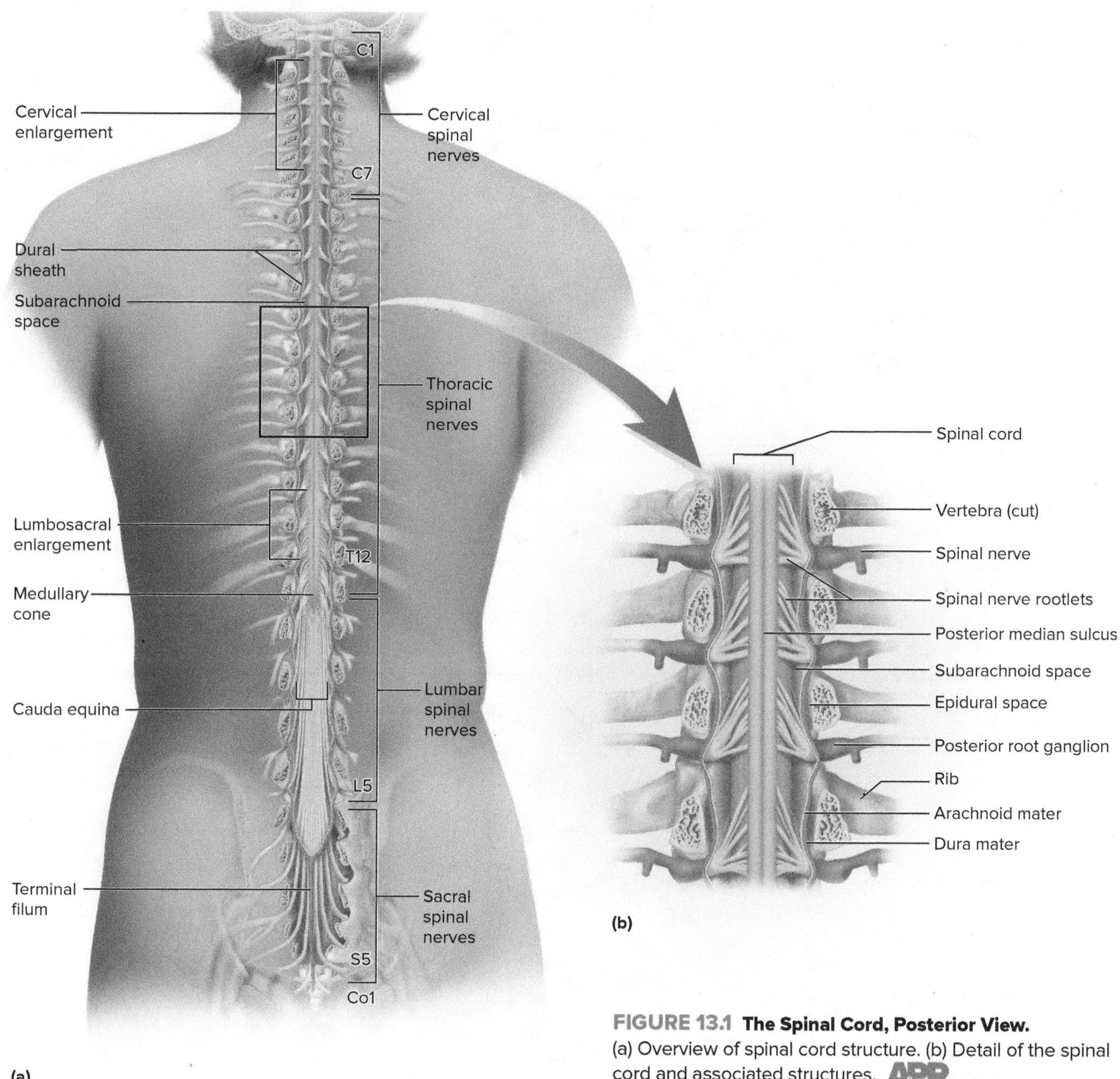


**FIGURE 13.1 The Spinal Cord, Posterior View.** (a) Overview of spinal cord structure. (b) Detail of the spinal cord and associated structures. APR

region and lower limbs. Inferior to the lumbosacral enlargement, the cord tapers to a point called the **medullary cone.** Arising from the lumbosacral enlargement and medullary cone is a bundle of nerve roots that occupy the vertebral canal from L2 to S5. This bundle, named the **cauda equina**[1] (CAW-duh ee-KWY-nah) for its resemblance to a horse's tail, innervates the pelvic organs and lower limbs.

**APPLY WHAT YOU KNOW**

*Spinal cord injuries commonly result from fractures of vertebrae C5 to C6, but never from fractures of L3 to L5. Explain both observations.*

[1]*cauda* = tail; *equin* = horse

## 13.1c Meninges of the Spinal Cord

The spinal cord and brain are enclosed in three fibrous membranes called **meninges**[2] (meh-NIN-jeez)—singular, *meninx* (MEN-inks) (fig. 13.2). These membranes separate the soft tissue of the central nervous system from the bones of the vertebrae and skull. From superficial to deep, they are the dura mater, arachnoid mater, and pia mater.

The **dura mater**[3] (DOO-ruh MAH-tur) forms a loose-fitting sleeve called the **dural sheath** around the spinal cord. It is a tough membrane about as thick as a rubber kitchen glove, composed of multiple layers of dense irregular connective tissue. The space between the sheath and vertebral bones, called the **epidural space,** is occupied by

[2]*menin* = membrane
[3]*dura* = tough; *mater* = mother, womb

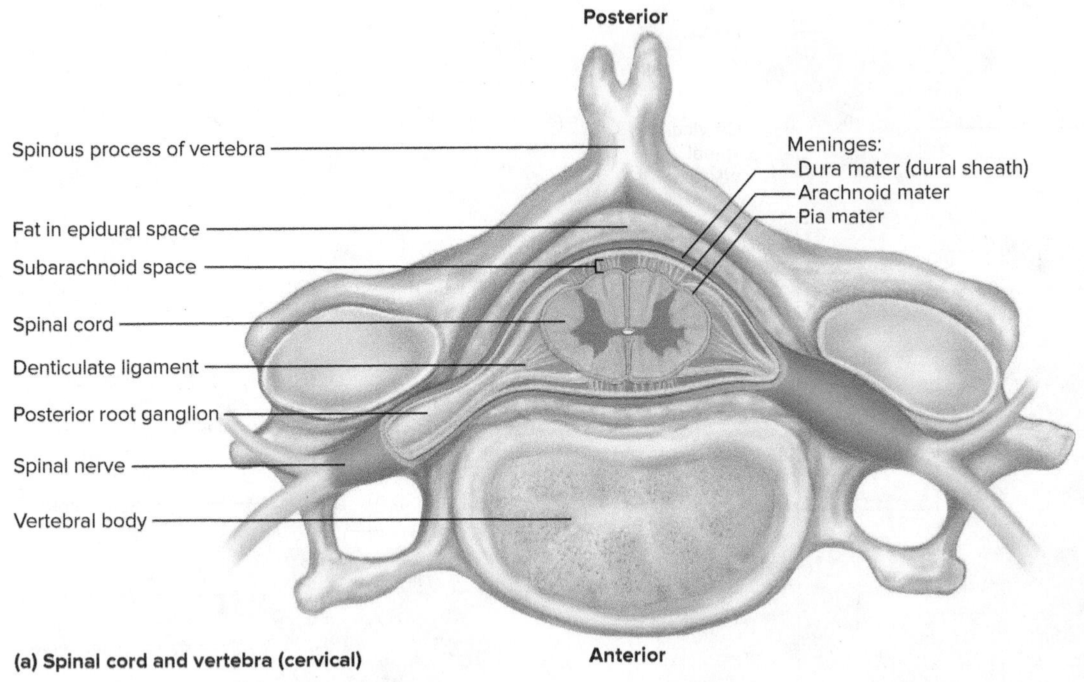


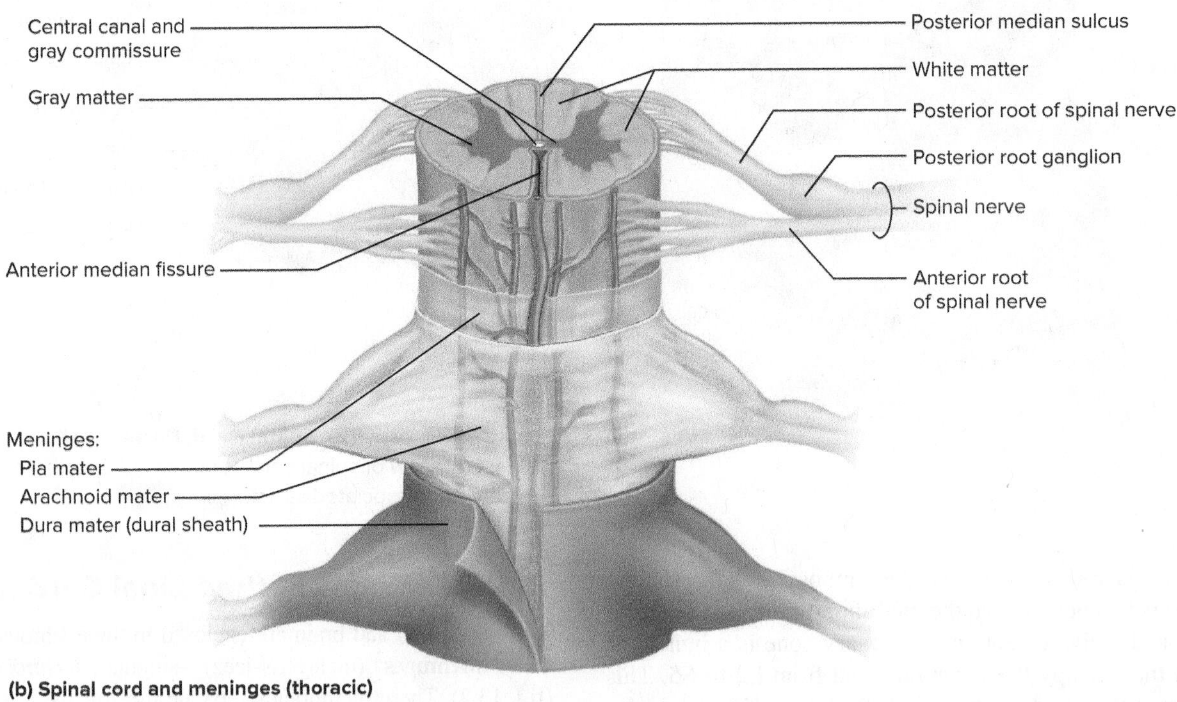


**FIGURE 13.2 Cross-Sectional Anatomy of the Spinal Cord.** (a) Relationship to the vertebra, meninges, and spinal nerves. (b) Detail of the spinal cord, meninges, and spinal nerve roots. See figure 13.3 for details of the gray and white matter.

blood vessels, adipose tissue, and loose connective tissue. Anesthetics can be introduced to this space to block pain signals during childbirth or surgery; this procedure is called *epidural anesthesia.*

The **arachnoid**[4] **mater** (ah-RACK-noyd) consists of the *arachnoid membrane*—five or six layers of squamous to cuboidal cells adhering to the inside of the dura—and a looser array of cells and collagenous and elastic fibers spanning the gap between the arachnoid membrane and the pia mater. This gap, the **subarachnoid space,** is filled with **cerebrospinal fluid (CSF)** (see section 14.2b). Inferior to the medullary cone, the subarachnoid space is called the **lumbar cistern** and is occupied by the cauda equina and CSF. When a sample of CSF is needed for clinical purposes, it is

[4]*arachn* = spider, spider web; *oid* = resembling

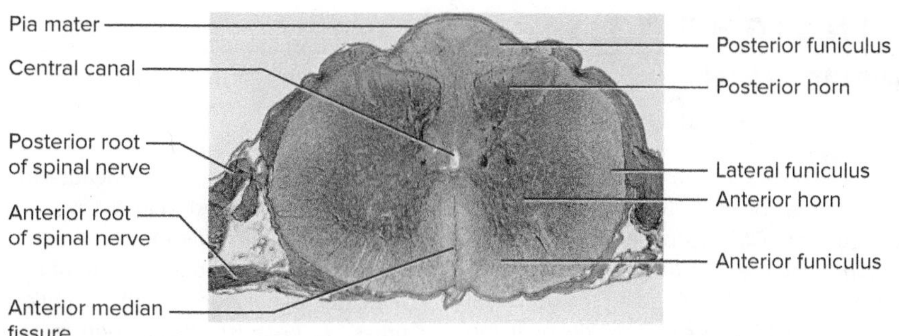


**FIGURE 13.3 Cross Section of the Spinal Cord (Lumbar Region).**
Jose Luis Calvo/Shutterstock

taken from the lumbar cistern by a procedure called a **spinal tap** or **lumbar puncture** (see Deeper Insight 13.1).

The **pia**[5] **mater** (PEE-uh) is a delicate, transparent membrane composed of one or two layers of squamous to cuboidal cells and delicate collagenous and elastic fibers. It closely follows the contours of the spinal cord. It continues beyond the medullary cone as a fibrous strand, the **terminal filum,** within the lumbar cistern. At the level of vertebra S2, it exits the lower end of the cistern and fuses with the dura mater, and the two form a **coccygeal ligament** that anchors the cord and meninges to vertebra Co1. At regular intervals along the cord, extensions of the pia called **denticulate**[6] **ligaments** extend through the arachnoid to the dura, anchoring the cord and limiting side-to-side movements.

## 13.1d Cross-Sectional Anatomy

Figure 13.2a shows the relationship of the spinal cord to a vertebra and spinal nerve, and **figure 13.3** shows the cord itself in more detail. The spinal cord, like the brain, consists of two kinds of nervous tissue called gray and white matter. **Gray matter** has a relatively dull color because it contains little myelin. It contains the somas, dendrites, and proximal parts of the axons of neurons. It is the site of synaptic contact between neurons, and therefore the site of all neural integration in the spinal cord. **White matter,** by contrast, has a bright, pearly white appearance due to an abundance of myelin. It is composed of bundles of axons, called **tracts,** that carry signals from one level of the CNS to another. Both gray and white matter also have an abundance of glial cells. Nervous tissue is often histologically stained with silver compounds, which give the gray matter a brown or golden color and white matter a lighter tan to amber color on slides that you may study.

### Gray Matter

The spinal cord has a central core of gray matter that looks somewhat butterfly- or H-shaped in cross sections. The core consists mainly of two **posterior (dorsal) horns,** which extend toward the posterolateral surfaces of the cord, and two thicker **anterior (ventral) horns,** which extend toward the anterolateral surfaces. The right and left sides of the gray matter are connected by a median bridge called the **gray commissure.** In the middle of the commissure is the **central canal,** which is collapsed in most areas of the adult spinal cord, but in some places (and in young children) remains open, lined with ependymal cells, and filled with CSF.

The posterior horn receives sensory nerve fibers from the spinal nerves, which usually synapse with networks of interneurons in the horn. The anterior horn contains the large neurosomas of motor neurons whose axons lead out to the skeletal muscles. The interneurons and motor neurons are especially abundant in the cervical and lumbosacral enlargements and are quite conspicuous in histological sections from these levels. The high density of neurons in these regions is related to motor control and sensation in the upper and lower limbs.

An additional **lateral horn** is visible on each side of the gray matter from segments T2 through L1 of the cord. It contains neurons of the sympathetic nervous system, which send their axons out of the cord by way of the anterior root along with the somatic efferent fibers.

### White Matter

The white matter of the spinal cord surrounds the gray matter. It consists of bundles of axons that course up and down the cord and provide avenues of communication between different levels of the CNS. These bundles are arranged in three pairs called **funiculi**[7] (few-NIC-you-lie)—a **posterior (dorsal), lateral,** and **anterior (ventral) funiculus** on each side. Each column consists of subdivisions called **tracts** or **fasciculi**[8] (fah-SIC-you-lye).

## 13.1e Spinal Tracts

Knowledge of the locations and functions of the spinal tracts is essential in diagnosing and managing spinal cord injuries. **Ascending tracts** carry sensory information up the

[5]*pia* = through mistranslation, now construed as tender, thin, or soft
[6]*denti* = tooth; *cul* = little; *ate* = resembling
[7]*funicul* = little rope, cord
[8]*fascicul* = little bundle

## DEEPER INSIGHT 13.1

### CLINICAL APPLICATION

### Spinal Tap

Several neurological diseases are diagnosed in part by examining cerebrospinal fluid (CSF) for bacteria, blood, white blood cells, or abnormalities of chemical composition. CSF is obtained by a procedure called a *spinal tap,* or *lumbar puncture.* The patient leans forward or lies on one side with the spine flexed, thus spreading the vertebral laminae and spinous processes apart **(fig. 13.4)**. The skin over the lumbar vertebrae is anesthetized, and a needle is inserted between the spinous processes of L3 and L4 (sometimes L4 and L5). This is the safest place to obtain CSF because the spinal cord doesn't extend this far and isn't exposed to injury by the needle. At a depth of 4 to 6 cm, the needle punctures the dura mater and enters the lumbar cistern. CSF normally drips out at a rate of about 1 drop per second. A lumbar puncture is not performed if a patient has signs of high intracranial pressure, because the sudden release of pressure (causing CSF to jet from the puncture) can cause fatal herniation of the brainstem and cerebellum into the vertebral canal.

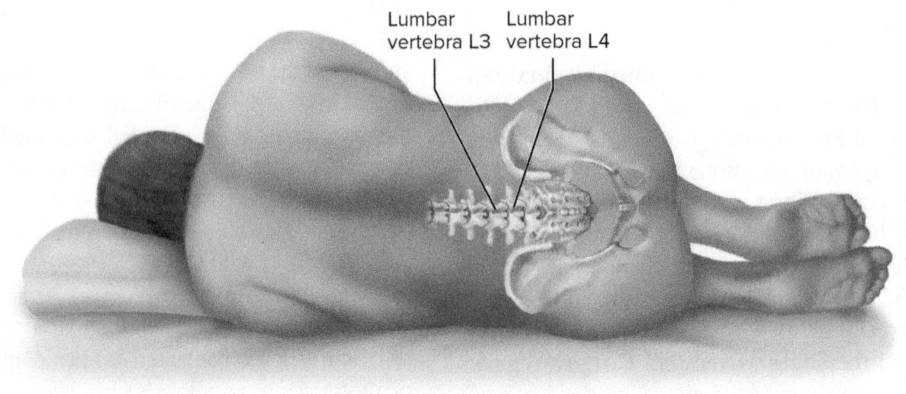


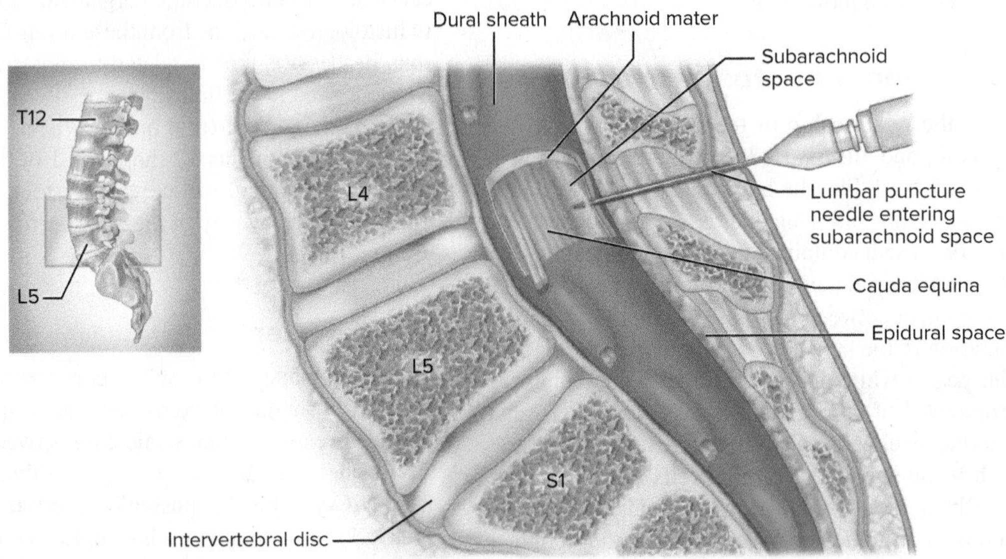


**FIGURE 13.4 Spinal Tap (Lumbar Puncture).**

cord, and **descending tracts** conduct motor impulses down **(fig. 13.5).** All nerve fibers in a given tract have a similar origin, destination, and function. Many of these fibers have their origin or destination in a region called the *brainstem.* Described more fully in section 14.3 (see fig. 14.1), this is a vertical stalk that supports the large *cerebellum* at the rear of the head and, even larger, two *cerebral hemispheres* that dominate the brain. In the following discussion, you will find references to brainstem and other regions where spinal tracts begin and end. Spinal cord anatomy will grow in meaning as you study the brain.

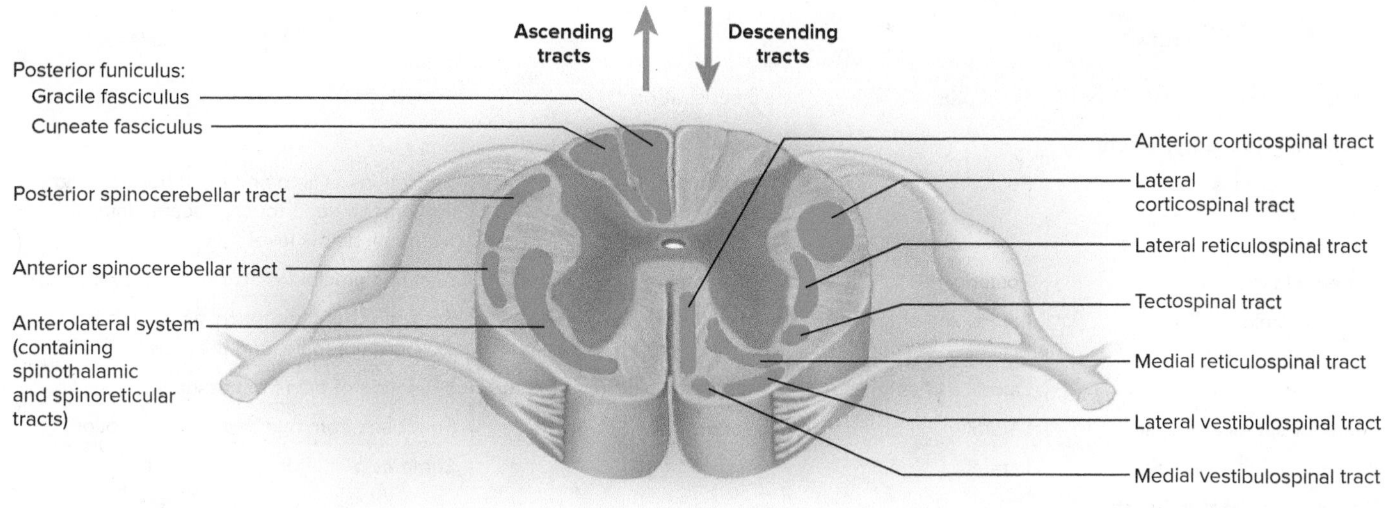


**FIGURE 13.5 Tracts of the Spinal Cord.** All of the illustrated tracts occur on both sides of the cord, but only the ascending sensory tracts are shown on the left (red), and only the descending motor tracts on the right (green).

? *If you were told that this cross section is either at level T4 or T10, how could you determine which is correct?*

Several of these tracts undergo **decussation**[9] (DEE-cuh-SAY-shun) as they pass up or down the brainstem and spinal cord—meaning that they cross over from the left side of the body to the right, or vice versa. As a result, the left side of the brain receives sensory information from the right side of the body and sends motor commands to that side, while the right side of the brain senses and controls the left side of the body. Therefore, a stroke that damages motor centers of the right side of the brain can cause paralysis of the left limbs and vice versa.

When the origin and destination of a tract are on opposite sides of the body, we say they are **contralateral**[10] to each other. When a tract doesn't decussate, its origin and destination are on the same side of the body and we say they are **ipsilateral.**[11]

The major spinal tracts are summarized in **table 13.1** and the following text. Bear in mind that each tract is repeated on the right and left sides of the spinal cord.

## Ascending Tracts

Ascending tracts carry sensory signals up the spinal cord. Sensory signals typically travel across three neurons from their origin in the receptors to their destination in the brain: a **first-order neuron** that detects a stimulus and transmits a signal to the spinal cord or brainstem; a **second-order neuron** that continues as far as a "gateway" called the *thalamus* at the upper end of the brainstem; and a **third-order neuron** that carries the signal the rest of the way to the cerebral cortex. The axons of these neurons are called the *first-* through *third-order nerve fibers* **(fig. 13.6).**

The major ascending tracts are as follows. The names of most of them consist of the prefix *spino-* followed by a root denoting the destination of its fibers in the brain, although this naming system does not apply to the first two.

- The posterior funiculus consists of the **cuneate**[12] **fasciculus** (CUE-nee-ate) and **gracile**[13] **fasciculus** (GRAS-el) from level T6 to the brain, and only the gracile fasciculus from T7 down (fig. 13.6a). The gracile fasciculus carries sensory signals from the lower trunk and lower limbs, and the cuneate fasciculus from the chest and upper limbs. These signals include the senses of vibration, visceral pain, deep touch, and especially proprioception from the lower limbs and lower trunk. **Proprioception**[14] is one's nonvisual sense of the position and movements of the body and its parts, coming from sensory nerve endings in the muscles, tendons, and joints. The brain uses this information to adjust muscle tone and actions to maintain equilibrium (balance), posture, and coordination. The first-order nerve fibers of these fasciculi end in the medulla oblongata of the brainstem, but the second-order fibers decussate there to the other side of the brain. Thus, the right brain receives signals from the left side of the body and vice versa.
- The **spinothalamic tract** (SPY-no-tha-LAM-ic) (fig. 13.6b) and some smaller tracts form the *anterolateral system,* which passes up the anterior and lateral funiculi of the spinal cord. The spinothalamic tract carries signals for pain, temperature, pressure, tickle, itch, and light touch. Light touch is the

[9] *decuss* = to cross, form an X
[10] *contra* = opposite; *later* = side
[11] *ipsi* = the same; *later* = side

[12] *cune* = wedge
[13] *gracil* = thin, slender
[14] *proprio* = one's own; *ception* = sensation

**TABLE 13.1 Major Spinal Tracts**

| Tract | Funiculus | Decussation | Functions |
|---|---|---|---|
| **Ascending (Sensory) Tracts** | | | |
| Gracile fasciculus | Posterior | In medulla | Sensations of limb and trunk position and movement, deep touch, visceral pain, and vibration, below level T6 |
| Cuneate fasciculus | Posterior | In medulla | Same as gracile fasciculus, from level T6 up |
| Spinothalamic | Lateral and anterior | In spinal cord | Sensations of light touch, tickle, itch, temperature, pain, and pressure |
| Spinoreticular | Lateral and anterior | In spinal cord (some fibers) | Sensation of pain from tissue injury |
| Posterior spinocerebellar | Lateral | None | Feedback from muscles (proprioception) |
| Anterior spinocerebellar | Lateral | In spinal cord | Same as posterior spinocerebellar |
| **Descending (Motor) Tracts** | | | |
| Lateral corticospinal | Lateral | In medulla | Fine control of limbs |
| Anterior corticospinal | Anterior | In spinal cord | Fine control of limbs |
| Tectospinal | Anterior | In midbrain | Reflexive head turning in response to visual and auditory stimuli |
| Lateral reticulospinal | Lateral | None | Balance and posture; regulation of awareness of pain |
| Medial reticulospinal | Anterior | None | Same as lateral reticulospinal |
| Lateral vestibulospinal | Anterior | None | Balance and posture |
| Medial vestibulospinal | Anterior | In medulla (some fibers) | Control of head position |

sensation produced, for example, by stroking hairless skin with a feather or cotton wisp, without indenting the skin. In this pathway, first-order neurons end in the posterior horn of the spinal cord near the point of entry. Here they synapse with second-order neurons, which decussate and form the contralateral ascending spinothalamic tract. These fibers lead all the way to the thalamus. Therefore, here again, each hemisphere of the brain receives sensory input from the opposite side of the body.

- The **spinoreticular tract** carries pain signals up the anterolateral system. First-order pain fibers enter the posterior horn and immediately synapse with second-order neurons. These decussate to the opposite anterolateral system, ascend the cord, and end in a loosely organized core of gray matter called the *reticular*[15] *formation* in the medulla oblongata and pons. Pain pathways are further discussed in chapter 16.
- The **posterior** and **anterior spinocerebellar tracts** (SPY-no-SERR-eh-BEL-ur) travel through the lateral funiculus and carry proprioceptive signals from the limbs and trunk to the cerebellum at the rear of the brain. Their first-order neurons originate in muscles and tendons and end in the posterior horn of the spinal cord. Second-order neurons send their fibers up the spinocerebellar tracts and end in the cerebellum. Both tracts provide the cerebellum with feedback needed to coordinate muscle action.

[15]*reticul* = little network

## Descending Tracts

Descending tracts carry motor signals down the brainstem and spinal cord. A descending motor pathway typically involves two neurons called the upper and lower motor neurons. The **upper motor neuron** begins with a neurosoma in the cerebral cortex or brainstem and has an axon that terminates on a **lower motor neuron** in the brainstem or spinal cord. The axon of the lower motor neuron then leads the rest of the way to the muscle or other target organ. The names of most descending tracts consist of a word root denoting the point of origin in the brain, followed by the suffix *-spinal.* The major descending tracts are described here.

- The **lateral** and **anterior corticospinal tracts** (COR-tih-co-SPY-nul) **(fig. 13.7)** carry motor signals from the cerebral cortex for precise, finely coordinated limb movements. The fibers of this system form ridges called *pyramids* on the anterior surface of the medulla oblongata, so these tracts were once called *pyramidal tracts.* Their fibers decussate either in the lower medulla or lower in the spinal cord, so each cerebral hemisphere controls muscles on the contralateral side of the body. The anterior tract gets smaller as it descends and gives off nerve fibers, and usually disappears by the midthoracic level.
- The **tectospinal**[16] **tract** (TEC-toe-SPY-nul) begins in the roof of the midbrain and descends the contralateral spinal

[16]*tectum* = roof (of the midbrain)

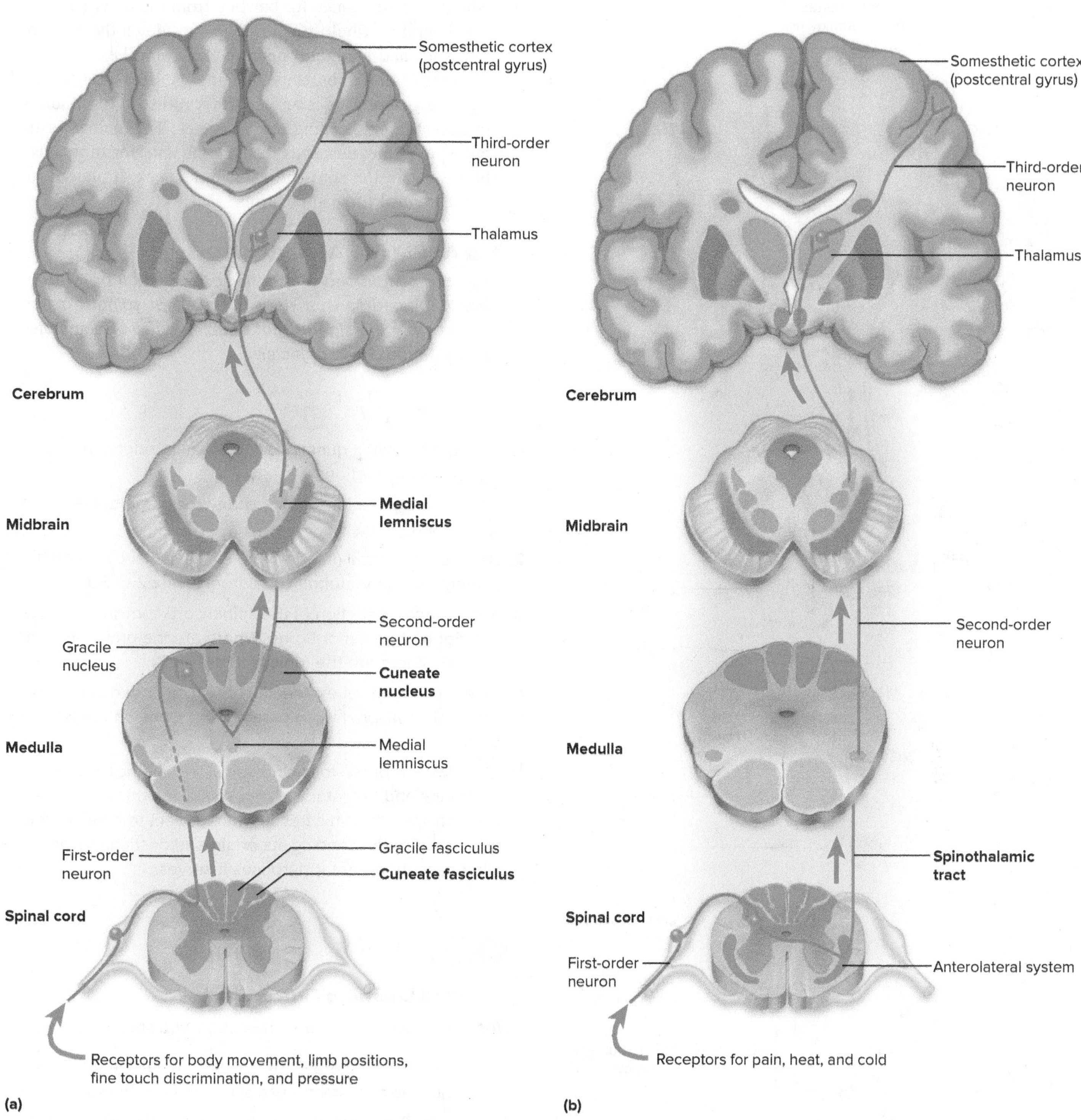


**FIGURE 13.6 Some Ascending Pathways of the CNS.** The spinal cord, medulla, and midbrain are shown in cross section and the cerebrum and thalamus (top) in frontal section. Nerve signals enter the spinal cord at the bottom of the figure and carry somatosensory information up to the cerebral cortex. (a) The cuneate fasciculus. (b) The spinothalamic tract.

cord only as far as the neck. It is involved in reflex turning of the head, especially in response to sights and sounds.

- The **lateral** and **medial reticulospinal tracts** (reh-TIC-you-lo-SPY-nul) originate in the reticular formation of the brainstem. They control muscles of the upper and lower limbs, especially to maintain posture and balance. They also contain *descending analgesic pathways* that regulate the transmission of pain signals to the brain.
- The **lateral** and **medial vestibulospinal tracts** (vess-TIB-you-lo-SPY-nul) begin in the brainstem *vestibular nuclei,*

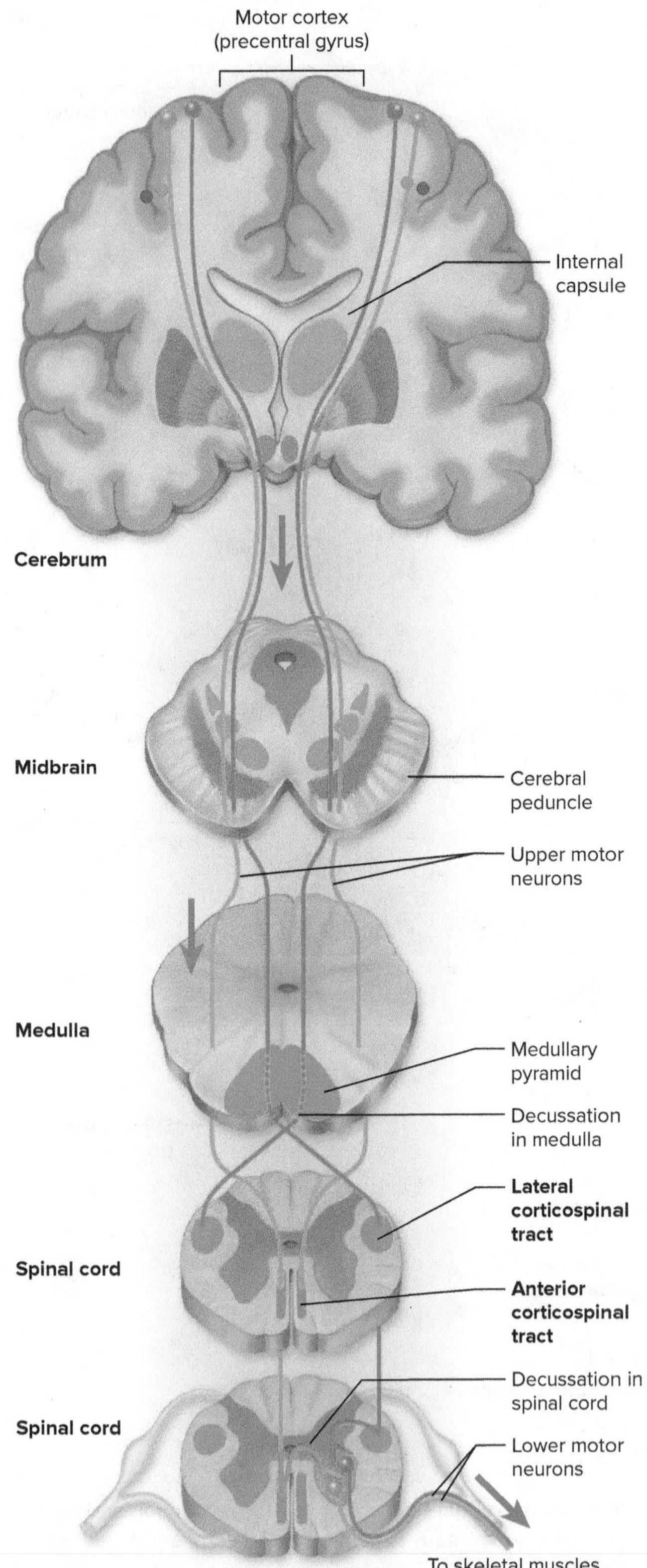


**FIGURE 13.7 Two Descending Pathways of the CNS.** The lateral and anterior corticospinal tracts, which carry signals for voluntary muscle contraction. Nerve signals originate in the cerebral cortex at the top of the figure and carry motor commands down the spinal cord.

which receive signals for balance from the inner ear. The lateral vestibulospinal tract passes down the anterior funiculus and facilitates neurons that control extensor muscles of the limbs, thus inducing the limbs to stiffen and straighten. This is an important reflex in responding to body tilt and keeping one's balance. The medial vestibulospinal tract descends through the anterior funiculus on both sides of the cord and ends in the neck. It plays a role in the control of head position.

**▶▶▶APPLY WHAT YOU KNOW**

*You are blindfolded and either a tennis ball or an iron ball is placed in your right hand. What spinal tract(s) would carry the signals that enable you to discriminate between these two objects?*

**BEFORE YOU GO ON**

Answer the following questions to test your understanding of the preceding section:

1. Name the four major regions and two enlargements of the spinal cord.
2. Describe the distal (inferior) end of the spinal cord and the contents of the vertebral canal from level L2 to S5.
3. Sketch a cross section of the spinal cord showing the anterior and posterior horns. Where are the gray and white matter? Where are the funiculi and tracts?
4. Give an anatomical explanation of why a stroke in the right cerebral hemisphere can paralyze the limbs on the left side of the body.
5. Identify each of the following spinal tracts—the gracile fasciculus and the lateral corticospinal, lateral reticulospinal, and spinothalamic tracts—with respect to whether it is ascending or descending; its origin and destination; and what sensory or motor purposes it serves.

## 13.2 The Spinal Nerves

### Expected Learning Outcomes

When you have completed this section, you should be able to

a. describe the anatomy of nerves and ganglia in general;
b. describe the attachments of a spinal nerve to the spinal cord;
c. trace the branches of a spinal nerve distal to its attachments;
d. name the five plexuses of spinal nerves and describe their general anatomy;
e. name some major nerves that arise from each plexus and identify what they innervate; and
f. explain the relationship of dermatomes to the spinal nerves.

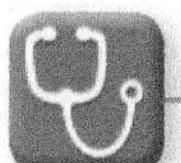

## DEEPER INSIGHT 13.2

### CLINICAL APPLICATION

### *Poliomyelitis and Amyotrophic Lateral Sclerosis*

*Poliomyelitis*[17] and *amyotrophic lateral sclerosis*[18] *(ALS)* are two diseases that involve destruction of motor neurons. In both diseases, the skeletal muscles atrophy from lack of innervation.

Poliomyelitis is caused by the poliovirus, which destroys motor neurons in the brainstem and anterior horn of the spinal cord. Signs of polio include muscle pain, weakness, and loss of some reflexes, followed by paralysis, muscular atrophy, and sometimes respiratory arrest. The virus spreads by fecal contamination of water. Historically, polio afflicted many children who contracted the virus from swimming in contaminated pools. For a time, the polio vaccine nearly eliminated new cases, but the disease has lately begun to reemerge among children in some parts of the world because of antivaccination politics.

ALS is also known as Lou Gehrig[19] disease after the baseball player who had to retire from the sport because of it. It is marked not only by the degeneration of motor neurons and atrophy of the muscles, but also sclerosis (scarring) of the lateral regions of the spinal cord—hence its name. Most cases occur when astrocytes fail to reabsorb the neurotransmitter glutamate from the tissue fluid, allowing it to accumulate to a neurotoxic level. The early signs of ALS include muscular weakness and difficulty in speaking, swallowing, and using the hands. Sensory and intellectual functions remain unaffected, as evidenced by the accomplishments of astrophysicist and best-selling author Stephen Hawking **(fig. 13.8),** who was stricken with ALS in college. Despite near-total paralysis, he had a slowly progressing form of the disease, remained intellectually undiminished, and communicated with the aid of a speech synthesizer and computer. Tragically, many people are quick to assume that those who have lost most of their ability to communicate their ideas and feelings have few ideas and feelings to communicate. To a victim, this may be more unbearable than the loss of motor function itself.

FIGURE 13.8 **Stephen Hawking (1942–2018).** "When I was first diagnosed with ALS, I was given two years to live. Now 45 years later, I am doing pretty well" (CNN interview, 2010).

Geoff Robinson Photography/REX/Shutterstock

## 13.2a General Anatomy of Nerves and Ganglia

The spinal cord communicates with the rest of the body by way of the spinal nerves. Before we discuss those specific nerves, however, it is necessary to be familiar with the structure of nerves and ganglia in general.

A **nerve** is a cordlike organ composed of numerous nerve fibers (axons) bound together by connective tissue **(fig. 13.9).** If we compare a *nerve fiber* to a wire carrying an electrical current in one direction, a *nerve* would be comparable to an electrical cable composed of hundreds of wires carrying currents in opposite directions. A nerve contains anywhere from a few nerve fibers to (in the optic nerve) a million. Nerves usually have a pearly white color and resemble frayed string as they divide into smaller and smaller branches. As we move away from the spinal nerves proper, the smaller branches are called **peripheral nerves,** and their disorders are collectively called *peripheral neuropathy.*

Nerve fibers of the peripheral nervous system are ensheathed in Schwann cells, which form a neurilemma and often a myelin sheath around the axon (see section 12.3b). External to the neurilemma, each fiber is surrounded by a basal lamina and then a thin sleeve of loose connective tissue called the **endoneurium.** In most nerves, the fibers are gathered in bundles called **fascicles,** each wrapped in a sheath called the **perineurium.** The perineurium is composed of up to 20 layers of overlapping, squamous, epithelium-like cells. Several fascicles are then bundled together and wrapped in an outer **epineurium** to compose the nerve as a whole. The epineurium consists of dense irregular connective tissue and protects the nerve from stretching and injury. Nerves have a high metabolic rate and need a plentiful blood supply, which is furnished by blood vessels that penetrate these connective tissue coverings.

**APPLY WHAT YOU KNOW**

*How does the structure of a nerve compare to that of a skeletal muscle? Which of the descriptive terms for nerves have similar counterparts in muscle histology?*

[17]*polio* = gray matter; *myel* = spinal cord; *itis* = inflammation
[18]*a* = without; *myo* = muscle; *troph* = nourishment; *sclerosis* = hardening
[19]Lou Gehrig (1903–41), New York Yankees baseball player

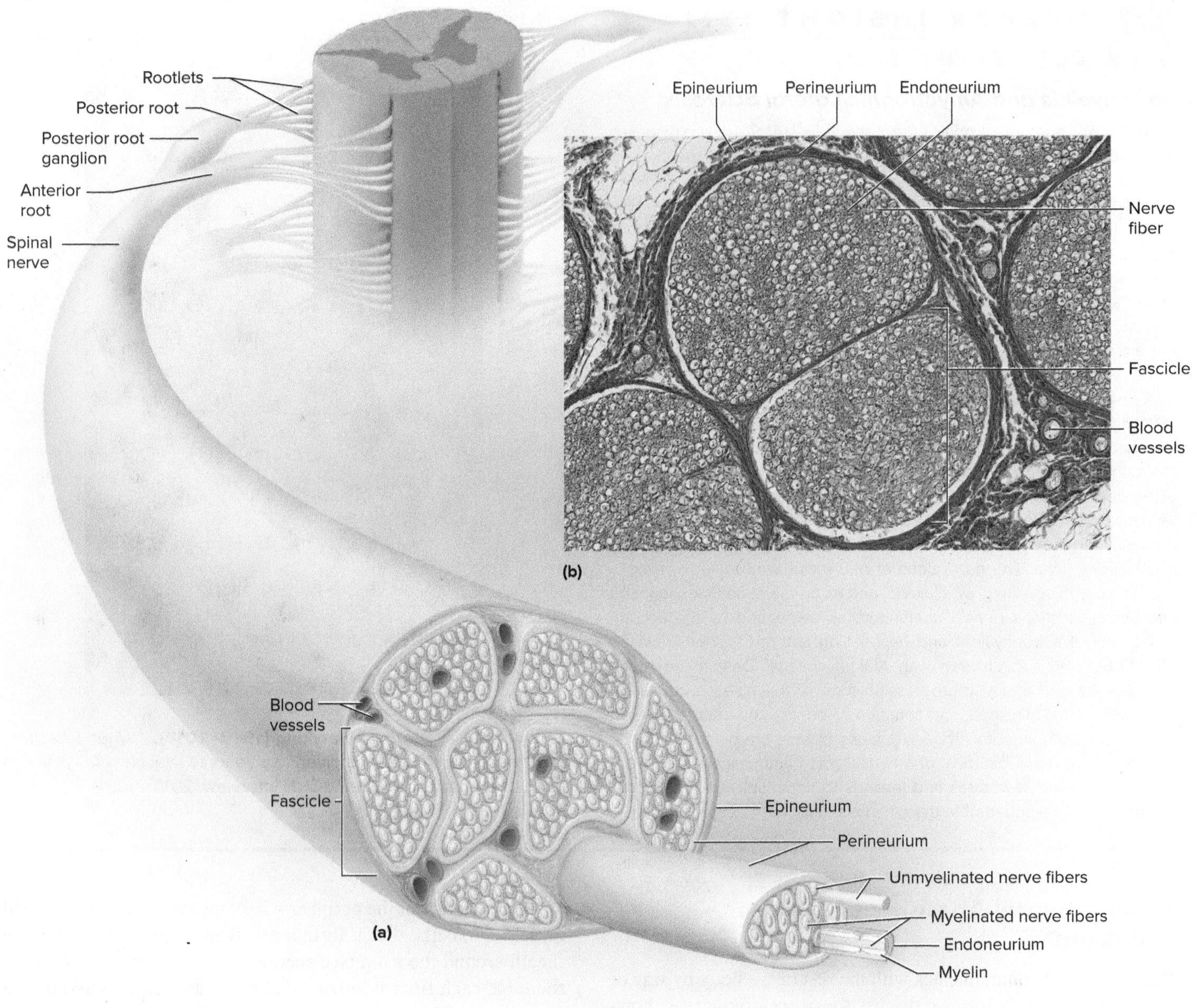


**FIGURE 13.9 Anatomy of a Nerve.** (a) A spinal nerve and its association with the spinal cord. (b) Cross section of a nerve. Individual nerve fibers show as tiny red dots, each surrounded by a light ring of myelin.

b: PASIEKA/Science Photo Library/Getty Images

As we saw in section 12.1, peripheral nerve fibers are of two kinds: sensory (afferent) fibers carrying signals from sensory receptors to the CNS, and motor (efferent) fibers carrying signals from the CNS to muscles and glands. Both types can be classified as *somatic* or *visceral* and as *general* or *special* depending on the organs they innervate **(table 13.2)**.

Purely **sensory nerves,** composed only of afferent fibers, are rare; they include nerves for smell and vision. **Motor nerves** carry only efferent fibers. Most nerves, however, are **mixed nerves,** which consist of both afferent and efferent fibers and therefore conduct signals in two directions. However, any one fiber in the nerve conducts signals in one direction only. Many nerves commonly described as motor are actually mixed because they carry sensory signals of proprioception from the muscle back to the CNS.

If a nerve resembles a thread, a **ganglion**[20] resembles a knot in the thread. A ganglion is a cluster of neurosomas outside the CNS. It is enveloped in an epineurium continuous with that of the nerve. Among the neurosomas are bundles of nerve fibers leading into and out of the ganglion. **Figure 13.10** shows a type of ganglion associated with the spinal nerves.

[20] *gangli* = knot

**TABLE 13.2 The Classification of Nerve Fibers**

| Class | Description |
|---|---|
| Afferent fibers | Carry sensory signals from receptors to the CNS |
| Efferent fibers | Carry motor signals from the CNS to effectors |
| Somatic fibers | Innervate skin, skeletal muscles, bones, and joints |
| Visceral fibers | Innervate blood vessels, glands, and viscera |
| General fibers | Innervate widespread organs such as muscles, skin, glands, viscera, and blood vessels |
| Special fibers | Innervate more localized organs in the head, including the eyes, ears, olfactory and taste receptors, and muscles of chewing, swallowing, and facial expression |

## 13.2b Spinal Nerves

There are 31 pairs of **spinal nerves:** 8 cervical (C1–C8), 12 thoracic (T1–T12), 5 lumbar (L1–L5), 5 sacral (S1–S5), and 1 coccygeal (Co1) **(fig. 13.11).** The first cervical nerve emerges between the skull and atlas, and the others emerge through intervertebral foramina, including the anterior and posterior foramina of the sacrum and the sacral hiatus. Thus, spinal nerves C1 through C7 emerge superior to the correspondingly numbered vertebrae (nerve C5 above vertebra C5, for example); nerve C8 emerges inferior to vertebra C7; and below this, all the remaining nerves emerge inferior to the correspondingly numbered vertebrae (nerve L3 inferior to vertebra L3, for example).

### Proximal Branches

Each spinal nerve arises from two points of attachment to the spinal cord. In each segment of the cord, six to eight nerve **rootlets** emerge from the anterior surface and converge to form the **anterior (ventral) root** of the spinal nerve. Another six to eight rootlets emerge from the posterior surface and converge to form the **posterior (dorsal) root (figs. 13.12, 13.13).** A short distance away from the spinal cord, the posterior root swells into a **posterior (dorsal) root ganglion,** which contains the neurosomas of sensory neurons (fig. 13.10). There is no corresponding ganglion on the anterior root because the neurosomas are in the anterior horns of the spinal cord.

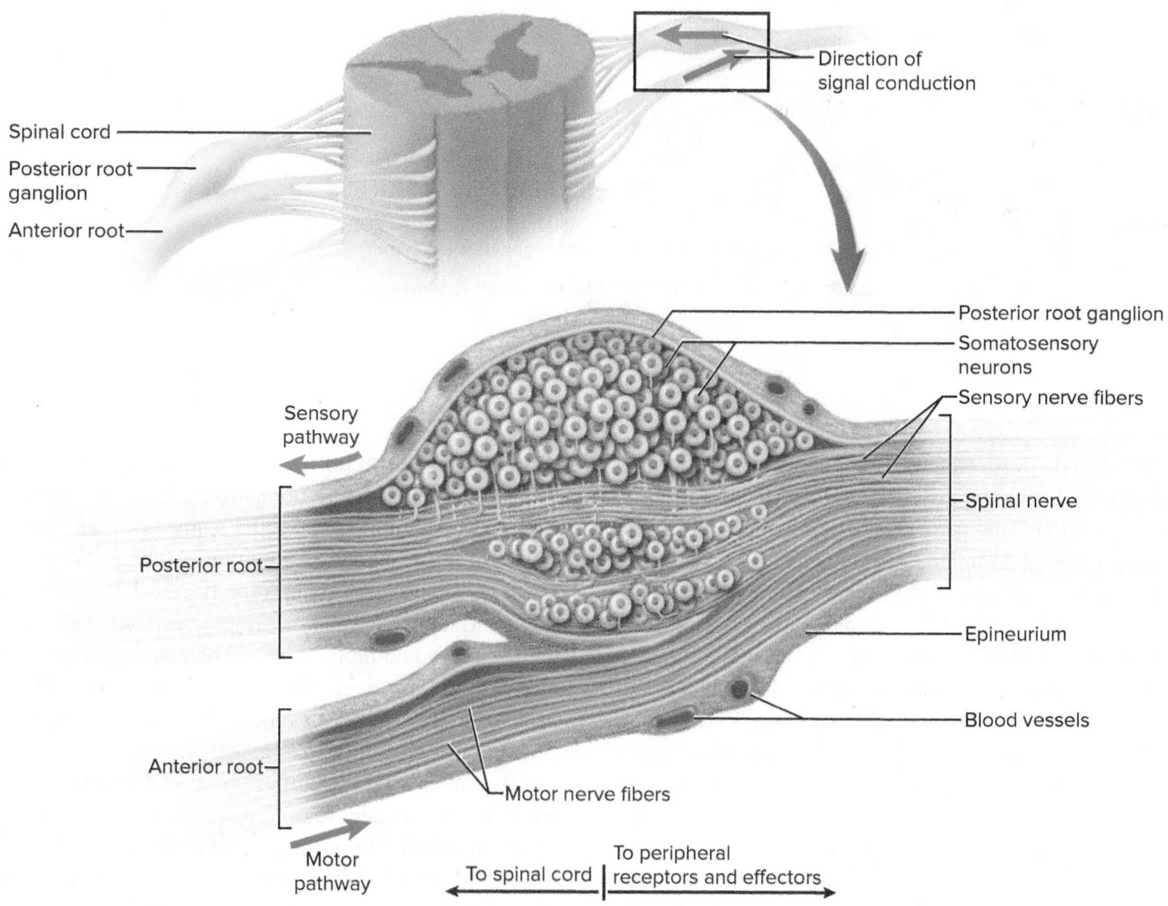


**FIGURE 13.10 Anatomy of a Ganglion (Longitudinal Section).** The posterior root ganglion contains the neurosomas of unipolar sensory neurons conducting signals from peripheral sense organs toward the spinal cord. Below this is the anterior root of the spinal nerve, which conducts motor signals away from the spinal cord, toward peripheral effectors. (The anterior root is not part of the ganglion.)

? *Where are the neurosomas of the neurons that give rise to the motor nerve fibers seen here?*

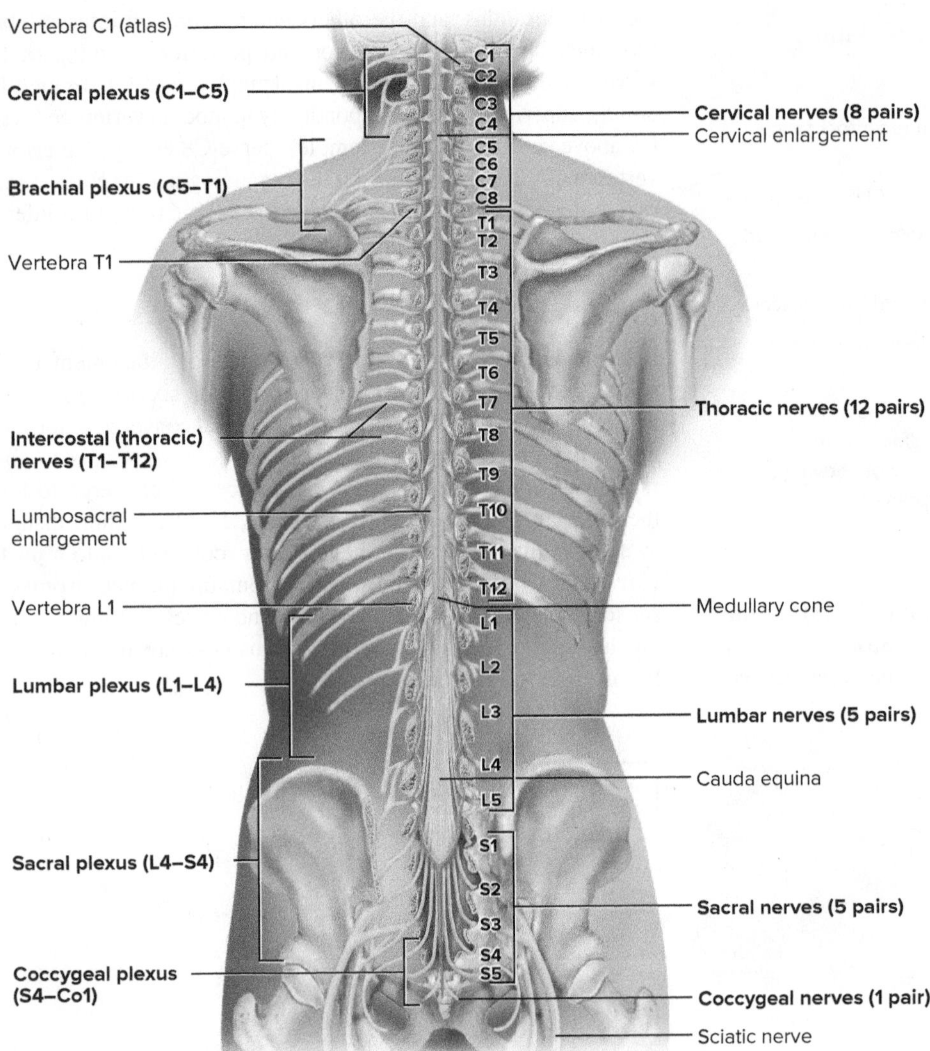


**FIGURE 13.11 The Spinal Nerve Roots and Plexuses, Posterior View.**

Slightly distal to the posterior root ganglion, the anterior and posterior roots merge, leave the dural sheath, and form the spinal nerve proper (fig. 13.12). The nerve then exits the vertebral canal through the intervertebral foramen. The spinal nerve is a mixed nerve, carrying sensory signals to the spinal cord by way of the posterior root and ganglion, and motor signals out to more distant parts of the body by way of the anterior root.

The anterior and posterior roots are shortest in the cervical region and become longer inferiorly. The roots that arise from segments L2 to Co1 of the cord form the cauda equina. Some viruses invade the CNS by way of the spinal nerve roots (see Deeper Insight 13.3).

## Distal Branches

Distal to the vertebrae, the branches of a spinal nerve are more complex **(fig. 13.14).** Immediately after emerging from the intervertebral foramen, the nerve divides into an **anterior ramus**[21] (RAY-mus), **posterior ramus,** and a small **meningeal branch.** Thus, each spinal nerve branches on both ends—into anterior and posterior *roots* approaching the spinal cord, and anterior and posterior *rami* leading away from the vertebral column.

The meningeal branch (see fig. 13.12) reenters the vertebral canal and innervates the meninges, vertebrae, and spinal ligaments with sensory and motor fibers. The posterior ramus innervates the muscles and joints in that region of the spine and the skin of the back. The larger anterior ramus innervates the anterior and lateral skin and muscles of the trunk, and gives rise to nerves of the limbs.

The anterior ramus differs from one region of the trunk to another. In the thoracic region, it forms an **intercostal nerve,** which travels along the inferior margin of a rib and innervates the skin and intercostal muscles (thus contributing to breathing). Sensory fibers of the intercostal nerve branches to the skin are the most common routes of viral migration in the painful disease known as shingles (see Deeper Insight 13.3). Motor fibers of the intercostal nerves innervate the internal oblique, external oblique, and transverse abdominal muscles. All other anterior rami form the *nerve plexuses,* described next.

[21]*ramus* = branch

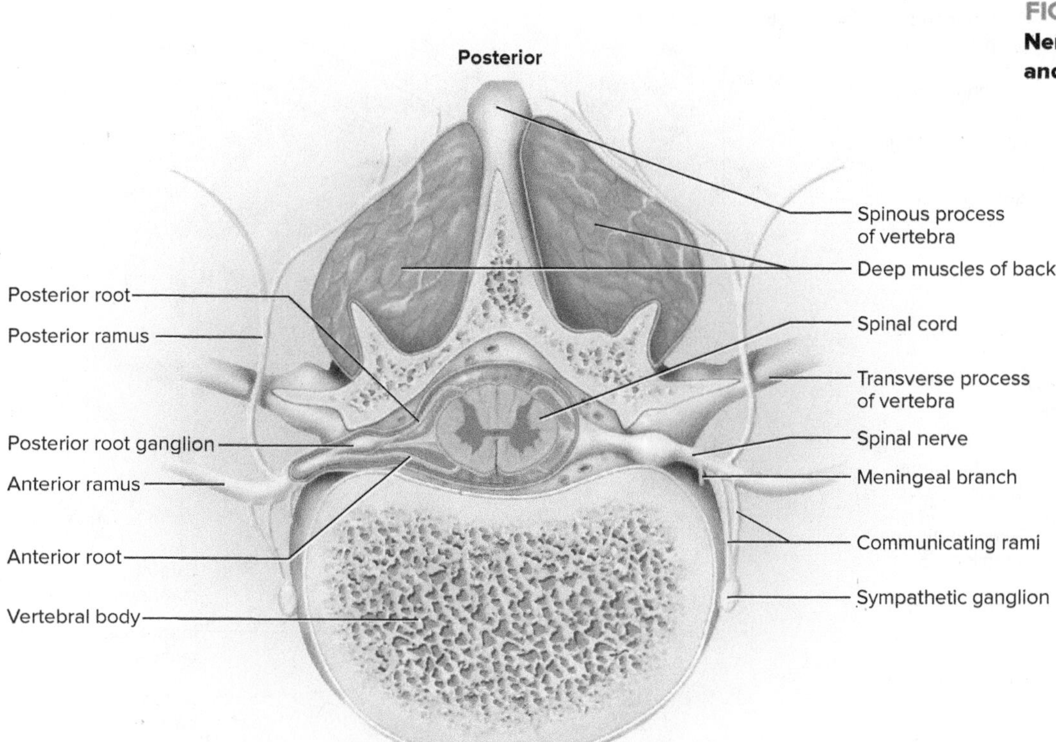

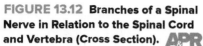

**FIGURE 13.12 Branches of a Spinal Nerve in Relation to the Spinal Cord and Vertebra (Cross Section).** APR

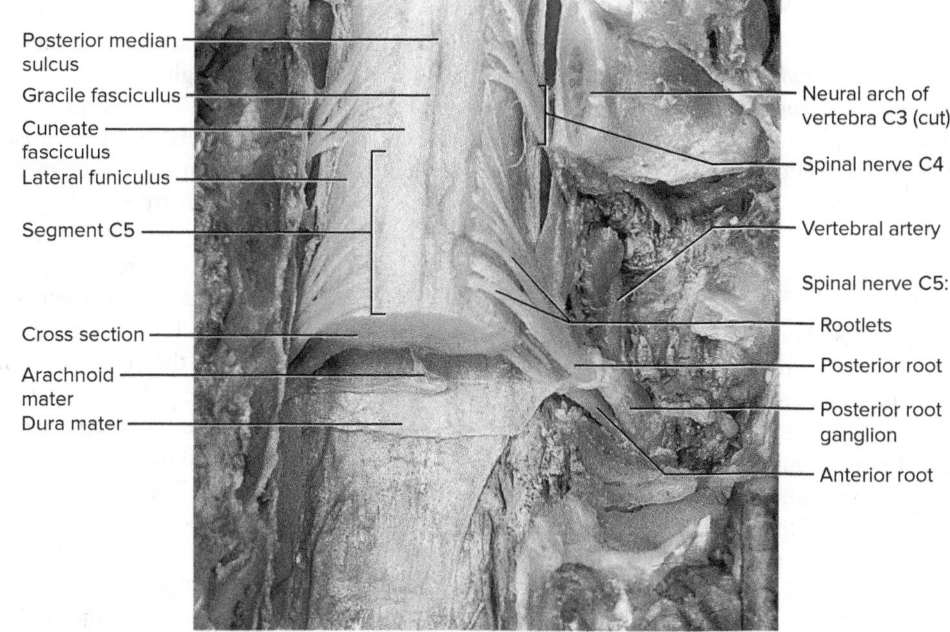


**FIGURE 13.13 The Point of Entry of Two Spinal Nerves into the Spinal Cord.** Posterior (dorsal) view with vertebrae cut away. Note that each posterior root divides into several rootlets that enter the spinal cord. A segment of the spinal cord is the portion receiving all the rootlets of one spinal nerve.

Courtesy of Dr. Robert A. Chase, M.D.

? *In the labeled rootlets of spinal nerve C5, are the nerve fibers afferent or efferent? How do you know?*

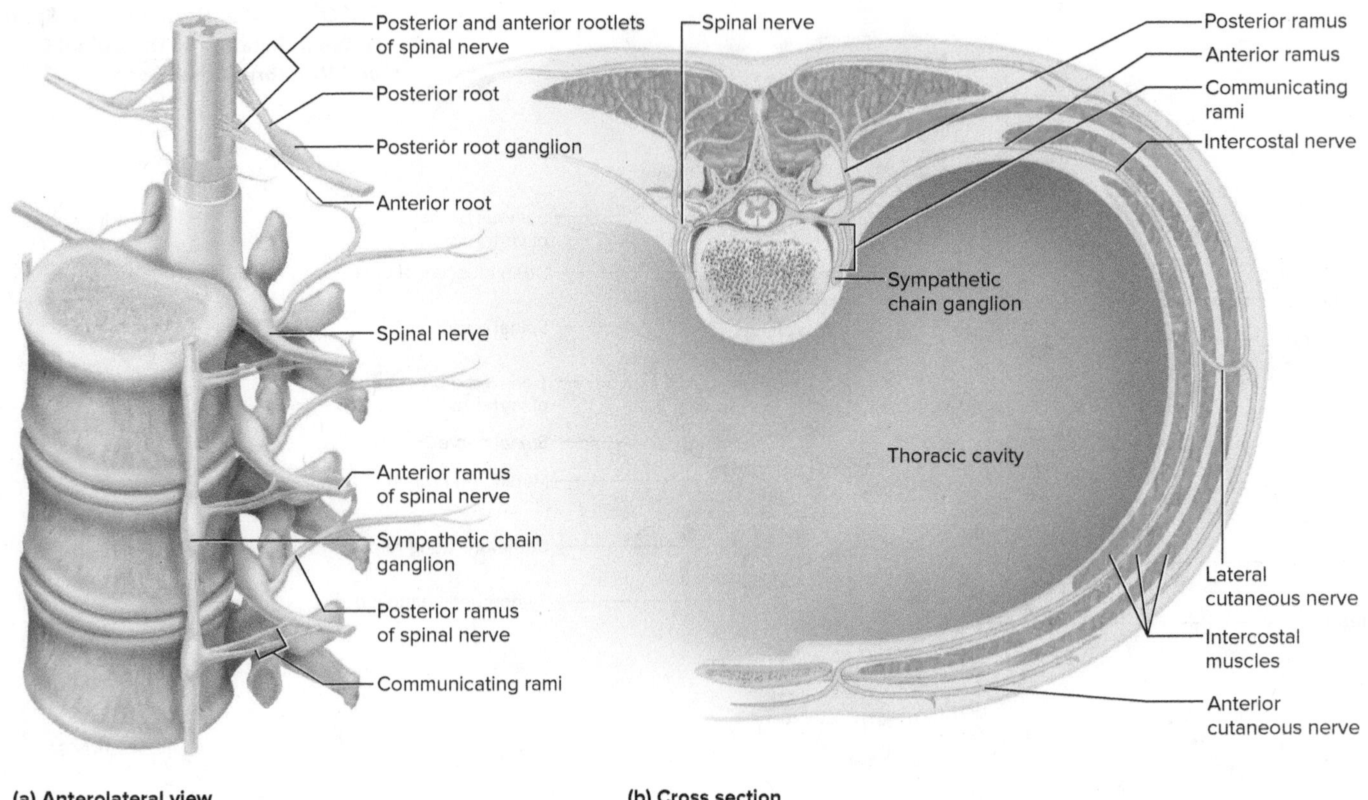


**FIGURE 13.14 Rami of the Spinal Nerves.** (a) Anterolateral view of the spinal nerves and their subdivisions in relation to the spinal cord and vertebrae. (b) Cross section of the thorax showing innervation of muscles and skin of the chest and back. This section is cut through the intercostal muscles between two ribs.

As shown in figure 13.14, the anterior ramus also gives off a pair of *communicating rami,* which connect with a string of *sympathetic chain ganglia* alongside the vertebral column. These are seen only in spinal nerves T1 through L2. They are components of the sympathetic nervous system and are discussed more fully in section 15.2a.

### 13.2c Nerve Plexuses

Except in the thoracic region, the anterior rami branch and anastomose (merge) repeatedly to form five webs called nerve plexuses: the small **cervical plexus** in the neck, the **brachial plexus** near the shoulder, the **lumbar plexus** of the lower back, the **sacral plexus** immediately inferior to this, and finally, the tiny **coccygeal plexus** adjacent to the lower sacrum and coccyx. A general view of these plexuses is shown in figure 13.11; they are described in the next four tables, beginning with table 13.3. The spinal nerve roots that give rise to each plexus are indicated in violet in each illustration. Some of these roots give rise to smaller branches called *trunks, anterior divisions, posterior divisions,* and *cords,* which are color-coded and explained in the individual figures. Two of the nerves arising from these plexuses, the *radial* and *sciatic,* are sites of unique nerve injuries described in Deeper Insight 13.4.

The nerves tabulated here have somatosensory and motor functions. *Somatosensory* means that they carry sensory signals from bones, joints, muscles, and the skin, in contrast to sensory input from the viscera or from special sense organs such as the eyes and ears. Somatosensory signals are for touch, heat, cold, stretch, pressure, pain, and other sensations. One of the most important somatosensory roles of these nerves is proprioception.

The motor function of these nerves is primarily to stimulate the contraction of skeletal muscles. They also innervate the bones of the corresponding regions, and carry autonomic fibers to some viscera and blood vessels, thus adjusting blood flow to local needs.

The following tables identify the areas of skin innervated by the sensory fibers and the muscle groups innervated by the motor fibers of the individual nerves. The muscle tables in chapter 10 provide a more detailed breakdown of the muscles supplied by each nerve and the actions they perform. You may assume that for each muscle, these nerves also carry sensory fibers from its proprioceptors. Throughout these tables, *nerve* is abbreviated *n.* and *nerves* as *nn.*

## The Cervical Plexus

The cervical plexus on each side of the neck **(fig. 13.15)** receives fibers from the anterior rami of nerves C1 to C5 and gives rise to the nerves listed in **table 13.3,** in order from superior to inferior. The most important of these are the *phrenic*[22] *nerves* (FREN-ic), which travel down each side of the mediastinum, innervate the diaphragm, and play an indispensable role in breathing (see fig. 15.3). In addition to the major nerves listed in table 13.3, the cervical plexus gives off several motor branches that innervate the geniohyoid, thyrohyoid, scalene, levator scapulae, trapezius, and sternocleidomastoid muscles.

[22]*phren* = diaphragm

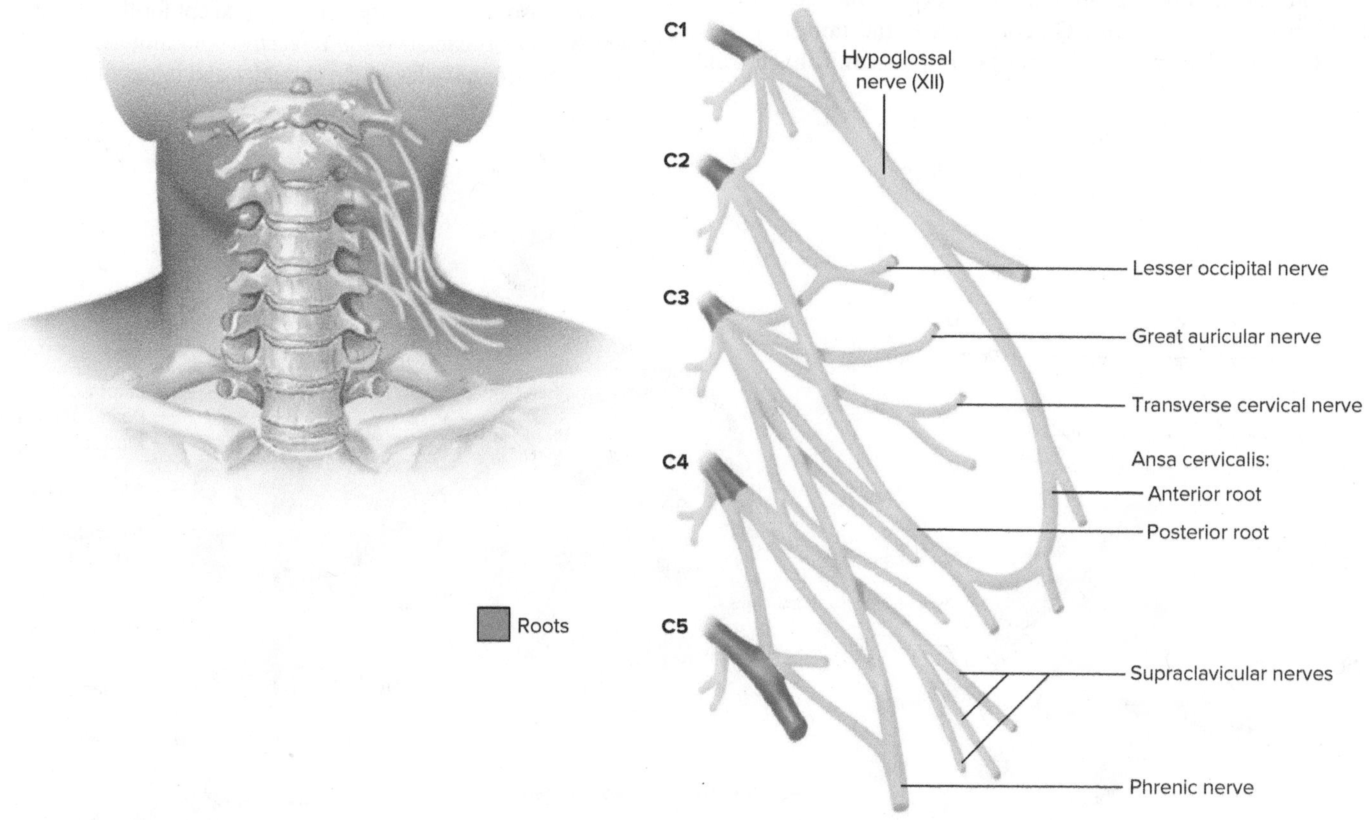


**FIGURE 13.15 The Cervical Plexus.** APR

*Predict the consequences of a surgical accident in which a phrenic nerve is severed.*

**TABLE 13.3 The Cervical Plexus**

| Nerve | Composition | Cutaneous and Other Sensory Innervation | Muscular Innervation (Motor and Proprioceptive) |
|---|---|---|---|
| Lesser occipital n. | Somatosensory | Upper third of medial surface of external ear, skin posterior to ear, posterolateral neck | None |
| Great auricular n. | Somatosensory | Most of the external ear, mastoid region, region from parotid salivary gland (see fig. 10.7) to slightly inferior to angle of mandible | None |
| Transverse cervical n. | Somatosensory | Anterior and lateral neck, underside of chin | None |
| Ansa cervicalis | Motor | None | Omohyoid, sternohyoid, and sternothyroid muscles (see table 10.2) |
| Supraclavicular nn. | Somatosensory | Lower anterior and lateral neck, shoulder, anterior chest | None |
| Phrenic n. | Mixed | Diaphragm, pleura, and pericardium | Diaphragm (see table 10.4) |

## The Brachial Plexus

The **brachial plexus (figs. 13.16, 13.17)** is formed predominantly by the anterior rami of nerves C5 to T1 (C4 and T2 make small contributions). It passes over the first rib into the axilla and innervates the upper limb and some muscles of the neck and shoulder. This plexus is well known for its conspicuous M or W shape seen in cadaver dissections.

The subdivisions of this plexus are called *roots, trunks, divisions,* and *cords* (color-coded in fig. 13.16).The five **roots** are the anterior rami of C5 through T1. Roots C5 and C6 converge to form the **upper trunk;** C7 continues as the **middle trunk;** and C8 and T1 converge to form the **lower trunk.** Each trunk divides into an **anterior** and **posterior division.** As the body is dissected from the anterior side of the shoulder inward, the anterior divisions are found in front of the posterior ones. Finally, the six divisions merge to form three large fiber bundles—the **lateral, posterior,** and **medial cords.** From these cords arise the five major nerves listed in **table 13.4** in the order of figure 13.16 from superior to inferior.

Among other functions, these nerves carry sensory signals from the skin of the shoulder and upper limb to the spinal cord. **Figure 13.18** shows the regions of the wrist and hand innervated by the sensory fibers of these nerves (except for the axillary nerve, which doesn't extend to the forearm). The motor fibers of these nerves control muscles of the shoulder and upper limb.

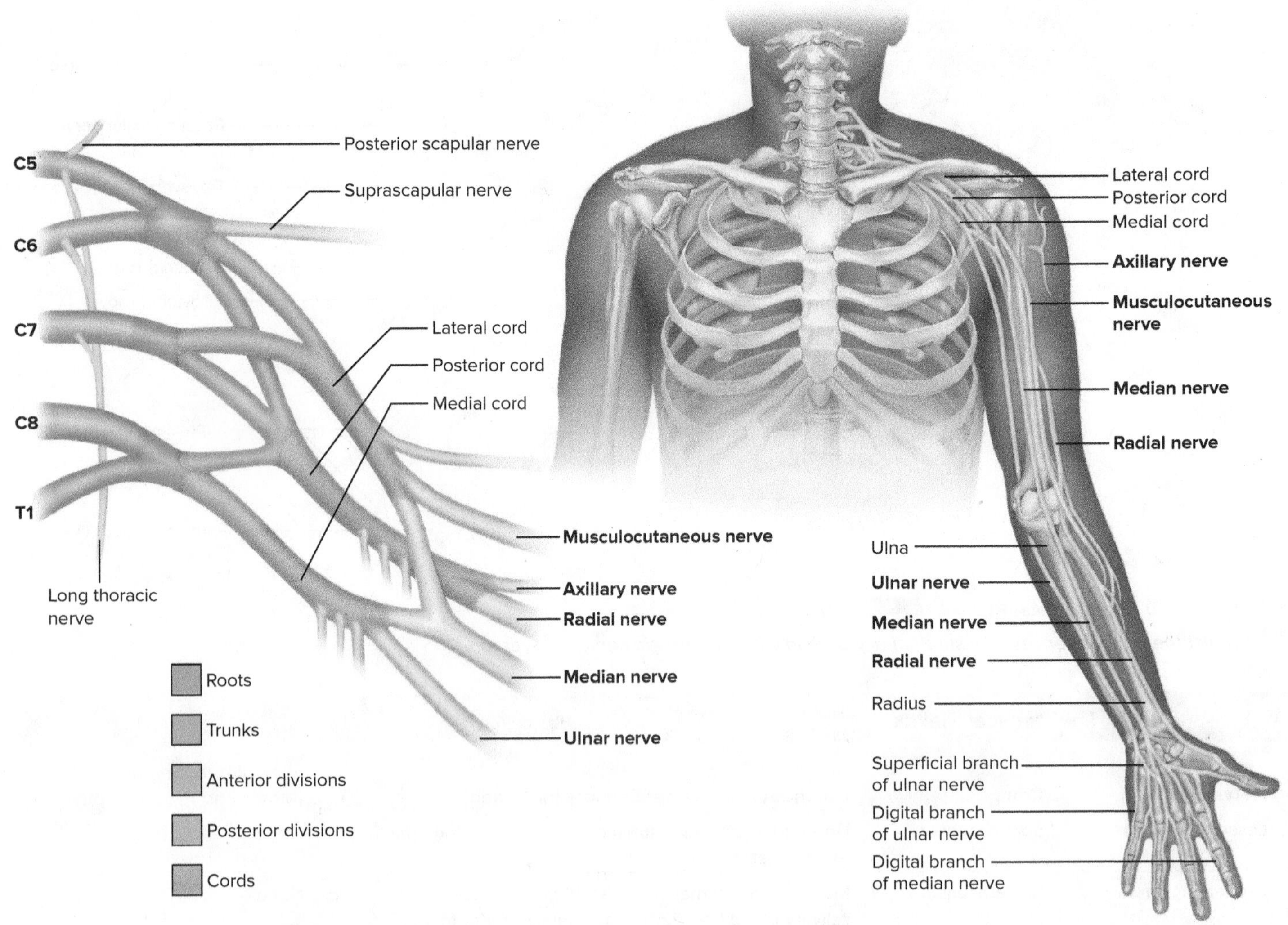


**FIGURE 13.16 The Brachial Plexus.** The labeled nerves innervate muscles tabulated in chapter 10, and those in boldface are further detailed in this table. APR

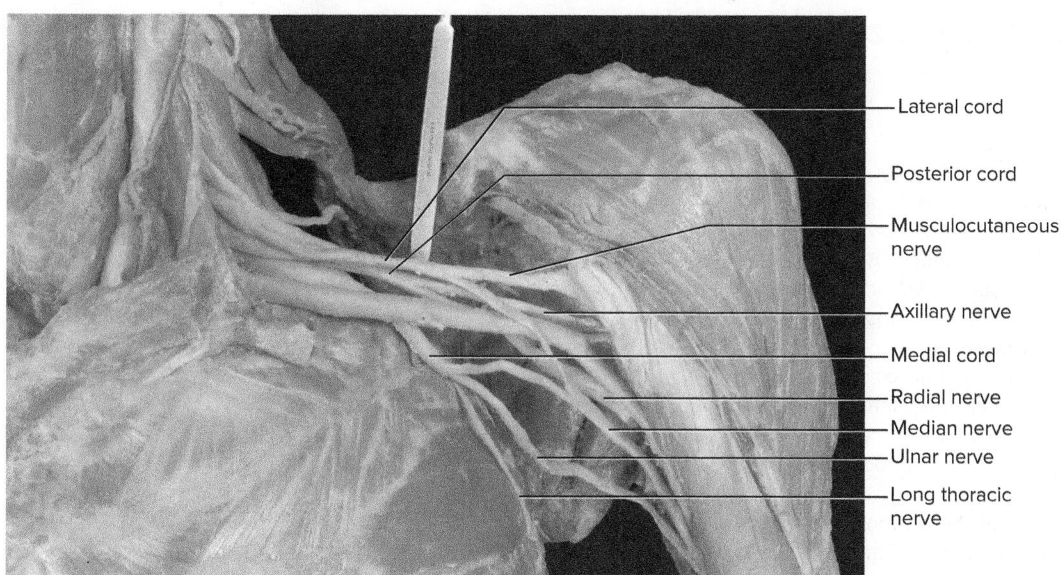


**FIGURE 13.17 Brachial Plexus of the Cadaver.** Anterior view of the left shoulder. Most of the other structures resembling nerves in this photograph are blood vessels.

Christine Eckel/McGraw-Hill Education

**TABLE 13.4 The Brachial Plexus**

| Nerve | Composition | Cord of Origin | Cutaneous and Joint Innervation (Sensory) | Muscular Innervation (Motor and Proprioceptive) |
|---|---|---|---|---|
| Musculocutaneous n. | Mixed | Lateral | Skin of anterolateral forearm; elbow joint | Brachialis, biceps brachii, and coracobrachialis muscles (see tables 10.9, 10.10) |
| Axillary n. | Mixed | Posterior | Skin of lateral shoulder and arm; shoulder joint | Deltoid and teres minor muscles (see table 10.9) |
| Radial n. | Mixed | Posterior | Skin of posterior arm; posterior and lateral forearm and wrist; joints of elbow, wrist, and hand | Mainly extensor muscles of posterior arm and forearm (see tables 10.10, 10.11) |
| Median n. | Mixed | Lateral and medial | Skin of lateral two-thirds of hand; tips of digits I–IV; joints of hand | Mainly forearm flexors; thenar group and lumbricals I–II of hand (see tables 10.10–10.12) |
| Ulnar n. | Mixed | Medial | Skin of palmar and medial hand and digits III–V; joints of elbow and hand | Some forearm flexors; adductor pollicis; hypothenar group; interosseous muscles; lumbricals III–IV (see tables 10.11, 10.12) |

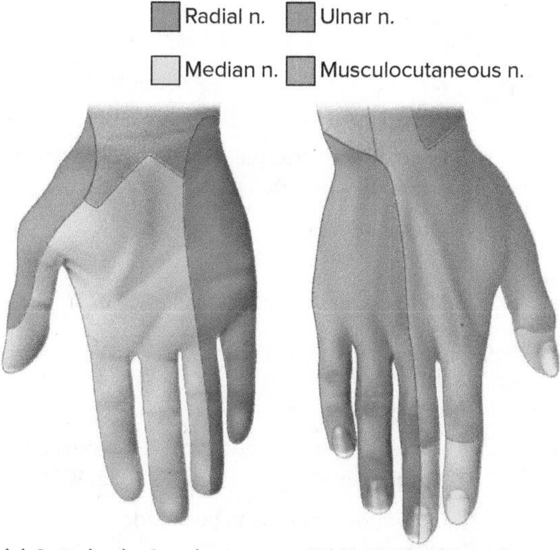


**FIGURE 13.18 Cutaneous Innervation of the Hand by Nerves from the Brachial Plexus.** (a) Anterior (palmar) view. (b) Posterior (dorsal) view.

## DEEPER INSIGHT 13.3

### CLINICAL APPLICATION

### *Shingles*

Chickenpox *(varicella),* a common disease of early childhood, is caused by the *varicella-zoster*[23] virus. It produces an itchy rash that usually clears up without complications. The virus, however, remains for life in the posterior root ganglia, kept in check by the immune system. If the immune system is compromised, however, the virus can travel along the sensory nerve fibers by *fast axonal transport* (see section 12.2d) and cause *shingles (herpes*[24] *zoster).* The signs of shingles are a painful trail of skin discoloration and fluid-filled vesicles along the path of the nerve **(fig. 13.19).** These usually appear in the chest and waist, often on just one side of the body. In some cases, lesions appear on one side of the face, especially in and around the eye, and occasionally in the mouth.

There is no cure, and the vesicles usually heal spontaneously in 1 to 3 weeks. In the meantime, aspirin and steroidal ointments can help to relieve the pain and inflammation of the lesions. Antiviral drugs such as acyclovir can shorten the course of an episode of shingles, but only if taken within the first 2 to 3 days of outbreak. Even after the lesions disappear, however, some people suffer intense pain along the course of the nerve *(postherpetic neuralgia, PHN),* lasting for months or even years. PHN is difficult to treat, but pain relievers and antidepressants are of some help. Shingles is particularly common after the age of 50. Childhood vaccination against varicella reduces the risk of shingles later in life. Adult vaccination is recommended in the United States for healthy persons over age 60.

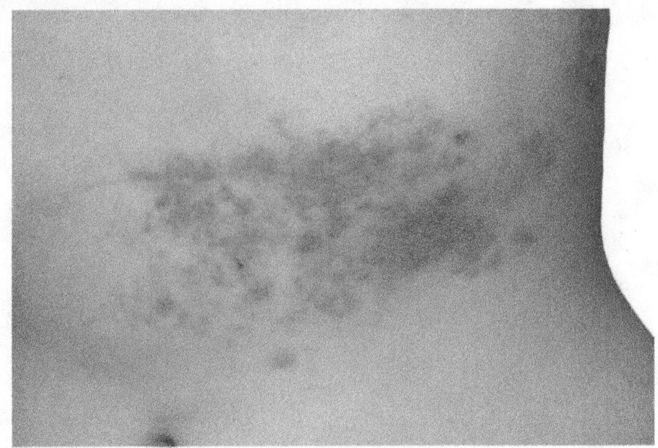

**FIGURE 13.19 Shingles Lesion Tracking the Course of a Sensory Nerve.**

Franciscodiazpagador/Getty Images

[23]*varicella* = little spot; zoster = girdle
[24]*herpes* = creeping

## The Lumbar Plexus

The **lumbar plexus (fig. 13.20)** is formed from the anterior rami of nerves L1 to L4 and some fibers from T12. With only five roots and two divisions, it is less complex than the brachial plexus. It gives rise to six major nerves, listed in **table 13.5** in anatomically descending order.

The sensory fibers of these nerves carry signals from the hip and knee joints and from skin of the genitalia, lower abdominal and gluteal regions, and the thigh, leg, and foot. The motor fibers control muscles of the hip, thigh, and scrotum.

**TABLE 13.5 The Lumbar Plexus**

| Nerve | Composition | Cutaneous and Joint Innervation (Sensory) | Muscular Innervation (Motor and Proprioceptive) |
|---|---|---|---|
| Iliohypogastric n. | Mixed | Skin of lower anterior abdominal and posterolateral gluteal regions | Internal and external oblique and transverse abdominal muscles (see table 10.5) |
| Ilioinguinal n. | Mixed | Skin of upper medial thigh; male scrotum and root of penis; female labia majora | Internal oblique |
| Genitofemoral n. | Mixed | Skin of middle anterior thigh; male scrotum; female labia majora | Male cremaster muscle (see fig. 27.7) |
| Lateral femoral cutaneous n. | Somatosensory | Skin of anterior and upper lateral thigh | None |
| Femoral n. | Mixed | Skin of anterior, medial, and lateral thigh and knee; skin of medial leg and foot; hip and knee joints | Iliacus, pectineus, quadriceps femoris, and sartorius muscles (see tables 10.13, 10.14) |
| Obturator n. | Mixed | Skin of medial thigh; hip and knee joints | Obturator externus; medial (adductor) thigh muscles (see table 10.13) |

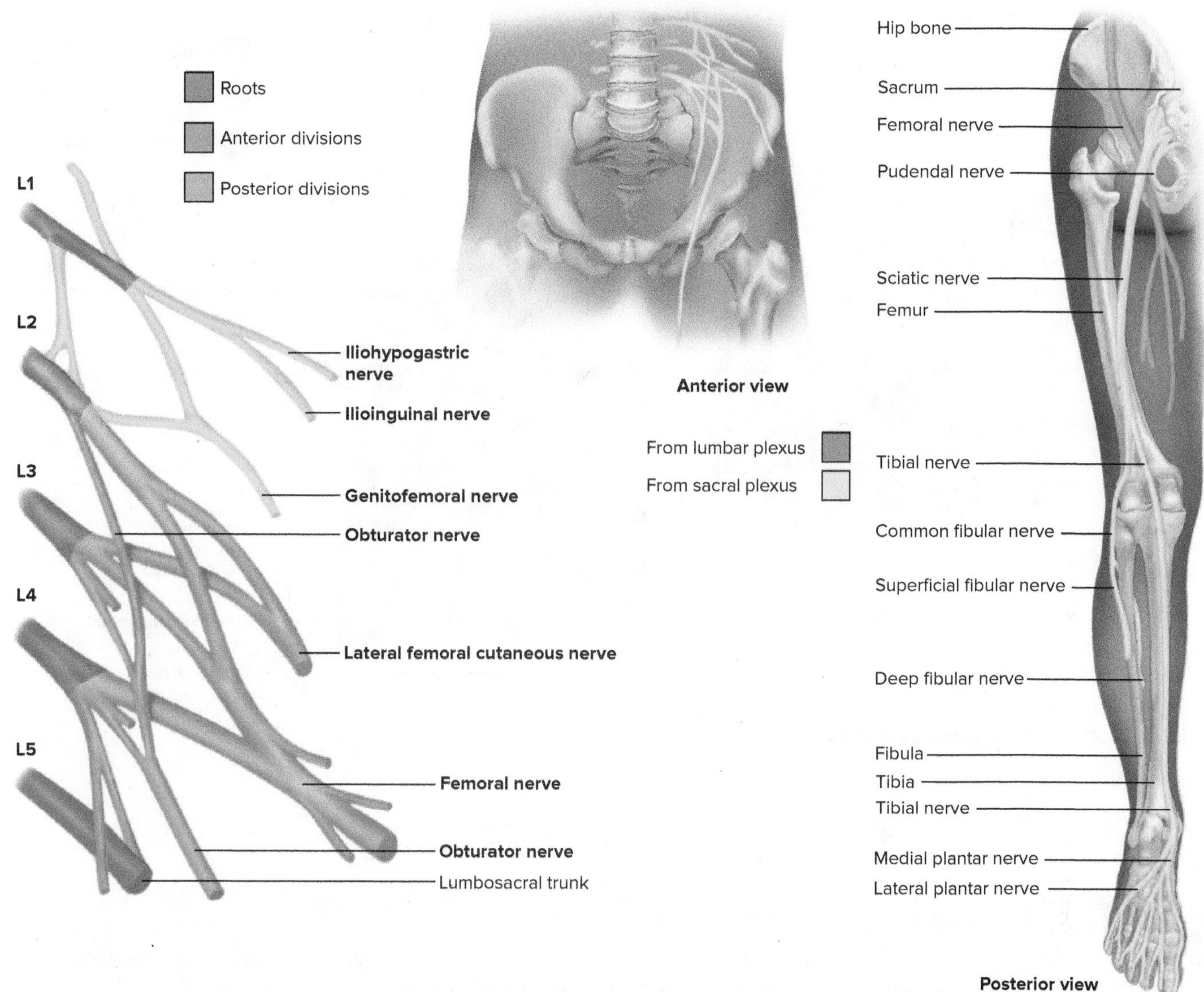


FIGURE 13.20 **The Lumbar Plexus.** APR

## The Sacral and Coccygeal Plexuses

The **sacral plexus** is formed from the anterior rami of nerves L4, L5, and S1 through S4. It has six roots and anterior and posterior divisions. Since it is connected to the lumbar plexus by fibers that run through the *lumbosacral trunk,* the two plexuses are sometimes referred to collectively as the *lumbosacral plexus.* The **coccygeal plexus** is a tiny plexus formed from the anterior rami of S4, S5, and Co1 **(fig. 13.21; table 13.6).**

The *tibial* and *common fibular nerves* travel together through a connective tissue sheath; they are referred to collectively as the **sciatic nerve** (sy-AT-ic), a common focus of injury and pain (see Deeper Insight 13.4). The sciatic nerve passes through the greater sciatic notch of the hip bone, extends for the length of the thigh, and ends at the popliteal fossa (back of the knee). Here, the tibial and common fibular nerves diverge and follow their separate paths into the leg. The tibial nerve descends through the leg and then gives rise to the *medial* and *plantar nerves* of the foot. The common fibular nerve divides into *deep* and *superficial fibular nerves.*

The sensory fibers of these nerves carry signals from joints of the hip, knee, and foot; from the gluteal and perineal regions and the genitals; and from skin from the gluteal region to the foot. The motor fibers control muscles of the gluteal and perineal regions, thigh, leg, and foot.

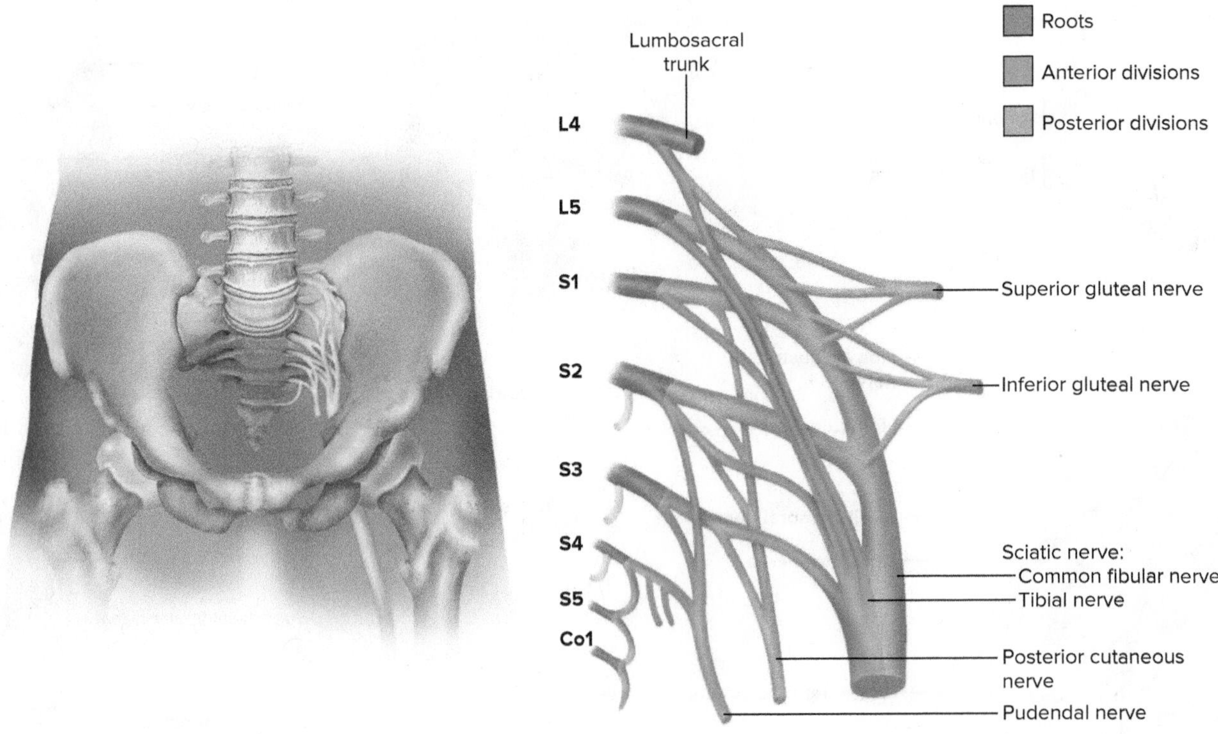


**FIGURE 13.21 The Sacral and Coccygeal Plexuses.** APR

## TABLE 13.6 The Sacral and Coccygeal Plexuses

| Nerve | Composition | Cutaneous and Joint Innervation (Sensory) | Muscular Innervation (Motor and Proprioceptive) |
|---|---|---|---|
| Superior gluteal n. | Mixed | Hip joint | Gluteus minimus, gluteus medius, and tensor fasciae latae muscles (see table 10.13) |
| Inferior gluteal n. | Mixed | None | Gluteus maximus muscle (see table 10.13) |
| Posterior cutaneous n. | Somatosensory | Skin of gluteal region, perineum, posterior and medial thigh, popliteal fossa, and upper posterior leg | None |
| Tibial n. | Mixed | Skin of posterior leg; plantar skin; knee and foot joints | Hamstring muscles; posterior muscles of leg (see tables 10.14, 10.15); most intrinsic foot muscles (via plantar nerves) (see table 10.16) |
| Fibular (peroneal) nn. (common, deep, and superficial) | Mixed | Skin of anterior distal third of leg, dorsum of foot, and toes I–II; knee joint | Biceps femoris muscle; anterior and lateral muscles of leg; extensor digitorum brevis muscle of foot (see tables 10.14–10.16) |
| Pudendal n. | Mixed | Skin of penis and scrotum of male; clitoris, labia majora and minora, and lower vagina of female | Muscles of perineum (see table 10.7) |

## DEEPER INSIGHT 13.4
### CLINICAL APPLICATION

### *Nerve Injuries*

The radial and sciatic nerves are especially vulnerable to injury. The radial nerve, which passes through the axilla, may be compressed against the humerus by improperly adjusted crutches, causing *crutch paralysis.* A similar injury often resulted from the now-discredited practice of correcting a dislocated shoulder by putting a foot in a person's armpit and pulling on the arm. One consequence of radial nerve injury is *wrist drop*—the fingers, hand, and wrist are chronically flexed because the extensor muscles supplied by the radial nerve are paralyzed and cannot oppose the flexors.

Because of its position and length, the sciatic nerve of the hip and thigh is the most vulnerable nerve in the body. Trauma to this nerve produces *sciatica,* a sharp pain that travels from the gluteal region along the posterior side of the thigh and leg as far as the ankle. Ninety percent of cases result from a herniated intervertebral disc or osteoarthritis of the lower spine, but sciatica can also be caused by pressure from a pregnant uterus, dislocation of the hip, injections in the wrong area of the buttock, or sitting for a long time on the edge of a hard chair. Men sometimes suffer sciatica because of the habit of sitting on a wallet carried in the hip pocket.

## 13.2d Cutaneous Innervation and Dermatomes

Each spinal nerve except C1 receives sensory input from a specific area of skin called a **dermatome.**[25] A *dermatome map* **(fig. 13.22)** is a diagram of the cutaneous regions innervated by each spinal nerve. Such a map is oversimplified, however, because the dermatomes overlap at their edges by as much as 50%. Therefore, severance of one sensory nerve root does not entirely deaden sensation from a dermatome. It is necessary to sever or anesthetize three sequential spinal nerves to produce a total loss of sensation from one dermatome. Spinal nerve damage is assessed by testing the dermatomes with pinpricks and noting areas in which the patient has no sensation.

### BEFORE YOU GO ON

Answer the following questions to test your understanding of the preceding section:

6. What is meant by the *anterior and posterior roots* of a spinal nerve? Which of these is sensory and which is motor?
7. Where are the neurosomas of the posterior root located? Where are the neurosomas of the anterior root?
8. List the five plexuses of spinal nerves and state where each one is located.
9. Identify which plexus gives rise to each of the following nerves: axillary, ilioinguinal, obturator, phrenic, pudendal, radial, and sciatic.

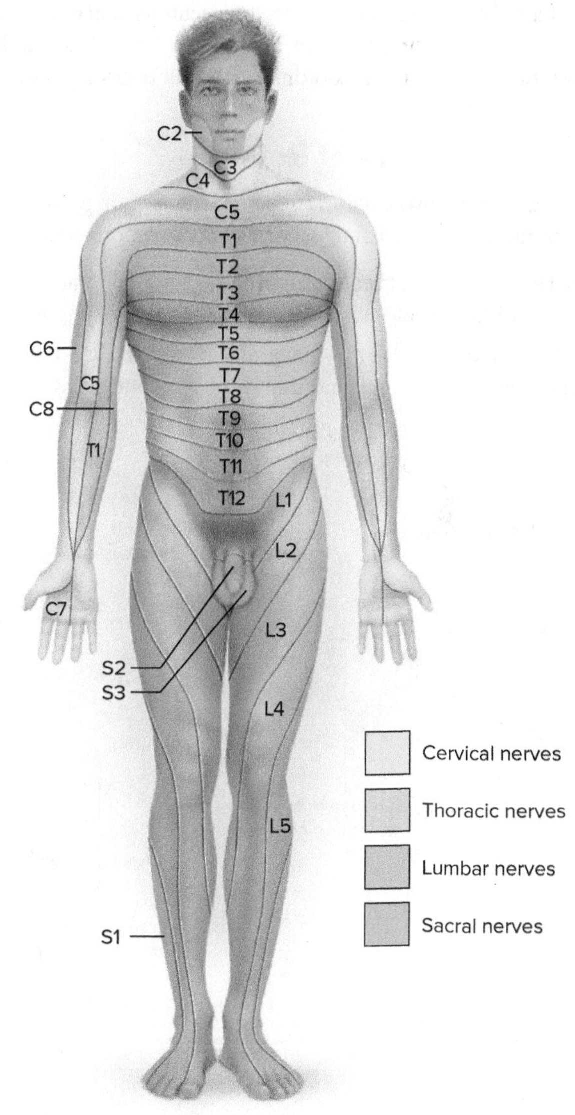


**FIGURE 13.22 A Dermatome Map of the Anterior Aspect of the Body.** Each zone of the skin is innervated by sensory branches of the spinal nerves indicated by the labels. Nerve C1 does not innervate the skin.

[25] *derma* = skin; *tome* = segment, part

## 13.3 Somatic Reflexes

**Expected Learning Outcomes**

When you have completed this section, you should be able to

a. define *reflex* and explain how reflexes differ from other motor actions;
b. describe the general components of a typical reflex arc; and
c. explain how the basic types of somatic reflexes function.

Most of us have had our reflexes tested with a little rubber hammer; a tap below the knee produces an uncontrollable jerk of the leg, for example. In this section, we discuss what reflexes are and how they are produced by an assembly of receptors, neurons, and effectors. We also survey the different types of neuromuscular reflexes and how they are important in motor coordination of our everyday tasks.

### 13.3a The Nature of Reflexes

**Reflexes** are quick, involuntary, stereotyped reactions of glands or muscles to stimulation. This definition sums up four important properties:

1. Reflexes *require stimulation*—they are not spontaneous actions like muscle tics but responses to sensory input.
2. Reflexes are *quick*—they generally involve only a few interneurons, or none, and minimum synaptic delay.
3. Reflexes are *involuntary*—they occur without intent, often without our awareness, and they are difficult to suppress. Given an adequate stimulus, the response is essentially automatic. You may become conscious of the stimulus that evoked a reflex, and this awareness may enable you to correct or avoid a potentially dangerous situation, but awareness is not a part of the reflex itself. It may come after the reflex action has been completed, and somatic reflexes can occur even if the spinal cord has been severed so that no stimuli reach the brain.
4. Reflexes are *stereotyped*—they occur in essentially the same way every time; the response is very predictable, unlike the variability of voluntary movement.

Reflexes include glandular secretion and contractions of all three types of muscle. The reflexes of skeletal muscle are called **somatic reflexes,** since they involve the somatic nervous system. Chapter 15 concerns the *visceral reflexes* of organs such as the heart and intestines. Somatic reflexes have traditionally been called *spinal reflexes,* but this is a misleading expression for two reasons: (1) Spinal reflexes are not exclusively somatic; visceral reflexes also involve the spinal cord. (2) Some somatic reflexes are mediated more by the brain than by the spinal cord.

A somatic reflex employs a **reflex arc,** in which signals travel along the following pathway **(fig. 13.23):**

1. *somatic receptors* in the skin, muscles, and tendons;
2. *afferent nerve fibers,* which carry information from these receptors to the posterior horn of the spinal cord or to the brainstem;

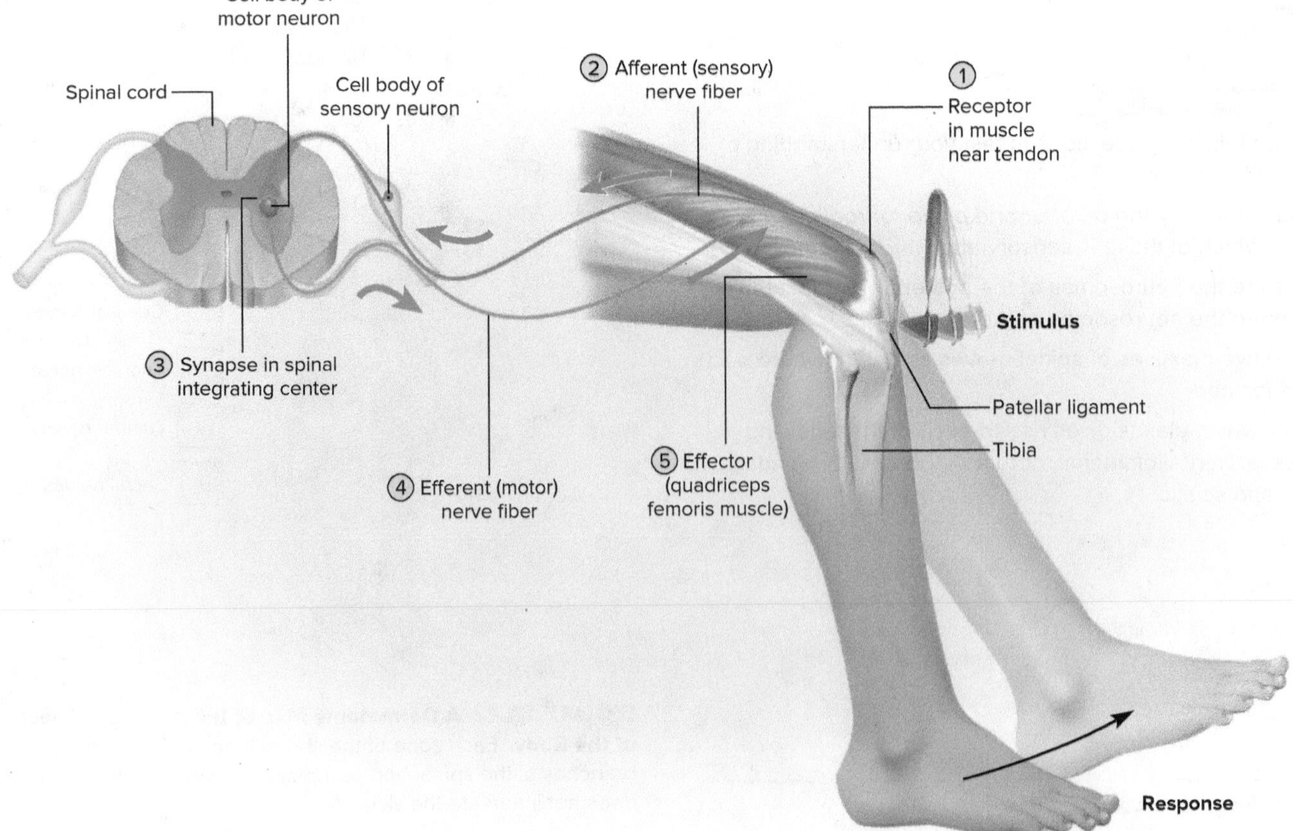


**FIGURE 13.23 A Representative Reflex Arc.**

3. an *integrating center,* a point of synaptic contact between neurons in the gray matter of the cord or brainstem;
4. *efferent nerve fibers,* which carry motor impulses to the muscles; and
5. *effectors,* the muscles that carry out the response.

In most reflex arcs, the integrating center includes one or more interneurons. Synaptic events in the integrating center determine whether the efferent neurons issue signals to the muscles. The more interneurons there are, the more complex the information processing can be, but with more synapses, there is a longer delay between input and output.

### 13.3b The Muscle Spindle

Many somatic reflexes involve stretch receptors called **muscle spindles** embedded in the muscles. These are among the body's **proprioceptors,** sense organs specialized to monitor the position and movement of body parts. The function of muscle spindles is to inform the brain of muscle length and body movements. This enables the brain to send motor commands back to the muscles that control muscle tone, posture, coordinated movement, and corrective reflexes (for example, to keep one's balance). Spindles are especially abundant in muscles that require fine control. Hand and foot muscles have 100 or more spindles per gram of muscle, whereas there are relatively few in large muscles with coarse movements, and none at all in the middle-ear muscles.

A muscle spindle is a bundle of usually seven or eight small, modified muscle fibers enclosed in an elongated fibrous capsule about 5 to 10 mm long **(fig. 13.24).** Spindles are especially concentrated at the ends of a muscle, near its tendons. The modified muscle fibers within the spindle are called

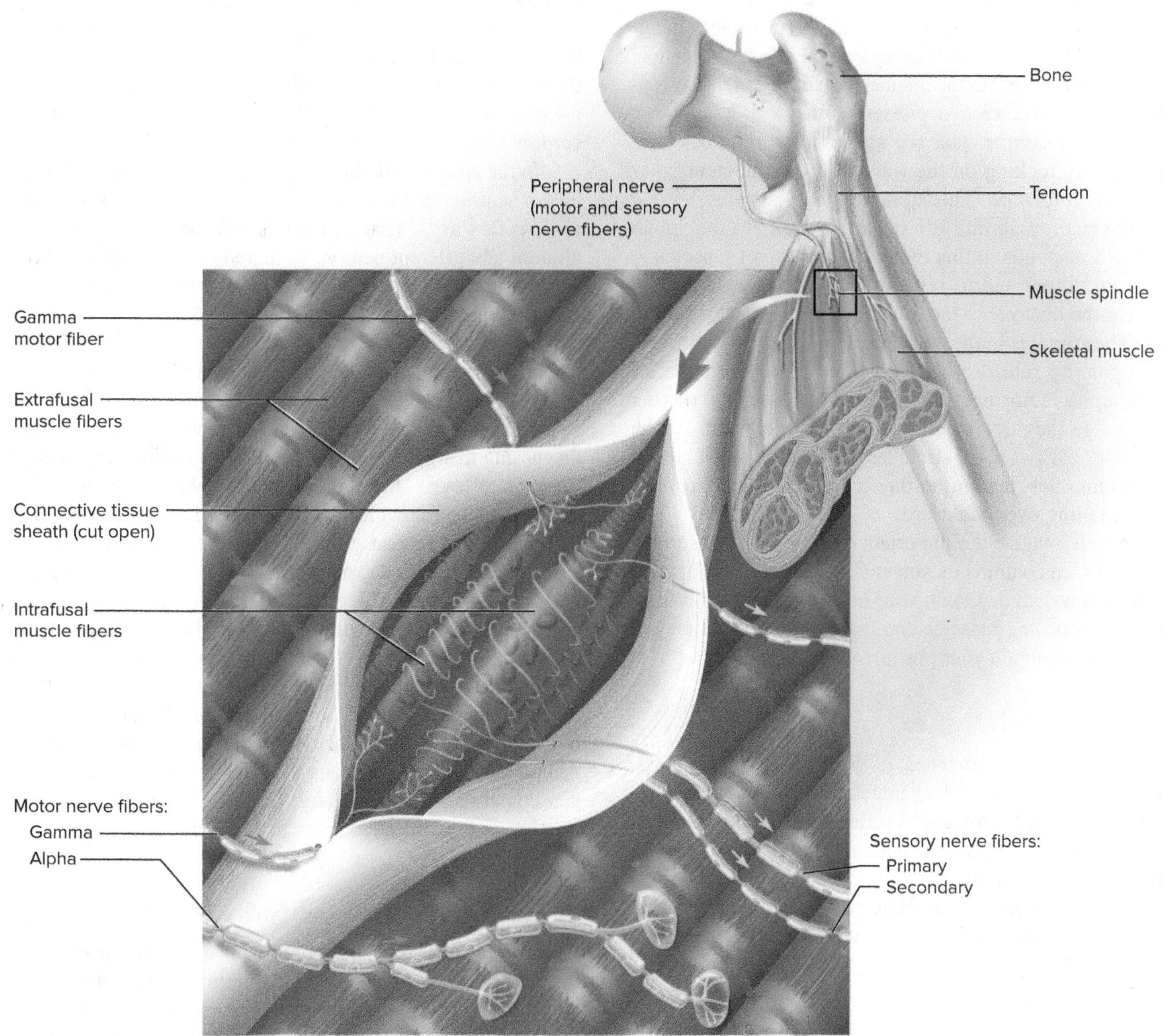


**FIGURE 13.24 A Muscle Spindle and Its Innervation.**

**intrafusal**[26] **fibers,** whereas those that make up the rest of the muscle and do its work are called **extrafusal fibers.**

Each end of an intrafusal fiber has a few sarcomeres. A **gamma motor neuron** of the spinal cord innervates each end and stimulates its contraction. This maintains tension and sensitivity of the intrafusal fiber, preventing it from going slack like an unstretched rubber band when a muscle shortens. Spinal motor neurons that supply the extrafusal muscle fibers are called **alpha motor neurons.** Up to now, we have studied only that type and the neuromuscular junctions they form with muscle, but nearly one-third of all spinal motor neurons are the gamma type—evidence of the great importance of muscle spindles.

The long midportion of an intrafusal fiber lacks sarcomeres and cannot contract, but is supplied by two types of sensory nerve fibers: *primary afferent fibers* that monitor muscle length and how rapidly it changes, which are therefore very responsive to sudden body movements; and *secondary afferent fibers* that monitor length only, not rate of change. Both of these sensory fiber types enter the posterior horn of the spinal cord, synapse on the alpha motor neurons and regulate their firing, and also send branches up the spinal cord to the brain. Through these fibers, the brain constantly but subconsciously monitors the length and tension of nearly every skeletal muscle throughout the body. This input is vital to the maintenance of posture, fine control of movements, and corrective reflexes.

Suppose, for example, you are standing on the deck of a boat that is gently rocking on the waves. At one moment, your body begins to tip forward. This stretches your calf muscles and their muscle spindles, setting off sensory signals to the spinal cord. The CNS responds to this by tensing your calf muscles to keep you from falling and to restore or maintain your upright posture. Then the boat rocks the other way and you begin to tip to the rear. The spindles in the calf muscles are now compressed and their signaling rate drops. Such input from the spindles inhibits the alpha motor neurons of the calf muscles, relaxing those muscles so they don't pull you farther backward. At the same time, your backward tilt stretches spindles in your anterior leg and thigh muscles, leading to their contraction and preventing you from falling over backward.

You can well imagine the importance of these reflexes to the coordination of such common movements as walking and dancing. In more subtle ways, all day long, your brain monitors input from the spindles of opposing muscles and makes fine adjustments in muscle tension to maintain your posture and coordination.

### 13.3c The Stretch Reflex

When a muscle is suddenly stretched, it "fights back"—it contracts, increases tone, and feels stiffer than an unstretched muscle. This response, called the **stretch (myotatic**[27]**) reflex,** helps to maintain equilibrium and posture, as we just saw in the rocking boat example. To take another case, if your head starts to tip forward, it stretches muscles at the back of your neck. This stimulates their muscle spindles, which send signals to the cerebellum by way of the brainstem. The cerebellum integrates this information and relays it to the cerebral cortex, and the cortex sends signals back, via the brainstem, to the muscles. The muscles contract and raise your head.

Stretch reflexes often feed back not to a single muscle but to a set of synergists and antagonists. Since the contraction of a muscle on one side of a joint stretches the antagonist on the other side, the flexion of a joint creates a stretch reflex in the extensors, and extension creates a stretch reflex in the flexors. (Think of the way your biceps brachii is stretched when you extend your elbow, for example.) Consequently, stretch reflexes are valuable in stabilizing joints by balancing the tension of the extensors and flexors. They also dampen (smooth out) muscle action. Without stretch reflexes, a person's movements tend to be jerky. Stretch reflexes are especially important in coordinating vigorous and precise movements such as dance.

A stretch reflex is mediated primarily by the brain and is not, therefore, strictly a spinal reflex, but a weak component of it is spinal and occurs even if the spinal cord is severed from the brain. The spinal component can be more pronounced if a muscle is stretched very suddenly. This occurs in the reflexive contraction of a muscle when its tendon is tapped, as in the familiar *patellar* (knee-jerk) *reflex.* Tapping the patellar ligament with a reflex hammer abruptly stretches the quadriceps femoris muscle of the thigh **(fig. 13.25).** This stimulates numerous muscle spindles in the quadriceps and sends an intense volley of signals to the spinal cord, mainly by way of primary afferent fibers.

In the spinal cord, these fibers synapse directly with the alpha motor neurons that return to the muscle, thus forming **monosynaptic reflex arcs.** That is, there is only one synapse between the afferent and efferent neuron, so there is little synaptic delay and a very prompt response. The alpha motor neurons excite the quadriceps, making it contract and creating the knee jerk.

There are many other tendon reflexes. A tap on the calcaneal tendon causes plantar flexion of the foot, a tap on the triceps brachii tendon causes extension of the elbow, and a tap on the masseter causes clenching of the jaw. Testing somatic reflexes is valuable in diagnosing many diseases that cause exaggeration, inhibition, or absence of reflexes—for example, neurosyphilis and other infectious diseases, diabetes mellitus, multiple sclerosis, alcoholism, hormone and electrolyte imbalances, and lesions of the nervous system.

Stretch reflexes and other muscle contractions often depend on **reciprocal inhibition,** a reflex that prevents muscles from working against each other by inhibiting antagonists. In the knee jerk, for example, the quadriceps wouldn't produce much joint movement if its antagonists, the hamstring muscles, contracted at the same time. But reciprocal inhibition prevents that from happening. Some branches of the sensory fibers from the quadriceps muscle spindles stimulate spinal interneurons that, in turn, *inhibit* the alpha motor neurons of the hamstrings (fig. 13.25). The hamstrings remain relaxed and allow the quadriceps to extend the knee.

### 13.3d The Flexor (Withdrawal) Reflex

A **flexor reflex** is the quick contraction of flexor muscles resulting in the withdrawal of a limb from an injurious stimulus. For example, suppose you are wading in a lake and step on a broken bottle with your right foot **(fig. 13.26).** Even before you are consciously

[26]*intra* = within; *fus* = spindle
[27]*myo* = muscle; *tat* (from *tasis*) = stretch

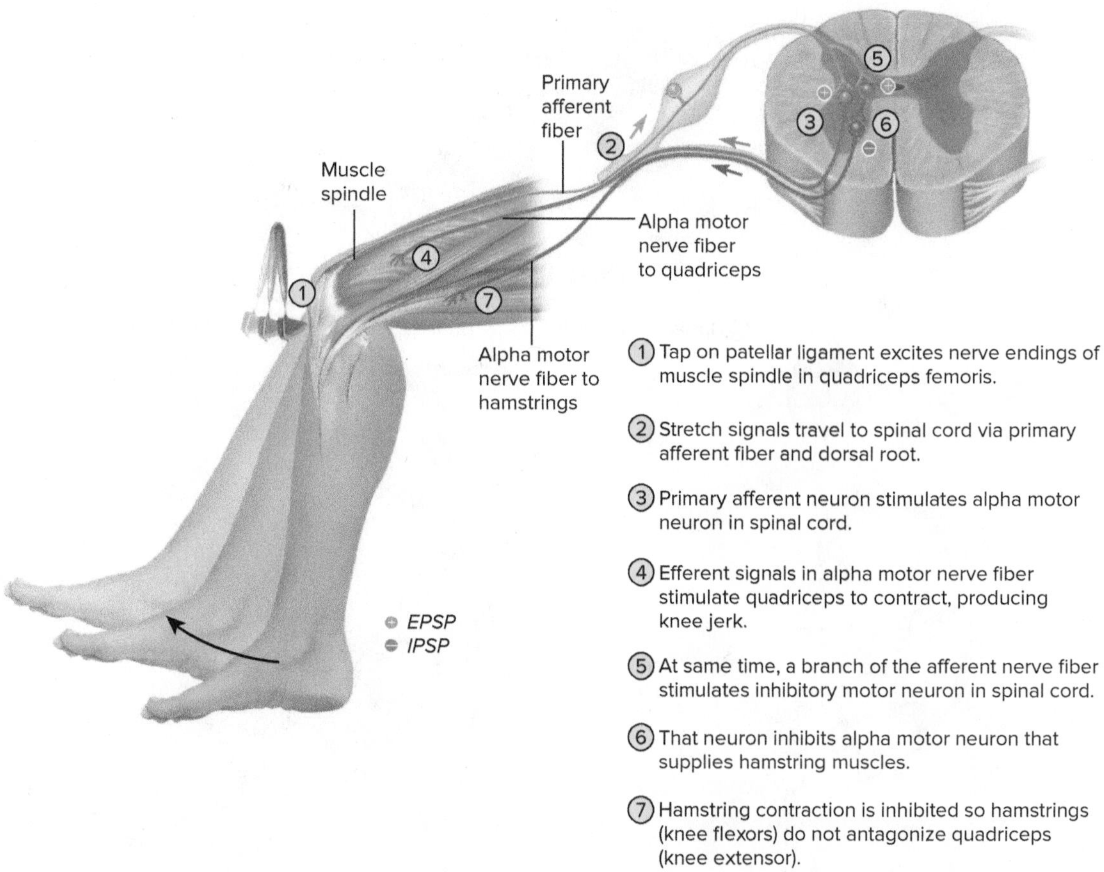

Primary afferent fiber
Muscle spindle
Alpha motor nerve fiber to quadriceps
Alpha motor nerve fiber to hamstrings
EPSP
IPSP
1 Tap on patellar ligament excites nerve endings of muscle spindle in quadriceps femoris.
2 Stretch signals travel to spinal cord via primary afferent fiber and dorsal root.
3 Primary afferent neuron stimulates alpha motor neuron in spinal cord.
4 Efferent signals in alpha motor nerve fiber stimulate quadriceps to contract, producing knee jerk.
5 At same time, a branch of the afferent nerve fiber stimulates inhibitory motor neuron in spinal cord.
6 That neuron inhibits alpha motor neuron that supplies hamstring muscles.
7 Hamstring contraction is inhibited so hamstrings (knee flexors) do not antagonize quadriceps (knee extensor).


**FIGURE 13.25 The Patellar Tendon Reflex Arc and Reciprocal Inhibition of the Antagonistic Muscle.** Plus signs indicate excitation of a postsynaptic cell (EPSP), and the minus sign indicates inhibition (IPSP). The tendon reflex occurs in the quadriceps femoris muscle, while the hamstring muscles exhibit reciprocal inhibition so they don't contract and oppose the quadriceps.

*Why is no IPSP shown at point 7 if the contraction of this muscle is being inhibited?*

aware of the pain, you quickly pull your foot away before the glass penetrates any deeper. This action involves contraction of the flexors and relaxation of the extensors in that limb; the latter is another case of reciprocal inhibition.

The protective function of this reflex requires more than a quick jerk like a tendon reflex, so it involves more complex neural pathways. Sustained contraction of the flexors is produced by a parallel after-discharge circuit in the spinal cord (see fig. 12.32). This circuit is part of a **polysynaptic reflex arc**—a pathway in which signals travel over many synapses on their way back to the muscle. Some signals follow routes with only a few synapses and return to the flexor muscles quickly. Others follow routes with more synapses, and therefore more delay, so they reach the flexor muscles a little later. Consequently, the flexor muscles receive prolonged output from the spinal cord and not just one sudden stimulus as in a stretch reflex. By the time these efferent signals begin to die out, you will probably be consciously aware of the pain and begin taking voluntary action to prevent further harm.

## 13.3e The Crossed Extension Reflex

In the preceding situation, if *all* you did was to quickly lift the injured leg from the lake bottom, you would fall over. To prevent this and maintain your balance, other reflexes shift your center of gravity over the leg that is still planted on the ground. The **crossed extension reflex** is the contraction of extensor muscles in the limb opposite from the one that is withdrawn (fig. 13.26). It extends and stiffens that limb and enables you to keep your balance. To produce this reflex, branches of the afferent nerve fibers cross from the stimulated side of the body to the contralateral side of the spinal cord. There, they synapse with interneurons, which, in turn, excite or inhibit alpha motor neurons to the muscles of the contralateral limb.

In the ipsilateral leg (the side that was hurt), you would contract your flexors and relax your extensors to lift the leg from the ground. On the contralateral side, you would relax your flexors and contract the extensors to stiffen that leg, since it must suddenly support your entire body. At the same time, signals travel up the spinal cord and cause contraction of contralateral muscles of the hip and abdomen, such as your internal and external obliques, to shift your center of gravity over the extended leg. To a large extent, the coordination of all these muscles and maintenance of equilibrium are mediated by the cerebellum and cerebral cortex.

The flexor reflex employs an **ipsilateral reflex arc**—one in which the sensory input and motor output are on the same side of the spinal cord. The crossed extension reflex employs a **contralateral reflex arc,** in which the input and output are on opposite sides. An

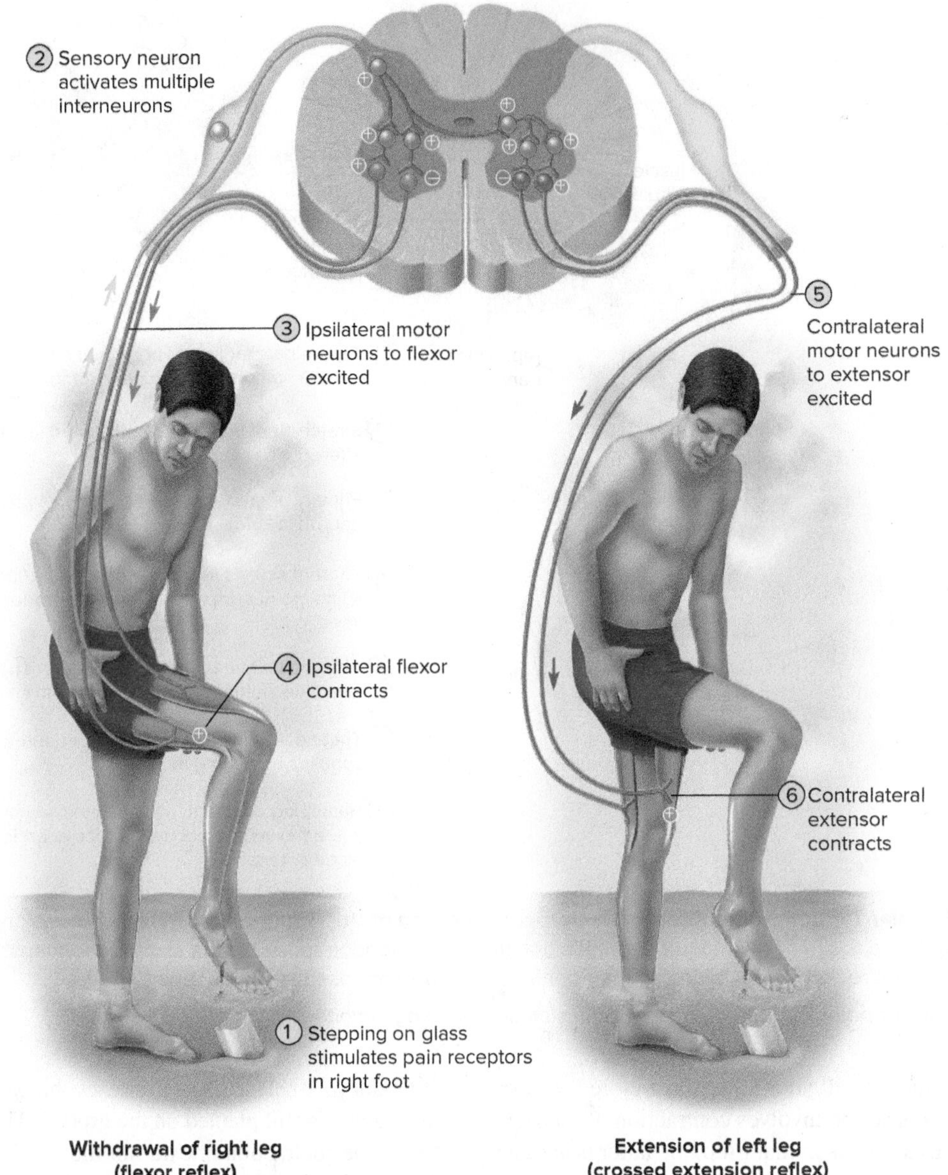

2 Sensory neuron activates multiple interneurons
3 Ipsilateral motor neurons to flexor excited
5 Contralateral motor neurons to extensor excited
4 Ipsilateral flexor contracts
6 Contralateral extensor contracts
1 Stepping on glass stimulates pain receptors in right foot
Withdrawal of right leg (flexor reflex)
Extension of left leg (crossed extension reflex)

**FIGURE 13.26 The Flexor and Crossed Extension Reflexes.** A pain stimulus triggers a withdrawal reflex, which results in contraction of flexor muscles of the injured limb. At the same time, a crossed extension reflex results in contraction of extensor muscles of the opposite limb. The latter reflex aids in balance when the injured limb is raised. Note that for each limb, while the agonist contracts, the alpha motor neuron to its antagonist is inhibited, as indicated by the red minus signs in the spinal cord. APR

*Would you expect this reflex arc to show more synaptic delay, or less, than the ones in figure 13.25? Why?*

**intersegmental reflex arc** is one in which the input and output occur at different levels (segments) of the spinal cord—for example, when pain to the foot causes contractions of abdominal and hip muscles higher up the body. Note that all of these reflex arcs can function simultaneously to produce a coordinated protective response to pain.

**APPLY WHAT YOU KNOW**

*In section 12.6d, you read of serial and parallel processing. Which of these do you think best describes the stretch reflex, flexor reflex, and crossed extension reflex? Explain.*

## 13.3f The Tendon Reflex

**Tendon organs** are proprioceptors located in a tendon near its junction with a muscle **(fig. 13.27).** A tendon organ is about 0.5 mm long. It consists of an encapsulated bundle of small, loose collagen fibers and one or more nerve fibers that penetrate the capsule and end in flattened leaflike processes between the collagen fibers. As long as the tendon is slack, its collagen fibers are slightly spread and put little pressure on the nerve endings. When muscle contraction pulls on the tendon, the collagen fibers come together like the two sides of a stretched rubber band and squeeze the nerve endings

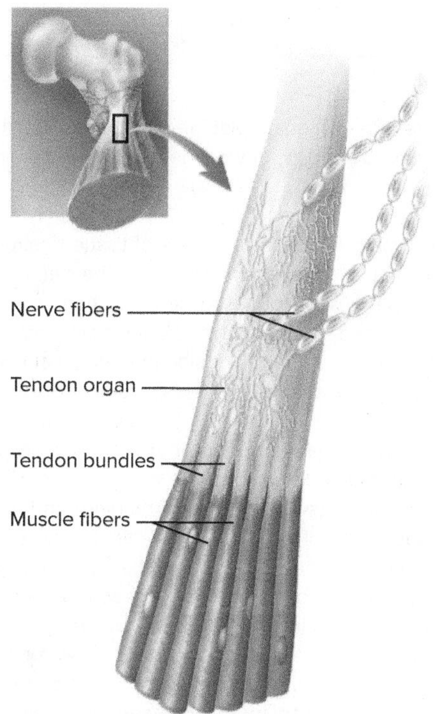


**FIGURE 13.27 A Tendon Organ.**

between them. The nerve fiber sends signals to the spinal cord that provide the CNS with feedback on the degree of muscle tension at the joint.

The **tendon reflex** is a response to excessive tension on the tendon. It inhibits alpha motor neurons to the muscle so the muscle doesn't contract as strongly. This moderates muscle contraction before it tears a tendon or pulls it loose from the muscle or bone. Nevertheless, strong muscles and quick movements sometimes damage a tendon before the reflex can occur, causing such athletic injuries as a ruptured calcaneal tendon.

The tendon reflex also functions when some parts of a muscle contract more than others. It inhibits the muscle fibers connected with overstimulated tendon organs so their contraction is more comparable to the contraction of the rest of the muscle. This spreads the workload more evenly over the entire muscle, which is beneficial in such actions as maintaining a steady grip on a tool.

**Table 13.7** and Deeper Insight 13.5 describe some injuries and other disorders of the spinal cord and spinal nerves.

**BEFORE YOU GO ON**

Answer the following questions to test your understanding of the preceding section:

10. Name five structural components of a typical somatic reflex arc. Which of these is absent from a monosynaptic arc?
11. State the function of each of the following in a muscle spindle: intrafusal fibers, gamma motor neurons, and primary afferent fibers.
12. Explain how nerve fibers in a tendon sense the degree of tension in a muscle.
13. Why must the withdrawal reflex, but not the stretch reflex, involve a polysynaptic reflex arc?
14. Explain why the crossed extension reflex must accompany a withdrawal reflex of the leg.

| TABLE 13.7 | Some Disorders of the Spinal Cord and Spinal Nerves |
|---|---|
| Guillain–Barré syndrome | An acute demyelinating nerve disorder often triggered by viral infection, resulting in muscle weakness, elevated heart rate, unstable blood pressure, shortness of breath, and sometimes death from respiratory paralysis |
| Neuralgia | General term for nerve pain, often caused by pressure on spinal nerves from herniated intervertebral discs |
| Paresthesia | Abnormal sensations of prickling, burning, numbness, or tingling in the absence of actual stimulation; a symptom of peripheral nerve disorders |
| Peripheral neuropathy | Any loss of sensory or motor function due to nerve injury; also called *nerve palsy* |
| Rabies (hydrophobia) | A disease usually contracted from animal bites, involving viral infection that spreads via somatic motor nerve fibers to the CNS and then autonomic nerve fibers; leads to seizures, coma, and death; invariably fatal if not treated before CNS symptoms appear |
| Spinal meningitis | Inflammation of the spinal meninges due to viral, bacterial, or other infection |

***You can find other spinal cord and peripheral nerve disorders described in the following places:***

*Carpal tunnel syndrome* in Deeper Insight 10.5; *multiple sclerosis* and *Tay–Sachs disease* in Deeper Insight 12.2; *polio* and *amyotrophic lateral sclerosis* in Deeper Insight 13.2; *shingles* in Deeper Insight 13.3; *crutch paralysis* and *sciatica* in Deeper Insight 13.4; spinal cord trauma and the forms of paralysis in Deeper Insight 13.5; *leprosy* and *diabetic neuropathy* in section 16.2d, and the latter also in section 17.7e.

## DEEPER INSIGHT 13.5

### CLINICAL APPLICATION

### *Spinal Cord Trauma*

In the United States, 10,000 to 12,000 people are newly paralyzed each year by spinal cord trauma, usually as a result of vertebral fractures. The greatest incidence is among males from 16 to 30 years old, because of their high-risk behaviors. Fifty-five percent of their injuries are from automobile and motorcycle accidents, 18% from sports, and 15% from gunshot and stab wounds. Elderly people are also at above-average risk because of falls, and in times of war, battlefield injuries account for many cases.

#### Effects of Injury

Complete *transection* (severance) of the spinal cord causes immediate loss of motor control at and below the level of the injury. Transection superior to segment C4 presents a threat of respiratory failure. Victims also lose sensation from the level of injury and below, although some patients temporarily feel burning pain within one or two dermatomes of the level of the lesion.

In the early stage, victims exhibit a syndrome called *spinal shock*. Muscles below the level of injury exhibit flaccid paralysis (inability to contract) and an absence of reflexes because of the lack of stimulation from higher levels of the CNS. For 8 days to 8 weeks after the accident, the patient typically lacks bladder and bowel reflexes and thus retains urine and feces. Lacking sympathetic stimulation to the blood vessels, a patient may exhibit *neurogenic shock* in which the vessels dilate and blood pressure drops dangerously low. Fever may occur because the hypothalamus cannot induce sweating to cool the body. Spinal shock can last from a few days to several weeks (usually 7 to 20 days).

As spinal shock subsides, somatic reflexes begin to reappear, at first in the toes and progressing to the feet and legs. Autonomic reflexes also reappear. Contrary to the earlier urinary and fecal retention, a patient now has the opposite problem, incontinence, as the rectum and bladder empty reflexively in response to stretch. Both the somatic and autonomic nervous systems typically exhibit exaggerated reflexes, a state called *hyperreflexia* or the *mass reflex reaction.* Stimuli such as a full bladder or cutaneous touch can trigger an extreme cardiovascular reaction. The systolic blood pressure, normally about 120 mm Hg, jumps to as high as 300 mm Hg. This causes intense headaches and sometimes a stroke. Pressure receptors in the major arteries sense this rise in blood pressure and activate a reflex that slows the heart, sometimes to a rate as low as 30 or 40 beats/minute (*bradycardia*), compared with a normal rate of 70 to 80. The patient may also experience profuse sweating and blurred vision.

Men at first lose the capacity for erection and ejaculation. They may recover these functions later and become capable of ejaculating and fathering children, but without sexual sensation. In females, menstruation may become irregular or cease.

The most serious permanent effect of spinal cord trauma is paralysis. The flaccid paralysis of spinal shock later changes to spastic paralysis as spinal reflexes are regained but lack inhibitory control from the brain. Spastic paralysis typically starts with chronic flexion of the hips and knees (flexor spasms) and progresses to a state in which the limbs become straight and rigid (extensor spasms). Three forms of muscle paralysis are *paraplegia,* a paralysis of both lower limbs resulting from spinal cord lesions at levels T1 to L1; *quadriplegia,* the paralysis of all four limbs resulting from lesions above level C5; and *hemiplegia,* paralysis of one side of the body, usually resulting not from spinal cord injuries but from a stroke or other brain lesion. Spinal cord lesions from C5 to C7 can produce a state of partial quadriplegia—total paralysis of the lower limbs and partial paralysis (*paresis,* or weakness) of the upper limbs.

#### Pathogenesis

Spinal cord trauma produces two stages of tissue destruction. The first is instantaneous—the destruction of cells by the traumatic event itself. The second stage, a wave of tissue death by necrosis and apoptosis, begins in minutes and lasts for days. It is far more destructive than the initial injury, typically converting a lesion in one spinal cord segment to a lesion that spans four or five segments, two above and two below the original site.

Microscopic hemorrhages appear in the gray matter and pia mater within minutes and grow larger over the next 2 hours. The white matter becomes edematous (swollen). Hemorrhaging and edema spread to adjacent segments of the cord and can fatally affect respiration or brainstem function when it occurs in the cervical region. *Ischemia* (iss-KEE-me-uh), the lack of blood, quickly leads to necrosis. The white matter regains circulation in about 24 hours, but the gray matter remains ischemic. Inflammatory cells (leukocytes and macrophages) infiltrate the lesion as the circulation recovers, and while they clean up necrotic tissue, they also contribute to the damage by releasing destructive free radicals and other toxic chemicals. The necrosis worsens, and is accompanied by another form of cell death, apoptosis. Apoptosis of the spinal oligodendrocytes, the myelinating glial cells of the CNS, results in demyelination of spinal nerve fibers, followed by death of the neurons.

In as little as 4 hours, this second wave of destruction, called *post-traumatic infarction,* consumes about 40% of the cross-sectional area of the spinal cord; within 24 hours, it destroys 70%. As many as five segments of the cord become transformed into a fluid-filled cavity, which is replaced with collagenous scar tissue over the next 3 to 4 weeks. This scar is one of the obstacles to the regeneration of lost nerve fibers.

#### Treatment

The first priority in treating a spinal injury patient is to immobilize the spine to prevent further trauma. Respiratory or other life support may also be required. Methylprednisolone, a steroid, dramatically improves recovery. Given within 3 hours of the trauma, it reduces injury to cell membranes and inhibits inflammation and apoptosis.

After these immediate requirements are met, reduction (repair) of the fracture is important. If a CT or MRI scan indicates spinal cord compression by the vertebral canal, a *decompression laminectomy* may be performed, in which vertebral laminae are removed from the affected region. CT and MRI have helped a great deal in recent decades for assessing vertebral and spinal cord damage, guiding surgical treatment, and improving recovery. Physical therapy is important for maintaining muscle and joint function as well as promoting the patient's psychological recovery.

Treatment strategies for spinal cord injuries are a vibrant field of contemporary medical research. Some current interests are the use of antioxidants to reduce free radical damage, and the implantation of pluripotent stem cells, which has produced significant (but not perfect) recovery from spinal cord lesions in rats. Public hopes have often been raised by promising studies reported in the scientific literature and news media, only to be dashed by the inability of other laboratories to repeat and confirm the results.

# STUDY GUIDE

## Assess Your Learning Outcomes

*To test your knowledge, discuss the following topics with a study partner or in writing, ideally from memory.*

### 13.1 The Spinal Cord

1. Functions of the spinal cord
2. Skeletal landmarks that mark the extent of the adult spinal cord, and what occupies the vertebral canal inferior to the spinal cord
3. The four regions of the spinal cord and the basis for their names
4. What defines one segment of the cord
5. Two enlargements of the cord and why the cord is wider at these points
6. Names and structures of the three spinal meninges, in order from superficial to deep, and the relationships of the epidural and subarachnoid spaces to the meninges
7. The two types of ligaments that arise from the pia mater; where they are found and what purpose they serve
8. Organization of spinal gray and white matter as seen in cross sections of the cord; how gray and white matter differ in composition; and why they are called *gray* and *white matter*
9. The position of the posterior and anterior horns of the gray matter; where lateral horns are also found, and the functions of all three
10. The anatomical basis for dividing white matter into three funiculi on each side of the cord, and for dividing each funiculus into tracts
11. Names and functions of the ascending tracts of the spinal cord
12. The meanings of *first-* through *third-order* neurons in an ascending tract
13. Names and functions of the descending tracts
14. The locations and distinctions between upper and lower motor neurons in the descending tracts
15. Decussation and its implications for cerebral function in relation to sensation and motor control of the lower body, and for the effects of a stroke
16. What it means to say that the origin and destination of a tract, or any two body parts, are ipsilateral or contralateral

### 13.2 The Spinal Nerves

1. Structure of a nerve, especially the relationship of the endoneurium, perineurium, and epineurium to nerve fibers and fascicles
2. The basis for classifying nerve fibers as afferent or efferent, somatic or visceral, and special or general
3. The basis for classifying entire nerves as sensory, motor, or mixed
4. The definition and structure of a *ganglion*
5. The number of spinal nerves and their relationship to the spinal cord and intervertebral foramina
6. Anatomy of the posterior and anterior roots of a spinal nerve; the rootlets; and the posterior root ganglion
7. Anatomy of the anterior ramus, posterior ramus, and meningeal branch of a spinal nerve
8. What arises from the anterior ramus in the thoracic region as opposed to all other regions of the spinal cord
9. General structure of a spinal nerve plexus and the names and locations of the five plexuses
10. Distinctions between the roots, trunks, anterior and posterior divisions, and cords of a spinal nerve plexus; which of these five features occur in each of the five plexuses
11. Nerves that arise from each plexus and the body regions or structures to which each nerve provides sensory innervation, motor innervation, or both
12. Dermatomes and why they are relevant to the clinical diagnosis of nerve disorders

### 13.3 Somatic Reflexes

1. Four defining criteria of a reflex; how somatic reflexes differ from other types; and the flaw in calling somatic reflexes spinal reflexes
2. The pathway and constituents of a somatic reflex arc
3. The role of proprioceptors in somatic reflexes
4. Structure and function of muscle spindles
5. Stretch reflexes; one or more examples; the purpose they serve in everyday function; the mechanism of a stretch reflex; and an anatomical reason why stretch reflexes are often quicker than other types of somatic reflexes
6. Reciprocal inhibition and why it is important that it often accompany a stretch reflex
7. Flexor reflexes; a common purpose that they serve; and why it is beneficial for flexor reflexes to employ polysynaptic reflex arcs
8. Crossed extension reflexes and why it is important for this type of reflex to accompany a withdrawal reflex
9. The structure, location, and function of a tendon organ

# STUDY GUIDE

## Testing Your Recall

Answers in Appendix A

1. Below L2, the vertebral canal is occupied by a bundle of spinal nerve roots called
   a. the terminal filum.
   b. the descending tracts.
   c. the gracile fasciculus.
   d. the medullary cone.
   e. the cauda equina.
2. The brachial plexus gives rise to all of the following nerves *except*
   a. the axillary nerve.
   b. the radial nerve.
   c. the obturator nerve.
   d. the median nerve.
   e. the ulnar nerve.
3. Nerve fibers that adjust the tension in a muscle spindle are called
   a. intrafusal fibers.
   b. extrafusal fibers.
   c. alpha motor neurons.
   d. gamma motor neurons.
   e. primary afferent fibers.
4. A stretch reflex requires the action of ______ to prevent an antagonistic muscle from interfering with the agonist.
   a. gamma motor neurons
   b. a withdrawal reflex
   c. a crossed extension reflex
   d. reciprocal inhibition
   e. a contralateral reflex
5. A patient has a gunshot wound that caused a bone fragment to nick the spinal cord. The patient now feels no pain or temperature sensations from that level of the body down. Most likely, the ______ was damaged.
   a. gracile fasciculus
   b. medial lemniscus
   c. tectospinal tract
   d. lateral corticospinal tract
   e. spinothalamic tract
6. Which of these is *not* a region of the spinal cord?
   a. cervical
   b. thoracic
   c. pelvic
   d. lumbar
   e. sacral
7. In the spinal cord, the somas of the lower motor neurons are found in
   a. the cauda equina.
   b. the posterior horns.
   c. the anterior horns.
   d. the posterior root ganglia.
   e. the fasciculi.
8. The outermost connective tissue wrapping of a nerve is called the
   a. epineurium.
   b. perineurium.
   c. endoneurium.
   d. arachnoid mater.
   e. dura mater.
9. The intercostal nerves between the ribs arise from which spinal nerve plexus?
   a. cervical
   b. brachial
   c. lumbar
   d. sacral
   e. none of them
10. All somatic reflexes share all of the following properties *except*
    a. they are quick.
    b. they are monosynaptic.
    c. they require stimulation.
    d. they are involuntary.
    e. they are stereotyped.
11. Outside the CNS, the somas of neurons are clustered in swellings called ______.
12. Distal to the intervertebral foramen, a spinal nerve branches into an anterior and posterior ______.
13. The cerebellum receives feedback from the muscles and joints by way of the ______ tracts of the spinal cord.
14. In the ______ reflex, contraction of flexor muscles in one limb is accompanied by the contraction of extensor muscles in the contralateral limb.
15. Modified muscle fibers serving primarily to detect stretch are called ______.
16. The ______ nerves arise from the cervical plexus and innervate the diaphragm.
17. The crossing of a nerve fiber or tract from the right side of the CNS to the left, or vice versa, is called ______.
18. The nonvisual awareness of the body's position and movements is called ______.
19. The ______ ganglion contains the somas of neurons that carry sensory signals to the spinal cord.
20. The sciatic nerve is a composite of two nerves, the ______ and ______.

## Building Your Medical Vocabulary

Answers in Appendix A

*State a meaning of each word element, and give a medical term from this chapter that uses it or a slight variation of it.*

1. arachno-
2. caudo-
3. contra-
4. cune-
5. ipsi-
6. phreno-
7. pia
8. proprio-
9. ram-
10. tecto-

# STUDY GUIDE

## What's Wrong with These Statements?

Answers in Appendix A

*Briefly explain why each of the following statements is false, or reword it to make it true.*

1. The gracile fasciculus is a descending spinal tract.
2. The adult spinal cord terminates in the sacral canal.
3. Each spinal nerve rootlet is connected to its own segment of the spinal cord.
4. Some spinal nerves are sensory and others are motor.
5. The dura mater adheres tightly to the bone of the vertebral canal.
6. The anterior and posterior horns of the spinal cord are composed of white matter.
7. The corticospinal tracts carry sensory signals from the spinal cord to the cerebral cortex.
8. The dermatomes are nonoverlapping regions of skin innervated by different spinal nerves.
9. Somatic reflexes are those that do not involve the brain.
10. Ipsilateral reflex arcs are monosynaptic whereas contralateral arcs are polysynaptic.

## Testing Your Comprehension

1. Jillian is thrown from a horse. She strikes the ground with her chin, causing severe hyperextension of the neck. Emergency medical technicians properly immobilize her neck and transport her to a hospital, but she dies 5 minutes after arrival. An autopsy shows multiple fractures of vertebrae C1, C6, and C7 and extensive damage to the spinal cord. Explain why she died rather than being left quadriplegic.
2. Wallace is the victim of a hunting accident. A bullet grazed his vertebral column, and bone fragments severed the left half of his spinal cord at segments T8 through T10. Since the accident, Wallace has had a condition called *dissociated sensory loss,* in which he feels no sensations of deep touch or limb position on the *left* side of his body below the injury, and no sensations of pain or heat from the *right* side. Explain what spinal tract(s) the injury has affected and why these sensory losses are on opposite sides of the body.
3. Anthony gets into a fight between rival gangs. As an attacker comes at him with a knife, he turns to flee, but stumbles. The attacker stabs him on the medial side of the right gluteal fold and Anthony collapses. He loses all use of his right limb, being unable to extend his hip, flex his knee, or move his foot. He never fully recovers these lost functions. Explain what nerve injury Anthony has most likely suffered.
4. Stand with your right shoulder, hip, and foot firmly against a wall. Raise your left foot from the floor without losing contact with the wall at any point. What happens? Why? What principle of this chapter does this demonstrate?
5. When a patient needs a tendon graft, surgeons sometimes use the tendon of the palmaris longus, a relatively dispensable muscle of the forearm. The median nerve lies nearby and looks very similar to this tendon. There have been cases in which a surgeon mistakenly removed a section of this nerve instead of the tendon. What effects do you think such a mistake would have on the patient?

CHAPTER 14

# THE BRAIN AND CRANIAL NERVES

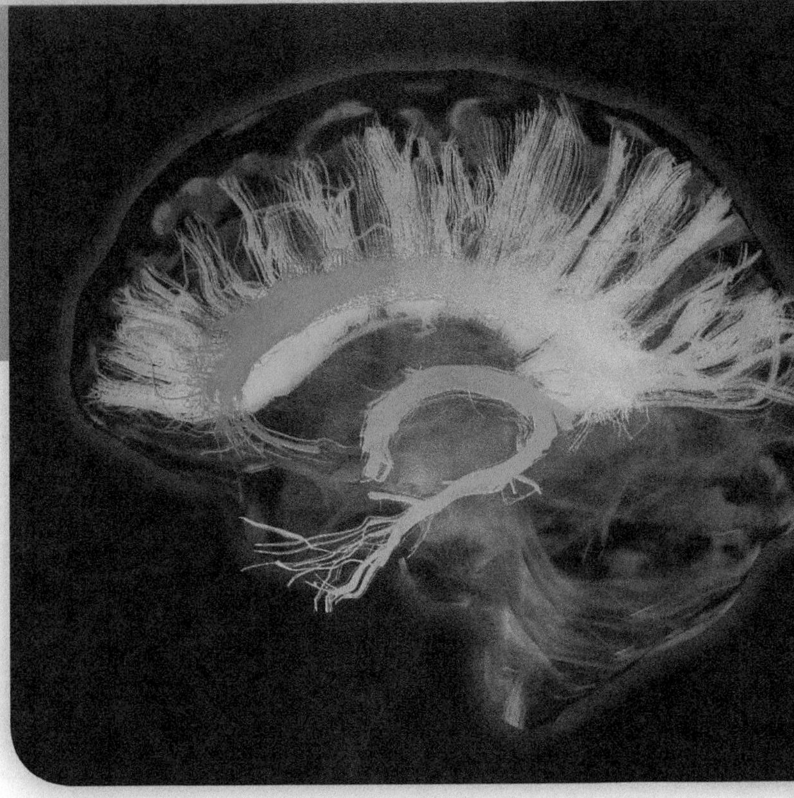

**Diffusion tensor image of white matter tracts in a lateral view of the brain**
Sherbrooke Connectivity Imaging Lab (SCIL)/Getty Images

## CHAPTER OUTLINE



## DEEPER INSIGHTS

**Module 7: Nervous System**

## BRUSHING UP

- The anatomy of the brain and cranial nerves is, in many respects, described in relation to the skull. Therefore, it may be helpful to review the cranial bones and major foramina in section 8.2a.
- You must be familiar with neuron structure (see section 12.2c) and with glial cells and their functions (see section 12.3a).
- The brainstem contains extensions of the spinal cord tracts, so you will find it helpful to know those or refer back to table 13.1 as you study the brainstem.
- To best understand the cranial nerves, you should be familiar with the general structure of nerves and ganglia, afferent and efferent nerve fibers, and the distinction between sensory, motor, and mixed nerves (see section 13.2a).

The human brain has a high opinion of itself, often claiming to be the most complex object in the known universe. It would be hard to argue otherwise. It has a mystique that intrigues modern biologists and psychologists even as it did the philosophers of antiquity. Aristotle thought it was just a radiator for cooling the blood, but generations earlier, Hippocrates had expressed a more accurate view. "Men ought to know," he said, "that from the brain, and from the brain only, arise our pleasures, joy, laughter and jests, as well as our sorrows, pains, griefs and tears. Through it, in particular, we think, see, hear, and distinguish the ugly from the beautiful, the bad from the good, the pleasant from the unpleasant."

Brain function is so strongly associated with what it means to be alive and human that the cessation of brain activity is taken as a clinical criterion of death even when other organs of the body are still functioning. With its hundreds of neural pools and trillions of synapses, the brain performs sophisticated tasks beyond our present understanding. Still, all of our mental functions, no matter how complex, are ultimately based on the cellular activities described in chapter 12. The relationship of the mind and personality to the cellular function of the brain is a question that will provide fertile ground for scientific study and philosophical debate long into the future.

This chapter is a study of the brain and the cranial nerves directly connected to it. Here we will plumb some of the mysteries of motor control, sensation, emotion, thought, language, personality, memory, dreams, and plans. Brain circuitry and function easily fill many books the size of this one, and we can barely scratch the surface of this complex subject here. This coverage will, however, provide some intriguing insights and lay a foundation for further study in other courses.

## 14.1 Overview of the Brain

### Expected Learning Outcomes

When you have completed this section, you should be able to

a. describe the major subdivisions and anatomical landmarks of the brain;
b. describe the locations of its gray and white matter; and
c. describe the embryonic development of the CNS and relate this to adult brain anatomy.

In the evolution of the central nervous system from the simplest vertebrates to humans, the spinal cord changed very little while the brain changed a great deal. In fishes and amphibians, the brain weighs about the same as the spinal cord, but in humans, it weighs 55 times as much. It averages about 1,600 g (3.5 lb) in men and 1,450 g in women. The difference between the sexes is proportional to body size, not intelligence. The Neanderthal people had larger brains than modern humans do.

Ours is the most sophisticated brain when compared to others in awareness of the environment, adaptability to environmental variation and change, quick execution of complex decisions, fine motor control and mobility of the body, and behavioral complexity. Over the course of human evolution, it has shown its greatest growth in areas concerned with vision, memory, abstract thought, and motor control of the prehensile hand.

### 14.1a Major Landmarks

We begin with a general overview of the major landmarks of the brain. These will provide important reference points as we progress through a more detailed study.

Two directional terms used in descriptions of CNS anatomy are *rostral* and *caudal.* **Rostral**[1] means "toward the nose" and **caudal**[2] means "toward the tail." These are apt descriptions for an animal such as a laboratory rat, on which so much brain research has been done. The terms are retained for human neuroanatomy as well, but in references to the brain, *rostral* means "toward the forehead" and *caudal* means "toward the spinal cord." In the spinal cord and brainstem, which are vertically oriented, *rostral* means "higher" and *caudal* means "lower."

We can conceptually divide the brain into three major portions—the *forebrain, cerebellum,* and *brainstem.* The most prominent part of the forebrain is the **cerebrum** (seh-REE-brum or SER-eh-brum). It constitutes about 83% of the brain's volume and consists of a pair of half globes called the **cerebral hemispheres (fig. 14.1a).** Each hemisphere is marked by thick folds called **gyri**[3] (JY-rye; singular, *gyrus*) separated by shallow grooves called **sulci**[4] (SUL-sye;

[1] *rostr* = nose
[2] *caud* = tail
[3] *gyr* = turn, twist
[4] *sulc* = furrow, groove

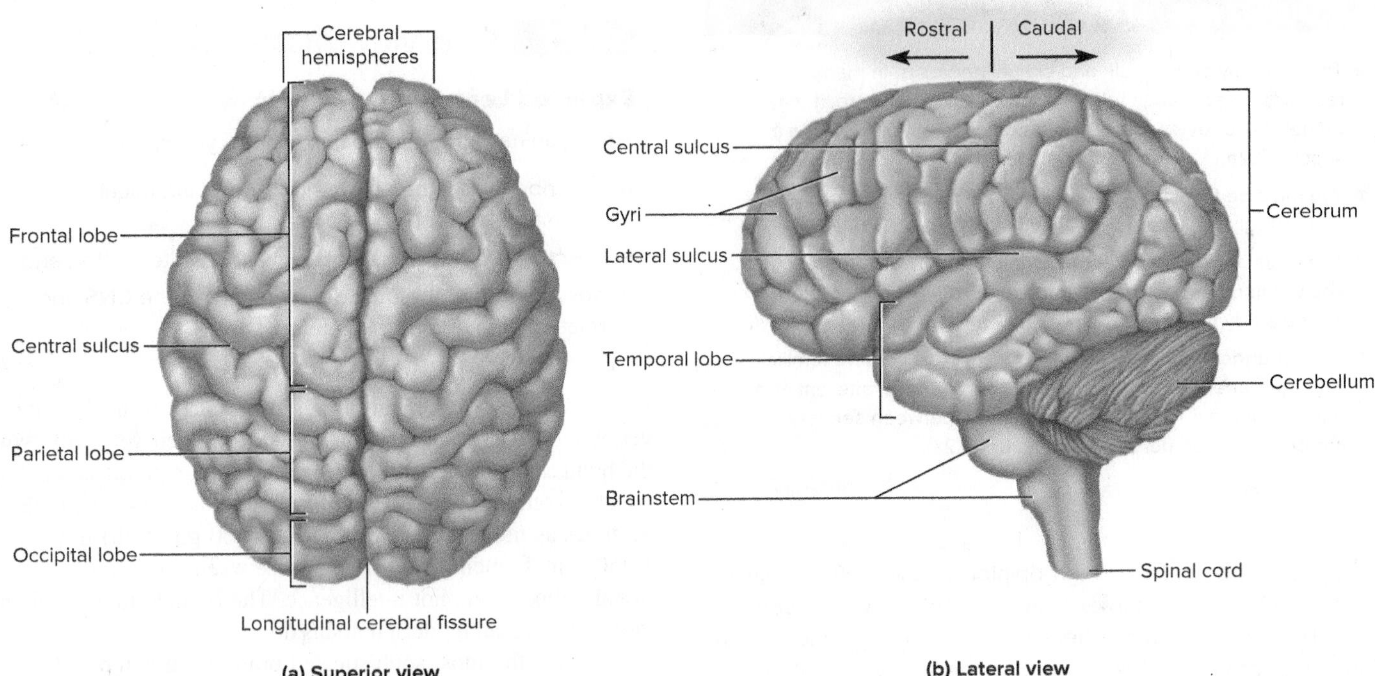


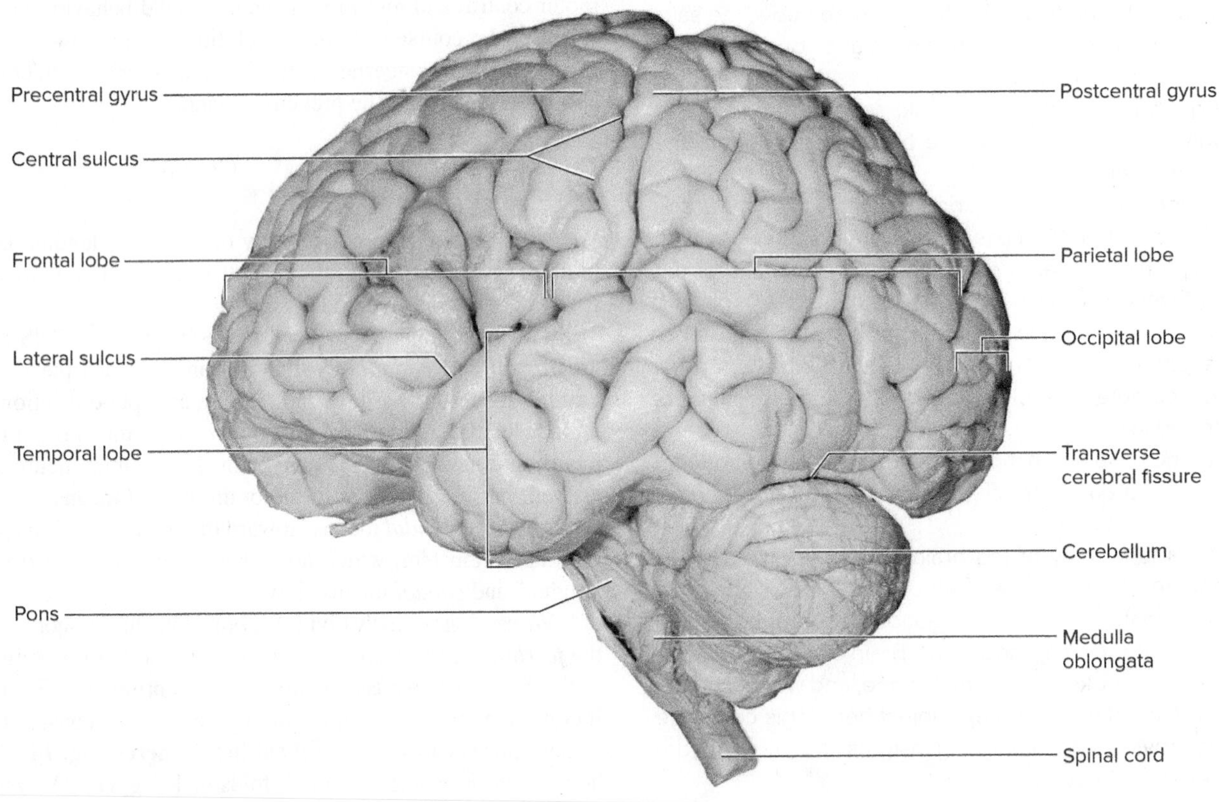


**FIGURE 14.1 Surface Anatomy of the Brain.** (a) Superior view of the cerebral hemispheres. (b) Left lateral view. (c) Lateral view of the cadaver brain. APR

singular, *sulcus*). A deep median groove, the **longitudinal cerebral fissure,** separates the right and left hemispheres from each other. At the bottom of this fissure, the hemispheres are connected by a thick bundle of nerve fibers called the **corpus callosum**[5]—a prominent landmark for anatomical description with a distinctive C shape in sagittal section **(fig. 14.2).**

The **cerebellum**[6] (SER-eh-BEL-um) occupies the posterior cranial fossa inferior to the cerebrum, separated from it by the **transverse cerebral fissure** (**fig. 14.1b, c;** also see fig. 8.9). It is also marked by fissures, sulci, and gyri (called *folia* in the cerebellum). The cerebellum is the second-largest region of the brain, constituting about 10% of its volume but containing over 50% of its neurons.

The **brainstem** is all of the brain except the forebrain and cerebellum. Its components, from rostral to caudal, are the *midbrain, pons,* and *medulla oblongata* (fig. 14.2).

In a living person, the brainstem is oriented like a vertical stalk with the forebrain perched on top like a mushroom cap. Postmortem changes give it a more oblique angle in the cadaver and, consequently, in many medical illustrations. Caudally, the brainstem ends at the foramen magnum of the skull, and the CNS continues below this as the spinal cord.

## 14.1b Gray and White Matter

The brain, like the spinal cord, is composed of gray and white matter (see figs. 14.5, 14.6c). Gray matter—the seat of the neurosomas, dendrites, and synapses—forms a surface layer called the **cortex** over the cerebrum and cerebellum, and deeper masses called **nuclei** surrounded by white matter. White matter lies deep to the cortical gray matter in most of the brain, opposite from the relationship of gray and white matter in the spinal cord. As in the spinal cord, white matter is composed of **tracts,** or bundles of axons, which here connect one part of the brain to another and to the spinal cord. These are described later in more detail.

## 14.1c Embryonic Development

Mature brain anatomy is often described in terms of *forebrain, midbrain,* and *hindbrain*—three terms that can be fully appreciated only with some awareness of the embryonic development of the CNS.

The nervous system develops from ectoderm, the outermost tissue layer of an embryo. Within the first 3 weeks, a *neural plate* forms along the dorsal midline of the embryo and sinks into the tissues to form a *neural groove,* with a raised *neural fold* along each side **(fig. 14.3).** The neural folds roll toward each other and fuse, somewhat like a closing zipper, beginning in the cervical region and progressing both caudally and rostrally. By day 26, this process creates a hollow channel called the **neural tube.** Following closure, the neural tube separates from the overlying ectoderm, sinks a little deeper, and grows lateral processes that later form motor nerve fibers. The lumen of the neural tube becomes a fluid-filled space that later constitutes the *central canal* of the spinal cord and *ventricles* of the brain.

As the neural tube develops, some ectodermal cells that originally lay along the margin of the groove separate from the rest and form a longitudinal column on each side called the **neural crest.** Neural crest cells give rise to the two inner meninges (arachnoid mater and pia mater); most of the peripheral nervous system, including the sensory and autonomic nerves and ganglia and Schwann cells; and some other structures of the skeletal, integumentary, and endocrine systems.

By the fourth week, the neural tube exhibits three anterior dilations, or *primary vesicles,* called the **forebrain** *(prosencephalon*[7]*)* (PROSS-en-SEF-uh-lon), **midbrain** *(mesencephalon*[8]*)* (MES-en-SEF-uh-lon), and **hindbrain** *(rhombencephalon*[9]*)* (ROM-ben-SEF-uh-lon) **(fig. 14.4).** By the fifth week, it subdivides into five *secondary vesicles.* The forebrain divides into two of them, the **telencephalon**[10] (TEL-en-SEFF-uh-lon) and **diencephalon**[11] (DY-en-SEF-uh-lon); the midbrain remains undivided and retains the name **mesencephalon;** and the hindbrain divides into two vesicles, the **metencephalon**[12] (MET-en-SEF-uh-lon) and **myelencephalon**[13] (MY-el-en-SEF-uh-lon). The telencephalon has a pair of lateral outgrowths that later become the cerebral hemispheres. The diencephalon will become chiefly the *thalamus* and *hypothalamus,* and has a pair of cuplike lateral outgrowths, the *optic vesicles,* which will become the retinas of the eyes. The metencephalon will give rise to the pons and cerebellum, and the myelencephalon to the medulla oblongata. Figure 14.4 is color-coded to show which mature brain regions develop from each vesicle.

**BEFORE YOU GO ON**

Answer the following questions to test your understanding of the preceding section:

1. List the three major parts of the brain and describe their locations.
2. Define *gyrus* and *sulcus.*
3. Contrast the composition and locations of gray and white matter in the brain.
4. Explain how the five secondary brain vesicles arise from the neural tube.

[5]*corpus* = body; *call* = thick
[6]*cereb* = brain; *ellum* = little

[7]*pros* = before, in front; *encephal* = brain
[8]*mes* = middle
[9]*rhomb* = rhombus
[10]*tele* = end, remote
[11]*di* = through, between
[12]*met* = behind, beyond, distal to
[13]*myel* = spinal cord

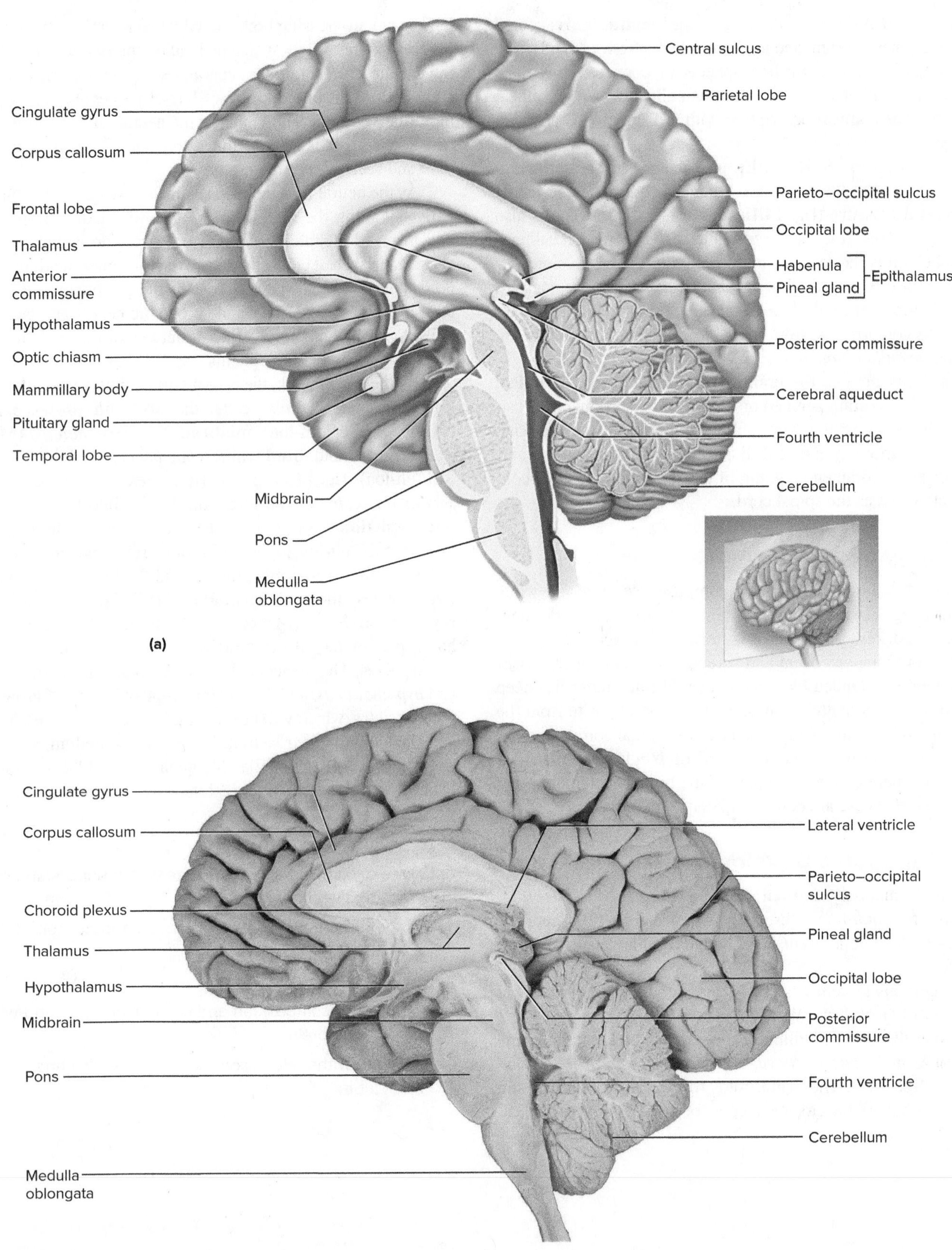


**FIGURE 14.2 Medial Aspect of the Brain.** (a) Major anatomical landmarks of the medial surface. (b) Median section of the cadaver brain. APR

Photo: Christine Eckel/McGraw-Hill Education

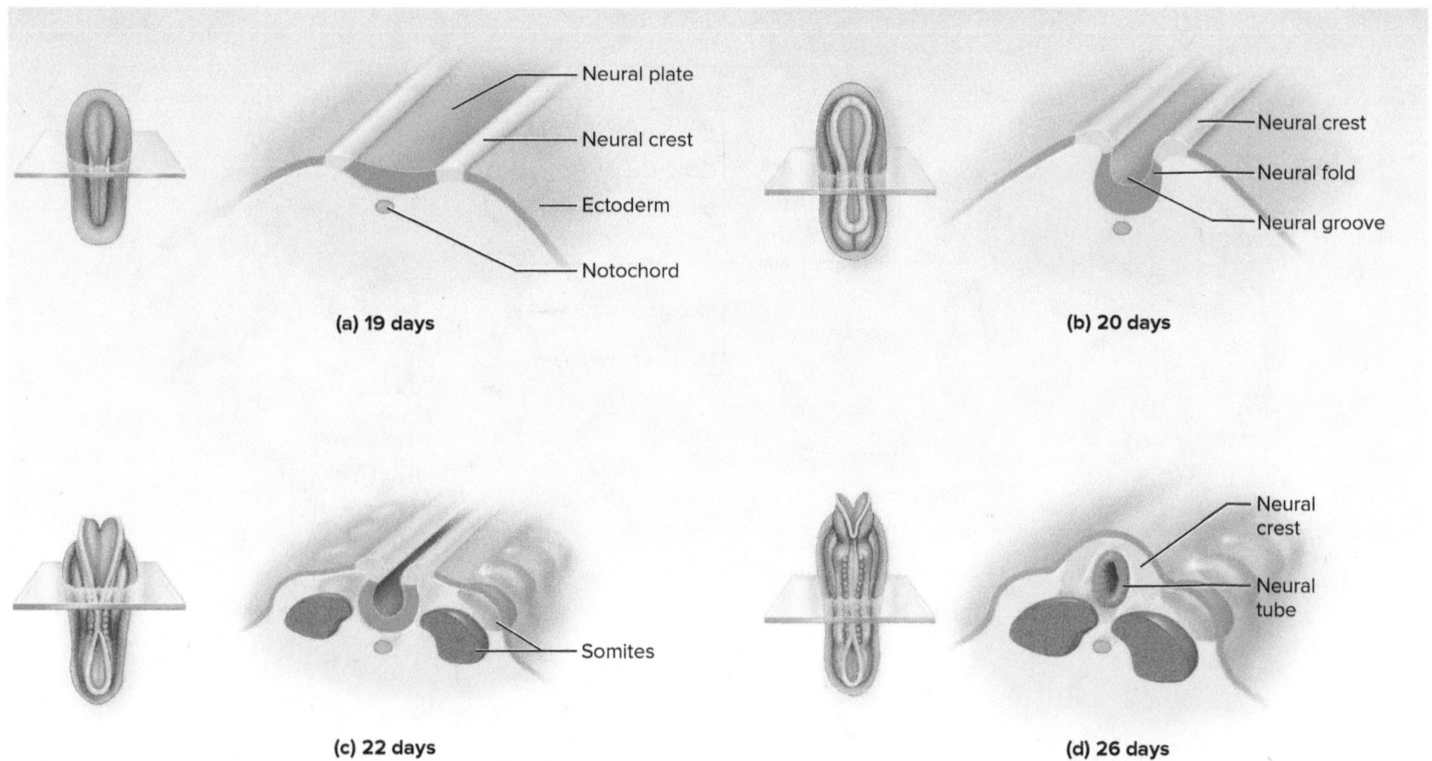


FIGURE 14.3 **Formation of the Embryonic Neural Tube.** The left-hand figure in each case is a dorsal view of the embryo, and the right-hand figure is a three-dimensional representation of the tissues at the indicated level of the respective embryo. (a) Neural plate at 19 days. (b) Neural groove at 20 days. (c) Neural groove closing at 22 days. (d) Neural tube at 26 days.

## 14.2 Meninges, Ventricles, Cerebrospinal Fluid, and Blood Supply

### Expected Learning Outcomes

When you have completed this section, you should be able to

a. describe the meninges of the brain;
b. describe the fluid-filled chambers within the brain;
c. discuss the production, circulation, and function of the cerebrospinal fluid that fills these chambers; and
d. explain the significance of the brain barrier system.

### 14.2a Meninges

The brain is enveloped in three membranes, the *meninges,* which lie between the nervous tissue and bone. They protect the brain and provide a structural framework for its arteries and veins. As in the spinal cord, these are the *dura mater, arachnoid mater,* and *pia mater* **(fig. 14.5).** Their histological composition is described in section 13.1c and is similar in the cranium. However, the cranial dura mater consists of two layers—an outer *periosteal layer* equivalent to the periosteum of the cranial bones, and an inner *meningeal layer.* Only the meningeal layer continues into the vertebral canal, where it forms the dural sheath around the spinal cord. The cranial dura mater is pressed closely against the cranial bone, with no intervening epidural space like the one around the spinal cord. It isn't attached to the bone, however, except in limited places: around the foramen magnum, the sella turcica, the crista galli, and the sutures of the skull.

In some places, the two layers of dura are separated by **dural sinuses,** spaces that collect blood that has circulated through the brain. Two major, superficial ones are the **superior sagittal sinus,** found just under the calvaria along the median line, and the **transverse sinus,** which runs horizontally from the rear of the head toward each ear. These sinuses meet like an inverted T at the back of the brain and ultimately empty into the internal jugular veins of the neck. These and other sinuses of the brain are more fully described and pictured along with other cerebral blood vessels in section 20.7c.

In certain places, the meningeal layer of the dura folds inward to separate major parts of the brain from each other and limit brain movements within the cranium, as when one receives a jolt to the head. There are three of these: (1) the *falx*[14] *cerebri* (falks SER-eh-bry), which extends into the longitudinal cerebral fissure as a tough, crescent-shaped wall between the right and left cerebral hemispheres; (2) the *tentorium*[15] *cerebelli* (ten-TOE-ree-um), which stretches like a roof over the posterior cranial fossa and separates the cerebellum from the overlying cerebrum; and (3) the *falx cerebelli,* a vertical partition between the right and left halves of the cerebellum on the inferior side.

[14]*falx* = sickle
[15]*tentorium* = tent

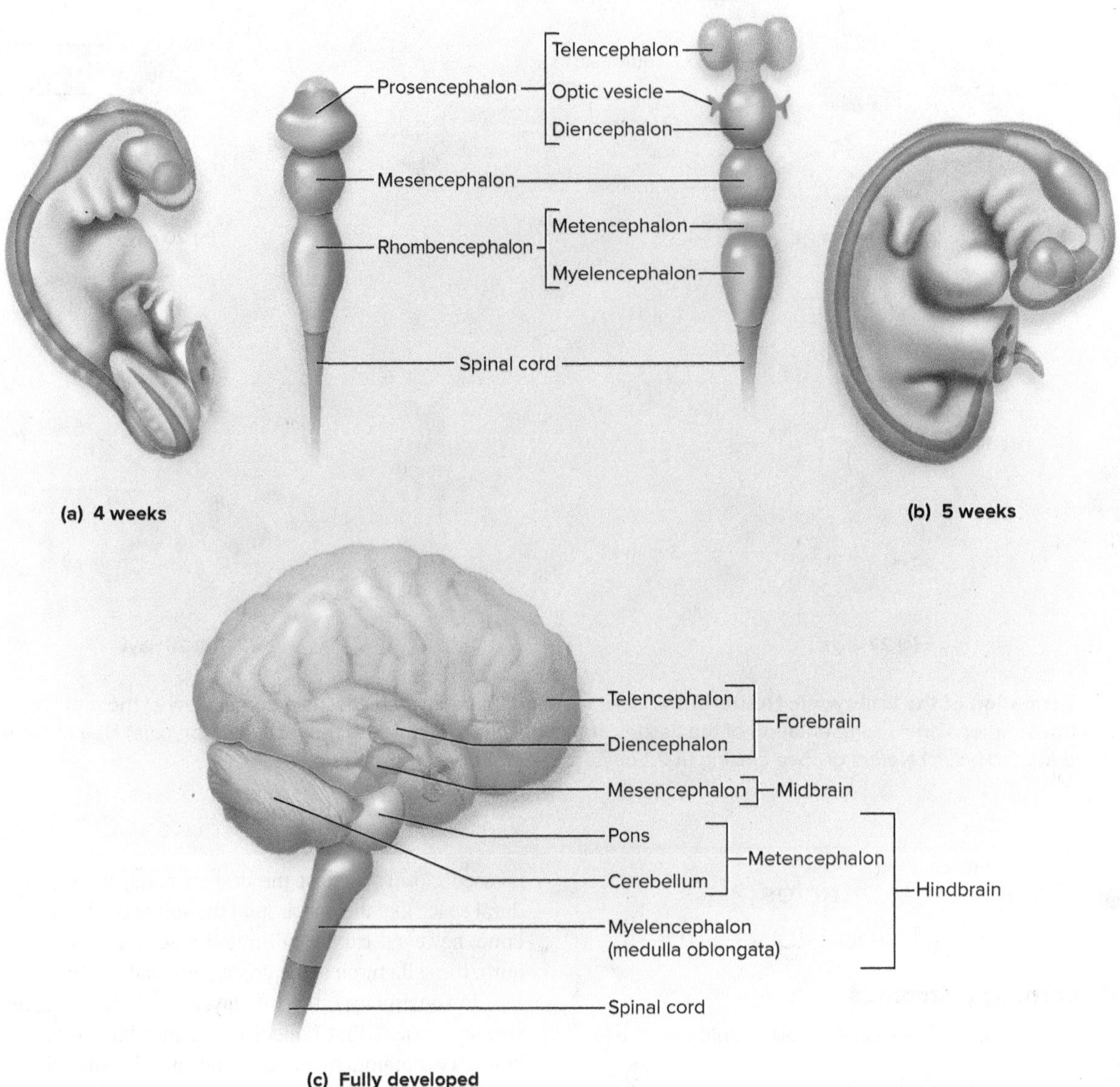


**FIGURE 14.4 Primary and Secondary Vesicles of the Embryonic Brain.** (a) The primary vesicles at 4 weeks. (b) The secondary vesicles at 5 weeks. (c) The fully developed brain, color-coded to relate its structures to the secondary embryonic vesicles.

The arachnoid mater and pia mater are similar to those of the spinal cord. The arachnoid mater is a transparent membrane over the brain surface, deep to the dura. A *subarachnoid space* separates it from the pia below; it contains the largest blood vessels of the cerebral surface. The pia mater is a very thin, delicate membrane, not usually visible without a microscope. Whereas the arachnoid meninx only overlies the sulci of the cerebral surface, the pia mater dips down into them, closely follows all the contours of the brain, and follows arteries for a short distance as they penetrate into the cerebrum.

## 14.2b Ventricles and Cerebrospinal Fluid

The brain has four internal chambers called **ventricles (fig. 14.6).** The largest and most rostral ones are the two **lateral ventricles,** which form an arc in each cerebral hemisphere. Through a tiny pore called the **interventricular foramen,** each lateral ventricle is connected to the **third ventricle,** a narrow median space inferior to the corpus callosum. From here, a canal called the **cerebral aqueduct** passes down the core of the midbrain and leads to the **fourth ventricle,** a small triangular chamber between the

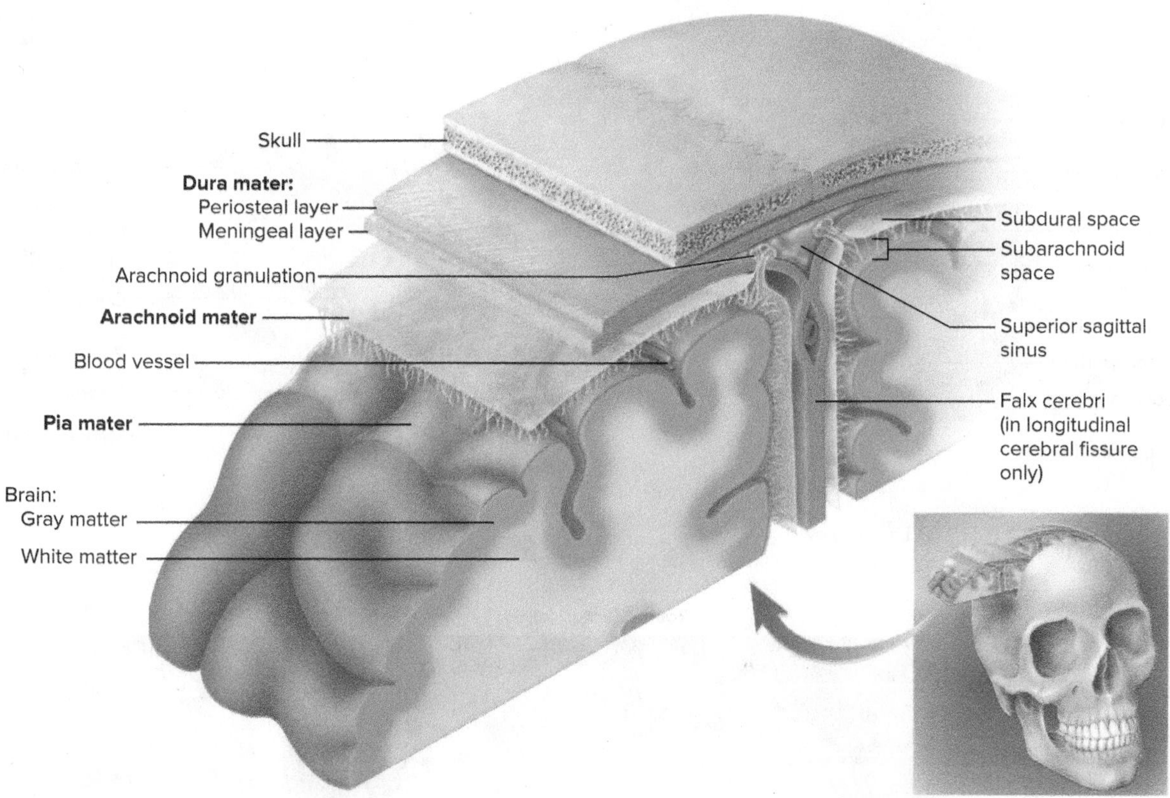


**FIGURE 14.5 The Meninges of the Brain.** Frontal section of the head.

## DEEPER INSIGHT 14.1
### CLINICAL APPLICATION

### *Meningitis*

*Meningitis*—inflammation of the meninges—is one of the most serious diseases of infancy and childhood. It occurs especially between 3 months and 2 years of age. Meningitis is caused by a variety of bacteria and viruses that invade the CNS by way of the nose and throat, often following respiratory, throat, or ear infections. The pia and arachnoid mater are most often affected, and from there the infection can spread to the adjacent nervous tissue. Meningitis can cause swelling of the brain, cerebral hemorrhaging, and sometimes death within mere hours of the onset of symptoms. Signs and symptoms include high fever, stiff neck, drowsiness, intense headache, and vomiting. Meningitis is diagnosed partly by examining the cerebrospinal fluid (CSF) for bacteria and white blood cells. The CSF is obtained by lumbar puncture (described in section 13.1c).

Death from meningitis can occur so suddenly that infants and children with a high fever should therefore receive immediate medical attention. Freshman college students show a slightly elevated incidence of meningitis, especially those living in crowded dormitories rather than off campus.

pons and cerebellum. Caudally, this space narrows and forms a **central canal** that extends through the medulla oblongata into the spinal cord.

On the floor or wall of each ventricle is a spongy mass of blood capillaries called a **choroid plexus** (CO-royd), named for its histological resemblance to a fetal membrane called the chorion. *Ependyma,* a type of neuroglia that resembles a cuboidal epithelium, lines the ventricles and canals and covers the choroid plexuses. It produces cerebrospinal fluid.

**Cerebrospinal fluid (CSF)** is a clear, colorless liquid that fills the ventricles and canals of the CNS and bathes its external surface. The brain produces about 500 mL of CSF per day, but the fluid is constantly reabsorbed at the same rate and only 100 to 160 mL is normally present at one time. About 40% of it is formed in the subarachnoid space external to the brain, 30% by the general ependymal lining of the brain ventricles, and 30% by the choroid plexuses. CSF production begins with the filtration of blood plasma through the capillaries of the brain. Ependymal cells modify the filtrate as it passes through them, so the CSF has more sodium chloride than blood plasma, but less potassium, calcium, and glucose and very little protein.

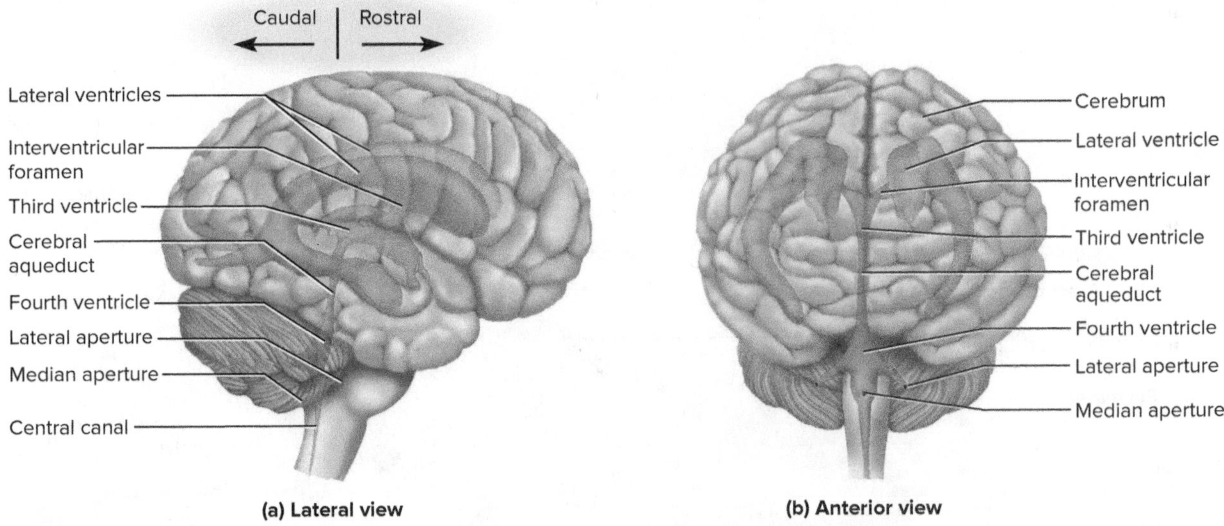


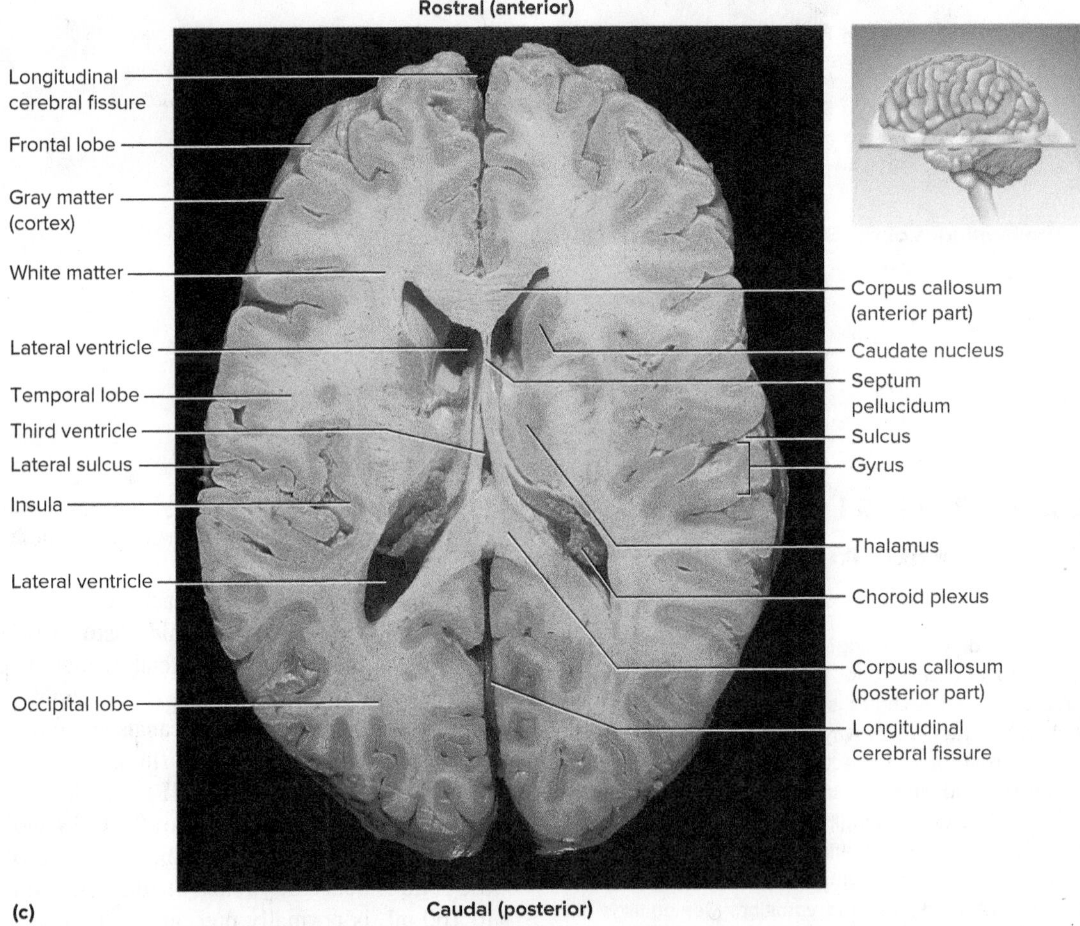


**FIGURE 14.6 Ventricles of the Brain.** (a) Right lateral view. (b) Anterior view. (c) Superior view of a horizontal section of the cadaver brain, showing the lateral ventricles and some other features of the cerebrum. APR

c: Rebecca Gray/Don Kincaid/McGraw-Hill Education

CSF continually flows through and around the CNS, driven partly by its own pressure, partly by the beating of ependymal cilia, and partly by rhythmic pulsations of the brain produced by each heartbeat. The CSF of the lateral ventricles flows through the interventricular foramina into the third ventricle, then down the cerebral aqueduct to the fourth ventricle (**fig. 14.7**). The third and fourth ventricles and their choroid plexuses add more CSF along the way. A small amount of CSF fills the central canal of the spinal cord, but ultimately, all of it escapes through three pores in the fourth ventricle—a *median aperture* and two *lateral apertures.* These lead into the subarachnoid space on the brain and spinal cord surface. From there, CSF is reabsorbed by **arachnoid granulations,** extensions of the arachnoid meninx shaped like little sprigs of cauliflower, protruding through the dura mater into the superior sagittal sinus. CSF penetrates the walls of the granulations and mixes with blood in the sinus.

Cerebrospinal fluid serves three purposes:

1. **Buoyancy.** Because the brain and CSF are similar in density, the brain neither sinks nor floats in the CSF. It hangs from delicate strands of the arachnoid meninx. A human brain removed from the body has a dead weight of about 1,500 g, but when suspended in CSF, its effective weight is only about 50 g. By analogy, consider how much easier it is to lift another person when you're immersed in a lake than it is on land. This buoyancy allows the brain to attain considerable size without being impaired by its own weight. If the brain rested heavily on the floor of the cranium, the pressure would kill the nervous tissue.
2. **Protection.** CSF also protects the brain from striking the cranium when the head is jolted. If the jolt is severe, however, the brain still may strike the inside of the cranium or suffer shearing injury from contact with the angular surfaces of the cranial floor. This is one of the common findings in child abuse (shaken child syndrome) and in concussions and other *traumatic brain injury (TBI)* from auto accidents, boxing and football, and the like.

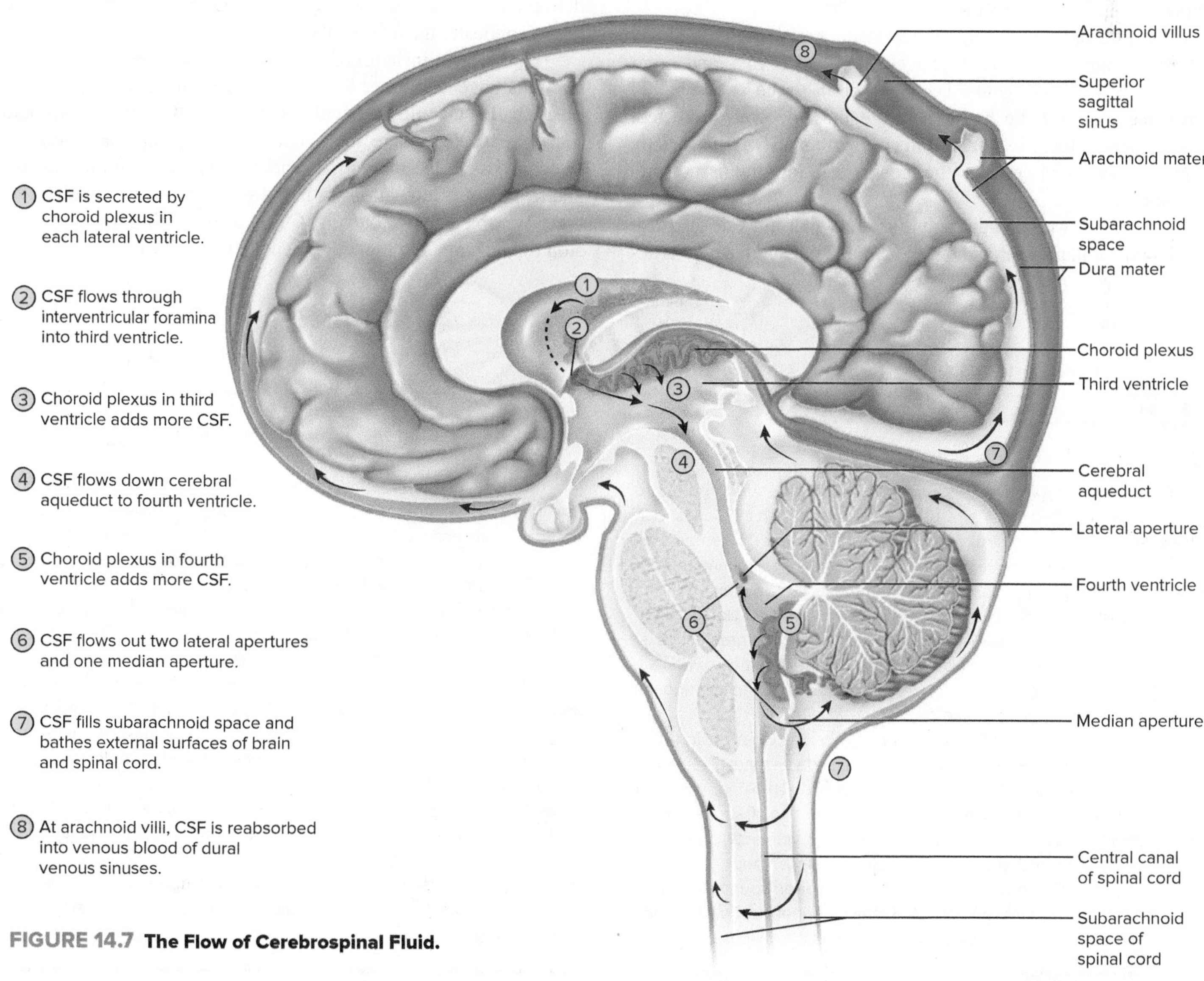

(1) CSF is secreted by choroid plexus in each lateral ventricle.
(2) CSF flows through interventricular foramina into third ventricle.
(3) Choroid plexus in third ventricle adds more CSF.
(4) CSF flows down cerebral aqueduct to fourth ventricle.
(5) Choroid plexus in fourth ventricle adds more CSF.
(6) CSF flows out two lateral apertures and one median aperture.
(7) CSF fills subarachnoid space and bathes external surfaces of brain and spinal cord.
(8) At arachnoid villi, CSF is reabsorbed into venous blood of dural venous sinuses.
Arachnoid villus
Superior sagittal sinus
Arachnoid mater
Subarachnoid space
Dura mater
Choroid plexus
Third ventricle
Cerebral aqueduct
Lateral aperture
Fourth ventricle
Median aperture
Central canal of spinal cord
Subarachnoid space of spinal cord

**FIGURE 14.7 The Flow of Cerebrospinal Fluid.**

3. **Chemical stability.** CSF rinses metabolic wastes from the nervous tissue and regulates its chemical environment. Slight changes in CSF composition can cause malfunctions of the nervous system. For example, a high glycine concentration disrupts the control of body temperature and blood pressure, and a high pH causes dizziness and fainting.

### 14.2c Blood Supply and the Brain Barrier System

The blood vessels that serve the brain are detailed in sections 20.7b and 20.7c. The brain constitutes only 2% of the adult body weight, yet it receives 15% of the blood flow (about 750 mL/min.) and consumes 20% of its oxygen and glucose. Because neurons have such a high demand for ATP, and therefore glucose and oxygen, the constancy of blood supply is especially critical to the nervous system. A mere 10-second interruption in blood flow can cause loss of consciousness; an interruption of 1 to 2 minutes can significantly impair neural function; and 4 minutes without blood usually causes irreversible brain damage (see Deeper Insight 14.2). For more on cerebral blood flow, see section 20.5a.

Despite its critical importance to the brain, blood is also a source of antibodies, macrophages, bacterial toxins, and other potentially harmful agents. Damaged brain tissue is essentially irreplaceable, and the brain therefore must be well protected. Consequently, there is a **brain barrier system (BBS)** that strictly regulates what can get from the bloodstream into the tissue fluid of the brain.

There are two potential points of entry that must be guarded: the blood capillaries throughout the brain tissue and the capillaries of the choroid plexuses. At the former site, the brain is well protected by the **blood–brain barrier,** which consists of tight junctions between the endothelial cells that form the capillary walls. In the developing brain, astrocytes reach out and contact the capillaries with their perivascular feet, stimulating the endothelial cells to form tight junctions that completely seal off the gaps between them. This ensures that anything leaving the blood must pass through the cells and not between them. The endothelial cells are more selective than gaps between them would be, and can exclude harmful substances from the brain tissue while allowing necessary ones to pass through. At the choroid plexuses, the brain is protected by a similar **blood–CSF barrier** formed by tight junctions between the ependymal cells. Tight junctions are absent from ependymal cells elsewhere, because it is important to allow exchanges between the brain tissue and CSF. That is, there is no brain–CSF barrier.

The BBS is highly permeable to water, glucose, and lipid-soluble substances such as oxygen, carbon dioxide, alcohol, caffeine, nicotine, and anesthetics. It is slightly permeable to sodium, potassium, chloride, and the waste products urea and creatinine. While the BBS is an important protective device, it is an obstacle to the delivery of medications such as antibiotics and cancer drugs, and thus complicates the treatment of brain diseases.

Trauma and inflammation sometimes damage the BBS and allow pathogens to enter the brain tissue. Furthermore, there are places called **circumventricular organs (CVOs)** in the third and fourth ventricles where the barrier is absent and the blood has direct access to brain neurons. These enable the brain to monitor and respond to fluctuations in blood glucose, pH, osmolarity, and other variables. Unfortunately, CVOs also afford a route of invasion by the human immunodeficiency virus (HIV).

## DEEPER INSIGHT 14.2
### CLINICAL APPLICATION

#### *Stroke*

A *stroke,* or *cerebral vascular accident (CVA),* is the sudden death of brain tissue resulting from an abrupt interruption of its blood supply. There are two kinds of stroke distinguished by cause: a *hemorrhagic stroke* resulting from the rupture of a cerebral or subarachnoid blood vessel, and more common, an *ischemic stroke* (iss-KEE-mic) resulting from the obstruction of a blood vessel, usually by a blood clot (thrombosis) or lipid deposit (atherosclerosis). Stroke is the second greatest cause of death after coronary artery disease; about one-half of those who have a stroke live less than one year longer. Stroke can occur at any age, but about two-thirds occur in people over 65 years old.

Aside from age, risk factors for stroke include hypertension; high blood cholesterol; obesity; diabetes mellitus; and such lifestyle choices as inadequate physical activity, overuse of alcohol, smoking, and using drugs such as amphetamines and cocaine. The risk of stroke can be reduced with statin drugs (to lower cholesterol level); antihypertensive drugs (to control blood pressure); and other lifestyle, medical, and surgical methods. Daily low-dose aspirin has not been found helpful for *primary prevention* of a first stroke, but may be beneficial for *secondary prevention* of recurrence in those who have had a previous stroke.

The signs and symptoms of a stroke depend on the function of the tissues downstream from the hemorrhage or obstruction, where neuron death occurs. They can include paralysis (usually on the side of the body opposite from a cerebral stroke), blindness or other loss of sensation, aphasia (loss of speech), or cognitive deficits (dysfunctions in awareness, memory, or reason). Similar symptoms lasting less than 24 hours are called *transient ischemic attack (TIA),* colloquially called a "mini-stroke." A TIA can foreshadow a true stroke later.

To be prepared to accurately recognize a stroke in another person and get quick help, think of the acronym **FAST: F**acial weakness (sagging or drooping on one side of the face), **A**rm drift (inability to prevent one arm from drifting down when asked to hold both arms above the head), **S**peech difficulty, and **T**ime to call emergency services. Some other signs include defects in the visual field, inability to stick the tongue out and move it left and right on command, and loss of memory (such as for one's name and the date). Irreversible brain damage (neuron death) occurs after about 3 hours and is therefore preventable with prompt emergency treatment—as stressed by the slogan, Time is brain!

**BEFORE YOU GO ON**

Answer the following questions to test your understanding of the preceding section:

5. Name the three meninges from superficial to deep. How does the dura mater of the brain differ from that of the spinal cord?
6. Describe three functions of the cerebrospinal fluid.
7. Where does the CSF originate and what route does it take through and around the CNS?
8. Name the two components of the brain barrier system and explain the importance of this system.

## 14.3 The Hindbrain and Midbrain

**Expected Learning Outcomes**

When you have completed this section, you should be able to

a. list the components of the hindbrain and midbrain and their functions; and
b. describe the location and functions of the reticular formation.

The study of the brain in the following pages will be organized around the five secondary vesicles of the embryonic brain and their mature derivatives. We will proceed in a caudal to rostral direction, beginning with the hindbrain and its relatively simple functions and progressing to the forebrain, the seat of such complex functions as thought, memory, and emotion.

### 14.3a The Medulla Oblongata

As noted earlier, the embryonic hindbrain differentiates into two subdivisions: the myelencephalon and metencephalon (see fig. 14.4). The myelencephalon becomes just one adult structure, the **medulla oblongata** (meh-DULL-uh OB-long-GAH-ta).

The medulla (**fig. 14.8;** also see fig. 14.2) begins at the foramen magnum of the skull and extends for about 3 cm rostrally, ending at a transverse groove between the medulla and pons. It looks superficially like an extension of the spinal cord, but slightly wider. Significant differences are apparent, however, on closer inspection of its gross and microscopic anatomy. Externally, the anterior surface features a pair of ridges called the **pyramids.** Resembling side-by-side baseball bats, these are wider at the rostral end, taper caudally, and are separated by a longitudinal groove, the *anterior median fissure,* continuous with that of the spinal cord. Lateral to each pyramid is a prominent bulge called the **olive.** Posteriorly, the *gracile* and *cuneate fasciculi* of the spinal cord continue as two pairs of ridges on the medulla.

All nerve fibers connecting the brain to the spinal cord pass through the medulla. As we saw in the cord, some of these are ascending (sensory) and some are descending (motor) fibers. The ascending fibers include first-order sensory fibers of the gracile and cuneate fasciculi, which end in the **gracile** and **cuneate nuclei** seen in **figure 14.9c.** Here, they synapse with second-order fibers that decussate and form the ribbonlike **medial lemniscus**[16] on each side. The second-order fibers rise to the thalamus, synapsing there with third-order fibers that complete the path to the cerebral cortex (compare fig. 13.6a).

The largest group of descending fibers is the pair of **corticospinal tracts** filling the pyramids on the anterior surface. These carry motor signals from the cerebral cortex on the way to the spinal cord, ultimately to stimulate the skeletal muscles. Any time you carry out a body movement below the neck, the signals en route to your muscles pass through here. About 90% of these fibers cross over at the *pyramidal decussation,* an externally visible point near the caudal end of the pyramids (fig. 14.8a). As a result, muscles below the neck are controlled by the contralateral side of the brain. A smaller *tectospinal tract* controls the neck muscles.

The medulla contains neural networks involved in a multitude of fundamental sensory and motor functions. The former include the senses of hearing, equilibrium, touch, pressure, temperature, taste, and pain; the latter include chewing, salivation, swallowing, gagging, vomiting, respiration, speech, coughing, sneezing, sweating, cardiovascular and gastrointestinal control, and head, neck, and shoulder movements. Signals for these functions enter and leave the medulla not only by way of the spinal cord, but also by four pairs of cranial nerves that begin or end here: cranial nerves VIII (in part), IX, X, and XII. At the level of the section in figure 14.9c, we see the origins of two of them, the vagus (X) and hypoglossal (XII). The names and functions of these nerves are detailed in section 14.6c.

Another feature seen in cross section is the wavy **inferior olivary nucleus,** a major relay center for signals going from many levels of the brain and spinal cord to the cerebellum. The *reticular formation,* detailed later, is a loose network of nuclei extending throughout the medulla, pons, and midbrain. In the medulla, it includes a **cardiac center,** which regulates the rate and force of the heartbeat; a **vasomotor center,** which regulates blood pressure and flow by dilating and constricting blood vessels; two **respiratory centers,** which regulate the rhythm and depth of breathing; and other nuclei involved in the aforementioned motor functions.

### 14.3b The Pons

The metencephalon develops into the pons and cerebellum. We will return to the cerebellum after finishing the brainstem. The **pons**[17] measures about 2.5 cm long. Most of it appears as a broad anterior bulge rostral to the medulla (see figs. 14.2, 14.8). Posteriorly, it consists mainly of two pairs of thick stalks called *cerebellar peduncles,* the cut edges in the upper half of **figure 14.9b.** They connect the cerebellum to the pons and midbrain (fig. 14.8b) and will be discussed with the cerebellum.

In cross section, the pons exhibits continuations of the previously mentioned reticular formation, medial lemniscus,

[16] *lemn* = ribbon; *iscus* = little
[17] *pons* = bridge

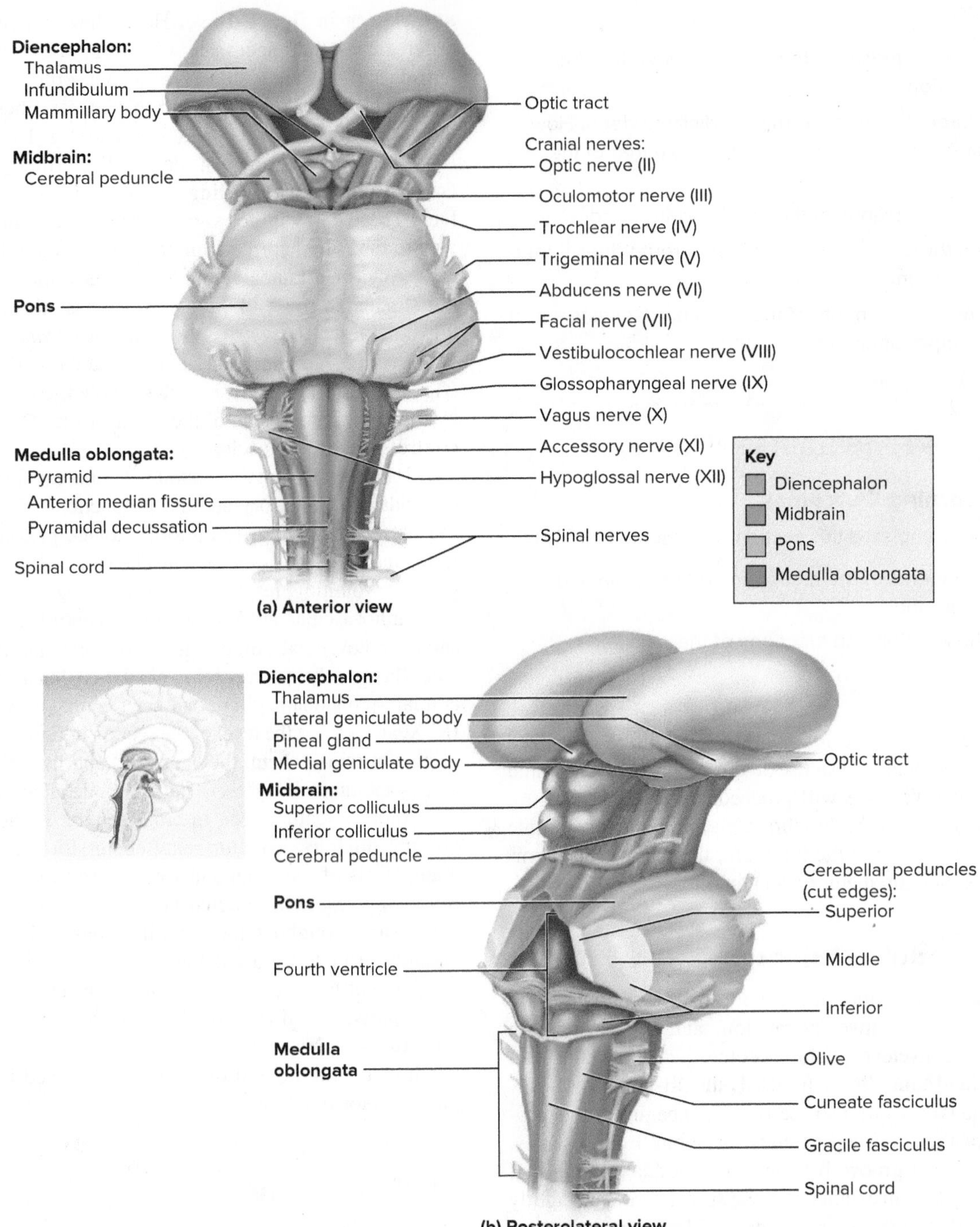


**FIGURE 14.8 The Brainstem and Diencephalon.** (a) Anterior view. (b) Posterolateral view. Color-coded to match the embryonic origins in figure 14.4. The boundary between the middle and inferior cerebellar peduncles is indistinct. APR

tectospinal tract, and other spinal tracts. The anterior half of the pons (lower half of fig. 14.9b) is dominated by tracts of white matter, including transverse fascicles that cross between left and right and connect the two hemispheres of the cerebellum, and longitudinal fascicles that carry sensory and motor signals up and down the brainstem.

Cranial nerves V to VIII begin or end in the pons, although we see only the trigeminal nerve (V) at the level of figure 14.9b. The other three emerge from the groove between the pons and medulla. The functions of these four nerves, detailed in table 14.1, include sensory roles in hearing, equilibrium, and taste; facial sensations such as touch and pain; and motor roles in eye movement, facial expressions, chewing, swallowing, urination, and the secretion of saliva and tears. The reticular formation in the pons contains additional nuclei concerned with sleep, respiration, and posture.

Posterior

Tectum

Reticular formation

Cerebral peduncle:

Tegmentum

Substantia nigra

Cerebral crus

Superior colliculus

Cerebral aqueduct

Medial geniculate nucleus

Central gray substance

Oculomotor nucleus

Medial lemniscus

Red nucleus

Oculomotor nerve (III)

Anterior

**(a) Midbrain**

(a) Midbrain

(b) Pons

(c) Medulla

Vermis of cerebellum

Superior cerebellar peduncle

Middle cerebellar peduncle

Trigeminal nerve nuclei

Sensory root of trigeminal nerve

Trigeminal nerve

Reticular formation

Medial lemniscus

Fourth ventricle

Tectospinal tract

Transverse fascicles

Longitudinal fascicles

**(b) Pons**

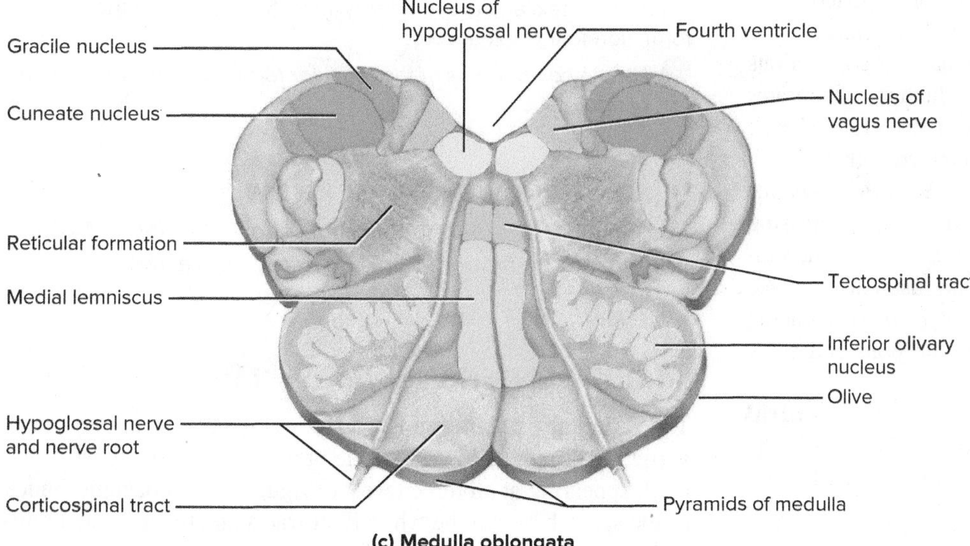


**(c) Medulla oblongata**

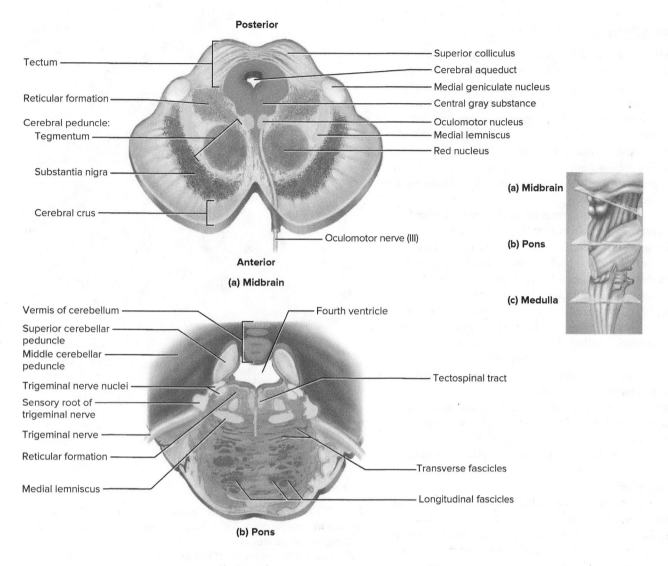

**FIGURE 14.9 Cross Sections of the Brainstem.** The level of each section is shown in the figure on the right. (a) The midbrain, cut obliquely to pass through the superior colliculi. (b) The pons. The straight edges indicate cut edges of the peduncles where the cerebellum was removed. (c) The medulla oblongata. APR

? *Trace the route taken through all three of these figures by fibers from the gracile and cuneate fasciculi described in section 13.1e.*

### 14.3c The Midbrain

The mesencephalon becomes just one mature brain structure, the **midbrain**—a short segment of brainstem that connects the hindbrain and forebrain (see figs. 14.2, 14.8). It contains the cerebral aqueduct, continuations of the medial lemniscus and reticular formation, and the motor nuclei of two cranial nerves that control eye movements: cranial nerves III (oculomotor) and IV (trochlear). Only the first of these is seen at the level of the cross section in **figure 14.9a.** (The *medial geniculate nucleus* seen in this figure is not part of the midbrain, but a part of the thalamus that happens to lie in the plane of this section.)

The part of the midbrain posterior to the cerebral aqueduct is a rooflike **tectum.**[18] It exhibits four bulges. The upper (rostral) pair, called the **superior colliculi**[19] (col-LIC-you-lye), control the *extrinsic muscles* of the eyes, enabling us to direct our gaze at a target; to track moving objects; and to turn the eyes and head in response to a visual stimulus (for example, to look at something that you catch sight of in your peripheral vision). Between the superior colliculi and thalamus are other visual control centers, the **pretectal nuclei,** that control pupillary diameter and focusing of the lens. The lower (caudal) pair, called the **inferior colliculi,** receives signals from the inner ear and relays them to other parts of the brain, especially the thalamus. These colliculi are sensitive to the time delays between sounds heard by the two ears and thus aid in locating the source of a sound in space. They also process fluctuations in pitch, which is important for such purposes as understanding another person's speech. They also mediate the reflexive turning of the head in response to a sound and one's tendency to jump when startled by a sudden noise.

Anterior to the cerebral aqueduct, the midbrain consists mainly of the **cerebral peduncles**—two stalks that anchor the cerebrum to the brainstem. Each peduncle has three main components: tegmentum, substantia nigra, and cerebral crus. The **tegmentum**[20] is dominated by the **red nucleus,** named for a pink color imparted by its high density of blood vessels. Fibers from the red nucleus form the *rubrospinal tract* in most mammals, but in humans its connections go mainly to and from the cerebellum, with which it collaborates in fine motor control. The **substantia nigra**[21] (sub-STAN-she-uh NY-gruh) is a dark gray to black nucleus pigmented with melanin. It is a motor center that relays inhibitory signals to the thalamus and basal nuclei (both of which are discussed later), suppressing unwanted body movement. Degeneration of the neurons in the substantia nigra leads to the muscle tremors of Parkinson disease (see Deeper Insight 12.4). The **cerebral crus** (plural, *crura*) is a bundle of nerve fibers that connect the cerebrum to the pons and carry the corticospinal nerve tracts.

The cerebral aqueduct is encircled by the **central (periaqueductal) gray substance.** This is involved with the reticular formation in controlling awareness of pain, as further described in section 16.2d.

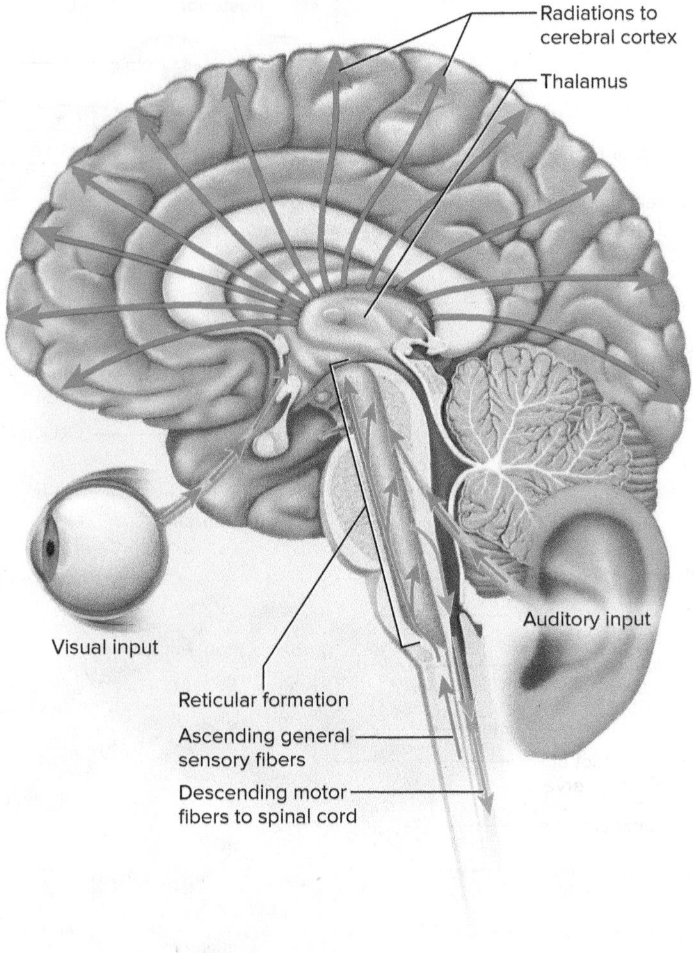

[18]*tectum* = roof, cover
[19]*colli* = hill; *cul* = little
[20]*tegmen* = cover
[21]*substantia* = substance; *nigra* = black

Radiations to cerebral cortex
Thalamus
Visual input
Auditory input
Reticular formation
Ascending general sensory fibers
Descending motor fibers to spinal cord

**FIGURE 14.10 The Reticular Formation.** The formation consists of over 100 nuclei scattered throughout the brainstem. Red arrows indicate routes of input to the reticular formation; blue arrows indicate the radiating relay of signals from the thalamus to the cerebral cortex; and green arrows indicate output from the reticular formation to the spinal cord.

*Locate components of the reticular formation in all three parts of figure 14.9.*

**APPLY WHAT YOU KNOW**

*Why are the inferior colliculi shown in figure 14.8b but not in figure 14.9a? How are these two figures related?*

### 14.3d The Reticular Formation

The **reticular**[22] **formation** is a loose web of gray matter that runs vertically through all levels of the brainstem and the upper spinal cord, appearing at all three levels of figure 14.9. It occupies much of the space between the white fiber tracts and the more anatomically distinct brainstem nuclei, and has connections with many areas of the cerebrum **(fig. 14.10).** It consists of more than 100 small neural networks defined less by anatomical boundaries than

[22]*ret* = network; *icul* = little

by their use of different neurotransmitters. The functions of these networks include the following:

- **Somatic motor control.** Some motor neurons of the cerebral cortex send their axons to reticular formation nuclei, which then give rise to the *reticulospinal tracts* of the spinal cord. These tracts adjust muscle tension to maintain tone, balance, and posture, especially during body movements. The reticular formation also relays signals from the eyes and ears to the cerebellum so the cerebellum can integrate visual, auditory, and vestibular (balance and motion) stimuli into its role in motor coordination. Other motor nuclei include *gaze centers,* which enable the eyes to track and fixate objects, and *central pattern generators*—neural pools that produce rhythmic signals to the muscles of breathing and swallowing.
- **Cardiovascular control.** The reticular formation includes the previously mentioned cardiac and vasomotor centers of the medulla oblongata.
- **Pain modulation.** The reticular formation is one route by which pain signals from the lower body reach the cerebral cortex. It is also the origin of the *descending analgesic pathways* mentioned in the description of the reticulospinal tracts in section 13.1e. Under certain circumstances, the nerve fibers in these pathways act in the spinal cord to deaden one's awareness of pain.
- **Sleep and consciousness.** The reticular formation has projections to the thalamus and cerebral cortex that allow it some control over what sensory signals reach the cerebrum and come to our conscious attention. It plays a central role in states of consciousness such as alertness and sleep. Injury to the reticular formation can result in irreversible coma.
- **Habituation.** This is a process in which the brain learns to ignore repetitive, inconsequential stimuli while remaining sensitive to others. In a noisy city, for example, a person can sleep through traffic sounds but wake promptly to the sound of an alarm clock or a crying baby. Reticular formation nuclei that modulate activity of the cerebral cortex are called the *reticular activating system* or *extrathalamic cortical modulatory system.*

### 14.3e The Cerebellum

The cerebellum is the largest part of the hindbrain and second-largest part of the brain as a whole **(fig. 14.11).** It consists of right and left **cerebellar hemispheres** connected by a narrow wormlike bridge called the **vermis.**[23] Each hemisphere exhibits slender, transverse, parallel folds called **folia**[24] separated by shallow sulci. The cerebellum has a surface cortex of gray matter and a deeper layer of white matter. In a sagittal section, the white matter exhibits a branching, fernlike pattern called the **arbor vitae.**[25] Each hemisphere has four masses of gray matter called **deep nuclei** embedded in the white matter. All input to the cerebellum goes to the cortex and all of its output comes from the deep nuclei.

Although the cerebellum is only about 10% of the mass of the brain, it has about 60% as much surface area as the cerebral cortex and it contains more than half of all brain neurons. Its tiny, densely spaced **granule cells** are the most abundant type of neuron in the entire brain. Its most distinctive neurons, however, are the unusually large, globose **Purkinje**[26] **cells** (pur-KIN-jee). These have a tremendous profusion of dendrites compressed into a single plane like a flat tree (see fig. 12.5 and the photo on the opening page of chapter 12). The Purkinje cells are arranged in a single file, with these thick dendritic planes parallel to each other like books on a shelf. Their axons travel to the deep nuclei, where they synapse on output neurons that issue fibers to the brainstem.

The cerebellum is connected to the brainstem by three pairs of stalks called **cerebellar peduncles**[27] (peh-DUN-culs): a pair of *inferior peduncles* connected to the medulla oblongata, a pair of *middle peduncles* to the pons, and a pair of *superior peduncles* to the midbrain (see fig. 14.8b). These consist of thick bundles of nerve fibers that carry signals to and from the cerebellum. Connections between the cerebellum and brainstem are very complex, but overlooking some exceptions, we can draw a few generalizations. Most spinal input enters the cerebellum by way of the inferior peduncles; most input from the rest of the brain enters by way of the middle peduncles; and cerebellar output travels mainly by way of the superior peduncles.

The function of the cerebellum was unknown in the 1950s. By the 1970s, it had come to be regarded as a center for monitoring muscle contractions and aiding in motor coordination. People with cerebellar lesions exhibit serious deficits in coordination and locomotor ability; more will be said later in this chapter about the role of the cerebellum in movement. But cerebellar lesions also affect several sensory, linguistic, emotional, and other nonmotor functions. Recent studies by positron emission tomography (PET) and functional magnetic resonance imaging (fMRI) (both described in Deeper Insight 1.5), and behavioral studies of people with cerebellar lesions, have created a much more expansive view of cerebellar function. It appears that its general role is the evaluation of certain kinds of sensory input, and monitoring muscle movement is only part of its broader function.

The cerebellum is highly active when a person explores objects with the fingertips, for example, to compare the textures of two objects without looking at them. (Tactile nerve fibers from a rat's snout and a cat's forepaws also feed into the cerebellum.) Some spatial perception also resides here. The cerebellum is much more active when a person is required to solve a pegboard puzzle than when moving pegs randomly around the same puzzle board. People with cerebellar lesions also have difficulty identifying different views of a three-dimensional object as belonging to the same object.

The cerebellum is also a timekeeper. PET scans show increased cerebellar activity when a person is required to judge the elapsed time between two stimuli. People with cerebellar lesions have difficulty with rhythmic finger-tapping tasks and other tests of

[23] *verm* = worm
[24] *foli* = leaf
[25] *arbor* = tree; *vitae* = of life

[26] Johannes E. von Purkinje (1787–1869), Bohemian anatomist
[27] *ped* = foot; *uncle* = little

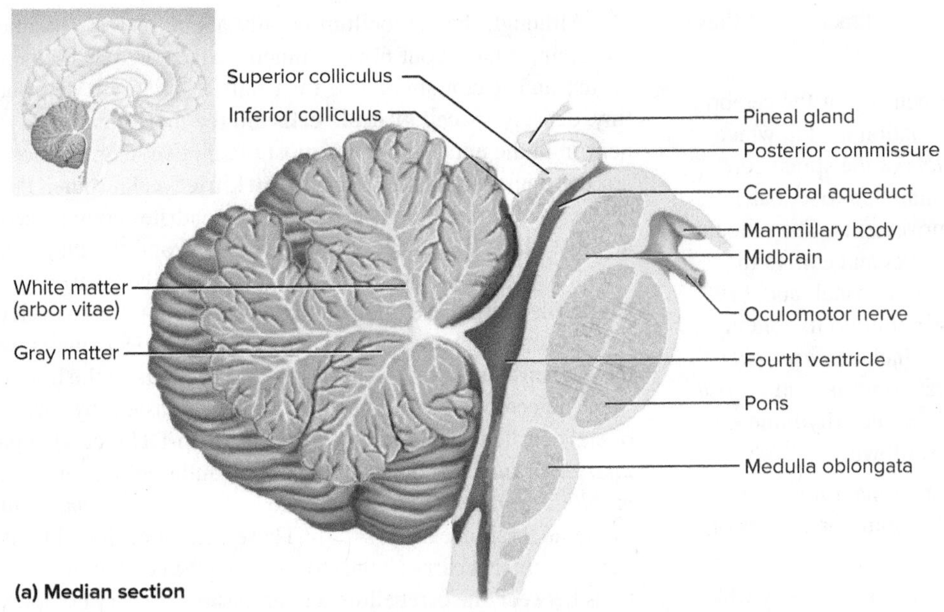


(a) Median section

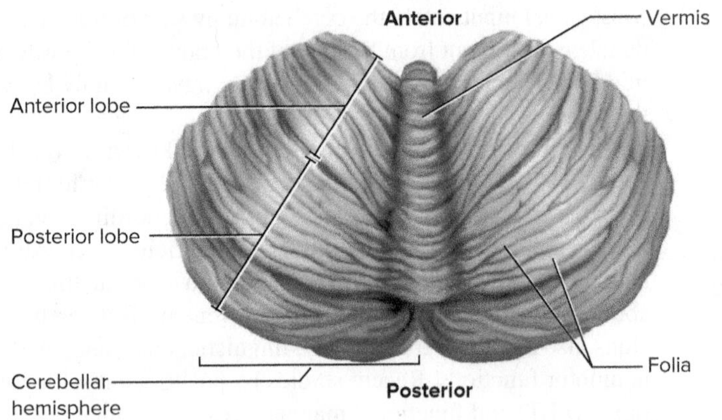


(b) Superior view

**FIGURE 14.11 The Cerebellum.** (a) Median section, showing relationship to the brainstem. (b) Superior view. APR

temporal judgment. An important aspect of cerebellar timekeeping is the ability to predict where a moving object will be in the next second or so. You can imagine the importance of this to a predator chasing its prey, to a tennis player, or in driving a car in heavy traffic. The cerebellum also helps to predict how much the eyes must move in order to compensate for head movements and remain fixed on an object.

Even hearing has some newly discovered and surprising cerebellar components. Cerebellar lesions impair a person's ability to judge differences in pitch between two tones and to distinguish between similar-sounding words such as *rabbit* and *rapid.* Language output also involves the cerebellum. If a person is given a noun such as *apple* and told to think of a related verb such as *eat,* the cerebellum shows higher PET activity than if the person is told merely to repeat the word *apple.*

People with cerebellar lesions also have difficulty planning and scheduling tasks. They tend to overreact emotionally and have difficulty with impulse control. Many children with attention-deficit/hyperactivity disorder (ADHD) have abnormally small cerebellums.

**BEFORE YOU GO ON**

Answer the following questions to test your understanding of the preceding section:

9. List several visceral functions controlled by nuclei of the medulla. What general function would be lost if the pyramids of the medulla were severed?
10. List several sensory and motor functions of the pons.
11. What functions are served by the superior and inferior colliculi? To what portion of the brainstem do they belong?
12. Where is the reticular formation found? Define *reticular formation* in a single sentence.
13. List several functions of the cerebellum.

## 14.4 The Forebrain

### Expected Learning Outcomes

When you have completed this section, you should be able to

a. name the three major components of the diencephalon and describe their locations and functions;
b. identify the five lobes of the cerebrum and their functions;
c. describe the three types of tracts in the cerebral white matter;
d. describe the distinctive cell types and histological arrangement of the cerebral cortex; and
e. describe the location and functions of the basal nuclei and limbic system.

The forebrain consists of the diencephalon and telencephalon. The diencephalon encloses the third ventricle and is immediately rostral to the brainstem. The telencephalon develops chiefly into the cerebrum.

### 14.4a The Diencephalon

Three structures arise from the embryonic diencephalon: the *thalamus, hypothalamus,* and *epithalamus.*

#### The Thalamus

Each side of the brain has a **thalamus,**[28] an ovoid mass perched at the superior end of the brainstem beneath the cerebral hemisphere (see figs. 14.6c, 14.8, 14.17). The two thalami form about four-fifths of the diencephalon. Laterally, they protrude into the lateral ventricles. Medially, they protrude into the third ventricle and are joined to each other by a narrow *interthalamic adhesion* in about 70% of people.

The thalamus consists of at least 23 nuclei, most of which fall into five groups: anterior, posterior, medial, lateral, and ventral. These groups and their functions are shown in **figure 14.12a.**

Broadly speaking, the thalamus is the "gateway to the cerebral cortex." Nearly all input to the cerebrum passes by way of synapses in the thalamic nuclei, including signals for taste, smell, hearing, equilibrium, vision, and such general senses as touch, pain, pressure, heat, and cold. (Some smell signals also get to the cerebrum by routes that bypass the thalamus.) The thalamic nuclei process this information, screen out much of it, and relay a small portion of it to the cerebral cortex.

The thalamus also serves in motor control by relaying signals from the cerebellum to the cerebrum and providing feedback loops between the cerebral cortex and the *basal nuclei* (deep cerebral motor centers). Finally, the thalamus is involved in the memory and emotional functions of the *limbic system,* a complex of structures that include some cerebral cortex of the temporal and frontal lobes and some of the anterior thalamic nuclei. The role of the thalamus in motor and sensory circuits is further discussed later in this chapter and chapter 16.

#### The Hypothalamus

The **hypothalamus** (see fig. 14.2) forms the floor and part of the walls of the third ventricle. It extends anteriorly to the *optic chiasm* (ky-AZ-um), where the optic nerves meet, and posteriorly to a pair of humps called the **mammillary**[29] **bodies.** Each mammillary body contains three or four *mammillary nuclei.* Their primary function is to relay signals from the limbic system to the thalamus. The pituitary gland is attached to the hypothalamus by a stalk *(infundibulum)* between the optic chiasm and mammillary bodies.

The hypothalamus is the major control center of the endocrine and autonomic nervous systems. It plays an essential role in the homeostatic regulation of nearly all organs of the body. Its nuclei include centers concerned with a wide variety of visceral functions **(fig. 14.12b):**

- **Hormone secretion.** The hypothalamus secretes hormones that control the anterior pituitary gland, thereby regulating growth, metabolism, reproduction, and stress responses. It also produces two hormones that are stored in the posterior pituitary gland, concerned with labor contractions, lactation, and water conservation. These relationships are explored especially in sections 17.2b and 17.2d.
- **Autonomic effects.** The hypothalamus is a major integrating center for the autonomic nervous system. It sends descending fibers to lower brainstem nuclei that influence heart rate, blood pressure, gastrointestinal secretion and motility, and pupillary diameter, among other functions.
- **Thermoregulation.** The *hypothalamic thermostat* consists of a collection of neurons, concentrated especially in the preoptic nucleus, that monitor body temperature. When the temperature deviates too much from its set point, this center activates mechanisms for lowering or raising the body temperature (see section 26.5c).
- **Food and water intake.** The hypothalamus regulates sensations of hunger and satiety. One nucleus in particular, the *arcuate nucleus,* contains receptors for hormones that increase hunger and energy expenditure, other hormones that reduce both, and hormones that exert long-term control over body mass (see section 26.1b). Hypothalamic neurons called *osmoreceptors* monitor blood osmolarity and stimulate water-seeking and drinking behavior when the body is dehydrated. Dehydration also stimulates the hypothalamus to produce *antidiuretic hormone,* which conserves water by reducing urine output.
- **Sleep and circadian rhythms.** The caudal part of the hypothalamus is part of the reticular formation. It contains nuclei that regulate the rhythm of sleep and waking.

[28] *thalamus* = chamber, inner room

[29] *mammill* = nipple

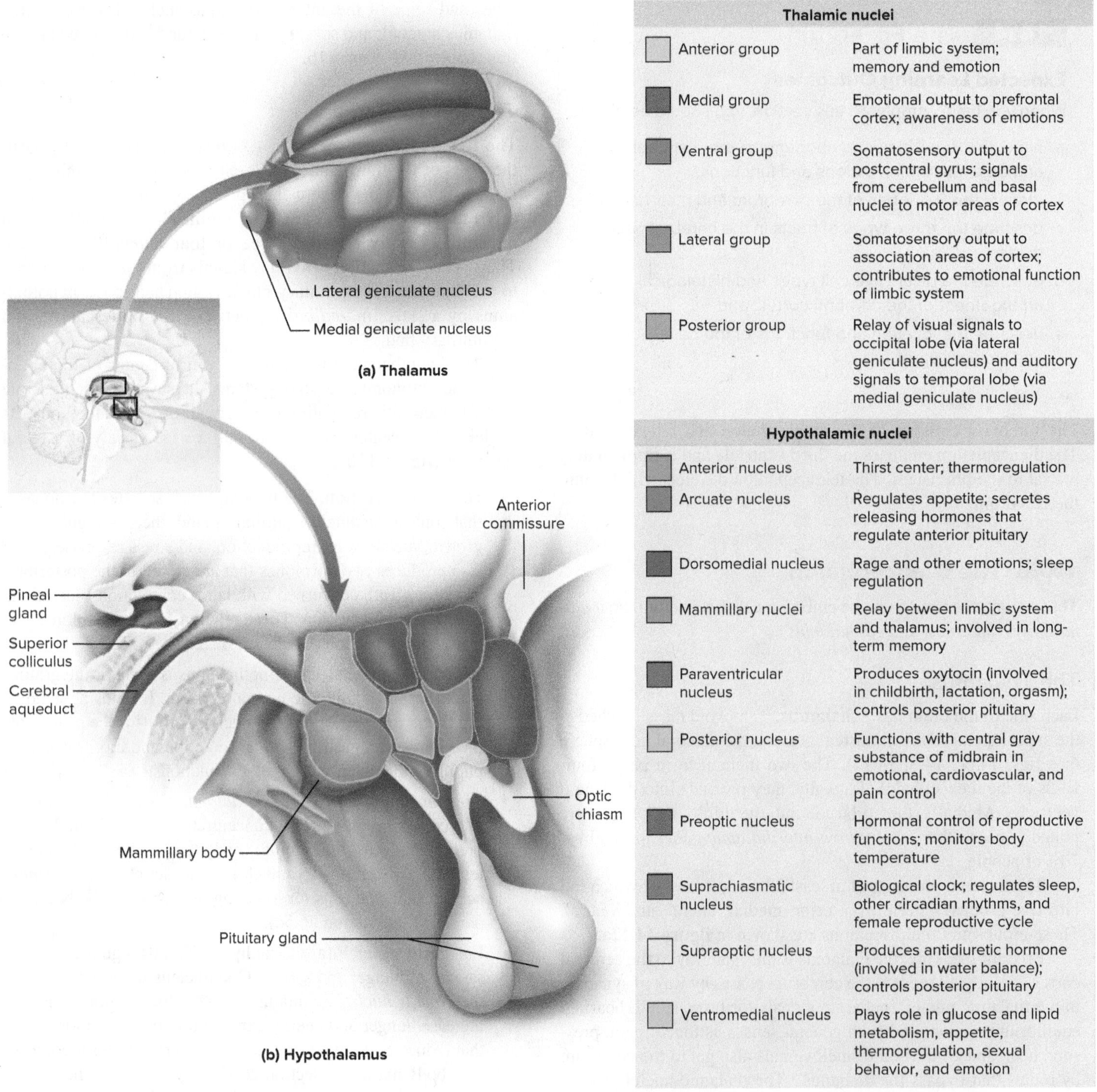


| Thalamic nuclei | |
|---|---|
| Anterior group | Part of limbic system; memory and emotion |
| Medial group | Emotional output to prefrontal cortex; awareness of emotions |
| Ventral group | Somatosensory output to postcentral gyrus; signals from cerebellum and basal nuclei to motor areas of cortex |
| Lateral group | Somatosensory output to association areas of cortex; contributes to emotional function of limbic system |
| Posterior group | Relay of visual signals to occipital lobe (via lateral geniculate nucleus) and auditory signals to temporal lobe (via medial geniculate nucleus) |
| **Hypothalamic nuclei** | |
| Anterior nucleus | Thirst center; thermoregulation |
| Arcuate nucleus | Regulates appetite; secretes releasing hormones that regulate anterior pituitary |
| Dorsomedial nucleus | Rage and other emotions; sleep regulation |
| Mammillary nuclei | Relay between limbic system and thalamus; involved in long-term memory |
| Paraventricular nucleus | Produces oxytocin (involved in childbirth, lactation, orgasm); controls posterior pituitary |
| Posterior nucleus | Functions with central gray substance of midbrain in emotional, cardiovascular, and pain control |
| Preoptic nucleus | Hormonal control of reproductive functions; monitors body temperature |
| Suprachiasmatic nucleus | Biological clock; regulates sleep, other circadian rhythms, and female reproductive cycle |
| Supraoptic nucleus | Produces antidiuretic hormone (involved in water balance); controls posterior pituitary |
| Ventromedial nucleus | Plays role in glucose and lipid metabolism, appetite, thermoregulation, sexual behavior, and emotion |

**FIGURE 14.12 The Diencephalon.** (a) Nuclei of the thalamus. (b) Nuclei of the hypothalamus. Only some of the nuclei of the thalamus and hypothalamus are shown, and some of their functions are listed. These lists are by no means complete. APR

Superior to the optic chiasm, the hypothalamus contains a *suprachiasmatic nucleus* that controls our 24-hour (circadian) rhythm of activity.

- **Memory.** The mammillary nuclei lie in the pathway of signals traveling from the hippocampus, an important memory center of the brain, to the thalamus. Thus, they are important in memory, and lesions to the mammillary nuclei cause memory deficits. (For a more complete discussion, see section 14.5d.)
- **Emotional behavior and sexual response.** Hypothalamic centers are involved in a variety of emotional responses including anger, aggression, fear, pleasure, and contentment; and in sexual drive, copulation, and orgasm.

## The Epithalamus

The **epithalamus** is a very small mass of tissue composed mainly of the **pineal gland** (an endocrine gland discussed in section 17.3), the **habenula**[30] (a relay from the limbic system to the midbrain), and a thin roof over the third ventricle (see fig. 14.2a).

## 14.4b The Cerebrum

The embryonic telencephalon becomes the cerebrum, the largest and most conspicuous part of the human brain. Your cerebrum enables you to turn these pages, read and comprehend the words, remember ideas, talk about them with your peers, and take an examination. It is the seat of voluntary motor control and our most distinctly human mental processes. It is the most complex and challenging frontier of neurobiology.

### Gross Anatomy

The cerebrum so dwarfs and conceals the other structures that people often think of "cerebrum" and "brain" as synonymous. Its major anatomical landmarks were described at the beginning of this chapter and should be reviewed if necessary (see figs. 14.1 and 14.2); most important are the two *cerebral hemispheres,* separated by the *longitudinal cerebral fissure* but connected by a prominent fiber tract, the *corpus callosum;* and the conspicuous wrinkles, or *gyri,* of each hemisphere, separated by grooves called *sulci.* The folding of the cerebral surface into gyri allows a greater amount of cortex to fit in the cranial cavity. The gyri give the cerebrum a surface area of about 2,500 $cm^2$. If the cerebrum were smooth-surfaced, it would have only one-third as much area and proportionately less information-processing capability. This extensive folding is one of the greatest differences between the human brain and the relatively smooth-surfaced brains of most other mammals.

Some gyri have consistent and predictable anatomy, while others vary from brain to brain and even from the right hemisphere to the left in the same person. Certain unusually prominent sulci divide each hemisphere into five anatomically and functionally distinct lobes, as follows. The first four are visible superficially and are named for the cranial bones overlying them; the fifth lobe *(insula)* is not visible from the surface.

It is difficult to summarize the functions of the cerebral lobes in any simple way; many functions such as vision, memory, speech, and emotion are distributed over multiple lobes, and different lobes contribute only part of the overall function. With that caveat, **figure 14.13** and the following list survey the anatomical distribution of many key cerebral functions.

1. The **frontal lobe** lies immediately behind the frontal bone, superior to the eyes. From the forehead, it extends caudally to a wavy vertical groove, the **central sulcus.** It is the seat of our conscious, abstract thought; explicit or declarative memory (see section 12.6e); cognitive and emotional processes such as mood, motivation, foresight, planning, decision making, emotional control, and judging socially

[30]*haben* = strap, rein; *ula* = little

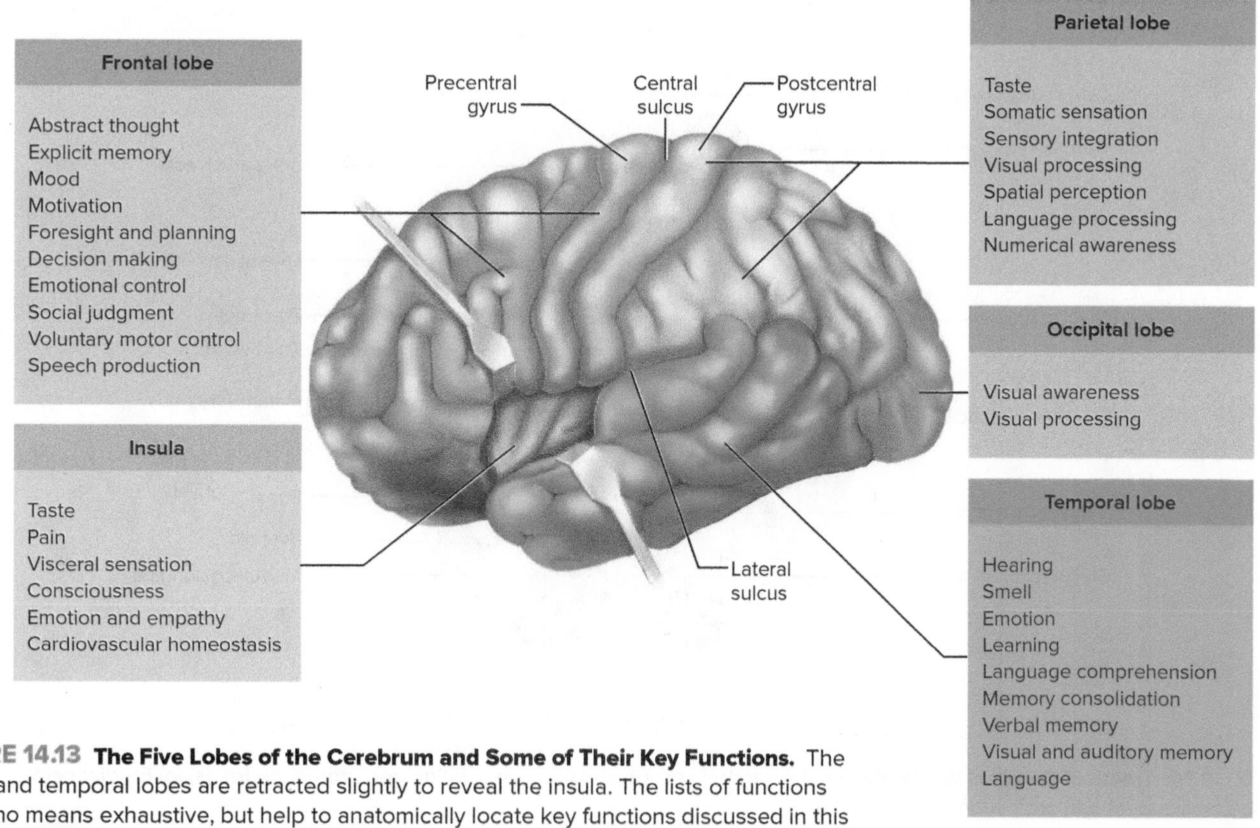


**FIGURE 14.13 The Five Lobes of the Cerebrum and Some of Their Key Functions.** The frontal and temporal lobes are retracted slightly to reveal the insula. The lists of functions are by no means exhaustive, but help to anatomically locate key functions discussed in this chapter. APR

appropriate behavior; and in speech production and other voluntary motor control.

2. The **parietal lobe** forms the uppermost part of the brain and underlies the parietal bone. Starting at the central sulcus, it extends caudally to the **parieto–occipital sulcus,** visible on the medial surface of each hemisphere (see fig. 14.2). It is concerned with taste, somatic sensation (such as touch, heat, and pain), and visual processing; multisensory integration such as correlating sights and sounds to holistically comprehend our sensory world; spatial perception and awareness of body orientation; language processing; and numerical awareness (a sense of the quantity of things we see before us).
3. The **occipital lobe** is at the rear of the head, caudal to the parieto–occipital sulcus and underlying the occipital bone. It is the principal visual center of the brain, where we first become aware of visual stimuli and process them to identify what we see.
4. The **temporal lobe** is a lateral, horizontal lobe deep to the temporal bone, separated from the frontal and parietal lobes above it by a deep **lateral sulcus.** It is concerned with hearing; smell; emotion; learning; language comprehension and memory of the grammar and vocabulary of the languages we speak; memory consolidation (formation of new long-term memories); and storage of verbal, visual, and auditory memories.
5. The **insula**[31] is a small mass of cortex deep to the lateral sulcus, made visible only by retracting or cutting away some of the overlying cerebrum (see fig. 14.6c). It plays roles in taste; pain; visceral sensation; consciousness; emotional responses and empathy (sympathetic awareness of the feelings of others); and cardiovascular homeostasis (such as heart rate and blood pressure responses to exercise).

[31]*insula* = island

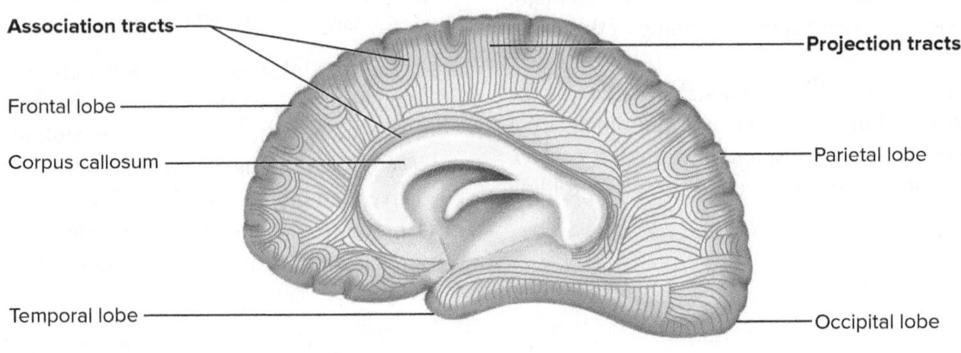


**(a) Sagittal section**

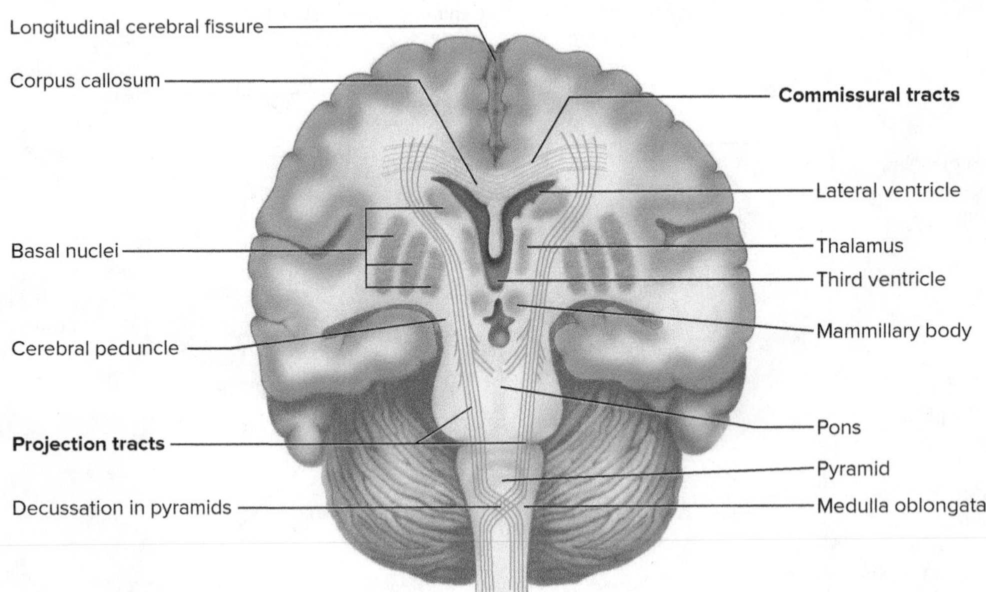


**(b) Frontal section**

**FIGURE 14.14 Tracts of Cerebral White Matter.** (a) Sagittal section showing association and projection tracts. (b) Frontal section showing commissural and projection tracts.

*What route can commissural tracts take between the right and left cerebral hemispheres other than the one shown here?*

## The Cerebral White Matter

Most of the volume of the cerebrum is white matter. This is composed of glia and myelinated nerve fibers that transmit signals from one region of the cerebrum to another and between the cerebrum and lower brain centers. These fibers form bundles, or *tracts,* of three kinds **(fig. 14.14):**

1. **Projection tracts** extend vertically between higher and lower brain and spinal cord centers. They carry information between the cerebrum and the rest of the body. The corticospinal tracts, for example, carry motor signals from the cerebrum to the brainstem and spinal cord. Other projection tracts carry signals upward to the cerebral cortex. Such tracts form a broad, dense sheet called the *internal capsule* between the thalamus and basal nuclei (described shortly), then radiate in a diverging, fanlike array (the *corona radiata*[32]) to specific areas of the cortex.
2. **Commissural tracts** cross from one cerebral hemisphere to the other through bridges called **commissures** (COM-ih-shurs). The great majority of commissural tracts pass through the large corpus callosum (see fig. 14.2). A few tracts pass through the much smaller **anterior** and **posterior commissures.** Commissural tracts enable the two sides of the cerebrum to communicate with each other.
3. **Association tracts** connect different regions within the same cerebral hemisphere. *Long association fibers* connect different lobes of a hemisphere to each other, whereas *short association fibers* connect different gyri within a single lobe. Among their roles, association tracts link perceptual and memory centers of the brain; for example, they enable you to see a rose, name it, and imagine its scent.

[32]*corona* = crown; *radiata* = radiating

## The Cerebral Cortex

Neural integration is carried out in the gray matter of the cerebrum, which is found in three places: the cerebral cortex, basal nuclei, and limbic system. We begin with the **cerebral cortex,**[33] a layer covering the surface of the hemispheres (see fig. 14.6c). Even though it is only 2 to 3 mm thick, the cortex constitutes about 40% of the mass of the brain and contains 14 to 16 billion neurons. It possesses two principal types of neurons **(fig. 14.15)** called *stellate cells* and *pyramidal cells.* **Stellate cells** have spheroidal neurosomas with short axons and dendrites projecting in all directions. They are concerned largely with receiving sensory input and processing information on a local level. **Pyramidal cells** are tall and conical. Their apex points toward the brain surface and has a thick dendrite with many branches and small, knobby *dendritic spines* (see fig. 12.5a). The base gives rise to horizontally oriented dendrites and an axon that passes into the white matter below. Pyramidal cells include the output neurons of the cerebrum—the only cerebral neurons whose fibers leave the cortex and connect with other parts of the CNS. Pyramidal cell axons have collaterals that synapse with other neurons in the cortex or in deeper regions of the brain.

About 90% of the human cerebral cortex is a six-layered tissue called **neocortex**[34] because of its relatively recent evolutionary origin. Although vertebrate animals have existed for about 600 million years, the neocortex didn't develop significantly until about 60 million years ago, when there was a sharp increase in the diversity

[33]*cortex* = bark, rind
[34]*neo* = new

## DEEPER INSIGHT 14.3

### CLINICAL APPLICATION

### *Tracking the Tracts of White Matter*

This chapter's opening photo was made with a relatively new application of magnetic resonance imaging (MRI) called *diffusion tensor imaging (DTI).* DTI is a method of detecting the diffusion of water molecules to trace parallel bundles of myelinated nerve fibers in the white matter of the CNS. In most places, water diffusion is random and generates no useful signal. The parallel paths of nerve fibers and the insulating effect of their myelin sheaths, however, give a directionality to diffusion, since more water diffuses along the nerve fibers than across them. The vectors of diffusion can be color-coded so tracts passing between the left and right brain are colored red, anterior–posterior tracts are green, and superior–inferior tracts are blue. The most often mapped tract has been the corticospinal tract, the main output pathway for cerebral control of the muscles; the tract of second greatest interest is called the *arcuate fasciculus,* which connects the Wernicke and Broca speech areas (see section 14.5h). The mapping of fiber tracts by DTI is called *tractography.* The ultimate aim of cerebral tractography is to determine the brain's *connectome,* a complete map of the physical connections (circuitry) between brain regions.

DTI dates to the 1990s but has only more recently gained application to living patients, making it a highly sensitive imaging method for neuropathology. Its greatest use to date is the assessment of acute ischemic stroke, and the second greatest is diagnosis of brain tumors and their effects on movement, language, and vision. DTI is employed by neurosurgeons for locating tumors and lesions that don't show up on conventional MRI. This enables the surgeon to precisely target a problem area and avoid injury to other critical tracts nearby. It is helpful in monitoring the maturation of myelin in children, degenerative changes in old age, the progress of demyelinating diseases such as multiple sclerosis, the extent of traumatic brain injury (TBI), and brain responses to therapy. It has found clinical applications as well to Alzheimer disease, epilepsy, autism, and cocaine addiction. Clinicians hope that it will soon prove useful in the prognosis of diseases—predicting their developmental course to allow for earlier and more effective intervention. DTI has also been used in assessments of cardiac muscle, prostate disease, and athletic injuries to muscles and tendons.

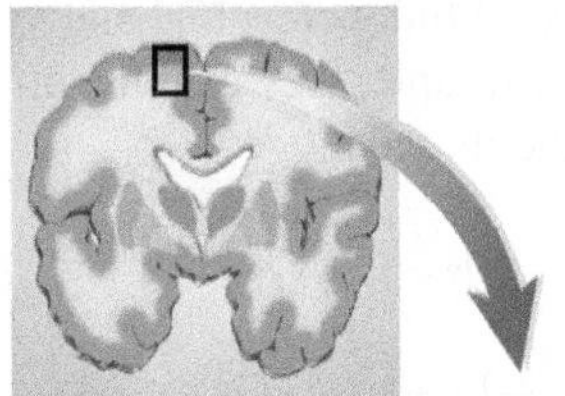

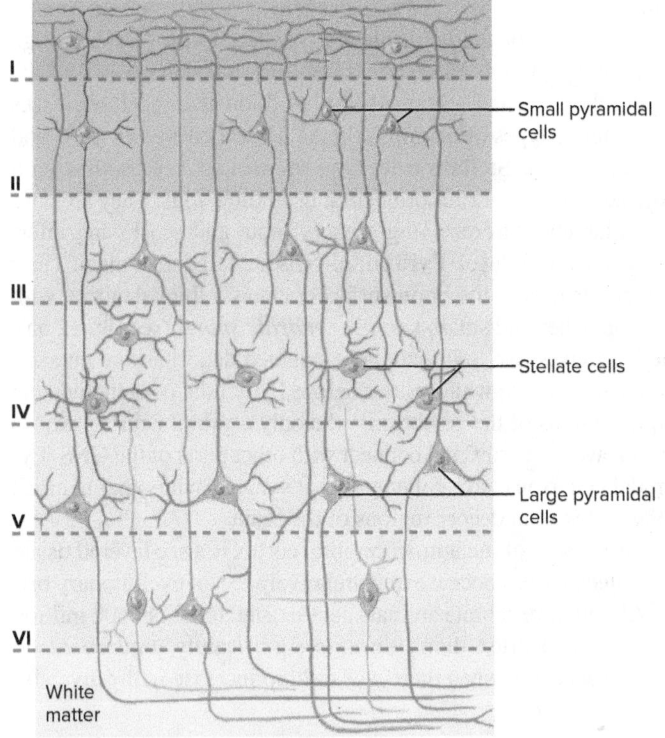


**FIGURE 14.15 Histology of the Neocortex.** Neurons are arranged in six layers.

? *Note the long processes leading upward from each pyramidal cell body. Are those axons or dendrites? Explain your answer.*

of mammals. It attained its highest development by far in the primates. The six layers of neocortex, numbered in figure 14.15, vary from one part of the cerebrum to another in relative thickness, cellular composition, synaptic connections, size of the neurons, and destination of their axons. Layer IV is thickest in sensory regions and layer V in motor regions, for example. All axons that leave the cortex and enter the white matter arise from layers III, V, and VI.

Some regions of cerebral cortex have fewer layers. The earliest type of cortex to appear in vertebrate evolution was a one- to five-layered tissue called *paleocortex* (PALE-ee-oh-COR-tex), limited in humans to part of the insula and certain areas of the temporal lobe concerned with smell. The next to evolve was a three-layered *archicortex* (AR-kee-COR-tex), found in the human hippocampus, a memory-forming center in the temporal lobe. The neocortex was the last to evolve.

## The Limbic System

The **limbic**[35] **system** is an important center of emotion and learning. It is a ring of cortex on the medial side of each hemisphere, encircling the corpus callosum and thalamus. Its most anatomically prominent components are the **cingulate**[36] **gyrus** (SING-you-let), which arches over the top of the corpus callosum in the frontal and parietal lobes; the **hippocampus**[37] in the medial temporal lobe **(fig. 14.16);** and the **amygdala**[38] (ah-MIG-da-luh) immediately rostral to the hippocampus, also in the temporal lobe. There are still differences of opinion on what structures to consider as parts of the limbic system, but these three are agreed upon. Other components include the mammillary bodies and other hypothalamic nuclei, some thalamic nuclei, parts of the basal nuclei, and parts of the frontal lobe called *prefrontal* and *orbitofrontal cortex.* Limbic system components are interconnected through a complex loop

[35]*limbus* = border
[36]*cingul* = girdle
[37]*hippocampus* = sea horse, named for its shape
[38]*amygdala* = almond

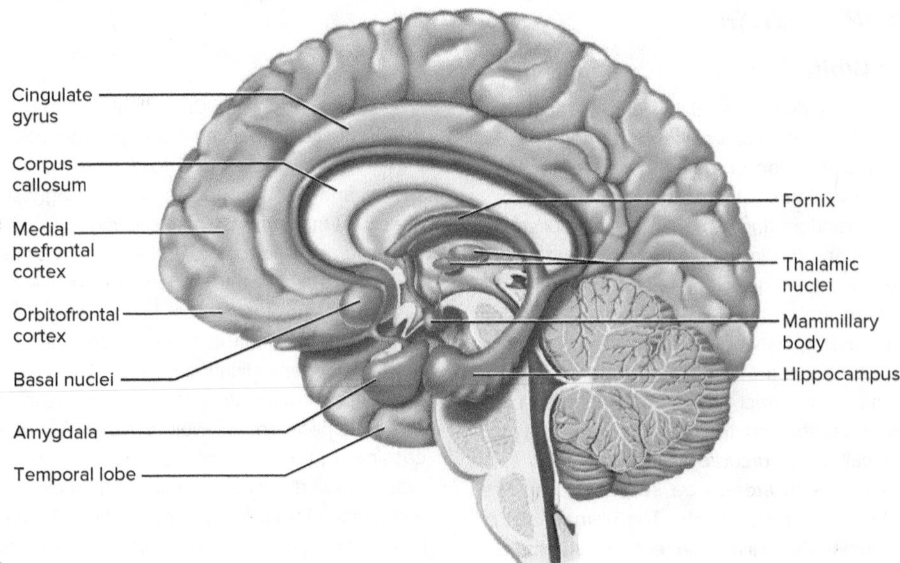


**FIGURE 14.16 The Limbic System.** This ring of structures (shown in violet) includes important centers of learning and emotion. In the frontal lobe, there is no sharp rostral boundary to limbic system components.

of fiber tracts allowing for somewhat circular patterns of feedback among its nuclei and cortical neurons. All of these structures are bilaterally paired; there is a limbic system in each cerebral hemisphere.

The limbic system was long thought to be associated with smell because of its close association with olfactory pathways, but beginning in the early 1900s and continuing even now, experiments have abundantly demonstrated more significant roles in emotion and memory. Most limbic system structures have centers for both gratification and aversion. Stimulation of a gratification center produces a sense of pleasure or reward; stimulation of an aversion center produces unpleasant sensations such as fear or sorrow. Gratification centers dominate some limbic structures, such as the *nucleus accumbens* (not illustrated), while aversion centers dominate others such as the amygdala. The roles of the amygdala in emotion and the hippocampus in memory are described in section 14.5d.

## The Basal Nuclei

The basal nuclei are masses of cerebral gray matter buried deep in the white matter, lateral to the thalamus **(fig. 14.17).** They are

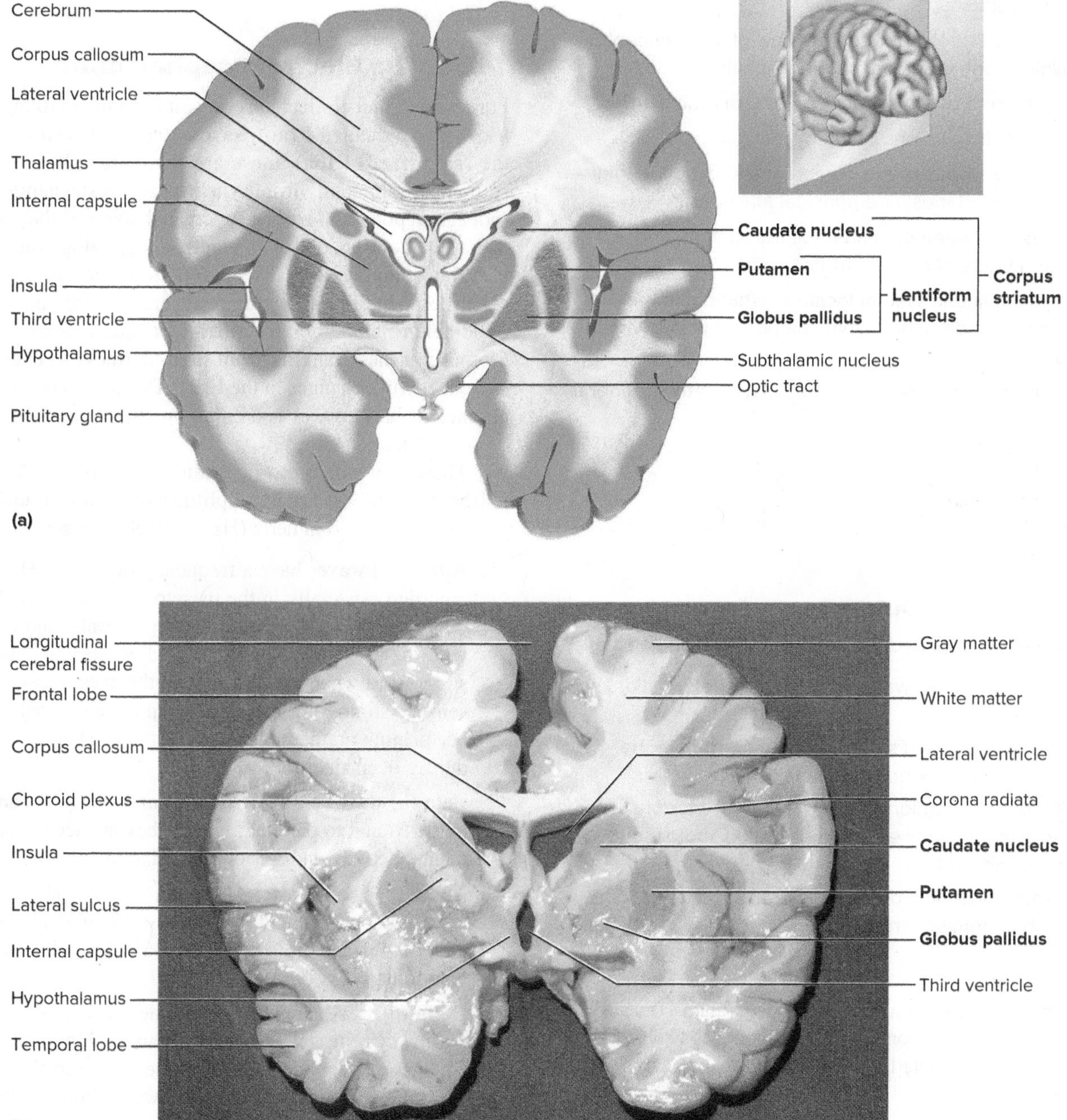


**FIGURE 14.17 The Basal Nuclei.** (a) Frontal section of the brain. (b) Corresponding slice of fresh brain tissue. The basal nuclei are labeled in boldface. APR

Photo: Biophoto Associates/Science Source

often called *basal ganglia,* but the word *ganglion* is best restricted to clusters of neurons outside the CNS. Neuroanatomists disagree on how many brain centers to classify as basal nuclei, but agree on at least three: the **caudate**[39] **nucleus, putamen**[40] (pyu-TAY-men), and **globus pallidus.**[41] These three are collectively called the *corpus striatum*[42] because of their striped appearance. The putamen and globus pallidus together are also called the *lentiform*[43] *nucleus,* because they form a lens-shaped body. They are involved in motor control and are further discussed in a later section on that topic.

**BEFORE YOU GO ON**

Answer the following questions to test your understanding of the preceding section:

14. What are the three major components of the diencephalon? Which ventricle does the diencephalon enclose?
15. What is the role of the thalamus in sensory function?
16. List at least six functions of the hypothalamus.
17. Name the five lobes of the cerebrum and describe their locations, boundaries, and principal functions.
18. Distinguish between commissural, association, and projection tracts of the cerebrum.
19. Where is the limbic system located? What component of it is involved in emotion? What component is involved in memory?
20. Where are the basal nuclei located? What is their general function?

## 14.5 Integrative Functions of the Brain

### Expected Learning Outcomes

When you have completed this section, you should be able to

a. list the types of brain waves and discuss their relationship to mental states;
b. describe the stages of sleep, their relationship to the brain waves, and the neural mechanisms of sleep;
c. identify the brain regions concerned with consciousness and thought, memory, emotion, sensation, motor control, and language; and
d. discuss the functional differences between the right and left cerebral hemispheres.

This section concerns such "higher" brain functions as sleep, memory, cognition, emotion, sensation, motor control, and language. These are associated especially with the cerebral cortex, but not exclusively; they involve interactions between the cerebral cortex and such areas as the basal nuclei, brainstem, and cerebellum. It is impossible in many cases to assign these functions to one specific brain region; as we have already seen (see fig. 14.13), functions of the brain don't have such easily defined anatomical boundaries. Some functions overlap anatomically and some cross anatomical boundaries from one region to another, often remote region. Thus, we will consider these as *integrative* functions of the brain, focusing especially on the cerebrum but in many cases involving the combined action of multiple levels of the brain. Some of these present the most difficult challenges for neurobiology, but they are the most intriguing functions of the brain and involve its largest areas.

### 14.5a The Electroencephalogram

For research and clinical purposes, it is common to monitor electrical activity called **brain waves.** Recorded with electrodes on the scalp **(fig. 14.18a),** these are rhythmic voltage changes resulting predominantly from synchronized postsynaptic potentials (not action potentials) in the superficial layers of the cerebral cortex. The recording, called an **electroencephalogram**[44] **(EEG),** is useful in studying normal brain functions such as sleep and consciousness, and in diagnosing degenerative brain diseases, metabolic abnormalities, brain tumors, trauma, and so forth. States of consciousness ranging from high alertness to deep sleep are correlated with changes in the EEG. The complete and persistent absence of brain waves is a common clinical and legal criterion of brain death.

There are four types of brain waves **(fig. 14.18b),** distinguished by differences in amplitude (mV) and frequency. Frequency is expressed in hertz (Hz), or cycles per second:

1. **Alpha (α) waves** have a frequency of 8 to 13 Hz and are recorded especially in the parieto-occipital area. They dominate the EEG when a person is awake and relaxed, with the eyes closed and the mind wandering. They are suppressed when a person opens the eyes, receives specific sensory stimulation, or engages in a mental task such as performing mathematical calculations. They are absent during deep sleep.
2. **Beta (β) waves** have a frequency of 14 to 30 Hz and occur in the frontal to parietal region. They are accentuated during mental activity and sensory stimulation.
3. **Theta (θ) waves** have a frequency of 4 to 7 Hz. They are normal in children and in drowsy or sleeping adults, but a predominance of theta waves in awake adults suggests emotional stress or brain disorders.
4. **Delta (δ) waves** are high-amplitude "slow waves" with a frequency of less than 3.5 Hz. Infants exhibit delta waves when awake, and adults exhibit them in deep sleep. A predominance of delta waves in awake adults indicates serious brain damage.

[39]*caudate* = tailed, tail-like
[40]*putam* = pod, husk
[41]*glob* = globe, ball; *pall* = pale
[42]*corpus* = body; *striat* = stripe
[43]*lenti* = lens; *form* = shape

[44]*electro* = electricity; *encephalo* = brain; *gram* = record

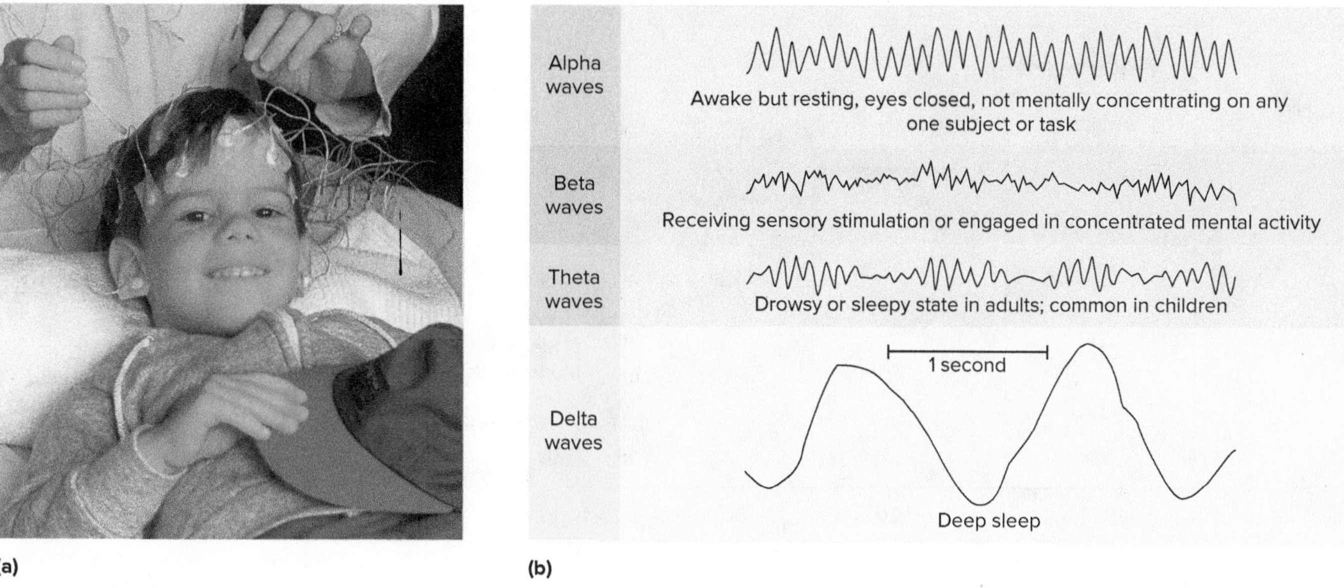


**FIGURE 14.18 The Electroencephalogram (EEG).** (a) An EEG is recorded from electrodes on the forehead and scalp. (b) Four classes of brain waves are seen in EEGs.

a: Larry Mulvehill/Science Source

## 14.5b Sleep

**Sleep** can be defined as a temporary, reversible loss of consciousness from which (in contrast to coma) one can awaken when stimulated. It is one of many bodily functions that occur in cycles called **circadian**[45] **rhythms** (sur-CAY-dee-an), so named because they are marked by events that recur at intervals of about 24 hours. Sleep superficially resembles other states of prolonged unconsciousness such as coma and animal hibernation, except that individuals cannot be aroused from those states by sensory stimulation.

Sleep occurs in distinct stages recognizable from changes in the EEG. In the first 30 to 45 minutes, the EEG waves drop in frequency but increase in amplitude as one passes through four sleep stages **(fig. 14.19a):**

- **Stage 1.** This stage usually lasts for 1 to 7 minutes. One feels drowsy, closes the eyes, and begins to relax. The EEG transitions from alpha waves to waves of mixed frequency. Thoughts come and go, often accompanied by a drifting sensation. One awakens easily if stimulated.
- **Stage 2.** This stage usually lasts for 10 to 25 minutes in the initial sleep cycle. One passes into light sleep. Brain waves have a lower frequency but higher voltage. They occasionally show 1 or 2 seconds of *sleep spindles,* high spikes resulting from interactions between neurons of the thalamus and cerebral cortex.
- **Stage 3.** This is moderate to deep sleep, typically beginning about 20 minutes after stage 1. Sleep spindles occur less often, and theta and delta waves appear. The muscles relax, and the *vital signs* (body temperature, blood pressure, and heart and respiratory rates) fall.
- **Stage 4.** The muscles are now very relaxed, vital signs are at their lowest levels, and one becomes difficult to awaken. Stage 4 sleep usually occurs only in the first one-third of the night **(fig. 14.19b).**

About five times a night, a sleeper backtracks from stage 3 or 4 to stage 2 and exhibits bouts of **rapid eye movement (REM) sleep.** This is so named because the eyes oscillate back and forth as if watching a movie. It is also called *paradoxical sleep* because the EEG resembles the waking state, yet the sleeper is harder to arouse than in any other stage. Vital signs increase and the brain consumes even more oxygen than when awake. Sleep paralysis is especially strong during REM sleep and usually prevents the sleeper from acting out his or her dreams.

Bouts of REM sleep become longer and longer as the night progresses, and we usually wake in the morning from either stage 3 or REM sleep. Dreams occur in both REM and non-REM sleep, but REM dreams tend to be longer, more vivid, and more emotional than non-REM dreams. Most nightmares, however, occur during non-REM sleep. The parasympathetic nervous system is very active during REM sleep, causing constriction of the pupils and erection of the penis or clitoris. Erection, however, is seldom accompanied by sexual dream content.

Humans are a diurnal (daytime-active) species in whom falling light intensity induces sleepiness. As the light fades at the end of the day, certain retinal cells called *ganglion cells* transmit signals to part of the hypothalamus called the **suprachiasmatic nucleus (SCN)** (SOO-pra-KY-az-MAT-ic) (see fig. 14.12b).

[45]*circa* = approximately; *dia* = a day, 24 hours

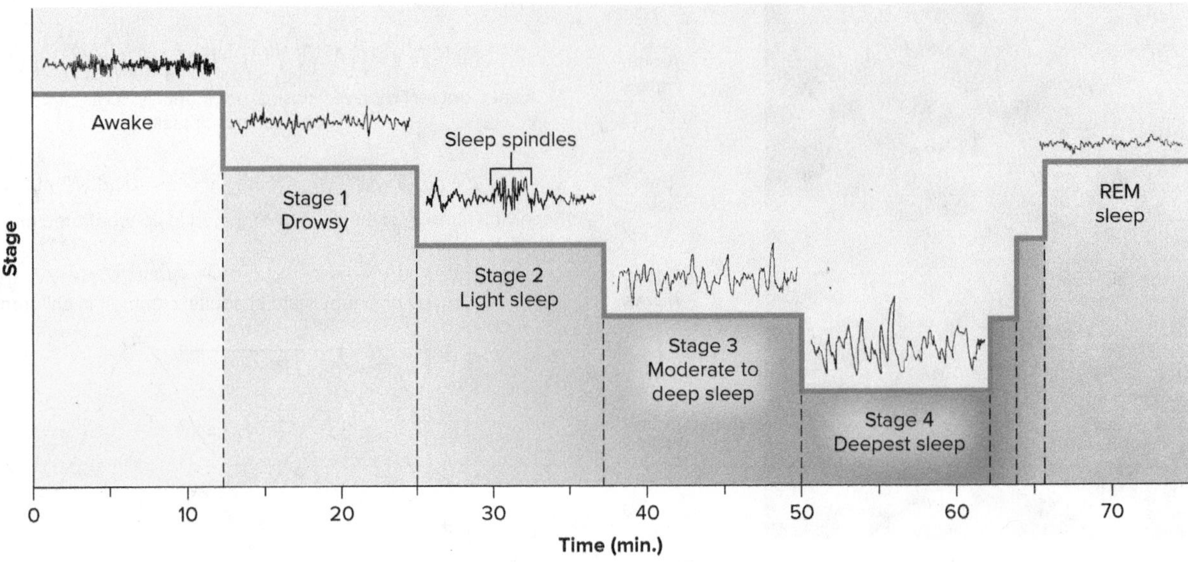


(a) One sleep cycle

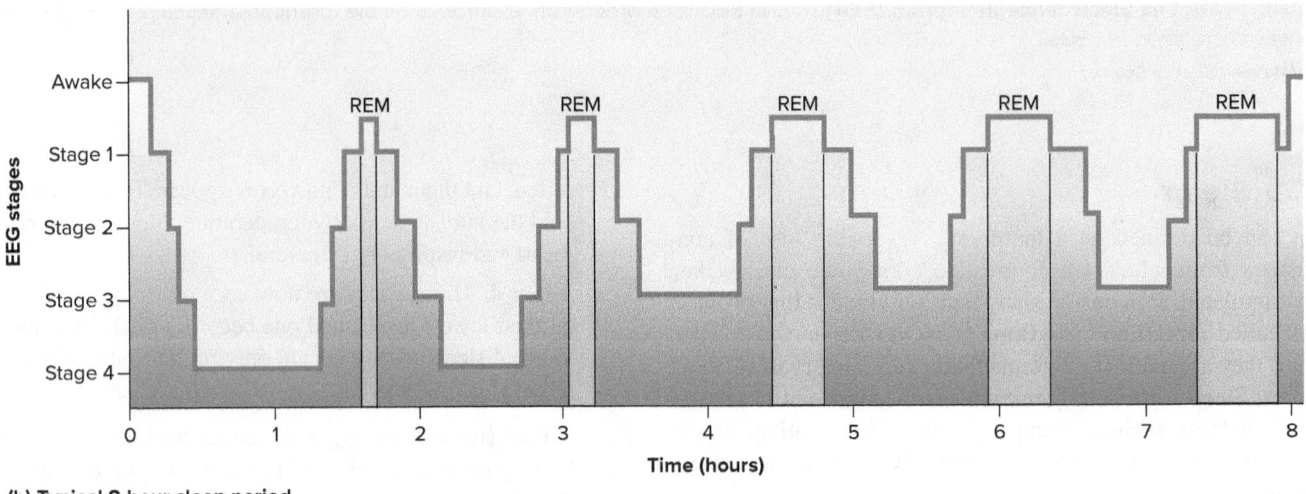


(b) Typical 8-hour sleep period

**FIGURE 14.19 Sleep Stages and Brain Activity.** (a) A single sleep cycle, from waking to deep sleep, followed by 10 minutes of REM sleep. (b) Stages of sleep over an 8-hour night in a typical young adult. Stage 4 is attained only in the first two cycles. Periods of REM sleep increase from about 10 minutes in the first cycle to as long as 50 minutes in the last hour of sleep. Most dreaming occurs during REM sleep.

Located just above the optic chiasm, the SCN is the body's master biological clock. It regulates not only sleep but also circadian rhythms of body temperature, urine production, hormone secretion, and other functions.

The SCN has two major output pathways leading to the nearby **dorsomedial nucleus (DMN)** and the pineal gland. The pineal gland responds to SCN input by secreting the hormone **melatonin.** Melatonin and the DMN together act on the reticular activating system (RAS) of the brainstem. The RAS now blocks signals from the thalamus to the cerebral cortex, so a drowsy person becomes less and less aware of environmental stimuli and lapses into sleep.

Waking is brought on by **orexins,** neuropeptides secreted by the hypothalamus. These stimulate the reticular activating system, which then stimulates the thalamus. As a person begins to wake, electrical activity increases in the thalamus and then spreads through the cerebral cortex. Thus, the cerebral awareness of environmental stimuli increases and the sleeper wakes up. The excitatory pathway from RAS to thalamus and cortex involves multiple excitatory neurotransmitters including histamine; this is why antihistamines, antagonizing this pathway, can make one drowsy.

Orexins are absent or at low levels in a disorder called **narcolepsy,** in which a person experiences excessive daytime sleepiness and fatigue and may often fall asleep at work or school, with abnormally quick onset of REM sleep. Narcolepsy seems to be an autoimmune disease caused by antibody-mediated destruction of the orexin-producing neurons.

**▶▶▶APPLY WHAT YOU KNOW**

*Some animals have been shown to exhibit narcolepsy as the result of a mutation in the gene for an orexin receptor. Looking ahead in the book to type 2 diabetes mellitus in section 17.7e, can you identify a common thread in these two disorders?*

We spend about one-third of our lives asleep, and we might well regret such a terrible "waste of time." Yet sleep deprivation can cause widespread dysfunctions ranging from cognitive decline or hallucinations to weight loss, reduced immunity, and even death. Yet the reasons for sleep and dreaming remain elusive. Non-REM sleep has a restorative, refreshing effect, but it is unclear why quiet bed rest alone can't serve these purposes; why must we lose consciousness?

Sleep is associated with restorative anabolic processes in the immune, nervous, endocrine, and other systems. During waking hours, brain glycogen levels go down, while ATP consumption generates a sleep-inducing metabolite, adenosine (see Deeper Insight 15.2). Non-REM sleep reduces cerebral metabolic rate and ATP consumption, allowing glycogen and ATP levels to rebound while adenosine levels fall and other metabolites are cleared from the brain. Growth hormone secretion rises during slow-wave sleep.

REM sleep appears to be a time in which the brain either "consolidates" and strengthens memories by reinforcing synaptic connections, or purges superfluous information from memory by weakening or eliminating other synapses. When REM sleep is blocked in experimental animals without waking them, they forget tasks they had recently learned. Theta wave activity and the sleep spindles of stage 2 sleep are also associated with memory consolidation. Sleep research subjects who have just learned a new task show a higher density of sleep spindles than controls who have not.

## 14.5c Cognition

**Cognition**[46] is the range of mental processes by which we acquire and use knowledge—sensory perception, thought, reasoning, judgment, memory, imagination, and intuition. Such functions are widely distributed over regions of cerebral cortex called **association areas,** which constitute about 75% of all brain tissue. This is the most difficult area of brain research and the most incompletely understood aspect of cerebral function. Much of what we know about it has come from studies of patients with brain lesions—areas of tissue destruction resulting from cancer, stroke, and trauma. The many brain injuries incurred in World Wars I and II yielded an abundance of insights into regional brain functions. More recently, imaging methods such as PET and fMRI have yielded much more sophisticated insights. These methods allow a researcher to scan a person's brain during various cognitive or motor tasks and to see which brain regions are most active in different mental and task states (see Deeper Insight 14.5).

[46]*cognit* = to know

A few examples of the cognitive effects of cerebral lesions reveal some functions of the association areas:

- Parietal lobe lesions can cause people to become unaware of objects, or even their own limbs, on the other side of the body—a condition called *contralateral neglect syndrome.* In typical cases, men shave only half of the face, women apply makeup to only one side, patients dress only half of the body, and some people deny that one arm or leg belongs to them. Such patients are unable to find their way around—say, to describe the route from home to work or navigate within a familiar building.
- Temporal lobe lesions often result in *agnosia*[47] (ag-NO-zee-ah), the inability to recognize, identify, and name familiar objects. In *prosopagnosia,*[48] a person cannot remember familiar faces, even his or her own reflection in a mirror.
- Frontal lobe lesions are especially devastating to the qualities we think of as personality. The frontal lobe integrates information from sensory and motor regions of the cortex and from other association areas. It gives us a sense of our relationship to the rest of the world, enabling us to think about it and to plan and execute appropriate behavior. Lesions here may produce profound personality disorders and socially inappropriate behaviors.

## 14.5d Memory

**Memory** is one of the cognitive functions, but warrants special attention. We studied its forms and its neural and molecular mechanisms earlier (see section 12.6e). Now that you have been introduced to the gross anatomy of the brain, we can consider where those processes occur anatomically.

Our subject is really a little broader than memory per se. Information management by the brain entails learning (acquiring new information), memory proper (information storage and retrieval), and forgetting (eliminating trivial information). Brain-injured people are sometimes unable to recall things they once knew **(retrograde amnesia)** or unable to store new information **(anterograde amnesia).** *Amnesia* refers to defects in *explicit* memory (such as the ability to describe past events), not *implicit* memory (such as the ability to tie one's shoes).

The **hippocampus** of the limbic system is an important memory-forming center (see fig. 14.16). It doesn't store memories, but organizes sensory and cognitive experiences into a unified long-term memory. The hippocampus learns from sensory input while an experience is happening, but it has a short memory. Later, especially during sleep, it plays this memory repeatedly to the cerebral cortex, which is a "slow learner" but forms longer-lasting memories. This process of "teaching the cerebral cortex" until a long-term memory is established is called **memory consolidation.** Long-term memories are held in various areas of cortex. One's vocabulary and memory of faces and familiar

[47]*a* = without; *gnos* = knowledge
[48]*prosopo* = face, person

objects, for example, reside in the superior temporal lobe, and memories of one's plans and social roles are in the prefrontal cortex (see fig. 14.13).

Lesions of the hippocampus can cause profound anterograde amnesia. For example, in 1953, a famous patient known in the literature as H. M. (Henry Molaison, 1926–2008) underwent surgical removal of a large portion of both temporal lobes, including both hippocampi, to treat severe epilepsy. The operation had no adverse effect on his intelligence or explicit memory for things that had happened early in his life, but it left him with an inability to establish new explicit memories. He could hold a conversation with his psychologist, but a few minutes later deny that it had taken place. He worked with the same psychologist for more than 40 years after his operation, but couldn't remember who she was from day to day. He was nevertheless able to learn new motor skills, thus showing explicit and implicit memory to involve separate brain regions.

Other parts of the brain involved in memory include the cerebellum, with a role in learning motor skills, and the amygdala, with a role in emotional memory.

### 14.5e Emotion

Emotional feelings and memories are not exclusively cerebral functions, but result from an interaction between areas of the prefrontal cortex and diencephalon. Emotional control centers of the brain have been identified by studying people with brain lesions and by such techniques as surgical removal, ablation (destruction) of small regions with electrodes, and stimulation with electrodes and chemical implants, especially in experimental animals. Changes in behavior following such procedures give clues to the functions that a region performs. However, interpretation of the results is difficult and controversial because of the complex connections between the emotional brain and other regions.

The **prefrontal cortex (frontal association area)** is the most rostral part of the frontal lobe, just behind the forehead. It is well developed only in primates, especially humans. It is the seat of judgment, intent, and control over the expression of our emotions. However we may feel, it is here that we decide the appropriate way to show those feelings. But the feelings themselves, and emotional memories, arise from deeper regions of the brain, especially the hypothalamus and amygdala. Here lie the nuclei that stimulate us to recoil in fear from a rattlesnake or yearn for a lost love.

The amygdala is a major component of the limbic system described earlier (see fig. 14.16). It receives processed information from the general senses and from vision, hearing, taste, and smell. Such input enables it to mediate emotional responses to such stimuli as a disgusting odor, a foul taste, a beautiful sight, pleasant music, or a stomachache. It is especially important in the sense of fear, but also plays roles in decision making, food intake, sexual behavior, and drawing our attention to novel stimuli.

Output from the amygdala goes in two directions of special interest: (1) Some goes to the hypothalamus and lower brainstem and influences somatic and visceral motor systems. An emotional response to a stimulus may, through these connections, make one's heart race, raise the blood pressure, make the hair stand on end, or induce vomiting. (2) Other output goes to areas of the prefrontal cortex that mediate conscious control and expression of the emotions, such as the ability to express love, control anger, or overcome fear.

Many important aspects of personality depend on an intact, functional amygdala and hypothalamus. When specific regions are destroyed or artificially stimulated, humans and other animals exhibit either blunted or exaggerated expressions of anger, fear, aggression, self-defense, pleasure, pain, love, sexuality, and parental affection, as well as abnormalities in learning, memory, and motivation. Lesions of the amygdala, for example, can abolish the sense of fear.

Much of our behavior is shaped by learned associations between stimuli, our responses to them, and the rewards or punishments that result. Nuclei involved in feelings of reward and punishment have been identified in the hypothalamus of cats, rats, monkeys, and other animals. In a representative experiment, an electrode is implanted in an area of an animal's hypothalamus called the **median forebrain bundle (MFB).** The animal is placed in a chamber with a foot pedal wired to that electrode. When the animal steps on the pedal, it receives a mild electrical stimulus to the MFB. Apparently the sensation is strongly rewarding, because the animal soon starts to press the pedal over and over and may spend most of its time doing so—even to the point of neglecting food and water. Rats have been known to bar-press 5,000 to 12,000 times an hour, and monkeys up to 17,000 times an hour, to stimulate their MFBs.

These animals cannot tell us what they are feeling, but electrode implants have also been used to treat people who suffer otherwise incurable schizophrenia, pain, or epilepsy. These patients also repeatedly press a button to stimulate the MFB, but they do not report feelings of joy or ecstasy. Some are unable to explain why they enjoy the stimulus, and others report "relief from tension" or "a quiet, relaxed feeling." With electrodes misplaced in other areas of the hypothalamus, subjects report feelings of fear or terror when stimulated.

**▶▶▶APPLY WHAT YOU KNOW**

*MRI scans show that John has a pea-size tumor in his hippocampus and Allan has a tumor of the same size in his amygdala. One of these patients is in prison for violent crimes in which he seemed to show no fear or sense of self-preservation. The other patient cannot remember the name of his new granddaughter, no matter how many times he is told. Which behavioral outcome do you associate with each patient? Why?*

### 14.5f Sensation

A great deal of the cerebrum is concerned with the senses—most cortex of the insula and of the parietal, occipital, and temporal lobes. Regions called **primary sensory cortex** are the sites where sensory input is first received and one becomes conscious of a stimulus. Adjacent to these are association areas where this information is interpreted. For example, the primary visual cortex, which receives input from the eyes, is bordered by the visual association area, which interprets and makes cognitive sense of the visual stimuli so we know what we are looking at. Some association

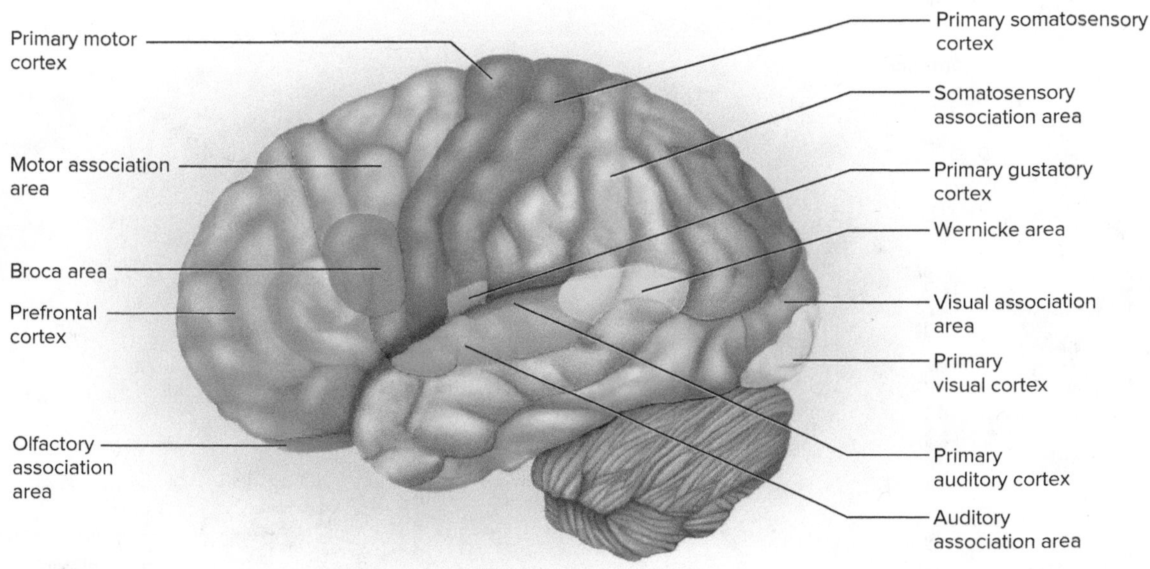


**FIGURE 14.20 Some Functional Regions of the Left Cerebral Cortex.** The Broca and Wernicke areas for language abilities are found in only one hemisphere, usually the left. The other regions shown here are mirrored in both hemispheres.

areas are *multimodal*—instead of processing information from a single sensory source, they receive input from multiple senses and integrate this into our overall perception of our surroundings. For example, in the frontal lobe just above the eyes, there is a patch of multimodal cortex called the *orbitofrontal cortex,* which receives taste, smell, and visual input to form our overall impression of the desirability of a particular food.

The sense organs and their signaling pathways in the CNS are the subject of chapter 16. Here we will examine only the areas of cerebral cortex involved in sensory perception.

## The Special Senses

The **special senses** are limited to the head, and some employ relatively complex sense organs. They are vision, hearing, equilibrium, taste, and smell. Their primary cortices and association areas are located as follows **(fig. 14.20).**

- **Vision.** Visual signals are received by the **primary visual cortex** in the far posterior region of the occipital lobe. This is bordered anteriorly by the **visual association area,** which includes all the remainder of the occipital lobe, some of the posterior parietal lobe (concerned with spatial perception), and much of the inferior temporal lobe, where we recognize faces and other familiar objects.
- **Hearing.** Auditory signals are received by the **primary auditory cortex** in the superior region of the temporal lobe and in the nearby insula. The **auditory association area** occupies areas of temporal lobe inferior to the primary auditory cortex and deep within the lateral sulcus. This is where we become capable of recognizing spoken words, a familiar piece of music, or a voice on the telephone.
- **Equilibrium.** Signals from the inner ear for equilibrium project mainly to the cerebellum and several brainstem nuclei concerned with head and eye movements and visceral functions. Some fibers of this system, however, are routed through the thalamus to areas of association cortex in the roof of the lateral sulcus and near the lower end of the central sulcus. This is the seat of consciousness of our body movements and orientation in space.
- **Taste and smell.** Gustatory (taste) signals are received by the **primary gustatory cortex** in the inferior end of the postcentral gyrus of the parietal lobe (discussed shortly) and an anterior region of the insula. Olfactory (smell) signals are received by the **primary olfactory cortex** in the medial surface of the temporal lobe and inferior surface of the frontal lobe. The *orbitofrontal cortex* mentioned earlier serves as a multimodal association area for both taste and smell, and is thus highly important in our enjoyment or rejection of various foods and drinks.

## The General Senses

The **general (somatosensory, somesthetic,**[49] **or somatic) senses** are distributed over the entire body and employ relatively simple receptors. They include such senses as touch, pressure, stretch, movement, heat, cold, and pain. Coming from the head, such signals reach the brain by way of certain cranial nerves, especially the trigeminal nerve; from the rest of the body, they ascend sensory tracts of the spinal cord such as the spinothalamic tract. In both routes, they decussate to the contralateral thalamus.

[49]*som* = body; *esthet* = feeling

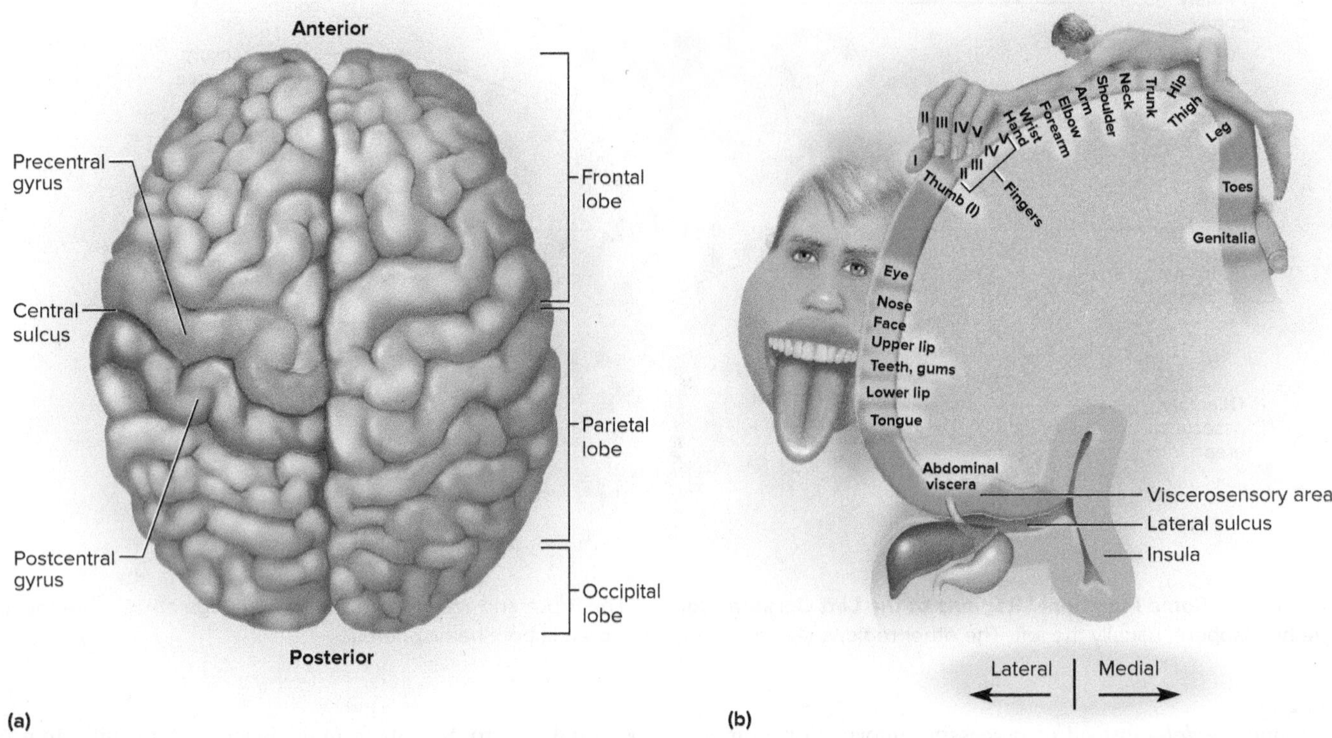


**FIGURE 14.21 The Primary Somatosensory Cortex (Postcentral Gyrus).** (a) Superior view of the brain showing the location of the postcentral gyrus (violet). (b) The sensory homunculus, drawn so that body parts are in proportion to the amount of cortex dedicated to their sensation. This gyrus also includes centers for visceral sensation from the intra-abdominal organs (the viscerosensory area). APR

The thalamus processes the input and selectively relays signals to the **postcentral gyrus.** This is a fold of the cerebrum that lies immediately caudal to the central sulcus and thus forms the rostral border of the parietal lobe **(fig. 14.21).** We can trace it from just above the lateral sulcus to the crown of the head and then downward into the longitudinal cerebral fissure. Its cortex is called the **primary somatosensory cortex.** Adjacent to it is a **somatosensory association area,** caudal to the gyrus and in the roof of the lateral sulcus (fig. 14.20). Awareness of stimulation occurs in the primary somatosensory cortex, but making cognitive sense of it is a function of the association area.

Because of the aforementioned decussation in sensory pathways, the right postcentral gyrus receives input from the left side of the body and vice versa. The primary somatosensory cortex is like an upside-down sensory map of the contralateral side of the body, traditionally diagrammed as a *sensory homunculus*[50] (fig. 14.21b). As the diagram shows, receptors in the lower limb project to superior and medial parts of the gyrus, and receptors in the face project to the inferior and lateral parts. Such point-for-point correspondence between an area of the body and an area of the CNS is called **somatotopy.**[51] The reason for the bizarre, distorted appearance of the homunculus is that the amount of cerebral tissue devoted to a given body region is proportional to how richly innervated and sensitive that region is, not to its size. Thus, the hands and face are represented by a much larger region of somatosensory cortex than the trunk is.

## 14.5g Motor Control

The intention to contract a skeletal muscle begins in the **motor association (premotor) area** of the frontal lobe (fig. 14.20). This is where we plan our behavior—where neurons compile a program for the degree and sequence of muscle contractions required for an action such as dancing, typing, or speaking. The program is then transmitted to neurons of the **precentral gyrus (primary motor area),** which is the most posterior gyrus of the frontal lobe, immediately anterior to the central sulcus **(fig. 14.22).** Neurons here send signals to the brainstem and spinal cord, which ultimately results in muscle contractions.

The precentral gyrus, like the postcentral one, exhibits somatotopy. The neurons for toe movements, for example, are deep in the longitudinal cerebral fissure on the medial side of the gyrus. The summit of the gyrus controls the trunk, shoulder, and arm, and the inferolateral region controls the facial muscles. This map is diagrammed as a *motor homunculus* (fig. 14.22b). Like the sensory homunculus, it has a distorted look because the amount of cortex devoted to a given body region is proportional to the number of muscles and motor units in that region, not to the size of the region. The amount of cerebral tissue dedicated to the hands, face,

[50]*hom* = man; *unculus* = little
[51]*somato* = body; *topy* = place

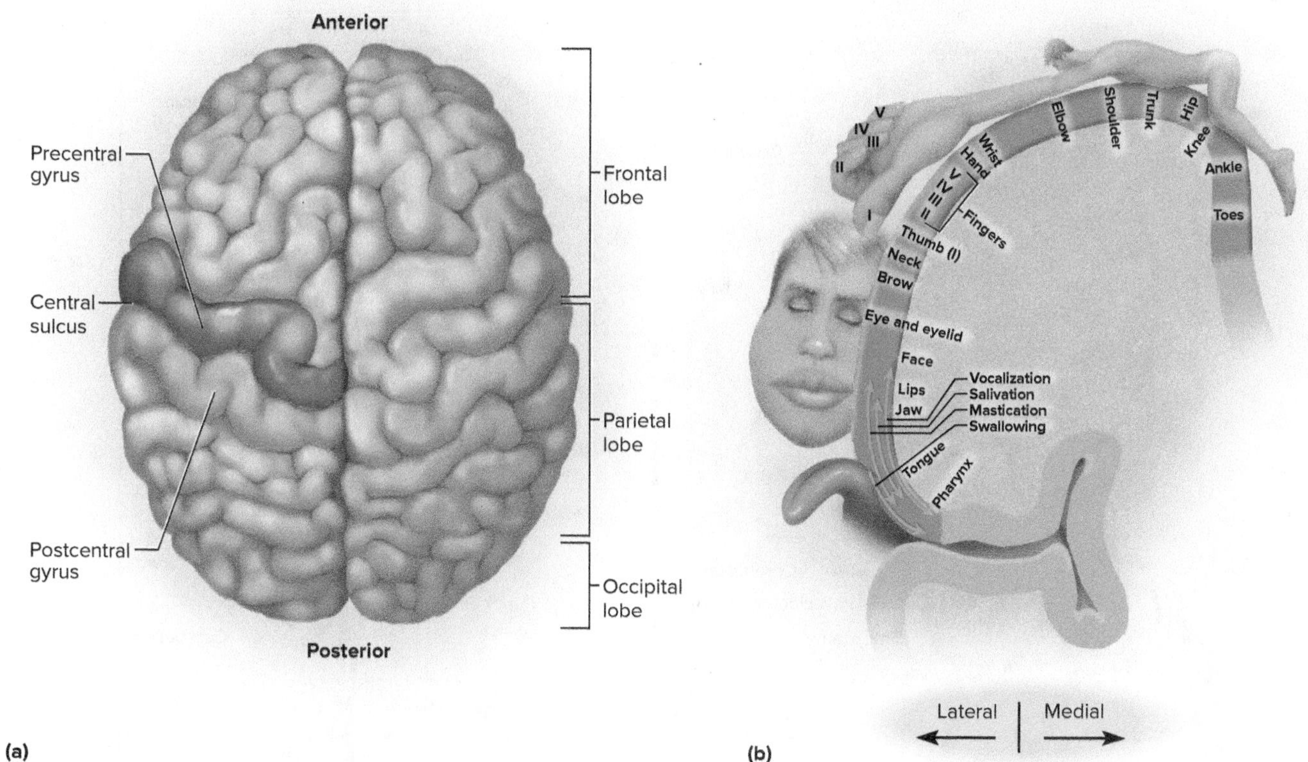


**FIGURE 14.22 The Primary Motor Cortex (Precentral Gyrus).** (a) Superior view of the brain showing the location of the precental gyrus (blue). (b) Motor homunculus, drawn so that body parts are in proportion to the amount of primary motor cortex dedicated to their control. APR

*Which body regions are controlled by the largest areas of motor cortex—regions with a few large muscles or regions with numerous small muscles?*

and tongue reflects the importance of fine motor control in speech, facial expression, and use of the hands.

There is no exact point-for-point correspondence between an area of the precentral gyrus and a given muscle. A muscle is controlled by neurons at several points within a general area of the gyrus. Also, a given neuron in the gyrus may ultimately affect more than one muscle, such as muscles of shoulder and elbow movement that both contribute to the coordinated positioning of one's hand. Although the homunculus identifies cortical areas that are broadly responsible for motor control of a given region, the boundaries between these cortical areas overlap and are not sharply defined.

The pyramidal cells of the precentral gyrus are called **upper motor neurons.** Their fibers project caudally, with about 19 million fibers ending in nuclei of the brainstem and 1 million forming the corticospinal tracts. Most of these fibers decussate in the lower medulla oblongata (at the pyramidal decussation) and form the *lateral corticospinal tract* on each side of the spinal cord. A smaller number of fibers pass through the medulla without decussation and form the *anterior corticospinal tracts,* which cross over lower in the spinal cord. Each precentral gyrus thus controls muscles on the contralateral side of the body. In the brainstem or spinal cord, the fibers from the upper motor neurons synapse with **lower motor neurons** whose axons innervate the skeletal muscles (see fig. 13.7).

Other areas of the brain important in muscle control are the basal nuclei (see fig. 14.17) and cerebellum. Among the roles of the basal nuclei are determining the onset and cessation of intentional movements; the repetitive hip and shoulder movements that occur in walking; and highly practiced, learned behaviors that one carries out with little thought—for example, writing, driving a car, and tying one's shoes. The basal nuclei lie in a feedback circuit from the cerebrum to the basal nuclei to the thalamus and back to the cerebrum. They receive signals from the substantia nigra of the midbrain and from all areas of cerebral cortex, except for the primary visual and auditory cortices. The basal nuclei process these and issue their output to the thalamus, which relays these signals back to the midbrain and cerebral cortex—especially to the prefrontal cortex, motor association area, and precentral gyrus.

Lesions of the basal nuclei cause movement disorders called **dyskinesias.**[52] These are sometimes characterized by abnormal difficulty initiating movement, such as rising from a chair or beginning to walk, and by a slow shuffling walk. Such motor dysfunctions are seen in Parkinson disease (see Deeper Insight 12.4). Smooth, easy movements require the excitation of agonistic muscles and inhibition of their antagonists. In Parkinson disease, the antagonists

[52] *dys* = bad, abnormal, difficult; *kines* = movement

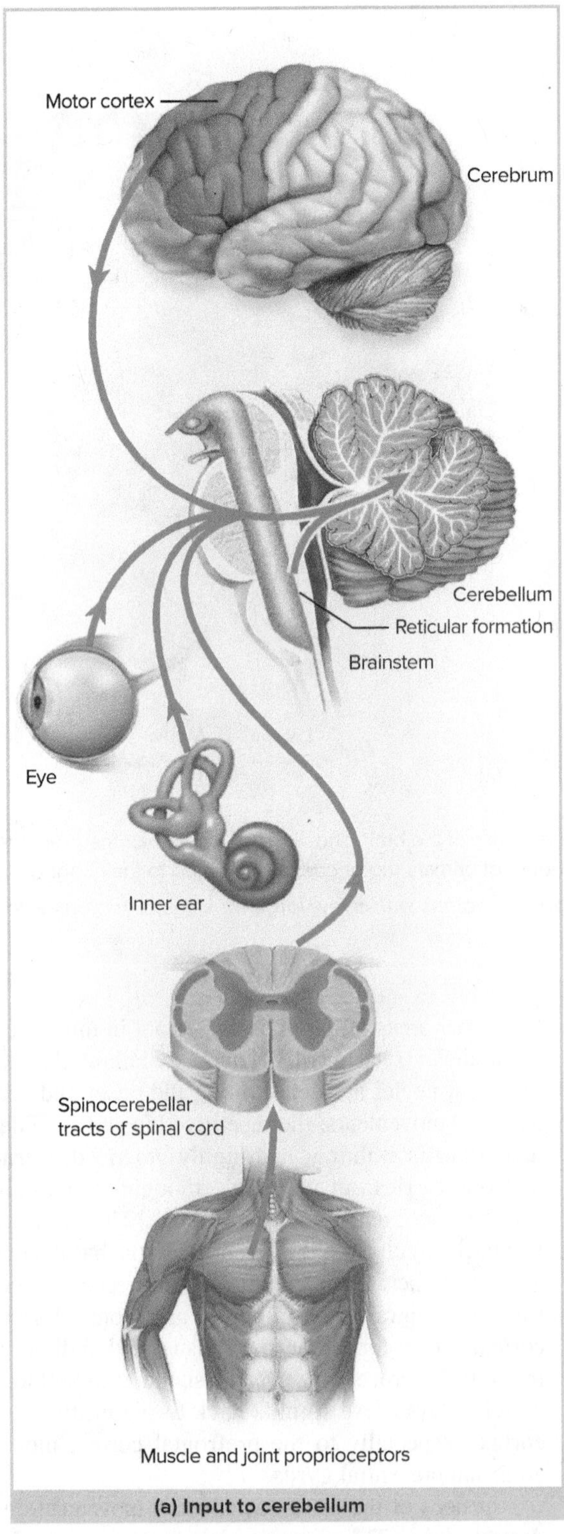


(a) Input to cerebellum

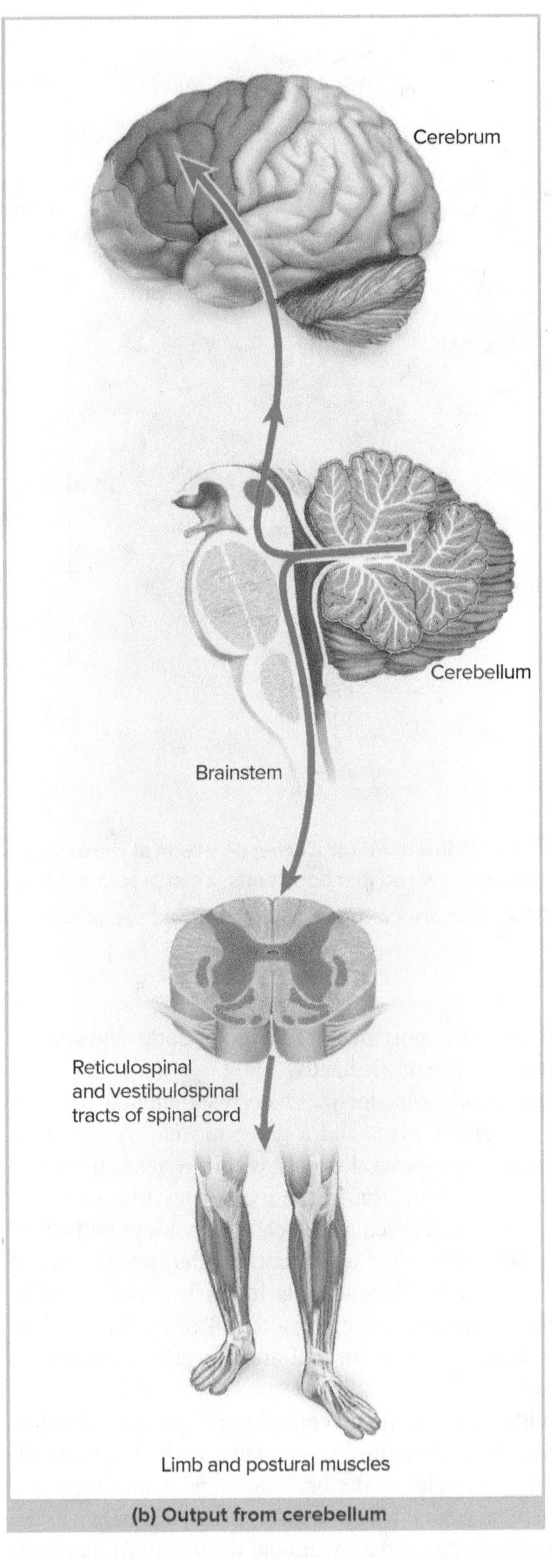


(b) Output from cerebellum

**FIGURE 14.23 Motor Pathways Involving the Cerebellum.** (a) Afferent (input) pathways from the cerebrum and sense organs to the cerebellum. (b) Efferent (output) pathways from the cerebellum to the skeletal muscles.

are not inhibited. Therefore, opposing muscles at a joint fight each other, making it a struggle to move as one wishes. Other dyskinesias are characterized by exaggerated or unwanted movements, such as flailing of the limbs *(ballismus)* in Huntington disease.

The cerebellum is highly important in motor coordination. In addition to its cognitive functions described earlier, it aids in learning motor skills, maintains muscle tone and posture, smooths muscle contractions, coordinates eye and body movements, and helps to coordinate the motions of different joints with each other (such as the shoulder and elbow in pitching a baseball). The cerebellum acts as a comparator in motor control. Through the middle peduncles, it receives information from the upper motor neurons of the cerebrum about the movements one intends to make, and information about body movement from the eyes and inner ears. Through the spinocerebellar tracts and inferior peduncles, it receives information from proprioceptors in the muscles and joints about the actual performance of the movement **(fig. 14.23a).** The Purkinje cells of the cerebellum compare the two. If there is a discrepancy between the intent and the performance, they signal the deep cerebellar nuclei. These, in turn, issue signals to the thalamus and lower brainstem, ultimately ascending to the motor association area of the cerebrum and the reticulospinal and vestibulospinal tracts of the spinal cord **(fig. 14.23b).** Output from these areas corrects the muscle performance to match the intent. Lesions of the cerebellum can result in a clumsy, awkward gait *(ataxia)* and make some tasks such as climbing stairs virtually impossible.

## 14.5h Language

Language includes several abilities—reading, writing, speaking, sign language, and understanding words—assigned to different regions of cerebral cortex **(fig. 14.24).** The **posterior speech area,** or **Wernicke**[53] **area** (WUR-ni-keh), is responsible for the recognition of spoken and written language. It lies just posterior to the lateral sulcus, usually in the left hemisphere, at the crossroad between visual, auditory, and somatosensory areas of cortex, receiving input from all these neighboring regions. The *angular gyrus,* part of the parietal lobe just caudal and superior to the Wernicke area, is important in the ability to read and write.

When we intend to speak, the Wernicke area formulates phrases according to learned rules of grammar and transmits a plan of speech to the **motor language area,** or **Broca**[54] **area,** located in the inferior prefrontal cortex of the same hemisphere. PET scans show a rise in the metabolic activity of the Broca area as one prepares to speak or sign (see fig. 14.41). This area generates a motor program for the muscles of the larynx, tongue, cheeks, and lips to produce speech, as well as for the hand motions of signing. It transmits this program to the primary motor cortex, which executes it—that is, it issues commands to the lower motor neurons that supply the relevant muscles.

The emotional aspect of language is controlled by regions in the opposite hemisphere that mirror the Wernicke and Broca areas. Opposite the Broca area is the *affective language area.* Lesions to this area result in *aprosody*—flat, emotionless speech. The cortex opposite the Wernicke area is concerned with recognizing the emotional content of another person's speech. Lesions here can result in such problems as inability to understand a joke.

**▶▶▶APPLY WHAT YOU KNOW**

*Of all the language centers just described, which one best fits the concept of multimodal association cortex?*

**Aphasia**[55] (ah-FAY-zee-uh) is any language deficit resulting from lesions in the hemisphere (usually the left) containing the Wernicke and Broca areas. The many forms of aphasia are difficult to classify. *Nonfluent (Broca) aphasia,* due to a lesion in the Broca area, results in slow speech, difficulty choosing words, or use of words that only approximate the correct word. For example, a person may say "tssair" when asked to identify a picture of a chair. In extreme cases, the person's entire vocabulary consists of two or three words, sometimes those that were being spoken when a stroke occurred. Such patients feel very frustrated with themselves and often maintain a tight-lipped reluctance to talk. A lesion to the Wernicke area may cause *fluent (Wernicke) aphasia,* in which a person speaks normally and sometimes excessively, but uses jargon and invented words that make little sense (for example, "choss" for chair). Such a person may be unable to comprehend

[53]Karl Wernicke (1848–1905), German neurologist
[54]Pierre Paul Broca (1824–80), French surgeon and anthropologist
[55]*a* = without; *phas* = speech

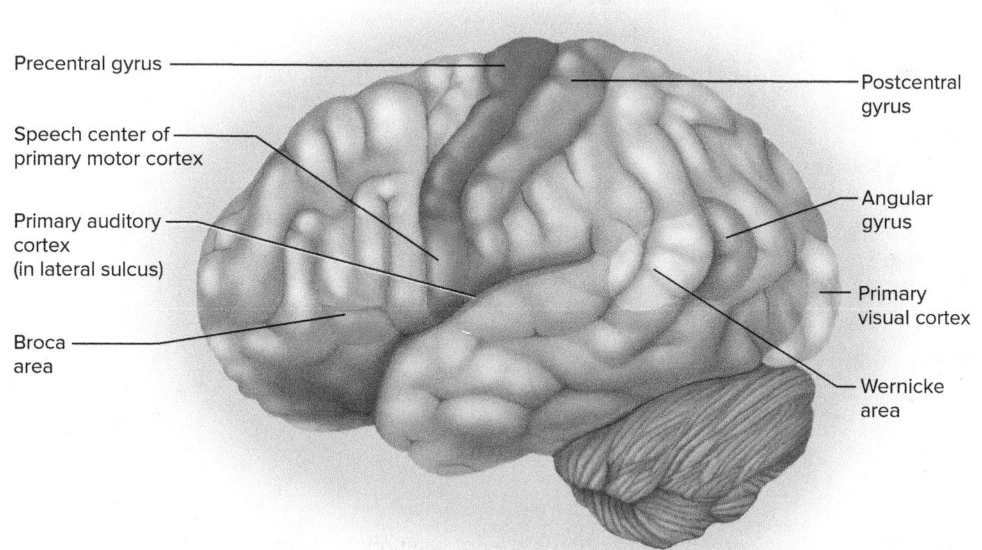


**FIGURE 14.24 Language Centers of the Left Hemisphere.**

written and spoken words. In *anomic aphasia,* a person can speak normally and understand speech, but cannot identify written words or pictures. Shown a picture of a chair, the person may say, "I know what it is; I have a lot of them," but be unable to name the object.

This represents only a small sample of the complex and puzzling linguistic effects of brain lesions. Other lesions to small areas of cortex can cause impaired mathematical ability, a tendency to write only consonants, or difficulty understanding the second half of each word a person reads.

## 14.5i Cerebral Lateralization

The two cerebral hemispheres look identical at a glance, but close examination reveals a number of differences. For example, in many women the left temporal lobe is longer than the right. In left-handed people, the left frontal, parietal, and occipital lobes are usually wider than those on the right. The two hemispheres also differ in some of their functions **(fig. 14.25).** Neither hemisphere is "dominant," but each is specialized for certain tasks. This difference in function is called **cerebral lateralization.** The idea, however, that some people are "left-brained" (such as a mathematician or scientist) and others "right-brained" (such as a musician or artist) is only a discredited popular myth. Everyone uses the two hemispheres about equally.

One hemisphere, usually the left, is called the *categorical hemisphere.* It is specialized for spoken and written language and for the sequential and analytical reasoning employed in such fields as science and mathematics. This hemisphere seems to break information into fragments and analyze it in a linear way. The other hemisphere, usually the right, is called the *representational hemisphere.* It perceives information in a more integrated, holistic way. It is a seat of imagination and insight; musical and artistic skill; perception of patterns and spatial relationships; and comparison of sights, sounds, smells, and tastes. It is better than the left hemisphere at recognizing the intonation, rhythm, and emotional content of other people's speech.

Cerebral lateralization is highly correlated with handedness. The left hemisphere is the categorical one in 96% of right-handed people, and the right hemisphere in 4%. Among left-handed people, the right hemisphere is categorical in 15% and the left in 70%, whereas in the remaining 15%, neither hemisphere is distinctly specialized.

Lateralization develops with age. In young children, if one cerebral hemisphere is damaged or removed (for example, because of brain cancer), the other hemisphere can often take over its functions. Adult males exhibit more lateralization than females and suffer more functional loss when one hemisphere is damaged. When the left hemisphere is damaged, men are three times as likely as women to become aphasic. The reason for this difference is not yet clear.

**BEFORE YOU GO ON**

Answer the following questions to test your understanding of the preceding section:

**21.** Suppose you are reading a novel and gradually fall asleep and begin to dream. How would your brain waves change during this sequence of events?

**22.** Describe the locations and functions of the somatosensory, visual, auditory, and frontal association areas.

**23.** Describe the somatotopy of the primary motor area and primary sensory area.

**24.** What are the roles of the Wernicke area, Broca area, and precentral gyrus in language?

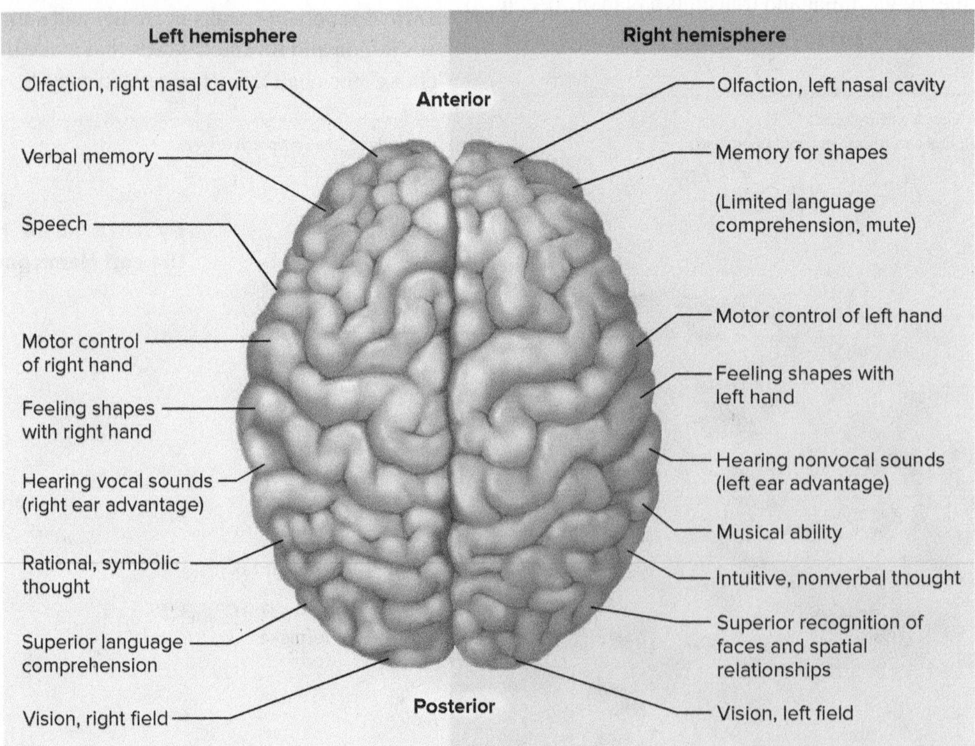


**FIGURE 14.25 Lateralization of Cerebral Functions.** The two cerebral hemispheres are not functionally identical.

## 14.6 The Cranial Nerves

### Expected Learning Outcomes

When you have completed this section, you should be able to

a. list the 12 cranial nerves by name and number;
b. identify where each cranial nerve originates and terminates; and
c. state the functions of each cranial nerve.

To be functional, the brain must communicate with the rest of the body. Most of its input and output travels by way of the spinal cord, but it also communicates by way of 12 pairs of **cranial nerves.** These arise primarily from the base of the brain, exit the cranium through its foramina, and lead to muscles and sense organs located mainly in the head and neck. The cranial nerves are numbered I to XII starting with the most rostral pair **(fig. 14.26).** Each nerve also has a descriptive name such as *optic nerve* and *vagus nerve.*

### 14.6a Cranial Nerve Pathways

Most motor fibers of the cranial nerves begin in nuclei of the brainstem and lead to glands and muscles. The sensory fibers begin in receptors located mainly in the head and neck and lead mainly to the brainstem. These include the special senses such as vision and hearing, as well as general senses such as touch and proprioception. Pathways for the special senses are detailed in chapter 16. Sensory fibers for proprioception begin in the muscles innervated by motor fibers of the cranial nerves, but they often travel to the brain in a different nerve from the one that supplies the motor innervation.

Most cranial nerves carry fibers between the brainstem and ipsilateral receptors and effectors. Thus, a lesion in one side of the brainstem causes a sensory or motor deficit on the same side of the head. This contrasts with lesions of the motor and somatosensory cortex of the cerebrum, which, as we saw earlier, cause sensory and motor deficits on the *contralateral* side of the body. The exceptions are the optic nerve (II), where half the fibers decussate to the opposite side of the brain (see fig. 16.45), and the trochlear nerve (IV), in which all efferent fibers lead to a muscle of the contralateral eye.

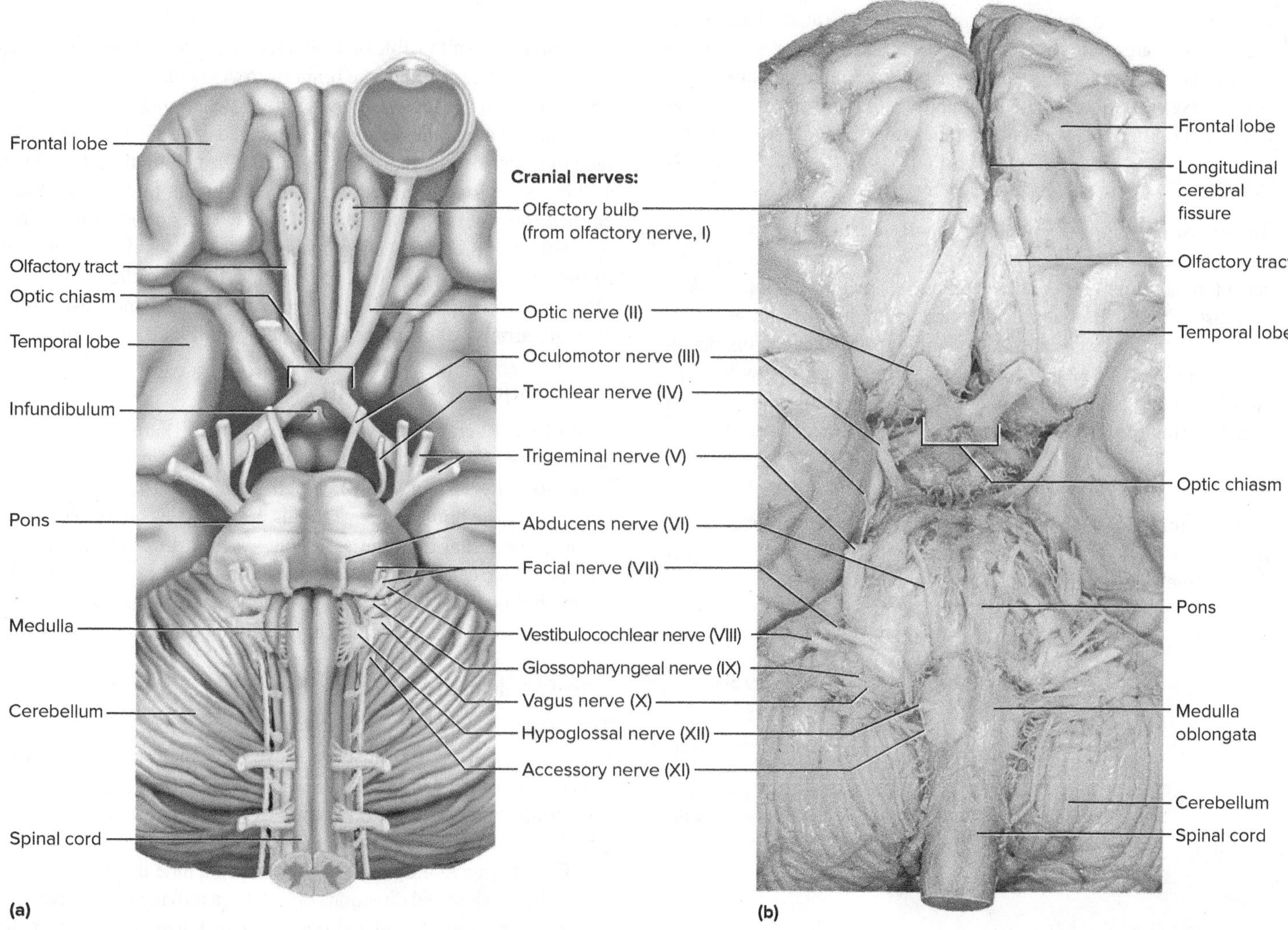


**FIGURE 14.26 The Cranial Nerves.** (a) Base of the brain, showing the 12 cranial nerves. (b) Photograph of the cranial nerves. APR

b: Rebecca Gray/Don Kincaid/McGraw-Hill Education

### 14.6b Cranial Nerve Classification

Cranial nerves are traditionally classified as sensory (I, II, VIII), motor (III, IV, VI, XI, XII), or mixed (V, VII, IX, X). In reality, only cranial nerves I and II (for smell and vision) are purely sensory, whereas all of the rest contain both afferent and efferent fibers and are therefore mixed nerves. Those traditionally classified as motor not only stimulate muscle contractions but also contain sensory fibers of proprioception, which provide the brain with feedback for controlling muscle action and make one aware of such things as the position of the tongue and orientation of the head. Cranial nerve VIII, concerned with hearing and equilibrium, is traditionally classified as sensory, but it also has motor fibers that return signals to the inner ear and tune it to sharpen the sense of hearing. The nerves traditionally classified as mixed have sensory functions quite unrelated to their motor functions. For example, the facial nerve (VII) has a sensory role in taste and a motor role in controlling facial expressions.

The traditional classification of these nerves as sensory, motor, or mixed may remain relevant for such purposes as board examinations and comparisons to other books. Therefore, in order to teach the traditional classification while reminding you that all but the first two of these nerves are actually mixed, this section will characterize such nerves as *predominantly* sensory or motor rather than implying that they are exclusively so. Nerves described here as *mixed* or *sensory* are agreed upon by all authorities to be mixed or purely sensory. Nerves described as predominantly motor or sensory are traditionally classified that way but contain some fibers of the other type.

### 14.6c Cranial Nerve Survey

The following pages survey the key characteristics of each of the 12 pairs of cranial nerves. For each nerve, we begin with a general description of its functions and any unique characteristics it may have; an illustration of its anatomical course; and remarks on the effects of damage to that nerve and how neurologists assess its functionality or deficits. At the end of the descriptive survey, you will find a summary table and illustration, as well as a helpful mnemonic for remembering the names of these nerves in anatomical order.

#### The Olfactory Nerve (CN I)

The olfactory nerve **(fig. 14.27)** is a purely sensory nerve for smell. It consists of several separate fascicles that pass independently through the cribriform plate of the ethmoid bone in the roof of the nasal cavity. It isn't visible on isolated brains because these fascicles are severed by removal of the brain from the skull, but on most such brains one can see the *olfactory bulbs* in which these nerves end.

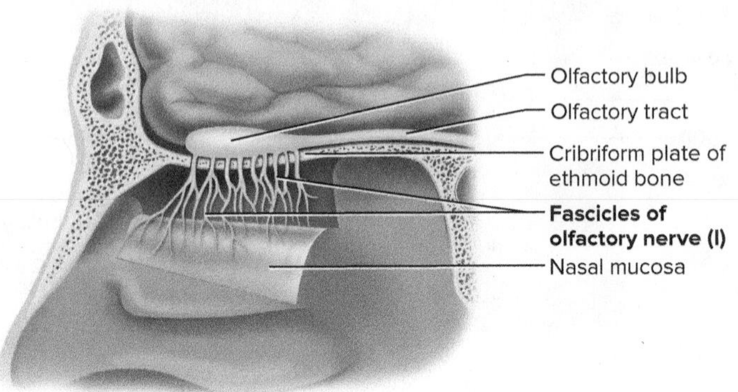


**FIGURE 14.27 The Olfactory Nerve (I).** APR

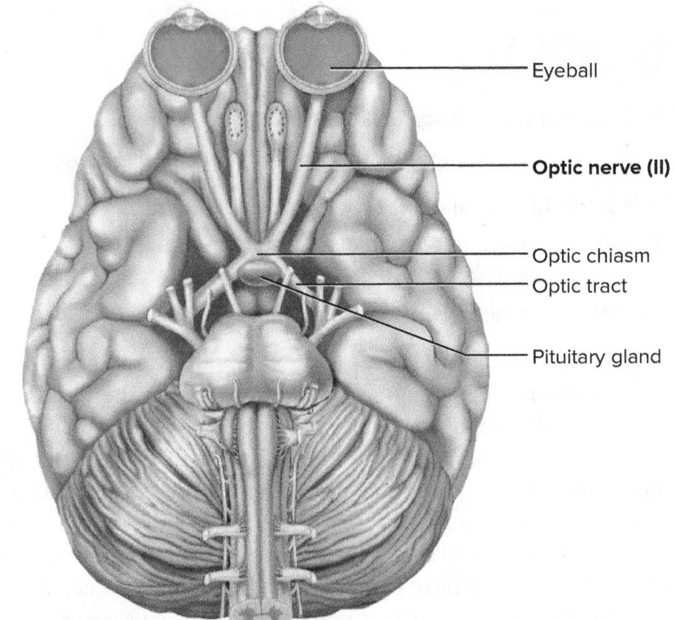


**FIGURE 14.28 The Optic Nerve (II).** APR

The olfactory nerve can be damaged by sharp blows to the face that break the ethmoid bone, such as a person might suffer in striking an automobile dashboard in a collision. Such damage can cause **anosmia,** loss of the sense of smell. This not only diminishes some of life's pleasures, but can also be dangerous if a person fails to detect smoke, a gas leak, or spoiled food. A clinical sign of olfactory nerve damage is that a patient cannot smell even such strongly aromatic substances as coffee, vanilla, clove oil, or soap.

#### The Optic Nerve (CN II)

Four of the 12 cranial nerves (II, III, IV, and VI) are concerned exclusively with the eyes. The only purely sensory nerve among these is the **optic nerve (fig. 14.28),** which carries all visual signals from the retina to the brain. Damage to this nerve causes blindness in part or all of the visual field in the affected eye. Part of the optic nerve, the optic disc, can be seen and assessed in an eye examination with an ophthalmoscope (see fig. 16.30). Optic nerve function is also assessed by tests of visual acuity and range of peripheral vision.

#### The Oculomotor Nerve (CN III)

The **oculomotor[56] nerve (fig. 14.29)** is predominantly motor. It controls four of the six muscles of eye movement (see fig. 16.25), which direct the gaze up, down, and medially. It also controls the *levator palpebrae superioris muscle* of the upper eyelid and the internal eye muscles of focusing and pupillary diameter.

Clinical signs of damage to this nerve include inability to move the eye in the aforesaid directions or to track a moving object, a drooping eyelid, a fixed and dilated pupil, unequal size and shape of the

[56]*oculo* = eye; *motor* = mover

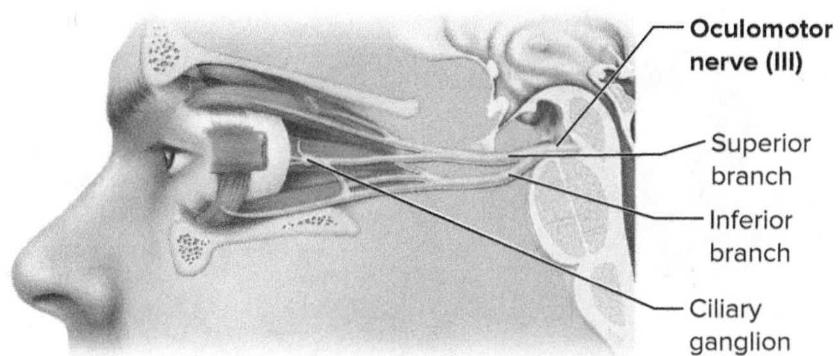


FIGURE 14.29 **The Oculomotor Nerve (III).** APR

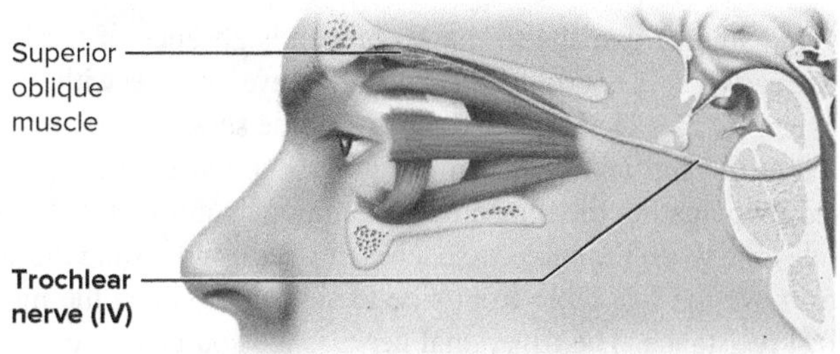


FIGURE 14.30 **The Trochlear Nerve (IV).** The tendon of the superior oblique muscle passes through a fibrous pulleylike sling, the trochlea (best seen in figure 16.25). APR

right and left pupils, lack of pupillary responses to light, double vision, difficulty focusing, and a tendency of the eye to rotate laterally at rest.

## The Trochlear Nerve (CN IV)

The **trochlear**[57] **nerve** (TROCK-lee-ur) **(fig. 14.30),** like the oculomotor, is a predominantly motor nerve for eye movement, but its only action is to direct the gaze slightly downward and rotate the top of the eyeball toward the nose, especially in compensating for head movements (see fig. 16.25). This is the only cranial nerve that arises from the posterior side of the brainstem. It is also unique in being the only one to completely decussate; the trochlear nerve roots cross each other within the brainstem before emerging from the surface, so the left trochlear nerve controls the right eye and vice versa.

Signs of trochlear nerve damage include double vision and a weak ability to look downward. The affected eye often points superolaterally and a patient tends to tuck in the chin and tilt the head downward to minimize the double vision. One assessment of trochlear nerve function is *Bielschowsky's head tilt test*—if the subject tilts the head toward one shoulder, the eye on that side shows an upward deviation.

## The Trigeminal Nerve (CN V)

The **trigeminal**[58] **nerve** (tri-JEM-ih-nul) is the largest of all cranial nerves and the most important sensory nerve of the face. Its name refers to the fact that it divides into three prominent branches shortly after leaving the brainstem—the *ophthalmic* ($V_1$), *maxillary* ($V_2$), and *mandibular* ($V_3$) *divisions* **(fig. 14.31a).** $V_1$ and $V_2$ are sensory nerves, whereas $V_3$ is mixed. Damage to one of these divisions results in loss of sensation from the respective region of the face **(fig. 14.31b).** Division $V_3$ also has a motor function in mastication **(fig. 14.31c),** which is impaired by damage to this branch.

[57]trochlea = pulley (for a loop through which the muscle's tendon passes)

[58]*tri* = three; *gem* = born (*trigem* = triplets)

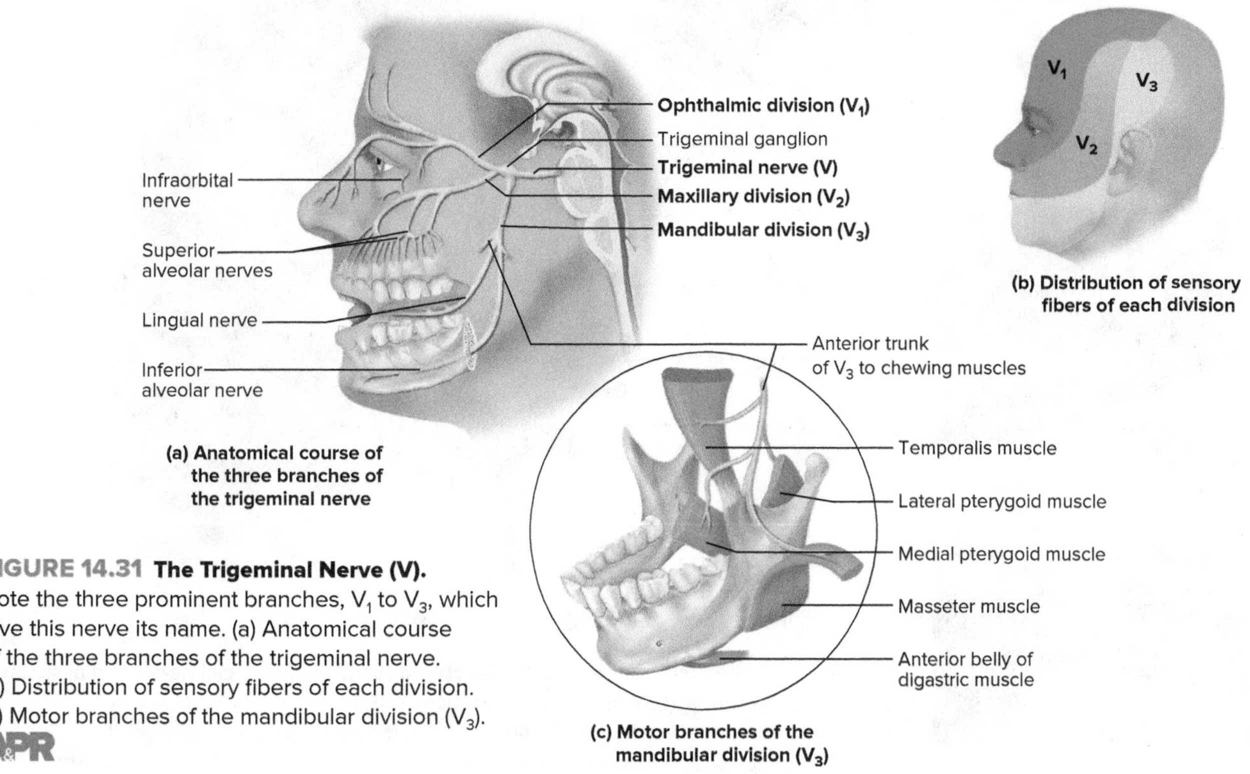


FIGURE 14.31 **The Trigeminal Nerve (V).** Note the three prominent branches, $V_1$ to $V_3$, which give this nerve its name. (a) Anatomical course of the three branches of the trigeminal nerve. (b) Distribution of sensory fibers of each division. (c) Motor branches of the mandibular division ($V_3$). APR

One sign of damage to the $V_1$ branch is absence of the blink reflex, as when a neurologist touches the eye surface with a cotton wisp. $V_2$ damage is marked by loss of the senses of touch, pain (tested with pinpricks), and temperature (hot and cold). $V_3$ is assessed by palpating the masseter and temporalis muscles to feel for muscle tone when the subject clenches the teeth, and testing the ability to move the mandible from side to side and to open the mouth against resistance. The trigeminal nerve is the source of a common pain disorder called *trigeminal neuralgia* (see Deeper Insight 14.4).

## The Abducens Nerve (CN VI)

The **abducens**[59] **nerve** (ab-DOO-senz) **(fig. 14.32),** like the oculomotor and trochlear, is also a predominantly motor nerve for eye movement. It controls a muscle, the *lateral rectus,* that directs the gaze laterally (see fig. 16.25). Damage to this nerve causes a medial deviation of the eye, as the medial rectus muscle is unopposed by the lateral rectus. Abducens nerve function is assessed by testing the subject's ability to direct the gaze laterally.

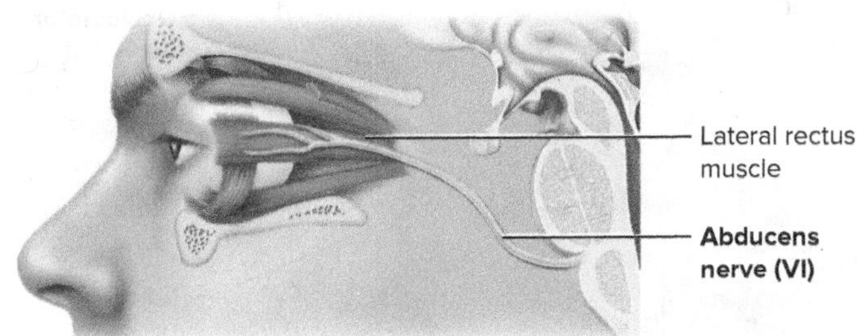


**FIGURE 14.32 The Abducens Nerve (VI).** By innervating the lateral rectus muscle, this nerve makes the eye turn away from the facial midline, as its name implies ("to turn away"). APR

## The Facial Nerve (CN VII)

The **facial nerve (fig. 14.33)** is the major motor nerve to the facial muscles (see table 10.1), but also contains sensory fibers from

[59]*ab* = away; *duc* = to lead or turn

Facial nerve (VII)
Geniculate ganglion
Pterygopalatine ganglion
Lacrimal (tear) gland
Chorda tympani branch (taste and salivation)
Submandibular ganglion
Sublingual gland
Parasympathetic fibers
Submandibular gland
Motor branch to muscles of facial expression
to (b)
(a)

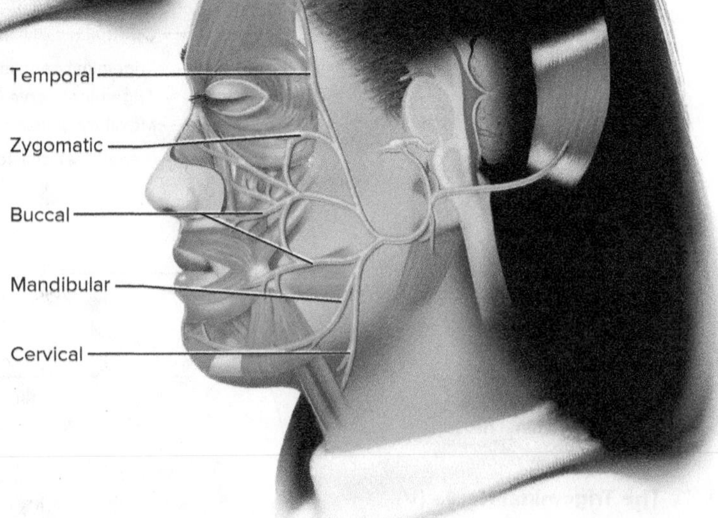

(b)

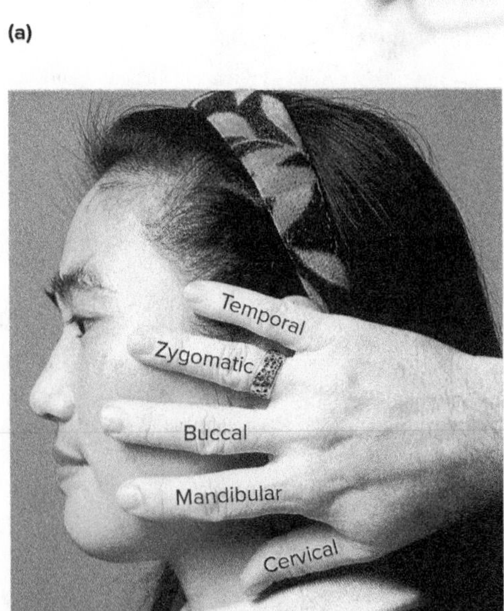

(c)

**FIGURE 14.33 The Facial Nerve (VII).** (a) The facial nerve and associated organs. (b) The five major branches of the facial nerve. (c) A way to remember the distribution of the five major branches. APR

c: Joe DeGrandis/McGraw-Hill Education

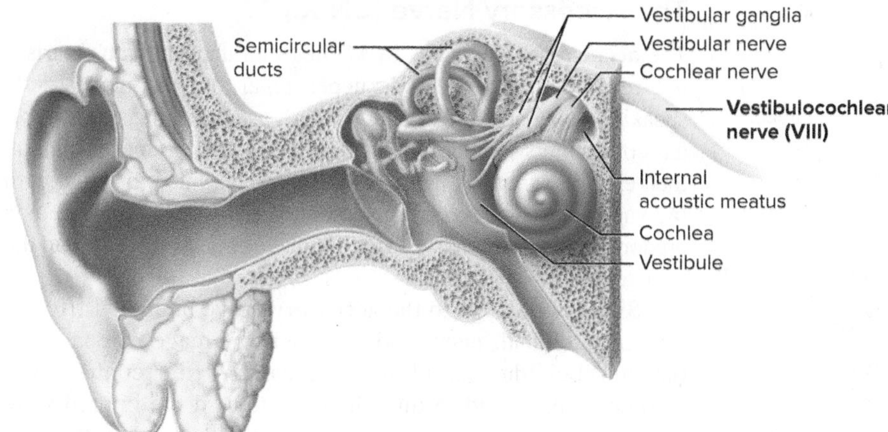


**FIGURE 14.34 The Vestibulocochlear Nerve (VIII).** Note how the nerve arises by convergence of the vestibular nerve and cochlear nerve, as its name implies. APR

taste buds of the anterior two-thirds of the tongue. It divides into five prominent branches: the *temporal, zygomatic, buccal, mandibular,* and *cervical branches.* Damage to the facial nerve can distort a person's sense of taste, especially for sweets, and cause sagging of facial muscles for lack of muscle tone (see Deeper Insight 14.4).

Motor functionality of the facial nerve is assessed by testing the subject's ability to smile, frown, whistle, raise the eyeballs, close the eyes, and perform other facial actions. Sensory function is assessed by testing sensitivity of the anterior tongue to substances such as sugar, salt, vinegar, and quinine, and testing the response of the tear glands to ammonia fumes.

## The Vestibulocochlear Nerve (CN VIII)

The **vestibulocochlear**[60] **nerve** (vess-TIB-you-lo-COC-lee-ur) **(fig. 14.34)** is a predominantly sensory nerve of hearing and equilibrium, but it also has a motor effect on the inner ear to tune the sense of hearing (see section 16.4c). It forms by convergence of the *cochlear nerve* from the cochlea and *vestibular nerve* from the semicircular ducts and vestibule of the inner ear. Damage to this nerve can cause *sensorineural deafness* (see Deeper Insight 16.3), dizziness, nausea, and *nystagmus* (involuntary rhythmic oscillations of the eyes from side to side). CN VIII function is assessed by looking for nystagmus and testing a patient's hearing, balance, and ability to walk a straight line.

## The Glossopharyngeal Nerve (CN IX)

The **glossopharyngeal**[61] **nerve** (GLOSS-oh-fah-RIN-jee-ul) **(fig. 14.35)** is a complex, mixed nerve with numerous sensory and motor functions in the head, neck, and thoracic region, including sensations from the tongue, throat, and outer ear; control of food intake; and even some aspects of cardiovascular and respiratory function. Signs of damage to this nerve include difficulty swallowing and loss of the bitter and sour taste sensations. It can be assessed by testing the rear of the tongue with bitter and sour substances, noting any speech impediments, and testing the gag reflex, swallowing, and coughing.

Glossopharyngeal nerve (IX)
Superior ganglion
Inferior ganglion
Otic ganglion
Parotid salivary gland
Carotid sinus
Pharyngeal muscles

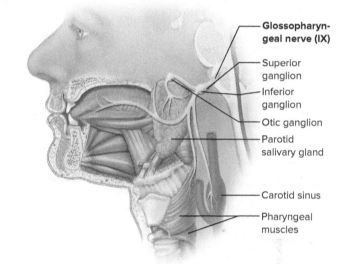

**FIGURE 14.35 The Glossopharyngeal Nerve (IX).** Note how the nerve branches go to the tongue and pharynx, as its name implies. APR

## The Vagus Nerve (CN X)

The **vagus**[62] **nerve** (VAY-gus) **(fig. 14.36)** has the most extensive distribution of all cranial nerves, supplying organs not only in the head and neck but also most viscera of the thoracic and abdominopelvic cavities. It is a mixed nerve with major roles in the control of cardiac, pulmonary, digestive, and urinary functions. It carries 90% of all the fibers of the parasympathetic nervous system (see chapter 15).

Damage to both vagus nerves (right and left) is generally fatal. Signs of damage to just one vagus nerve include impaired swallowing and gastrointestinal motility, and hoarseness or loss of the voice. Vagal function is assessed by examining movements of the palate during speech; observing hoarseness or weakness of the voice or the inability to cough forcibly; and checking for swallowing difficulty or absence of the gag reflex.

[60] *vestibulo* = entryway (vestibule of inner ear); *cochlea* = conch, snail (cochlea of ear)
[61] *glosso* = tongue; *pharyng* = throat
[62] *vag* = wandering

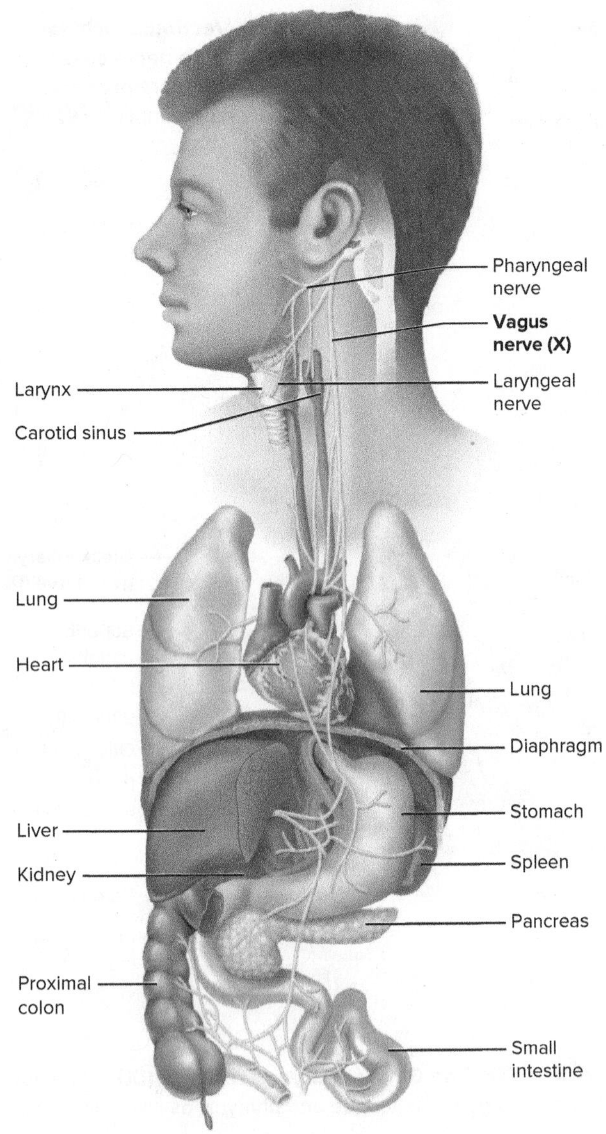


**FIGURE 14.36 The Vagus Nerve (X).** Note how this nerve "wanders" through much of the thoracic and abdominal cavities, as its name implies. APR

## The Accessory Nerve (CN XI)

The **accessory nerve (fig. 14.37)** takes an unusual path. It arises not from the brain but from the upper spinal cord; therefore, strictly speaking, it is not a true cranial nerve. It ascends alongside the spinal cord, enters the cranial cavity through the foramen magnum, then exits the cranium through the jugular foramen, bundled with the vagus and glossopharyngeal nerves. The accessory nerve is a predominantly motor nerve that controls mainly swallowing and the neck and shoulder muscles.

Signs of damage to the accessory nerve include difficulty moving the head, neck, and shoulders. Damage can paralyze the sternocleidomastoid muscle, causing the contralateral sternocleidomastoid to turn the head toward the injured side. Accessory nerve function can be assessed by testing the subject's ability to rotate the head and shrug the shoulders against resistance.

## The Hypoglossal Nerve (CN XII)

The **hypoglossal**[63] **nerve** (HY-po-GLOSS-ul) **(fig. 14.38)** is a predominantly motor nerve controlling tongue movements of speech, food manipulation, and swallowing. Injury to the hypoglossal nerve impairs speech and swallowing. Damage to one nerve may cause the tongue to atrophy on that side, and the tongue may deviate laterally when the subject is asked to protrude it. Damage to both may render a person unable to protrude the tongue against resistance from a tongue depressor.

## Cranial Nerve Learning Aid

Generations of biology and medical students have relied on mnemonic (memory-aiding) phrases and ditties, ranging from the sublimely silly to the unprintably ribald, to help them remember the cranial nerves. An old classic began, "On old Olympus' towering

[63]*hypo* = below; *gloss* = tongue

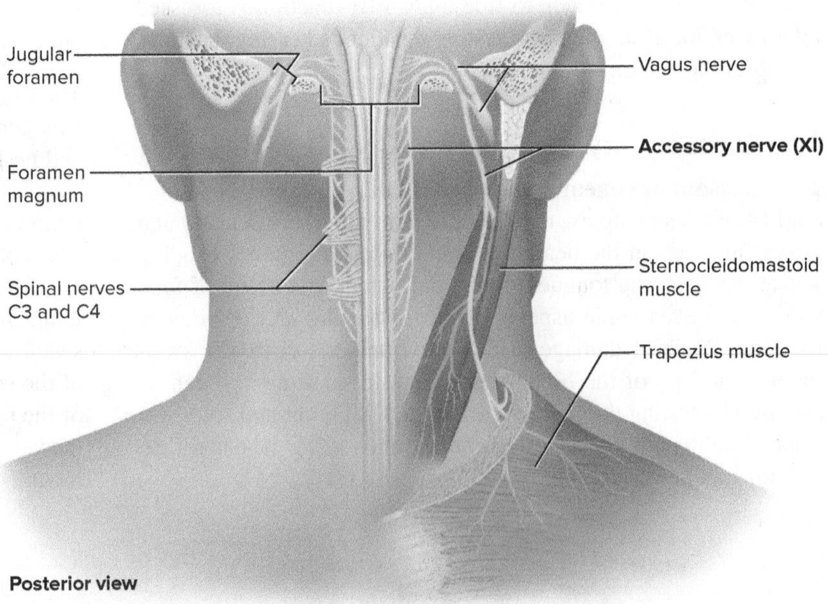

**FIGURE 14.37 The Accessory Nerve (XI).** This nerve used to be named the *spinal accessory,* referring to its origins in the spinal cord. APR

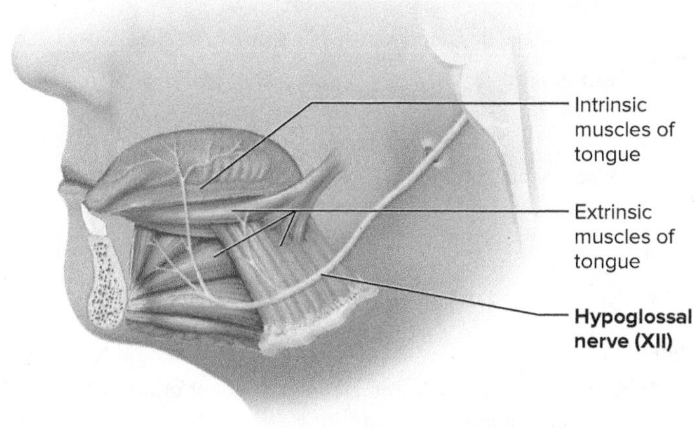


FIGURE 14.38 **The Hypoglossal Nerve (XII).** Note how this nerve approaches the tongue from below, as its name implies.

tops . . . ," with the first letter of each word matching the first letter of each cranial nerve (olfactory, optic, oculomotor, etc.). Some cranial nerves have changed names, however, since that mnemonic was invented. One of the author's former students, now a neurologist, devised the following "Old Opie" mnemonic that can remind you of the first two to four letters (indicated in boldface) of most cranial nerve names:

| | |
|---|---|
| **Old** | **ol**factory (I) |
| **Op**ie | **op**tic (II) |
| **oc**casionally | **oc**ulomotor (III) |
| **tr**ies | **tr**ochlear (IV) |
| **trig**onometry | **trig**eminal (V) |
| **a**nd | **a**bducens (VI) |
| **f**eels | **f**acial (VII) |
| **ve**ry | **ve**stibulocochlear (VIII) |
| **glo**omy, | **glo**ssopharyngeal (IX) |
| **vag**ue, | **vag**us (X) |
| **a**nd | **a**ccessory (XI) |
| **hypo**active. | **hypo**glossal (XII) |

**Table 14.1** summarizes the cranial nerves with respect to their sensory, motor, or mixed composition, functions, origin and termination, and cranial passages (mostly foramina) through which the nerves pass on their way to or from the peripheral organs. **Figure 14.40** reviews their locations on the base of the brain and their sensory and motor connections with the peripheral organs.

## DEEPER INSIGHT 14.4
### CLINICAL APPLICATION

### *Some Cranial Nerve Disorders*

*Trigeminal neuralgia*[64] *(tic douloureux*[65]*)* is a syndrome characterized by recurring episodes of intense stabbing pain on one side of the face, often compared to an electrical shock, with painless intervals between attacks. It is usually caused by a nearby blood vessel, but sometimes a tumor, putting pressure on the trigeminal nerve. It can be triggered by touch, toothbrushing, drinking, shaving, face washing, or even a breeze on the face. The pain lasts from a few seconds to a minute or two, but may strike up to 100 times a day; it can be so unbearable that it drove some sufferers to suicide before treatments became available. It affects women more often than men, and usually strikes after age 50. It can be treated with medications; vascular surgery to relieve pressure on the nerve; or gamma knife radiosurgery, which uses targeted gamma rays to deliberately injure a small spot on the nerve and stimulate a healing process.

*Bell*[66] *palsy* is a degenerative disorder of the facial nerve, probably due to the herpesvirus that causes cold sores. It is characterized by paralysis or weakness of the facial muscles on one side with resulting distortion of the facial features, such as sagging of the mouth or eyelid. **(fig. 14.39).** The paralysis may interfere with speech, prevent closure of the eye, and sometimes inhibit tear secretion, thus causing dry eyes. There may also be a partial loss of the sense of taste. Bell palsy may appear abruptly, sometimes overnight, and often disappears spontaneously within 3 to 5 weeks.

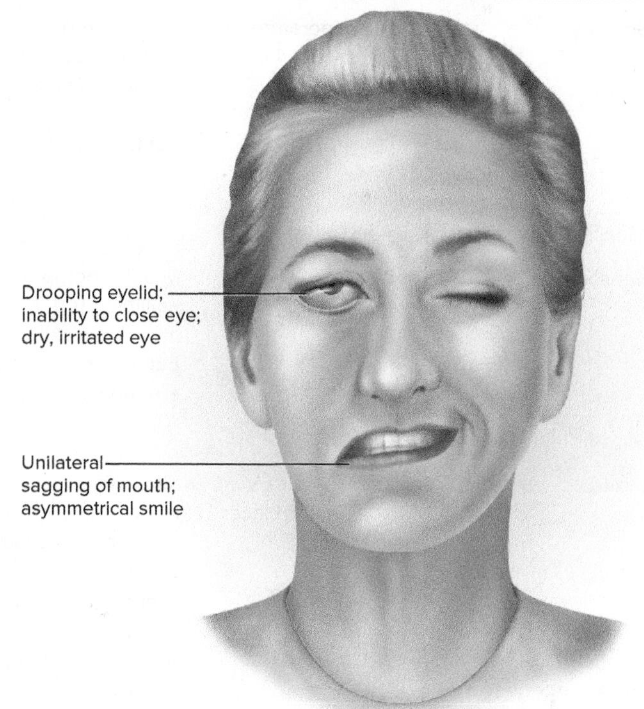


FIGURE 14.39 **Bell Palsy.** Signs of damage to the right facial nerve.

[64]*neur* = nerve; *algia* = pain
[65]*tic* = twitch, spasm; *douloureux* = painful (French)
[66]Sir Charles Bell (1774–1842), Scottish physician

**TABLE 14.1 The Cranial Nerves**

| Composition | Function | Origin | Termination | Cranial Passage |
|---|---|---|---|---|
| **I. Olfactory Nerve** | | | | |
| Sensory | Smell | Olfactory mucosa in nasal cavity | Olfactory bulbs | Cribriform foramina of ethmoid bone |
| **II. Optic Nerve** | | | | |
| Sensory | Vision | Retina | Thalamus and midbrain | Optic foramen |
| **III. Oculomotor Nerve** | | | | |
| Predominantly motor | Eye movements, opening of eyelid, pupillary constriction, focusing | Midbrain | Somatic fibers to levator palpebrae superioris; superior, medial, and inferior rectus muscles; and inferior oblique muscle of eye. Autonomic fibers enter eyeball and lead to constrictor of iris and ciliary muscle of lens. | Superior orbital fissure |
| **IV. Trochlear Nerve** | | | | |
| Predominantly motor | Eye movements | Midbrain | Superior oblique muscle of eye | Superior orbital fissure |
| **V. Trigeminal Nerve** | | | | |
| **Ophthalmic division ($V_1$)** | | | | |
| Sensory | Touch, temperature, and pain sensations from upper face | Superior region of face as illustrated; surface of eyeball; lacrimal (tear) gland; superior nasal mucosa; frontal and ethmoidal sinuses | Pons | Superior orbital fissure |
| **Maxillary division ($V_2$)** | | | | |
| Sensory | Same as $V_1$, lower on face | Middle region of face as illustrated; nasal mucosa; maxillary sinus; palate; upper teeth and gums | Pons | Foramen rotundum and infraorbital foramen |
| **Mandibular division ($V_3$)** | | | | |
| Mixed | *Sensory:* Same as $V_1$ and $V_2$, lower on face *Motor:* Mastication | *Sensory:* Inferior region of face as illustrated; anterior two-thirds of tongue (but not taste buds); lower teeth and gums; floor of mouth; dura mater *Motor:* Pons | *Sensory:* Pons *Motor:* Anterior belly of digastric; masseter, temporalis, mylohyoid, and pterygoid muscles; tensor tympani muscle of middle ear | Foramen ovale |
| **VI. Abducens Nerve** | | | | |
| Predominantly motor | Lateral eye movement | Inferior pons | Lateral rectus muscle of eye | Superior orbital fissure |

| TABLE 14.1 | The Cranial Nerves *(continued)* | | | |
|---|---|---|---|---|
| **VII. Facial Nerve** | | | | |
| Mixed | *Sensory:* Taste<br>*Motor:* Facial expression; secretion of tears, saliva, nasal and oral mucus | *Sensory:* Taste buds of anterior two-thirds of tongue<br>*Motor:* Pons | *Sensory:* Thalamus<br>*Motor:* Somatic fibers to digastric muscle, stapedius muscle of middle ear, stylohyoid muscle, muscles of facial expression. Autonomic fibers to submandibular and sublingual salivary glands, tear glands, nasal and palatine glands. | Internal acoustic meatus and stylomastoid foramen |
| **VIII. Vestibulocochlear Nerve** | | | | |
| Predominantly sensory | Hearing and equilibrium | *Sensory:* Cochlea, vestibule, and semicircular ducts of inner ear<br>*Motor:* Pons | *Sensory:* Fibers for hearing end in medulla; fibers for equilibrium end at junction of medulla and pons<br>*Motor:* Outer hair cells of cochlea of inner ear | Internal acoustic meatus |
| **IX. Glossopharyngeal Nerve** | | | | |
| Mixed | *Sensory:* Taste; touch, pressure, pain, and temperature sensations from tongue and outer ear; regulation of blood pressure and respiration<br>*Motor:* Salivation, swallowing, gagging | *Sensory:* Pharynx; middle and outer ear; posterior one-third of tongue (including taste buds); internal carotid artery<br>*Motor:* Medulla oblongata | *Sensory:* Medulla oblongata<br>*Motor:* Parotid salivary gland; glands of posterior tongue; stylopharyngeal muscle (which dilates pharynx during swallowing) | Jugular foramen |
| **X. Vagus Nerve** | | | | |
| Mixed | *Sensory:* Taste; sensations of hunger, fullness, and gastrointestinal discomfort<br>*Motor:* Swallowing, speech, deceleration of heart, bronchoconstriction, gastrointestinal secretion and motility | *Sensory:* Thoracic and abdominopelvic viscera, root of tongue, pharynx, larynx, epiglottis, outer ear, dura mater<br>*Motor:* Medulla oblongata | *Sensory:* Medulla oblongata<br>*Motor:* Tongue, palate, pharynx, larynx, lungs, heart, liver, spleen, digestive tract, kidney, ureter | Jugular foramen |
| **XI. Accessory Nerve** | | | | |
| Predominantly motor | Swallowing; head, neck, and shoulder movements | Spinal cord segments C1 to C6 | Palate, pharynx, trapezius and sternocleidomastoid muscles | Jugular foramen |
| **XII. Hypoglossal Nerve** | | | | |
| Predominantly motor | Tongue movements of speech, food manipulation, and swallowing | Medulla oblongata | Intrinsic and extrinsic muscles of tongue | Hypoglossal canal |

**FIGURE 14.40 Review of Cranial Nerve Pathways.** Pathways concerned with sensory function are shown in green, and those concerned with motor function in red. All cranial nerves except I and II carry sensory fibers, but these functions are omitted in cases where the nerve is essentially motor and its sensory function is limited to proprioception from the muscles.

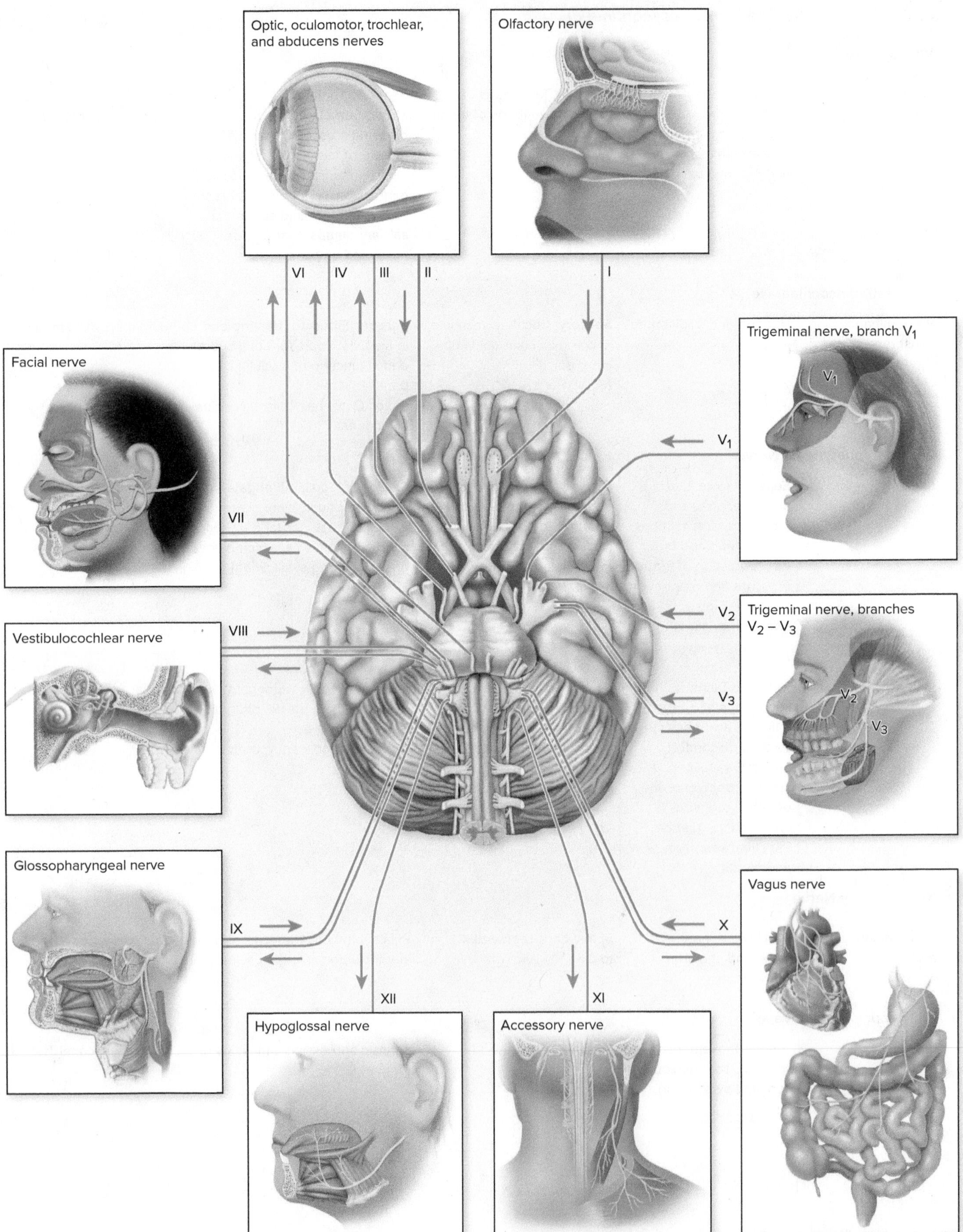

| TABLE 14.2 | Some Disorders Associated with the Brain and Cranial Nerves |
|---|---|
| Cerebral palsy | Muscular incoordination resulting from damage to the motor areas of the brain during fetal development, birth, or infancy; causes include prenatal rubella infection, drugs, or radiation exposure; oxygen deficiency during birth; and hydrocephalus |
| Concussion | Damage to the brain typically resulting from a blow, often with loss of consciousness, disturbances of vision or equilibrium, and short-term amnesia |
| Encephalitis | Inflammation of the brain, accompanied by fever, usually caused by mosquito-borne viruses or herpes simplex virus; causes neuronal degeneration and necrosis; can lead to delirium, seizures, and death |
| Epilepsy | Disorder causing sudden, massive discharge of neurons (seizures) resulting in motor convulsions, sensory and psychic disturbances, and often impaired consciousness; may result from congenital brain malformation birth trauma, later brain trauma, tumors, drug or alcohol abuse, or infections |
| Migraine headache | Recurring headaches often accompanied by nausea, vomiting, dizziness, and aversion to light, often triggered by such factors as weather changes, stress, hunger, red wine, or noise; more common in women and sometimes running in families |
| Schizophrenia | A thought disorder involving delusions, hallucinations, inappropriate emotional responses to situations, incoherent speech, and withdrawal from society, resulting from hereditary or developmental abnormalities in neural networks |

***You can find other brain and cranial nerve disorders described in the following places:***

*Hydrocephalus* in Deeper Insight 8.2; brain tumors in Deeper Insight 12.1; *multiple sclerosis* and *Tay-Sachs disease* in Deeper Insight 12.2; *Parkinson* and *Alzheimer diseases* in Deeper Insight 12.4; *Parkinson disease, Huntington disease,* and *cerebellar ataxia* in section 14.5g; *meningitis* in Deeper Insight 14.1; *stroke* in Deeper Insight 14.2; *amnesia* in section 14.5d; *aprosody* and *aphasia* in section 14.5h; and *trigeminal neuralgia* and *Bell palsy* in Deeper Insight 14.4.

Like a machine with a great number of moving parts, the nervous system is highly subject to malfunctions. **Table 14.2** lists a few well-known brain and cranial nerve dysfunctions. The effects of aging on the CNS are described in section 29.4a.

**BEFORE YOU GO ON**

Answer the following questions to test your understanding of the preceding section:

**25.** List the purely sensory cranial nerves and state the function of each.

**26.** What is the only cranial nerve to extend beyond the head–neck region?

**27.** If the oculomotor, trochlear, or abducens nerve was damaged, the effect would be similar in all three cases. What would that effect be?

**28.** Which cranial nerve carries sensory signals from the greatest area of the face?

**29.** Name two cranial nerves involved in the sense of taste and describe where their sensory fibers originate.

## DEEPER INSIGHT 14.5
### CLINICAL APPLICATION

### *Images of the Mind*

Enclosed as it is in the cranium, there is no easy way to observe a living brain directly. This has long frustrated neurobiologists, who once had to content themselves with glimpses of brain function afforded by electroencephalograms, patients with brain lesions, and patients who remained awake and conversant during brain surgery and consented to experimentation while the brain was exposed. Newer imaging methods, however, have yielded dramatic perspectives on brain function. Two of these—positron emission tomography (PET) and magnetic resonance imaging (MRI)—were explained in Deeper Insight 1.5. Both techniques rely on transient increases in blood flow to parts of the brain called into action to perform specific tasks. By monitoring these changes, neuroscientists can identify which parts of the brain are involved in specific tasks.

To produce a PET scan of the brain, the subject is given an injection of radioactively labeled glucose and a scan is made in a *control state* before any specific mental task is begun. Then the subject is given a task—for example, to read the word *car* and speak a verb related to it, such as *drive*. While the subject does so, new *task-state* scans are made. Neither control- nor task-state images are very revealing by themselves, but the computer subtracts the control-state data from the task-state data and presents a color-coded image of the difference.

In such images, the busiest areas of the brain "light up" on the computer screen from moment to moment as the task is performed **(fig. 14.41)**. This identifies the regions used for various stages of the task, such as reading the word, thinking of a verb to go with it, planning to say *drive*, and actually saying it. Among other things, such experiments demonstrate that the Broca and Wernicke areas aren't involved in simply repeating words; they are active, however, when a subject must evaluate a word and choose an appropriate response—that is, they function in formulating the new word the subject is going to say. PET scans also show that different neural pools take over a task as we practice and become more proficient at it.

*Functional magnetic resonance imaging (fMRI)* depends on the role of astrocytes in brain metabolism. The main excitatory neurotransmitter secreted by cerebral neurons is glutamate. After a neuron releases glutamate and stimulates the next neuron, astrocytes quickly remove it from the synapse and convert it to glutamine. Astrocytes acquire the energy for this from the anaerobic fermentation of glucose. High activity in an area of cortex thus requires an increased blood flow to supply this glucose, but it doesn't elevate oxygen consumption from that blood. Thus, the oxygen supply exceeds demand in that part of the brain, and blood leaving the region contains more oxygen than the blood leaving less active regions. Since the magnetic properties of hemoglobin depend on how much oxygen is bound to it, fMRI can detect changes in brain circulation.

fMRI is more precise than PET and pinpoints regions of brain activity with a precision of 1 to 2 mm. It also has the advantages of requiring no injected substances and no exposure to radioisotopes. While it takes about 1 minute to produce a PET scan, fMRI produces images much more quickly, which makes it more useful for determining how the brain responds immediately to sensory input or mental tasks.

Cutting-edge advances in PET and fMRI technology have enhanced our knowledge of shifting patterns of brain activity associated with attention and consciousness, sensory perception, memory, emotion, motor control, reading, speaking, musical judgment, planning a chess strategy, and so forth. In addition to their contribution to basic neuroscience, these techniques are highly valuable to neurosurgery and psychopharmacology. They have enhanced our understanding of dysfunctions such as depression, schizophrenia, and attention-deficit/hyperactivity disorder (ADHD). Such methods ushered in an exciting era of safe visualization of brain function, producing pictures of the mind at work.

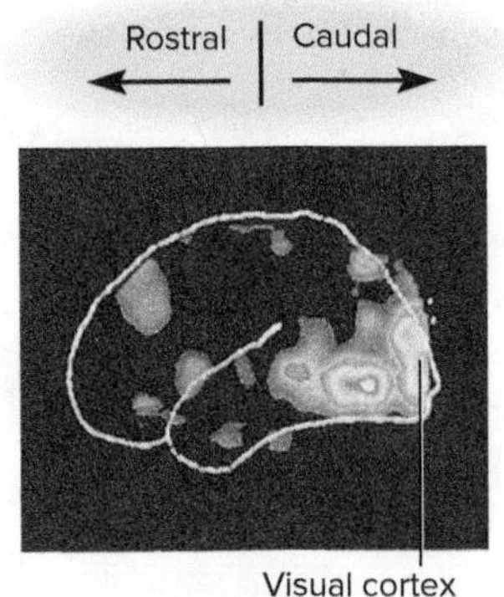


(1) The word *car* is seen in the visual cortex.

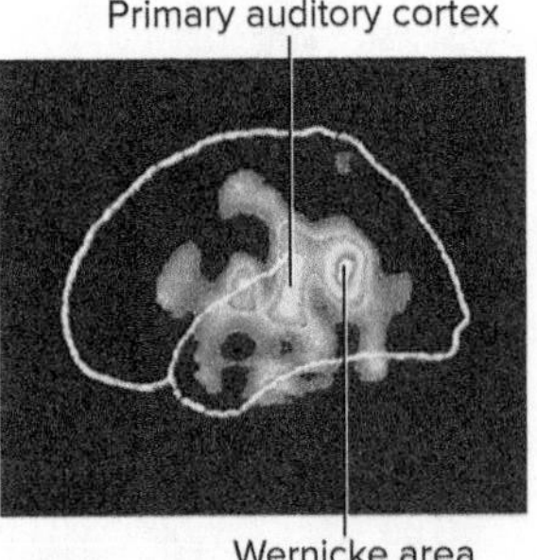


(2) Wernicke area conceives of the verb *drive* to go with it.

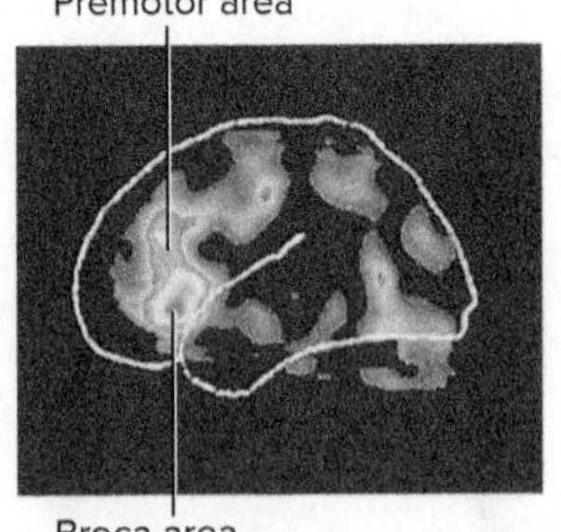


(3) Broca area compiles a motor program to speak the word *drive*.

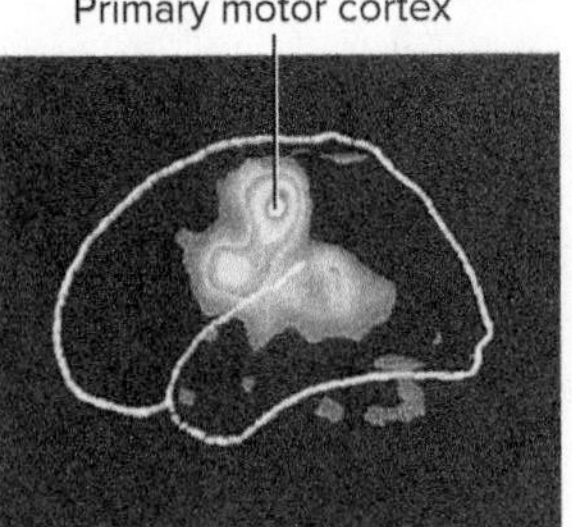


(4) The primary motor cortex executes the program and the word is spoken.

**FIGURE 14.41 PET Scans of the Brain Made During the Performance of a Language Task.** These images show the cortical regions that are active when a person reads words and then speaks them. The most active areas are shown in red and less active areas in blue.

(all): Courtesy Dr. Marcus E. Raichle, MD, Washington University School of Medicine

# STUDY GUIDE

## Assess Your Learning Outcomes

*To test your knowledge, discuss the following topics with a study partner or in writing, ideally from memory.*

### 14.1 Overview of the Brain

1. Typical mass of the adult brain
2. Meanings of the directional terms *rostral* and *caudal* in brain anatomy
3. Three principal divisions of the brain
4. Names of the tissue folds and shallow grooves in the cerebrum and cerebellum, and the names of the deep grooves between the two cerebral hemispheres and between the cerebrum and cerebellum
5. Locations of the gray and white matter in the cerebrum and cerebellum; the composition of gray and white matter and how this relates to their colors; and the meaning of *cortex, nucleus,* and *tract* in relation to brain gray and white matter
6. Embryonic development of the brain from neural plate to neural tube stage; differentiation into forebrain, midbrain, and hindbrain; development of the five embryonic brain vesicles; and the name and destiny of each vesicle

### 14.2 Meninges, Ventricles, Cerebrospinal Fluid, and Blood Supply

1. The three meninges of the brain; two subdivisions of the dura mater; and the relationship of the dural sinuses and subarachnoid space to the meninges
2. Ventricles of the brain, their names and locations, and the passages that connect them
3. The relationship of the ependymal cells and choroid plexuses to the brain ventricles and canals
4. The sources, flow, reabsorption, and functions of the cerebrospinal fluid (CSF)
5. The brain's demands for blood flow, glucose, and oxygen in relation to its percentage of the body weight
6. Structure and function of the blood–brain and blood–CSF barriers, and the clinical relevance of the brain barrier system
7. The locations, structural nature, function, and clinical relevance of circumventricular organs

### 14.3 The Hindbrain and Midbrain

1. The medulla oblongata: its location, gross anatomy, and general functions; which cranial nerves arise from it; and the specific functions of each of its tracts and nuclei
2. The pons: its location, gross anatomy, and functions; which cranial nerves arise from the pons and from the groove between pons and medulla; and its contributions to the anterolateral system and anterior spinocerebellar tract
3. The midbrain: its location, gross anatomy, and general functions; which cranial nerves arise from it; and the specific functions of its colliculi, substantia nigra, and central gray substance
4. How the reticular formation relates to the foregoing brainstem regions in location, structure, and functions
5. The cerebellum: its location, gross anatomy, unique neuron types, its three pairs of peduncles, and their relationship to cerebellar input and output
6. The classical view of cerebellar function and how this has lately expanded as a result of brain imaging studies and studies of people with cerebellar lesions

### 14.4 The Forebrain

1. The two major parts of the forebrain
2. Three principal parts of the diencephalon
3. Thalamic functions, location, and gross anatomy
4. Hypothalamic functions, location, gross anatomy, and anatomical and physiological relationships with the pituitary gland
5. The location, components, and functions of the epithalamus
6. Gross anatomy of the cerebral hemispheres, their five lobes, and the functions of each lobe
7. Three types of cerebral tracts and their defining anatomical and functional differences
8. Three locations of cerebral gray matter
9. The thickness, extent, and relative amount of tissue and number of neurons in the cerebral cortex
10. Two types of neurons in the cerebral cortex and their morphology
11. Evolutionary and structural distinctions between archicortex, paleocortex, and neocortex, and where each occurs in the human brain
12. The location, constituents, and functions of the limbic system
13. Names, locations, and functions of the basal nuclei

### 14.5 Integrative Functions of the Brain

1. Four kinds of brain waves in the EEG, the states in which each type normally dominates the EEG, and the clinical relevance of the EEG
2. Stages of sleep; physiological characteristics of each; roles of the hypothalamus, reticular formation, melatonin, and orexins in regulating the sleep cycle; and hypotheses on the functions of sleep
3. Association areas of the cerebral cortex; the involvement of some of these in cognitive function; and the contributions of brain injury patients and brain imaging methods to understanding the regional distribution of cognitive functions
4. Brain regions involved in memory; forms of amnesia
5. Brain regions involved in emotion, and insights into the neurobiology of emotion from brain trauma, ablation, and brain stimulation studies
6. Brain regions involved in the special and general senses
7. The functional relationship between primary sensory cortex and sensory association areas
8. Location of the postcentral gyrus; its somatosensory function; its somatotopy as charted in the sensory homunculus; and the effect of decussation on its function
9. Locations of the precentral gyrus and motor association area; their roles in motor control; the somatotopy of the gyrus as charted in the motor homunculus; and the effect of decussation on its function
10. Upper and lower motor neurons and the course of their axons
11. Roles of the basal nuclei and cerebellum in motor coordination and learned motor skills
12. Effects of Parkinson disease and basal nuclei lesions on motor control
13. Locations of the Wernicke and Broca areas; their roles in language; interaction of the Broca area and precentral gyrus in speech;

## STUDY GUIDE

and forms of aphasia and other language deficits resulting from damage to the language centers

14. Cerebral lateralization; functional differences between the categorical and representational hemispheres; and why it cannot be said that a particular function is necessarily "right-brained" or "left-brained"

**14.6 The Cranial Nerves**

1. Names and numbers of the 12 pairs of cranial nerves, and their relationships to the brainstem and skull foramina
2. Which cranial nerves are purely sensory, which are mixed, which have traditionally been regarded as motor, and why it is not entirely accurate to simply call them motor nerves
3. For each cranial nerve, its location, functions, origin, termination, and passage through the skull
4. Signs of damage to each cranial nerve, and clinical methods of testing for damage

## Testing Your Recall

*Answers in Appendix A*

1. Which of these is caudal to the hypothalamus?
   a. the thalamus
   b. the optic chiasm
   c. the cerebral aqueduct
   d. the pituitary gland
   e. the corpus callosum

2. If the telencephalon was removed from a 5-week-old embryo, which of the following structures would fail to develop in the fetus?
   a. cerebral hemispheres
   b. the thalamus
   c. the midbrain
   d. the medulla oblongata
   e. the spinal cord

3. The blood–CSF barrier is formed by
   a. blood capillaries.
   b. endothelial cells.
   c. protoplasmic astrocytes.
   d. oligodendrocytes.
   e. ependymal cells.

4. The pyramids of the medulla oblongata contain
   a. descending corticospinal fibers.
   b. commissural fibers.
   c. ascending spinocerebellar fibers.
   d. fibers going to and from the cerebellum.
   e. ascending spinothalamic fibers.

5. Which of the following does *not* receive any input from the eyes?
   a. the hypothalamus
   b. the frontal lobe
   c. the thalamus
   d. the occipital lobe
   e. the midbrain

6. While studying in a noisy cafeteria, you get sleepy and doze off for a few minutes. You awaken with a start and realize that all the cafeteria sounds have just "come back." While you were dozing, this auditory input was blocked from reaching your auditory cortex by
   a. the temporal lobe.
   b. the hypothalamus.
   c. the reticular activating system.
   d. the medulla oblongata.
   e. the vestibulocochlear nerve.

7. Because of a brain lesion, a certain patient never feels full, but eats so excessively that she now weighs nearly 270 kg (600 lb). The lesion is most likely in her
   a. hypothalamus.
   b. amygdala.
   c. hippocampus.
   d. basal nuclei.
   e. pons.

8. The ______ is most closely associated with the cerebellum in embryonic development and remains its primary source of input fibers throughout life.
   a. telencephalon
   b. thalamus
   c. midbrain
   d. pons
   e. medulla

9. Damage to the ______ nerve could result in defects of eye movement.
   a. optic
   b. vagus
   c. trigeminal
   d. facial
   e. abducens

10. All of the following *except* the ______ nerve begin or end in the orbit.
    a. optic
    b. oculomotor
    c. trochlear
    d. abducens
    e. accessory

11. The right and left cerebral hemispheres are connected to each other by a thick C-shaped bundle of fibers called the ______.

12. The brain has four chambers called ______ filled with ______ fluid.

13. On a sagittal plane, the cerebellar white matter exhibits a branching pattern called the ______.

14. The only cranial nerve with direct control over the lower digestive tract is the ______.

15. Cerebrospinal fluid is secreted partly by a mass of blood capillaries called the ______ in each ventricle.

16. The primary motor area of the cerebrum is the ______ gyrus of the frontal lobe.

17. A lesion in which lobe of the cerebrum is most likely to cause a radical alteration of the personality?

18. Areas of cerebral cortex that identify or interpret sensory information are called ______.

19. Linear, analytical, and verbal thinking occurs in the ______ hemisphere of the cerebrum, which is on the left in most people.

20. The motor pattern for speech is generated in an area of cortex called the ______ and then transmitted to the primary motor cortex to be carried out.

# STUDY GUIDE

## Building Your Medical Vocabulary

*Answers in Appendix A*

*State a meaning of each word element, and give a medical term from this chapter that uses it or a slight variation of it.*

1. -algia
2. cephalo-
3. cerebro-
4. corpo-
5. encephalo-
6. -gram
7. insulo-
8. oculo-
9. trochle-
10. -uncle

## What's Wrong with These Statements?

*Answers in Appendix A*

*Briefly explain why each of the following statements is false, or reword it to make it true.*

1. Eye movements are controlled mainly by the optic nerve and oculomotor nerve.
2. The cerebral hemispheres would fail to develop if the neural crests of the embryo were destroyed.
3. The midbrain is caudal to the pons.
4. The Broca area is contralateral to the Wernicke area.
5. Most of the cerebrospinal fluid is produced by the choroid plexuses.
6. Hearing is a function of the occipital lobe.
7. Respiration is controlled by nuclei in the hypothalamus.
8. The facial nerve carries sensory signals from a larger area of the face than any other cranial nerve does.
9. All cranial nerves innervate organs of the head–neck region.
10. Most of the brain's neurons are found in the cerebral cortex.

## Testing Your Comprehension

1. Which cranial nerve conveys pain signals to the brain in each of the following situations? (a) Sand blows into your eye; (b) you bite the back of your tongue; and (c) your stomach hurts from eating too much.
2. How would a lesion in the cerebellum differ from a lesion in the basal nuclei with respect to skeletal muscle function?
3. Suppose that a neuroanatomist performed two experiments on an animal with the same basic brainstem structure as a human's: In experiment 1, he selectively transected (cut across) the pyramids on the anterior side of the medulla oblongata; and in experiment 2, he selectively transected the gracile and cuneate fasciculi on the posterior side. How would the outcomes of the two experiments differ?
4. A person can survive destruction of an entire cerebral hemisphere but cannot survive destruction of the hypothalamus, which is a much smaller mass of brain tissue. Explain this difference and describe some ways that destruction of a cerebral hemisphere could affect one's quality of life.
5. What would be the most obvious effects of lesions that destroyed each of the following: (a) the hippocampus, (b) the amygdala, (c) the Broca area, (d) the occipital lobe, and (e) the hypoglossal nerve?

CHAPTER

# 15

# THE AUTONOMIC NERVOUS SYSTEM AND VISCERAL REFLEXES

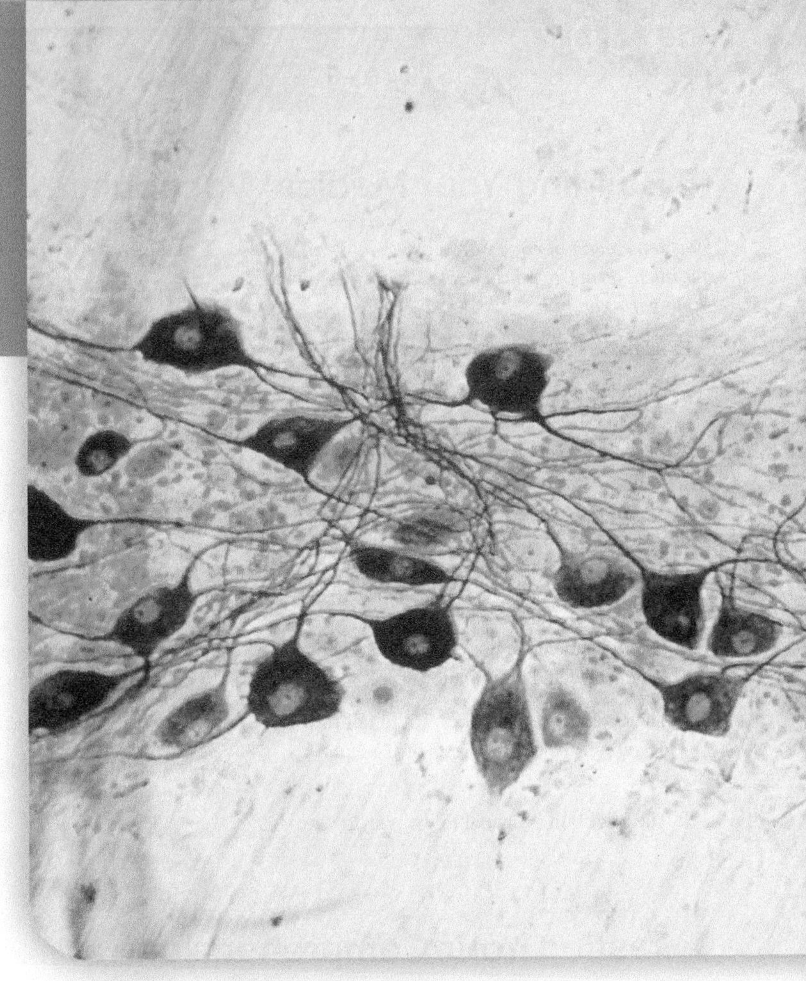

**Autonomic neurons in the enteric nervous system of the digestive tract**

Biophoto Associates/Science Source

## CHAPTER OUTLINE



## DEEPER INSIGHTS

**Module 7: Nervous System**

**BRUSHING UP**

- The function of the autonomic nervous system is heavily grounded in the concepts of negative feedback and homeostasis (see section 1.6c).
- Figure 12.2 provides a helpful perspective on how the autonomic nervous system (ANS) fits into the scheme of the nervous system as a whole.
- It is important that you clearly understand neurotransmitters and receptors and why neurotransmitters can have either excitatory or inhibitory effects on different target cells (see sections 12.5c, 12.5d).
- Many effects of the ANS are carried out by smooth muscle. The innervation of smooth muscle will help in understanding the effects described in this chapter (see section 11.7b).
- You should be familiar with the anatomy and functions of the hypothalamus, a highly important autonomic integrating center (see section 14.4a).
- Autonomic signals travel to their target organs by way of the spinal nerves described in section 13.2b and cranial nerves III, VII, IX, and X, detailed in section 14.6c.

We are consciously aware of many of the activities of our nervous system discussed in the preceding chapters—the general and special senses, our cognitive processes and emotions, and our voluntary movements. But there is another branch of the nervous system that operates in comparative secrecy, usually without our willing it, thinking about it, or even being able to consciously modify or suppress it.

This secretive agent is called the *autonomic nervous system (ANS).* Its name means "self-governed," as it is almost fully independent of our will. Its job is to regulate such fundamental states and life processes as heart rate, blood pressure, body temperature, respiratory airflow, pupillary diameter, digestion, energy metabolism, defecation, urination, and sexual functions. In short, the ANS quietly manages a multitude of involuntary processes responsible for the body's homeostasis.

Walter Cannon (1871–1945), the American physiologist who coined such expressions as *homeostasis* and the *fight-or-flight reaction,* dedicated his career to the study of the autonomic nervous system. He found that an animal can live without a functional sympathetic nervous system (one of the two divisions of the ANS), but it must be kept warm and free of stress. It cannot regulate its body temperature, tolerate any strenuous exertion, or survive on its own. Indeed, the ANS is more necessary for survival than are many functions of the somatic nervous system; an absence of autonomic function is fatal because the body can't maintain homeostasis without it. Thus, for an understanding of bodily function, the mode of action of many drugs, and other aspects of health care, we must be especially aware of how the ANS works.

## 15.1 General Properties of the Autonomic Nervous System

**Expected Learning Outcomes**

When you have completed this section, you should be able to

a. explain how the autonomic and somatic nervous systems differ in form and function; and
b. explain how the two divisions of the autonomic nervous system differ in general function.

The **autonomic**[1] **nervous system (ANS)** can be narrowly defined as a motor nervous system that controls glands, cardiac muscle, and smooth muscle. It is also called the **visceral motor system** to distinguish it from the somatic motor system that controls the skeletal muscles. The primary target organs of the ANS are viscera of the thoracic and abdominopelvic cavities and some structures of the body wall, including cutaneous blood vessels, sweat glands, and arrector muscles (arrector pili) of the hairs.

The ANS usually carries out its actions involuntarily, without our intent or awareness, in contrast to the voluntary nature of the somatic motor system. This voluntary–involuntary distinction is not, however, as clear-cut as it may seem. Some skeletal muscle responses are quite involuntary, such as the somatic reflexes, and some muscles are difficult or impossible to control, such as the middle-ear muscles. On the other hand, therapeutic uses of biofeedback have shown that some people can learn to voluntarily control such visceral functions as blood pressure and heart rate.

Visceral effectors don't depend on the autonomic nervous system to function, but only to adjust their activity to the body's changing needs. The heart, for example, goes on beating even if all the nerves to it are severed, but the ANS normally modulates the heart rate in conditions of rest or exercise. If the somatic nerves to a skeletal muscle are severed, the muscle exhibits flaccid paralysis—it no longer functions. But if the autonomic nerves to cardiac or smooth muscle are severed, the muscle exhibits exaggerated responses *(denervation hypersensitivity).*

### 15.1a Visceral Reflexes

The ANS is responsible for the body's **visceral**[2] **reflexes**—unconscious, automatic, stereotyped responses to stimulation, much like the somatic reflexes discussed in section 13.3, but involving visceral receptors and effectors and slower responses. Some authorities regard the visceral afferent (sensory) pathways as part of the ANS, but most prefer to limit the term *ANS* to the efferent (motor) pathways. Regardless of this preference, however, autonomic activity involves a visceral reflex arc that includes (1) **receptors** (nerve endings that detect stretch, tissue damage, blood chemistry, body

[1] *auto* = self; *nom* = rule (self-governed)
[2] *viscero* = internal organs

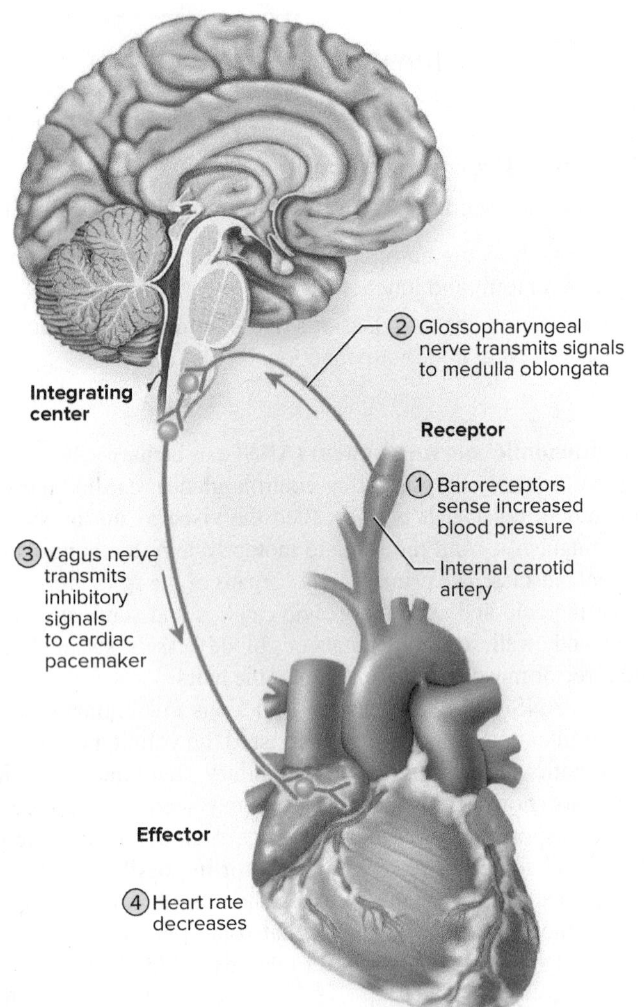

② Glossopharyngeal nerve transmits signals to medulla oblongata
Integrating center
Receptor
① Baroreceptors sense increased blood pressure
Internal carotid artery
③ Vagus nerve transmits inhibitory signals to cardiac pacemaker
Effector
④ Heart rate decreases

**FIGURE 15.1 An Autonomic Reflex Arc.** This pathway produces the baroreflex, which compensates for blood pressure fluctuations in arteries above the heart.

temperature, and other internal stimuli), (2) **afferent neurons** leading to (3) an **integrating center** and interneurons in the CNS, (4) **efferent neurons** carrying motor signals away from the CNS, and finally (5) an **effector** that carries out the end response.

For example, high blood pressure activates a visceral *baroreflex.*[3] It stimulates stretch receptors called *baroreceptors* in the internal carotid arteries and aorta, and they transmit signals via the glossopharyngeal nerves to the brainstem **(fig. 15.1).** The medulla integrates this with other information and transmits signals back to the heart by way of the vagus nerves. The vagus nerves slow down the heart and reduce blood pressure, thus completing a homeostatic negative feedback loop. A separate autonomic reflex accelerates the heart when blood pressure drops below normal—for example, when we move from a reclining to a standing position and gravity draws blood away from the upper body (see fig. 1.8).

[3]*baro* = pressure

## 15.1b Divisions of the Autonomic Nervous System

The ANS has two subsystems: sympathetic and parasympathetic. They differ in anatomy and function, but often innervate the same target organs and may have cooperative or contrasting effects on them. The **sympathetic division** adapts the body in many ways for physical activity—it increases alertness, heart rate, blood pressure, pulmonary airflow, blood glucose concentration, and blood flow to cardiac and skeletal muscle, but at the same time, it reduces blood flow to the skin and digestive tract. Cannon referred to extreme sympathetic responses as the *fight-or-flight reaction* because it comes into play when an animal must attack, defend itself, or flee from danger. In our own lives, this reaction occurs in situations involving arousal, exercise, competition, stress, danger, trauma, anger, or fear. Ordinarily, however, the sympathetic division has more subtle effects that we notice barely, if at all.

The **parasympathetic division,** by comparison, has a calming effect on many body functions. It is associated with reduced energy expenditure and normal bodily maintenance, including such functions as digestion and waste elimination. This is often called the *resting-and-digesting state.*

This does not mean that the body alternates between states where one system or the other is active. Normally, both systems are active simultaneously. They exhibit a background rate of activity called **autonomic tone,** and the balance between *sympathetic tone* and *parasympathetic tone* shifts in accordance with the body's changing needs. Parasympathetic tone, for example, maintains smooth muscle tone in the intestines and holds the resting heart rate down to about 70 to 80 beats/min. If the parasympathetic vagus nerves to the heart are cut, the heart beats at its own intrinsic rate of about 100 beats/min. Sympathetic tone keeps most blood vessels partially constricted and thus maintains blood pressure. A loss of sympathetic tone can cause such a rapid drop in blood pressure that a person goes into shock and may faint.

Neither division has universally excitatory nor inhibitory effects. The sympathetic division, for example, excites the heart but inhibits digestive and urinary functions, whereas the parasympathetic division has the opposite effects. We will later examine how differences in neurotransmitters and receptors account for these differences of effect.

## 15.1c Autonomic Output Pathways

Although usually defined only as part of the peripheral nervous system, the ANS has components in both the CNS and PNS. It includes control nuclei in the hypothalamus and other regions of the brainstem, motor neurons in the spinal cord and peripheral ganglia, and nerve fibers that travel through the cranial and spinal nerves you have already studied.

The autonomic motor pathway to a target organ differs significantly from somatic motor pathways. In somatic pathways, a motor neuron in the brainstem or spinal cord issues a myelinated axon that reaches all the way to a skeletal muscle. In autonomic pathways, the signal travels across *two* nerve fibers to get to the target organ, and it must cross a synapse where these two neurons meet in an autonomic ganglion **(fig. 15.2).** The first fiber is called the **preganglionic fiber.** It begins with a neurosoma in the brainstem or spinal cord. Its axon

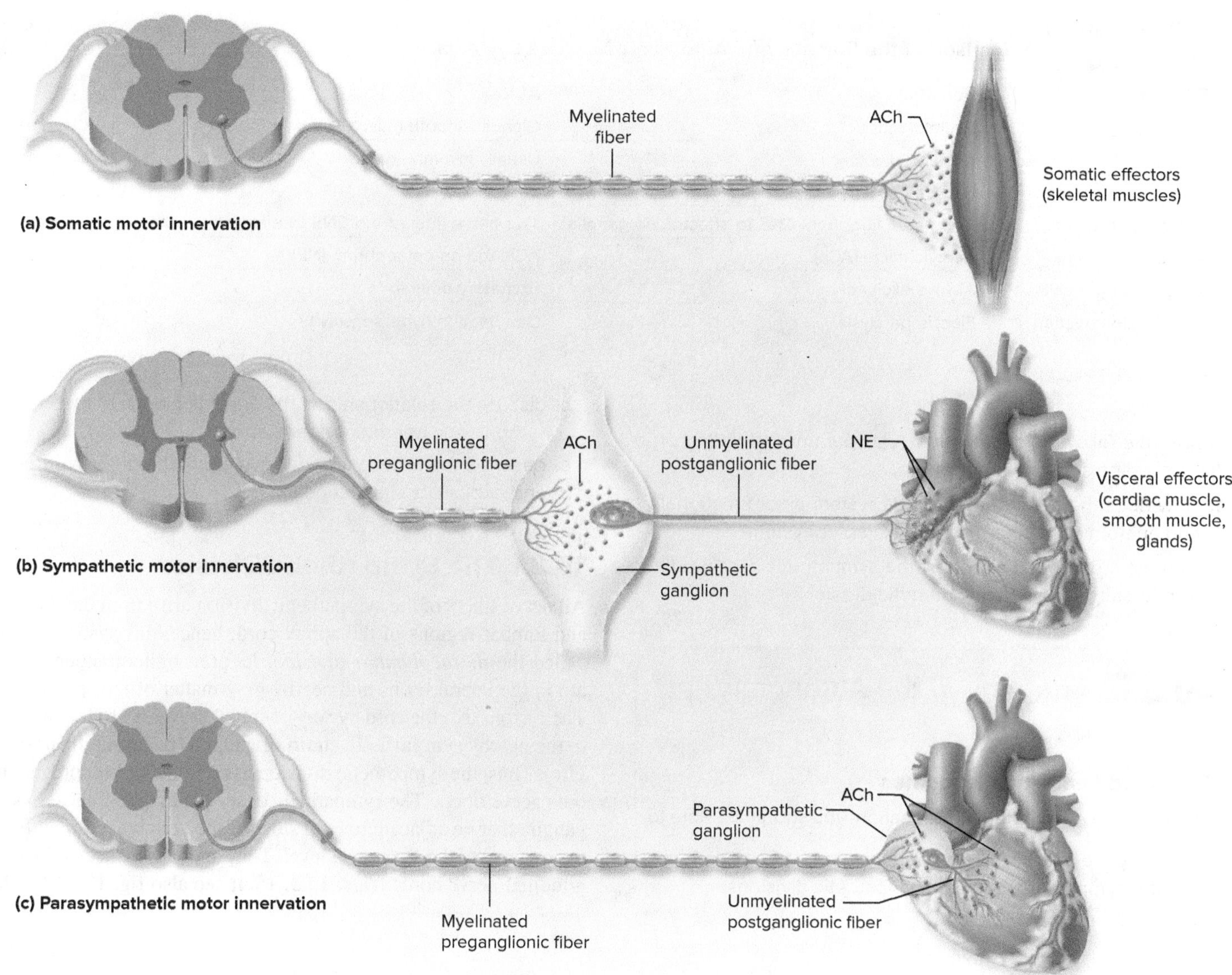


**FIGURE 15.2 Comparison of Somatic and Autonomic Efferent Pathways.** (a) In the somatic nervous system, each motor nerve fiber extends all the way from the CNS to a skeletal muscle. (b) In the sympathetic nervous system, a short preganglionic fiber extends from the spinal cord to a sympathetic ganglion usually near the vertebral column. A longer postganglionic fiber extends from there to the target organ. (c) In the parasympathetic nervous system, a long preganglionic fiber extends from the CNS to a ganglion in or near the target organ, and a short postganglionic fiber completes the path to specific effector cells in that organ (smooth or cardiac muscle or glands). (ACh = acetylcholine; NE = norepinephrine)

extends from there to an autonomic ganglion somewhere outside the CNS—often in a chain near the vertebral column or located in or near the target organ. Here, it meets the second neuron and secretes the neurotransmitter acetylcholine (ACh) to stimulate it. The axon from the second neuron, called the **postganglionic fiber,** leaves the ganglion and extends the rest of the way to the target organ or cells. Depending on the fiber type, it secretes either ACh or norepinephrine (NE). Autonomic preganglionic fibers are myelinated and the postganglionic fibers are unmyelinated. In contrast to somatic motor neurons, postganglionic fibers of the ANS don't usually synapse with a specific target cell, but end in a beadlike chain of varicosities that diffusely release neurotransmitter into the tissue and stimulate many cells simultaneously (see section 11.7b and fig. 11.21).

In summary, the autonomic nervous system is a division of the nervous system responsible for homeostasis, acting through mostly unconscious and involuntary control of glands, smooth muscle, and cardiac muscle. Its target organs are mainly thoracic and abdominopelvic viscera, but also include some cutaneous and other effectors. It acts through motor pathways that involve two nerve fibers, preganglionic and postganglionic, reaching from CNS to effector. The ANS has two divisions, sympathetic and parasympathetic, that often have cooperative or contrasting effects on the same target organ. Both divisions have excitatory effects on some target cells and inhibitory effects on others. These and other differences between the somatic and autonomic nervous systems are summarized in **table 15.1.**

**TABLE 15.1 Comparison of the Somatic and Autonomic Nervous Systems**

| Feature | Somatic | Autonomic |
|---|---|---|
| Effectors | Skeletal muscle | Glands, smooth muscle, cardiac muscle |
| Control | Usually voluntary | Usually involuntary |
| Distal nerve endings | Neuromuscular junctions | Varicosities |
| Efferent pathways | One nerve fiber from CNS to effector; no ganglia | Two nerve fibers from CNS to effector; synapse at a ganglion |
| Neurotransmitters | Acetylcholine (ACh) | ACh and norepinephrine (NE) |
| Effect on target cells | Always excitatory | Excitatory or inhibitory |
| Effect of denervation | Flaccid paralysis | Denervation hypersensitivity |

**BEFORE YOU GO ON**

Answer the following questions to test your understanding of the preceding section:

1. How does the autonomic nervous system differ functionally and anatomically from the somatic motor system?
2. How do the general effects of the sympathetic division differ from those of the parasympathetic division?

## 15.2 Anatomy of the Autonomic Nervous System

### Expected Learning Outcomes

When you have completed this section, you should be able to

a. identify the anatomical components and nerve pathways of the sympathetic and parasympathetic divisions;

b. discuss the relationship of the adrenal glands to the sympathetic nervous system; and

c. describe the enteric nervous system of the digestive tract and explain its significance.

### 15.2a The Sympathetic Division

All nerve fibers of the sympathetic division arise from the thoracic and lumbar regions of the spinal cord; hence, this system is also called the *thoracolumbar division.* Its preganglionic neurosomas are in the lateral horns and nearby gray matter of the spinal cord. Their axons exit the cord by way of spinal nerves T1 to L2 and lead to the nearby **sympathetic chain** of ganglia **(paravertebral**[4] **ganglia).** Thus, the sympathetic division has relatively short preganglionic nerve fibers. The sympathetic chain is a longitudinal series of ganglia that lie adjacent to both sides of the vertebral column from the cervical to the coccygeal level. They are interconnected by longitudinal nerve cords (**figs. 15.3, 15.4;** see also fig. 13.14 for the

[4] *para* = next to; *vertebr* = vertebral column

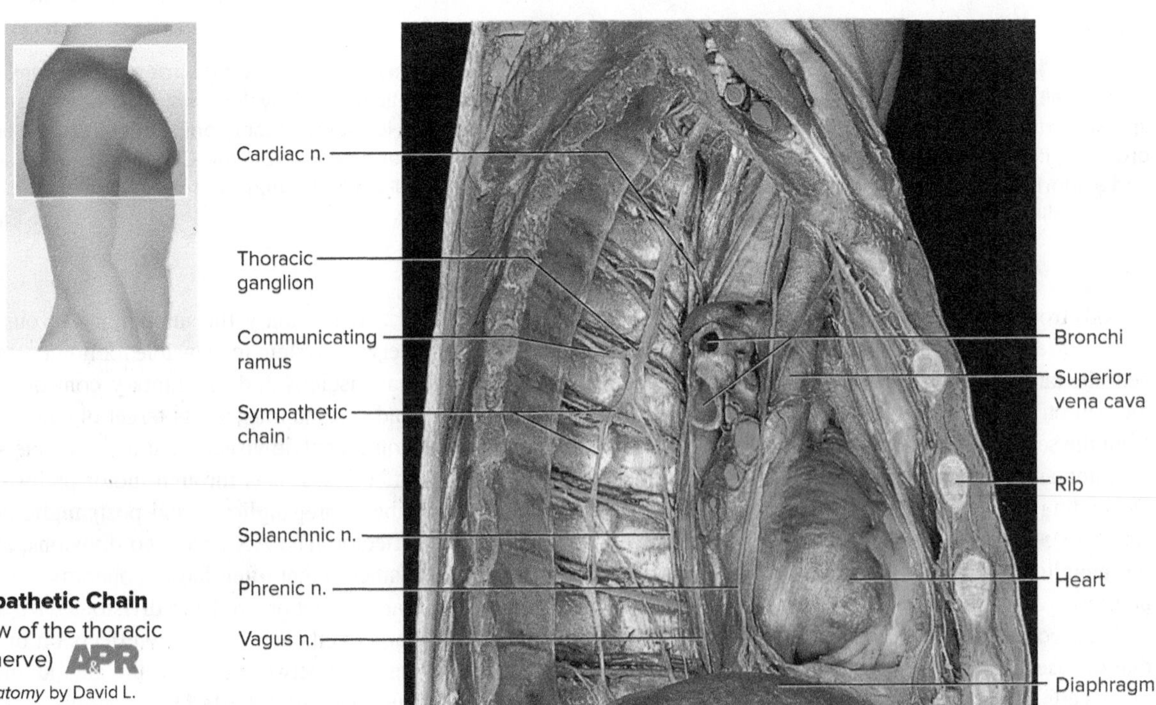


**FIGURE 15.3 The Sympathetic Chain Ganglia.** Right lateral view of the thoracic cavity of a cadaver. (n. = nerve) APR

From *A Stereoscopic Atlas of Anatomy* by David L. Bassett. Courtesy of Dr. Robert A. Chase, M.D.

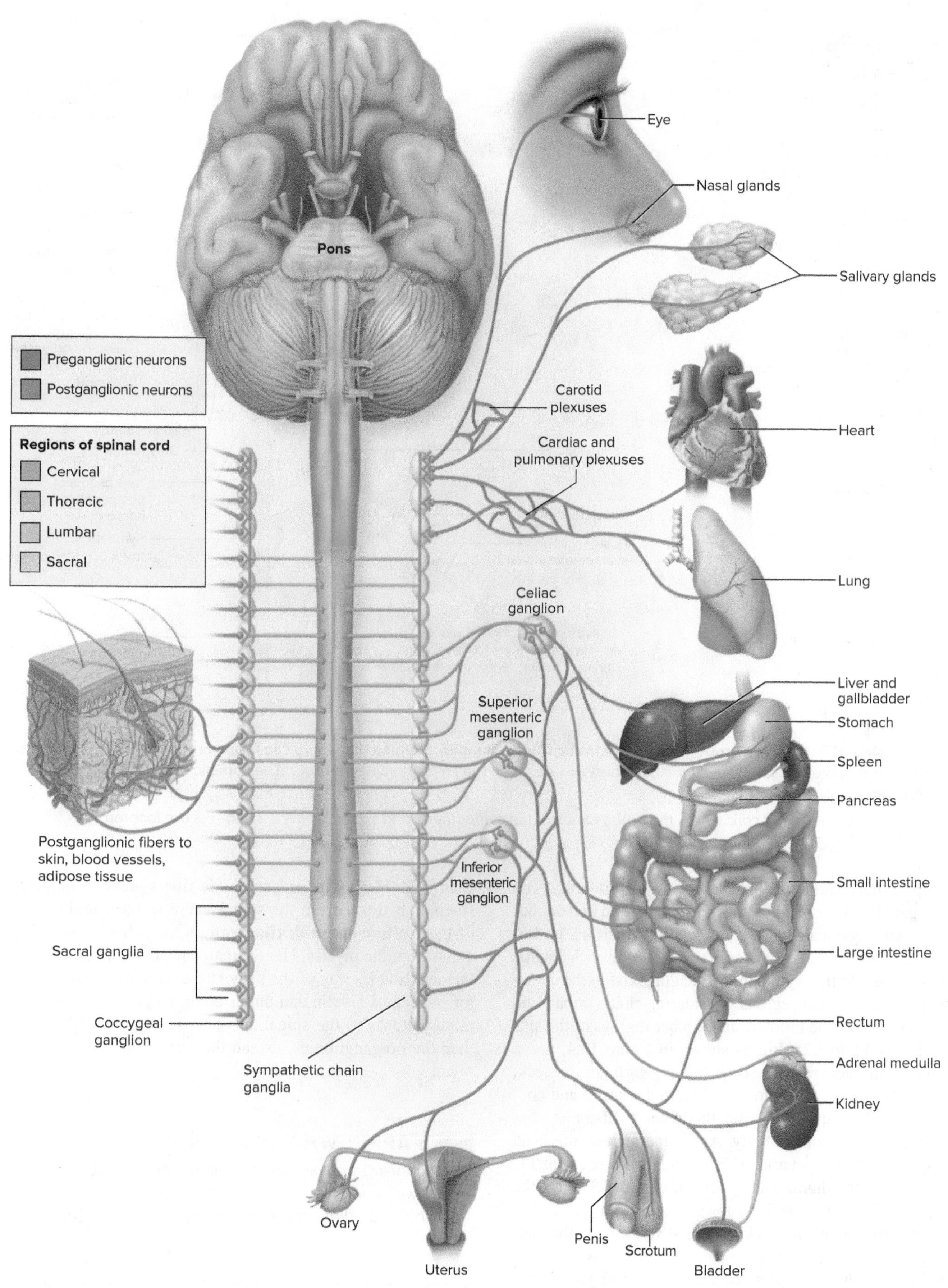


**FIGURE 15.4 Schematic of the Sympathetic Nervous System.** APR

? *Does the sympathetic innervation of the lungs make a person inhale and exhale? Explain.*

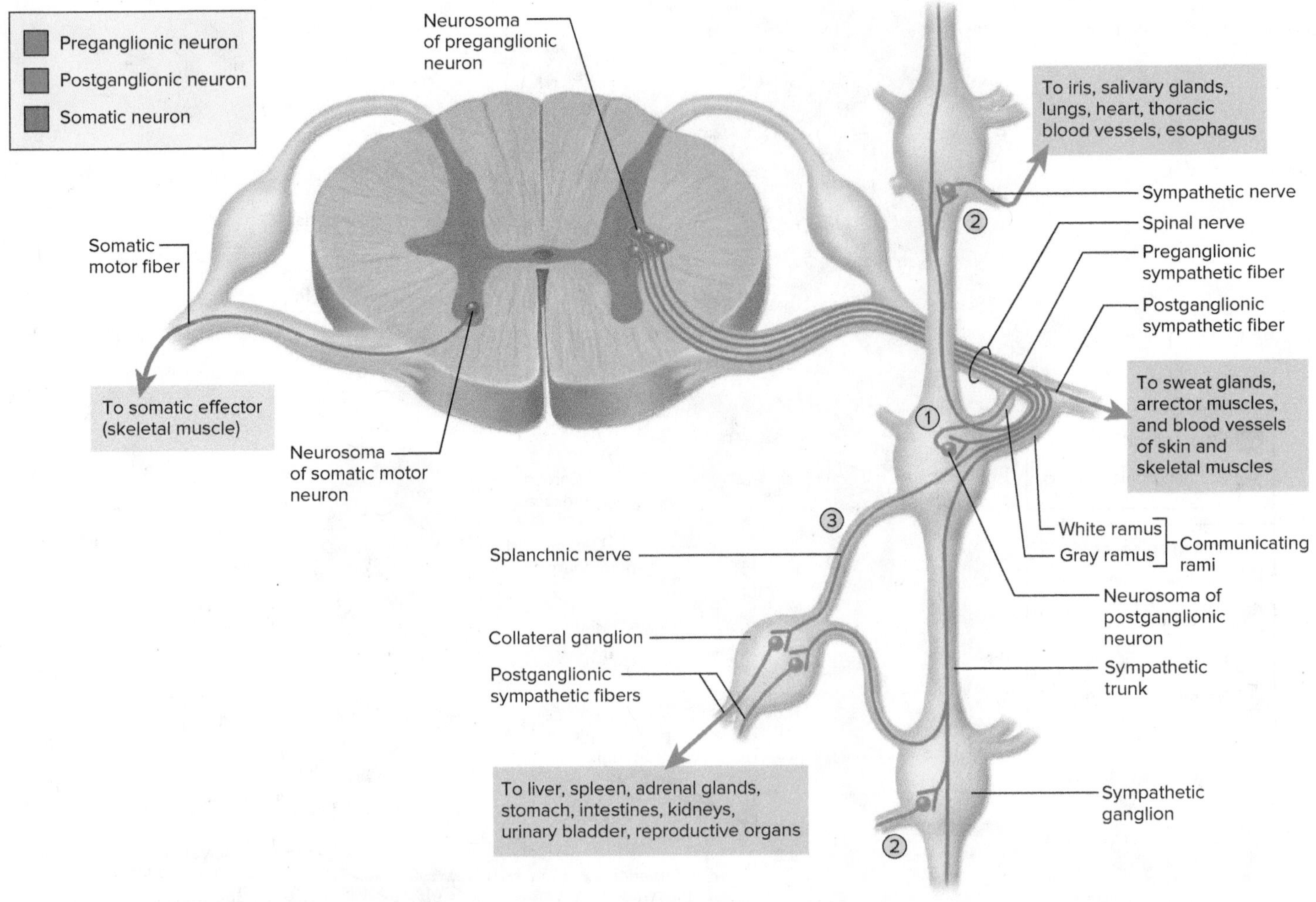


**FIGURE 15.5 Neural Pathways Through the Sympathetic Chain Ganglia.** Sympathetic fibers can follow any of the three numbered routes: (1) the spinal nerve route, (2) the sympathetic nerve route, or (3) the splanchnic nerve route. The somatic efferent pathway is shown on the left for comparison.

*Name the parts of the spinal cord where the neurosomas of the sympathetic and somatic efferent neurons are located.*

relationship of this chain to the spinal nerves and vertebrae). The number of ganglia in this chain varies from person to person, but usually there are 3 cervical *(superior, middle,* and *inferior),* 11 thoracic, 4 lumbar, 4 sacral, and 1 coccygeal ganglion in each chain.

It may seem odd that sympathetic ganglia exist in the cervical, sacral, and coccygeal regions considering that sympathetic fibers arise only from the thoracic and lumbar regions of the spinal cord (levels T1 to L2). But as shown in figure 15.4, nerve cords from the thoracic region ascend to the ganglia in the neck, and cords from the lumbar region descend to the sacral and coccygeal ganglia. Consequently, sympathetic nerve fibers are distributed to every level of the body. As a general rule, the head receives sympathetic output arising from spinal cord segment T1, the neck from T2, the thorax and upper limbs from T3 to T6, the abdomen from T7 to T11, and the lower limbs from T12 to L2. There is considerable overlap and individual variation in this pattern, however.

In the thoracolumbar region, each paravertebral ganglion is connected to a spinal nerve by two branches called *communicating rami* **(fig. 15.5).** The preganglionic fibers are small myelinated fibers that travel from the spinal nerve to the ganglion by way of the **white communicating ramus,**[5] which gets its color and name from the myelin. Unmyelinated postganglionic fibers leave the ganglion by way of the **gray communicating ramus,** named for its lack of myelin and duller color, and by other routes. This ramus returns to the spinal nerve. Postganglionic fibers, longer than the preganglionics, extend the rest of the way to the target organ.

### ▶▶▶APPLY WHAT YOU KNOW

*Would autonomic postganglionic fibers have faster or slower conduction speeds than somatic motor fibers? Why? (See hints in section 12.3d.)*

[5] *ramus* = branch

**TABLE 15.2 Innervation to and from the Collateral Ganglia**

| Sympathetic Ganglia | → | Collateral Ganglia | → | Postganglionic Target Organs |
|---|---|---|---|---|
| Thoracic ganglion 5 to 9 or 10 | → | Celiac ganglion | → | Stomach, spleen, liver, pancreas, small intestine, and kidneys |
| Thoracic ganglia 9 to 12 | → | Celiac and superior mesenteric ganglia | → | Small intestine, colon, and kidneys |
| Lumbar ganglia | → | Inferior mesenteric ganglion | → | Rectum, urinary bladder, and reproductive organs |

After entering the sympathetic chain, preganglionic fibers may follow any of three courses:

- Some end in the ganglion they enter and synapse immediately with a postganglionic neuron.
- Some travel up or down the chain and synapse in ganglia at other levels. It is these fibers that link the paravertebral ganglia into a chain. They are the only route by which ganglia at the cervical, sacral, and coccygeal levels receive input.
- Some pass through the chain without synapsing and continue as *splanchnic nerves* (SPLANK-nic), to be considered shortly.

Nerve fibers leave the sympathetic chain by three routes. These are numbered in figure 15.5 to correspond to the following descriptions:

① **The spinal nerve route.** Some postganglionic fibers exit a ganglion by way of the gray ramus, return to the spinal nerve or its subdivisions, and travel the rest of the way to the target organ. This is the route to most sweat glands, arrector muscles, and blood vessels of the skin and skeletal muscles.

② **The sympathetic nerve route.** Other postganglionic fibers leave by way of sympathetic nerves that extend to the heart, lungs, esophagus, and thoracic blood vessels. These nerves form a **carotid plexus** around each carotid artery of the neck and issue fibers from there to effectors in the head—including sweat, salivary, and nasal glands; arrector muscles; blood vessels; and dilators of the iris. Some fibers from the superior and middle cervical ganglia form the *cardiac nerves* to the heart (which also contain parasympathetic fibers).

③ **The splanchnic[6] nerve route.** Some of the fibers that arise from spinal nerves T5 to T12 pass through the sympathetic ganglia without synapsing. Beyond the ganglia, they continue as **splanchnic nerves,** which lead to a second set of ganglia called **collateral ganglia.** Here the preganglionic fibers synapse with the postganglionics.

The collateral ganglia contribute to a network called the **abdominal aortic plexus** wrapped around the aorta **(fig. 15.6).** There are three major collateral ganglia in this plexus—the **celiac, superior mesenteric,** and **inferior mesenteric ganglia**—located at points where arteries of the same names branch off the aorta. The postganglionic fibers accompany these arteries and their branches to the target organs. **Table 15.2** summarizes the innervation to and from the three major collateral ganglia.

The term *solar plexus* is used by some authorities as a collective name for the celiac and superior mesenteric ganglia, and by others as a synonym for the celiac ganglion only. The term comes from the nerves radiating from the ganglion like rays of the sun.

In summary, effectors in the muscles and body wall are innervated mainly by sympathetic fibers in the spinal nerves, effectors in the head and thoracic cavity by sympathetic nerves, and effectors in the abdominopelvic cavity by splanchnic nerves.

There is no simple one-to-one relationship between preganglionic and postganglionic fibers in the sympathetic division. For one thing, each postganglionic neuron may receive synapses from multiple preganglionic fibers, thus exhibiting the principle of *neural convergence.* Furthermore, each preganglionic fiber branches out to multiple postganglionic neurons, thus showing *neural divergence.* (See section 12.6d to review diverging and converging circuits.) Most sympathetic preganglionic fibers synapse with 10 to 20 postganglionic neurons. Therefore, when one preganglionic neuron fires, it can excite multiple postganglionic fibers leading to different target organs. The sympathetic division thus tends to have relatively widespread effects—as suggested by the name *sympathetic.*[7]

## 15.2b The Adrenal Glands

The paired **adrenal[8] (suprarenal) glands** rest like hats on the superior poles of the kidneys (fig. 15.6). Each adrenal is actually two glands with different functions and embryonic origins. The outer rind, the **adrenal cortex,** secretes steroid hormones discussed in section 17.3e. The inner core, the **adrenal medulla,** is essentially a sympathetic ganglion. It consists of modified postganglionic neurons without dendrites or axons. Sympathetic preganglionic fibers penetrate through the cortex and terminate on these cells. The sympathetic nervous system and adrenal medulla are so closely related in development and function that they are referred to collectively as the *sympathoadrenal system.*

[6]*splanchn* = viscera

[7]*sym* = together; *path* = feeling
[8]*ad* = near; *ren* = kidney

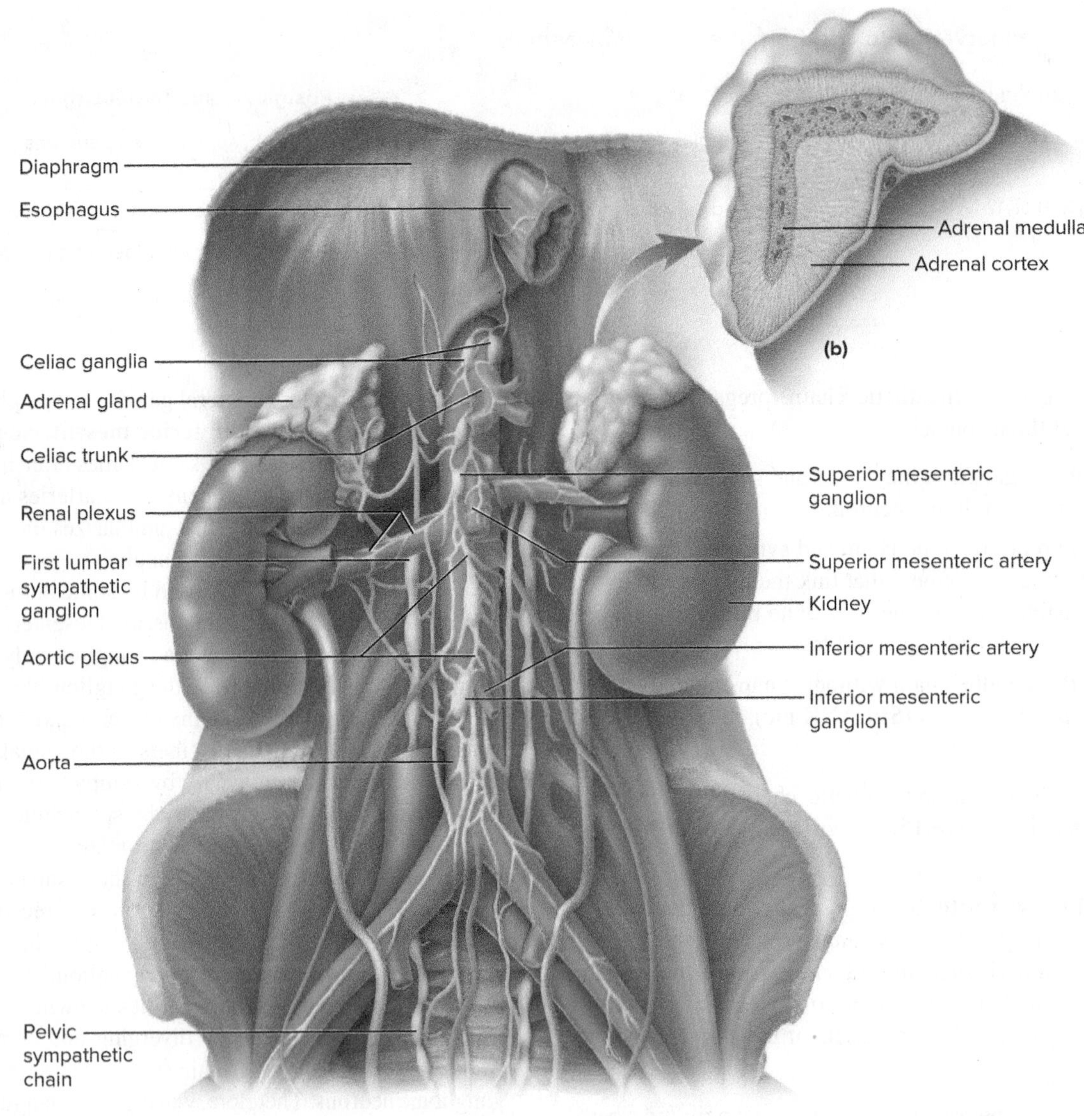


**FIGURE 15.6 Abdominopelvic Components of the Sympathetic Nervous System.** (a) Collateral ganglia, abdominal aortic plexus, and adrenal glands. (b) The adrenal gland, frontal section. Only the adrenal medulla plays a role in the sympathetic nervous system; the adrenal cortex has unrelated roles described in section 17.3e.

When stimulated, the adrenal medulla secretes a mixture of hormones into the bloodstream—about 85% epinephrine (adrenaline), 15% norepinephrine (noradrenaline), and a trace of dopamine. These hormones, the *catecholamines,* were briefly considered in section 12.5c because they also function as neurotransmitters.

## 15.2c The Parasympathetic Division

The parasympathetic division is also called the *craniosacral division* because its nerve fibers arise from the brain and sacral region of the spinal cord; they travel in certain cranial and sacral nerves. Neurosomas of the preganglionic neurons are located in the midbrain, pons, medulla oblongata, and segments S2 to S4 of the spinal cord **(fig. 15.7).** They issue long preganglionic fibers that end in **terminal ganglia** in or near the target organ. (If a terminal ganglion is embedded in the wall of a target organ, it is also called an *intramural*[9] *ganglion.*) Thus, the parasympathetic division has long preganglionic fibers, reaching almost all the way to the target cells, and short postganglionic fibers that cover the rest of the distance.

There is some neural divergence in the parasympathetic division, but much less than in the sympathetic. The parasympathetic division has a ratio of fewer than five postganglionic fibers to every preganglionic fiber. Furthermore, the preganglionic fiber reaches the target organ before even this slight divergence occurs. The parasympathetic division is therefore relatively selective in its stimulation of target organs.

[9] *intra* = within; *mur* = wall

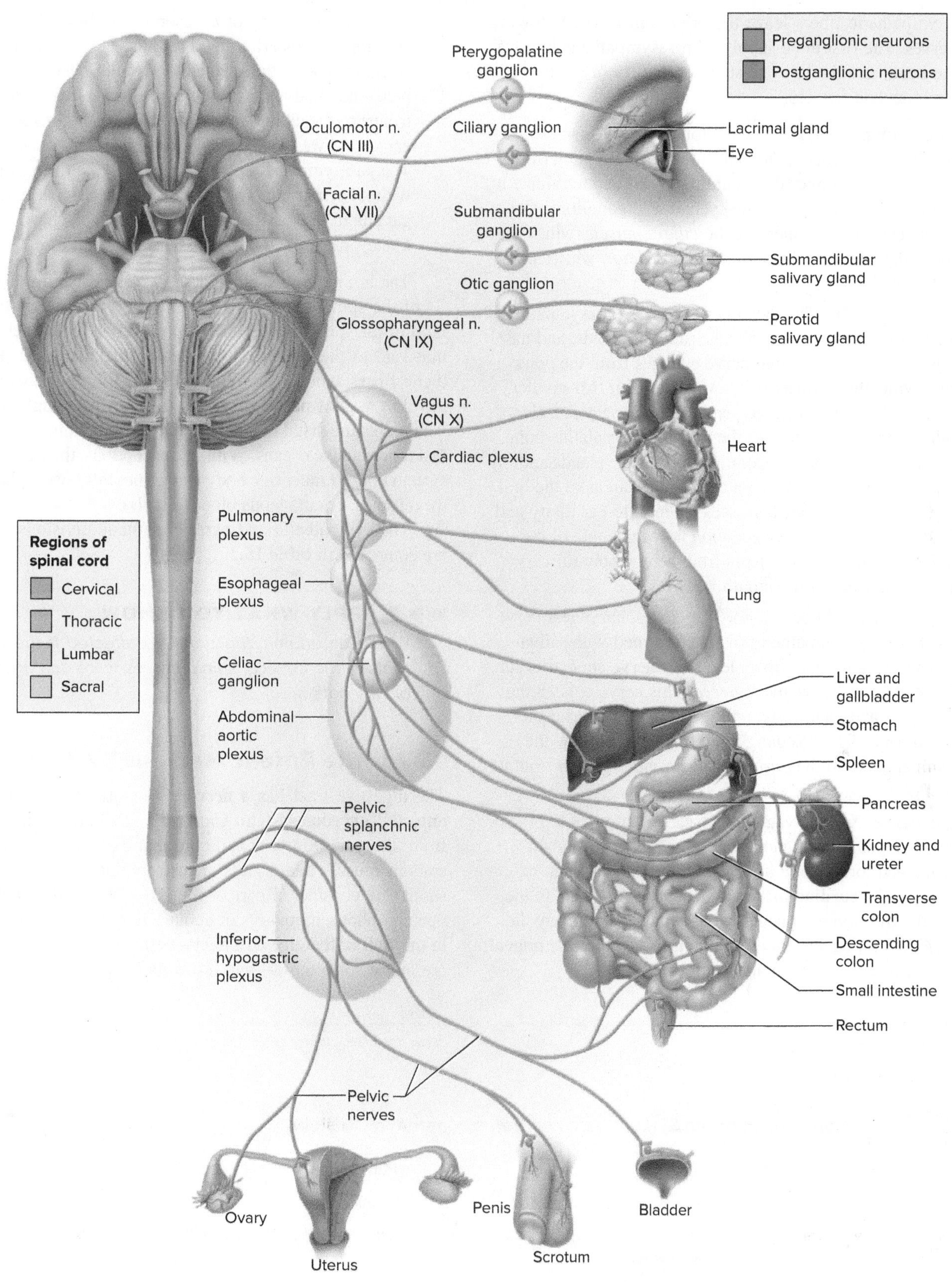


**FIGURE 15.7 Schematic of the Parasympathetic Nervous System.** APR

*Which nerve carries the most parasympathetic nerve fibers?*

Parasympathetic fibers leave the brainstem in the following cranial nerves. The first three supply all parasympathetic innervation to the head, and the last one supplies viscera of the thoracic and abdominopelvic cavities.

1. **Oculomotor nerve (III).** The oculomotor nerve carries parasympathetic fibers that control the lens and pupil of the eye. The preganglionic fibers enter the orbit and terminate in the *ciliary ganglion* behind the eyeball. Postganglionic fibers enter the eyeball and innervate the *ciliary muscle,* which thickens the lens, and the *pupillary constrictor,* which narrows the pupil.
2. **Facial nerve (VII).** The facial nerve carries parasympathetic fibers that regulate the tear glands, salivary glands, and nasal glands. Soon after the facial nerve emerges from the pons, its parasympathetic fibers split away and form two smaller branches. The superior branch ends at the *pterygopalatine ganglion* near the junction of the maxilla and palatine bone. Postganglionic fibers then continue to the tear glands and glands of the nasal cavity, palate, and other areas of the oral cavity. The inferior branch crosses the middle-ear cavity and ends at the *submandibular ganglion* near the angle of the mandible. Postganglionic fibers from here supply salivary glands in the floor of the mouth.
3. **Glossopharyngeal nerve (IX).** The glossopharyngeal nerve also carries parasympathetic fibers concerned with salivation. The preganglionic fibers leave this nerve soon after its origin and form the *tympanic nerve.* This nerve crosses the middle-ear cavity and ends in the *otic*[10] *ganglion* near the foramen ovale. The postganglionic fibers then follow the trigeminal nerve to the *parotid salivary gland* just in front of the earlobe.
4. **Vagus nerve (X).** The vagus nerve carries about 90% of all parasympathetic preganglionic fibers. It travels down the neck and forms three networks in the mediastinum of the chest—the **cardiac plexus,** which supplies fibers to the heart; the **pulmonary plexus,** whose fibers accompany the bronchi and blood vessels into the lungs; and the **esophageal plexus,** whose fibers regulate swallowing.

At the lower end of the esophagus, these plexuses give off anterior and posterior **vagal trunks,** each of which contains fibers from both the right and left vagus nerves. These trunks penetrate the diaphragm, enter the abdominal cavity, and contribute to the extensive *abdominal aortic plexus* mentioned earlier. As we have seen, sympathetic fibers synapse here. The parasympathetic fibers, however, pass through the plexus without synapsing. They synapse farther along, in terminal ganglia in or near the liver, pancreas, stomach, small intestine, kidney, ureter, and proximal half of the colon.

The remaining parasympathetic fibers arise from levels S2 to S4 of the spinal cord. They travel a short distance in the anterior rami of the spinal nerves and then form **pelvic splanchnic nerves** that lead to the **inferior hypogastric plexus.** Some parasympathetic fibers synapse here, but most pass through this plexus and travel by way of **pelvic nerves** to the terminal ganglia in their target organs: the distal half of the colon, the rectum, urinary bladder, and reproductive organs. With few exceptions, the parasympathetic system doesn't innervate body wall structures (sweat glands, arrector muscles, or cutaneous blood vessels).

The sympathetic and parasympathetic divisions of the ANS are compared in **table 15.3.**

**APPLY WHAT YOU KNOW**

*Would autonomic functions be affected if the anterior roots of the cervical spinal nerves were damaged? Why or why not?*

### 15.2d The Enteric Nervous System

The digestive tract has a nervous network of its own called the **enteric**[11] **nervous system.** Unlike the ANS proper, it doesn't arise from the brainstem or spinal cord, but like the ANS, it innervates smooth muscle and glands. Thus, opinions differ on whether it should be considered part of the ANS. Pictured in this chapter's opening photo, it consists of about 100 million neurons embedded in the wall of the digestive tract—perhaps more neurons than there are in the spinal cord—and it has its own reflex arcs. The enteric

[10] *ot* = ear; *ic* = pertaining to

[11] *enter* = intestines; *ic* = pertaining to

**TABLE 15.3 Comparison of the Sympathetic and Parasympathetic Divisions**

| Feature | Sympathetic | Parasympathetic |
|---|---|---|
| Origin in CNS | Thoracolumbar | Craniosacral |
| Location of ganglia | Paravertebral ganglia adjacent to spinal column and prevertebral ganglia anterior to it | Terminal ganglia near or within target organs |
| Fiber lengths | Short preganglionic | Long preganglionic |
| | Long postganglionic | Short postganglionic |
| Neural divergence | Extensive | Minimal |
| Effects of system | Often widespread and general | More specific and local |

nervous system regulates the motility of the esophagus, stomach, and intestines and the secretion of digestive enzymes and acid. To function normally, however, these digestive activities also require regulation by the sympathetic and parasympathetic systems. The enteric nervous system is discussed in more detail in section 25.1b. Its importance in intestinal motility becomes dramatically apparent when the system is absent (see Deeper Insight 15.1).

**BEFORE YOU GO ON**

Answer the following questions to test your understanding of the preceding section:

3. Explain why the sympathetic division is also called the thoracolumbar division even though its paravertebral ganglia extend all the way from the cervical to the sacral region.
4. Describe or diagram the structural relationships among the following: preganglionic fiber, postganglionic fiber, gray ramus, white ramus, and sympathetic ganglion.
5. Explain in anatomical terms why the parasympathetic division affects target organs more selectively than the sympathetic division does.
6. Trace the pathway of a parasympathetic fiber of the vagus nerve from the medulla oblongata to the small intestine.

**DEEPER INSIGHT 15.1**

**CLINICAL APPLICATION**

### *Megacolon*

The importance of the enteric nervous system becomes vividly clear when it is absent. Such is the case in a hereditary defect called *Hirschsprung*[12] disease. During normal embryonic development, neural crest cells migrate to the large intestine and establish the enteric nervous system. In Hirschsprung disease, however, they fail to supply the distal parts of the large intestine, leaving the sigmoid colon and rectum (see fig. 25.33) without enteric ganglia. In the absence of these ganglia, the sigmoidorectal region lacks motility, constricts permanently, and obstructs the passage of feces. Feces accumulate and become impacted above the constriction, resulting in *megacolon*—a massive dilation of the bowel accompanied by abdominal distension and chronic constipation. The most life-threatening complications are colonic gangrene, perforation of the bowel, and bacterial infection of the peritoneum *(peritonitis).* The treatment of choice is surgical removal of the affected segment and attachment of the healthy colon directly to the anal canal.

Hirschsprung disease is usually evident even in the newborn, which fails to have its first expected bowel movement. It affects four times as many infant boys as girls, and although its incidence in the general population is about 1 in 5,000 live births, it occurs in about 1 out of 10 infants with Down syndrome.

Hirschsprung disease is not the only cause of megacolon. In Central and South America, biting insects called *kissing bugs* transmit parasites called *trypanosomes* to humans. These parasites, similar to the ones that cause African sleeping sickness, cause *Chagas*[13] disease. Among other effects, they destroy the autonomic ganglia of the enteric nervous system, leading to a massively enlarged and often gangrenous colon.

[12]Harald Hirschsprung (1830–1916), Danish physician
[13]Carlos Chagas (1879–1934), Brazilian physician

## 15.3 Autonomic Effects on Target Organs

**Expected Learning Outcomes**

When you have completed this section, you should be able to

a. name the neurotransmitters employed at different synapses of the ANS;
b. name the receptors for these neurotransmitters and explain how they relate to autonomic effects;
c. explain how the ANS controls many target organs through dual innervation; and
d. explain how control is exerted in the absence of dual innervation.

### 15.3a Neurotransmitters and Their Receptors

As noted earlier, the divisions of the ANS often have contrasting effects on an organ. The sympathetic division accelerates the heartbeat and the parasympathetic division slows it down, for example. But each division of the ANS also can have contrasting effects on different organs. For example, the parasympathetic division contracts the wall of the urinary bladder but relaxes the male internal urethral sphincter; both actions are necessary for the expulsion of urine. It employs acetylcholine for both purposes. Similarly, the sympathetic division constricts most blood vessels but dilates the bronchioles of the lungs, and it achieves both effects with norepinephrine.

How can different autonomic neurons have such contrasting effects? There are two fundamental reasons: (1) Sympathetic and parasympathetic fibers secrete different neurotransmitters, and (2) target cells respond in different ways even to the same neurotransmitter depending on what type of receptors they have for it. All autonomic nerve fibers secrete either acetylcholine or norepinephrine, and each of these neurotransmitters has two major classes of receptors **(fig. 15.8).**

- **Acetylcholine (ACh).** ACh is secreted by the preganglionic fibers in both divisions and the postganglionic fibers of the parasympathetic division **(table 15.4).** A few sympathetic postganglionics also secrete ACh—those that innervate sweat glands and some blood vessels. Any nerve fiber that secretes ACh is called a **cholinergic fiber** (CO-lin-UR-jic), and any receptor that binds it is called a **cholinergic receptor.** There are two categories of cholinergic receptors:
  - **Muscarinic receptors** (MUSS-cuh-RIN-ic). These are named for muscarine, a mushroom toxin used in their discovery. All cardiac muscle, smooth muscle, and gland cells with cholinergic innervation have muscarinic receptors. There are different subclasses of muscarinic receptors with different effects; thus ACh excites intestinal

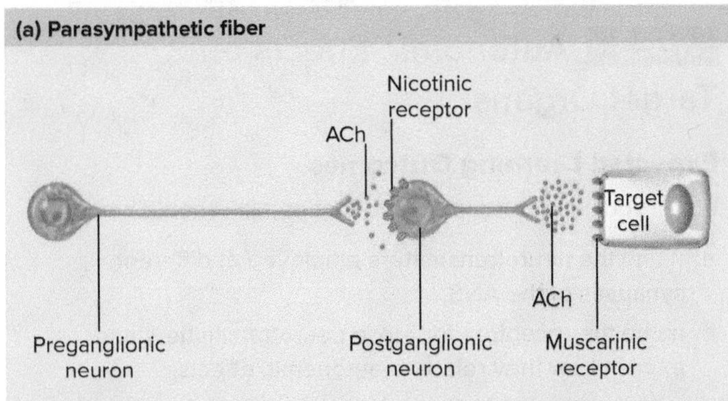


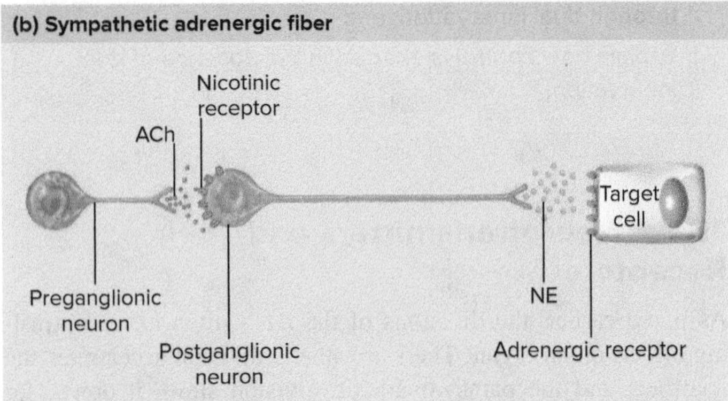


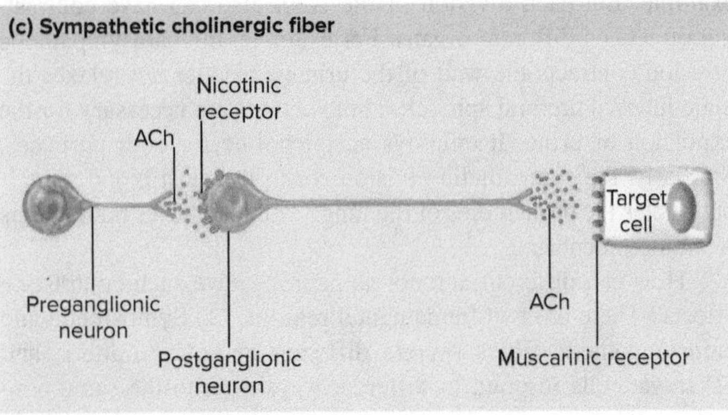


**FIGURE 15.8 Neurotransmitters and Receptors of the Autonomic Nervous System.** (a) All parasympathetic fibers are cholinergic. (b) Most sympathetic postganglionic fibers are adrenergic; they secrete norepinephrine (NE), and the target cell bears adrenergic receptors. (c) A few sympathetic postganglionic fibers are cholinergic; they secrete acetylcholine (ACh), and the target cell has cholinergic receptors of the muscarinic class.

smooth muscle by binding to one type of muscarinic receptor, and inhibits cardiac muscle by binding to a different type. Muscarinic receptors work through a variety of second-messenger systems.

- **Nicotinic receptors** (NIC-oh-TIN-ic). These are named for another botanical toxin helpful to their discovery—nicotine. They occur at all synapses in the autonomic ganglia, where the preganglionic fibers stimulate the postganglionic cells; on cells of the adrenal medulla; and at the neuromuscular junctions of skeletal muscle fibers. The binding of ACh to a nicotinic receptor is always excitatory. Nicotinic receptors work by opening ligand-gated ion channels and producing an excitatory postsynaptic potential in the target cell.

**TABLE 15.4 Locations of Cholinergic and Adrenergic Fibers in the ANS**

| Division | Preganglionic Fibers | Postganglionic Fibers |
|---|---|---|
| Sympathetic | Always cholinergic | Mostly adrenergic; a few cholinergic |
| Parasympathetic | Always cholinergic | Always cholinergic |

- **Norepinephrine (NE).** This neurotransmitter is secreted by nearly all sympathetic postganglionic fibers (table 15.4). Nerve fibers that secrete it are called **adrenergic fibers,** and the receptors for it are called **adrenergic receptors.** (NE is also called noradrenaline, the origin of the term *adrenergic.*) There are two principal categories of NE receptors:
  - **α-adrenergic receptors.** These usually have excitatory effects. For example, the binding of NE to α-adrenergic receptors promotes labor contractions, stimulates piloerection, and constricts dermal blood vessels, yet it inhibits intestinal motility. These contrasting effects result from the different actions of two subclasses of α-adrenergic receptors—$\alpha_1$ and $\alpha_2$. Receptors of the $\alpha_1$ type act through calcium ions as a second messenger, whereas $\alpha_2$ receptors inhibit the synthesis of cyclic AMP (cAMP).
  - **β-adrenergic receptors.** These are usually inhibitory. For example, NE relaxes and dilates the bronchioles (thus enhancing respiratory airflow) when it binds to β-adrenergic receptors of the smooth muscle. Yet when it binds to the β-adrenergic receptors of cardiac muscle, it has an excitatory effect. Such contrasting effects—increased pulmonary airflow and a stronger, faster heartbeat—are obviously appropriate to a state of exercise. Here again there are two receptor subclasses, $\beta_1$ and $\beta_2$, which mediate different effects. Both types, however, act through cAMP as a second messenger.

**Table 15.5** summarizes the effects of sympathetic and parasympathetic stimulation on different target organs and shows how some of these effects hinge on the receptor type. Knowledge of these receptor types is also vital to the field of neuropharmacology (see Deeper Insight 15.2). Many naturally occurring drugs bind

**TABLE 15.5 Effects of the Sympathetic and Parasympathetic Nervous Systems**

| Target | Sympathetic Effect and Receptor Type | Parasympathetic Effect (All Muscarinic) |
|---|---|---|
| ***Adipose Tissue*** | Decreased fat breakdown (α) | No effect |
| | Increased fat breakdown (α, β) | |
| **Eye** | | |
| Iris | Pupillary dilation (α) | Pupillary constriction |
| Ciliary muscle and lens | Relaxation for far vision (β) | Contraction for near vision |
| Lacrimal (tear) gland | None | Secretion |
| **Integumentary System** | | |
| Merocrine sweat glands (cooling) | Secretion (muscarinic) | No effect |
| Apocrine sweat glands (scent) | Secretion (α) | No effect |
| Arrector pili muscles | Hair erection (α) | No effect |
| **Endocrine System** | | |
| ***Adrenal Medulla*** | Hormone secretion (nicotinic) | No effect |
| **Circulatory System** | | |
| Heart rate and force | Increased (β) | Decreased |
| Deep coronary arteries | Vasodilation (β) | Slight vasodilation |
| | Vasoconstriction (α) | |
| Blood vessels of most viscera | Vasoconstriction (α) | Vasodilation |
| Blood vessels of skin | Vasoconstriction (α) | Vasodilation, blushing |
| Platelets (blood clotting) | Increased clotting (α) | No effect |
| **Respiratory System** | | |
| Bronchi and bronchioles | Bronchodilation (β) | Bronchoconstriction |
| Mucous glands | Decreased secretion (α) | No effect |
| | Increased secretion (β) | |
| **Urinary System** | | |
| Kidneys | Reduced urine output (α) | No effect |
| Bladder wall | No effect | Contraction |
| Internal urinary sphincter | Contraction, urine retention (α) | Relaxation, urine release |
| **Digestive System** | | |
| Salivary glands | Thick mucous secretion (α) | Thin serous secretion |
| Gastrointestinal motility | Decreased (α, β) | Increased |
| Gastrointestinal secretion | Decreased (α) | Increased |
| Liver | Glycogen breakdown (α, β) | Glycogen synthesis |
| Pancreatic enzyme secretion | Decreased (α) | Increased |
| Pancreatic insulin secretion | Decreased (α) | No effect |
| | Increased (β) | |
| **Reproductive System** | | |
| Penile or clitoral erection | No effect | Stimulation |
| Glandular secretion | No effect | Stimulation |
| Orgasm, smooth muscle roles | Stimulation (α) | No effect |
| Uterus | Relaxation (β) | No effect |
| | Labor contractions (α) | |

selectively to one or another class or subclass of receptor. Atropine binds only to muscarinic receptors and curare only to nicotinic receptors, for example. Many synthetic drugs are designed to be similarly selective.

The autonomic effects on glandular secretion are often the indirect results of action on blood vessels. Many glandular secretions begin as a filtrate of the blood, which is then modified by the gland cells. Increasing the blood flow through a gland (such as a salivary or sweat gland) tends to increase secretion, and reducing the blood flow reduces secretion.

Sympathetic effects tend to last longer than parasympathetic effects. After a parasympathetic fiber secretes ACh into a synapse, it is quickly broken down by acetylcholinesterase (AChE) and its effect lasts only a few seconds. The NE released by a sympathetic fiber, however, has various fates: (1) Some is reabsorbed by the nerve fiber, where it is either reused or broken down by an enzyme called *monoamine oxidase (MAO).* (2) Some diffuses into the adjacent tissues, where it is degraded by another enzyme, *catechol-O-methyltransferase (COMT).* (3) Much of it passes into the bloodstream, where MAO and COMT are absent. This NE and epinephrine from the adrenal gland circulate throughout the body and may exert their effects for several minutes before they are finally degraded by the liver.

ACh and NE are not the only neurotransmitters employed by the ANS. Although all autonomic fibers secrete one of these, many of them also secrete neuropeptides that modulate ACh or NE function. Sympathetic fibers may also secrete enkephalin, substance P, neuropeptide Y, somatostatin, neurotensin, or gonadotropin-releasing hormone. Some parasympathetic fibers relax blood vessels by stimulating the endothelial cells to release nitric oxide (NO), a gas. NO inhibits smooth muscle tone in the vessel wall, thus allowing the vessel to dilate. This increases the blood flow through the vessel. Among other functions, this mechanism is crucial to penile erection (see Deeper Insight 27.4).

**▶▶▶APPLY WHAT YOU KNOW**

*Table 15.5 notes that the sympathetic nervous system has an α-adrenergic effect on blood platelets and promotes clotting. How can the sympathetic nervous system stimulate platelets, considering that platelets are drifting cell fragments in the bloodstream with no nerve fibers leading to them?*

## 15.3b Dual Innervation

Most of the viscera receive nerve fibers from both the sympathetic and parasympathetic divisions and thus are said to have **dual innervation.** In such cases, the two divisions may have either *antagonistic* or *cooperative* effects on the same organ.

**Antagonistic effects** oppose each other. For example, the sympathetic division speeds up the heart and the parasympathetic division slows it down; the sympathetic division inhibits digestion and the parasympathetic division stimulates it; the sympathetic division dilates the pupil and the parasympathetic division constricts it. In some cases, these effects are exerted through dual innervation of the same effector cells, as in the heart, where nerve fibers of both divisions stimulate some of the same cells. In other cases, antagonistic effects arise because each division innervates different effector cells with opposite effects on organ function. In the iris of the eye, for example, sympathetic fibers innervate pupillary dilator cells and parasympathetic fibers innervate constrictor cells **(fig. 15.9).**

**Cooperative effects** are seen when the two divisions act on different effectors to produce a unified overall effect. Salivation is a good example. The parasympathetic division stimulates serous cells of the salivary glands to secrete a watery, enzyme-rich secretion, while the sympathetic division stimulates mucous cells of the same glands to secrete mucus. The enzymes and mucus are both necessary components of the saliva.

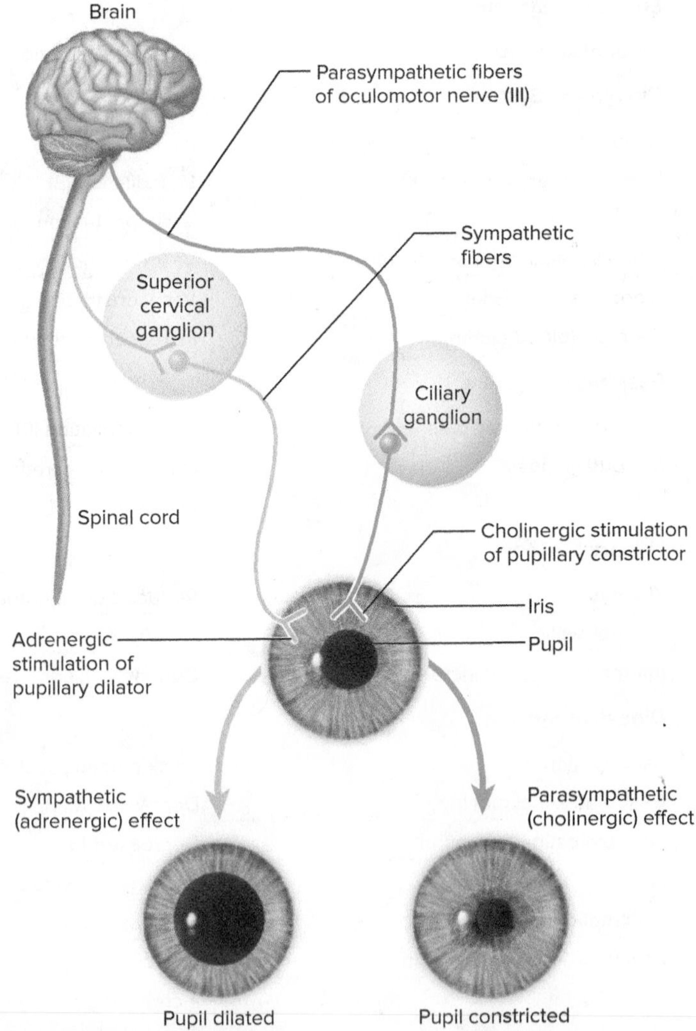


**FIGURE 15.9 Dual Innervation of the Iris.** Shows antagonistic effects of the sympathetic (yellow) and parasympathetic (blue) divisions on the iris.

? *If a person is in a state of fear, would you expect the pupils to be dilated or constricted? Why?*

Even when both divisions innervate a single organ, they don't always innervate it equally or exert equal influence. For example, the parasympathetic division forms an extensive plexus in the wall of the digestive tract and exerts much more influence over it than the sympathetic division does. In the ventricles of the heart, by contrast, there is much less parasympathetic than sympathetic innervation.

## 15.3c Control Without Dual Innervation

Dual innervation isn't always necessary for the ANS to produce opposite effects on an organ. The adrenal medulla, arrector muscles, sweat glands, and many blood vessels receive only sympathetic fibers. The most significant example of control without dual innervation is regulation of blood pressure and routes of blood flow. The sympathetic fibers to a blood vessel have a baseline sympathetic tone, which keeps the vessels in a state of partial constriction called **vasomotor tone (fig. 15.10).** An increase in firing rate constricts a vessel by increasing smooth muscle contraction. A drop in firing frequency dilates a vessel by allowing the smooth muscle to relax. The blood pressure in the vessel, pushing outward on its wall, then dilates the vessel. Thus, the sympathetic division alone exerts opposite effects on the vessels.

Sympathetic control of vasomotor tone can shift blood flow from one organ to another according to the changing needs of the body. In times of emergency, stress, or exercise, the skeletal muscles and heart receive a high priority and the sympathetic division dilates the arteries that supply them. Processes such as digestion, nutrient absorption, and urine formation can wait; thus the sympathetic division constricts arteries to the gastrointestinal tract and kidneys. It also reduces blood flow through the skin, which may help to minimize bleeding in the event that the stress-producing situation leads to injury. Furthermore, since there isn't enough blood in the body to supply all the organ systems equally, it is necessary to temporarily divert blood away from some organs in order to supply an adequate amount to the muscular system.

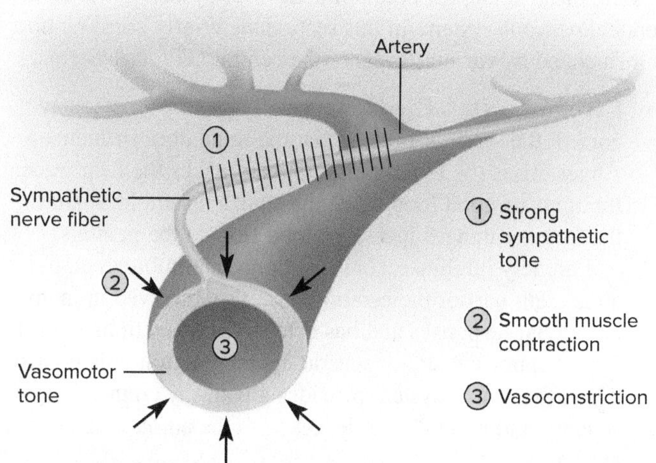


**(a) Vasoconstriction**

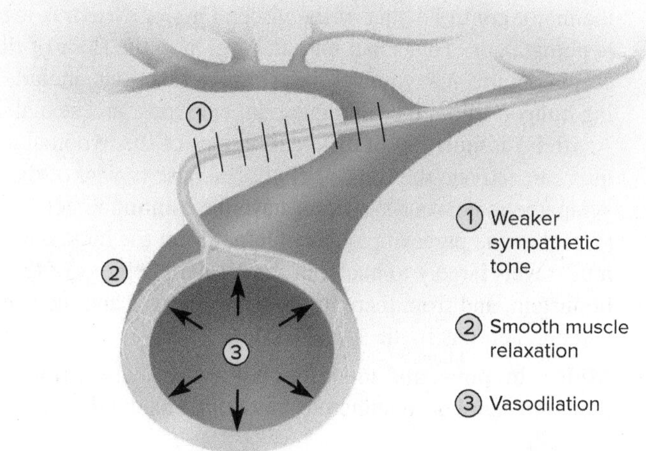


**(b) Vasodilation**

FIGURE 15.10 **Sympathetic and Vasomotor Tone.** (a) Vasoconstriction in response to a high rate of sympathetic nerve firing. (b) Vasodilation in response to a low rate of sympathetic nerve firing. Smooth muscle relaxation allows blood pressure within the vessel to push the vessel wall outward. Black lines crossing each nerve fiber represent action potentials, with a high firing frequency in part (a) and a lower frequency in part (b).

**BEFORE YOU GO ON**

Answer the following questions to test your understanding of the preceding section:

7. What neurotransmitters are secreted by adrenergic and cholinergic fibers?
8. Why do sympathetic effects last longer than parasympathetic effects?
9. How can the sympathetic division cause smooth muscle to relax in some organs but contract in others?
10. What are the two ways in which the sympathetic and parasympathetic systems can affect each other when they both innervate the same target organ? Give examples.
11. How can the sympathetic nervous system have contrasting effects in a target organ without dual innervation?

# 15.4 Central Control of Autonomic Function

### Expected Learning Outcomes

When you have completed this section, you should be able to

a. identify what parts of the brain influence the autonomic nervous system;
b. give examples of emotional influences on autonomic function; and
c. give examples of spinal cord control over autonomic functions.

In spite of its name, the autonomic nervous system is not an independent nervous system. In this section we briefly consider how it is influenced by various levels of the central nervous system.

- **Cerebral cortex.** Even if we usually cannot consciously control the ANS, it is clear that the mind does influence it. Anger raises the blood pressure, fear makes the heart race, thoughts of good food make the stomach rumble, sexual thoughts or images increase blood flow to the genitals, and anxiety inhibits sexual function. The limbic system, an ancient part of the cerebral cortex, is involved in many emotional responses and has extensive connections with the hypothalamus, a site of several nuclei of autonomic control. Thus, the limbic system provides a pathway connecting sensory and mental experiences with the autonomic nervous system.
- **Hypothalamus.** Although the major site of CNS control over the somatic motor system is the primary motor cortex, the major control center of the visceral motor system is the hypothalamus. This small but vital region in the floor of the brain contains many nuclei for primitive functions, including hunger, thirst, thermoregulation, emotions, and sexuality. Artificial stimulation of different regions of the hypothalamus can activate the fight-or-flight response typical of the sympathetic nervous system or have the calming effects typical of the parasympathetic. Output from the hypothalamus travels largely to nuclei in more caudal regions of the brainstem, and from there to the cranial nerves and the sympathetic neurons in the spinal cord.
- **Midbrain, pons, and medulla oblongata.** These regions of the brainstem house numerous autonomic nuclei described in section 14.3: centers for cardiac and vasomotor control, salivation, swallowing, sweating, gastrointestinal secretion, bladder control, pupillary constriction and dilation, and other primitive functions. Many of these nuclei belong to the reticular formation, which extends from the medulla to the hypothalamus. Autonomic output from these nuclei travels by way of the spinal cord and the oculomotor, facial, glossopharyngeal, and vagus nerves.
- **Spinal cord.** Finally, the spinal cord integrates such autonomic reflexes as micturition (urination), defecation, erection, and ejaculation (details are in sections 23.7d, 25.7f, and 27.5). Fortunately, the brain is able to inhibit defecation and urination consciously, but when injuries sever the spinal cord from the brain, the autonomic spinal reflexes alone control the elimination of urine and feces.

**Table 15.6** describes some dysfunctions of the autonomic nervous system.

**BEFORE YOU GO ON**

Answer the following questions to test your understanding of the preceding section:

12. What system in the brain connects our conscious thoughts and feelings with the autonomic control centers of the hypothalamus?
13. List some autonomic responses that are controlled by nuclei in the hypothalamus.
14. What are the roles of the midbrain, pons, and medulla in autonomic control?
15. Name some visceral reflexes controlled by the spinal cord.

| TABLE 15.6 | Some Disorders of the Autonomic Nervous System |
|---|---|
| Horner syndrome | Chronic unilateral pupillary constriction, sagging of the eyelid, withdrawal of the eye into the orbit, flushing of the skin, and lack of facial perspiration; results from lesions in the cervical ganglia, upper thoracic spinal cord, or brainstem that interrupt sympathetic innervation of the head. |
| Raynaud disease | Intermittent attacks of paleness, cyanosis, and pain in the fingers and toes, caused when cold or emotional stress triggers excessive vasoconstriction in the digits; most common in young women. In extreme cases, causes gangrene and may require amputation. Sometimes treated by severing sympathetic nerves to the affected regions. |

***You can find other autonomic nervous system disorders described in the following places:***

The *mass reflex reaction* in Deeper Insight 13.5; *autonomic effects of cranial nerve injuries* in section 14.6c; *Hirschsprung disease* and *Chagas disease* in Deeper Insight 15.1; and *orthostatic hypotension* in table 20.2.

## DEEPER INSIGHT 15.2
### CLINICAL APPLICATION

### *Drugs and the Nervous System*

*Neuropharmacology* is a branch of medicine that deals with the effects of drugs on the nervous system, especially drugs that mimic, enhance, or inhibit the action of neurotransmitters. A few examples will illustrate the clinical relevance of neurotransmitter and receptor functions.

A number of drugs work by stimulating adrenergic and cholinergic neurons or receptors. *Sympathomimetics*[14] are drugs that enhance sympathetic action. They stimulate adrenergic receptors or promote norepinephrine release. For example, phenylephrine, found in such cold medicines as Dimetapp and Sudafed PE, aids breathing by stimulating alpha receptors, dilating the bronchioles, and constricting nasal blood vessels, thus reducing swelling in the nasal mucosa. *Sympatholytics*[15] are drugs that suppress sympathetic action by inhibiting norepinephrine release or by binding to adrenergic receptors without stimulating them. Propranolol, for example, is a *beta-blocker.* It reduces hypertension partly by blocking β-adrenergic receptors. This interferes with the effects of epinephrine and norepinephrine on the heart and blood vessels. (It also reduces the production of *angiotensin II,* a hormone that stimulates vasoconstriction and raises blood pressure.)

*Parasympathomimetics* enhance parasympathetic effects. Pilocarpine, for example, relieves glaucoma (excessive pressure in the eyeball) by dilating a vessel that drains fluid from the eye. *Parasympatholytics* inhibit ACh release or block its receptors. Atropine, for example, blocks muscarinic receptors. It is sometimes used to dilate the pupils for eye examinations and to dry the mucous membranes of the respiratory tract before inhalation anesthesia. It is an extract of the deadly nightshade plant, *Atropa belladonna.*[16] Women of the Middle Ages used nightshade to dilate their pupils, which was regarded as a beauty enhancement.

The drugs we have mentioned so far act on the peripheral nervous system and its effectors. Many others act on the central nervous system. Strychnine, for example, blocks the inhibitory action of glycine on spinal motor neurons. The neurons then overstimulate the muscles, causing spastic paralysis and sometimes death by suffocation.

Sigmund Freud predicted that psychiatry would eventually draw upon biology and chemistry to deal with emotional problems once treated only by counseling and psychoanalysis. A branch of neuropharmacology called *psychopharmacology* has fulfilled his prediction. This field dates to the 1950s when chlorpromazine, an antihistamine, was incidentally found to relieve the symptoms of schizophrenia.

The management of clinical depression is one example of how contemporary psychopharmacology has supplemented counseling approaches. Some forms of depression result from deficiencies of the monoamine neurotransmitters. Thus, they yield to drugs that prolong the effects of the monoamines already present at the synapses. Prozac (fluoxetine), for example, blocks serotonin reuptake and prolongs its mood-elevating effect; thus Prozac is called a *selective serotonin reuptake inhibitor (SSRI).* It is also used to treat fear of rejection, excess sensitivity to criticism, lack of self-esteem, and inability to experience pleasure, all of which were long handled only through counseling, group therapy, or psychoanalysis. After monoamines are taken up from the synapse, they are degraded by monoamine oxidase (MAO). Drugs called *MAO inhibitors* slow down the breakdown of monoamine neurotransmitters and provide another pharmacological approach to depression.

Our growing understanding of neurochemistry also gives us more insight into the action of addictive drugs of abuse such as amphetamines and cocaine. Amphetamines ("speed") chemically resemble norepinephrine and dopamine, two neurotransmitters associated with elevated mood. Dopamine is especially important in sensations of pleasure. Cocaine blocks dopamine reuptake and thus produces a brief rush of good feelings. But when dopamine is not reabsorbed by the neurons, it diffuses out of the synaptic cleft and is degraded elsewhere. Cocaine thus depletes the neurons of dopamine faster than they can synthesize it, so finally there is no longer an adequate supply to maintain normal mood. The postsynaptic neurons make new dopamine receptors as if "searching" for the neurotransmitter—all of which leads ultimately to anxiety, depression, and the inability to experience pleasure without the drug.

Caffeine exerts its stimulatory effect by competing with adenosine. Adenosine, which you know as a component of DNA, RNA, and ATP, also functions as a neuromodulator in the brain, inhibiting ACh release by cholinergic neurons. One theory of sleepiness is that it results when prolonged metabolic activity breaks down so much ATP that the accumulated adenosine has a noticeably inhibitory effect. Caffeine has enough structural similarity to adenosine **(fig. 15.11)** to bind to its receptors, but it doesn't produce the inhibitory effect. Thus, it prevents adenosine from exerting its effect, more ACh is secreted, and a person feels more alert.

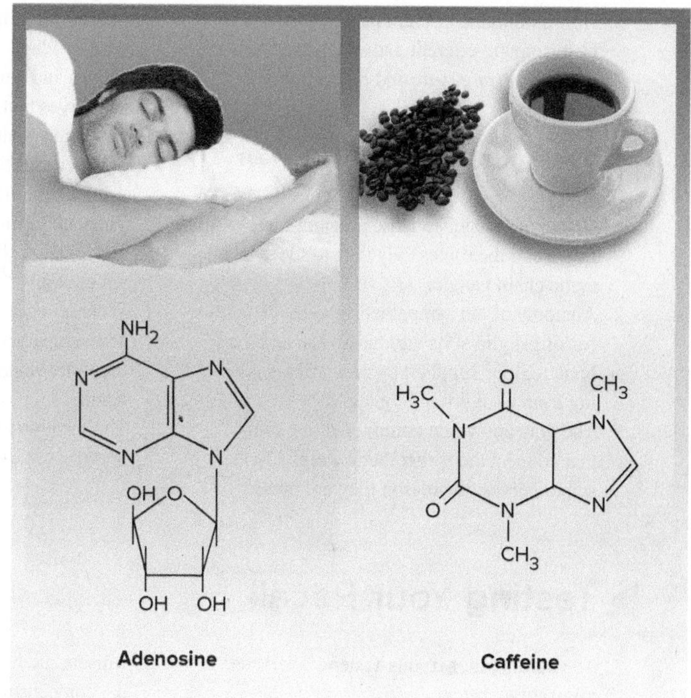


**FIGURE 15.11 Adenosine and Caffeine.** Adenosine, a breakdown product of ATP and other chemicals, inhibits ACh release and produces a sense of sleepiness. Caffeine is similar enough to block the action of adenosine by binding to its receptors. This results in increased ACh release and heightened arousal.

**left:** Stockbyte/Getty Images; **right:** Duncan Walker/Getty Images

[14] *mimet* = imitate, mimic
[15] *lyt* = break down, destroy
[16] *bella* = beautiful, fine; *donna* = woman

# STUDY GUIDE

## Assess Your Learning Outcomes

*To test your knowledge, discuss the following topics with a study partner or in writing, ideally from memory.*

### 15.1 General Properties of the Autonomic Nervous System

1. The fundamental function and effectors of the autonomic nervous system (ANS)
2. Why this system is called *autonomic;* how it differs from the somatic motor system
3. The fundamental, contrasting functions of the sympathetic and parasympathetic divisions of the ANS
4. Why it cannot be said that at any given moment, either the sympathetic or the parasympathetic division is active; the meaning of *autonomic tone*
5. Basic anatomical components of the ANS
6. How autonomic efferent pathways differ from somatic efferent pathways; the meanings of *preganglionic* and *postganglionic fibers*

### 15.2 Anatomy of the Autonomic Nervous System

1. Origin of the sympathetic preganglionic fibers and the routes they take to the sympathetic chain ganglia
2. Anatomy of the sympathetic chain; the number of ganglia at its various levels; and the body regions supplied by nerve fibers issuing from each group of ganglia
3. The gray and white communicating rami that connect the sympathetic ganglia to the spinal nerves; the reason they are named *gray* and *white;* and the path that sympathetic nerve fibers take through these rami
4. Differences between the spinal nerve route, sympathetic nerve route, and splanchnic nerve route by which fibers leave the sympathetic chain
5. Various places in which a sympathetic preganglionic fiber may synapse with a postganglionic neuron
6. Locations of the celiac, superior mesenteric ganglia, and inferior mesenteric ganglia; the collective name for them; and the varied meanings of the expression *solar plexus*
7. The degree and significance of neural divergence in the sympathetic nervous system, and the effect of this on target organ stimulation
8. Why the adrenal medulla can be considered part of the sympathetic nervous system; what products it secretes when stimulated
9. Names and numbers of the cranial and spinal nerves that carry preganglionic fibers of the parasympathetic nervous system; which nerve carries the largest percentage of parasympathetic fibers
10. The path of the vagus nerve, and the names and locations of the plexuses and trunks to which it gives rise
11. Where, in general, terminal ganglia of the parasympathetic division are found, and therefore where the postganglionic fibers begin
12. The location and functions of the enteric nervous system

### 15.3 Autonomic Effects on Target Organs

1. Why the autonomic effect on a target cell depends on both the neurotransmitter released and the type of receptor on the target cell
2. The difference between cholinergic and adrenergic fibers and where each can be found in the ANS
3. What nicotinic and muscarinic receptors have in common, how they differ, and where they occur in the ANS
4. What $\alpha$- and $\beta$-adrenergic receptors have in common, how they differ, and where they occur in the ANS
5. Neurotransmitter stability and how it relates to the duration of sympathetic versus parasympathetic effects
6. The variety of neurotransmitters and neuromodulators employed by them
7. Autonomic control of certain organs by dual innervation, and examples of antagonistic and cooperative effects on an organ
8. How the ANS can regulate organs that lack dual innervation

### 15.4 Central Control of Autonomic Function

1. Examples of the influence of the cerebral cortex, hypothalamus, midbrain, pons, medulla oblongata, and spinal cord on the autonomic nervous system, and their involvement in autonomic effects

## Testing Your Recall

*Answers in Appendix A*

1. The autonomic nervous system innervates all of these *except*
   a. cardiac muscle.
   b. skeletal muscle.
   c. smooth muscle.
   d. salivary glands.
   e. blood vessels.

2. Muscarinic receptors bind
   a. epinephrine.
   b. norepinephrine.
   c. acetylcholine.
   d. cholinesterase.
   e. neuropeptides.

3. All of the following cranial nerves *except* the ______ carry parasympathetic fibers.
   a. vagus
   b. facial
   c. oculomotor
   d. glossopharyngeal
   e. hypoglossal

# STUDY GUIDE

4. Which of the following cranial nerves carries sympathetic fibers?
   a. oculomotor
   b. facial
   c. trigeminal
   d. vagus
   e. none of them

5. Which of these ganglia is *not* involved in the sympathetic division?
   a. intramural
   b. superior cervical
   c. paravertebral
   d. inferior mesenteric
   e. celiac

6. Epinephrine is secreted by
   a. sympathetic preganglionic fibers.
   b. sympathetic postganglionic fibers.
   c. parasympathetic preganglionic fibers.
   d. parasympathetic postganglionic fibers.
   e. the adrenal medulla.

7. The most significant autonomic control center within the CNS is
   a. the cerebral cortex.
   b. the limbic system.
   c. the midbrain.
   d. the hypothalamus.
   e. the sympathetic chain ganglia.

8. The gray communicating ramus contains
   a. visceral sensory fibers.
   b. parasympathetic motor fibers.
   c. sympathetic preganglionic fibers.
   d. sympathetic postganglionic fibers.
   e. somatic motor fibers.

9. Throughout the autonomic nervous system, the neurotransmitter released by the preganglionic fiber binds to _____ receptors on the postganglionic neuron.
   a. nicotinic
   b. muscarinic
   c. adrenergic
   d. alpha
   e. beta

10. Which of these does *not* result from sympathetic stimulation?
    a. dilation of the pupil
    b. acceleration of the heart
    c. digestive secretion
    d. enhanced blood clotting
    e. piloerection

11. Certain nerve fibers are called _____ fibers because they secrete norepinephrine.

12. _____ is a state in which a target organ receives both sympathetic and parasympathetic fibers.

13. _____ is a state of continual background activity of the sympathetic and parasympathetic divisions.

14. Most parasympathetic preganglionic fibers are found in the _____ nerve.

15. The digestive tract has a semi-independent nervous system called the _____ nervous system.

16. MAO and COMT are enzymes that break down _____ at certain ANS synapses.

17. The adrenal medulla consists of modified postganglionic neurons of the _____ nervous system.

18. The sympathetic nervous system has short _____ and long _____ nerve fibers.

19. Adrenergic receptors classified as $\alpha_1$, $\beta_1$, and $\beta_2$ act by changing the level of _____ in the target cell.

20. Sympathetic fibers to blood vessels maintain a state of partial vasoconstriction called _____.

## Building Your Medical Vocabulary

*Answers in Appendix A*

*State a meaning of each word element, and give a medical term from this chapter that uses it or a slight variation of it.*

1. baro-
2. lyto-
3. muro-
4. nomo-
5. oto-
6. patho-
7. reno-
8. splanchno-
9. sym-
10. viscero-

## What's Wrong with These Statements?

*Answers in Appendix A*

*Briefly explain why each of the following statements is false, or reword it to make it true.*

1. The parasympathetic nervous system shuts down when the sympathetic nervous system is active, and vice versa.
2. The parasympathetic nervous system controls dilation and constriction of the blood vessels of the skin.
3. Voluntary control of the ANS is not possible.
4. The sympathetic nervous system stimulates digestion.
5. All sympathetic postganglionic fibers are adrenergic.
6. Urination and defecation cannot occur without signals from the brain to the bladder and rectum.
7. Some parasympathetic nerve fibers are adrenergic.
8. Sympathetic effects are more localized and organ-specific than parasympathetic effects.
9. The oculomotor, facial, hypoglossal, and vagus nerves carry the parasympathetic fibers that arise from the brain.
10. The two divisions of the ANS have cooperative effects on the iris.

# STUDY GUIDE

## ▶ Testing Your Comprehension

1. You are dicing raw onions while preparing dinner, and the vapor makes your eyes water. Describe the afferent and efferent pathways involved in this response.
2. Suppose you are walking alone at night when you hear a dog growling close behind you. Describe the ways your sympathetic nervous system would prepare you to deal with this situation.
3. Suppose that the cardiac nerves were destroyed. How would this affect the heart and the body's ability to react to a stressful situation?
4. What would be the advantage to a wolf in having its sympathetic nervous system stimulate the arrector muscles? What happens in a human when the sympathetic system stimulates these muscles?
5. Pediatric literature has reported many cases of poisoning in children with Lomotil, an antidiarrheal medicine. Lomotil works primarily by means of the morphinelike effects of its chief ingredient, diphenoxylate, but it also contains atropine. Considering the mode of action described for atropine in Deeper Insight 15.2, why might it contribute to the antidiarrheal effect of Lomotil? In atropine poisoning, would you expect the pupils to be dilated or constricted? The skin to be moist or dry? The heart rate to be elevated or depressed? The bladder to retain urine or void uncontrollably? Explain each answer. Atropine poisoning is treated with physostigmine, a cholinesterase inhibitor. Explain the rationale of this treatment.

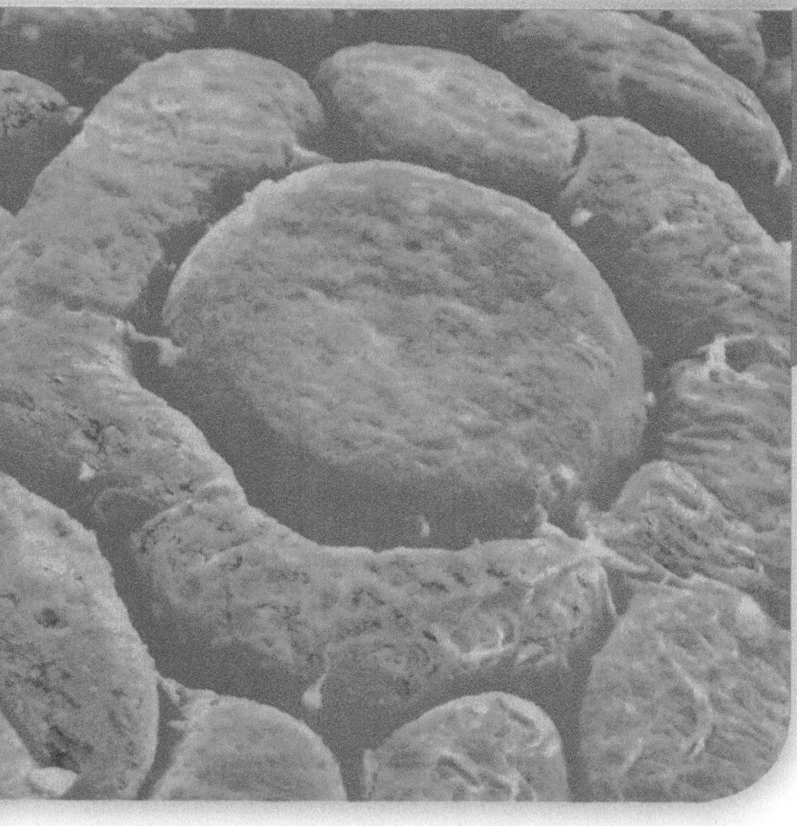

CHAPTER 16

# SENSE ORGANS

**A vallate papilla of the tongue, where most taste buds are located (SEM)**
Omikron/Science Source

## CHAPTER OUTLINE



## DEEPER INSIGHTS

**Module 7: Nervous System**

## BRUSHING UP

- Understanding how some senses work—including taste and smell—hinges on a knowledge of G proteins, cAMP, and second-messenger systems, explained in figure 3.8 and the associated text.
- This chapter's description of the hearing process assumes prior knowledge of mechanically gated membrane channels (see section 3.2a) and ion flow down an electrochemical gradient (see section 11.3c).
- Several concepts in section 12.6 are important for understanding sensory processes: postsynaptic potentials (EPSPs and IPSPs), temporal and spatial summation, neural coding, and converging neural circuits.
- You will need to remember the concepts of spinal cord tracts and decussation (see section 13.1e) to understand sensory pathways from lower-body receptors to the brain.
- Familiarity with certain cranial nerves is necessary for understanding other sensory pathways to the brain—especially the olfactory, optic, trigeminal, facial, vestibulocochlear, glossopharyngeal, and vagus nerves, all described in table 14.1.
- You must know the gross anatomy of the brain, especially lobes and gyri of the cerebral cortex, to understand where sensory signals are received and processed (see section 14.4b).
- To understand the anatomy of the ear, it will be helpful to recall the anatomy of the temporal bone (see "The Temporal Bones" in section 8.2a).

Anyone who enjoys music, art, fine food, or a good conversation appreciates the human senses. Yet their importance extends far beyond deriving pleasure from the environment. In the 1950s, behavioral scientists at Princeton University studied the methods used by Soviet Communists to extract confessions from political prisoners, including solitary confinement and sensory deprivation. Student volunteers were immobilized in dark soundproof rooms or suspended in dark chambers of water. In a short time, they experienced visual, auditory, and tactile hallucinations, incoherent thought patterns, deterioration of intellectual performance, and sometimes morbid fear or panic. Similar effects are seen in some burn patients who are immobilized and extensively bandaged (including the eyes) and thus suffer prolonged lack of sensory input. Patients connected to life-support equipment and confined under oxygen tents sometimes become delirious. Sensory input is vital to the integrity of personality and intellectual function.

Furthermore, much of the information communicated by the sense organs never comes to our conscious attention—blood pressure, body temperature, and muscle tension, for example. By monitoring such conditions, however, the sense organs initiate somatic and visceral reflexes that are indispensable to homeostasis and to our very survival in a ceaselessly changing and challenging environment.

## 16.1 Properties and Types of Sensory Receptors

**Expected Learning Outcomes**

When you have completed this section, you should be able to

a. define *receptor* and *sense organ;*
b. list the four kinds of information obtained from sensory receptors, and describe how the nervous system encodes each type; and
c. outline three ways of classifying receptors.

A sensory **receptor** is any structure specialized to detect a stimulus. Some receptors are simple, bare nerve endings, such as the receptors for heat and pain, whereas others are true sense organs. A **sense organ** is a structure that combines nervous tissue with other tissues that enhance its response to a certain type of stimulus. The accessory tissues may include epithelial, muscular, or connective tissue. Sense organs can be as complex as the eye and ear or as microscopic and simple as a dendrite wrapped in a little bit of connective tissue.

### 16.1a General Properties of Receptors

The fundamental purpose of any sensory receptor is **transduction,** the conversion of one form of energy to another—light, sound, heat, touch, vibration, or other forms of stimulus energy into nerve signals. (Any device that converts one energy form to another is a *transducer*—whether a sense organ, gasoline engine, or lightbulb.)

The initial effect of a stimulus on a sensory cell is a small local electrical change called a **receptor potential.** In many cases, such as the senses of touch and smell, the sensory cell is a neuron. If the receptor potential is strong enough, the neuron fires off a volley of action potentials, generating a nerve signal to the CNS. In other cases, such as taste and hearing, the sensory cell isn't a neuron but an epithelial cell. Nevertheless, it has synaptic vesicles at its base; it releases a neurotransmitter in response to a stimulus; and it stimulates an adjacent neuron. That neuron then generates signals to the CNS.

Not all sensory signals go to the brain, but when they do, we may experience a **sensation**—a subjective awareness of the stimulus. Yet most sensory signals delivered to the CNS produce no conscious sensation at all. Most of them are filtered out in the brainstem before reaching the cerebral cortex, a valuable function that keeps us from being driven mad by innumerable unimportant stimuli detected by the sense organs. Other nerve signals concern functions that don't require conscious awareness, such as monitoring blood pH and body temperature.

Sensory receptors transmit four kinds of information—*modality, location, intensity,* and *duration:*

1. **Modality** refers to the type of stimulus or the sensation it produces. Vision, hearing, and taste are examples of sensory modalities, as are subcategories of these such as red or blue light, bass or treble sounds. The action potentials for vision

are identical to the action potentials for taste or any other modality—so how can the brain tell a visual signal from a taste signal? Modality is determined by where the sensory signals end in the brain. Hypothetically, if we could rewire the brain so signals from the ear were routed to the visual cortex of the occipital lobe, we would perceive acoustic signals as light rather than sound.

2. **Location** is also encoded by which nerve fibers issue signals to the brain. Any sensory neuron detects stimuli within an area called its **receptive field.** In the sense of touch, for example, a single sensory neuron may cover an area of skin as large as 7 cm in diameter. No matter where the skin is touched within that field, it stimulates the same neuron. The brain may be unable to determine whether the skin was touched at "point A" or at some other point 1 or 2 cm away. If the skin is simultaneously touched at two places in the same field, it can feel like a single touch **(fig. 16.1a).** In some areas of the body such as the back, however, it isn't necessary to make finer distinctions. On the other hand, we must be able to localize touch sensations much more precisely with the fingertips. Here, each sensory neuron may cover a receptive field 1 mm or less in diameter—there is a much higher density of tactile nerve fibers. Two points of contact just 2 mm apart will be felt as separate touches **(fig. 16.1b).** That is, the fingertips have finer *two-point touch discrimination* than the skin of the back. You can imagine the importance of this in reading braille, appreciating the texture of a fine fabric, or manipulating an object as small as a sesame seed. The receptive field concept pertains not only to touch, but also to other senses such as vision.
3. **Intensity** refers to whether a sound is loud or soft, a light is bright or dim, a pain is mild or excruciating, and so forth. It is encoded in three ways: (a) As stimulus intensity rises, the firing frequencies of sensory nerve fibers rise (see fig. 12.30); (b) intense stimuli recruit greater numbers of neurons to fire; and (c) weak stimuli activate only the most sensitive neurons, whereas strong stimuli can activate a less sensitive group of neurons with higher thresholds. Thus, the brain can distinguish intensities based on which neurons are firing, how many are doing so, and how fast they are firing.
4. **Duration,** or how long a stimulus lasts, is encoded by changes in firing frequency with the passage of time. All receptors exhibit the property of **sensory adaptation**—if the stimulus is prolonged, the firing of the neuron gets slower

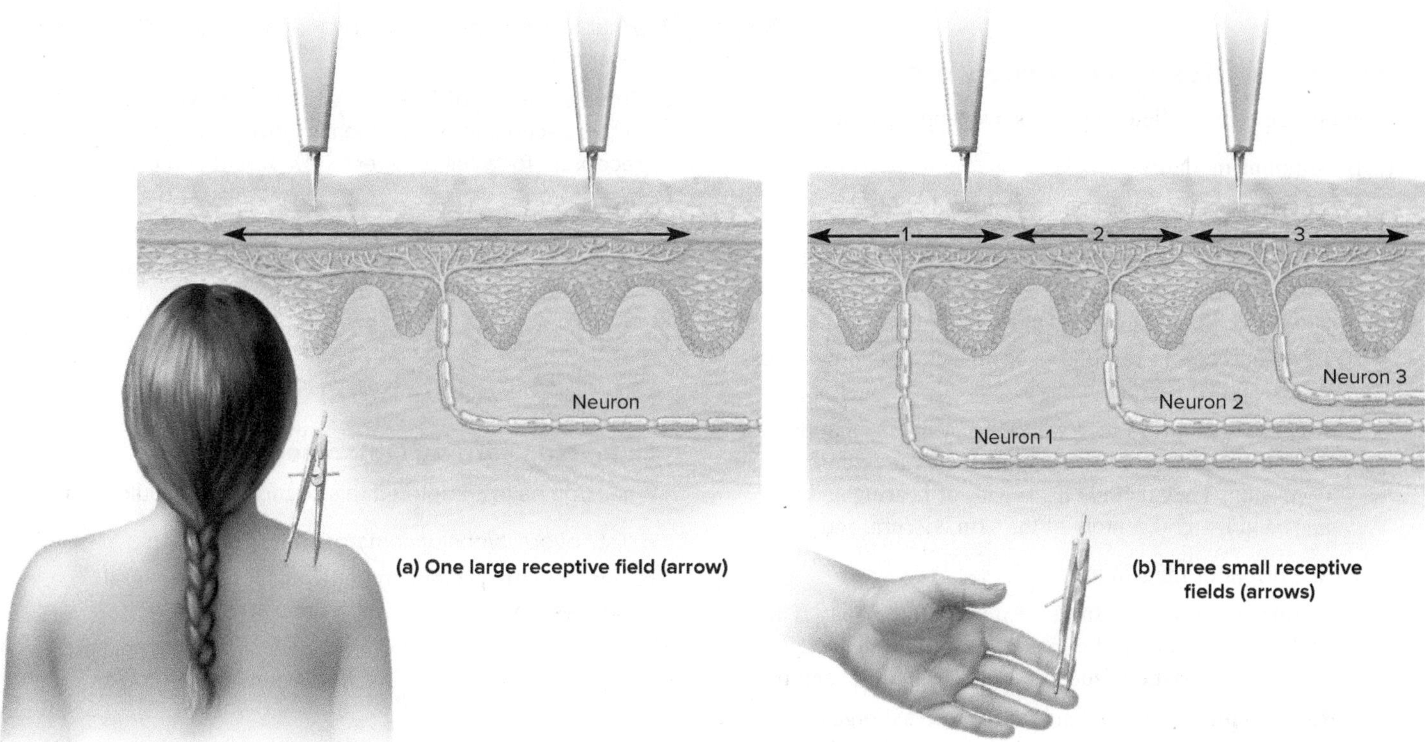


**FIGURE 16.1 Receptive Fields.** (a) A neuron with a large receptive field, as found in the skin of the back. If the skin is touched in two close-together places within this receptive field, the brain senses it as only one point of contact. (b) Neurons with small receptive fields, as found in the fingertips. Two close-together points of contact here are likely to stimulate two different neurons and be felt as separate touches.

? *If the receptive field in part (a) is 7 cm in diameter, is it ever possible for two touches 1 cm apart to be felt separately?*

over time, and with it, we become less aware of the stimulus. Adapting to hot bathwater is an example of this. Receptors are classified according to how quickly they adapt. **Phasic receptors** generate a burst of action potentials when first stimulated, then quickly adapt and sharply reduce or stop signaling even if the stimulus continues. Some of them fire again when the stimulus ceases. Phasic receptors are found in the senses of smell, hair movement, and cutaneous pressure and vibration. Their phasic nature explains why we may notice a suspicious odor such as a gas leak for several seconds, then the sensation fades in intensity even if the stimulus is still there. If we don't find the gas leak quickly, it becomes difficult to find it at all. **Tonic receptors** adapt more slowly and generate signals more steadily. Proprioceptors and pain receptors are among the most persistently responding tonic receptors because the brain must always be aware of body position, muscle tension, joint motion, or a pain.

**▶▶▶ APPLY WHAT YOU KNOW**

*Although you may find it difficult to immerse yourself in a tub of hot water or a cold lake, you soon adapt and become more comfortable. In light of this, do you think cold and warm receptors are phasic or tonic? Explain.*

### 16.1b Classification of Receptors

Receptors can be classified by various overlapping systems:

1. By stimulus modality:
   - **Thermoreceptors** respond to heat and cold.
   - **Photoreceptors,** the eyes, respond to light.
   - **Nociceptors,**[1] pain receptors, respond to tissue injury or situations that threaten to damage a tissue.
   - **Chemoreceptors** respond to chemicals, including odors, tastes, and body fluid composition.
   - **Mechanoreceptors** respond to physical deformation of a cell or tissue caused by vibration, touch, pressure, stretch, or tension. They include the organs of hearing and balance and many receptors of the skin, viscera, and joints.
2. By the origin of the stimulus:
   - **Exteroceptors** sense stimuli external to the body. They include the receptors for vision, hearing, taste, smell, and cutaneous sensations such as touch, heat, cold, and pain.
   - **Interoceptors** detect stimuli in the internal organs such as the stomach, intestines, and bladder, and produce feelings of stretch, pressure, visceral pain, and nausea.
   - **Proprioceptors** sense the position and movements of the body or its parts. They occur in muscles, tendons, and joint capsules.
3. By the distribution of receptors in the body. There are two broad classes of senses:
   - **General (somatosensory, somesthetic) senses** employ widely distributed receptors in the skin, muscles, tendons, joints, and viscera. These include touch, pressure, stretch, heat, cold, and pain, as well as many stimuli that we do not perceive consciously, such as blood pressure and composition. Their receptors are relatively simple—sometimes nothing more than a bare dendrite.
   - **Special senses** are limited to the head, are innervated by the cranial nerves, and employ relatively complex sense organs. The special senses are vision, hearing, equilibrium, taste, and smell.

**BEFORE YOU GO ON**

Answer the following questions to test your understanding of the preceding section:

1. Not every sensory *receptor* is a sense *organ*. Explain.
2. What does it mean to say sense organs are transducers? What form of energy do all receptors have as their output?
3. Not every sensory signal results in conscious awareness of a stimulus. Explain.
4. What is meant by the *modality* of a stimulus? Give some examples.
5. Three schemes of receptor classification were presented in this section. In each scheme, how would you classify the receptors for a full bladder? How would you classify taste receptors?
6. Nociceptors are tonic rather than phasic receptors. Speculate on why this is beneficial to homeostasis.

## 16.2 The General Senses

**Expected Learning Outcomes**

When you have completed this section, you should be able to

a. list several types of somatosensory receptors;
b. describe the projection pathways for the general senses; and
c. describe the types and mechanisms of pain, and explain how the brain modulates one's sensitivity to pain.

Receptors for the general senses are relatively simple in structure and physiology. They consist of one or a few sensory nerve fibers and, usually, a sparse amount of connective tissue. These receptors are shown in **figure 16.2** and described in **table 16.1.**

[1]*noci* = pain

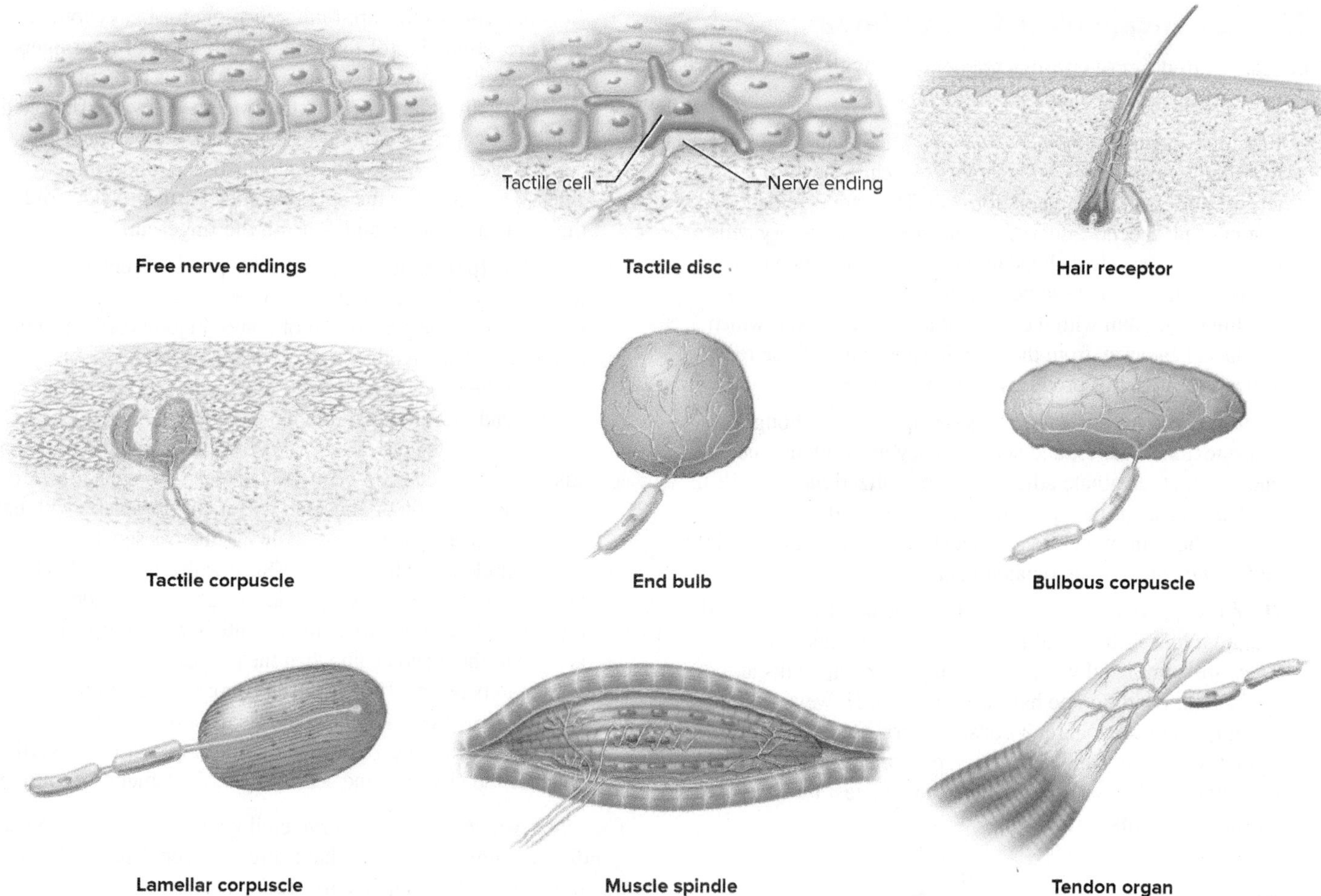


**FIGURE 16.2 Receptors of the General Senses.** See table 16.1 for functions.

**TABLE 16.1 Receptors of the General Senses**

| Receptor Type | Locations | Modality |
|---|---|---|
| **Unencapsulated Endings** | | |
| Free nerve endings | Widespread, especially in epithelia and connective tissues | Pain, heat, cold |
| Tactile discs | Stratum basale of epidermis | Light touch, pressure |
| Hair receptors | Around hair follicle | Light touch, movement of hairs |
| **Encapsulated Nerve Endings** | | |
| Tactile corpuscles | Dermal papillae of fingertips, palms, eyelids, lips, tongue, nipples, and genitals | Light touch, texture |
| End bulbs | Mucous membranes | Similar to tactile corpuscles |
| Bulbous corpuscles | Dermis, subcutaneous tissue, and joint capsules | Heavy continuous touch or pressure; joint movements |
| Lamellar corpuscles | Dermis, joint capsules, periosteum, breasts, genitals, and some viscera | Deep pressure, stretch, tickle, vibration |
| Muscle spindles | Skeletal muscles near tendon | Muscle stretch (proprioception) |
| Tendon organs | Tendons | Tension on tendons (proprioception) |

### 16.2a Unencapsulated Nerve Endings

**Unencapsulated nerve endings** are dendrites with no connective tissue wrapping. They include the following:

- **Free nerve endings** include *warm receptors,* which respond to rising temperature; *cold receptors,* which respond to falling temperature; and *nociceptors* for pain. They are bare dendrites that have no special association with specific accessory cells or tissues. They are most abundant in the skin and mucous membranes. You can locate some of your cold receptors by gently touching your skin with the point of a graphite pencil, which conducts heat away from the skin. In spots where these receptors are located, this produces a sensation of cold.
- **Tactile discs** are tonic receptors for light touch, thought to sense textures, edges, and shapes. They are flattened nerve endings that terminate adjacent to specialized *tactile cells* in the basal layer of the epidermis. They respond to compression of the skin, which releases a chemical from the tactile cell that excites the associated nerve fiber.
- **Hair receptors (root hair plexuses)** are dendrites that coil around a hair follicle and respond to movements of the hair. They are stimulated when, for example, an ant walks across one's skin, bending one hair after another. However, they adapt quickly, so we aren't constantly irritated by the feel of clothing against the skin. Hair receptors are particularly important in the eyelashes, where the slightest touch evokes a protective blink reflex.

### 16.2b Encapsulated Nerve Endings

**Encapsulated nerve endings** are nerve fibers wrapped in glial cells or connective tissue. Most of them are mechanoreceptors for touch, pressure, and stretch. The connective tissue either enhances the sensitivity of the nerve fiber or makes it more selective with respect to which modality it responds to. The principal encapsulated nerve endings are as follows:

- **Tactile corpuscles** are phasic receptors for light touch and texture. They are tall, ovoid to pear-shaped, and consist of two or three nerve fibers meandering upward through a fluid-filled capsule of flattened Schwann cells. They are mechanically linked to the edges of the dermal papillae of the skin. Tactile corpuscles are especially concentrated in sensitive hairless areas such as the fingertips, palms, eyelids, lips, nipples, and genitals. Drag your fingernail lightly across the back of your hand, and then across your palm. The difference in sensation you feel is due to the high concentration of tactile corpuscles in the palmar skin. Tactile corpuscles enable you to tell the difference between silk and sandpaper, for example, by light strokes of your fingertips.
- **End bulbs** are functionally similar to tactile corpuscles, but instead of occurring in the skin, they are found in the mucous membranes of the lips and tongue, in the conjunctiva on the anterior surface of the eye, and in the epineurium of large nerves. They are ovoid bodies composed of a connective tissue sheath around a sensory nerve fiber.
- **Bulbous corpuscles** are tonic receptors for heavy touch, pressure, stretching of the skin, deformation of the fingernails, and joint movements. They aid in our perception of the shapes of objects held in the fingers. They are flattened, elongated capsules containing a few nerve fibers and are located in the dermis, subcutaneous tissue, and joint capsules. They connect the subcutaneous tissues to skin folds in the joints and palms and beneath the fingernails.
- **Lamellar (pacinian[2]) corpuscles** are phasic receptors chiefly for vibration. They are large ovoid receptors, up to 1 or 2 mm long, found in the periosteum of bones; in joint capsules; in the pancreas and some other viscera; and deep in the dermis, especially on the hands, feet, breasts, and genitals. They consist of a single dendrite running through the core of the organ, encapsulated by multiple concentric layers of cells. The innermost capsule layers are flattened Schwann cells, but the greater bulk of the capsule consists of concentric layers of fibroblasts with narrow fluid-filled spaces between them. In cross section, a lamellar corpuscle looks like an onion slice with a dot, the dendrite, in the middle. Lamellar corpuscles are phasic receptors that respond with one or two action potentials when pressure is applied to them and again when the pressure is taken away, but not in between. They are usually considered to function as vibration receptors, stimulated by such actions as stroking a surface with the fingertips. The friction ridges of the fingertips enhance the vibration and sensitivity of the lamellar corpuscles.

The other two encapsulated nerve endings in figure 16.2—muscle spindles and tendon organs—have already been discussed in relation to muscle reflexes in section 13.3.

### 16.2c Somatosensory Projection Pathways

**Sensory projection** is the transmission of information from a receptor, or a receptive field, to a specific locality in the cerebral cortex, enabling the brain to detect and identify the stimulus. The identifiable origin can be a small and specific area within a receptor, such as a small area of the retina or the skin. The pathways followed by sensory signals to their ultimate destinations in the CNS are called **projection pathways.** From the receptor to the final destination in the brain, most somatosensory signals travel by way of three neurons called the **first-, second-,** and **third-order neurons.** Their axons are called first- through third-order nerve fibers. The first-order fibers for touch, pressure, and proprioception are large, myelinated, and fast; those for heat and cold are small, unmyelinated or lightly myelinated, and slower.

Somatosensory signals from the head, such as facial sensations, travel by way of several cranial nerves (especially CN V, the trigeminal nerve) to the pons and medulla oblongata. In the brainstem, the first-order fibers of these neurons synapse with second-order neurons that decussate and lead to the contralateral thalamus. Third-order neurons then complete the projection pathway to the cerebrum. Proprioceptive signals from the head are an exception, as the second-order fibers carry these signals to the cerebellum.

Below the head, the first-order fibers enter the posterior horn of the spinal cord. Signals ascend the cord in the spinothalamic and

[2]Filippo Pacini (1812–83), Italian anatomist

other pathways detailed in table 13.1 and figure 13.6. These pathways decussate either at or near the point of entry into the cord, or in the brainstem, so the primary somatosensory cortex in each cerebral hemisphere receives signals from the contralateral side of the body.

Signals for proprioception below the head travel up the spinocerebellar tracts to the cerebellum. Signals from the thoracic and abdominal viscera travel to the medulla oblongata by way of sensory fibers in the vagus nerve (CN X). Visceral pain signals also ascend the spinal cord in the gracile fasciculus.

### 16.2d Pain

From a clinical standpoint, the sense of pain arguably deserves the most attention of all the senses we cover in this chapter, for it is the number one reason people seek medical attention. It is also one of the most difficult problems to treat.

**Pain** can be defined as an uncomfortable perception of tissue injury or noxious stimulation. It is not a disease in itself, but a symptom of an underlying condition. Its function is to motivate one to avoid, minimize, or escape danger—for example, by favoring a sprained ankle, withdrawing one's hand from a burn, or avoiding things that have caused pain in the past. Few of us enjoy pain and we may wish that no such thing existed, but it is an adaptive and necessary sensation—we'd be far worse off without it. We see evidence of this in such diseases as leprosy and diabetes mellitus, where nerve damage *(peripheral neuropathy)* can deaden the sense of pain and make a person unaware of minor injuries or not care enough about them. The resulting neglect can allow injuries to become gangrenous and cost people their fingers, toes, feet, or entire limbs.

#### Types of Pain

There are two clinical categories of pain—*nociceptive and neuropathic.* **Nociceptive pain** stems from tissue injury such as cuts, burns, and chemical irritation, detected by the nerve endings called nociceptors. These are especially abundant in the skin and mucous membranes and occur in nearly all organs, although not in the brain or liver. In some brain surgery, the patient must remain conscious and able to talk with the surgeon; such patients need only local anesthesia. Nociceptors occur in the meninges, however, and play an important role in headaches. Nociceptive pain is associated with tissue inflammation and responds to anti-inflammatory drugs such as aspirin, ibuprofen, and naprosyn.

Nociceptive pain is sudivided into three kinds according to origin:

1. **Visceral pain,** which arises from the internal organs of the body cavities. This type of pain is diffuse, dull, and hard to locate. Among its causes are stretch (such as an overfull bladder or stomach), chemical irritation (as in intestinal cramps and acid reflux), and ischemia (deficient blood flow, as in heart attacks and menstrual cramps). It is often associated with sensations of squeezing, cramping, and nausea.
2. **Deep somatic pain,** which arises from bones, joints, muscles, and related sources. Examples include the pain of arthritis, sprains, and bone fractures. It often results from excessive stretch (as in an ankle sprain or pulled muscle), but can have other causes.
3. **Superficial somatic pain,** which usually arises from the skin. Examples include the pain of cuts, burns, and insect stings.

**Neuropathic pain** stems from injuries to the nerves, spinal cord, meninges, or brain. It is often characterized by stabbing, burning, tingling, or "electrical" sensations. Examples include headache; phantom limb pain; fibromyalgia; and the pain of multiple sclerosis, postherpetic neuralgia (see Deeper Insight 13.3), and cancer (from tumor invasion of nerves or neurotoxic effects of chemotherapy).

Two types of nerve fibers mediate pain responses and contrasting qualities of pain called *fast pain* and *slow pain.* **Fast pain** is the immediate, sharp pain one feels from a cut, burn, or bee sting, for example. It is mediated by myelinated *A-delta (Aδ)* nerve fibers. These conduct signals at speeds of 12 to 30 m/s, so the pain is felt quickly upon injury. It is a sharp, localized, often stabbing feel. It is described as *discriminative pain* because we can usually tell exactly where it is coming from. **Slow pain** originates in small unmyelinated *type C* nerve fibers, which conduct at only 0.5 to 2.0 m/s. It has a delayed and more burning or aching feel, and it's harder to tell exactly where the pain is coming from. If you bang your shin on a piece of furniture, you may feel both of these: a sharp fast pain immediately, then after a few seconds, an even more intense and longer-lasting slow pain.

#### Projection Pathways for Pain

It is notoriously difficult for clinicians to locate the origin of a patient's pain, because pain travels by diverse and complex routes and the sensation can originate anywhere along the way. Pain signals reach the brain by two main pathways:

1. Signals from the head travel to the brainstem by way of four cranial nerves: mainly the trigeminal (CN V), but also the facial (CN VII), glossopharyngeal (CN IX), and vagus (CN X) nerves. Trigeminal fibers enter the pons and descend to synapses in the medulla. Pain fibers of the other three cranial nerves lead directly to the medulla. Second-order neurons arise in the medulla and ascend to the thalamus, which relays the message to the cerebral cortex, as detailed shortly.
2. Pain signals from the neck and below travel by way of three ascending spinal cord tracts: the spinothalamic tract, spinoreticular tract, and gracile fasciculus (**fig. 16.3;** see also section 13.1, fig. 13.6). The spinothalamic tract carries most of the somatic pain signals that ultimately reach the cortex and make us conscious of pain. The spinoreticular tract carries signals to the reticular formation of the brainstem, and these are ultimately relayed to the hypothalamus and limbic system. Here, they activate visceral, emotional, and behavioral reactions such as nausea, fear, and some reflexes. The gracile fasciculus carries signals to the thalamus for visceral pain, such as the pain of a stomachache or from passing a kidney stone.

When the thalamus receives pain signals from these sources, it relays most of them through third-order neurons to their final destination in the postcentral gyrus of the cerebrum. This is the site of discriminative pain perception—judgment of the location of injury and the quality and intensity of the sensation. Exactly what part of this gyrus receives the signals depends on where the pain originated, as described by the concept of somatotopy in section 14.5g (see fig. 14.21). Most of this gyrus is somatosensory. A region of the gyrus deep within the lateral sulcus of the brain, however, is a viscerosensory area, which receives the visceral signals conveyed by

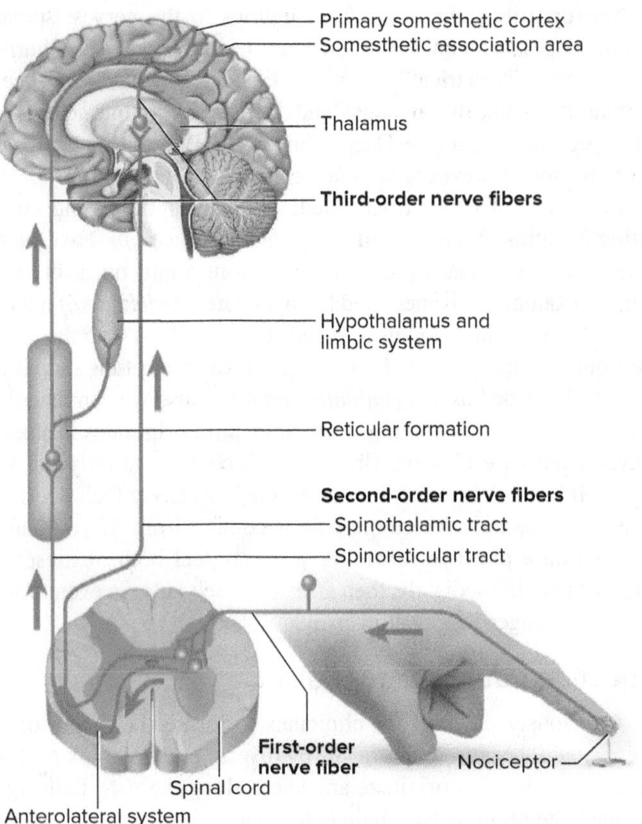


**FIGURE 16.3 Projection Pathways for Pain.** A first-order neuron conducts a pain signal to the posterior horn of the spinal cord, a second-order neuron conducts it to the thalamus, and a third-order neuron conducts it to the cerebral cortex. Signals from the spinothalamic tract pass through the thalamus. Signals from the spinoreticular tract bypass the thalamus on the way to the sensory cortex.

the gracile fasciculus. The emotional aspects of pain register in the hypothalamus and the prefrontal cortex, limbic system, insula, and anterior cingulate gyrus of the cerebrum (see figs. 14.16, 14.17).

Pain in the viscera is often mistakenly thought to come from the skin or other superficial sites—for example, the pain of a heart attack is felt "radiating" along the left shoulder and medial side of the arm **(fig. 16.4).** This phenomenon, called **referred pain,** results from the convergence of neural pathways in the CNS. In the case of cardiac pain, for example, spinal cord segments T1 to T5 receive input from the heart as well as from the chest and arm. Pain fibers from the heart and skin in this region converge and follow the same pathway from here to the thalamus and cerebral cortex. The brain can't distinguish which source the arriving signals are coming from. It acts as if it assumes they are most likely from the skin, since skin has more pain receptors than the heart and suffers injury more often. Knowledge of the origins of referred pain is important for the diagnosis of organ dysfunctions.

## CNS Modulation of Pain

Regardless of expressions such as "pain in the joints" and "muscle pain," it must be realized that pain doesn't exist in these peripheral locations, but only in the brain; it is a conscious *perception* of signals from other organs. Because of this, it is subjective, highly variable, and influenced by a person's physical and mental state—for example, one's expectation of pain, fixation on it, or conversely, achieving pain relief by redirecting one's attention to distractors. This is why such techniques as acupuncture, meditation, hypnosis, placebos, exercise therapy, and Lamaze childbirth can effectively lessen pain.

Some examples show how pain originates in cerebral perception and not in the outlying organs. **Fibromyalgia** is a syndrome of sometimes excruciating, even disabling pain that seems to come from the muscles or bones; yet those distant organs are sending no abnormal nerve signals to the brain. The pain lies entirely in the brain's abnormal responses to normal incoming signals.

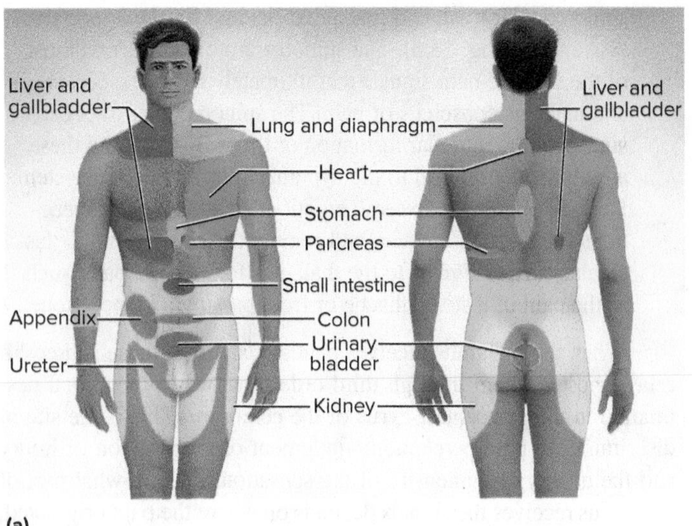


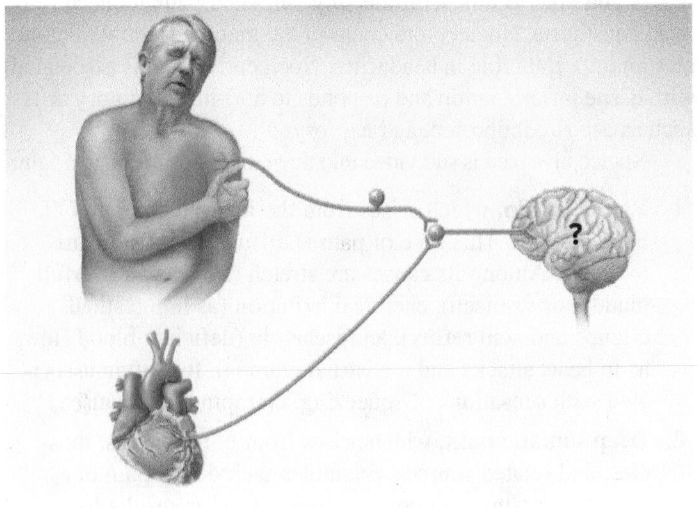


**FIGURE 16.4 Referred Pain.** (a) Areas of referred pain. Pain in these areas of the skin is often a symptom of problems in the indicated viscera. (b) The basis of referred pain in a heart attack.

**Phantom limb pain** is an eerie sensation of pain, sometimes intense, coming from a limb that has been lost by trauma or amputation. It is commonly accompanied by nonpainful *phantom limb sensations* such as the bulk and weight of the absent limb; or feelings of touch, itching, tingling, pressure, heat, or cold; or the illusion that one can even control the limb. Phantom pain can also occur when other body parts have been removed, such as after a tooth extraction or mastectomy. The neurological mechanism of phantom limb pain isn't known with certainty, and it doesn't respond to conventional pain medications. One might think that cutting nerves or even the spinal cord along pain pathways could eliminate the pain, but it doesn't. Battlefield trauma, in contrast to these other cases, shows strikingly how the brain can powerfully suppress the painful awareness of severe injury—many mortally wounded soldiers have reported little or no pain even in their dying hour. So as one neurologist has put it, the bane of pain lies mainly in the brain.

The central nervous system has **analgesic**[3] (pain-relieving) mechanisms related to the long-known analgesic effects of opium, morphine, and heroin. In 1974, neurophysiologists discovered receptor sites in the brain for these drugs. Since these opiates don't occur naturally in the body, physiologists wondered what normally binds to such receptors. They soon found two analgesic oligopeptides with 200 times the potency of morphine, and named them **enkephalins.**[4] Larger analgesic neuropeptides, the **endorphins**[5] and **dynorphins,**[6] were discovered later. All three are known as **endogenous opioids** (which means "internally produced opium-like substances").

These opioids are secreted by the CNS, pituitary gland, digestive tract, and other organs in states of stress or exercise. In the CNS, they are found especially in the central gray substance of the midbrain (see fig. 14.9a) and posterior horn of the spinal cord. They are *neuromodulators* that can block the transmission of pain signals and produce feelings of pleasure and euphoria. Their secretion rises sharply in women giving birth, and they may even be responsible for the aforementioned battlefield reports. However, efforts to employ them in pain therapy have been disappointing.

How do these opioids block pain? For pain to be perceived, signals from the nociceptors must get beyond the posterior horn of the spinal cord and travel to the brain. Through mechanisms called **spinal gating,** pain signals can be stopped at the posterior horn. Two of these mechanisms are described here.

One of these involves **descending analgesic fibers**—nerve fibers that arise in the brainstem, travel down the spinal cord in the reticulospinal tract, and block pain signals from traveling to the brain. **Figure 16.5** depicts one relatively simple mechanism

[3]*an* = without; *alges* = pain

[4]*en* = within; *kephal* = head
[5]acronym from *endogenous morphine*
[6]*dyn* = pain

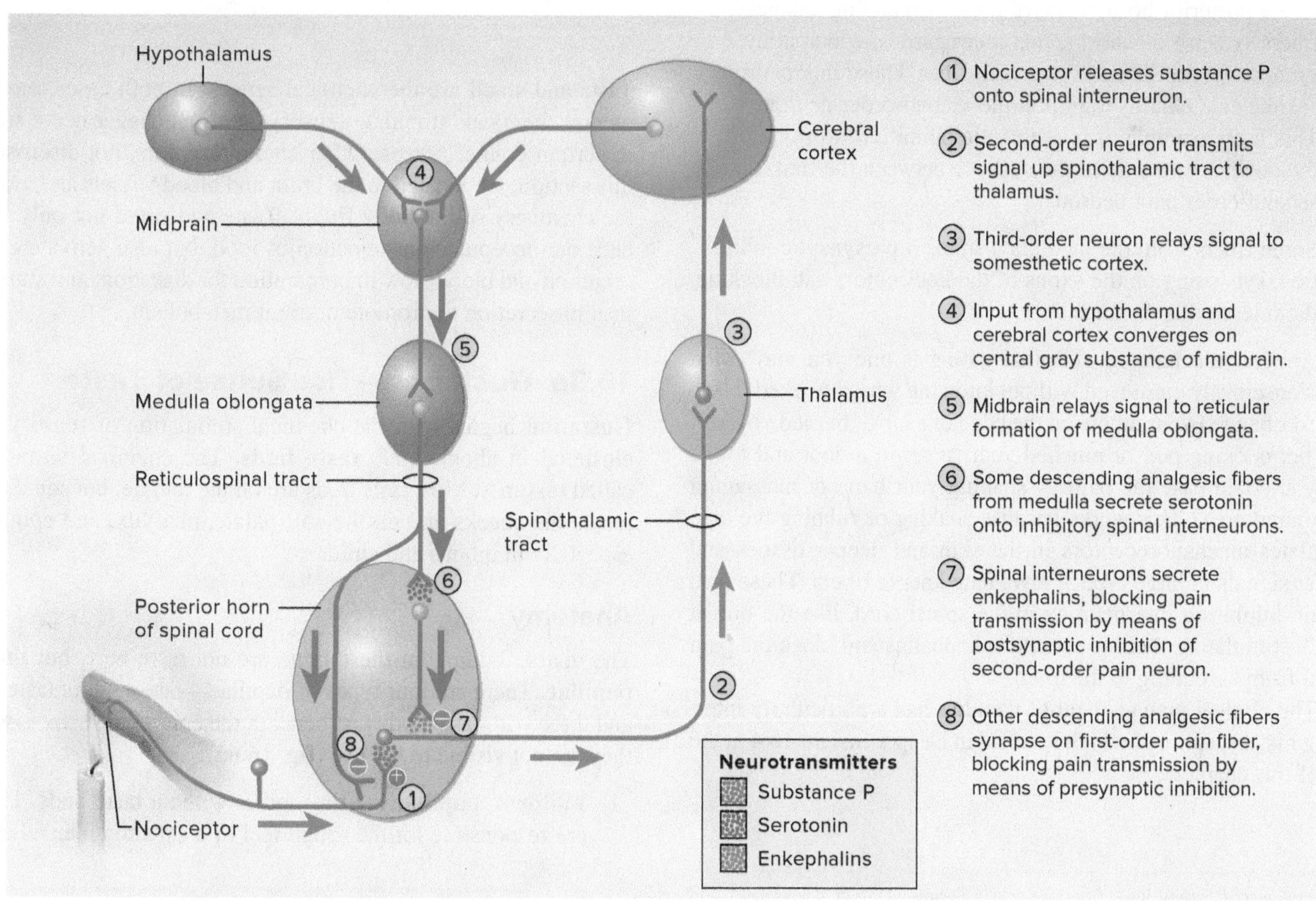


**FIGURE 16.5 Spinal Gating of Pain Signals.**

of pain modulation in the posterior horn. The normal route of pain transmission is indicated by the red arrows and steps 1 through 3:

1. A nociceptor stimulates a second-order nerve fiber. The neurotransmitter at this synapse is called **substance P** (think *P* for "pain"[7]).
2. The second-order nerve fiber transmits signals up the spinothalamic tract to the thalamus.
3. The thalamus relays the signals through a third-order neuron to the cerebral cortex, where one becomes conscious of pain.

The pathway for pain modulation is indicated by descending green arrows and steps 4 through 8:

4. Signals from the hypothalamus and cerebral cortex feed into the central gray substance of the midbrain, allowing both autonomic and conscious effects on pain perception.
5. The midbrain relays signals to certain nuclei in the reticular formation of the medulla oblongata.
6. The medulla issues descending, serotonin-secreting analgesic fibers to the spinal cord. These fibers travel the reticulospinal tract and end in the posterior horn at all levels of the cord.
7. In the posterior horn, some of these descending analgesic fibers synapse on short spinal interneurons, which in turn synapse on the second-order pain fiber. These interneurons secrete enkephalins to inhibit the second-order neuron. This is an example of postsynaptic inhibition, working on the downstream side of the synapse between the first- and second-order pain neurons.
8. Some fibers from the medulla also exert presynaptic inhibition, synapsing on the axons of the nociceptors and blocking the release of substance P.

Another mechanism of spinal gating is one you may often have consciously employed without knowing why it worked. Have you ever banged your elbow on the edge of a table, burned yourself on a hot cooking pot, or pinched your finger in a door and found that you could ease the pain by shaking your hand or massaging the injured area? This works because shaking or rubbing the area stimulates mechanoreceptors in the skin and deeper tissues and trigger signals in large type A myelinated nerve fibers. These lead to pain-inhibiting interneurons in the spinal cord, like the one at step 7, stimulating them to secrete enkephalins and block the pain signal from ascending to the brain.

The clinical management of pain has had a particularly interesting history, some of which is retold in Deeper Insight 16.4 at the end of this chapter.

[7]named *substance P* because it was first discovered in a *powdered* extract of brain and intestine

**BEFORE YOU GO ON**

Answer the following questions to test your understanding of the preceding section:

7. What stimulus modalities are detected by free nerve endings?
8. Name any four encapsulated nerve endings and identify their stimulus modalities.
9. Where do most second-order somatosensory neurons synapse with third-order neurons?
10. Distinguish between nociceptive and neuropathic pain, and describe the three categories of nociceptive pain.
11. Outline the pathways that pain signals take to and within the brain.
12. Describe two ways that the CNS can modify a person's perception of incoming pain signals.

## 16.3 The Chemical Senses

**Expected Learning Outcomes**

When you have completed this section, you should be able to

a. explain how taste and smell receptors are stimulated; and
b. describe the receptors and projection pathways for these two senses.

Taste and smell are the chemical senses. In both cases, environmental chemicals stimulate sensory cells and trigger nerve signals in certain cranial nerves. Other chemoreceptors, not discussed in this section, are located in the brain and blood vessels and monitor the chemistry of the body fluids. Taste and smell not only influence our acceptance or rejection of food, but also activate gastric secretion and blood flow in preparation for digestion, and stimulate insulin secretion to promote nutrient metabolism.

### 16.3a Gustation—The Sense of Taste

**Gustation** begins with the chemical stimulation of sensory cells clustered in about 4,000 **taste buds.** The chemical stimuli are called **tastants.** Most taste buds are on the tongue, but some occur inside the cheeks and on the soft palate, pharynx, and epiglottis, especially in infants and children.

#### Anatomy

The visible bumps on the tongue are not taste buds but **lingual papillae.** There are four types of papillae—one without taste buds and three with taste buds just beneath the epithelial surface, where they are not visible to the eye **(fig. 16.6a):**

1. **Filiform**[8] **papillae** are tiny spikes without taste buds. They are responsible for the rough feel of a cat's tongue and are

[8]*fili* = thread; *form* = shaped

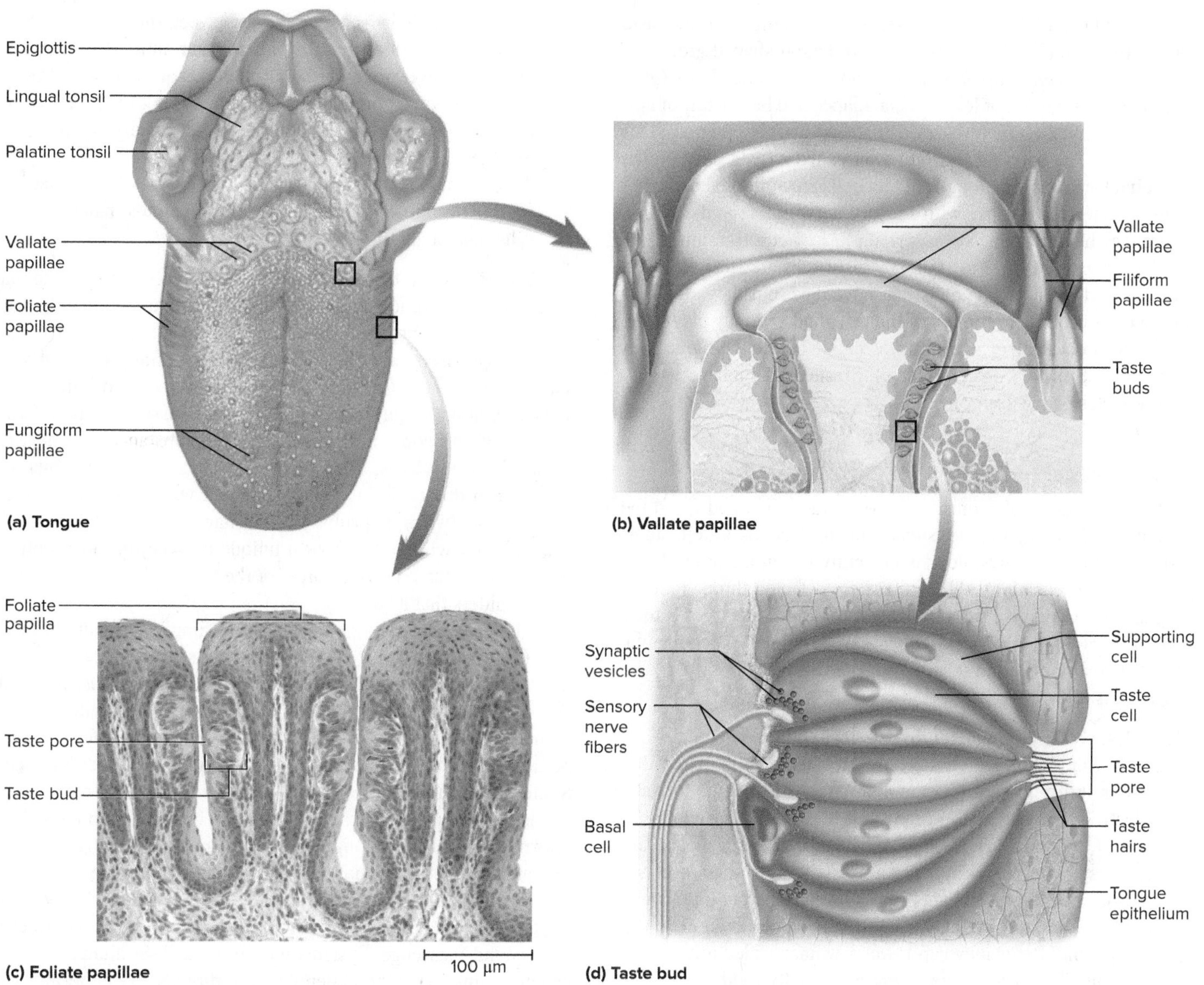


**FIGURE 16.6 Gustatory (Taste) Receptors.** (a) Superior surface of the tongue and locations of its papillae. (b) Detail of the vallate papillae (compare this chapter's opening photo). (c) Taste buds on the walls of two adjacent foliate papillae. (d) Structure of a taste bud. APR

c: Jose Luis Calvo/Shutterstock.com

important to many mammals for grooming the fur. They are the most abundant papillae on the human tongue, but they are small. They are innervated, however, and serve in one's sense of the texture of food, called *mouthfeel.*

2. **Foliate**[9] **papillae** are also weakly developed in humans. They form parallel ridges on the sides of the tongue about two-thirds of the way back from the tip, adjacent to the molar and premolar teeth, where most chewing occurs and most flavor chemicals are released from the food. Most of their taste buds degenerate by the age of 2 or 3 years. This may partially explain why children so often reject foods that are tolerated or enjoyed by adults.

3. **Fungiform**[10] **papillae** (FUN-jih-form) are shaped somewhat like mushrooms. Each has about three taste buds, located mainly on the apex. These papillae are widely distributed, but especially concentrated at the tip and sides of the tongue. These respond not only to taste but, like filiform papillae, also to food texture.

4. **Vallate**[11] **papillae** are large papillae arranged in a V at the rear of the tongue. Each is surrounded by a deep circular trench. There are only 7 to 12 vallate papillae, but they contain up to half of all taste buds—around 250 each, located on the walls of the papilla facing the trench **(fig. 16.6b).**

[9] *foli* = leaf; *ate* = like

[10] *fungi* = mushroom; *form* = shaped

[11] *vall* = wall; *ate* = like, possessing

Regardless of location and sensory specialization, all taste buds look alike **(fig. 16.6c, d).** They are lemon-shaped groups of 50 to 150 *taste cells, supporting cells,* and *basal cells.* **Taste (gustatory) cells** are more or less banana-shaped and have a tuft of apical microvilli called **taste hairs,** which serve as receptor surfaces for tastants. The hairs project into a pit called a **taste pore** on the epithelial surface of the tongue. Taste cells are epithelial cells, not neurons, but they synapse with sensory nerve fibers at their base, where they have synaptic vesicles and release neurotransmitters. A taste cell lives for only 7 to 10 days. **Basal cells** are stem cells that multiply and replace taste cells that have died, but they also synapse with sensory nerve fibers of the taste bud and may play some role in the processing of sensory information before the signal goes to the brain. **Supporting cells** resemble taste cells but have no synaptic vesicles or sensory role.

## Physiology

To be tasted, molecules must dissolve in the saliva and flood the taste pore. On a dry tongue, sugar and salt have as little taste as a sprinkle of sand. Physiologists currently recognize at least five primary taste sensations. All of these are detected throughout the tongue; physiologists have abandoned the old concept of a taste map of the tongue that supposedly showed regional specialization of taste buds for different sensations. The five primary taste sensations are as follows:

1. **Salty,** produced by metal ions such as sodium and potassium. Since salts are vital electrolytes, there is obvious value in our ability to taste them and in having an appetite for salt. Electrolyte intake is also important in the osmotic regulation of the body's fluid balance. Electrolyte deficiencies can cause a craving for salt; many animals as diverse as insects, parrots, deer, and elephants seek salt deposits ranging from mud puddles and wet clay to the sweat on larger animals and people. Pregnancy can lower a woman's electrolyte concentrations and create a craving for salty food.
2. **Sweet,** produced by many organic compounds, especially sugars. Sweetness is associated with carbohydrates and foods of high caloric value. Many flowering plants have evolved sweet nectar and fruits that entice animals to eat them and disperse their pollen and seeds. Our fondness for fruit and sugar has coevolved with plant reproductive strategies.
3. **Umami** is a "meaty" taste produced by amino acids such as aspartic and glutamic acids—the savory taste of beef or chicken broth, cheese, and mushrooms. Pronounced "ooh-mommy," the word is Japanese slang for "delicious" or "yummy." The umami taste motivates protein intake.
4. **Sour,** usually associated with acids in such foods as citrus fruits. Sour is usually an aversive taste that helps one avoid spoiled foods and overloading the body's acid–base balance.
5. **Bitter,** associated with spoiled foods and alkaloids such as nicotine, caffeine, quinine, and morphine. Alkaloids are often poisonous, and the bitter taste sensation usually induces a human or animal to reject a food. While flowering plants make their fruits temptingly sweet, they often load their leaves with bitter alkaloids to deter animals from eating them. However, many bitter compounds are not very toxic, and many toxic compounds in nature are not bitter. There is little correlation between bitterness and toxicity, so the sense of bitter taste is suspected of having other functions not yet discovered. The threshold for bitter is lowest of all—that is, we can taste lower concentrations of alkaloids than of acids, salts, and sugars.

The first three of these sensations reinforce the appetite and desire for three fundamental classes of nutrients—minerals, carbohydrates, and proteins. Sour and bitter are usually aversive stimuli that discourage the ingestion of potentially harmful substances, but many of us cultivate a taste for sour and bitter foods such as lemons, yogurt, turnip greens, and Brussels sprouts. Variations between people in the taste for such substances has at least a partial genetic basis. Two important categories of nutrients not included in this classical list are fats and water. Recent research suggests that two more primary tastes may warrant inclusion in the list, as they each have their own unique oropharyngeal receptors: **oleogustus,**[12] the proposed name for the taste of fats, and **water** (if one considers that a "taste").

The many flavors we perceive aren't simply a mixture of these five (or seven) primary tastes, but are also influenced by food texture, aroma, temperature, appearance, and one's state of mind, among other things. Many flavors depend on smell; without their aromas, cinnamon merely has a faintly sweet taste, coffee and peppermint are bitter, and apples and onions taste almost identical. Some flavors such as pepper are due to stimulation of free endings of the trigeminal nerve rather than taste buds. Filiform and fungiform papillae of the tongue are innervated by the *lingual nerve* (a branch of the trigeminal) and are sensitive to texture.

Sugars, alkaloids, and glutamate stimulate taste cells by binding to receptors on the cell surface, which then activate G proteins and second-messenger systems within the cell. Sodium and acids penetrate into the cell and depolarize it directly. By either mechanism, taste cells then release neurotransmitters that stimulate the sensory dendrites at their base.

## Projection Pathways

The facial nerve (CN VII) collects sensory information from taste buds of the anterior two-thirds of the tongue, the glossopharyngeal nerve (CN IX) from the posterior one-third, and the vagus nerve (CN X) from taste buds of the palate, pharynx, and epiglottis. All taste fibers project to a site in the medulla oblongata called the *solitary nucleus.* Second-order neurons arise here and relay the signals to two destinations: (1) nuclei in the hypothalamus and amygdala that activate autonomic reflexes such as salivation, gagging, and vomiting, and that function in emotions and memory associated with taste; and (2) the thalamus, which relays signals to the primary gustatory cortex, located in the insula and roof of the lateral sulcus of the cerebrum, where we become conscious of the taste. Processed signals are further relayed to the orbitofrontal cortex (see fig. 14.16), where they

[12]*oleo* = oil; *gust* = taste

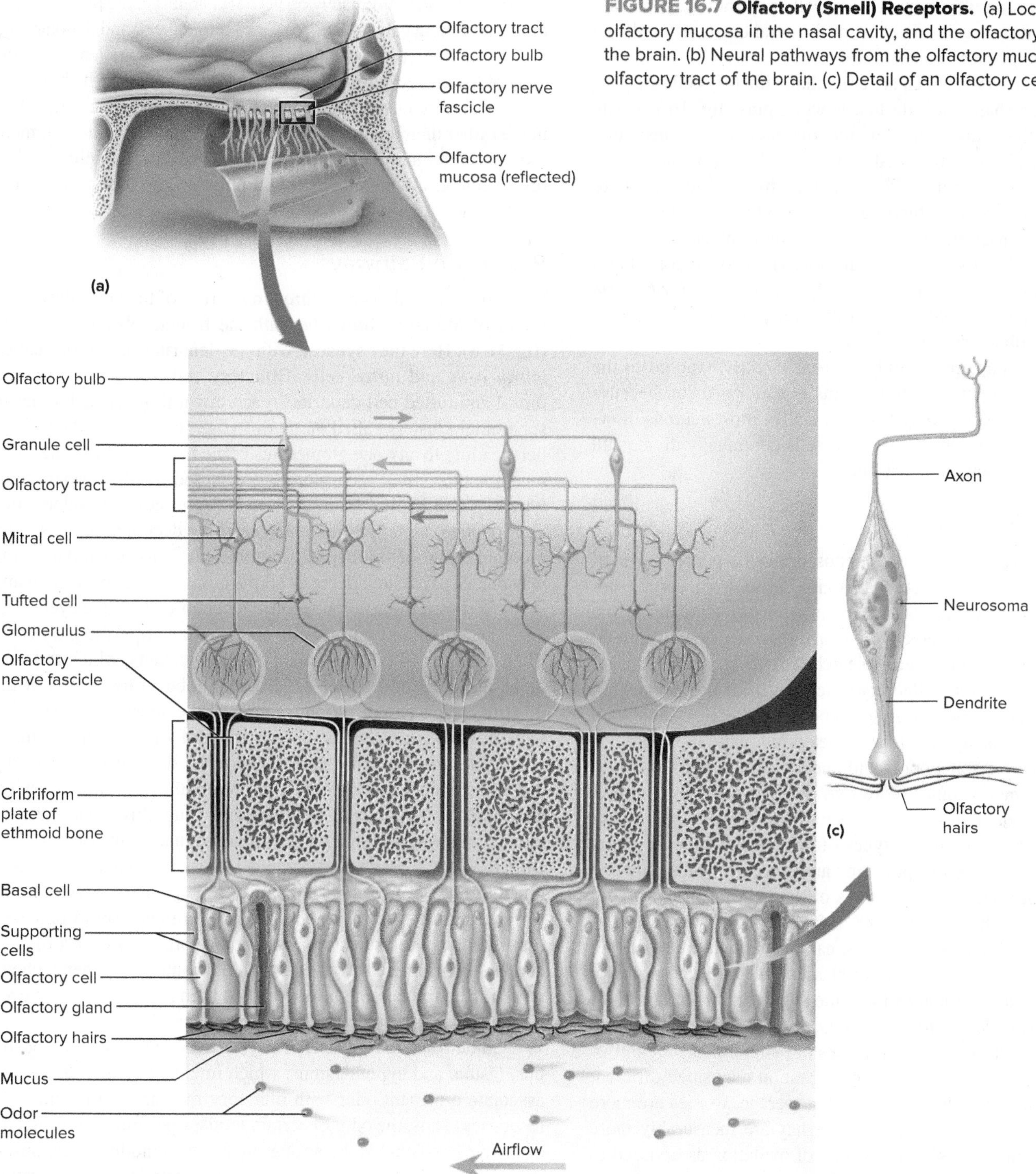


**FIGURE 16.7 Olfactory (Smell) Receptors.** (a) Location of the olfactory mucosa in the nasal cavity, and the olfactory bulb of the brain. (b) Neural pathways from the olfactory mucosa to the olfactory tract of the brain. (c) Detail of an olfactory cell.

are integrated with signals from the nose and eyes and we form an overall impression of the flavor and palatability of food.

### 16.3b Olfaction—The Sense of Smell

**Olfaction,** the sense of smell, is a response to airborne chemicals called **odorants.** These are detected by receptor cells in a patch of epithelium, the **olfactory mucosa,** in the roof of the nasal cavity **(fig. 16.7).** This location places the olfactory cells close to the brain, but it isn't as well ventilated as the lower nasal cavity; forcible sniffing is often needed to identify an odor or locate its source.

#### Anatomy

The olfactory mucosa covers about 5 $cm^2$ of the superior concha, cribriform plate, and nasal septum of each nasal fossa. It consists of 10 to 20 million **olfactory cells** as well as epithelial supporting cells and basal stem cells. The rest of the nasal cavity is lined by a nonsensory *respiratory mucosa.*

Unlike taste cells, which are epithelial, olfactory cells are neurons. They are shaped a little like bowling pins (fig. 16.7c). The widest part, the neurosoma, contains the nucleus. The neck and head of the cell are a modified dendrite with a swollen tip. The head bears 10 to 20 cilia called **olfactory hairs.** These cilia are immobile, but they have binding sites for odor molecules. They lie in a tangled mass embedded in a thin layer of mucus. The basal end of each cell tapers to become an axon. These axons collect into small fascicles that leave the nasal cavity through pores *(cribriform foramina)* in the ethmoid bone. Collectively, the fascicles are regarded as the olfactory nerve (CN I).

Olfactory cells are the only neurons directly exposed to the external environment. Apparently this is hard on them, because they have a life span of only 60 days. Unlike most neurons, however, they are replaceable. The basal cells continually divide and differentiate into new olfactory cells.

## Physiology

Humans do not, as commonly supposed, have a poorer sense of smell than other mammals; that notion arose from certain unsubstantiated nineteenth-century assumptions of Paul Broca and Sigmund Freud and suffered from confirmation bias in twentieth-century and even more recent research. We have only about one-third as many functional olfactory genes as rodents do, but we have more complex olfactory bulbs and orbitofrontal cortex—the brain regions where odor signals are interpreted. Humans outperform rodents and dogs for some odors and underperform them for others. Our sense of smell is much more sensitive than our sense of taste; we can detect odor concentrations as low as a few parts per trillion.

Humans have about 400 types of odor receptors; each olfactory cell has only one receptor type and therefore binds only one odorant. With various combinations of input, however, most people can distinguish 2,000 to 4,000 different odors; some, such as world-class food and wine experts, can distinguish up to 10,000. Attempts to group these into odor classes have been inconclusive and controversial; the names for some suggested classes have included *pungent, floral, musky,* and *earthy.* Our olfactory sense is very subject to "top-down" influences of emotional and cognitive states, so the same odorant and concentration may smell different to us under different circumstances. On average, women are more sensitive to odors than men are, and they are measurably more sensitive to some odors near the time of ovulation as opposed to other phases of the menstrual cycle. Human olfactory communication is now known to play a role in family relationships, stress and anxiety levels, and responses to the reproductive status of others, even when we're not consciously aware of this information.

The first step in smell is that an odorant molecule must bind to a receptor on one of the olfactory hairs. Hydrophilic odorants diffuse freely through the mucus of the olfactory epithelium and bind directly to a receptor. Hydrophobic odorants are transported to the receptor by an *odorant-binding protein* in the mucus. When the receptor binds an odorant, it activates a G protein and, through it, the cyclic adenosine monophosphate (cAMP) second-messenger system. The cAMP system ultimately opens ion channels in the plasma membrane, admitting cations ($Na^+$ or $Ca^{2+}$) into the cell and depolarizing it, creating a receptor potential. This triggers action potentials in the axon of the olfactory cell, and a signal is transmitted to the brain.

Some odorants, however, act on nociceptors of the trigeminal nerve rather than on olfactory cells. These include ammonia, menthol, chlorine, and the capsaicin of hot peppers. "Smelling salts" revive unconscious persons by stimulating the trigeminal nerve with ammonia fumes.

## Projection Pathways

When olfactory fibers pass through the roof of the nose, they enter a pair of **olfactory bulbs** beneath the frontal lobes of the brain **(fig. 16.8).** Here they synapse with the dendrites of neurons called *mitral cells* and *tufted cells.* Olfactory cell axons reach up and mitral and tufted cell dendrites reach down to meet each other in spheroidal clusters called *glomeruli* (fig. 16.7b). All olfactory fibers leading to any one glomerulus come from cells with the same receptor type; thus each glomerulus is dedicated to a particular type of odor. Higher brain centers interpret complex odors such as chocolate, wine, perfume, or coffee by decoding signals from a combination of odor-specific glomeruli. This is similar to the way our visual system decodes all the colors of the spectrum using input from just three color-specific receptor cells of the eye.

The tufted and mitral cells carry output from the glomeruli. Their axons form bundles called **olfactory tracts,** which run caudally along the underside of the frontal lobes. Most fibers of the olfactory tracts end in various regions of the inferior surface of the temporal lobe regarded as the **primary olfactory cortex.** This is where one first becomes conscious of the odor. It is noteworthy that olfactory signals can reach the cerebral cortex directly, without first passing through the thalamus; thus, this is an extrathalamic[13] pathway. Except for the spinoreticular pain pathway (see fig. 16.3), no other sensory signals bypass the thalamus. Even in olfaction, however, some signals from the primary olfactory cortex continue to a relay in the thalamus on their way to olfactory association areas elsewhere. The primary olfactory cortex of each cerebral hemisphere relays signals to the contralateral hemisphere, so all further processing is mirrored on both sides of the brain even if an odor is initially detected in only one nasal fossa.

On both sides, signals are relayed to the amygdala, hippocampus, insula, and hypothalamus, which interact in complex ways to associate a present odor with olfactory memories and emotional responses. Thus, the odor of certain foods, a perfume, a hospital, or decaying flesh can evoke strong memories, emotional responses, and visceral reactions such as sneezing or coughing, the secretion of saliva and stomach acid, or vomiting. The orbitofrontal cortex, just above the eyes, also receives signals from the primary olfactory cortex. Here is where we identify and discriminate among odors. This region also integrates odor, taste, and vision into an overall impression of the desirability or acceptability of food.

Most areas of olfactory cortex also send fibers back to the olfactory bulbs by way of neurons called *granule cells.* Granule cells

[13]*extra* = outside; *thalam* = chamber, thalamus

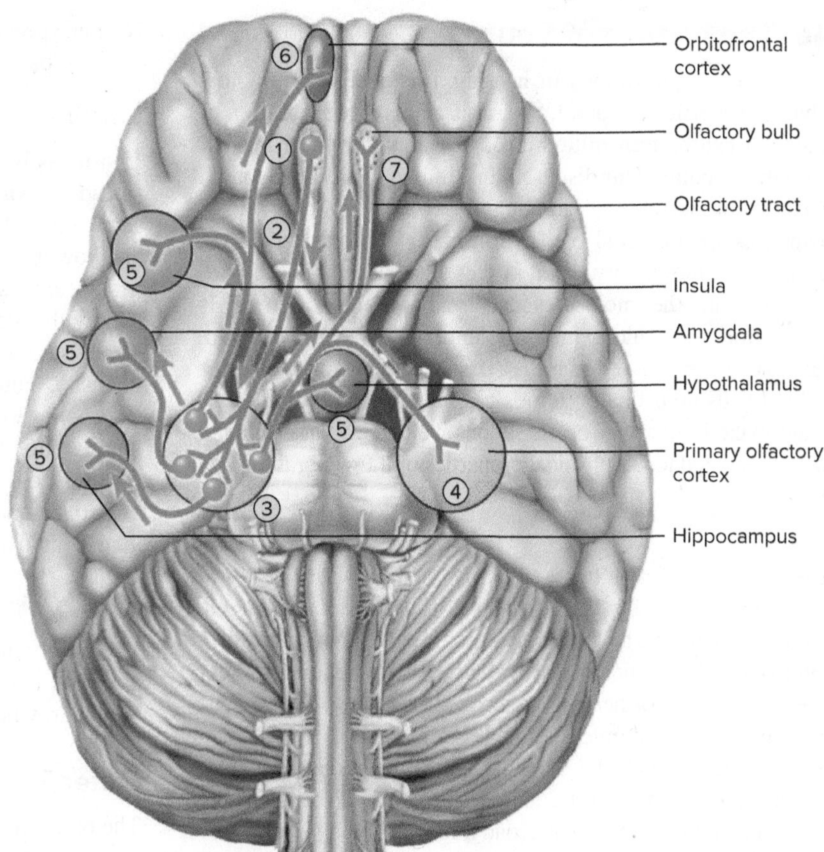
(1) Olfactory signals are received in olfactory bulbs.
(2) Signals are relayed caudally in olfactory tracts.
(3) Primary olfactory cortex in temporal lobe creates conscious perception of odor and relays signals to other brain destinations.
(4) Signals from each temporal lobe are relayed to contralateral temporal lobe, so all processing is mirrored in both cerebral hemispheres.
(5) Signals relayed to amygdala, hippocampus, insula, and hypothalamus relate odor to olfactory memory and produce emotional and visceral responses to odor.
(6) Signals received in orbitofrontal cortex combine with other information to identify and discriminate among odors and integrate odor into sense of flavor.
(7) Feedback to olfactory bulb modulates perception of odor according to circumstances such as hunger versus satiety.
Orbitofrontal cortex
Olfactory bulb
Olfactory tract
Insula
Amygdala
Hypothalamus
Primary olfactory cortex
Hippocampus

**FIGURE 16.8 Olfactory Projection Pathways in the Brain.** This shows only the extrathalamic pathways.

can inhibit the mitral and tufted cells. An effect of this feedback is that odors can change in quality and significance under different conditions. Food may smell more appetizing when you are hungry, for example, than when you have just eaten or when you are ill.

**▶▶▶ APPLY WHAT YOU KNOW**

*Which taste sensations could be lost after damage to (1) the facial nerve or (2) the glossopharyngeal nerve? A fracture of which cranial bone would most likely eliminate the sense of smell?*

**BEFORE YOU GO ON**

Answer the following questions to test your understanding of the preceding section:

13. What is the difference between a lingual papilla and a taste bud? Which is visible to the naked eye?
14. List the primary taste sensations and discuss their adaptive significance (survival value).
15. Which cranial nerves carry gustatory impulses to the brain?
16. What part of an olfactory cell binds odor molecules?
17. What brain regions serve the sense of smell and how do they differ in their olfactory functions?

## 16.4 Hearing and Equilibrium

**Expected Learning Outcomes**

When you have completed this section, you should be able to

a. identify the properties of sound waves that account for pitch and loudness;
b. describe the gross and microscopic anatomy of the ear;
c. explain how the ear converts vibrations to nerve signals and discriminates between sounds of different intensity and pitch;
d. explain how the vestibular apparatus enables the brain to interpret the body's position and movements; and
e. describe the pathways taken by auditory and vestibular signals to the brain.

**Hearing** is a response to vibrating air molecules, and **equilibrium** is the sense of body orientation, movement, and balance. Both senses reside in the inner ear, a maze of fluid-filled passages and sensory cells. We will study how the fluid is set in motion and how the sensory cells convert this motion into an informative nerve signal.

## 16.4a The Nature of Sound

To understand the physiology of hearing, it is necessary to know some basic properties of sound. **Sound** is any audible vibration of molecules. It can be transmitted through water, solids, or air, but not through a vacuum. Our discussion is limited to airborne sound.

Sound is produced by a vibrating object such as a tuning fork, a loudspeaker, or the vocal cords. Consider a loudspeaker. When the speaker cone moves forward, it pushes air molecules ahead of it. They collide with other molecules just ahead of them, and energy is transferred from molecule to molecule until it reaches the eardrum. No one molecule moves very far; they simply collide with each other like billiard balls until finally, some molecules collide with the eardrum and make it vibrate. The sensations we perceive as pitch and loudness are related to the physical properties of these vibrations.

### Pitch

**Pitch** is our sense of whether a sound is "high" (treble) or "low" (bass). It is determined by the frequency at which the sound source, eardrum, and other parts of the ear vibrate. One movement of a vibrating object back and forth is called a *cycle,* and the number of cycles per second (or hertz, Hz) is called **frequency.** The lowest note on a piano, for example, is 27.5 Hz, middle C is 261 Hz, and the highest note is 4,176 Hz. The most sensitive human ears, particularly in children, can hear frequencies from 20 to 20,000 Hz, but most of us cannot hear over that broad a range. The *infrasonic* frequencies below 20 Hz aren't detected by the ear, but we sense them through vibrations of the skull and skin and they play a significant role in our appreciation of music. The inaudible vibrations above 20,000 Hz are *ultrasonic.* Human ears are most sensitive to frequencies ranging from 1,500 to 5,000 Hz. In this range, we can hear sounds of relatively low energy (volume), whereas sounds above or below this range must be louder to be audible, as reflected in the steeply rising curves at both ends of the violet range in **figure 16.9.**

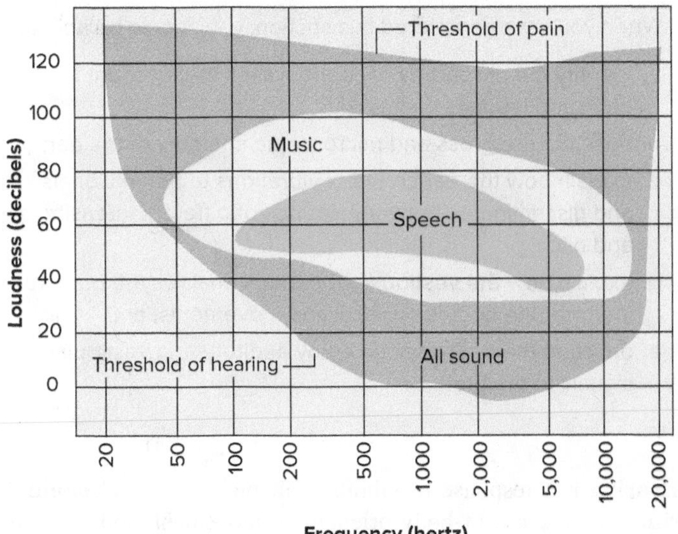


**FIGURE 16.9 The Range of Human Hearing.**

*How would the shape of this graph change in a case of moderate hearing loss between 200 and 5,000 Hz?*

Normal speech falls within the 1,500 to 5,000 Hz range. Most of the hearing loss suffered with age is in the range of 250 to 2,050 Hz.

### Loudness

**Loudness** is the perception of sound energy, intensity, or the **amplitude** of vibration. In the speaker example, amplitude is a measure of how far forward and back the cone vibrates on each cycle and how much it compresses the air molecules in front of it. Loudness is expressed in decibels (dB), with 0 dB defined by a sound energy that corresponds to the threshold of human hearing. Every 10 dB step up the scale represents a sound with 10 times greater intensity. Thus, 10 dB is 10 times threshold, 20 dB is 100 times threshold, 30 dB is 1,000 times threshold, and so forth. Normal conversation has a loudness of about 60 dB. At most frequencies, the threshold of pain is 120 to 140 dB, approximately the intensity of a loud thunderclap. Prolonged exposure to sounds greater than 90 dB can cause permanent loss of hearing.

## 16.4b Anatomy of the Ear

The ear has three sections called the *outer, middle,* and *inner ear.* The first two are concerned only with transmitting sound to the inner ear, where vibration is converted to nerve signals.

### Outer Ear

The **outer (external) ear** is essentially a funnel for conducting airborne vibrations to the *tympanic membrane* (eardrum). It begins with the fleshy **auricle (pinna)** on the side of the head, shaped and supported by elastic cartilage except for the earlobe, which is mostly adipose tissue. The auricle is an arrangement of named whorls and recesses that direct sound into the auditory canal **(fig. 16.10).**

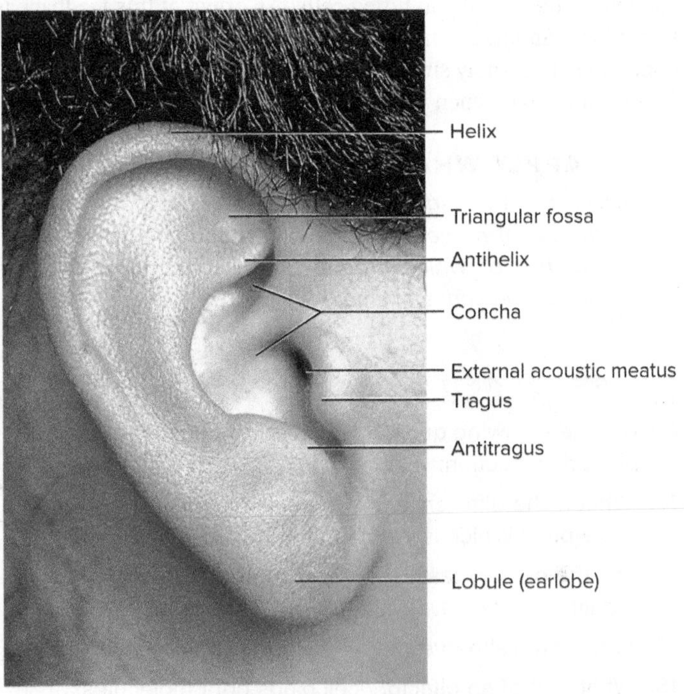


**FIGURE 16.10 Anatomy of the Auricle (Pinna) of the Ear.**

Joe DeGrandis/McGraw-Hill Education

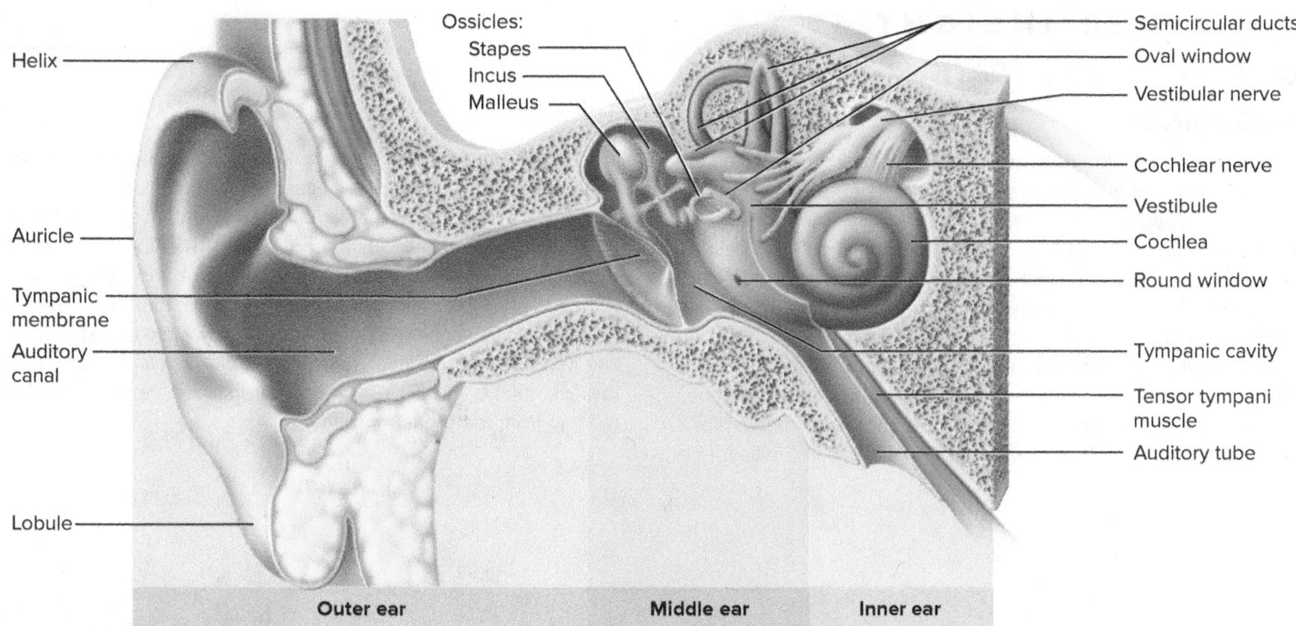


**FIGURE 16.11 Internal Anatomy of the Ear.**

The **auditory canal (external acoustic meatus)** is the passage leading through the temporal bone to the tympanic membrane. It follows a slightly S-shaped course for about 3 cm **(fig. 16.11).** It is lined with skin and supported by fibrocartilage at its opening and by the temporal bone for the rest of its length.

The outer end of the canal is protected by stiff **guard hairs.** The canal has ceruminous and sebaceous glands whose secretions mix with dead skin cells and form **cerumen** (earwax). Cerumen is sticky and coats the guard hairs, making them more effective in blocking foreign particles from the auditory canal. Its stickiness may also be a deterrent to insects, ticks, or other pests. In addition, it contains lysozyme and has a low pH, both of which inhibit bacterial growth; it waterproofs the canal and protects its skin and the tympanic membrane from absorbing water; and it keeps the tympanic membrane pliable. Cerumen normally dries and falls from the canal, but sometimes it becomes impacted and interferes with hearing.

## Middle Ear

The **middle ear** is located in the **tympanic cavity** of the temporal bone. What we colloquially call the eardrum is anatomically known as the **tympanic**[14] **membrane.** It closes the inner end of the auditory canal and separates it from the middle ear. The membrane is shaped like a Chinese farmer (coolie) hat—about 1 cm in diameter and slightly concave on its outer surface. It is suspended in a ring-shaped groove in the temporal bone and vibrates freely in response to sound. It is innervated by sensory branches of the vagus and trigeminal nerves and is highly sensitive to pain.

Posteriorly (behind the ear), the tympanic cavity is continuous with the *mastoid cells*—air-filled spaces in the mastoid process of the temporal bone. It is filled with air that enters by way of the **auditory (eustachian**[15] or **pharyngotympanic) tube,** a passageway to the nasopharynx. (Be careful not to confuse *auditory tube* with *auditory canal.*) The auditory tube serves to aerate and drain the middle ear. It is normally flattened and closed, but swallowing or yawning opens it and allows air to enter or leave the tympanic cavity. This equalizes air pressure on both sides of the tympanic membrane, allowing it to vibrate freely. Excessive pressure on one side or the other muffles the sense of hearing and may cause pain, as one commonly experiences in airline flight. Unfortunately, the auditory tube also allows throat infections to spread to the middle ear (see Deeper Insight 16.1).

The tympanic cavity, a space only 2 to 3 mm wide between the outer and inner ears, contains the three smallest bones and the two smallest skeletal muscles of the body. The bones, called the **auditory ossicles,**[16] connect the tympanic membrane to the inner ear. Progressing inward, the first is the **malleus,**[17] which has an elongated *handle* attached to the inner surface of the tympanic membrane, and a *head,* which articulates with the next ossicle. The second bone, the **incus,**[18] has a roughly triangular *body* that articulates with the malleus; a *long limb* that articulates with the stapes; and a *short limb* (not illustrated) suspended by a ligament from the wall of the cavity. The **stapes**[19] (STAY-peez), the body's smallest bone, is shaped like a stirrup. It has a *head* that articulates with the incus; two *limbs* that form an arch; and an elliptical *base (footplate).* The base is held by a ringlike ligament in an opening

[14] *tympan* = drum

[15] Bartholomeo Eustachio (1524–74), Italian anatomist
[16] *oss* = bone; *icle* = little
[17] *malleus* = hammer
[18] *incus* = anvil
[19] *stapes* = stirrup

## DEEPER INSIGHT 16.1

## CLINICAL APPLICATION

### *Middle-Ear Infection*

About 80% of children get middle-ear infections, or *otitis*[20] *media,* in the first 10 years of life. In the United States, it accounts for about 30 million doctor visits per year and about half of all antibiotic prescriptions for children; it affects about 11% of the entire world population each year.

Why is it so common in children? Up to the age of about 8 years, the auditory tubes are relatively short and horizontal **(fig. 16.12).** They allow upper respiratory infections to spread easily from the throat to the tympanic cavity and mastoid cells. Fluid accumulation in the cavity produces pressure, pain, and impaired hearing. If otitis media goes untreated, it may spread from the mastoid cells and cause meningitis, a potentially deadly infection (see Deeper Insight 14.1). Chronic otitis media can also cause fusion of the middle-ear bones and result in permanent hearing loss. It is sometimes necessary to drain fluid from the tympanic cavity by lancing the tympanic membrane and inserting a tiny drainage tube—a procedure called *tympanostomy.*[21] The tube, which is eventually sloughed out of the ear, relieves the pressure and permits the infection to heal. The great majority of children get a middle-ear infection in the first year of life. Holding an infant horizontally while breast feeding or putting it to bed with a bottle increases the risk of otitis media. To minimize the risk, infants should be held in an inclined, head-up position while feeding from the breast or bottle.

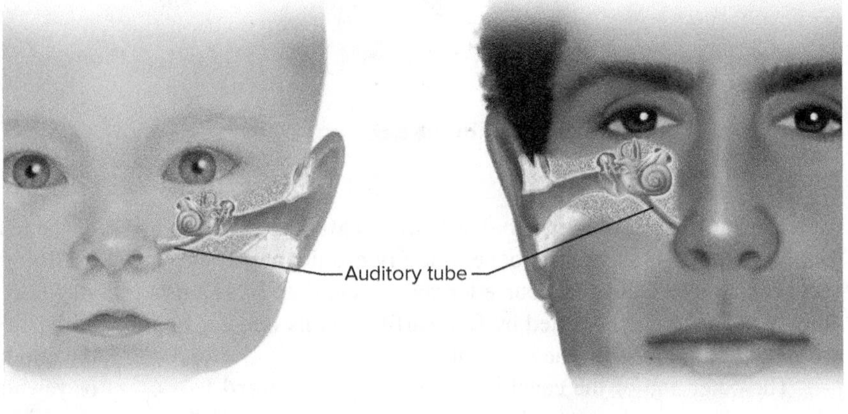


**FIGURE 16.12 The Auditory Tube of an Infant and Adult.** (a) The shorter, nearly horizontal tube of infants and young children makes it easy for them to get middle-ear infections. (b) The longer and more oblique tube of the adult.

[20]*ot* = ear; *itis* = inflammation

[21]*tympano* = eardrum; *stomy* = making an opening

called the **oval window,** where the inner ear begins. On the other side of the base is an inner-ear liquid called *perilymph.*

The muscles of the middle ear are the stapedius and tensor tympani. The **stapedius** (sta-PEE-dee-us) arises from the posterior wall of the cavity and inserts on the stapes. The **tensor tympani** (TEN-sor TIM-pan-eye) arises from the wall of the auditory tube, travels alongside it, and inserts on the malleus. The function of these muscles is discussed under the physiology of hearing.

## Inner Ear

The **inner (internal) ear** is housed in a maze of temporal bone passages called the **bony labyrinth,** which is lined by a system of fleshy tubes called the **membranous labyrinth (fig. 16.13).** Between the bony and membranous labyrinths is a cushion of fluid, the **perilymph** (PER-ih-limf), similar to cerebrospinal fluid. Within the membranous labyrinth is a fluid called **endolymph,** similar to intracellular fluid. The bony and membranous labyrinths form a tube-within-a-tube structure, somewhat like a bicycle inner tube within the tire.

The labyrinths begin with a chamber called the **vestibule,** which contains organs of equilibrium to be discussed later. The organ of hearing is the **cochlea**[22] (COC-lee-uh), a coiled tube that arises from the anterior side of the vestibule. In other vertebrates, the cochlea is straight or slightly curved. In most mammals, however, it assumes the form of a snail-like spiral, which allows a longer cochlea to fit in a compact space. In humans, the spiral is about 9 mm wide at the base and 5 mm high. Its apex points anterolaterally. The cochlea winds for about 2.5 coils around a screwlike bony axis called the **modiolus**[23] (mo-DY-oh-lus). The "threads of the screw" form a spiral platform that supports the fleshy tube of the cochlea.

A vertical section cuts through the cochlea about five times **(fig. 16.14a).** A single cross section looks like **figure 16.14b.** It is important to realize that the structures seen in cross section actually have the form of spiral strips winding around the modiolus from base to apex.

[22]*cochlea* = snail

[23]*modiolus* = hub

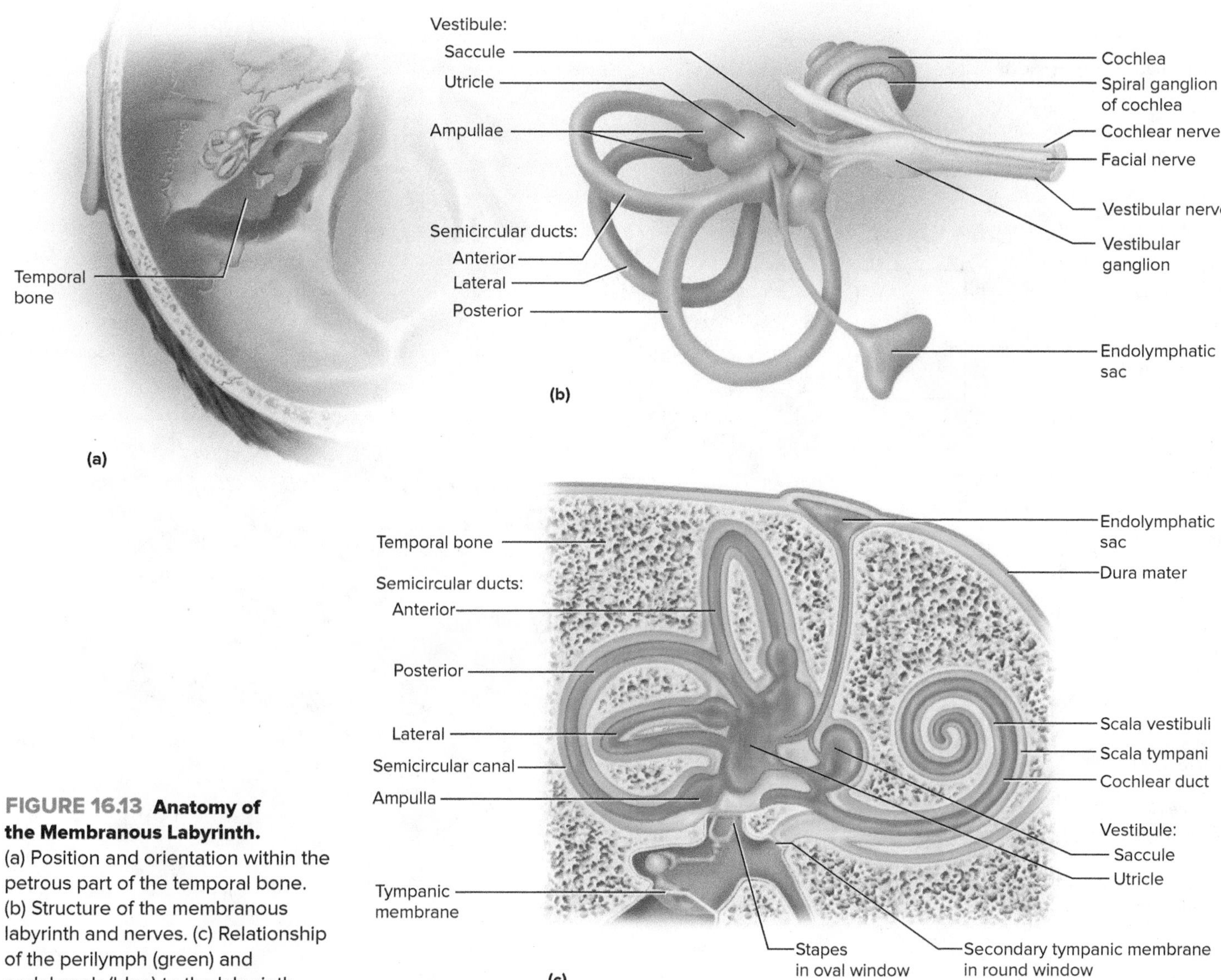


**FIGURE 16.13 Anatomy of the Membranous Labyrinth.** (a) Position and orientation within the petrous part of the temporal bone. (b) Structure of the membranous labyrinth and nerves. (c) Relationship of the perilymph (green) and endolymph (blue) to the labyrinth.

The cochlea has three fluid-filled chambers separated by membranes. The superior chamber is called the **scala**[24] **vestibuli** (SCAY-la vess-TIB-you-lye) and the inferior one is the **scala tympani.** These are filled with perilymph and communicate with each other through a narrow channel at the apex of the cochlea. The scala vestibuli begins near the oval window and spirals to the apex; from there, the scala tympani spirals back down to the base and ends at the **round window** (fig. 16.13). The round window is covered by a membrane called the *secondary tympanic membrane.*

The middle chamber is a triangular space, the **cochlear duct (scala media).** It is separated from the scala vestibuli above by a thin **vestibular membrane** and from the scala tympani below by a much thicker **basilar membrane.** Unlike those chambers, it is filled with endolymph rather than perilymph. The vestibular membrane separates the endolymph from the perilymph and helps to maintain a chemical difference between them. Within the cochlear duct, supported on the basilar membrane, is the **spiral (acoustic) organ**—a thick epithelium of sensory and supporting cells and associated membranes **(fig. 16.14c).** This is the device that converts vibrations into nerve impulses, so we must pay particular attention to its structural details.

The spiral organ has an epithelium composed of **hair cells** and **supporting cells.** Hair cells are named for the long, stiff microvilli called **stereocilia**[25] on their apical surfaces. (Stereocilia aren't true cilia. They don't have an axoneme of microtubules as seen in cilia, and they don't move by themselves.) Resting on top of the stereocilia is a gelatinous **tectorial**[26] **membrane.**

The spiral organ has four rows of hair cells spiraling along its length **(fig. 16.15).** About 3,500 of these, called **inner hair cells (IHCs),** are arranged in a row on the medial side of the basilar

[24] *scala* = staircase

[25] *stereo* = solid

[26] *tect* = roof

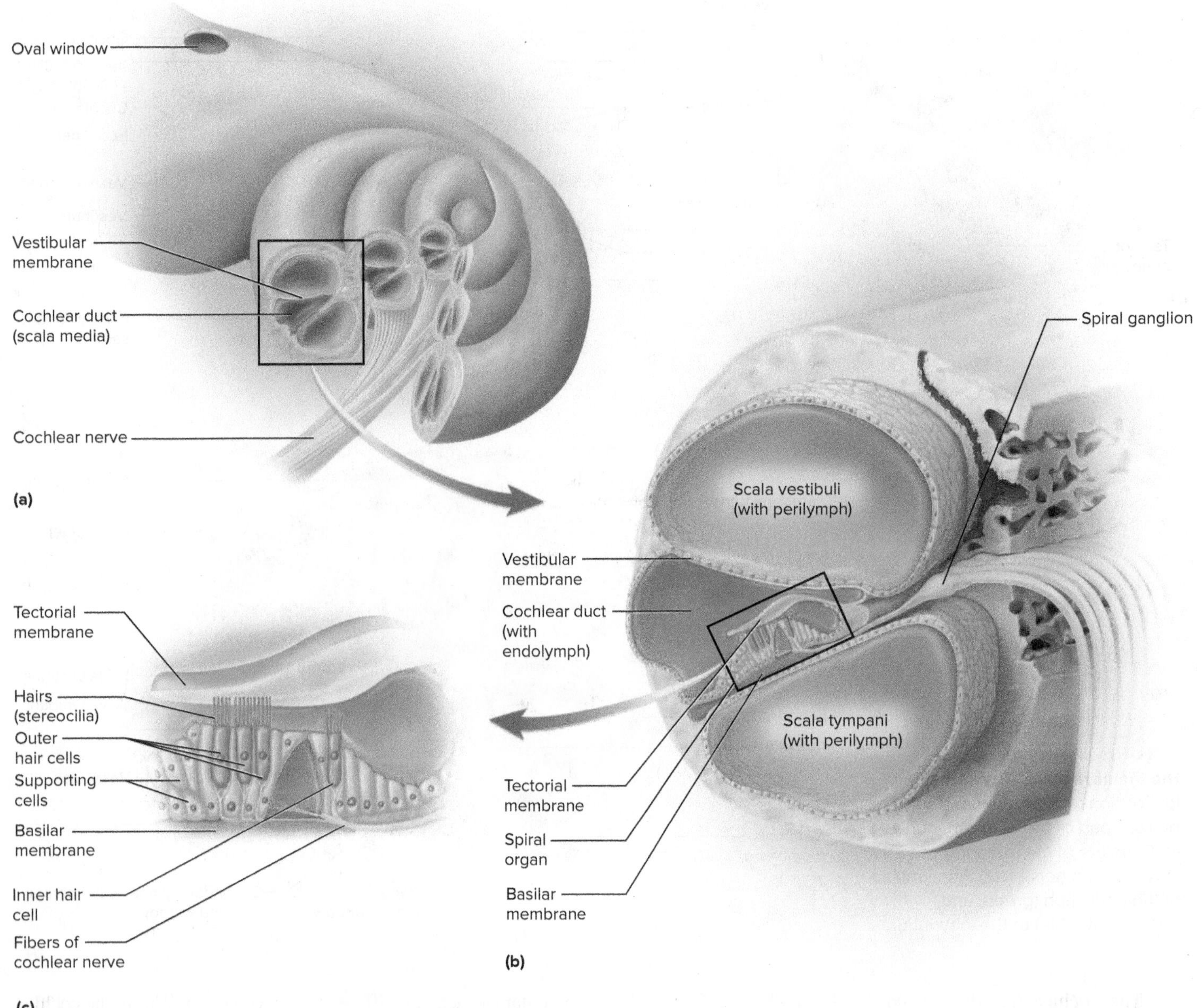


**FIGURE 16.14 Anatomy of the Cochlea.** (a) Vertical section. In anatomical position, the apex of the cochlea faces downward and anterolaterally. (b) Detail of one section through the cochlea. (c) Detail of the spiral organ.

membrane (facing the modiolus). Each of these has a cluster of 50 to 60 stereocilia, graded from short to tall. Another 20,000 **outer hair cells (OHCs)** are neatly arranged in three rows across from the inner hair cells. Each OHC has about 100 stereocilia arranged in the form of a V, with their tips embedded in the tectorial membrane. All that we hear comes from the IHCs, which supply 90% to 95% of the sensory fibers of the cochlear nerve. The function of the OHCs is to adjust the response of the cochlea to different frequencies and enable the IHCs to work with greater precision. We will see later how this is done. Hair cells are not neurons, but synapse with nerve fibers at their base—the OHCs with both sensory and motor neurons and the IHCs with sensory neurons only.

## 16.4c The Physiology of Hearing

We can now examine the way sound affects the ear and produces action potentials. Sound waves enter the auditory canal on one side and nerve signals exit the inner ear on the other. Connecting these is the middle ear, so we begin with an analysis of its contribution.

### The Middle Ear

One might wonder why we have a middle ear at all—why the tympanic membrane doesn't simply vibrate against the fluid-filled labyrinth of the inner ear. The reason is that the tympanic membrane, which moves in air, vibrates easily, whereas

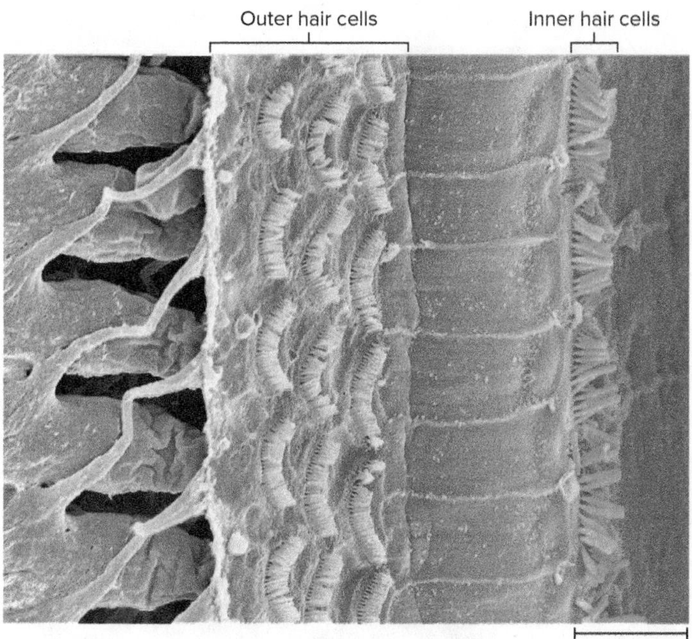


**FIGURE 16.15 Apical Surfaces of the Cochlear Hair Cells.** All signals that we hear come from the inner hair cells on the right.

SPL/Science Source

*What is the function of the three rows of hair cells on the left?*

the stapes must push against the perilymph of the inner ear. This fluid resists motion much more than air does. If the tympanic membrane had air on one side and fluid on the other, the sound waves wouldn't have enough energy to move the fluid adequately. The tympanic membrane, however, has 18 times the area of the oval window. By concentrating the energy of the vibrating tympanic membrane on an area one-eighteenth that size, the ossicles create a greater force per unit area at the oval window and overcome the inertia of the fluid.

The auditory ossicles do not, however, provide any mechanical advantage, any amplification of sound. Vibrations of the stapes against the inner ear normally have the same amplitude as vibrations of the tympanic membrane against the malleus. Why, then, have a lever system composed of three ossicles? Why not simply have one ossicle concentrating the mechanical energy of the tympanic membrane directly on the inner ear?

The answer is that the ossicles serve at times to *lessen* the transfer of energy to the inner ear. They and their muscles have a protective function. In response to a loud noise, the tensor tympani pulls the tympanic membrane inward and tenses it, while the stapedius reduces the motion of the stapes. This **tympanic reflex** muffles the transfer of vibrations to the oval window. The reflex probably evolved in part for protection from loud but slowly building natural sounds such as thunder. The reflex has a latency of about 40 ms, which isn't quick enough to protect the inner ear from sudden artificial noises such as gunshots. The tympanic reflex also doesn't adequately protect the ears from sustained loud noises such as factory noise or loud music. Such noises can irreversibly damage the hair cells of the inner ear. It is therefore imperative to wear ear protection when using firearms or working in noisy environments (even symphony orchestras).

The middle-ear muscles also help to coordinate speech with hearing. Without them, the sound of your own speech would be so loud it could damage your inner ear, and it would drown out soft or high-pitched sounds from other sources. Just as you are about to speak, however, the brain signals these muscles to contract. This dampens the sense of hearing in phase with the inflections of your own voice and makes it easier to hear other people while you are speaking.

**APPLY WHAT YOU KNOW**

*What type of muscle fibers—slow oxidative or fast glycolytic (see table 11.2)—do you think constitute the stapedius and tensor tympani? That is, which type would best suit the purpose of these muscles?*

## Stimulation of Cochlear Hair Cells

The next step in hearing is based on movement of the cochlear hair cells relative to stationary structures nearby. In this section, we will see how movements of the inner-ear fluids and basilar membrane move the hair cells and why it is important that the tectorial membrane near the hair cells remains relatively still.

A simple mechanical model of the ear can help in visualizing how this happens **(fig. 16.16).** (The vestibular membrane is omitted from the model for simplicity; it doesn't affect the mechanics of hearing.) As you listen to your favorite music, each inward movement of the tympanic membrane pushes the middle-ear ossicles inward. The stapes, in turn, pushes on the perilymph in the scala vestibuli. Perilymph, like other liquids, cannot be compressed, so it flows away from the stapes footplate. The resulting pressure in the scala vestibuli pushes the vestibular membrane downward; this pushes on the endolymph in the cochlear duct; the endolymph pushes down on the basilar membrane; the basilar membrane pushes on the perilymph in the scala tympani; and finally,

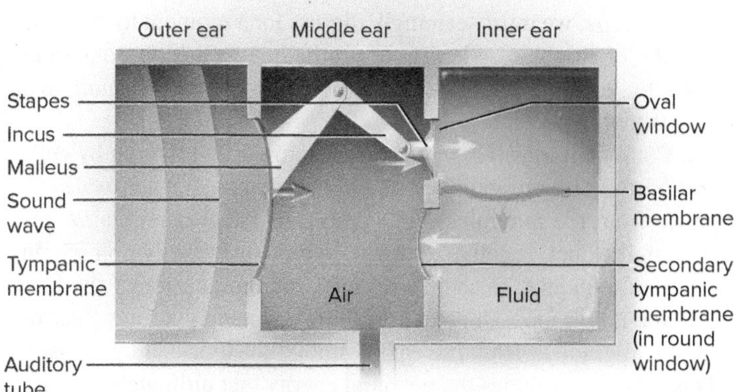


**FIGURE 16.16 Mechanical Model of Hearing.**

*Why would high air pressure in the middle ear reduce the movements of the basilar membrane of the inner ear?*

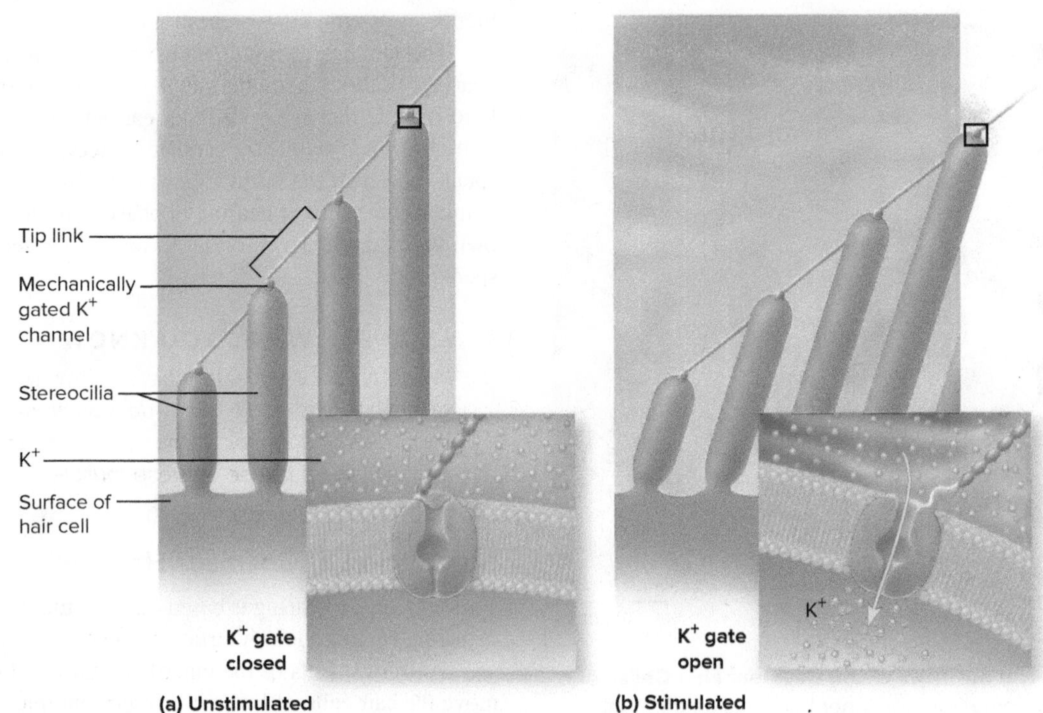


**FIGURE 16.17 Potassium Channels of the Cochlear Hair Cells.** Each stereocilium has a $K^+$ channel at its tip, shown at the small black box. (a) A hair cell at rest, unstimulated, with the potassium gates closed. (b) A stimulated hair cell, with the potassium gate of each stereocilium pulled open by the tip link leading to the next higher stereocilium.

the secondary tympanic membrane bulges outward to relieve the pressure. As the cycle of vibration continues, the stapes pulls back from the oval window and all of this happens in reverse.

In short, as the stapes goes in-out-in, the secondary tympanic membrane goes out-in-out, and the basilar membrane goes down-up-down. It is not difficult to see how this happens—the only thing hard to imagine is that it can happen as often as 20,000 times per second! The important thing about all this is that the hair cells, affixed to the basilar membrane, go along for the ride, bobbing up and down as the basilar membrane moves.

To understand how all of this leads to electrical excitation of the hair cells, we must seemingly digress for a moment to examine the tips of the hair cells. These are bathed in a high-potassium fluid, the endolymph. Why is this fluid so rich in potassium, and why is that important?

Potassium ions ($K^+$) are secreted into the endolymph by cells around the circumference of the cochlear duct (on the wall opposite from the modiolus). The vestibular membrane retains this fluid in the duct. Relative to the perilymph, the endolymph has an electrical potential of about +80 mV, and the interior of the hair cell about –40 mV. Thus there is an exceptionally strong electrochemical gradient from the endolymph to the hair cell cytoplasm. This gradient provides the potential energy that ultimately enables the hair cell to work.

On the inner hair cells—the ones that generate all the signals we hear—each stereocilium has a single transmembrane protein at its tip that functions as a mechanically gated ion channel. A fine, stretchy protein filament called a **tip link** extends like a spring from the ion channel of one stereocilium to the sidewall of the taller stereocilium next to it **(fig. 16.17).** The stereocilia increase in height progressively, so that every stereocilium but the tallest one has a tip link leading to a taller one beside it.

Now what of the tectorial membrane? This conspicuous structure of the spiral organ is anchored to the core of the cochlea and remains relatively still as the hair cells dance up and down to the beat of the music. Each time the basilar membrane rises upward toward the tectorial membrane, the hair cell stereocilia are pushed against that membrane and tilt toward the tallest one. As each taller stereocilium bends over, it pulls on the tip link of its neighbor. The tip link, connected to the ion gate of the next shorter stereocilium, pulls the gate open and allows ions to flood into the cell. The gate is nonselective, but since the predominant ion of the endolymph is $K^+$, the primary effect of this gating is to allow a quick burst of $K^+$ to flow into the hair cell. This depolarizes the hair cell while the gate is open, and when the basilar membrane drops and the stereocilium bends the other way, the gate closes and the cell becomes briefly hyperpolarized. During each moment of depolarization, a hair cell releases a burst of neurotransmitter from its base, exciting the sensory dendrite that synapses with the hair cell. Each depolarization thus generates a signal in the cochlear nerve.

To summarize: Each upward movement of the basilar membrane pushes the inner hair cells closer to the stationary tectorial membrane. This forces the stereocilia to bend in the direction of the tallest one. Each stereocilium has a tip link connecting it to an ion channel at the top of the next shorter stereocilium. When the taller one bends over, it pulls the channel open. Potassium ions flow into the hair cell and depolarize it. The hair cell releases a burst of neurotransmitter, exciting the sensory processes of the cochlear nerve cells below it. Thus a signal is generated in the cochlear nerve and transmitted to the brain.

## Sensory Coding

For sounds to carry any meaning, we must distinguish differences in loudness and pitch. Our ability to do so stems from the fact that the cochlea responds differently to sounds of different amplitude and frequency. Variations in loudness (amplitude) cause variations in the intensity of cochlear vibration. A soft sound produces relatively slight up-and-down movements of the basilar membrane. Hair cells are stimulated only moderately, and a given sound frequency stimulates hair cells in a relatively limited, or focused, region of the cochlea. A louder sound makes the basilar membrane vibrate more vigorously. Hair cells respond more intensely, generating a higher firing frequency in the cochlear nerve. In addition, for a given frequency, a loud sound vibrates a longer segment of the basilar membrane and thus excites a greater number of hair cells. If the brain detects moderate firing rates associated with hair cells in relatively narrow bands of the cochlea, it interprets this as a soft sound. If it detects a high firing frequency in nerve fibers associated with broader bands, it interprets this as a louder sound.

Frequency discrimination is based on a structural gradient in the basilar membrane resembling a piano's gradient in sound frequency from the short strings to long strings. At its proximal end (the base of the cochlea), the membrane is attached, narrow, and stiff, like the piano's short strings. At its distal end (the apex of the cochlea), it is unattached, five times wider, and more flexible. Think of the basilar membrane as analogous to a wire stretched tightly between two posts. If you pluck the wire at one end, a wave of vibration travels down its length and back. This produces a standing wave, with some regions of the wire vertically displaced more than others. Similarly, a sound causes a standing wave in the basilar membrane. The peak amplitude of this wave is near the distal end in the case of low-frequency sounds and nearer the proximal end with sounds of higher frequencies. When the brain receives signals mainly from inner hair cells at the distal end, it interprets the sound as low-pitched; when signals come mainly from the proximal end, it interprets the sound as high-pitched **(fig. 16.18).** Speech, music, and other everyday sounds, of course, aren't pure tones—they create complex, ever-changing patterns of vibration in the basilar membrane that must be decoded by the brain.

## Cochlear Tuning

Just as we tune a radio to receive a certain frequency, we also tune our cochlea to receive some frequencies better than others. The outer hair cells (OHCs) are supplied with a few sensory fibers (5% to 10% of those in the cochlear nerve), but more importantly, they receive motor fibers from the brain.

In response to sound, the OHCs send signals to the medulla oblongata by way of the sensory neurons, and the pons sends signals immediately back to the OHCs by way of the motor neurons. In response, the hair cells shorten as much as 15%. Remember that an OHC is anchored to the basilar membrane below and by its stereocilia to the tectorial membrane above. Therefore, tensing of an OHC reduces the basilar membrane's mobility. This results in some regions of the cochlea sending fewer signals to the brain than neighboring regions, so the brain can better distinguish between sound frequencies. When OHCs are experimentally incapacitated, the inner hair cells (IHCs) respond much less precisely to differences in pitch.

There is another mechanism of cochlear tuning involving the inner hair cells. The pons sends efferent fibers to the cochlea that synapse with the sensory nerve fibers near the base of the IHCs. The efferent fibers can inhibit the sensory fibers from firing in some areas of the cochlea, and thus enhance the contrast between signals from the more responsive and less responsive regions. Combined with the previously described role of the OHCs, this sharpens the tuning of the cochlea and our ability to discriminate pitch.

## The Auditory Projection Pathway

The sensory nerve fibers beginning at the bases of the hair cells belong to bipolar sensory neurons. Their somas form a coil, the **spiral ganglion,** around the modiolus (see fig. 16.14), and their axons lead away from the cochlea as the **cochlear nerve.** This nerve joins the *vestibular nerve,* discussed later, and the two together become the *vestibulocochlear nerve* (CN VIII).

Each ear sends fibers to both sides of the medulla oblongata. There, they end in the *cochlear nuclei,* synapsing with second-order neurons that ascend to the *superior olivary nucleus* of the

### DEEPER INSIGHT 16.2
**CLINICAL APPLICATION**

#### Deafness

*Deafness* means any hearing loss, from mild and temporary to complete and irreversible. *Conductive deafness* results from any condition that interferes with the transmission of vibrations to the inner ear. Such conditions include a damaged tympanic membrane, otitis media, blockage of the auditory canal, and otosclerosis. *Otosclerosis*[27] is fusion of the auditory ossicles to each other or fusion of the stapes to the oval window. Either way, it prevents the bones from vibrating freely. *Sensorineural (nerve) deafness* results from the death of hair cells or any of the nervous elements concerned with hearing. It is a common occupational disease of factory and construction workers, musicians, and other people exposed to frequent or sustained loud sounds. Deafness leads some people to develop delusions of being talked about, disparaged, or cheated. Beethoven said his deafness drove him nearly to suicide.

[27] *oto* = ear; *scler* = hardening; *osis* = process, condition

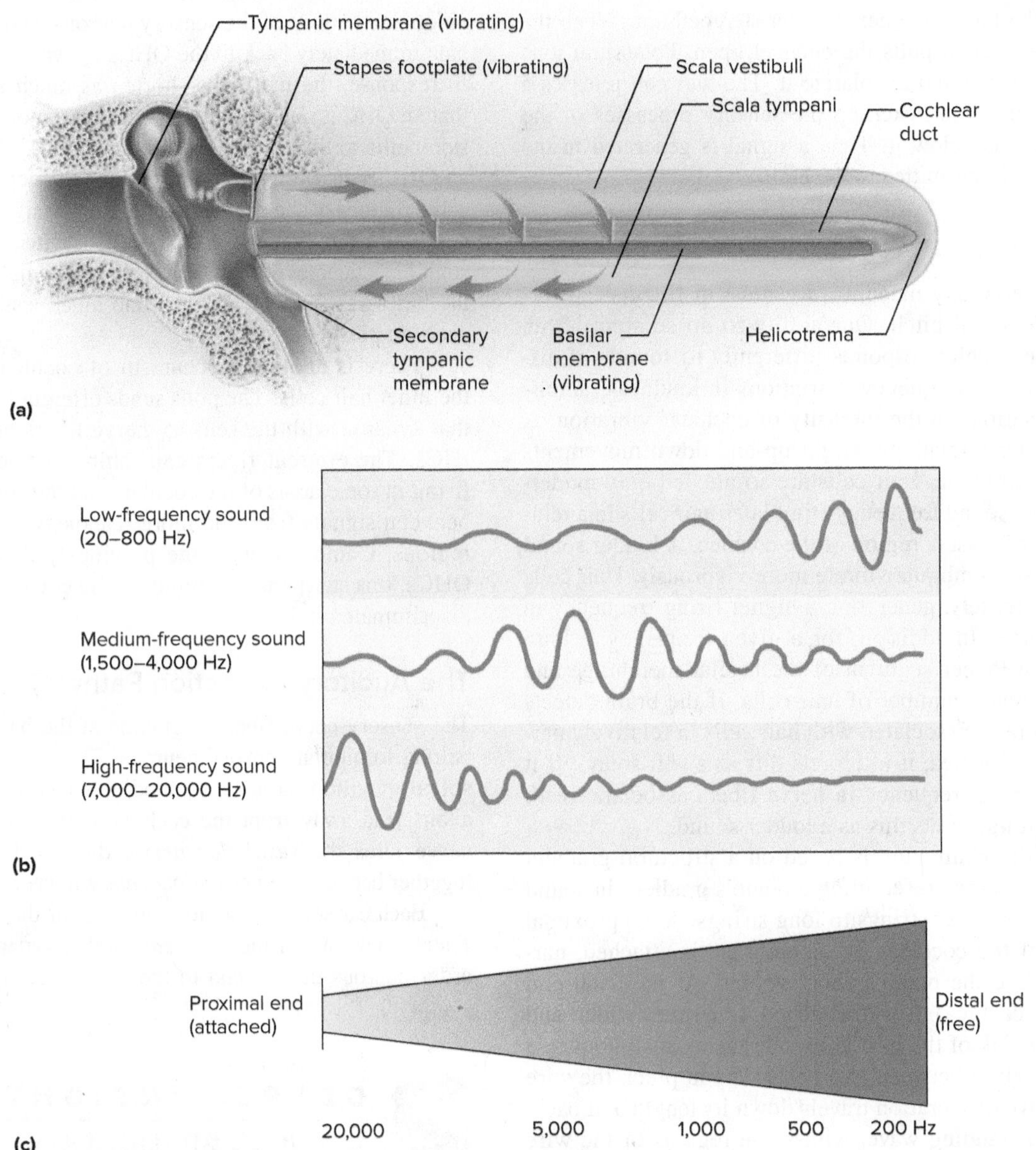


**FIGURE 16.18 Frequency Response of the Basilar Membrane of the Cochlea.** (a) The cochlea, uncoiled and laid out straight. (b) Sounds produce a standing wave of vibration along the basilar membrane. The peak amplitude of the wave varies with the frequency of the sound, as shown here. The amount of vibration is greatly exaggerated in this diagram to clarify the standing wave. (c) The taper of the basilar membrane and its correlation with sound frequencies. High frequencies (7,000–20,000 Hz) are best detected by hair cells near the narrow proximal end at the left, and low frequencies (20–800 Hz) by hair cells near the wider distal end at the right.

pons **(fig. 16.19)**. By way of CN VIII, the superior olivary nucleus issues the efferent fibers back to the cochlea that are involved in cochlear tuning. By way of CNs $V_3$ and VII, it also issues motor fibers to the tensor tympani and stapedius muscles, respectively. The superior olivary nucleus also functions in **binaural**[28] **hearing**—comparing signals from the right and left ears to identify the direction from which a sound is coming.

Other fibers from the cochlear nuclei ascend to the inferior colliculi of the midbrain. The inferior colliculi help to locate the origin of a sound in space, process fluctuations in pitch that are important for such purposes as understanding another person's speech, and mediate the startle response and rapid head turning that occur in reaction to loud or sudden noises.

Third-order neurons begin in the inferior colliculi and lead to the thalamus. Fourth-order neurons complete the pathway from there to the primary auditory cortex; thus the auditory pathway, unlike most other sensory pathways, involves not three but four neurons from receptor to cerebral cortex. The primary auditory cortex lies in the superior margin of the temporal lobe and extends deeply into the lateral sulcus (see fig. 14.20). The temporal lobe

[28] *bin* = two; *aur* = ears

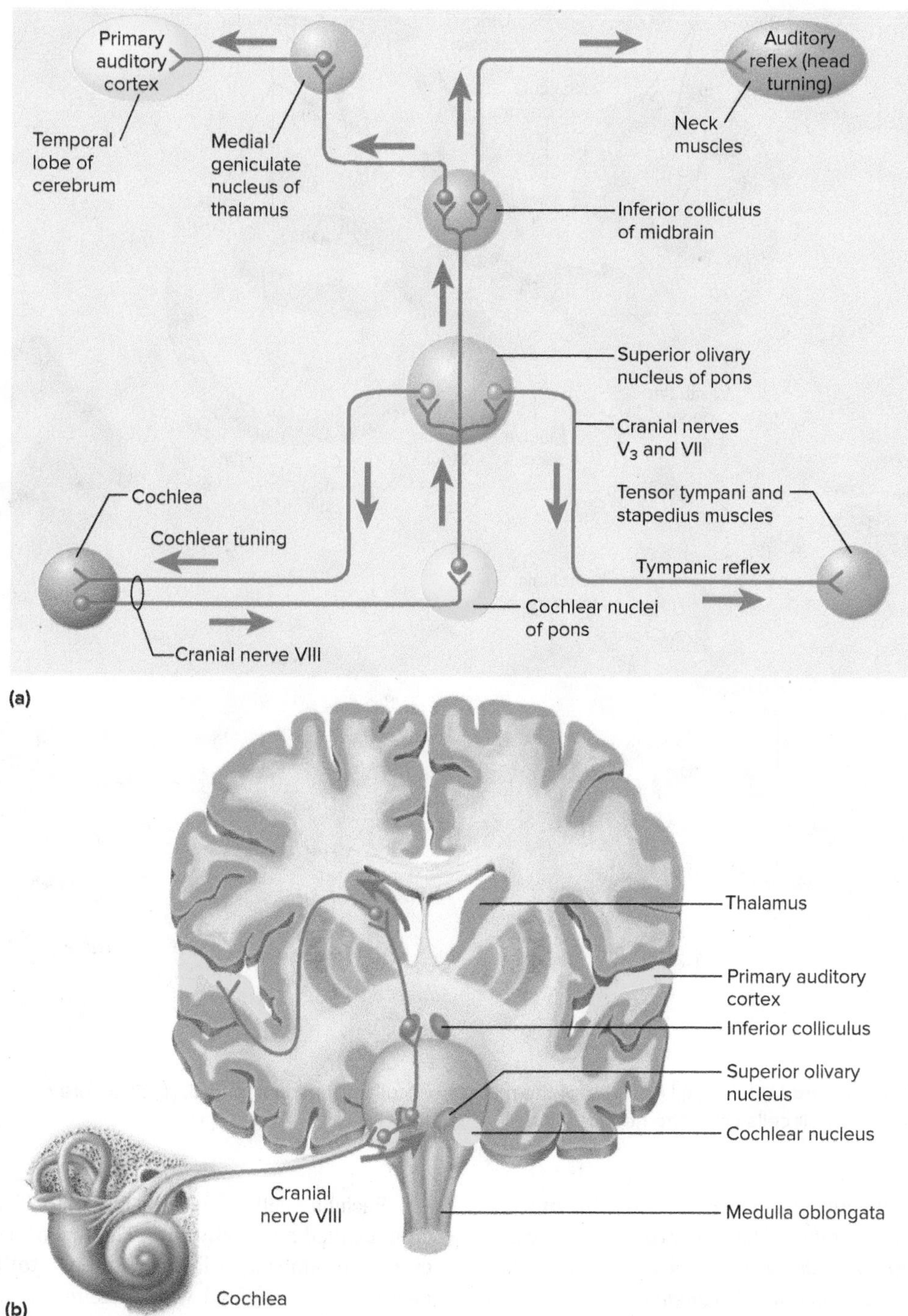


**FIGURE 16.19 Auditory Pathways in the Brain.** (a) Schematic. (b) Brainstem and frontal section of the cerebrum, showing the locations of auditory processing centers. (cranial nerve $V_3$ = trigeminal nerve, mandibular division; CN VII = facial nerve; CN VIII = vestibulocochlear nerve)

is the site of conscious perception of sound, and it completes the information processing essential to binaural hearing. Because of extensive decussation in the auditory pathway, damage to the right or left auditory cortex doesn't cause a unilateral loss of hearing.

## 16.4d The Physiology of Equilibrium

The original function of the ear in vertebrate evolution wasn't hearing, but equilibrium. Only later did vertebrates evolve the cochlea, outer- and middle-ear structures, and auditory function of the ear. In humans, the receptors for equilibrium constitute the **vestibular apparatus,** which consists of three **semicircular ducts** and two chambers—an anterior **saccule**[29] and a posterior **utricle**[30] (see fig. 16.13).

The sense of equilibrium is divided into **static equilibrium,** the perception of the orientation of the head in space (whether it

[29] *saccule* = little sac
[30] *utricle* = little bag

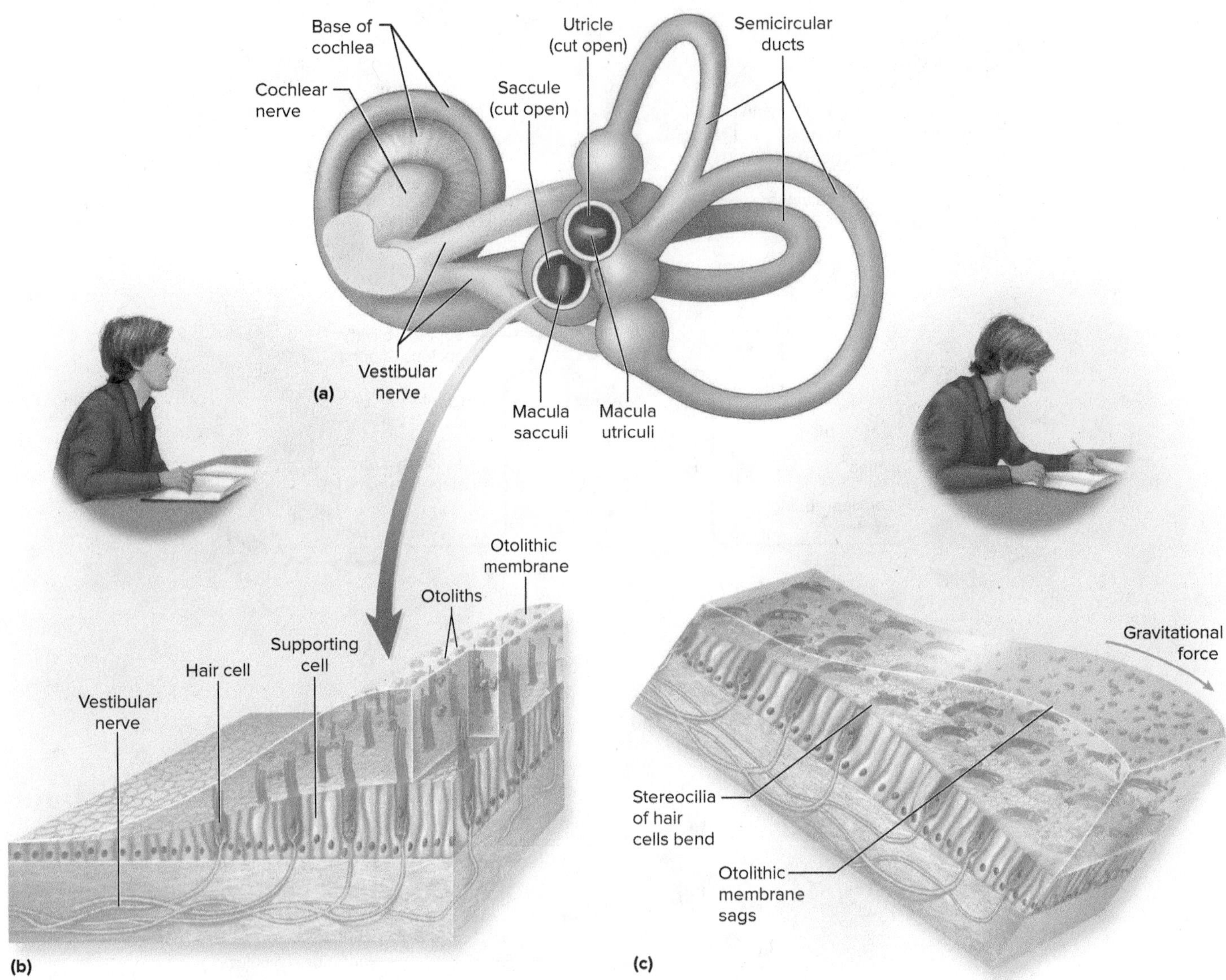


**FIGURE 16.20 The Saccule and Utricle.** (a) Locations of the macula sacculi and macula utriculi. (b) Structure of a macula. (c) Action of the otolithic membrane on the hair cells when the head is tilted.

is erect or tilted in any direction), and **dynamic equilibrium,** the perception of motion or acceleration. There are two kinds of acceleration: (1) *linear acceleration,* a change in velocity in a straight line, as when riding in a car or elevator; and (2) *angular acceleration,* a change in the rate of rotation, as when your car turns a corner or you swivel in a rotating chair. The saccule and utricle are responsible for static equilibrium and the sense of linear acceleration; the semicircular ducts detect only angular acceleration.

## The Saccule and Utricle

The saccule and utricle each contain a 2 × 3 mm patch of hair cells and supporting cells called a macula.[31] The **macula sacculi** lies almost vertically on the wall of the saccule, and the **macula utriculi** lies almost horizontally on the floor of the utricle **(fig. 16.20a).**

Each hair cell of a macula has 40 to 70 stereocilia and one true cilium called a **kinocilium.**[32] The tips of the stereocilia and kinocilium are embedded in a gelatinous **otolithic membrane.** This membrane is weighted with protein–calcium carbonate granules called **otoliths**[33] **(fig. 16.20b),** which add to the weight and inertia of the membrane and enhance the sense of gravity and motion.

**Figure 16.20c** shows how the macula utriculi detects tilt of the head. With the head erect, the otolithic membrane bears directly down on the hair cells, and stimulation is minimal. When you tilt your head down to read a book, however, the heavy otolithic membrane sags and bends the stereocilia, stimulating the hair cells. Any orientation of the head causes a combination of stimulation to the utricules and saccules of the two ears. The brain interprets head orientation by comparing these inputs to each other and to other input from the eyes

[31] *macula* = spot

[32] *kino* = moving

[33] *oto* = ear; *lith* = stone

and stretch receptors in the neck, thereby detecting whether only the head is tilted or the entire body is tipping.

The inertia of the otolithic membranes is especially important in detecting linear acceleration. Suppose you're sitting in a car at a stoplight and then begin to move. The membrane of the macula utriculi briefly lags behind the rest of the tissues, bends the stereocilia backward, and stimulates the cells. When you stop at the next light, the macula stops but the otolithic membrane keeps going for a moment, bending the stereocilia forward. The hair cells convert this stimulation to nerve signals, and the brain is thus advised of changes in your linear velocity.

The macula sacculi is nearly vertical and its hair cells therefore respond to vertical acceleration and deceleration. If you're standing in an elevator and it begins to move up, the membrane of the macula sacculi lags behind briefly and pulls down on the hairs. When the elevator stops, the membrane keeps going for a moment and bends the hairs upward. In both cases, the hair cells are stimulated and the brain is made aware of your vertical movements. These sensations are important in such ordinary actions as sitting down, and as your head bobs up and down during walking and running.

## The Semicircular Ducts

The head also experiences rotary movements, such as when you spin in a rotating chair, walk down a hall and turn a corner, or bend forward to pick something up from the floor. Such movements are detected by the three semicircular ducts **(fig. 16.21),** housed in the bony *semicircular canals* of the temporal bone. The *anterior* and *posterior semicircular ducts* are oriented vertically at right angles to each other. The *lateral semicircular duct* is about 30° from the

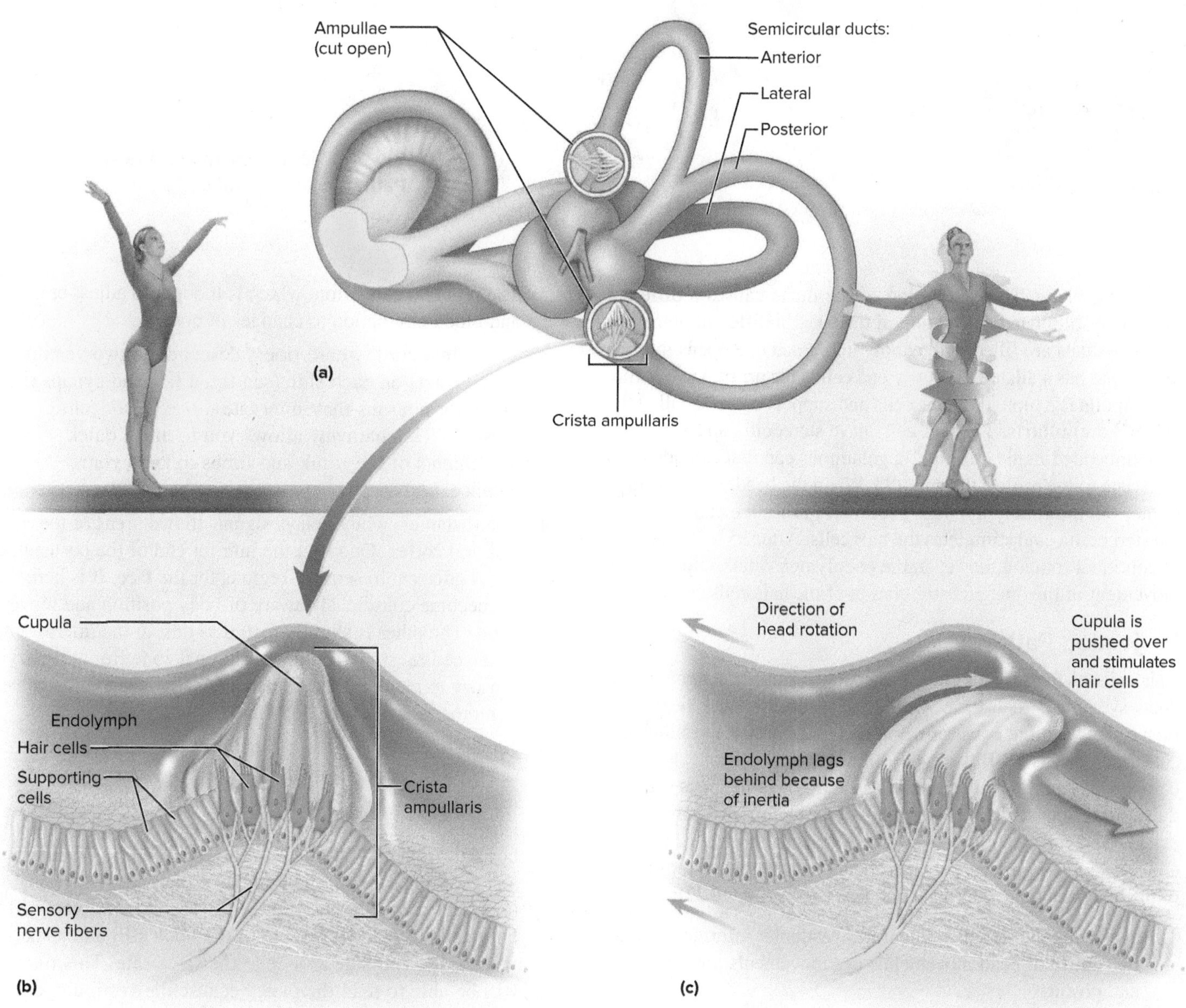


**FIGURE 16.21 The Semicircular Ducts.** (a) Structure of the semicircular ducts, with two ampullae opened to show the crista ampullaris and cupula. (b) Detail of the crista ampullaris. (c) Action of the endolymph on the cupula and hair cells when the head rotates.

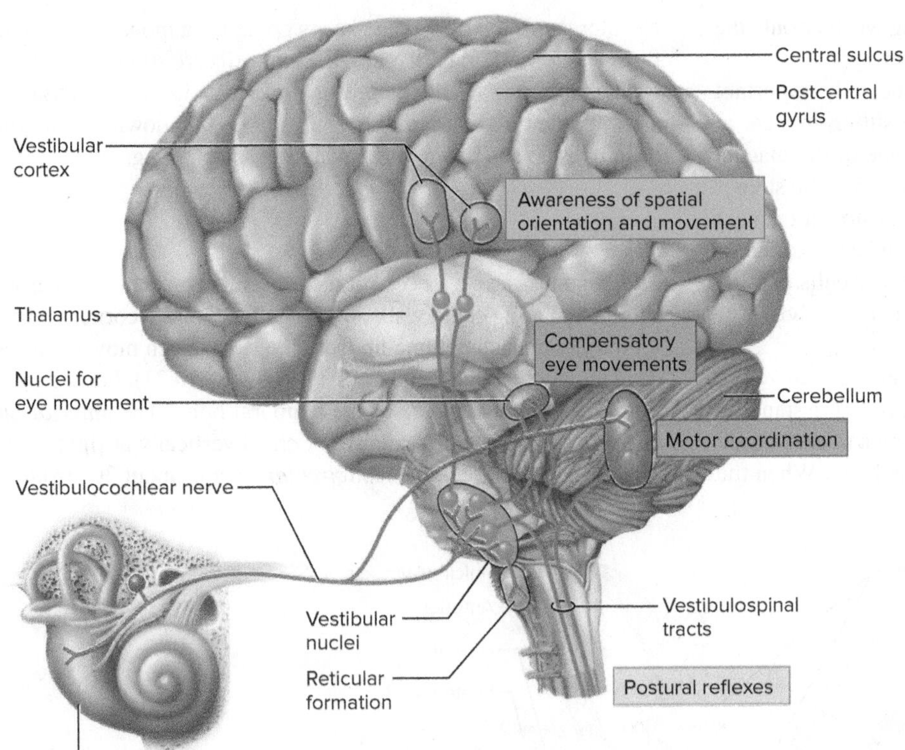


**FIGURE 16.22 Vestibular Projection Pathways in the Brain.**

horizontal plane. The orientation of the ducts causes a different duct to be stimulated by rotation of the head in different planes.

The ducts are filled with endolymph. Each one opens into the utricle and has a dilated sac at one end called the **ampulla.**[34] Within the ampulla is a mound of hair cells and supporting cells called the **crista**[35] **ampullaris.** The hair cells have stereocilia and a kinocilium embedded in the **cupula,**[36] a gelatinous cap that extends from the crista to the roof of the ampulla. When the head turns, the duct rotates but the endolymph lags behind. It pushes the cupula, bends the stereocilia, and stimulates the hair cells. After 25 to 30 seconds of continual rotation, however, the endolymph catches up with the movement of the duct and stimulation of the hair cells ceases.

## Projection Pathways

Hair cells of the macula sacculi, macula utriculi, and semicircular ducts synapse at their bases with sensory fibers of the **vestibular nerve.** This and the cochlear nerve merge to form the vestibulocochlear nerve (CN VIII). Fibers of the vestibular apparatus lead to a complex of four **vestibular nuclei** on each side of the pons and medulla. Nuclei on the right and left sides of the brainstem communicate extensively with each other, so each receives input from both the right and left ears. They process signals about the position and movement of the body and relay information to five targets **(fig. 16.22):**

1. The cerebellum, which integrates vestibular information into its control of head movements, eye movements, muscle tone, and posture.
2. The reticular formation, which is thought to adjust breathing and blood circulation to changes in posture.
3. The spinal cord, where fibers descend the two vestibulospinal tracts on each side (see fig. 13.5) and synapse on motor neurons that innervate the extensor (antigravity) muscles. This pathway allows you to make quick movements of the trunk and limbs to keep your balance.
4. The thalamus, which relays signals to two areas of the cerebral cortex. One is at the inferior end of the postcentral gyrus adjacent to sensory regions for the face. It is here that we become consciously aware of body position and movement. The other is slightly rostral to this, at the inferior end of the central sulcus in the transitional zone from primary sensory to motor cortex. This area is thought to be involved in motor control of the head and body.
5. Nuclei of the oculomotor, trochlear, and abducens nerves (CNs III, IV, and VI). These nerves produce eye movements that compensate for movements of the head (the *vestibulo–ocular reflex*). To observe this effect, hold a book in front of you at a comfortable reading distance and fix your gaze on the middle of the page. Move the book left and right about once per second, and you will be unable to read it. Now hold the book still and shake your head from side to side at the same rate. This time you will be able to read the page because the vestibulo–ocular reflex compensates for your head movements and keeps your eyes fixed on the target. This reflex enables you to keep your vision fixed on a distant object as you walk or run toward it.

[34]*ampulla* = little jar
[35]*crista* = crest, ridge
[36]*cupula* = little tub

**BEFORE YOU GO ON**

Answer the following questions to test your understanding of the preceding section:

**18.** What physical properties of sound waves correspond to the sensations of loudness and pitch?

**19.** What are the benefits of having auditory ossicles and muscles in the middle ear?

**20.** Explain how vibration of the tympanic membrane ultimately produces fluctuations of membrane voltage in a cochlear hair cell.

**21.** How does the brain recognize the difference between the musical notes high C and middle C? Between a loud sound and a soft one?

**22.** How does the function of the semicircular ducts differ from the function of the saccule and utricle?

**23.** How is sensory transduction in the semicircular ducts similar to that in the saccule and utricle?

## 16.5 Vision

**Expected Learning Outcomes**

When you have completed this section, you should be able to

a. describe the anatomy of the eye and its accessory structures;
b. discuss the structure of the retina and its receptor cells;
c. explain how the optical system of the eye creates an image on the retina;
d. discuss how the retina converts this image to nerve signals;
e. explain why different types of receptor cells and neural circuits are required for day and night vision;
f. describe the mechanism of color vision; and
g. trace the visual projection pathways in the brain.

### 16.5a Light and Vision

**Vision (sight)** is the perception of objects in the environment by means of the light they emit or reflect. **Light** is visible electromagnetic radiation. Human vision is limited to wavelengths ranging from about 400 to 700 nm. Most solar radiation of shorter and longer wavelengths is filtered out by ozone, carbon dioxide, and water vapor in the atmosphere. Therefore, the radiation that reaches the surface of the earth falls within that range, and vision is adapted to take advantage of the wavelenths available to us. The *ultraviolet (UV)* radiation just below 400 nm and the *infrared (IR)* radiation just above 700 nm are invisible to us. Furthermore, radiation in the ultraviolet range has such high energy that it destroys macromolecules rather than producing the controlled chemical reactions needed for vision, and radiation in the infrared range has such low energy that it merely warms the tissues, also failing to energize chemical reactions.

### 16.5b Accessory Structures of the Orbit

The eyeball occupies a bony socket called the **orbit.** This general area of the face, the *orbital region,* contains structures that protect and aid the eye **(figs. 16.23, 16.24):**

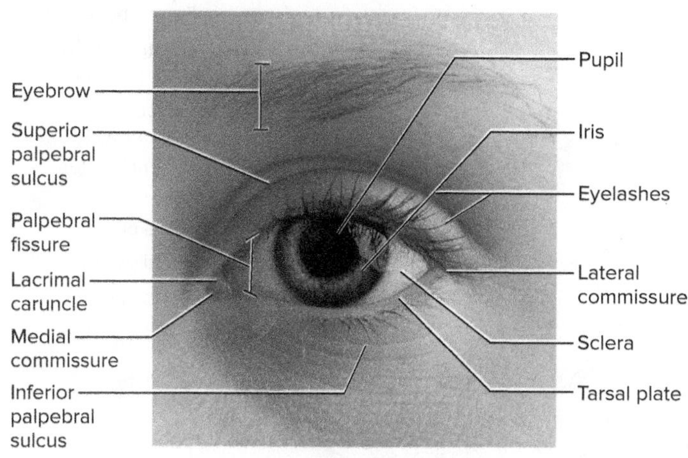


**FIGURE 16.23 External Anatomy of the Orbital Region.**
Joe DeGrandis/McGraw-Hill Education

- The **eyebrows** enhance facial expressions and nonverbal communication, but may also protect the eyes from glare and keep perspiration from running into the eye.
- The **eyelids,** or **palpebrae** (pal-PEE-bree), block foreign objects from the eye, prevent visual stimuli from disturbing one's sleep, and blink periodically to moisten the eye with tears and sweep debris from the surface. The eyelids are separated from each other by the **palpebral fissure** and meet each other at the corners called the **medial** and **lateral commissures.** The eyelid consists largely of the orbicularis oculi muscle covered with skin (fig. 16.24a). It also contains a supportive fibrous **tarsal plate** that is thickened along the margin of the eyelid. Within the plate are 20 to 25 **tarsal glands** that open along the edge of the eyelid. They secrete an oil that coats the eye and reduces tear evaporation. The **eyelashes** are guard hairs that help to keep debris from the eye. Touching the eyelashes stimulates hair receptors and triggers the blink reflex. They also disrupt airflow across the eye surface, thus protecting the eyes from drying. In windy or rainy conditions, we can squint so that the eyelashes protect the eyes even further, but without completely obstructing our vision.
- The **conjunctiva** (CON-junk-TY-vuh) is a transparent mucous membrane that covers the inner surface of the eyelid and anterior surface of the eyeball, except for the cornea. It secretes a thin mucous film that prevents the eyeball from drying. It is richly innervated and highly sensitive to pain. It is also very vascular, which is especially evident when the vessels are dilated and the eyes are "bloodshot." Because it is vascular and the cornea is not, the conjunctiva heals more readily than the cornea when injured.
- The **lacrimal**[37] **apparatus** (fig. 16.24b) consists of the lacrimal (tear) gland and a series of ducts that drain the tears into the nasal cavity. The **lacrimal gland,** about the size and shape of an almond, is nestled in a shallow fossa of the frontal bone in the superolateral corner of the orbit. About 12 short ducts lead from the gland to the surface of the conjunctiva. Tears cleanse and lubricate the eye surface, deliver oxygen and

[37]*lacrim* = tear

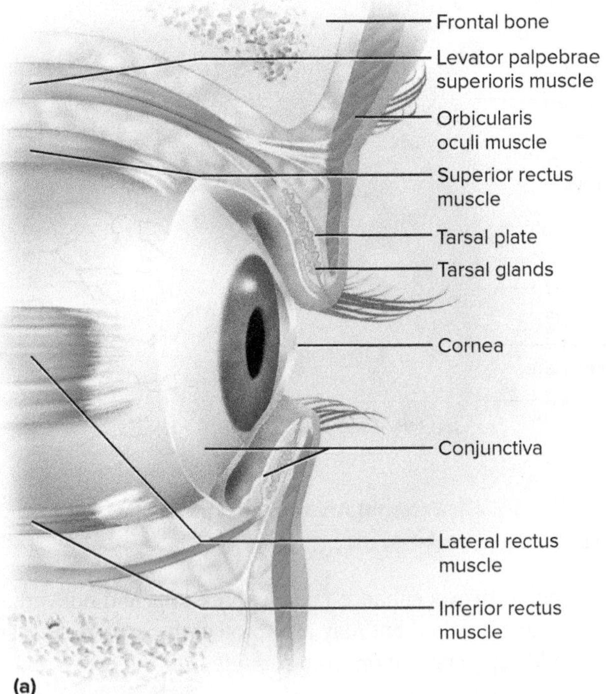


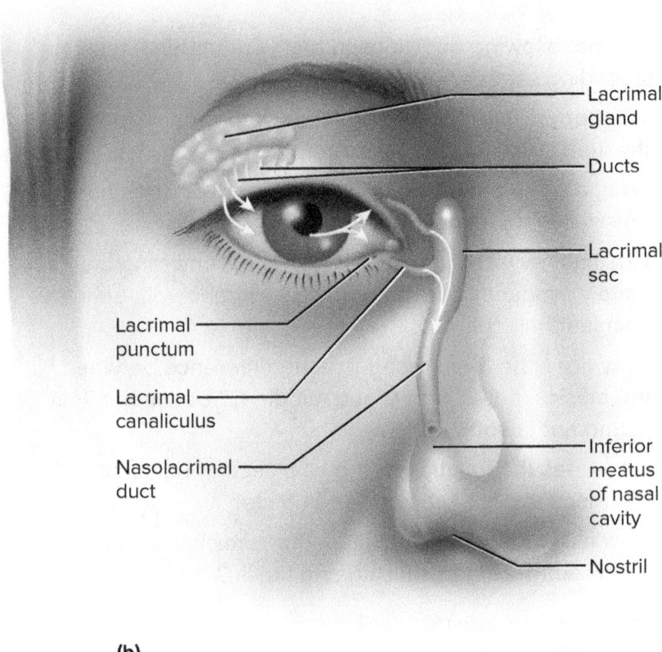


**FIGURE 16.24 Accessory Structures of the Orbit.** (a) Sagittal section of the eye and orbit. (b) The lacrimal apparatus. The arrows indicate the flow of tears from the lacrimal gland, across the front of the eye, into the lacrimal sac, and down the nasolacrimal duct.

*What would be the effect of a blockage of the lacrimal puncta?*

nutrients to the conjunctiva, and contain an antibacterial enzyme, *lysozyme,* which protects the eye from infection. After washing across the eye, tears collect near the medial commissure and flow into a tiny pore, the **lacrimal punctum,**[38] on the margin of each eyelid. The punctum opens into a short **lacrimal canaliculus,** which leads to the **lacrimal sac** in the medial wall of the orbit. From this sac, a **nasolacrimal duct** carries the tears to the inferior meatus of the nasal cavity; thus an abundance of tears from crying or watery eyes can result in a runny nose. Once the tears enter the nasal cavity, they normally flow back to the throat and are swallowed. When you have a cold, the nasolacrimal ducts become swollen and obstructed, the tears cannot drain, and they may overflow from the brim of the eye.

- Six **extrinsic eye muscles** attach to the walls of the orbit and the external surface of the eyeball. *Extrinsic* means "arising externally"; it distinguishes these from the *intrinsic* muscles inside the eye that control the lens and pupil. The extrinsic muscles move the eye **(fig. 16.25).** They include four *rectus* ("straight") muscles and two *oblique* muscles. The **superior, inferior, medial,** and **lateral rectus** originate from a shared tendinous ring on the posterior wall of the orbit and insert on the anterior region of the eyeball, just beyond the visible "white of the eye." They move the eye up, down, medially, and laterally. The **superior oblique** travels along the medial wall of the orbit. Its tendon passes through a fibrocartilage ring, the **trochlea**[39] (TROCK-lee-uh), and inserts on the superolateral aspect of the eyeball. The **inferior oblique** extends from the medial wall of the orbit to the inferolateral aspect of the eye. The oblique muscles slightly rotate the eyes when you tilt your head toward either shoulder, keeping the visual axes of the eyes aligned. People with weakness in the oblique muscles have to tilt their heads to fixate on objects; with the head erect, they have double vision. The oblique muscles also pull the eye forward, opposing tension in the rectus muscles that would otherwise pull the eye back more deeply into the orbit. The superior oblique muscle is innervated by the trochlear nerve (CN IV), the lateral rectus by the abducens (CN VI), and the other four muscles by the oculomotor nerve (CN III).
- **Orbital fat** surrounds the eye on the sides and back. It cushions the eye, allows it to move freely, and protects blood vessels and nerves in the rear of the orbit.

## 16.5c Anatomy of the Eye

The eyeball is a sphere about 24 mm in diameter **(fig. 16.26)** with three principal components: (1) three layers (tunics) that form its wall; (2) optical components that admit and focus light; and (3) neural components, the retina and optic nerve. The retina is not only a neural component but also part of the inner tunic. The cornea is part of the outer tunic as well as one of the optical components.

### The Tunics

The three tunics of the eyeball are as follows:

- The outer **fibrous layer.** This is divided into two regions: sclera and cornea. The **sclera**[40] (white of the eye) covers most

[38]*punct* = point
[39]*trochlea* = pulley

[40]*scler* = hard, tough

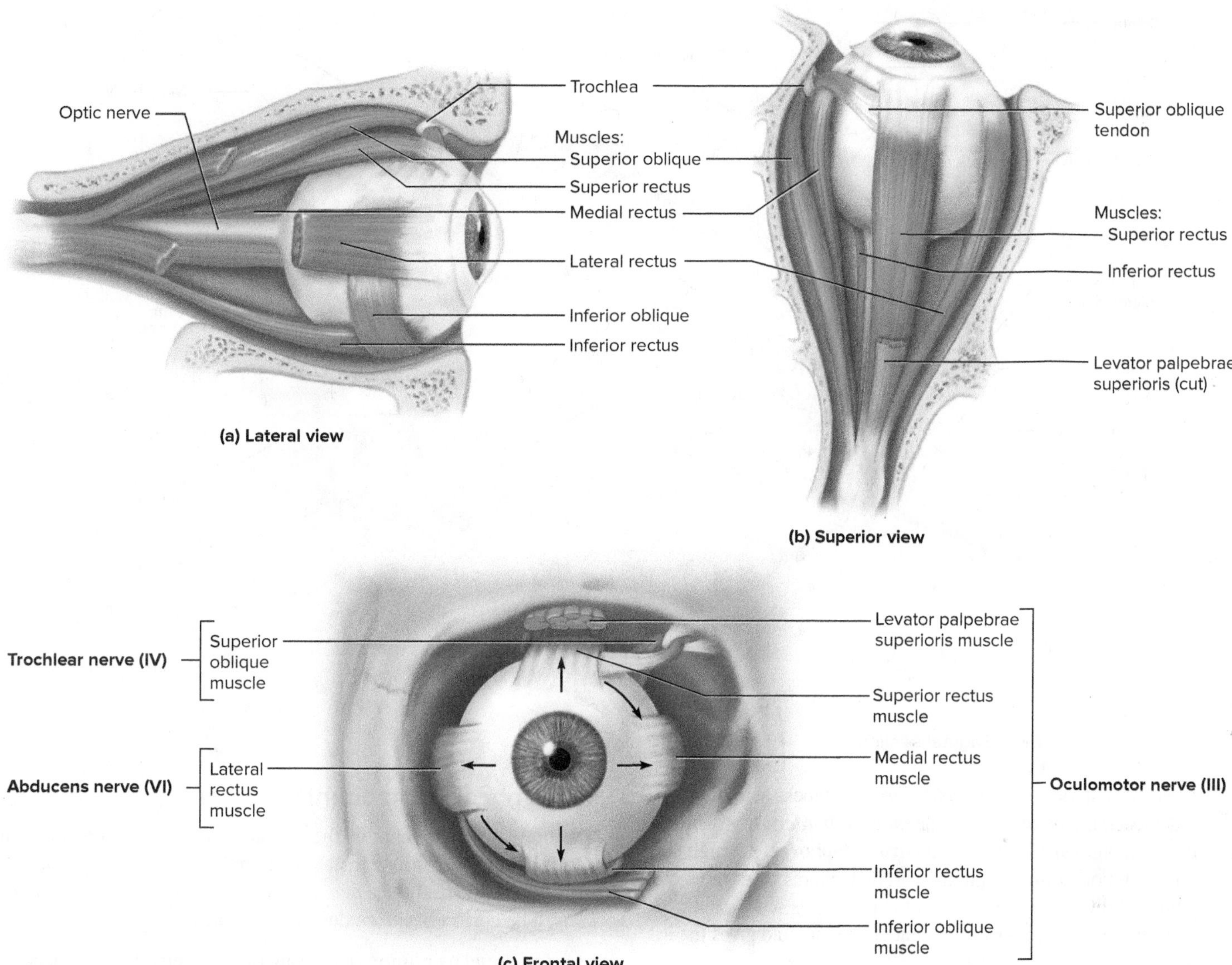


**FIGURE 16.25 Extrinsic Muscles of the Eye.** (a) Lateral view of the right eye. The lateral rectus muscle is cut to show a portion of the optic nerve. (b) Superior view of the right eye. (c) Innervation of the extrinsic muscles; arrows indicate the eye movement produced by each muscle.

*What would cause the greatest loss of visual function—trauma to cranial nerve III, IV, or VI? Why?*

of the eye surface and consists of dense collagenous connective tissue perforated by blood vessels and nerves. It serves as a tough fibrous protective cover for the eye and provides for attachment of the extrinsic muscles that move it. The **cornea** is the anterior transparent region of modified sclera that admits light into the eye. Most of it is composed of very compact layers of collagen fibrils and thin flat fibroblasts. It is covered by a thin stratified squamous epithelium anteriorly and a simple squamous epithelium posteriorly. Both epithelia pump sodium ions out of the corneal tissue. Water follows by osmosis, so this mechanism prevents the cornea from overhydrating, swelling, and losing transparency. When this ion pumping ceases at death, the cornea becomes cloudy. The anterior epithelium also is a source of stem cells that give the cornea a great capacity for regeneration if it is injured.

- The middle **vascular layer.** This is also called the **uvea**[41] (YOU-vee-uh) because it resembles a peeled grape in fresh dissection. It consists of three regions—the choroid, ciliary body, and iris. The **choroid** (CO-royd) is a highly vascular, deeply pigmented layer of tissue behind the retina. It gets its name from a histological resemblance to the chorion of the placenta. Its dense network of blood vessels provides all oxygenation, nourishment, and waste-removal services to the retina, which has no blood vessels of its own. The **ciliary body,** a thickened extension of the choroid, forms a muscular ring around the lens. It supports the iris and lens and secretes a fluid called aqueous humor. The **iris** is an adjustable diaphragm that controls the diameter of the **pupil,** its central opening. It has two pigmented

[41]*uvea* = grape

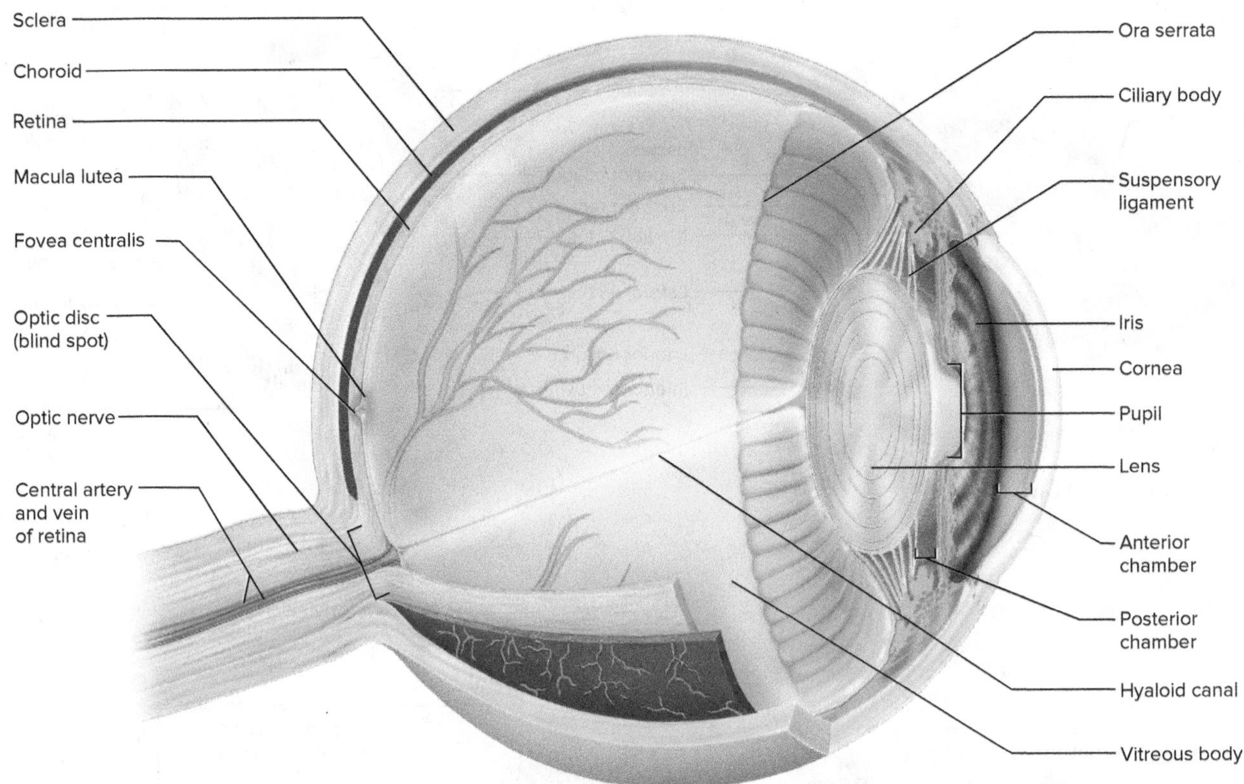


**FIGURE 16.26 The Eye.** Sagittal section.

layers: a posterior *pigment epithelium* that blocks stray light from reaching the retina, and the *anterior border layer,* which contains pigmented cells called **chromatophores.**[42] A high concentration of melanin in the chromatophores gives the iris a black, brown, or hazel color. If the melanin is scanty, light reflects from the posterior pigment epithelium and gives the iris a blue, green, or gray color.

- The **inner layer.** This consists of the retina and beginning of the optic nerve.

[42]*chromato* = color; *phore* = bearer

## The Optical Components

The optical components of the eye are transparent elements that admit light rays, bend (refract) them, and focus images on the retina. They include the *cornea, aqueous humor, lens,* and *vitreous body.* The cornea has been described already.

- The **aqueous humor** is a serous fluid secreted by the ciliary body into a space called the **posterior chamber** between the iris and lens **(fig. 16.27).** It flows through the pupil into the **anterior chamber** between the iris and cornea. From here, it is reabsorbed by a circular vein called the **scleral venous sinus.** Normally the rate of reabsorption balances the rate of secretion (see Deeper Insight 16.3 for an important exception).

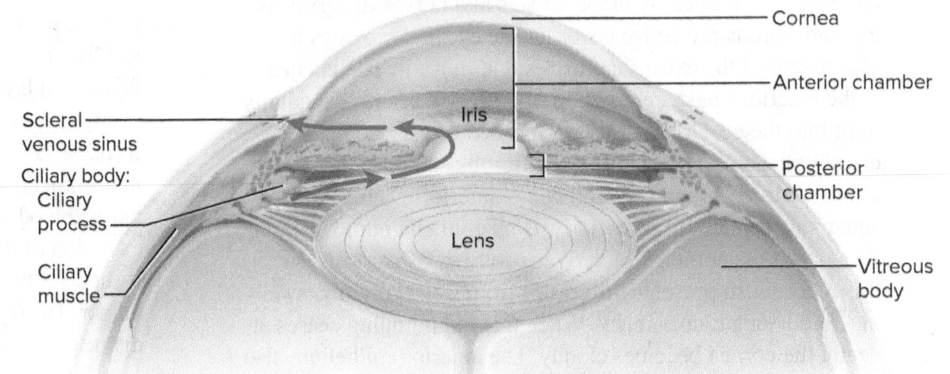


**FIGURE 16.27 Production and Reabsorption of Aqueous Humor.** Blue arrows indicate the flow of aqueous humor from the ciliary processes into the posterior chamber; through the pupil into the anterior chamber; and finally into the scleral venous sinus, the vein that reabsorbs the fluid.

- The **lens** is composed of flattened, tightly compressed, transparent cells called *lens fibers.* It is suspended behind the pupil by a ring of fibers called the **suspensory ligament (fig. 16.29;** also see fig. 16.26), which attaches it to the ciliary body. Tension on the ligament somewhat flattens the lens so it is about 9.0 mm in diameter and 3.6 mm thick at the middle.
- The **vitreous**[43] **body** is a transparent jelly that fills a space called the *vitreous chamber* behind the lens. The vitreous body maintains *intraocular pressure* within the eye, which supports its spherical shape and enables the extrinsic muscles to pull the eye in different directions without compressing and distorting it. It also keeps the retina smoothly pressed against the wall of the eye, which keeps it in close contact with its blood supply and is essential for focusing images on the retina. An oblique channel through this body called the *hyaloid canal* is the remnant of an artery present in the embryo (see fig. 16.26).

## The Neural Components

The neural components are the retina and optic nerve. The **retina** forms from a cup-shaped outgrowth of the diencephalon called the *optic vesicle* (see fig. 14.4b); it is actually a part of the brain—the only part that can be viewed without dissection. It is a thin transparent membrane attached to the rest of the eye at only two points: the **optic disc,** where the optic nerve leaves the rear *(fundus)* of the eye, and its scalloped anterior margin, the **ora serrata.**[44] The

[43]*vitre* = glassy

[44]*ora* = border, margin; *serrata* = notched, serrated

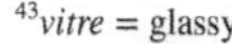

## DEEPER INSIGHT 16.3
### CLINICAL APPLICATION

### *Causes of Blindness*

The most common causes of blindness are cataracts, glaucoma, macular degeneration, and diabetic retinopathy.

*Cataracts* are clouding of the lenses **(fig. 16.28a).** They occur as the lens fibers darken with age, fluid-filled clefts appear between them, and the clefts accumulate debris from degenerating fibers. Cataracts are a common complication of diabetes mellitus, but can also be induced by heavy smoking, ultraviolet radiation, radiation therapy, certain viruses and drugs, and other causes. They cause the vision to appear milky or as if one was looking from behind a waterfall.[45] Cataracts can be treated by replacing the natural lens with a plastic one. The implanted lens improves vision almost immediately, but glasses still may be needed for near vision.

*Glaucoma* is a state of elevated pressure within the eye that occurs when the scleral venous sinus is obstructed so aqueous humor isn't reabsorbed as fast as it is secreted. Pressure in the anterior and posterior chambers drives the lens back and puts pressure on the vitreous body. The vitreous body presses the retina against the choroid and compresses the blood vessels that nourish the retina. Without a good blood supply, retinal cells die and the optic nerve may atrophy, producing blindness. Symptoms often go unnoticed until the damage is irreversible. Illusory flashes of light are an early symptom of glaucoma. Late-stage symptoms include dimness of vision,[46] a narrowed visual field **(fig. 16.28b),** and colored halos around artificial lights. Glaucoma can be detected early in the course of regular eye examinations by measurements of intraocular pressure and visual field. It can be halted with drugs or surgery, but lost vision can't be restored.

*Macular degeneration* is the death of receptor cells in the macula, the central part of the retina and location of the sharpest vision. It can develop so slowly that one fails to notice a change in vision, but eventually it results in loss of vision in the center of the visual field, often making it difficult or impossible to read, drive a car, or do fine daily tasks. It cannot yet be cured, but early detection can allow for treatments to slow its progression.

*Diabetic retinopathy* causes most adult blindness in the United States. It is a retinal degeneration caused by the effects of diabetes mellitus on the blood vessels that nourish the retina. With early detection and control of diabetes, blindness can be prevented in 90% of cases.

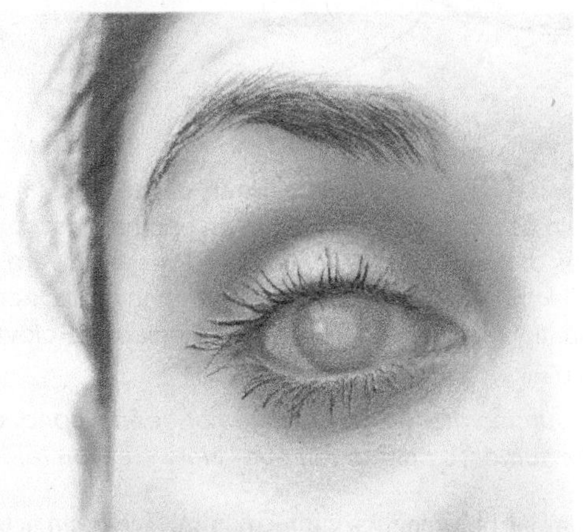

(a)

(b)

**FIGURE 16.28 Cataracts and Glaucoma.** (a) Lens clouded by cataracts. The visual effect of this is milky or blurry vision. (b) The visual field in advanced glaucoma, with tunnel vision.

a: sruilk/Shutterstock; b: Source: National Eye Institute, National Institutes of Health

[45]*cataract* = waterfall

[46]*glauco* = grayness

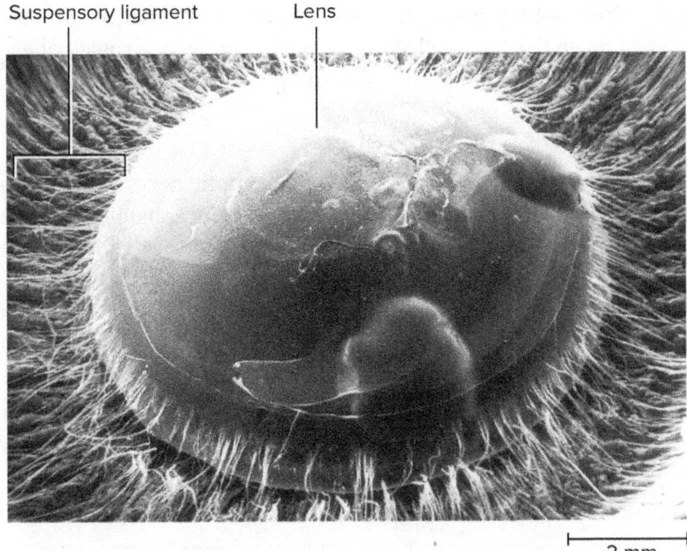


**FIGURE 16.29 The Lens of the Eye (SEM).** Posterior view of the lens and the suspensory ligament that anchors it to the ciliary body.

Ralph C Eagle Jr./Science Source/Getty Images Plus

(a)

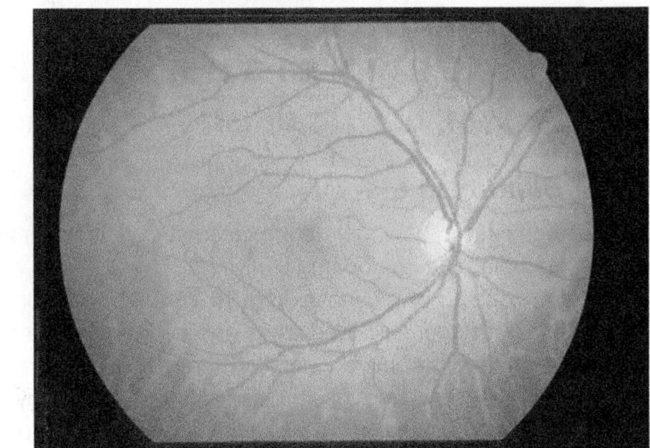

(b)

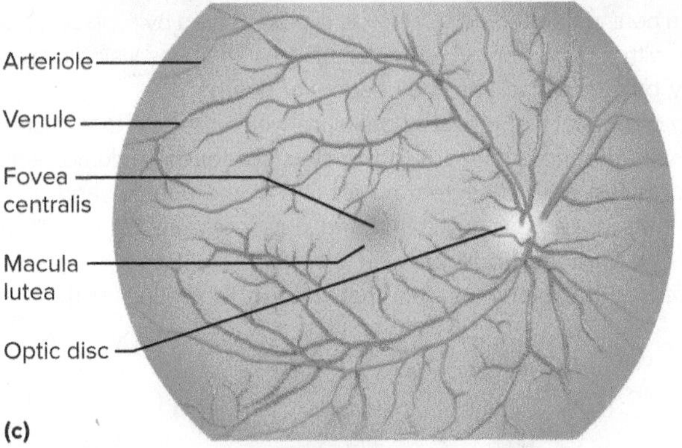


(c)

**FIGURE 16.30 The Fundus (Rear) of the Eye.** (a) Use of the ophthalmoscope. (b) As seen with an ophthalmoscope. (c) Anatomical features of the fundus. Note the blood vessels diverging from the optic disc, where they enter the eye with the optic nerve. An eye examination also serves as a partial check on cardiovascular health.

a: Peter Dazeley/Getty Images; b: Lisa Klancher

? *Assuming these figures have not been flipped, do they show the subject's right or left eye? How can you tell?*

retina can separate from the wall of the eyeball because of blows to the head or insufficient pressure from the vitreous body. Such a *detached retina* may cause blurry areas in the field of vision. It leads to blindness if the retina remains separated for too long from the blood supply in the choroid.

The retina is examined with an illuminating and magnifying instrument called an *ophthalmoscope* (**fig. 16.30**). Directly posterior to the center of the lens, on the visual axis of the eye, is a patch of cells called the **macula lutea**[47] about 3 mm in diameter. In the center of the macula is a tiny pit, the **fovea**[48] **centralis,** which produces the most finely detailed images for reasons explained later. About 3 mm medial to the macula lutea is the optic disc. Nerve fibers from all regions of the retina converge on this point and leave here in a bundle that constitutes the optic nerve. Blood vessels travel through the core of the optic nerve and enter and leave the eye at the optic disc. Eye examinations serve for more than evaluating the visual system; they allow for a direct, noninvasive examination of blood vessels for signs of hypertension, diabetes mellitus, atherosclerosis, and other vascular diseases.

The optic disc contains no receptor cells, so it produces a **blind spot** in the visual field of each eye. You can detect your blind spot and observe an interesting visual phenomenon with the help of **figure 16.31.** Close or cover your right eye and hold the image about 30 cm (1 ft) from your face. Fixate on the X with your left eye. Without taking your gaze off the X, move your head or the page slightly forward and back, or right and left, until the red dot disappears. This occurs because the image of the dot is falling on the blind spot of your left eye.

You should notice something else happen at the same time as the dot disappears—a phenomenon called **visual filling.** The green bar seems to fill in the space where the dot used to be. This occurs because the brain uses the image surrounding the blind spot to fill in the area with similar but imaginary information. The brain acts as if it is better to assume that the unseen area probably looks like its surroundings than to allow a dark blotch to disturb your vision. This is one reason why we don't see a blind patch in the visual field. Another is that the eyes continually undergo minute flickering movements **(saccades)** that ensure that the same area of the visual field doesn't always project onto the same area of retina. What an eye doesn't see at one moment, it will see just milliseconds later when the saccades redirect its visual axis.

[47]*macula* = spot; *lutea* = yellow
[48]*fovea* = pit, depression

FIGURE 16.31 **Demonstration of the Blind Spot and Visual Filling.** See text for explanation of how to conduct this demonstration. Some adjustment of the distance from your face may be needed depending on the print or electronic medium in which you view the image.

Eye saccades are the fastest muscular movements in the human body. Without them, you'd be unable to read this page.

## 16.5d Formation of an Image

The visual process begins when light rays enter the eye, focus on the retina, and produce a tiny inverted image. When fully dilated, the pupil admits five times as much light as it does when fully constricted. Its diameter is controlled by two sets of contractile elements in the iris: (1) The **pupillary constrictor** consists of smooth muscle cells that encircle the pupil. When stimulated by the parasympathetic nervous system, it narrows the pupil and admits less light to the eye. (2) The **pupillary dilator** consists of a spokelike arrangement of contractile *myoepithelial cells.* When stimulated by the sympathetic nervous system, these cells contract, widen the pupil, and admit more light to the eye (see fig. 15.9). Pupillary constriction and dilation occur in three situations: in response to emotions, changes in light intensity, and a shift in one's gaze between distant and nearby objects. Constriction in response to a shift in gaze is part of the *near response* described shortly.

Pupillary constriction in response to light is called the **photopupillary reflex.** It is mediated by an autonomic reflex arc. When light intensity rises, signals are transmitted from the eye to the *pretectal region* of the upper midbrain. Preganglionic parasympathetic fibers travel by way of the oculomotor nerve from here to the *ciliary ganglion* in the orbit. From the ganglion, postganglionic fibers continue into the eye, where they stimulate the pupillary constrictor.

Sympathetic innervation to the pupil originates, like all other sympathetic efferent fibers, in the spinal cord. Preganglionic fibers ascend from the thoracic cord to the superior cervical ganglion. From there, postganglionic fibers follow the carotid arteries into the head and lead ultimately to the pupillary dilator.

### Refraction

Image formation depends on **refraction,** the bending of light rays. Light travels at a speed of 300,000 km/s in a vacuum, but it slows down slightly in air, water, glass, and other media. The *refractive index* of a medium ($n$) is a measure of how much it retards light rays relative to air. The *refractive index* of air is arbitrarily set at $n = 1.00$. If light traveling through air strikes a medium of higher refractive index at a 90° *angle of incidence,* it slows down but doesn't change course—the light rays are not bent. If it strikes at any other angle, however, the light ray changes direction—it is refracted **(fig. 16.32a).** The greater the difference in refractive index between the two media, and the greater the angle of incidence, the stronger the refraction is.

As light enters the eye, it passes from air, with $n = 1.00$, to cornea, with $n = 1.38$. Light rays striking the very center of the cornea pass straight through, but because of the curvature of the cornea, rays striking off center are bent toward the center **(fig. 16.32b).** The aqueous humor has a refractive index of 1.33 and doesn't greatly alter the path of the light. The lens has a refractive index of 1.40. As light passes from air to cornea, the refractive index changes by 0.38; but as it passes from aqueous humor to lens, the refractive index changes by only 0.07. Therefore, the cornea refracts light more than the lens does. The lens merely fine-tunes the image, especially as you shift your focus between near and distant objects.

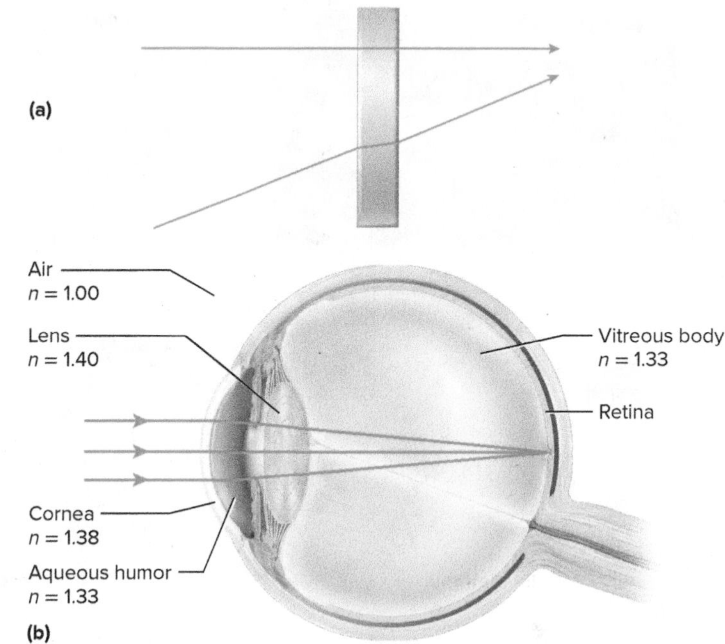


FIGURE 16.32 **Principles of Refraction.** (a) A refractive medium does not bend light rays that strike it at a 90° angle but does bend rays that enter or leave it at any other angle. (b) Refractive indices of the media from air to retina. The greater the difference between the refractive indices of two media, the more strongly light rays are refracted when passing from one to the next.

### The Near Response

**Emmetropia**[49] (EM-eh-TRO-pee-uh) is a state in which the eye is relaxed and focused on an object more than 6 m (20 ft) away, the light rays coming from that object are essentially parallel, and the rays are focused on the retina without effort. If the gaze shifts to something closer, light rays from the source are too divergent to be focused without effort. In other words, the eye is automatically focused on things in the distance unless you make an effort to focus elsewhere. For a wild animal or our prehistoric ancestors, this arrangement would be adaptive because it allows for alertness to predators or prey at a distance.

The **near response (fig. 16.33),** or adjustment to close-range vision, involves three processes to focus an image on the retina:

1. **Convergence of the eyes.** Move your finger gradually closer to a baby's nose and the baby will look cross-eyed at it. This **convergence** of the eyes orients the visual axis of each eye toward the object in order to focus its image on each fovea. If the eyes cannot converge accurately—for example, when the extrinsic muscles are weaker in one eye than in the other—double vision, or *diplopia,*[50] results. The images

[49] *em* = in; *metr* = measure; *opia* = vision
[50] *dipl* = double; *opia* = vision

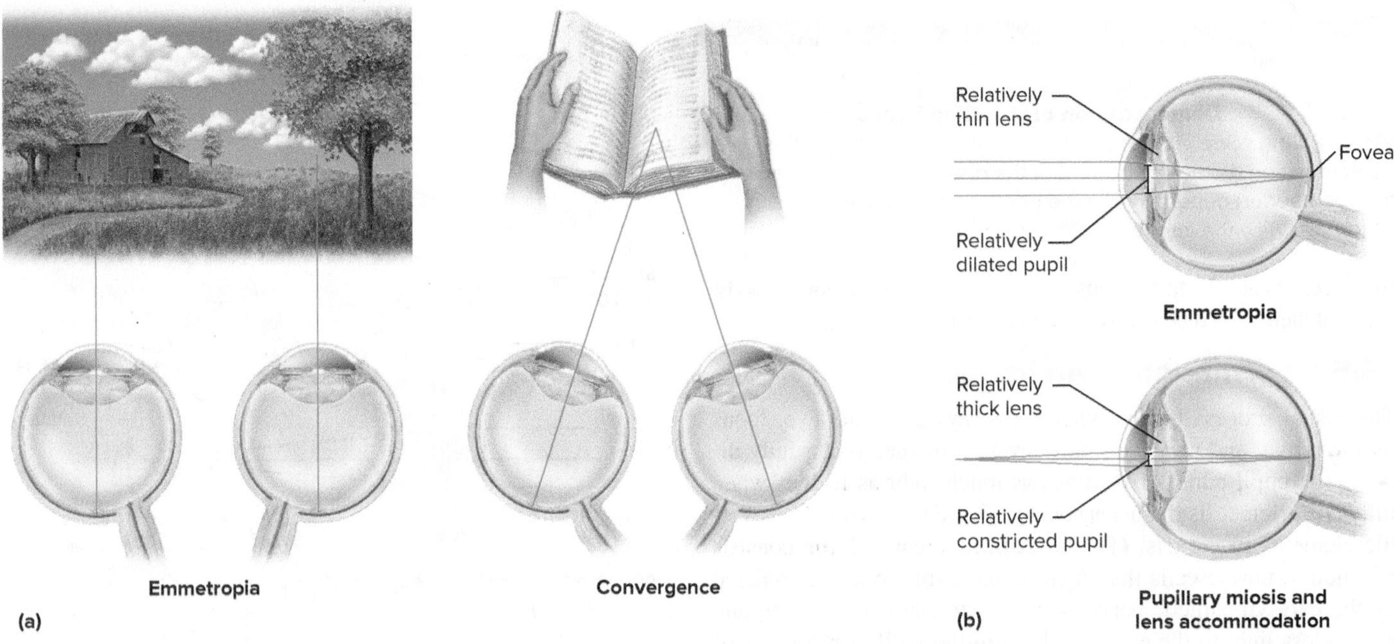


**FIGURE 16.33 Emmetropia and the Near Response.** (a) Superior view of both eyes fixed on an object more than 6 m away (left), and both eyes fixed on an object closer than 6 m (right). (b) Lateral view of the eye fixed on a distant object (top) and nearby object (bottom).

fall on different parts of the two retinas and the brain sees two images. You can simulate this effect by pressing gently on the corner of one eyelid as you look at this text; the image of the text will fall on noncorresponding regions of the two eyes and cause you to see double.

2. **Constriction of the pupil.** Lenses cannot refract light rays at their edges as well as they can closer to the center. The image produced by any lens is therefore somewhat blurry around the edges; this *spherical aberration* is quite evident in an inexpensive microscope. It can be minimized by screening out the peripheral light rays and looking only at the better-focused center. In the eye, the pupil serves this purpose by constricting as you focus on nearby objects. Like the diaphragm setting (f-stop) of a camera, the pupil thus has a dual purpose: to adjust the eye to variations in brightness and to reduce spherical aberration.
3. **Accommodation of the lens. Accommodation** is a change in the curvature of the lens that enables you to focus on a nearby object. When you look at something nearby, the ciliary muscle surrounding the lens contracts. This narrows the diameter of the ciliary body, relaxes the fibers of the suspensory ligament, and allows the lens to relax into a more convex shape **(fig. 16.34).** In emmetropia, the lens is about 3.6 mm thick at the center; in accommodation, it

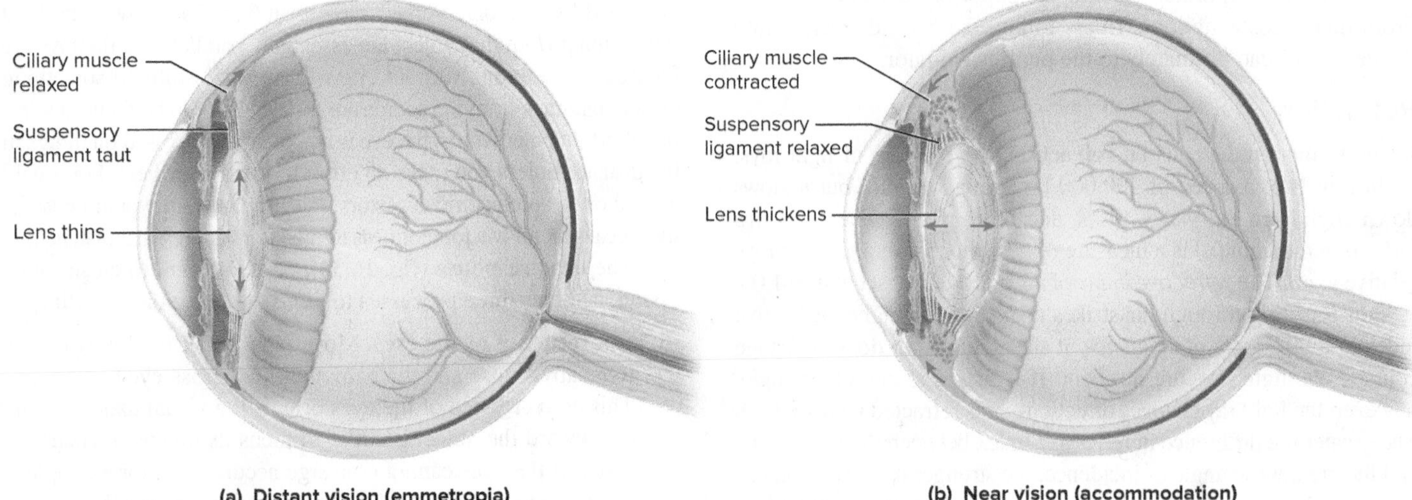


**FIGURE 16.34 Accommodation of the Lens.** (a) In the emmetropic eye, the ciliary muscle is relaxed and dilated. It puts tension on the suspensory ligament and flattens the lens. (b) In accommodation, the ciliary muscle contracts and narrows in diameter. This reduces tension on the suspensory ligament and allows the lens to relax into a more convex shape.

thickens to as much as 4.5 mm. A more convex lens refracts light more strongly and focuses the divergent light rays onto the retina. The closest an object can be and still come into focus is called the **near point of vision.** It depends on the flexibility of the lens. The lens stiffens with age, so the near point averages about 9 cm at the age of 10 and 83 cm by the age of 60.

Some common defects in image formation are described in **table 16.2.**

**▶▶▶APPLY WHAT YOU KNOW**

*Which extrinsic muscles of the eyes are the prime movers in convergence?*

## 16.5e Sensory Transduction in the Retina

The conversion of light energy into action potentials occurs in the retina. We begin our exploration of this process with the cellular layout of the retina **(fig. 16.36).** From there we go to the pigments that absorb light and then to what happens when light is absorbed.

**TABLE 16.2 Common Defects of Image Formation**

| | |
|---|---|
| Astigmatism[51] | Inability to simultaneously focus light rays that enter the eye on different planes. Focusing on vertical lines, such as the edge of a door, may cause horizontal lines, such as a tabletop, to go out of focus. Caused by a deviation in the shape of the cornea so that it is shaped like the back of a spoon rather than part of a sphere. Corrected with *cylindrical lenses,* which refract light more in one plane than another. |
| Hyperopia[52] | Farsightedness—a condition in which the eyeball is too short. The retina lies in front of the focal point of the lens, and the light rays have not yet come into focus when they reach the retina (see top of **fig. 16.35b**). Causes the greatest difficulty when viewing nearby objects. Corrected with *convex lenses,* which cause light rays to converge slightly before entering the eye, so they reach their focal point farther forward than usual, on the retina of the shortened eyeball. |
| Myopia[53] | Nearsightedness—a condition in which the eyeball is too long. Light rays come into focus before they reach the retina and begin to diverge again by the time they fall on it (see top of **fig. 16.35c**). Corrected with *concave lenses,* which cause light rays to diverge slightly before entering the eye, shifting the focal point posteriorly so that it falls on the retina of the elongated eyeball. |
| Presbyopia[54] | Reduced ability to accommodate for near vision with age. Caused by declining flexibility of the lens. Results in difficulty reading and doing close handwork. Corrected with *bifocal lenses* or reading glasses. |

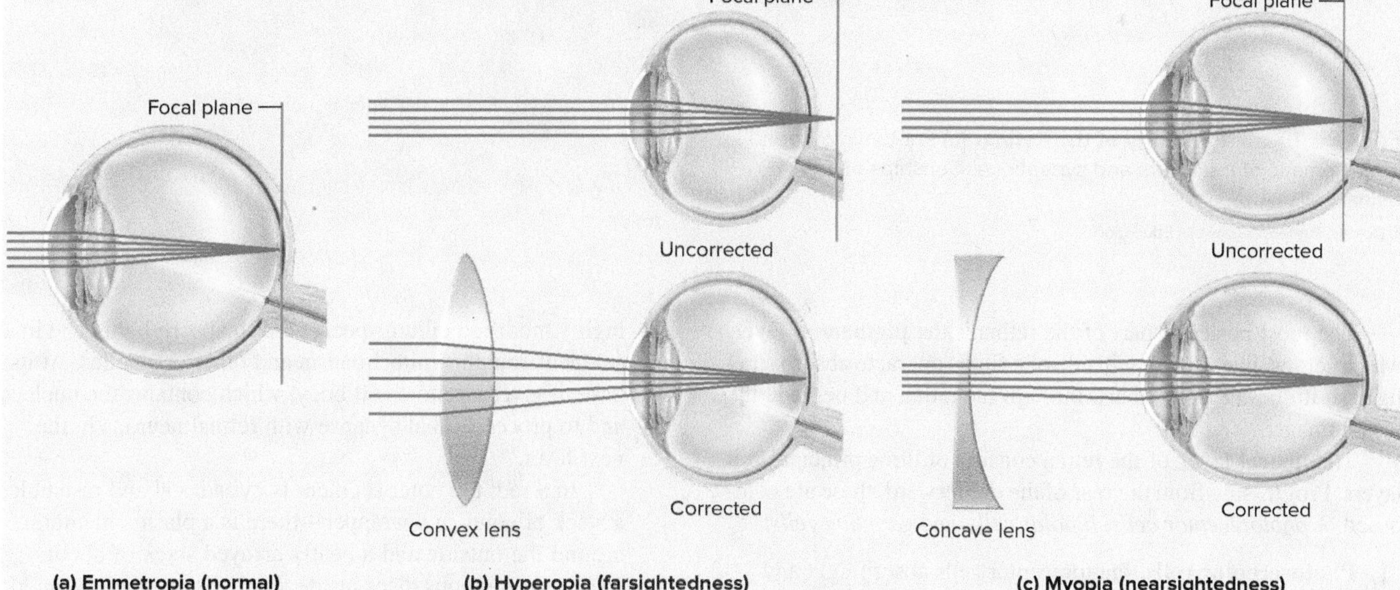


**FIGURE 16.35 Two Common Visual Defects and the Effects of Corrective Lenses.** (a) The normal emmetropic eye, with light rays converging on the retina. (b) Hyperopia (farsightedness) and the corrective effect of a convex lens. (c) Myopia (nearsightedness) and the corrective effect of a concave lens.

[51] *a* = not; *stigma* = point; *ism* = condition
[52] *hyper* = excessive; *op* = eye; *ia* = condition
[53] *my* = closed; *op* = eye; *ia* = condition
[54] *presby* = old; *op* = eye; *ia* = condition

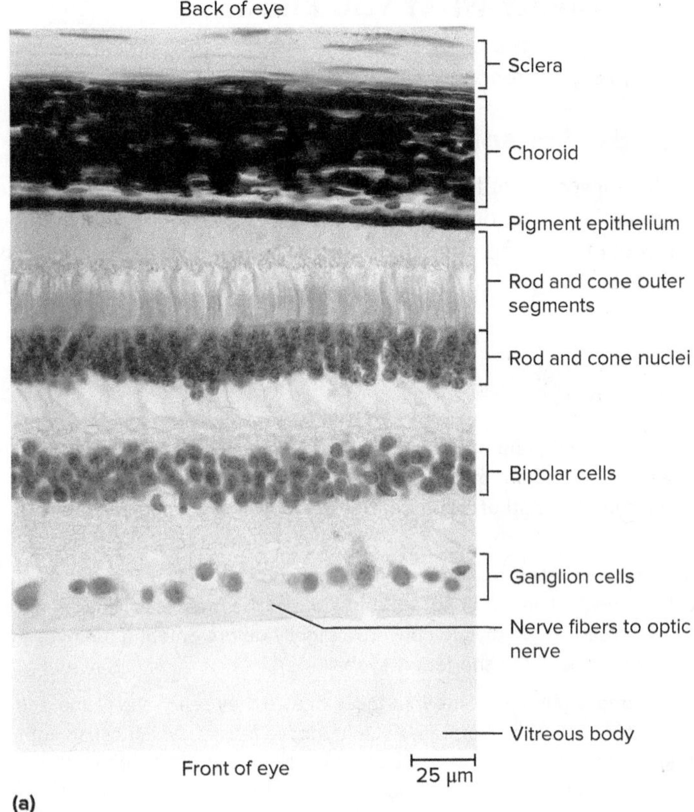


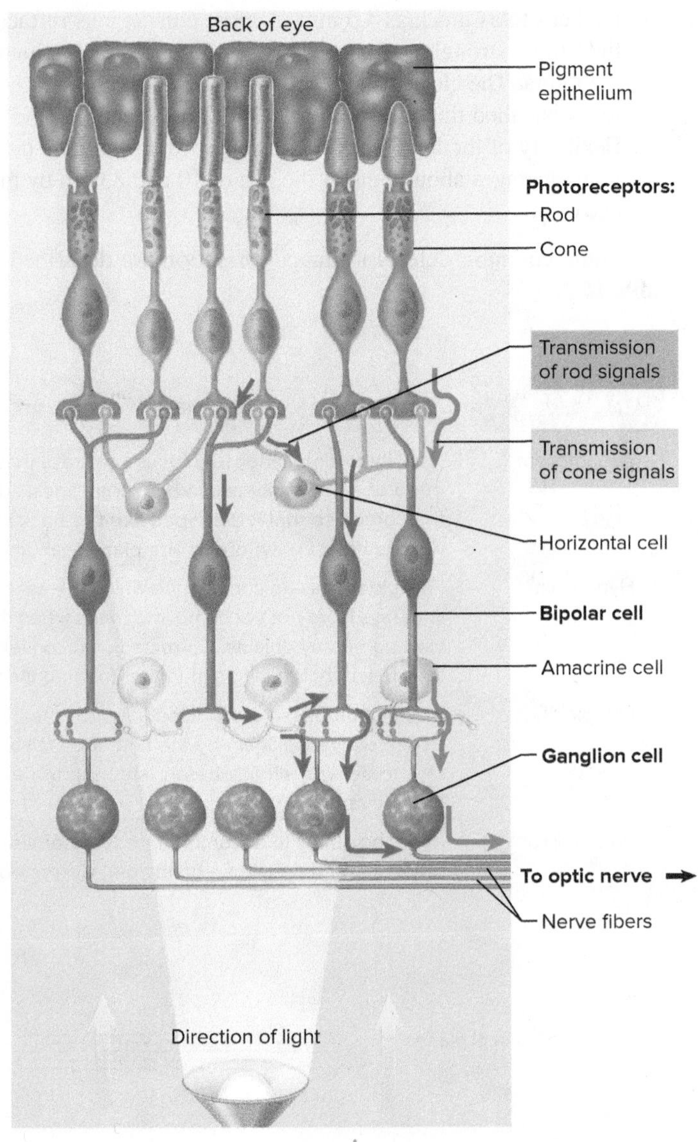

**FIGURE 16.36 Histology of the Retina.** (a) Photomicrograph. (b) Schematic of the layers and synaptic relationships of the retinal cells.

a: Dennis Strete/McGraw-Hill Education

The most posterior part of the retina is the **pigmented layer,** which serves, like the black inside of a film camera, to absorb stray light so it doesn't reflect back through the retina and degrade the visual image.

The **neural layer** of the retina consists of three principal cell layers. Progressing from the rear of the eye forward, these are composed of *photoreceptor cells, bipolar cells,* and *ganglion cells:*

1. **Photoreceptor cells.** Photoreceptor cells absorb light and generate a chemical or electrical signal. There are three kinds: rods, cones, and certain ganglion cells. Only rods and cones produce visual images; the ganglion cells are discussed later. **Rods** and **cones** aren't neurons, but are related to the ependymal cells of the brain. Each rod or cone has an **outer segment** that points toward the wall of the eye and an **inner segment** facing the interior **(fig. 16.37).** The two segments are separated by a constriction containing nine pairs of microtubules; the outer segment is actually a highly modified cilium specialized to absorb light. The inner segment contains mitochondria and other organelles. At its base, it gives rise to a cell body, which contains the nucleus, and to processes that synapse with retinal neurons in the next layer.

   In a rod, the outer segment is cylindrical and resembles a stack of coins in a wrapper—there is a plasma membrane around the outside and a neatly arrayed stack of about 1,000 membranous discs inside. Each disc is densely studded with globular proteins—the visual pigment *rhodopsin.* The membranes hold these pigment molecules in a position that results in the most efficient light absorption. Rod cells are responsible for **night (scotopic[55]) vision** and produce images only in shades of gray **(monochromatic vision).**

[55]*scot* = dark; *op* = vision

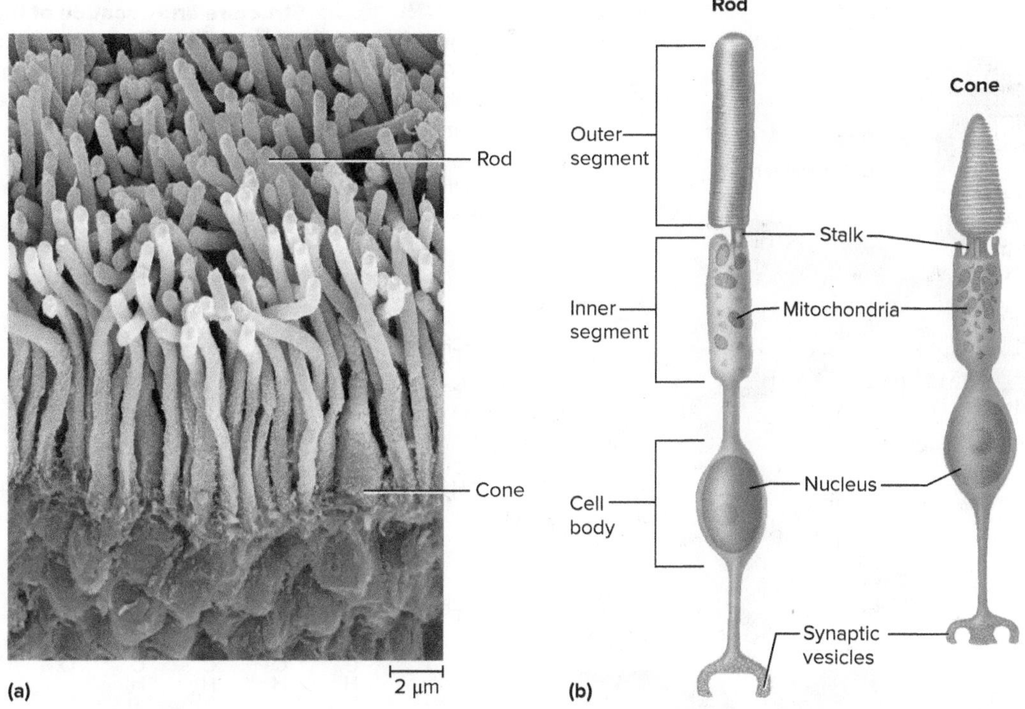


**FIGURE 16.37 Rod and Cone Cells.** (a) Rods and cones of a human retina (SEM). The outer segments are shown in tan (rods) and green (cones); cell bodies and inner segments are in violet. (b) Structure of human rods and cones. The rod outer segment is shown greatly shortened.

a: Steve Gschmeissner/Science Source

A cone cell is similar but shorter, its outer segment tapers to a point, and the discs are not detached from the plasma membrane but are parallel infoldings of it. Their visual pigment is called *photopsin*. Cones function in brighter light; they are responsible for **day (photopic[56]) vision** as well as **color (trichromatic) vision.**

Rods and cones continually renew their discs by addition of new ones at the proximal (basal) end of the outer segment, while old discs are shed from the distal tips of the cells and phagocytized by cells in the pigment epithelium.

2. **Bipolar cells.** Rods and cones synapse with the dendrites of **bipolar cells,** the first-order neurons of the visual pathway. They in turn synapse with the ganglion cells described next (fig. 16.36b).
3. **Ganglion cells. Ganglion cells** are the largest neurons of the retina, arranged in a single layer close to the vitreous body. They are the second-order neurons of the visual pathway. Most ganglion cells receive input from multiple bipolar cells. Their axons form the optic nerve. Some of the ganglion cells, however, are supplemental photoreceptors; they absorb light directly and transmit signals to brainstem nuclei that control pupillary diameter and the body's circadian rhythms. They don't contribute to visual images but detect only light intensity. Their sensory pigment is called **melanopsin.**

There are other retinal cells, but they don't form layers of their own. **Horizontal cells** and **amacrine[57] cells** form horizontal connections between rods, cones, and bipolar cells and intervene in the pathways from receptor cells to ganglion cells. They play diverse roles in enhancing the perception of contrast, the edges of objects, and changes in light intensity. In addition, much of the mass of the retina is composed of astrocytes and other types of glial cells.

There are approximately 130 million rods and 6.5 million cones in one retina, but only 1 million nerve fibers in the optic nerve. With a ratio of nearly 140 receptor cells to one optic nerve fiber, it is obvious that there must be substantial *neural convergence* and information processing in the retina itself before signals are conducted to the brain proper. Convergence occurs where multiple rods or cones synapse with one bipolar cell, and again where multiple bipolar cells feed into one ganglion cell. Later we will examine how convergence functions in visual resolution and night vision.

## Visual Pigments

The visual pigment of the rods is called **rhodopsin** (ro-DOP-sin), or **visual purple.** It consists of two major parts (moieties): a protein called **opsin** and a vitamin A derivative called **retinene** or **retinal** (rhymes with "pal") **(fig. 16.38).** A dietary deficiency of vitamin A can lead to **night blindness,** a difficulty seeing in dim light. Opsin is embedded in the disc membranes of the rod's outer segment. All rods contain a single kind of rhodopsin with an absorption peak at

[56]*phot* = light; *op* = vision

[57]*a* = without; *macr* = long; *in* = fiber (lacking axons)

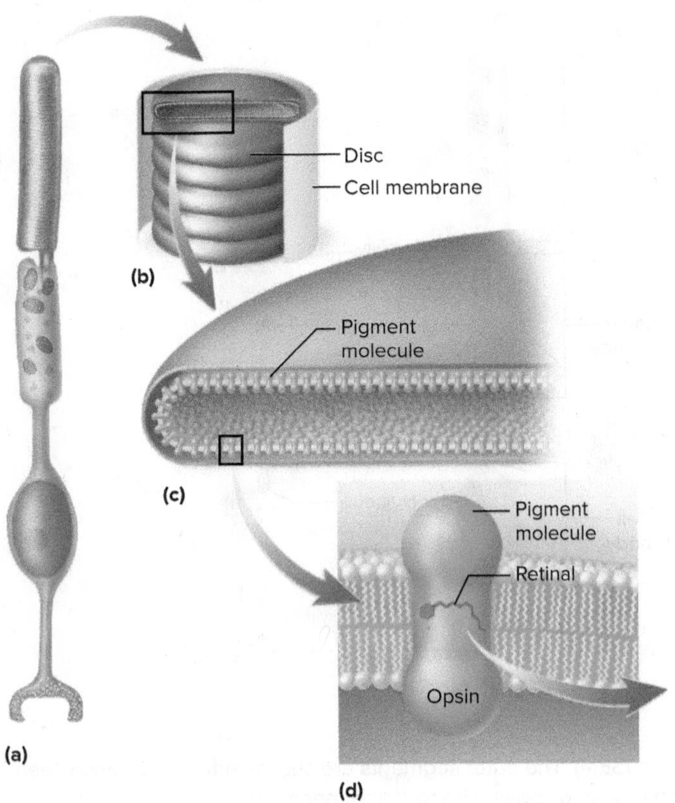


(e) *Cis*-retinal

(f) *Trans*-retinal (bleached)

**FIGURE 16.38 Structure and Location of the Visual Pigments.** (a) A rod cell. (b) Detail of the rod outer segment. (c) One disc of the outer segment showing the membrane studded with pigment molecules. (d) A pigment molecule, embedded in the unit membrane of the disc, showing the protein moiety, opsin, and the vitamin A derivative, retinal. (e) *Cis*-retinal, the isomer present in the absence of light. (f) *Trans*-retinal, the isomer produced when the pigment absorbs a photon of light.

a wavelength of 500 nm. Rods are less sensitive to light of other wavelengths and cannot distinguish one color from another.

In cones, the pigment is called **photopsin.** Its retinal moiety is the same as that of rhodopsin, but the opsin moiety has a different amino acid sequence that determines which wavelengths of light the pigment absorbs. There are three kinds of cones, which are identical in appearance but optimally absorb different wavelengths of light. These differences enable us to perceive different colors.

## Generating the Optic Nerve Signal

The events of sensory transduction are probably the same in rods and cones, but are better known in rods. In the dark, their retinal has a bent shape called ***cis*-retinal.** When it absorbs light, it changes to a straight form called *trans*-retinal and breaks away from the opsin **(fig. 16.39).** This is called **bleaching,** because purified rhodopsin changes from violet to colorless in the light. For a rod to continue functioning, *trans*-retinal has to be converted back to the *cis* form and reunited with opsin, producing functional rhodopsin at a rate that keeps pace with bleaching. Fifty percent of the bleached rhodopsin is regenerated in about 5 minutes. Cones are faster and their photopsin is 50% regenerated in about 90 seconds.

In the dark, rods don't sit quietly doing nothing. They steadily release the neurotransmitter glutamate from the basal end of the cell **(fig. 16.40a).** When a rod absorbs light, glutamate secretion ceases **(fig. 16.40b).** We won't delve into the mechanistic details of why this occurs. The important point is that the bipolar cells, next in line, are sensitive to these on and off pulses of glutamate secretion. Some bipolar cells are inhibited by glutamate and excited when its secretion stops; these cells are therefore excited by rising light intensities. Other bipolar cells are excited by glutamate and therefore respond when light intensity drops. As your eye scans a scene, it passes areas of greater and lesser brightness. Their images on the retina cause a rapidly changing pattern of bipolar cell responses as the light intensity on a patch of retina rises and falls.

When bipolar cells detect fluctuations in light intensity, they stimulate ganglion cells either directly (by synapsing with them) or indirectly (via pathways that go through amacrine cells). Ganglion cells are the only retinal cells that produce action potentials; all other retinal cells produce only graded local potentials. Ganglion cells respond to the bipolar cells with rising and falling firing frequencies. Via the optic nerve, these changes provide visual signals to the brain.

## 16.5f Light and Dark Adaptation

The human eye can detect light intensities ranging from a single photon at threshold (near-total darkness) to 10 billion times as bright (the intensity of bright sunlight reflected from snow). **Light adaptation** is an adjustment in vision that occurs when you go from a dark or dimly lit area into brighter light. If you wake up in the night and turn on a lamp, at first you see a harsh glare; you may experience discomfort from the overstimulated retinas. Your pupils quickly constrict to reduce the intensity of stimulation, but color vision and visual acuity (the ability to see fine detail) remain below normal for 5 to 10 minutes—the time needed for pigment bleaching to adjust retinal sensitivity to this light intensity. The

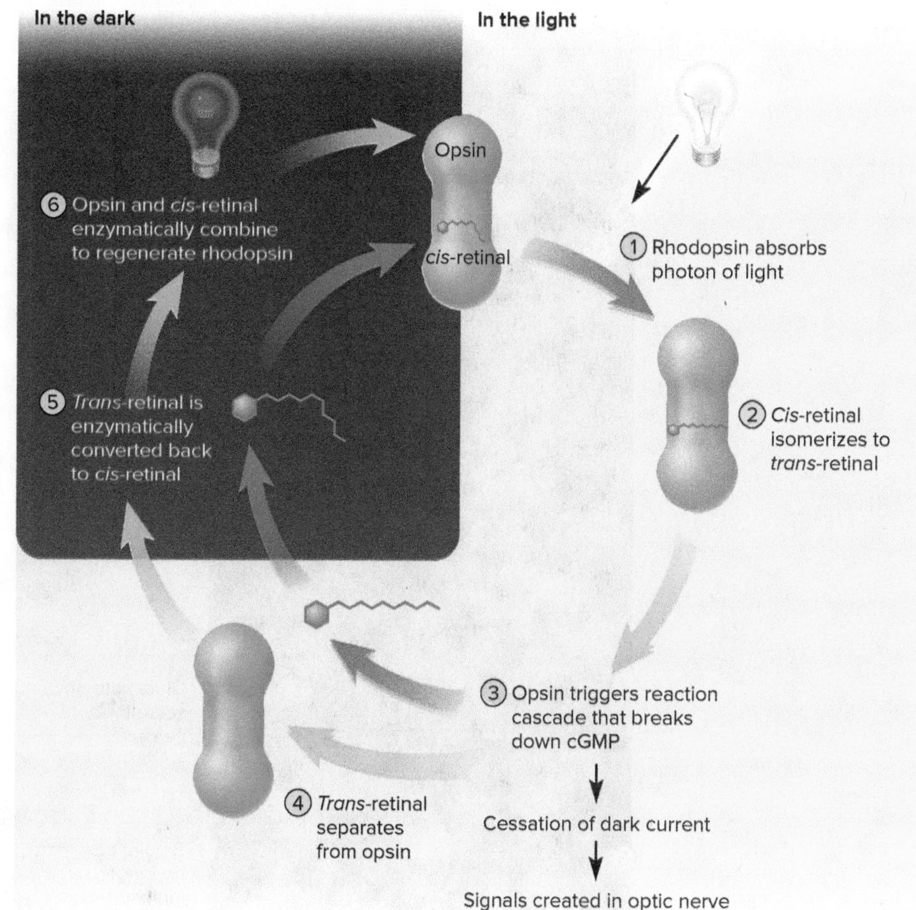
In the dark
In the light
Opsin
cis-retinal
1 Rhodopsin absorbs photon of light
2 Cis-retinal isomerizes to trans-retinal
3 Opsin triggers reaction cascade that breaks down cGMP
Cessation of dark current
Signals created in optic nerve
4 Trans-retinal separates from opsin
5 Trans-retinal is enzymatically converted back to cis-retinal
6 Opsin and cis-retinal enzymatically combine to regenerate rhodopsin

**FIGURE 16.39 The Bleaching and Regeneration of Rhodopsin.** Numbers 1 through 4 indicate the bleaching events that occur in the light; numbers 5 and 6 indicate the regenerative events that are independent of light. The regenerative events occur in light and dark, but in the light, they are outpaced by bleaching.

rods bleach quickly in bright light, and cones take over. Even in typical indoor light, rod vision is nonfunctional.

On the other hand, suppose you're sitting in a brightly lit room reading at night, and there is a power failure. Your eyes must undergo **dark adaptation** before you can see well enough to find your way in the dark. There isn't enough light for cone (photopic) vision, and it takes a little time for the rods (scotopic vision) to adjust to the dark. Your rod pigment was bleached by the lights in the room while the power was on, but now in the relative absence of light, rhodopsin regenerates faster than it bleaches. In a minute or two, scotopic vision begins to function, and after 20 to 30 minutes, the amount of regenerated rhodopsin is sufficient for your eyes to reach essentially maximum sensitivity. Dilation of the pupils also helps by admitting more light to the eye.

## 16.5g The Dual Visual System

You may wonder why we have both rods and cones. Why can't we simply have one type of receptor cell that produces detailed color vision, both day and night? The **duplicity theory** of vision holds that a single receptor system cannot produce both high sensitivity and high resolution. It takes one type of cell and neural circuit to provide sensitive night vision and a different type to provide high-resolution daytime vision.

The high sensitivity of rods in dim light stems partly from the extensive neural convergence that occurs between the rods and ganglion cells. Up to 600 rods converge on each bipolar cell, and many bipolar cells converge on each ganglion cell. This allows for a high degree of *spatial summation* **(fig. 16.41a).** Weak stimulation of many rods can produce an additive effect on one bipolar cell, and several bipolar cells can collaborate to excite one ganglion cell. Thus, a ganglion cell can respond in dim light that only weakly stimulates any individual rod. Scotopic vision is functional even at a light intensity less than starlight reflected from a sheet of white paper. A shortcoming of this system is that it cannot resolve finely detailed images. One ganglion cell receives input from all the rods in about 1 $mm^2$ of retina—its receptive field. What the brain perceives is therefore a coarse, grainy image similar to an overenlarged photograph or low-resolution digital image.

Around the edges of the retina, receptor cells are especially large and widely spaced. If you fixate on the middle of this page, you will notice that you can't read the words near the margins. Visual acuity decreases rapidly as the image falls away from the fovea centralis. Our peripheral vision is a low-resolution system that serves mainly to alert us to motion in the periphery and to stimulate us to look that way to identify what is there.

When you look directly at something, its image falls on the fovea, which is occupied by about 4,000 tiny cones and no rods. The other neurons of the fovea are displaced to one side so they won't interfere with light falling on the cones. The smallness of these cones is like the smallness of the dots or pixels in a fine-grained (high-resolution) photograph; it is partially responsible for

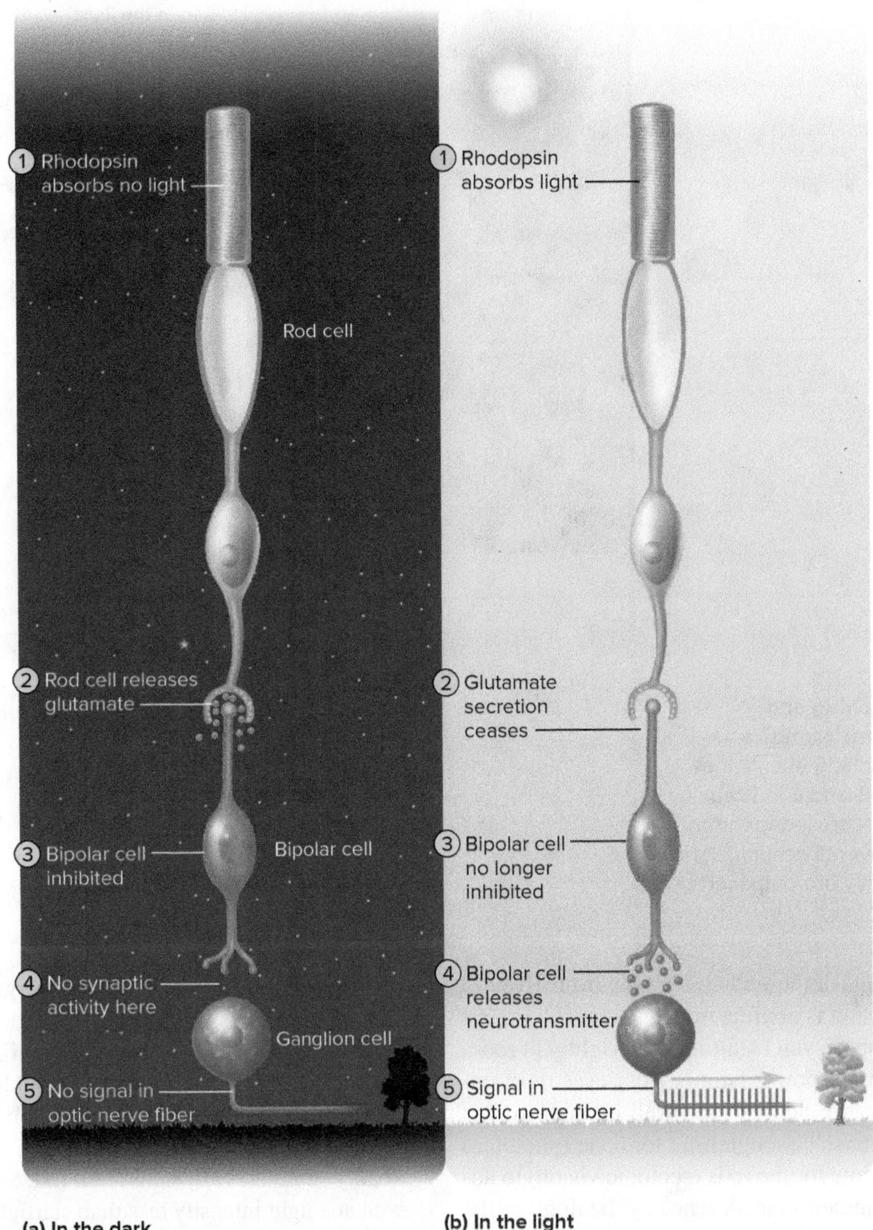

1 Rhodopsin absorbs no light
Rod cell
2 Rod cell releases glutamate
3 Bipolar cell inhibited
Bipolar cell
4 No synaptic activity here
Ganglion cell
5 No signal in optic nerve fiber
1 Rhodopsin absorbs light
2 Glutamate secretion ceases
3 Bipolar cell no longer inhibited
4 Bipolar cell releases neurotransmitter
5 Signal in optic nerve fiber
(a) In the dark
(b) In the light

**FIGURE 16.40 Mechanism of Generating Visual Signals.** (a) In complete darkness, rod cells are active whereas certain bipolar cells and the ganglion cells are not. (b) As rod cells absorb light, they are inhibited and these bipolar cells and ganglion cells are activated. Cones are believed to function similarly. Some bipolar cells behave differently from the type used in this example.

the high-resolution images formed at the fovea. In addition, the cones here show no neural convergence. Each cone synapses with only one bipolar cell and each bipolar cell with only one ganglion cell. This gives each foveal cone a "private line to the brain," and each ganglion cell of the fovea reports to the brain on a receptive field of just 2 μm$^2$ of retinal area **(fig. 16.41b).** Cones distant from the fovea exhibit some neural convergence but not nearly as much as rods do. The price of this lack of convergence at the fovea, however, is that cone cells are incapable of spatial summation, and the cone system is therefore less sensitive to light. The threshold of photopic (cone) vision lies between the intensity of starlight and moonlight reflected from white paper.

**▶▶▶APPLY WHAT YOU KNOW**

*If you look directly at a dim star in the night sky, it disappears, and if you look slightly away, it reappears. Why?*

## 16.5h Color Vision

Most nocturnal vertebrates have only rod cells, but many diurnal animals are endowed with cones and color vision. Color vision is especially well developed in primates for evolutionary reasons discussed in chapter 1 (see section 1.4b). It is based on three kinds of cones named for the absorption peaks of their photopsins: **short-wavelength (S) cones,** with peak sensitivity at a wavelength of

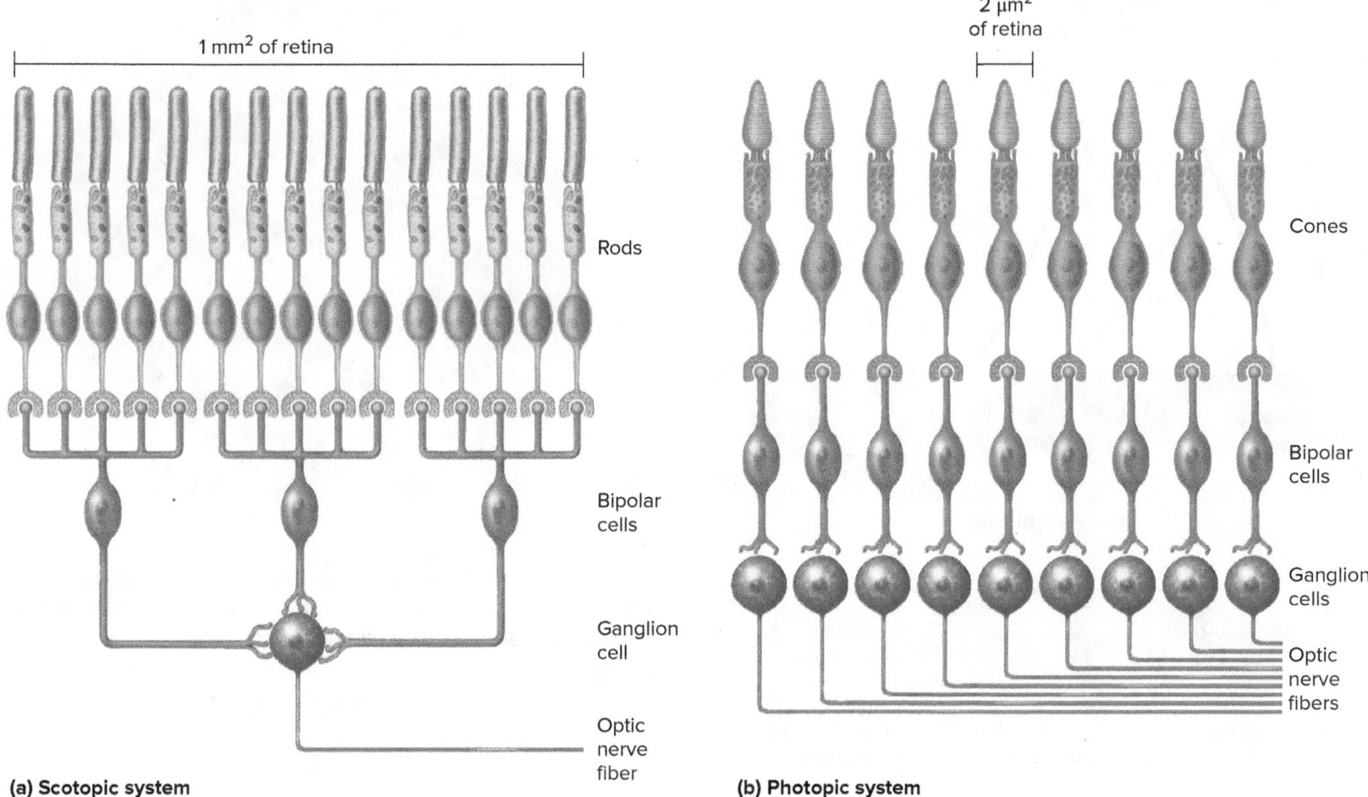


**FIGURE 16.41 Retinal Circuitry and Visual Sensitivity.** (a) In the scotopic (night vision) system, many rods converge on each bipolar cell and many bipolar cells converge on each ganglion cell. Note the large receptive field (1 mm$^2$), which makes this a low-resolution system. (b) In the photopic (day vision) system, there is little neural convergence. Note the small receptive field (2 µm$^2$), which makes this a high-resolution system.

420 nm; **medium-wavelength (M) cones,** which peak at 531 nm; and **long-wavelength (L) cones,** which peak at 558 nm. These were formerly called *blue, green,* and *red cones*—a less accurate terminology. "Red" cones, for example, don't peak in the red part of the spectrum (558 nm light is perceived as orange-yellow), but they are the only cones that respond at all to red light.

Our perception of colors is based on a mixture of nerve signals representing cones with different absorption peaks. In **figure 16.42,** note that light at 400 nm excites only S cones. At 500 nm, all three types of cones are stimulated; the L cones respond at 60% of their maximum capacity, M cones at 82% of their maximum, and S cones at 20%. The brain interprets this mixture as blue-green. The table in this figure shows how some other color sensations are generated by other response ratios.

Some individuals have a hereditary alteration or lack of one photopsin or another and thus exhibit **color blindness.** The most common form is *red–green color blindness,* which results from a lack of either L or M cones and causes difficulty distinguishing these and related shades from each other. For example, a person with normal *trichromatic* color vision sees **figure 16.43** as showing the number 74, whereas a person with red–green color blindness sees no number. Red–green color blindness is a sex-linked recessive trait. It occurs in about 8% of males and 0.5% of females.

## 16.5i Stereoscopic Vision

**Stereoscopic vision (stereopsis)** is depth perception—the ability to judge how far away objects are. It depends on having two eyes with overlapping visual fields, which allows each eye to look at the same object from a different angle. Stereoscopic vision contrasts with the *panoramic vision* of mammals such as rodents and horses, in which the eyes are on opposite sides of the head. Although stereoscopic vision covers a smaller visual field than panoramic vision and provides less alertness to sneaky predators, it has the advantage of depth perception. The evolutionary basis of our stereoscopic vision was also explained along with color vision in section 1.4b.

When you fixate on something within 30 m (100 ft), each eye views it from a slightly different angle and focuses its image on the fovea centralis. The point in space on which the eyes are focused is called the *fixation point.* Objects farther away than the fixation point cast an image somewhat medial to the foveas, and closer objects cast their images more laterally **(fig. 16.44).** The distance of an image from the two foveas provides the brain with information used to judge the position of other points relative to the fixation point.

## 16.5j The Visual Projection Pathway

The optic nerves arise from the retinal ganglion cells and leave each orbit through the optic canal. They converge to form an X, the

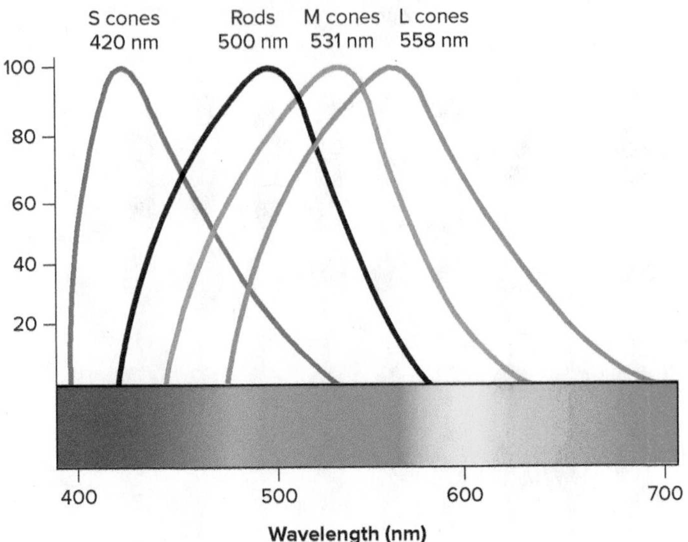


| Wavelength (nm) | Percentage of maximum cone response (S : M : L) | Perceived hue |
|---|---|---|
| 400 | 50 : 0 : 0 | Violet |
| 450 | 72 : 30 : 0 | Blue |
| 500 | 20 : 82 : 60 | Blue-green |
| 550 | 0 : 85 : 97 | Green |
| 625 | 0 : 3 : 35 | Orange |
| 675 | 0 : 0 : 5 | Red |

**FIGURE 16.42 Absorption Spectra of the Retinal Cells.** In the middle column of the table, each number indicates how strongly the respective cone cells respond as a percentage of their maximum capability for a given light intensity. At 550 nm, for example, L cones respond at 97% of their maximum, M cones at 85%, and S cones not at all. The result is a perception of green light.

? *If you were to add another row to this table for 600 nm, what would you enter in the middle and right-hand columns?*

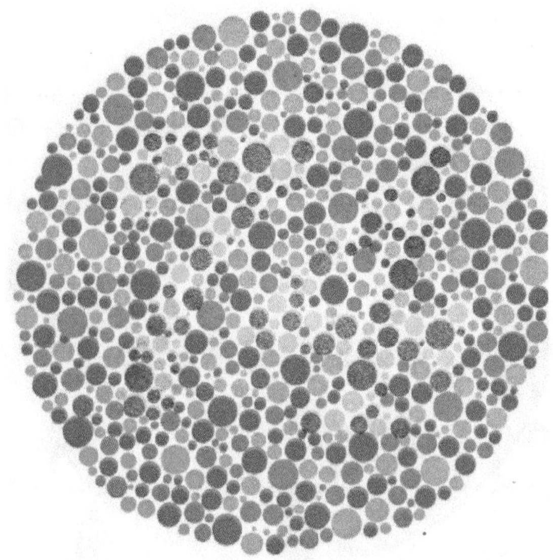

**FIGURE 16.43 A Test for Red–Green Color Blindness.** Persons with normal vision see the number 74. Persons with red–green color blindness see no discernible number.

Steve Allen/Getty Images

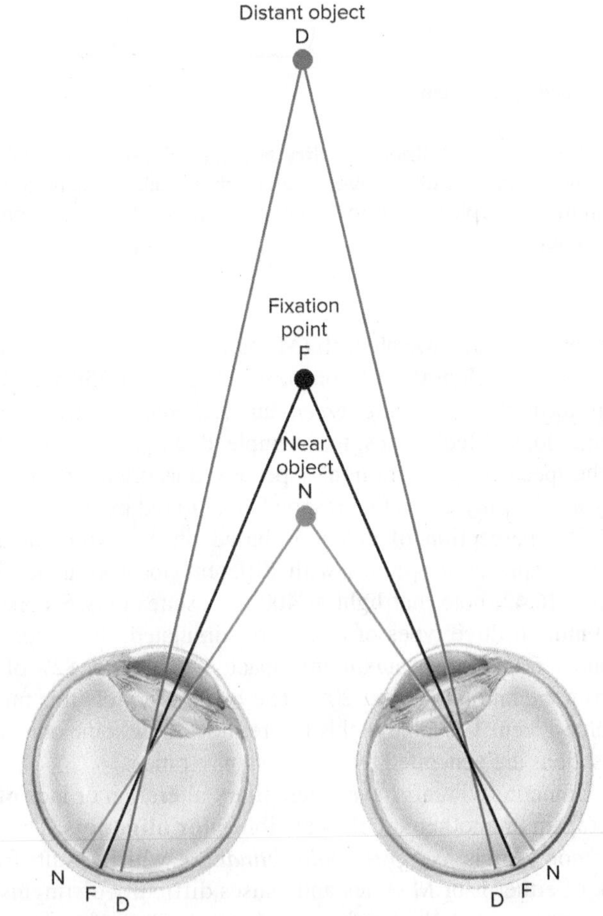


**FIGURE 16.44 The Retinal Basis of Stereoscopic Vision (Depth Perception).** When the eyes converge on the fixation point (F), more distant objects (D) are focused on the retinas medial to the fovea and the brain interprets them as being farther away than the fixation point. Nearby objects (N) are focused lateral to the fovea and interpreted as being closer.

**optic chiasm**[58] (ky-AZ-um), on the base of the brain anterior to the pituitary. Beyond this, the same fibers continue as a pair of **optic tracts.**

Within the chiasm, half of the fibers from each optic nerve cross over to the opposite side of the brain **(fig. 16.45).** This is called **hemidecussation,**[59] since only half of the fibers decussate. As a result, the right cerebral hemisphere sees objects in the left visual field, because their images fall on the right half of each retina (the medial half of the left eye and lateral half of the right eye). You can trace the nerve fibers from each half-retina in the figure to see that they lead to the right hemisphere. Conversely, the left hemisphere sees objects in the right visual field. Since the right brain controls motor responses on the left side of the body and vice versa, each side of the brain sees what is on the side of the body where it exerts motor control. In horses and other animals with panoramic vision, nearly 100% of the optic nerve fibers of the right eye decussate to the left brain and vice versa.

[58] *chiasm* = cross, X
[59] *hemi* = half; *decuss* = to cross, form an X

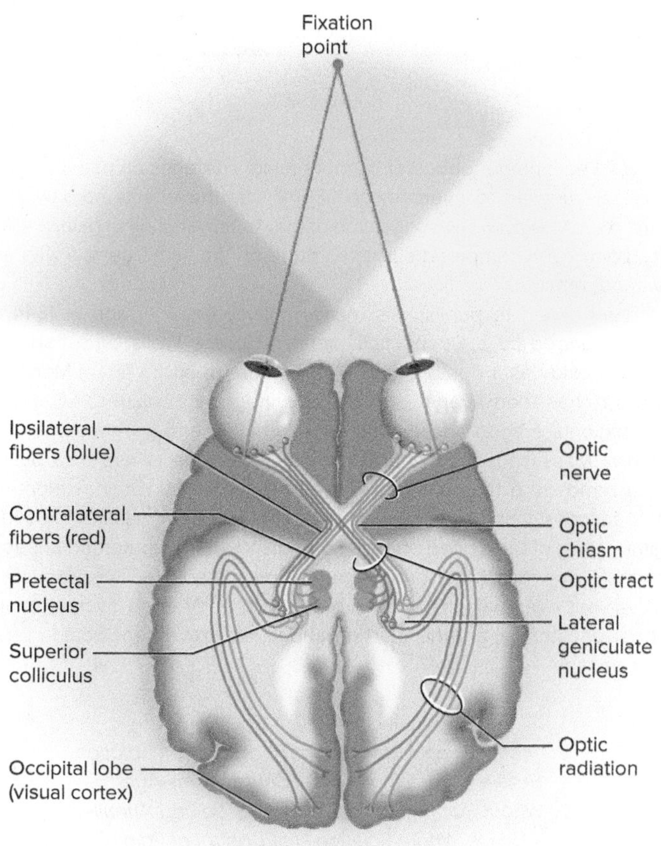


**FIGURE 16.45 The Visual Projection Pathway.** Diagram of hemidecussation and projection to the primary visual cortex. Blue and yellow indicate the visual fields of the left and right eyes; green indicates the area of overlap and stereoscopic vision. Nerve fibers from the medial side of the right eye (red) descussate to the left side of the brain, while fibers from the lateral side remain on the right side of the brain. The converse is true of the left eye. The right occipital lobe thus monitors the left side of the visual field and the left occipital lobe monitors the right side.

? *If a stroke destroyed the optic radiation of the right cerebral hemisphere, how would it affect a person's vision? Would it affect the person's visual reflexes?*

Most axons of the optic tracts end in the **lateral geniculate**[60] **nucleus** (jeh-NIC-you-late) of the thalamus. Third-order neurons arise here and form the **optic radiation** of fibers in the white matter of the cerebrum. These project to the primary visual cortex of the occipital lobe, where conscious visual sensation occurs. Lesions along these tracts or in the occipital lobe can cause blindness even if the eyes are fully functional, with various effects on one of both eyes, and part or all of the visual field of either eye, depending on where the lesion occurs.

[60]*geniculate* = bent like a knee

A few optic nerve fibers come from the photosensitive, melanopsin-containing ganglion cells and take a different route, ending in the superior colliculi and pretectal nuclei of the midbrain. The superior colliculi control the visual reflexes of the extrinsic eye muscles, and the pretectal nuclei are involved in the photopupillary and accommodation reflexes.

Space doesn't allow us to consider much about the very complex processes of visual information processing in the brain. Some processing, such as contrast, brightness, motion, and stereopsis, begins in the retina. The primary visual cortex in the occipital lobe is connected by association tracts to association areas in the temporal and parietal lobes. The primary visual cortex relays information forward to association areas in the temporal and parietal lobes for further processing. One pathway, called the **ventral stream,** runs forward through the lower temporal lobe. It carries signals mainly from cone cells and the central part of the retina. It is concerned with color vision, object recognition, and visual memory, including our ability to read, recognize faces, and identify other things we see. The other, called the **dorsal stream,** runs forward through the upper parietal lobe. It carries signals mainly from rods and the peripheral retina. It is concerned with recognizing the locations and spatial relationships of objects and with analysis of motion. What is yet to be learned about visual processing has important implications for biology, medicine, psychology, and even philosophy.

The effects of aging on the senses—especially taste, smell, hearing, and vision—are described at "Sense Organs" in section 29.4a.

## BEFORE YOU GO ON

Answer the following questions to test your understanding of the preceding section:

24. Why can't we see wavelengths of 350 nm or 750 nm?
25. Why are light rays bent (refracted) more by the cornea than by the lens?
26. List as many structural and functional differences between rods and cones as you can.
27. Explain how the absorption of a photon of light leads to excitation of an optic nerve fiber.
28. Discuss the duplicity theory of vision, summarizing the advantage of having separate types of retinal photoreceptor cells and neural circuits for photopic and scotopic vision.

## DEEPER INSIGHT 16.4
### MEDICAL HISTORY

### Anesthesia—From Ether Frolics to Modern Surgery

Surgery is as old as civilization. People from the Stone Age to the pre-Columbian civilizations of the Americas practiced *trephination*—cutting a hole in the skull to let out "evil spirits" that were thought to cause headaches. The ancient Hindus were expert surgeons for their time, and the Greeks and Romans pioneered military surgery. But until the nineteenth century, surgery was a miserable and dangerous business, done only as a last resort and with little hope of the patient's survival. Surgeons rarely attempted anything more complex than amputations or kidney stone removal. A surgeon had to be somewhat indifferent to the struggles and screams of his patient. Most operations had to be completed in 3 minutes or less, and a strong arm and stomach were more important qualifications for a surgeon than extensive anatomical knowledge.

At least three things were needed for surgery to be more effective: better knowledge of anatomy, *asepsis*[61] for the control of infection, and *anesthesia*[62] for the control of pain. Early efforts to control surgical pain were crude and usually ineffective, such as choking a patient into unconsciousness and trying to complete the surgery before he or she awoke. Alcohol and opium were often used as anesthetics, but the dosage was poorly controlled; some patients were underanesthetized and suffered great pain anyway, and others died of overdoses. Often there was no alternative but for a few strong men to hold the struggling patient down as the surgeon worked. Charles Darwin originally intended to become a physician, but left medical school because he was sickened by observing "two very bad operations, one on a child," in the days before anesthesia.

In 1799, the English chemist Sir Humphry Davy suggested using nitrous oxide to relieve pain. His student, Michael Faraday, later a distinguished physicist, suggested ether. Neither of these ideas caught on for several decades, however. Nitrous oxide ("laughing gas") was a popular amusement in the 1800s, when traveling showmen went from town to town demonstrating its effects on volunteers from the audience. In 1841, at a medicine show in Georgia, some students were impressed with the volunteers' euphoric giggles and antics and asked a young local physician, Crawford W. Long, if he could make some nitrous oxide for them. Long lacked the equipment to synthesize it, but he recommended they try ether. Ether was commonly used in small oral doses for toothaches and "nervous ailments," but its main claim to popularity was its use as a party drug for so-called ether frolics. Long himself was a bit of a bon vivant who put on demonstrations for some of the young ladies, with the disclaimer that he could not be held responsible for whatever he might do under the influence of ether (such as stealing a kiss).

At these parties, Long noted that people sometimes fell and suffered considerable cuts and bruises without feeling pain. In 1842, he had a patient who was terrified of pain but needed a tumor removed from his neck. Long excised the tumor without difficulty as his patient sniffed ether from a towel. The operation created a sensation in town, but other physicians ridiculed Long and pronounced anesthesia dangerous. His medical practice declined as people grew afraid of him, but over the next 4 years he performed eight more minor surgeries on patients under ether. Struggling to overcome criticisms that the effects he saw were due merely to hypnotic suggestion or individual variation in pain sensitivity, Long even compared surgeries done on the same person with and without ether.

Long failed to publish his results quickly enough, and in 1844 he was scooped by a Connecticut dentist, Horace Wells, who had tried nitrous oxide as a dental anesthetic. Another dentist, William Morton of Boston, had tried everything from champagne to opium to kill pain in his patients. He too became interested in ether and gave a demonstration at Massachusetts General Hospital, where he etherized a patient and removed a tumor before a medical audience. Within a month of this successful and sensational demonstration, ether was being used in other cities of the United States and England. Morton patented a "secret formula" he called Morton's Letheon,[63] which smelled suspiciously of ether, but eventually he went broke in a greedy effort to monopolize ether anesthesia, and he died a pauper. His grave near Boston bears the epitaph:

WILLIAM T. G. MORTON
*Inventor and Revealer of Anaesthetic Inhalation*
*Before Whom, in All Time, Surgery Was Agony.*
*By Whom Pain in Surgery Was Averted and Annulled.*
*Since Whom Science Has Control of Pain.*

Wells, who had engaged in a bitter feud to establish himself as the inventor of ether anesthesia, committed suicide at the age of 33. Crawford Long ran a successful medical practice in Athens, Georgia, but to his death he remained disappointed that he had not received credit as the first to perform surgery on etherized patients. The Emory University Hospital Midtown in Atlanta was named the Crawford W. Long Memorial Hospital from 1931 to 2009 in his honor.

Ether and chloroform became obsolete when safer anesthetics were developed. *General anesthetics* such as isoflurane render a patient unconscious by crossing the blood–brain barrier and blocking nervous transmission through the brainstem. Certain general anesthetics deaden pain by activating GABA receptors and causing an inflow of $Cl^-$, which hyperpolarizes neurons and makes them less likely to fire. Diazepam (Valium) also employs this mechanism. *Local anesthetics* such as procaine (Novocaine) and tetracaine selectively deaden specific nerves. They decrease the permeability of membranes to $Na^+$, thereby reducing their ability to produce action potentials.

A sound knowledge of anatomy, control of infection and pain, and development of better tools converged to allow surgeons time to operate more carefully. As a result, surgery became more intellectually challenging and interesting. It attracted a more educated class of practitioner, which put it on the road to becoming the remarkable lifesaving approach that it is today.

[61] *a* = without; *sepsis* = infection
[62] *an* = without; *esthesia* = feeling, sensation
[63] *lethe* = oblivion, forgetfulness

# STUDY GUIDE

## Assess Your Learning Outcomes

*To test your knowledge, discuss the following topics with a study partner or in writing, ideally from memory.*

### 16.1 Properties and Types of Sensory Receptors

1. The definition of *receptor* and the range of complexity in sensory receptors
2. The definition of *sensory transduction* and the relationship of neural action potentials to that concept
3. The production and role of the receptor potential in sensory transduction
4. Four kinds of stimulus information transmitted by sensory receptors
5. Five categories of receptors classified by stimulus modality
6. Three categories of receptors classified by origin of their stimuli
7. Differences between general (somatosensory) and special senses

### 16.2 The General Senses

1. Three types of unencapsulated sensory nerve endings, and what it means to say a nerve ending is *unencapsulated*
2. Six types of encapsulated nerve endings and how these differ from unencapsulated endings
3. The main routes for somatosensory signals from the head, and from the lower body, to the brainstem; the final destination of proprioceptive signals in the brain; and the final destination of most other sensory signals
4. Definitions of *pain* and *nociceptor*
5. Differences between fast pain and slow pain
6. Differences between nociceptive and neuropathic pain, and the three types of nociceptive pain
7. Differences between fast and slow pain, and the types of nerve fibers responsible for each
8. The general three-neuron pathway typically taken by pain signals to the cerebral cortex
9. Pain pathways from receptors in the head to the cerebral cortex, including the cranial nerves that carry pain signals
10. Pain pathways from the lower body to the cerebral cortex and reticular formation, including the spinal cord tracts that carry pain signals
11. Referred pain and its anatomical basis
12. Examples of the modulation of pain sensitivity by the brain
13. Spinal gating mechanisms that modify a person's sense of pain and awareness of body injury
14. Names of some analgesic neuropeptides and how they affect the sensation of pain

### 16.3 The Chemical Senses

1. Structure and locations of the taste buds
2. Types, locations, and functions of lingual papillae
3. Five primary taste sensations, and sensations other than taste that play a part in flavor
4. Mechanisms by which sugars, salts, alkaloids, acids, and glutamate excite taste cells
5. Which nerves carry taste signals, what routes they take to the brain, and what brain centers receive gustatory input
6. Structure and location of the olfactory mucosa and its receptor cells
7. How odor molecules excite olfactory cells
8. Which cranial nerve carries olfactory signals to the brain, and the route and point of termination of its nerve fibers
9. Sensory routes from the olfactory bulbs to the temporal lobes, insula, orbitofrontal cortex, hippocampus, amygdala, and hypothalamus; and the olfactory functions of these respective signal destinations
10. How the cerebral cortex influences olfactory bulb function and one's perception of smell

### 16.4 Hearing and Equilibrium

1. How sound is generated; what physical properties of a sound wave are measured in hertz and decibels; and what sensory qualities of sound correspond to those two physical properties
2. The total range of human hearing, in hertz, and the narrower range in which humans hear best
3. The decibel level of ordinary conversation and the thresholds of hearing and pain
4. Boundaries between the outer ear, middle ear, and inner ear
5. Anatomy of the outer ear and the function of its cerumen and guard hairs
6. Structure of the tympanic membrane and tympanic cavity; the names, structures, and anatomical arrangement of the auditory ossicles; the two middle-ear muscles; and anatomy of the auditory tube, its contribution to hearing, and its relevance to middle-ear infections
7. The bony and membranous labyrinths of the inner ear; the names and distribution of the two inner-ear fluids in relation to the labyrinths
8. Size and shape of the cochlea and its relationship to the modiolus
9. Cross-sectional anatomy of the cochlea
10. Structure of the spiral organ, especially the hair cells and tectorial membrane; differences between inner and outer hair cells
11. Function of the middle-ear ossicles and muscles; how the tympanic reflex works and how it protects one's hearing
12. How vibrations of the tympanic membrane lead to stimulation of the cochlear nerve
13. How the cochlea codes for differences in the pitch and loudness of sounds
14. How the outer hair cells tune the cochlea to improve its sensitivity to differences in pitch
15. The pathway from cochlear nerve to auditory centers of the brain; the feedback pathway from the pons back to the cochlea, and its purpose
16. Differences between static and dynamic equilibrium and between linear and angular acceleration
17. Structure of the saccule and utricle and the relevance of the spatial orientation of the macula in each one
18. How linear acceleration stimulates the hair cells of the saccule and utricle during linear acceleration; how the body senses the difference between vertical and horizontal acceleration
19. Structure of the semicircular ducts, especially the crista ampullaris and cupula
20. How acceleration stimulates hair cells of the crista ampullaris, and why the combined input of the six semicircular ducts enables the brain to sense tilting or rotation of the head in any direction
21. Why it cannot be said that the vestibular system senses motion of the head, but only changes in the rate of motion
22. The path taken by signals in the vestibular nerve to the cerebrum, cerebellum, reticular formation, spinal cord, and nuclei of the three cranial nerves for eye movements
23. Why it is important for eye movement to be coordinated with vestibular input

# STUDY GUIDE

### 16.5 Vision

1. The definition of *vision* and the range of electromagnetic wavelengths over which human vision occurs
2. Six extrinsic eye muscles, their anatomy, the eye motions they produce, and the cranial nerves that control them
3. Components of the lacrimal apparatus and the route taken by tears as they wash over the eye and drain into the nasal cavity
4. Anatomy and functions of the eyebrow, eyelids, eyelashes, and conjunctiva
5. Three tunics of the eyeball and the structural components of each
6. Optical components of the eye
7. The secretion, flow, and reabsorption of aqueous humor
8. General structure of the retina; its two points of attachment to the wall of the eye; and the locations, structure, and functional significance of the optic disc, optic nerve, macula lutea, and fovea centralis
9. The cause of the blind spot and how the brain compensates for it
10. Structure and action of the pupillary constrictor and dilator; anatomy of their autonomic innervation; and the photopupillary reflex
11. Principles of refraction; points at which refraction occurs as light enters the eye; relative contributions of the cornea and lens to image formation, and the reason for the difference
12. The difference between emmetropia and the near response, and three mechanisms of the near response
13. Histological layers and cell types of the retina; three types of photoreceptor cells and their respective functions; functions of the retinal bipolar, ganglion, horizontal, and amacrine cells
14. The structures of rods and cones; where visual pigments are contained in these cells; the general structure of rhodopsin and photopsin; and how these two pigments differ
15. Differences in rod and cone function
16. How light absorption generates an optic nerve signal
17. Mechanisms of light and dark adaptation
18. Why a single retinal receptor system cannot achieve both low-threshold night vision and high-resolution day vision; why rod vision works in very low light but sacrifices resolution to do so; and why cone vision gives high resolution but sacrifices light sensitivity
19. Difference between S, M, and L cones; how neural coding and three cone types produce sensitivity to innumerable colors; and what causes color blindness
20. The retinal basis of stereoscopic vision
21. Projection pathways from the eyes to the occipital lobe and to the superior colliculi and pretectal nuclei of the midbrain
22. Hemidecussation, where it occurs, and how it determines what areas of the visual field are seen by the right and left occipital lobes
23. Brain centers of higher-order spatial and object recognition

## ▶ Testing Your Recall

Answers in Appendix A

1. Hot and cold stimuli are detected by
   a. free nerve endings.
   b. proprioceptors.
   c. end bulbs.
   d. lamellar corpuscles.
   e. tactile corpuscles.

2. ______ is a neurotransmitter that transmits pain sensations to second-order spinal neurons.
   a. Endorphin
   b. Enkephalin
   c. Substance P
   d. Acetylcholine
   e. Norepinephrine

3. ______ is a neuromodulator that blocks the conduction of pain signals by second-order spinal neurons.
   a. Endorphin
   b. Enkephalin
   c. Substance P
   d. Acetylcholine
   e. Norepinephrine

4. Most taste buds occur in
   a. the vallate papillae.
   b. the fungiform papillae.
   c. the filiform papillae.
   d. the palate.
   e. the lips.

5. The higher the frequency of a sound,
   a. the louder it sounds.
   b. the harder it is to hear.
   c. the more it stimulates the distal end of the spiral organ.
   d. the faster it travels through air.
   e. the higher its pitch.

6. Cochlear hair cells rest on
   a. the tympanic membrane.
   b. the secondary tympanic membrane.
   c. the tectorial membrane.
   d. the vestibular membrane.
   e. the basilar membrane.

7. The acceleration you feel when an elevator begins to rise is sensed by
   a. the anterior semicircular duct.
   b. the spiral organ.
   c. the crista ampullaris.
   d. the macula sacculi.
   e. the macula utriculi.

8. The color of light is determined by
   a. its velocity.
   b. its amplitude.
   c. its wavelength.
   d. refraction.
   e. how strongly it stimulates the rods.

9. The retina receives its oxygen supply from
   a. the hyaloid canal.
   b. the vitreous body.
   c. the choroid.
   d. the pigment epithelium.
   e. the scleral venous sinus.

10. Which of the following statements about photopic vision is false?
    a. It is mediated by the cones.
    b. It has a low threshold.
    c. It produces fine resolution.
    d. It does not function in starlight.
    e. It does not employ rhodopsin.

11. The most finely detailed vision occurs when an image falls on a pit in the retina called the ______.

12. The only cells of the retina that generate action potentials are the ______ cells.

STUDY GUIDE

13. The visual pigment of a cone cell is ______.

14. The gelatinous membranes of the macula sacculi and macula utriculi are weighted by protein–calcium carbonate granules called ______.

15. Three rows of ______ in the cochlea have V-shaped arrays of stereocilia and tune the frequency sensitivity of the cochlea.

16. The ______ is a tiny bone that vibrates in the oval window and thereby transfers sound vibrations to the inner ear.

17. The ______ of the midbrain receives auditory input and triggers the head-turning auditory reflex.

18. The function of the ______ in a taste bud is to replace dead taste cells.

19. Olfactory neurons synapse with mitral cells and tufted cells in the ______, which lies inferior to the frontal lobe.

20. In the phenomenon of ______, pain from the viscera is perceived as coming from an area of the skin.

## Building Your Medical Vocabulary

*Answers in Appendix A*

*State a meaning of each word element, and give a medical term from this chapter that uses it or a slight variation of it.*

1. bin-
2. decuss-
3. hemi-
4. lacrimo-
5. litho-
6. maculo-
7. noci-
8. scoto-
9. -sepsis
10. tricho-

## What's Wrong with These Statements?

*Answers in Appendix A*

*Briefly explain why each of the following statements is false, or reword it to make it true.*

1. The sensory (afferent) nerve fibers for touch end in the thalamus.
2. Things we touch with the left hand are perceived in the left cerebral hemisphere.
3. Things we see with the left eye are perceived only in the right cerebral hemisphere.
4. All chemoreceptors can be classified as exteroceptors.
5. The vitreous body occupies the posterior chamber of the eye.
6. Descending analgesic fibers prevent pain signals from reaching the spinal cord.
7. Signals for hearing are carried in cranial nerve VIII and signals for equilibrium in cranial nerve IX.
8. The tympanic cavity and membranous labyrinth are filled with endolymph.
9. Rods and cones release their neurotransmitter when stimulated by light, but not in total darkness.
10. All of the extrinsic muscles of the eye are controlled by the oculomotor nerve.

## Testing Your Comprehensionn

1. The principle of neural convergence is explained under "Neural Pools and Circuits" in section 12.6d. Discuss its relevance to referred pain and scotopic vision.
2. What type of cutaneous receptor enables you to feel an insect crawling through your hair? What type enables you to palpate a patient's pulse? What type enables a blind person to read braille?
3. Contraction of a muscle usually puts more tension on a structure, but contraction of the ciliary muscle puts less tension on the lens. Explain how.
4. In figure 16.45, suppose a stroke or trauma destroyed just the red fibers in the circled area labeled "Optic radiation." Predict how this would affect the subject's visual field for each eye. Predict the same for a lesion that cut completely across the circled area labeled "Optic tract."
5. What would be the benefit of a drug that blocks the receptors for substance P?

# APPENDIX A

# ANSWER KEYS

This appendix provides answers to questions in the figure legends and the end-of-chapter questions in the "Testing Your Recall," "Building Your Medical Vocabulary," and "What's Wrong with These Statements?" sections. Answers to "Apply What You Know" and "Testing Your Comprehension" questions are available to instructors on the text Connect site at www.mcgrawhillconnect.com.

## CHAPTER 1

*Figure Legend Questions*

1.7 Vasodilation allows more blood to flow close to the body surface and to lose heat through the skin; thus, it cools the body.

1.9 Yes; one could say that pregnancy activates a series of events leading to childbirth, the termination of the pregnancy. Thus, it has the qualities of a negative feedback loop.

1.11 MRI is better than X-rays for visualizing nervous tissue, since X-rays do not penetrate bone very well. It also shows better contrast than X-rays in visualization of other soft tissues. X-rays are better than PET scans for visualizing bones, teeth, and other hard or dense tissues, as PET scans have relatively low resolution and do not serve well to visualize tissues with little regional variation in metabolic rate.

*Testing Your Recall*

1. a
2. e
3. d
4. a
5. c
6. c
7. a
8. c
9. d
10. b
11. dissection
12. gradient
13. deduction
14. psychosomatic
15. homeostasis
16. set point
17. negative feedback
18. organ
19. stereoscopic
20. prehensile, opposable

*Building Your Medical Vocabulary* (Answers may vary; these are acceptable examples.)

1. listen—auscultation
2. apart—dissection
3. the same—homeostasis
4. change—metabolism
5. touch—palpation
6. nature—physiology
7. cut—dissection
8. to stay—homeostasis
9. solid—stereoscopic
10. to cut—tomography

*What's Wrong with These Statements?*

1. Auscultation means listening to body sounds, not inspecting the body by touch.
2. MRI does not involve ionizing radiation and has no known risk to a fetus.
3. Positive feedback is beneficial in limited cases, but more often it causes rapid departure from the homeostatic set point and may cause illness or death.
4. Each cell has many organelles, so organelles far outnumber cells.
5. Matter will move spontaneously down a gradient without the need for application of external energy.
6. Leeuwenhoek was a textile merchant who built microscopes to examine fabric.
7. A scientific theory is founded on a large body of evidence and summarizes what is already known.
8. Both the treatment and control groups consist of volunteer patients.
9. Evolutionary biologists do not believe humans evolved from monkeys, but that humans and apes evolved from the same ancestor.
10. Negative feedback is a self-corrective process with a beneficial effect on the body.

## ATLAS A

*Figure Legend Questions*

A.4 Right lower quadrant (RLQ)

A.8 No, it is inferior to the peritoneal cavity, since the peritoneum passes over its superior surface.

*Testing Your Recall*

1. d
2. c
3. e
4. d
5. d
6. a
7. a
8. d
9. b
10. d
11. mesenteries
12. parietal
13. mediastinum
14. nuchal
15. hand, foot
16. meninges
17. retroperitoneal
18. medial
19. inferior
20. cubital, popliteal

*Building Your Medical Vocabulary* (Answers may vary; these are acceptable examples.)

1. before—antebrachium
2. neck—cervical
3. above—epigastric
4. below—hypochondriac
5. groin—inguinal
6. within—intraperitoneal
7. wall—parietal
8. around—peritoneum
9. behind—retroperitoneal
10. arrow—sagittal

*What's Wrong with These Statements?*

1. A sagittal section could only pass between the lungs or through one lung, not through both of them.
2. A frontal section passes from left to right and could include both eyes.
3. The knee is proximal to the ankle (tarsal region).
4. The diaphragm is inferior to the lungs.
5. The esophagus is superior to the stomach.
6. The liver extends from the hypochondriac to the epigastric region, superior to the lumbar region.
7. The heart is enfolded by the pericardial cavity but not contained within it.
8. The kidneys are retroperitoneal.
9. The peritoneum lines the outside of the stomach and intestines.
10. The sigmoid colon is in the lower left quadrant.

## CHAPTER 2

*Figure Legend Questions*

2.8 Because water molecules are attracted to each other, it requires more thermal energy for any one of them to break free and evaporate.

2.12 Decomposition

2.26 No, the amount of energy released is the same with or without an enzyme.

*Testing Your Recall*

1. a
2. c
3. a
4. c
5. a
6. e
7. b
8. c
9. b
10. d
11. cation
12. free radicals
13. catalyst, enzymes
14. anabolism
15. dehydration synthesis
16. -ose, -ase
17. phospholipids
18. cyclic adenosine monophosphate
19. anaerobic fermentation
20. substrate

*Building Your Medical Vocabulary* (Answers may vary; these are acceptable examples.)

1. not—atom
2. oxygen—aerobic
3. both—amphipathic
4. heat—calorie
5. glue—colloid
6. water—hydrolysis
7. part—polymer
8. one—monomer
9. few—oligosaccharide
10. loving—hydrophilic

*What's Wrong with These Statements?*

1. The monomers of a polysaccharide are monosaccharides (simple sugars).
2. ATP is not an energy-storage molecule. Most of our reserve energy is stored in fat.
3. Such molecules are called isomers, not isotopes.
4. Catabolism produces products with less energy than the reactants.
5. Peptide bonds join amino acids together, not sugars.
6. A saturated fat is one to which no more hydrogen can be added.
7. Enzymes, like all catalysts, are not consumed by the reactions they catalyze.
8. Above a certain temperature, enzymes denature and cease working.
9. These solutes have different molecular weights, so 2% solutions would not contain the same number of molecules per unit volume.
10. A solution with pH 8 has one-tenth the hydrogen ion concentration of one with pH 7.

## CHAPTER 3

*Figure Legend Questions*

3.8 Adenylate cyclase is a transmembrane protein. The G protein is peripheral.

3.19 The $Na^+$–$K^+$ pump requires ATP, whereas osmosis does not. ATP is quickly depleted after a cell dies.

3.22 Transcytosis is a combination of endocytosis and exocytosis.

3.27 Large molecules such as enzymes and RNA must pass through the nuclear pores, but pores in the plasma membrane must be small enough to prevent such large molecules from escaping the cell.

3.33 A centriole is composed of a cylinder of nine groups of microtubules, but in a centriole, there are three microtubules in each group and in an axoneme there are only two. Also, an axoneme usually has a central pair of microtubules, whereas a centriole does not.

*Testing Your Recall*

1. e
2. b
3. d
4. b
5. e
6. e
7. a
8. c
9. d
10. b
11. micrometers
12. second messenger
13. Voltage-gated
14. hydrostatic pressure
15. hypertonic
16. exocytosis
17. Ribosomes, proteasomes
18. smooth ER, peroxisomes
19. ligand-gated channel
20. cistern

*Building Your Medical Vocabulary* (Answers may vary; these are acceptable examples.)

1. opposite—antiport
2. color—chromatin
3. together—cotransport
4. cell—cytoplasm
5. into, within—endocytosis
6. easy—facilitated
7. spindle—fusiform
8. study of—cytology
9. process—pinocytosis
10. eat—phagocytosis

*What's Wrong with These Statements?*

1. Osmosis does not require ATP, so it can continue even after cell death.
2. Some cells have two or more nuclei and some cells have none.
3. Second messengers activate enzymes in the cell; they are not transport proteins.
4. Peroxisomes are produced by the endoplasmic reticulum, not by the Golgi complex.
5. A channel could not move material from the outside of a cell to the inside unless it extended all the way across the membrane; it must be a transmembrane protein.
6. The plasma membrane consists primarily of phospholipid molecules.
7. The brush border is composed of microvilli.
8. Cells in hypertonic saline will lose water and shrivel.
9. Osmosis is not a carrier-mediated process and therefore not subject to a transport maximum.
10. Many ribosomes lie free in the cytosol, not attached to the ER or nucleus.

## CHAPTER 4

*Figure Legend Questions*

4.1 The helix would bulge where two purines were paired and would be constricted where two pyrimidines were paired.

4.8 The ribosome would have no way of holding the partially completed peptide in place while adding the next amino acid.

*Testing Your Recall*

1. a
2. e
3. c
4. c
5. e
6. b
7. a
8. d
9. d
10. a
11. cytokinesis
12. cyclin-dependent kinases
13. genetic code
14. polyribosome
15. RNA polymerase
16. genome
17. 46, 92, 92
18. ribosome
19. growth factors
20. autosomes

*Building Your Medical Vocabulary* (Answers may vary; these are acceptable examples.)

1. different—allele
2. finger—polydactyly
3. double—diploid
4. half—haploid
5. different—heterozygous
6. nucleus—karyotype
7. next in a series—metaphase
8. shape—polymorphism
9. change—mutation
10. many—polydactyly

*What's Wrong with These Statements?*

1. There are no ribosomes on the Golgi complex; they are on the rough ER.
2. There are no genes for steroids, carbohydrates, or phospholipids, but only for proteins.
3. RNA is half the weight of a DNA of the same length because it has only one nucleotide strand, whereas DNA has two.
4. Each amino acid is represented by a triplet, a sequence of three bases, not one base pair.
5. A single gene can code for multiple proteins.

6. This law describes the pairing of bases between the two strands of DNA, not between mRNA and tRNA.
7. Only about 2% of the human DNA codes for proteins.
8. Mutations can be harmful, beneficial, or neutral.
9. Males have only one X chromosome, but have two sex chromosomes (the X and Y).
10. Several RNA polymerase molecules at once can transcribe a gene.

## CHAPTER 5

*Figure Legend Questions*

5.2 They are longitudinal sections. In a cross section, both the egg white and yolk would look circular. In an oblique section, the white would look elliptical but the yolk would still look circular.

5.12 The epithelia of the tongue, oral cavity, esophagus, and anal canal would look similar to this.

5.28 Gap junctions

5.30 Exocytosis

5.31 The sketch would look like one of the purple sacs in the middle figure, budding directly from the epithelial surface with no duct.

5.32 Holocrine glands, because entire cells break down to become the secretion, and these must be continually replaced.

*Testing Your Recall*

1. a
2. b
3. c
4. e
5. c
6. a
7. b
8. e
9. b
10. b
11. necrosis
12. mesothelium
13. lacunae
14. fibers
15. collagen
16. skeletal muscle
17. basement membrane
18. matrix (extracellular material)
19. multipotent
20. simple

*Building Your Medical Vocabulary* (Answers may vary; these are acceptable examples.)

1. away—apoptosis
2. cartilage—chondrocyte
3. outer—ectoderm
4. producing—collagen
5. tissue—histology
6. whole—holocrine
7. glassy—hyaline
8. dead—necrosis
9. formed—neoplasia
10. scale—squamous

*What's Wrong with These Statements?*

1. The esophageal epithelium is nonkeratinized.
2. All of them contact the basement membrane.
3. There are a few cases of skeletal muscles not attached to bones.
4. Glandular secretions are produced by cells of the parenchyma; the stroma is nonsecretory supportive connective tissue.
5. Adipose tissue is an exception; cells constitute most of its volume.
6. Adipocytes are also found in areolar tissue, either singly or in small clusters.
7. Tight junctions serve mainly to restrict the passage of material between cells.
8. Neoplasia is abnormal tissue growth, such as tumors; development of mature tissue types from nonspecialized tissues is called differentiation.
9. Excitability is characteristic of all living cells, but most highly developed in nerve and muscle cells.
10. Perichondrium is lacking from fibrocartilage and from hyaline articular cartilage.

## CHAPTER 6

*Figure Legend Questions*

6.5 Keratinocytes

6.8 Cuticle

6.11 Asymmetry (A), irregular border (B), and color (C). The photo does not provide enough information to judge the diameter of the lesion (D).

*Testing Your Recall*

1. d
2. c
3. d
4. b
5. a
6. e
7. c
8. a
9. a
10. d
11. Insensible perspiration
12. arrector muscle
13. debridement
14. cyanosis
15. dermal papillae
16. earwax
17. sebaceous glands
18. anagen
19. dermal papilla
20. third-degree

*Building Your Medical Vocabulary* (Answers may vary; these are acceptable examples.)

1. substance—melanin
2. white—albinism
3. skin—dermatology
4. through—diaphoresis
5. same—homograft
6. injure—lesion
7. black—melanoma
8. tumor—carcinoma
9. nail—eponychium
10. hair—piloerector

*What's Wrong with These Statements?*

1. Basal cell carcinoma is the most common form of skin cancer.
2. The number of melanocytes is about the same in all skin colors; dark skin results from the accumulation of melanin in keratinocytes.
3. Keratin is the protein of the epidermis; the dermis is composed mainly of collagen.
4. Vitamin D synthesis begins in the keratinocytes.
5. Epidermal cell multiplication occurs in the stratum basale.
6. Cells of the cortex are also dead; the only living hair cells are in and near the hair bulb.
7. The hypodermis is not considered to be a layer of the skin.
8. Different races have about the same density of melanocytes but different amounts of melanin.
9. A genetic lack of melanin causes albinism, not pallor. Pallor is a temporary, nonhereditary paleness of the skin.
10. Apocrine sweat glands develop at puberty.

## CHAPTER 7

*Figure Legend Questions*

7.1 The wider epiphyses provide surface area for muscle attachment and bone articulation, while the narrowness of the diaphysis minimizes weight.

7.6 Places where bone comes close to the skin, such as the sternum and hips

7.7 Temporal bone, parietal bone, and several others

7.9 Humerus, radius, ulna, femur, tibia, fibula

7.10 An infant's joints are still cartilaginous.

7.12 The zones of cell proliferation and cell hypertrophy

*Testing Your Recall*

1. e
2. a
3. d
4. c
5. d
6. a
7. d
8. e
9. b
10. d
11. hydroxyapatite
12. canaliculi
13. appositional
14. solubility product
15. hypocalcemia
16. Osteoblasts
17. calcitriol
18. osteoporosis
19. metaphysis
20. osteomalacia

*Building Your Medical Vocabulary* (Answers may vary; these are acceptable examples.)

1. calcium—hypocalcemia
2. destroy—osteoclast
3. softening—osteomalacia
4. marrow—osteomyelitis
5. straight—orthopedics
6. bone—osseous
7. bone—osteocyte
8. growth—diaphysis
9. dart—spicule
10. place—ectopic

*What's Wrong with These Statements?*

1 Flat cranial bones have a middle layer of spongy bone called the diploe.
2. Cartilage is removed and replaced by bone, not calcified and transformed into bone.
3. The most common bone disease is osteoporosis, not fractures.
4. Bones elongate at the epiphysial plate, not the articular cartilage.
5. Osteoclasts develop from stem cells in the bone marrow, not from osteoblasts.
6. Osteoblasts give rise only to osteocytes and are therefore unipotent.
7. Hydroxyapatite is the major mineral of bone; the major protein is collagen.
8. Osteons have blood vessels in their central canals, not in the canaliculi.
9. The major effect of vitamin D is bone resorption, though it also promotes deposition.
10. Parathyroid hormone indirectly promotes bone resorption, not deposition.

## CHAPTER 8

*Figure Legend Questions*

8.10 Any five of these: the occipital, parietal, sphenoid, zygomatic, and palatine bones, and the mandible and maxilla

8.12 Any five of these: the frontal, lacrimal, and sphenoid bones, and the vomer, maxilla, and inferior concha

8.25 Rupture of this ligament allows the atlas to slip anteriorly and the dens of the axis to tear into the spinal cord.

8.35 The adult hand lacks epiphysial plates, the growth zones of a child's long bones.

8.41 The three cuneiforms and the cuboid bone of the tarsus are arranged in a row similar to the distal carpal bones (trapezium, trapezoid, capitate, and hamate), with the trapezium corresponding to the median cuneiform (proximal to digit I in each case). In the proximal row, the navicular bone of the tarsus is somewhat similar to the scaphoid of the carpus, being proximal to digit I and articulating with three bones of the distal row, but the calcaneus and talus are very different, being adapted to their load-bearing role.

*Testing Your Recall*

1. b
2. e
3. a
4. d
5. a
6. e
7. c
8. b
9. e
10. b
11. fontanelles
12. temporal
13. sutures
14. sphenoid
15. anulus fibrosus
16. dens
17. auricular
18. styloid
19. foramina
20. medial longitudinal

*Building Your Medical Vocabulary* (Answers may vary; these are acceptable examples.)

1. rib—intercostal
2. helmet—cranium
3. tough—dura mater
4. tongue—hypoglossa
5. little—ossicle
6. breast—mastoid
7. foot—bipedal
8. wing—pterygoid
9. above—supraorbital
10. ankle—metatarsal

*What's Wrong with These Statements?*

1. It passes out the jugular foramen.
2. Each hand and foot has 14 phalanges.
3. The female pelvis is wider and shallower than the male's.
4. The carpal bones are in the base of the hand, not the narrow wrist region.
5. Muscles of the infraspinous fossa are easily palpated on the back, inferior to the scapular spine.
6. You would be resting your elbow on the olecranon.
7. The lumbar vertebrae have transverse processes but no transverse costal facets.
8. The most frequently broken bone is the clavicle.
9. *Arm* refers to the region containing only the humerus; *leg* refers to the region containing the tibia and fibula.
10. These extra bones in the cranium are called sutural bones, not sesamoid bones.

## CHAPTER 9

*Figure Legend Questions*

9.2 The gomphosis, because a tooth is not a bone

9.4 The pubic symphysis consists of the cartilaginous interpubic disc and the adjacent parts of the two pubic bones.

9.5 Interphalangeal joints are not subjected to a great deal of compression.

9.7 $MA = 1.0$. Shifting the fulcrum to the left would increase the *MA* of this lever, while the lever would remain first class.

9.19 The atlas (C1)

*Testing Your Recall*

1. c
2. b
3. a
4. e
5. c
6. c
7. a
8. d
9. b
10. d
11. synovial fluid
12. bursa
13. pivot
14. Kinesiology
15. gomphosis
16. serrate
17. extension
18. range of motion
19. articular disc
20. talus

*Building Your Medical Vocabulary* (Answers may vary; these are acceptable examples.)

1. away—abduction
2. joint—arthritis
3. characterized by—cruciate
4. letter X—cruciate
5. leg—talocrural
6. to lead—adduction
7. movement—kinesiology
8. moon—meniscus
9. to lay back—supination
10. to pull—protraction

*What's Wrong with These Statements?*

1. Osteoarthritis occurs in almost everyone after a certain age; rheumatoid arthritis is less common.
2. A kinesiologist studies joint movements; a rheumatologist treats arthritis.
3. Synovial joints are diarthroses and amphiarthroses, but never synarthroses.
4. There is no meniscus in the elbow.
5. This action involves hyperextension of the shoulder.
6. The cruciate ligaments are in the knee.
7. The round ligament is somewhat slack and probably does not secure the femoral head.
8. The knuckles are diarthroses.

9. Synovial fluid is secreted by the synovial membrane of the joint capsule and fills the bursae.
10. A tooth is not a bone.

## CHAPTER 10

*Figure Legend Questions*

10.4 The brachialis and lateral head of the triceps brachii have direct attachments; the biceps brachii and long head of the triceps brachii have indirect attachments.
10.8 The zygomaticus major, levator palpebrae superioris, and orbicularis oris
10.16 Pectoralis minor, serratus anterior, and all three layers of the upper intercostal muscles
10.27 *Teres* refers to the round or cordlike shape of the first muscle, and *quadratus* refers to the four-sided shape of the second.
10.28 Part (c) represents a cross section cut too high on the forearm to include these muscles.
10.34 Climbing stairs, walking, running, or riding a bicycle
10.38 The soleus

*Testing Your Recall*

1. b
2. b
3. a
4. c
5. e
6. e
7. b
8. a
9. d
10. c
11. buccinator
12. fascicle
13. prime mover (agonist)
14. hamstring
15. flexor retinacula
16. urogenital triangle
17. linea alba
18. synergist
19. bipennate
20. sphincter

*Building Your Medical Vocabulary* (Answers may vary; these are acceptable examples.)

1. head—splenius capitis
2. work—synergist
3. bundle—fascicle
4. lip—levator labii superioris
5. lower back—quadratus lumborum
6. mouse—muscle
7. muscle—perimysium
8. shoulder—omohyoid
9. feather—bipennate
10. third—peroneus tertius

*What's Wrong with These Statements?*

1. The connective tissue that encloses individual muscle fibers is endomysium.
2. The orbicularis was once thought to be a sphincter but is no longer interpreted as such.
3. The biceps brachii is fusiform.
4. A synergist aids an agonist in its function; it does not oppose the agonist.
5. Many skeletal muscles are innervated by cranial nerves (those in the head and neck).
6. Normally, no muscular effort is needed to exhale.
7. The hamstrings flex the knee and therefore would not aid in lifting the body to the next step.
8. The facial nerve innervates 16 of the facial muscles tabulated in this chapter. The trigeminal innervates 6 tabulated muscles, but they are muscles of chewing and swallowing, not facial expression.
9. The adductor pollicis is by far the strongest of the three listed muscles (important in the strength of the hand grip), but is not listed first.
10. They are on opposite sides of the tibia and act as antagonists.

## ATLAS B

*Figure Legend Questions*

B.1 Orbicularis oris; trapezius
B.5 The lungs, heart, liver, stomach, gallbladder, and spleen, among others
B.8 Sternocleidomastoids
B.11 Posterior
B.13 Fat (adipose tissue)
B.18 Five: one tendon proximally (at the humerus) and four distally (in the hand)
B.19 The mark would belong close to where the leader for the styloid process of the radius ends in figure B.19b.
B.20 The mark would belong close to where the leader for the rectus femoris ends; the vastus intermedius is deep to this.
B.21 The fibula
B.24 There is no such bone; digit I (the great toe) has only a proximal and distal phalanx.
B.25 Answers to the muscle test are as follows:

1. f
2. b
3. k
4. p
5. h
6. y
7. z
8. w
9. c
10. a
11. x
12. m
13. n
14. e
15. g
16. v
17. f
18. c
19. x
20. w
21. k
22. d
23. f
24. b
25. a
26. u
27. j
28. i
29. g
30. q

## CHAPTER 11

*Figure Legend Questions*

11.1 The striations distinguish it from smooth muscle; the multiple nuclei adjacent to the plasma membrane and the parallel fibers distinguish it from both cardiac and smooth muscle.
11.2 The electrical excitation spreading down the T tubule must excite the opening of calcium gates in the terminal cisterns.
11.13 ATP is needed to pump $Ca^{2+}$ back into the sarcoplasmic reticulum by active transport and to induce each myosin head to release actin so the sarcomere can relax.
11.16 The gluteus maximus and quadriceps femoris
11.17 The muscle tension curve would drop gradually while the muscle length curve would rise.

*Testing Your Recall*

1. a
2. c
3. b
4. d
5. c
6. c
7. e
8. c
9. e
10. b
11. threshold
12. oxidative
13. terminal cisterns
14. myosin
15. acetylcholine
16. myoglobin
17. Z discs
18. varicosities
19. muscle tone
20. Isometric contraction

*Building Your Medical Vocabulary* (Answers may vary; these are acceptable examples.)

1. weak—myasthenia
2. self—autorhythmic
3. abnormal—dystrophy
4. same—isometric
5. length—isometric
6. muscle—myocyte
7. flesh—sarcolemma
8. time—temporal
9. tension—isotonic
10. growth—dystrophy

*What's Wrong with These Statements?*

1. A motor neuron may supply 1,000 or more muscle fibers; a motor unit consists of one motor neuron and all the muscle fibers it innervates.
2. Somatic motor neurons do not innervate cardiac muscle.
3. Fast glycolytic fibers fatigue relatively quickly.
4. Thin myofilaments extend well into the A bands, where they overlap with thick myofilaments.
5. Thin and thick myofilaments do not shorten, but glide over each other.
6. Thick and thin myofilaments are present but not arranged in a way that produces striations.
7. Under natural conditions, a muscle seldom or never attains complete tetanus.
8. Even excitation would be impossible without ATP, because ATP drives the active transport ($Na^+$–$K^+$) pumps that maintain membrane potential and excitability.
9. A muscle produces most of its ATP during this time by anaerobic fermentation, which generates lactate; it does not consume lactate.
10. Autorhythmicity is limited to unitary smooth muscle.

## CHAPTER 12

*Figure Legend Questions*

12.9 Its conduction speed is relatively slow, but it has a small diameter and contributes relatively little bulk to the nervous tissue.

12.25 One EPSP is a voltage change of only 0.5 mV or so. A change of about 15 mV is required to reach threshold and make a neuron fire.

12.30 The CNS interprets a stimulus as more intense if it receives signals from high-threshold sensory neurons than if it receives signals only from low-threshold neurons.

12.32 A reverberating circuit, because a neuron early in the circuit is continually restimulated

*Testing Your Recall*

1. e
2. c
3. d
4. a
5. c
6. e
7. d
8. a
9. d
10. b
11. afferent
12. conductivity
13. absolute refractory period
14. dendrites
15. oligodendrocytes
16. myelin sheath gaps
17. axon hillock, initial segment
18. norepinephrine
19. facilitated zone
20. Neuromodulators

*Building Your Medical Vocabulary* (Answers may vary; these are acceptable examples.)

1. forward—anterograde
2. to touch—synapse
3. star—astrocyte
4. tree—dendrite
5. carry—afferent
6. knot—ganglion
7. to walk—retrograde
8. nerve—neuroglia
9. hard—sclerosis
10. body—somatic

*What's Wrong with These Statements?*

1. A neuron never has more than one axon.
2. Oligodendrocytes of the brain perform the same function as Schwann cells of the PNS.
3. The extracellular concentration of $Na^+$ is greater than its intracellular concentration.
4. Only a small fraction of the neuron's $Na^+$ and $K^+$ exchange places across the plasma membrane.
5. The threshold stays the same but an EPSP brings the membrane potential closer to the threshold.
6. The absolute refractory period sets an upper limit on firing frequency.
7. The effect of a neurotransmitter varies from place to place depending on the type of receptor present.
8. The signals travel rapidly through the internodal segments and slow down at each myelin sheath gap.
9. Learning involves modification of the synapses of existing neurons, not an increase in the neuron population.
10. Neurons cannot undergo mitosis to replace those that are lost, although limited replacement occurs through multiplication and differentiation of stem cells.

## CHAPTER 13

*Figure Legend Questions*

13.5 If it were T10, there would be no cuneate fasciculus; that exists only from T6 up.

13.10 They are in the anterior horn of the spinal cord.

13.13 They are afferent, because they arise from the posterior root of the spinal nerve.

13.15 Severing one phrenic nerve paralyzes the diaphragm on the ipsilateral side; severing both of them paralyzes the entire diaphragm and causes respiratory arrest.

13.25 Motor neurons are capable only of exciting skeletal muscle (end-plate potentials are always excitatory). To inhibit muscle contraction, it is necessary to inhibit the motor neuron at the CNS level (point 6).

13.26 They would show more synaptic delay, because there are more synapses in the pathway.

*Testing Your Recall*

1. e
2. c
3. d
4. d
5. e
6. c
7. c
8. a
9. e
10. b
11. ganglia
12. ramus
13. spinocerebellar
14. crossed extension
15. intrafusal fibers
16. phrenic
17. decussation
18. proprioception
19. posterior root
20. tibial, common fibular

*Building Your Medical Vocabulary* (Answers may vary; these are acceptable examples.)

1. spider—arachnoid
2. tail—cauda equina
3. opposite—contralateral
4. wedge—cuneate
5. same—ipsilateral
6. diaphragm—phrenic
7. tender—pia mater
8. oneself—proprioception
9. branch—ramus
10. roof—tectospinal

*What's Wrong with These Statements?*

1. The gracile fasciculus is an ascending (sensory) tract.
2. It terminates in the upper lumbar region of the vertebral column.
3. Each segment of the spinal cord has several rootlets.
4. All spinal nerves are mixed nerves; none are purely sensory or motor.
5. The dura is separated from the bone by a fat-filled epidural space.
6. The horns of the spinal cord are gray matter.
7. Corticospinal tracts are descending (motor) tracts, not sensory.
8. Dermatomes overlap each other by as much as 50%.
9. Some somatic reflexes are mediated primarily through the brainstem and cerebellum.
10. Many ipsilateral reflex arcs are also polysynaptic.

## CHAPTER 14

*Figure Legend Questions*

14.9 Signals in the cuneate fasciculus ascend to the cuneate nucleus in part (c), and signals in the gracile fasciculus ascend to the nearby gracile nucleus. Both of them decussate together to the contralateral medial lemnicus in parts (b) and (a) and travel this route to the thalamus.

14.10 The reticular formation is labeled on all three parts of the figure.

14.14 Commissural tracts also cross through the anterior and posterior commissures shown in figure 14.2.

14.15 Dendrites; the axons project downward into the white matter.

14.22 Regions with numerous small muscles

*Testing Your Recall*

1. c
2. a
3. e
4. a
5. b
6. c
7. a
8. d
9. e
10. e
11. corpus callosum
12. ventricles, cerebrospinal
13. arbor vitae
14. vagus nerve
15. choroid plexus
16. precentral
17. frontal
18. association areas
19. categorical
20. Broca area

*Building Your Medical Vocabulary* (Answers may vary; these are acceptable examples.)

1. pain—neuralgia
2. head—hydrocephalus
3. brain—cerebrospinal
4. body—corpus callosum
5. brain—encephalitis
6. record of—electroencephalogram
7. island—insula
8. eye—oculomotor
9. pulley—trochlea
10. little—peduncle

*What's Wrong with These Statements?*

1. The optic nerve is purely sensory. Eye movements are controlled by the oculomotor, trochlear, and abducens nerves.
2. The cerebral hemispheres do not develop from neural crest tissue.
3. The midbrain is rostral to the pons.
4. The Broca and Wernicke areas are ipsilateral, both in the left hemisphere in most people.
5. The choroid plexuses produce only 30% of the CSF.
6. Hearing is a temporal lobe function; vision resides in the occipital lobe.
7. Respiration is controlled by nuclei in the pons and medulla oblongata.
8. The trigeminal nerve carries sensory signals from the largest area of the face.
9. The vagus nerve (cranial nerve X) innervates organs of the thoracic and abdominopelvic cavities.
10. The cerebellum contains more than half of all brain neurons.

## CHAPTER 15

*Figure Legend Questions*

15.4 No; inhaling and exhaling are controlled by the somatic motor system and skeletal muscles.

15.5 The neurosoma of the somatic efferent neuron is in the anterior horn and the neurosoma of the sympathetic preganglionic neuron is in the lateral horn.

15.7 The vagus nerve

15.9 The pupils dilate because fear increases sympathetic output, which induces dilation.

*Testing Your Recall*

1. b
2. c
3. e
4. e
5. a
6. e
7. d
8. d
9. a
10. c
11. adrenergic
12. Dual innervation
13. Autonomic tone
14. vagus
15. enteric
16. norepinephrine
17. sympathetic
18. preganglionic, postganglionic
19. cAMP
20. vasomotor tone

*Building Your Medical Vocabulary* (Answers may vary; these are acceptable examples.)

1. pressure—baroreflex
2. dissolve—sympatholytic
3. wall—intramural
4. rule—autonomic
5. ear—otic
6. feeling—parasympathetic
7. kidney—adrenal
8. internal organs—splanchnic
9. together—sympathetic
10. internal organs—visceral

*What's Wrong with These Statements?*

1. Both systems are always simultaneously active.
2. Cutaneous blood vessels receive only sympathetic fibers.
3. In biofeedback and other circumstances, limited voluntary control of the ANS is possible.
4. The sympathetic division inhibits digestion.
5. The sympathetic division has a few cholinergic postganglionic fibers, although most are adrenergic.
6. Waste elimination can occur by autonomic spinal reflexes without necessarily involving the brain.
7. All parasympathetic fibers are cholinergic.
8. The sympathetic division has more neural divergence and therefore more widespread, less organ-specific, effects than the parasympathetic division.
9. The hypoglossal nerve carries no parasympathetic fibers.
10. They have antagonistic effects on the iris.

## CHAPTER 16

*Figure Legend Questions*

16.1 Yes; two touches are felt separately if they straddle the boundary between two separate receptive fields.

16.9 The lower margin of the violet zone ("all sound") would be higher in that frequency range.

16.15 They are the outer hair cells, which function to "tune the cochlea" and improve discrimination between sounds of different pitches.

16.16 It would oppose the inward movement of the tympanic membrane and, thus, reduce the amount of vibration transferred to the inner ear.

16.24 This would prevent tears from draining into the lacrimal canals, resulting in more watery eyes.

16.25 Cranial nerve III, because it controls more eye movements than IV or VI.

16.30 It is the right eye. The optic disc is always medial to the fovea, so this has to be a view of the observer's left and the subject's right.

16.42 Approximately 68:20:0, and yellow

16.45 It would cause blindness in the left half of the visual field. It would not affect the visual reflexes.

*Testing Your Recall*

1. a
2. c
3. b
4. a
5. e
6. e
7. d
8. c
9. c
10. b
11. fovea centralis
12. ganglion
13. photopsin
14. otoliths
15. outer hair cells
16. stapes
17. inferior colliculi
18. basal cells
19. olfactory bulb
20. referred pain

*Building Your Medical Vocabulary* (Answers may vary; these are acceptable examples.)

1. two—binaural
2. cross over—hemidecussation
3. half—hemidecussation
4. tears—lacrimal
5. stone—otolithic
6. spot—macula sacculi
7. pain—nociceptor
8. dark—scotopic
9. infection—asepsis
10. hair—peritrichial

*What's Wrong with These Statements?*

1. These fibers end in the medulla oblongata.
2. They are perceived in the right hemisphere because of decussation.
3. Because of hemidecussation, each hemisphere receives signals from both eyes.
4. Chemoreceptors that monitor blood chemistry, for example, are interoceptors.
5. The posterior chamber, the space between iris and lens, is filled with aqueous humor.
6. Descending analgesic fibers block signals that have reached the dorsal horn of the spinal cord.
7. Cranial nerve VIII carries both auditory and equilibrium signals.
8. The tympanic cavity is filled with air.
9. Rods release glutamate in the dark and stop when they are illuminated.
10. The trochlear and abducens nerves control the superior oblique and lateral rectus, respectively.

## CHAPTER 17

*Figure Legend Questions*

17.1 Heart, liver, stomach, small intestine, placenta (any three)
17.4 The posterior pituitary (neurohypophysis)
17.19 Steroids enter the target cell; they do not bind to membrane receptors or activate second messengers.
17.24 Such a drug would block leukotriene synthesis and thus inhibit allergic and inflammatory responses.

*Testing Your Recall*

1. b
2. d
3. a
4. c
5. c
6. c
7. d
8. c
9. a
10. e
11. adenohypophysis
12. tyrosine
13. acromegaly
14. cortisol
15. glucocorticoids
16. interstitial endocrine
17. negative feedback inhibition
18. hypophysial portal system
19. permissive
20. Up-regulation

*Building Your Medical Vocabulary* (Answers may vary; these are acceptable examples.)

1. gland—adenohypophysis
2. bile—cholecystokinin
3. flow through—diabetes
4. twenty—eicosanoid
5. yellow—luteinizing
6. resembling—thyroid
7. full of—glomerulosa
8. favoring—progesterone
9. turn—gonadotropin
10. urine—glycosuria

*What's Wrong with These Statements?*

1. Gonadotropin secretion would rise because of a lack of negative feedback inhibition from the testes.
2. Glycoproteins cannot enter the target cell; they bind to surface receptors of the plasma membrane.
3. Thyroglobulin can be synthesized, but it cannot be iodinated, so no thyroid hormone is produced.
4. Tumors can cause hypersecretion but can also destroy endocrine cells and lead to hyposecretion.
5. Hormones are also secreted by the heart, liver, kidneys, and other organs not generally regarded as glands.
6. Most cases of diabetes mellitus are caused by insensitivity to insulin, not a lack of insulin.
7. The pineal gland and thymus undergo involution with age; they are larger in children than they are later in life.
8. Without iodine, there is no thyroid hormone (TH); without TH, there can be no negative feedback inhibition.
9. The tissue at the center is the adrenal medulla.
10. There are also two testes, two ovaries, and four parathyroid glands.

## CHAPTER 18

*Figure Legend Questions*

18.1 (Answering this requires labeling the illustration.)
18.4 The sunken center represents the former location of the nucleus.
18.5 Hemoglobin consists of a noncovalent association of four protein chains. The prosthetic group is the heme moiety of each of the four chains.
18.18 *Myelo-* refers to the bone marrow, where these cells develop.
18.19 Although numerous, these WBCs are immature and incapable of performing their defensive roles.
18.21 A platelet plug lacks the fibrin mesh that a blood clot has.
18.22 It would affect only the intrinsic mechanism.
18.23 In both blood clotting and hormonal signal amplification, the product of one reaction step is an enzyme that catalyzes the production of many more molecules of the next product. Thus, there is a geometric increase in the number of product molecules at each step and ultimately, a large final result from a small beginning.
18.25 The older theory of leeching was that many disorders are caused by "bad blood," which could be removed painlessly by medicinal leeches. The modern practice is to take advantage of the anticoagulants in the leech saliva to promote blood flow to a tissue or to dissolve and remove clots that have already formed.

*Testing Your Recall*

1. b
2. c
3. c
4. a
5. b
6. d
7. d
8. c
9. d
10. c
11. hematopoiesis
12. hematocrit (packed cell volume)
13. thromboplastin
14. agglutinogens
15. hemophilia
16. hemostasis
17. Sickle-cell disease
18. polycythemia
19. vitamin $B_{12}$
20. erythropoietin

*Building Your Medical Vocabulary* (Answers may vary; these are acceptable examples.)

1. without—anemia
2. producing—erythroblast
3. red—erythrocyte
4. aggregate—agglutination
5. blood—hemostasis
6. white—leukocyte
7. deficiency—leukopenia
8. vein—phlebotomy
9. formation—hemopoiesis
10. clot—thrombosis

*What's Wrong with These Statements?*

1. Most of the volume is usually plasma.
2. Hyperproteinemia causes retention of more water in the circulatory system and raises blood pressure.
3. Oxygen deficiency is the result of anemia, not its cause.
4. Clotting (coagulation) is one mechanism of hemostasis, but hemostasis includes other mechanisms (vascular spasm and platelet plug), so it is not synonymous with the other two terms.
5. He can be the father if he is heterozygous for type A ($I^Ai$), the mother is heterzygous for type B ($I^Bi$), and both are heterzygous for

Rh type *(Dd)*. The baby could then inherit *ii* and *dd*, and have phenotype O–.

6. The most abundant WBCs are neutrophils.
7. Blood clotting requires $Ca^{2+}$ at several steps.
8. Even platelets arise ultimately from hematopoietic stem cells.
9. The heme is excreted; the globin is broken down into amino acids that can be reused.
10. In leukemia, there is an excess of WBCs. A WBC deficiency is leukopenia.

## CHAPTER 19

*Figure Legend Questions*

19.1 Both; they receive pulmonary arteries from the pulmonary circuit and bronchial arteries from the systemic circuit.

19.2 To the left

19.7 The trabeculae carneae

19.12 The right atrium

19.14 It ensures that wave summation and tetanus will not occur, thus ensuring relaxation and refilling of the heart chambers.

19.19 They prevent prolapse of the AV valves during ventricular systole.

19.20 This is the point at which the aortic valve opens and blood is ejected into the aorta, raising its blood pressure.

*Testing Your Recall*

1. d
2. b
3. d
4. a
5. a
6. d
7. d
8. c
9. a
10. c
11. systole, diastole
12. systemic
13. atrioventricular (coronary) sulcus
14. $Na^+$
15. gap junctions
16. T wave
17. vagus
18. myocardial infarction
19. endocardium
20. cardiac output

*Building Your Medical Vocabulary* (Answers may vary; these are acceptable examples.)

1. entryway—atrium
2. slow—bradycardia
3. heart—cardiology
4. crown—coronary
5. moon—semilunar
6. nipple—papillary
7. semi—semilunar
8. fast—tachycardia
9. vessel—vasomotor
10. belly—ventricle

*What's Wrong with These Statements?*

1. The coronary circulation is part of the systemic circuit; the other division is the pulmonary circuit.
2. There are no valves at the openings of the venae cavae.
3. The first two-thirds of ventricular filling occurs before the atria contract. The atria add only about 31% of the blood that fills the ventricles.
4. The vagus nerves affect heart rate but not contraction strength.
5. High $CO_2$ and low pH accelerate the heart rate.
6. The first heart sound occurs at the time of the QRS complex.
7. The heart has its own internal pacemaker and would continue beating; the nerves only alter the heart rate.
8. That would result from clamping the pulmonary veins, not the pulmonary arteries.
9. Cardiomyocytes do have a stable resting potential when they are at rest.
10. The ECG is a composite record of the electrical activity of the entire myocardium, not a record from a single myocyte. It looks much different from an action potential.

## CHAPTER 20

*Figure Legend Questions*

20.2 Veins are subjected to less pressure than arteries and have less need of elasticity.

20.5 Endocrine glands, kidneys, the small intestine, and choroid plexuses of the brain

20.8 Veins have less muscular and elastic tissue, so they expand more easily than arteries.

20.10 Arterial anastomoses: the arterial circle of the brain, the celiac circulation, encircling the heads of the humerus and femur, and the arterial arches of the hand and foot. Venous anastomoses: the jugular veins, the azygos system, the mesenteric veins, and venous networks of the hand and foot. Portal systems: the hepatic portal system and (outside of this chapter) the hypophysial portal system. Answers may vary.

20.20 Nothing would happen if he lifted his finger from point O because the valve at that point would prevent blood from flowing downward and filling the vein. If he lifted his finger from point H, blood would flow upward, fill the vein, and the vein between O and H would stand out.

20.27 Aorta → left common carotid a. → external carotid a. → superficial temporal a.

20.36 The ovaries and testes begin their embryonic development near the kidneys. The gonadal veins elongate as the gonads descend to the pelvic cavity and scrotum.

20.39 Joint movements may temporarily compress an artery. Anastomoses allow for continued blood flow through alternative routes to more distal regions.

20.40 The cephalic, basilic, and median cubital vv.

*Testing Your Recall*

1. c
2. b
3. a
4. e
5. b
6. c
7. e
8. a
9. e
10. d
11. systolic, diastolic
12. continuous capillaries
13. Anaphylactic
14. thoracic pump
15. oncotic pressure
16. transcytosis
17. sympathetic
18. baroreceptors
19. cerebral arterial circle
20. basilic, cephalic

*Building Your Medical Vocabulary* (Answers may vary; these are acceptable examples.)

1. vessel—angiogenesis
2. arm—brachiocephalic
3. abdomen—celiac
4. window—fenestrations
5. neck—jugular
6. belonging to—vasa vasorum
7. standing—saphenous
8. below—subclavian
9. chest—thoracoacromial
10. bladder—vesical

*What's Wrong with These Statements?*

1. Blood can bypass capillaries by flowing through an arteriovenous anastomosis.
2. Blood drains from the brain by way of the internal jugular veins.
3. The longest blood vessel is the great saphenous vein.
4. Some veins have valves, but arteries do not.
5. By the formula $F \propto r^4$, the flow increases in proportion to the fourth power of radius, or 16-fold.
6. The femoral triangle is bordered by the inguinal ligament, sartorius muscle, and adductor longus muscle.
7. The lungs also receive blood from the bronchial arteries of the systemic circuit.
8. Most capillaries reabsorb only a portion (typically about 85%) of the fluid they filter; the rest is absorbed by the lymphatic system.

9. An aneurysm is a weak, bulging vessel that *may* rupture.
10. The response to falling blood pressure is a corrective vasoconstriction.

## CHAPTER 21

*Figure Legend Questions*

21.2 There are much larger gaps between the endothelial cells of lymphatic capillaries than between those of blood capillaries.

21.3 There would be no consistent one-way flow of lymph. Lymph and tissue fluid would accumulate, especially in the lower regions of the body.

21.4 (1) Prevention of excess tissue fluid accumulation and (2) monitoring the tissue fluids for pathogens

21.5 Lymph flows from the breast to the axillary lymph nodes. Therefore, metastatic cancer cells tend to lodge first in those nodes.

21.13 Erythrocytes in the red pulp; lymphocytes and macrophages in the white pulp

21.15 Both of these produce a ring of proteins in the target-cell plasma membrane, opening a hole in the membrane through which the cell contents escape.

21.23 All three defenses depend on the action of helper T cells, which are destroyed by HIV.

21.26 The ER is the site of antibody synthesis.

*Testing Your Recall*

1. b
2. c
3. a
4. a
5. d
6. b
7. e
8. d
9. a
10. c
11. pathogen
12. lysozyme
13. Lymphadenitis
14. diapedesis (emigration)
15. opsonization
16. pyrogen
17. interleukins
18. antigen-binding site, epitope
19. clonal deletion
20. autoimmune

*Building Your Medical Vocabulary* (Answers may vary; these are acceptable examples.)

1. apart—anaphylactic
2. secrete—paracrine
3. outside—extravasated
4. arising—endogenous
5. freedom—immunology
6. set in motion—cytokine
7. water—lymphatic
8. enlargement—splenomegaly
9. disease—lymphadenopathy
10. fire—pyrogen

*What's Wrong with These Statements?*

1. Lysozyme is a bacteria-killing enzyme.
2. The principal birthplace of lymphocytes is the red bone marrow; T lymphocytes migrate from there to the thymus.
3. Interferons promote inflammation.
4. Helper T cells are also necessary to humoral and innate immunity.
5. Negative selection serves to eliminate or deactivate self-reactive T cells (not unresponsive ones), thus preventing immune attack on one's own tissues.
6. The thymus and spleen do not receive or filter any incoming lymph; only lymph nodes do this.
7. Only antibodies of the IgG and IgM classes employ complement fixation.
8. One can be HIV-positive without having AIDS. AIDS is defined by a low helper T cell count ($< 200/\mu L$), not by the presence of the virus.
9. Anergy is a loss of lymphocyte activity, whereas autoimmune diseases result from misdirected activity.
10. Plasma cells are antibody-synthesizing cells of the connective tissues that develop from B cells; they are not found in the blood plasma.

## CHAPTER 22

*Figure Legend Questions*

22.3 The line would cross the figure just slightly above the trachea label.

22.4 Epiglottic, corniculate, and arytenoid

22.7 The right main bronchus is slightly wider and more vertical than the left, making it easier for aspirated objects to fall into the right.

22.8 To secrete mucus

22.17 Any airflow through the nose would not be registered by the spirometer, and the spirometer could not give a correct reading of pulmonary ventilation.

22.19 $P_{O_2}$ drops from 104 to 95 mm Hg on its way out of the lungs because of some mixing with systemic blood. It drops farther to 40 mm Hg when the blood gives up $O_2$ to respiring tissues, and remains at this level until the blood is reoxygenated back in the lungs. $P_{CO_2}$ is 40 mm Hg leaving the lungs and rises to 46 mm Hg when $CO_2$ is picked up from respiring tissues. It remains at that level until the blood returns to the lungs and unloads $CO_2$.

22.23 About 60%

22.25 In the alveoli, $CO_2$ leaves the blood, $O_2$ enters, and all the chemical reactions are the reverse of those in figure 22.23. The blood bicarbonate concentration will be reduced following alveolar gas exchange because bicarbonate is taken up by the chloride shift antiport and converted to $CO_2$ and water.

22.26 A higher temperature suggests a relatively high metabolic rate and, thus, an elevated need for oxygen. Comparison of these curves shows that for a given $P_{O_2}$, hemoglobin gives up more oxygen at warmer temperatures.

*Testing Your Recall*

1. c
2. c
3. a
4. e
5. e
6. c
7. b
8. a
9. d
10. a
11. epiglottis
12. bronchial tree
13. pulmonary surfactant
14. atmospheric
15. Obstructive
16. anatomical dead space
17. compliance, elasticity
18. ventral respiratory group
19. ventilation–perfusion coupling
20. alkalosis, hypocapnia

*Building Your Medical Vocabulary* (Answers may vary; these are acceptable examples.)

1. imperfect—atelectasis
2. smoke—hypercapnia
3. cancer—carcinoma
4. horn—corniculate
5. true—eupnea
6. measuring device—spirometer
7. nose—nasofacial
8. breathing—dyspnea
9. breath—spirometry
10. shield—thyroid

*What's Wrong with These Statements?*

1. They also fire during expiration (although at a lower rate) to exert a braking action on the diaphragm.
2. The two lungs have a total of 18 segmental bronchi but only 5 lobes.
3. The most abundant cells are alveolar macrophages.
4. When volume increases, pressure decreases.
5. Atelectasis can have other causes such as airway obstruction.
6. The greatest effect is to lower the $CO_2$ level; accelerated breathing has little effect on blood $O_2$.
7. We inhale all the gases of the atmosphere, whether the body uses them or not; there is no way to separate one gas from another as we inhale.

8. In an average 500 mL tidal volume, 350 mL reaches the alveoli.
9. The lower the $P_{CO_2}$, the higher the pH.
10. Most blood $CO_2$ is transported as bicarbonate ions.

## CHAPTER 23

*Figure Legend Questions*

23.2 Ammonia is produced by the deamination of amino acids; urea is synthesized from ammonia and carbon dioxide; uric acid is produced from nucleic acids; and creatinine is produced from creatine phosphate.

23.3 It would be in the dark space at the top of the figure, where the spleen, colon, and small intestine are shown.

23.10 The afferent arteriole is larger. The relatively large inlet to the glomerulus and its small outlet result in high blood pressure in the glomerulus. This is the force that drives glomerular filtration.

23.16 It lowers the urine pH; the more $Na^+$ that is reabsorbed, the more $H^+$ is secreted into the tubular fluid. This is seen at the $Na^+$–$H^+$ antiport along the right margin of the figure.

23.23 The relatively short female urethra is less of an obstacle for bacteria traveling from the perineum to the urinary bladder.

*Testing Your Recall*

1. a
2. d
3. b
4. c
5. b
6. b
7. d
8. e
9. c
10. a
11. micturition
12. Renal autoregulation
13. trigone
14. macula densa
15. podocytes
16. transport maximum
17. Antidiuretic hormone
18. internal urethral
19. protein
20. arcuate

*Building Your Medical Vocabulary* (Answers may vary; these are acceptable examples.)

1. nitrogen—azotemia
2. bladder—cystitis
3. ball—glomerulus
4. next to—juxtaglomerular
5. middle—mesangial
6. kidney—nephron
7. foot—podocyte
8. sagging—nephroptosis
9. pus—pyelonephritis
10. straight—vasa recta

*What's Wrong with These Statements?*

1. Calcium and sodium reabsorption by the PCT are influenced by parathyroid hormone and angiotensin II.
2. Urine contains more urea and chloride than sodium.
3. There is one renal corpuscle per nephron and many nephrons drain into each collecting duct, so renal corpuscles substantially outnumber collecting ducts.
4. "Tight" junctions of the renal tubule are quite leaky, and a substantial amount of tubular fluid passes through them to be reabsorbed by the paracellular route.
5. Diabetes insipidus shows no glucose in the urine.
6. Dilation of the efferent arteriole reduces resistance and thus lowers the glomerular blood pressure and filtration rate.
7. Angiotensin II stimulates aldosterone secretion and $Na^+$ reabsorption, thus reducing urine output.
8. Urine can be as dilute as 50 mOsm/L.
9. Normally there is abundant sodium but no glucose in the urine.
10. Micturition is caused by contraction of the detrusor.

## CHAPTER 24

*Figure Legend Questions*

24.1 The tissue fluid compartment

24.8 Ingestion of water

24.10 It would decrease along with the pH.

24.13 Reverse both arrows to point to the left.

*Testing Your Recall*

1. c
2. a
3. a
4. a
5. d
6. c
7. e
8. b
9. d
10. b
11. $Na^+$
12. $K^+$ and $Mg^{2+}$
13. metabolic water
14. cutaneous transpiration
15. fluid sequestration
16. hyperkalemia
17. hyponatremia
18. respiratory acidosis
19. limiting pH
20. osmolarity

*Building Your Medical Vocabulary* (Answers may vary; these are acceptable examples.)

1. food—hyperalimentation
2. blood—hypoxemia
3. intestine—parenteral
4. potassium—hyperkalemia
5. sodium—hyponatremia
6. next to—parenteral
7. isolate—sequestration
8. breathing—transpiration
9. across—transpiration
10. volume—hypovolemia

*What's Wrong with These Statements?*

1. This is an effect of hypokalemia, not hyperkalemia.
2. Aldosterone has only a small influence on blood pressure.
3. Such injuries elevate the ECF potassium level.
4. Phosphate concentration is less critical than that of other electrolytes and can safely vary over a relatively broad range.
5. PTH promotes calcium absorption but phosphate excretion.
6. Protein buffers more acid than bicarbonate or phosphates do.
7. Increased sodium reabsorption increases urinary $H^+$ excretion and lowers the urine pH.
8. Alkalosis tends to cause a reduction of respiratory rate and pulmonary ventilation so the ECF pH will rise again.
9. More water than salt is lost in true dehydration, so the body fluids become hypertonic.
10. Oral wetting and cooling have only a short-term effect on thirst.

## CHAPTER 25

*Figure Legend Questions*

25.6 The first and second premolars and third molar

25.7 The enamel is a secretion, not a tissue; all the rest are living tissues.

25.11 Blockage of the mouth by the root of the tongue and blockage of the nose by the soft palate

25.12 The muscularis externa of the esophagus has two layers of muscle, with skeletal muscle in the upper to middle regions and smooth muscle in the middle to lower regions. In the stomach, it has three layers of muscle, all of which are smooth muscle.

25.14 It exchanges $H^+$ for $K^+$ ($H^+$–$K^+$ ATPase is an active transport pump).

25.20 The hepatic artery and the hepatic portal vein

25.32 Lipids do not enter the hepatic portal system that leads directly to the liver. Dietary fats are absorbed into the lacteals of the small intestine, then would have to travel the following route, at a minimum, to reach the liver: intestinal trunk → thoracic duct → left subclavian vein → heart → aorta → celiac trunk → common hepatic artery → hepatic artery proper → hepatic arteries → liver.

25.33 The internal anal sphincter is composed of smooth muscle and therefore controlled by the autonomic nervous system. The external anal sphincter is composed of skeletal muscle and therefore controlled by the somatic nervous system.

*Testing Your Recall*

1. b
2. d
3. c
4. e
5. a
6. c
7. a
8. a
9. a
10. a
11. occlusal
12. amylase, lipase
13. parotid
14. enteric
15. vagus
16. gastrin
17. sinusoids
18. dipeptidase
19. bile acids
20. iron

*Building Your Medical Vocabulary* (Answers may vary; these are acceptable examples.)

1. cavity—antrum
2. juice—chylomicron
3. little—micelle
4. vomiting—emetic
5. bridle—frenulum
6. liver—hepatocyte
7. dry—jejunum
8. gateway—portal
9. gateway—pyloric
10. S-shaped—sigmoid

*What's Wrong with These Statements?*

1. Fat digestion begins in the stomach.
2. Most of the tooth is dentin.
3. Hepatocytes secrete bile into the bile canaliculi.
4. The ileal papilla regulates the passage of residue from the ileum of the small intestine into the cecum of the large intestine.
5. The lacteals take up chylomicrons, not micelles.
6. Hepcidin inhibits iron absorption and prevents iron overload.
7. The small intestine absorbs not only glucose but also fructose and galactose.
8. Most of the water is absorbed by the small intestine.
9. Secretin stimulates the liver and pancreas to secrete bicarbonate and inhibits gastric secretion.
10. Water, glucose, and other nutrients pass between cells, through the tight junctions.

## CHAPTER 26

*Figure Legend Questions*

26.4 A high HDL:LDL ratio indicates that excess cholesterol is being transported to the liver for removal from the body. A high LDL:HDL ratio indicates a high rate of cholesterol deposition in the walls of the arteries.

26.7 NADH and $FADH_2$

26.11 Acidosis, ketoacidosis, or metabolic acidosis

26.12 Amino acids → keto acids → pyruvate → glucose

*Testing Your Recall*

1. a
2. c
3. b
4. e
5. b
6. e
7. c
8. a
9. d
10. d
11. incomplete
12. glycogenolysis
13. gluconeogenesis
14. urea
15. liver
16. insulin
17. core temperature
18. arcuate
19. cytochromes
20. ATP synthase, ATP

*Building Your Medical Vocabulary* (Answers may vary; these are acceptable examples.)

1. bag—ascites
2. bad—cachexia
3. color—cytochrome
4. producing—lipogenesis
5. sugar—hypoglycemia
6. like—ascites
7. thin—leptin
8. splitting—glycolysis
9. new—gluconeogenesis
10. push—chemiosmotic

*What's Wrong with These Statements?*

1. Leptin suppresses the appetite.
2. A nutrient is a dietary substance that is absorbed into the tissues and becomes part of the body; water meets this criterion and is considered a nutrient.
3. Fat has more than twice as many calories per gram as carbohydrate does.
4. Most of the cholesterol is endogenous, not dietary.
5. Excessive protein intake generates excess nitrogenous waste and can cause renal damage.
6. Excessive ketone production is an effect of high-fat diets.
7. The membrane reactions produce up to 28 ATP per glucose, whereas glycolysis and the matrix reactions produce only 4 ATP.
8. Gluconeogenesis is a postabsorptive phenomenon.
9. Brown fat does not generate ATP.
10. At 21°C, the body loses about 60% of its heat by radiation.

## CHAPTER 27

*Figure Legend Questions*

27.1 Both disorders result from defects in hormone receptors rather than from a lack of the respective hormone.

27.5 The word *vagina* means "sheath." The tunica vaginalis partially ensheathes the testis.

27.10 An enlarged prostate compresses the urethra and interferes with emptying of the bladder.

27.11 A tunica albuginea would allow excessive pressure to build in the corpus spongiosum, compressing the urethra and interfering with ejaculation.

27.13 The crossing-over in prophase I results in a mixture of maternal and paternal genes in each chromosome.

27.14 The next cell stage in meiosis, the secondary spermatocyte, is genetically different from the other cells of the body and would be subject to immune attack if not isolated from the antibodies in the blood.

*Testing Your Recall*

1. a
2. a
3. a
4. c
5. a
6. d
7. e
8. c
9. d
10. d
11. mesonephric
12. zinc
13. pampiniform plexus
14. secondary spermatocytes
15. tunica albuginea
16. seminal vesicles
17. nurse
18. secondary spermatocyte
19. deep
20. acrosome

*Building Your Medical Vocabulary* (Answers may vary; these are acceptable examples.)

1. hidden—cryptorchidism
2. twins—epididymis
3. out—ejaculation
4. union—gamete
5. condition—cryptorchidism
6. reduction—meiosis
7. testis—cryptorchidism
8. network—rete testis
9. body—acrosome
10. sheath—tunica vaginalis

*What's Wrong with These Statements?*

1. Testosterone is secreted by the interstitial endocrine cells.
2. The sperm DNA is contained in the nucleus in the sperm head.
3. Meiosis II is completed before spermiogenesis, which is the conversion of the four spermatids to mature sperm.
4. Only the testes are primary sex organs; the penis is a secondary sex organ.

5. Female fetal development results from a low testosterone level, not from estrogen.
6. The seminal vesicles contribute about 60% of the semen.
7. The pampiniform plexus prevents the testes from overheating.
8. Sperm have no testosterone receptors; testosterone binds to androgen-binding protein in the seminiferous tubules.
9. There is no such phenomenon as male menopause, and sperm production normally continues throughout old age.
10. Erection is the result of parasympathetic stimulation of the blood vessels of the erectile tissues.

## CHAPTER 28

*Figure Legend Questions*

28.4 To move the egg or conceptus toward the uterus

28.8 Paraurethral glands

28.9 They cause milk to flow from the acinus into the ducts of the mammary gland.

28.10 This results in a clearer image since the X-rays do not have to penetrate such a thick mass of tissue.

28.18 The rising ratio of estradiol to progesterone makes the uterus more irritable.

*Testing Your Recall*

1. a
2. d
3. c
4. a
5. e
6. b
7. b
8. b
9. c
10. c
11. follicle
12. endometrium
13. menarche
14. corpus luteum
15. corona radiata
16. antrum
17. climacteric
18. conceptus
19. infundibulum, fimbriae
20. lochia

*Building Your Medical Vocabulary* (Answers may vary; these are acceptable examples.)

1. beginning—menarche
2. of—gravidarum
3. mound—cumulus
4. pregnancy—progesterone
5. uterus—hysterectomy
6. milk—lactation
7. to tie—tubal ligation
8. uterus—endometrium
9. egg—oogenesis
10. first—primipara

*What's Wrong with These Statements?*

1. Only the ovum and cumulus oophorus cells enter the uterine tube, not the whole follicle.
2. HCG is secreted by the placenta.
3. Meiosis II is not completed until after ovulation, and only if the egg is fertilized.
4. Such girls often have lower than average body fat and delayed menarche because of this.
5. Many eggs and follicles undergo atresia during childhood, so their number is greatly reduced by the age of puberty.
6. Prolactin is secreted during pregnancy but does not induce lactation then.
7. Colostrum is lower in fat than milk is.
8. Up to two dozen follicles mature to the secondary follicle stage in each cycle, but usually only one of them ovulates.
9. Progesterone inhibits uterine contractions.
10. Only the superficial (functional) layer is shed.

## CHAPTER 29

*Figure Legend Questions*

29.2 An unfertilized egg dies long before it reaches the uterus.

29.8 About 8 weeks

29.13 XXY (Klinefelter syndrome) and YO (a zygote that would not survive)

29.15 Female, as seen from the two X chromosomes at the lower right

*Testing Your Recall*

1. b
2. b
3. c
4. c
5. a
6. e
7. c
8. a
9. d
10. d
11. teratogens
12. nondisjunction
13. life span
14. life expectancy
15. chorionic villi
16. acrosome
17. collagen
18. Down syndrome (trisomy-21)
19. foramen ovale
20. embryo

*Building Your Medical Vocabulary* (Answers may vary; these are acceptable examples.)

1. with—congenital
2. falling off—decidual
3. old age—progeria
4. mulberry—morula
5. flat cake—placenta
6. double—aneuploidy
7. aging—senescence
8. together—syncytiotrophoblast
9. end—telomere
10. monster—teratogen

*What's Wrong with These Statements?*

1. The ability to fertilize an egg increases in the first 10 hours as sperm become capacitated.
2. Fertilization occurs in the uterine tube.
3. Several early-arriving sperm clear a path for the one that fertilizes the egg.
4. Early cell divisions occur while the conceptus is still in the uterine tube, about 2 days before arrival in the uterus.
5. The individual is considered an embryo then; it is not a fetus until all of the major organs have formed.
6. As they develop, the chorionic villi become thinner and more permeable.
7. The kidneys exhibit one of the greatest degrees of senescence, shrinking 60% to 80% by age 90.
8. The foramen ovale is a shunt in the heart by which blood bypasses the lungs; the shunt that bypasses the liver is the ductus venosus.
9. Blood in the umbilical vein is returning from the placenta, where it has picked up oxygen and thus has a high $P_{O_2}$.
10. Telomerase is a telomere-repairing enzyme that prolongs cell life, as in stem cells and cancer cells.

## APPENDIX D

*Table D.2 Question*

Asn-Ile-Tyr-Val-Arg-Asp

# APPENDIX B

# SYMBOLS, WEIGHTS, AND MEASURES

## Units of Length

| | |
|---|---|
| m | meter |
| km | kilometer ($10^3$ m) |
| cm | centimeter ($10^{-2}$ m) |
| mm | millimeter ($10^{-3}$ m) |
| µm | micrometer ($10^{-6}$ m) |
| nm | nanometer ($10^{-9}$ m) |

## Units of Mass and Weight

| | |
|---|---|
| amu | atomic mass unit |
| MW | molecular weight |
| mole | MW in grams |
| g | gram |
| kg | kilograms ($10^3$ g) |
| mg | milligrams ($10^{-3}$ g) |
| µg | micrograms ($10^{-6}$ g) |

## Units of Pressure

| | |
|---|---|
| atm | atmospheres (1 atm = 760 mm Hg) |
| mm Hg | millimeters of mercury |
| $P_X$ | partial pressure of gas X (as in $Po_2$) |

## Conversion Factors

| | |
|---|---|
| 1 in. = 2.54 cm | 1 cm = 0.394 in. |
| 1 fl oz = 29.6 mL | 1 mL = 0.034 fl oz |
| 1 qt = 0.946 L | 1 L = 1.057 qt |
| 1 g = 0.0035 oz | 1 oz = 28.38 g |
| 1 lb = 0.45 kg | 1 kg = 2.2 lb |
| °C = (5/9)(°F − 32) | °F = (9/5)(°C) + 32 |

## Units of Volume

| | |
|---|---|
| L | liter |
| dL | deciliter (= 100 mL) ($10^{-1}$ L) |
| mL | milliliter ($10^{-3}$ L) |
| µL | microliter (= 1 $mm^3$) ($10^{-6}$ L) |

## Units of Heat

| | |
|---|---|
| cal | "small" calorie |
| kcal | kilocalorie (Calorie; 1 kcal = 1,000 cal) |
| Cal | "large" (dietary) calorie (1 Cal = 1,000 cal) |

## Greek Letters

| | |
|---|---|
| α | alpha |
| β | beta |
| γ | gamma |
| Δ | delta (uppercase) |
| δ | delta (lowercase) |
| η | eta |
| θ | theta |
| λ | lambda |
| µ | mu |
| π | pi |

## Units of Concentration

Chemical concentrations—the amounts of solute in a given volume of solution—are expressed in different ways for different scientific or clinical purposes. Some of these are explained here, particularly those used in this book.

### WEIGHT PER VOLUME

A simple way to express concentration is the weight of solute in a given volume of solution. For example, intravenous (I.V.) saline typically contains 8.5 grams of NaCl per liter of solution (8.5 g/L). For many biological purposes, however, we deal with smaller quantities such as *milligrams per deciliter (mg/dL)*. For example, a typical serum cholesterol concentration may be 200 mg/dL, also expressed as 200 mg/100 mL or 200 milligram-percent (mg-%).

### PERCENTAGES

Percentage concentration is also simple to compute, but it is necessary to specify whether the percentage refers to the weight or to the volume of solute in a given volume of solution. For example, if we begin with 5 g of dextrose (an isomer of glucose) and add enough water to make 100 mL of solution, the resulting concentration will be 5% weight per volume (w/v). A commonly used intravenous fluid is D5W, which stands for 5% w/v dextrose in distilled water.

If the solute is a liquid, such as ethanol, percentages refer to volume of solute per volume of solution. Thus, 70 mL of ethanol diluted with water to 100 mL of solution produces 70% volume per volume (70% v/v) ethanol.

### MOLARITY

Percentage concentrations are easy to prepare, but that unit of measurement is inadequate for many purposes. The physiological effect of a chemical depends on how many molecules of it are present in a given volume, not the weight of the chemical. Five percent glucose, for example, contains almost twice as many sugar molecules as the same volume of 5% sucrose. Each solution contains 50 g of sugar per liter, but glucose has a molecular weight (MW) of 180 and sucrose has a MW of 342. Since each molecule of glucose is lighter, 50 g of glucose contains more molecules than 50 g of sucrose.

To produce solutions with a known number of molecules per volume, we must factor in the molecular weight. If we know the MW and weigh out that many grams of the substance, we have a quantity known as 1 *mole.* One mole of glucose is 180 g and 1 mole of sucrose is 342 g. Each quantity contains the same number of molecules of the respective sugar—a number known as *Avogadro's number,* $6.023 \times 10^{23}$ molecules per mole.

*Molarity* (M) is the number of moles of solute per liter of solution. A one-molar (1.0 M) solution of glucose contains 180 g/L, and 1.0 M solution of sucrose contains 342 g/L. Both have the same number of solute molecules in a given volume. Body fluids and laboratory solutions usually are less concentrated than 1 M, so biologists and clinicians more often work with *millimolar* (mM, $10^{-3}$ M) and *micromolar* (μM, $10^{-6}$ M) concentrations.

## OSMOLARITY AND OSMOLALITY

The osmotic concentration of body fluids has a great effect on cellular function, body water distribution, nutrient absorption, urinary water loss, the sense of thirst, and blood pressure. Thus, it is important to quantify osmotic concentrations in physiology and in clinical practice (as when giving I.V. fluid therapy). Physiologists and clinicians usually express osmotic concentration in *milliosmoles per liter* (mOsm/L).

One *osmole* is 1 mole of dissolved particles. If a solute does not ionize in water, then 1 mole of the solute yields 1 osmole (osm) of dissolved particles. A solution of 1 M glucose, for example, is also 1 osm/L. If a solute does ionize, it yields two or more dissolved particles in solution. A 1 M solution of NaCl, for example, contains 1 mole/L of sodium ions and 1 mole/L of chloride ions; 1 M calcium chloride ($CaCl_2$) would (if it completely dissociated) yield 1 mole of calcium ions and 2 moles of chloride ions. All ions equally affect osmosis and must be separately counted in a measure of osmotic concentration. Thus,

$$1 \text{ M NaCl} = 2 \text{ osm/L, and}$$

$$1 \text{ M } CaCl_2 = 3 \text{ osm/L.}$$

*Osmolality* is the number of osmoles of solute per kilogram of water, and *osmolarity* is the number of osmoles per liter of solution. Most clinical calculations are based on osmolarity, since it is easier to measure the volume of a solution than the weight of water it contains. The difference between osmolality and osmolarity can be important in experimental work, but at the concentrations of human body fluids, there is less than 1% difference between the two, and the two are essentially interchangeable for clinical purposes.

All body fluids and many clinical solutions are mixtures of many chemicals. The osmolarity of such a solution is the total osmotic concentration of all of its dissolved particles.

A concentration of 1 osm/L is substantially higher than we find in most body fluids, so physiological concentrations are usually expressed in terms of milliosmoles per liter (mOsm/L) (1 mOsm/L = $10^{-3}$ osm/L). Blood plasma, tissue fluid, and intracellular fluid measure about 300 mOsm/L.

## MILLIEQUIVALENTS PER LITER

Electrolytes are important for their chemical, physical (osmotic), and electrical effects on the body. Their electrical effects, which determine such things as nerve, heart, and muscle actions, depend not only on their concentration but also on their electrical charge. A calcium ion ($Ca^{2+}$) has twice the electrical effect of a sodium ion ($Na^+$), for example, because it carries twice the charge. In measuring electrolyte concentrations, one must take the charges into account.

One *equivalent* (Eq) of an electrolyte is the amount that would electrically neutralize 1 mole of hydrogen ions ($H^+$) or hydroxide ions ($OH^-$). For example, 1 mole (58.4 g) of NaCl yields 1 mole, or 1 Eq, of $Na^+$ in solution. Thus, an NaCl solution of 58.4 g/L contains 1 equivalent of $Na^+$ per liter (1 Eq/L). One mole (98 g) of sulfuric acid ($H_2SO_4$) yields 2 moles of positive charges ($H^+$). Thus, 98 g of sulfuric acid per liter would be a solution of 2 Eq/L.

The electrolytes in human body fluids have concentrations less than 1 Eq/L, so we more often express their concentrations in *milliequivalents per liter* (mEq/L). If you know the millimolar concentration of an electrolyte, you can easily convert this to mEq/L by multiplying it by the valence (charge) of the ion:

$$1 \text{ mM } Na^+ = 1 \text{ mEq/L}$$

$$1 \text{ mM } Ca^{2+} = 2 \text{ mEq/L}$$

$$1 \text{ mM } Fe^{3+} = 3 \text{ mEq/L}$$

## ACIDITY AND ALKALINITY (PH)

Acidity is expressed in terms of pH, a measure derived from the molarity of $H^+$. Molarity is represented by square brackets, so the molarity of $H^+$ is symbolized $[H^+]$. pH is the negative logarithm of hydrogen ion molarity; that is,

$$\text{pH} = -\log [H^+].$$

In pure water, 1 in 10 million molecules of $H_2O$ ionizes into hydrogen and hydroxide ions: $H_2O \rightleftharpoons H^+ + OH^-$. Pure water has a neutral pH because it contains equal amounts of $H^+$ and $OH^-$. Since 1 in 10 million molecules ionize, the molarity of $H^+$ and the pH of water are as follows:

$$[H^+] = 0.0000001 \text{ M} = 10^{-7} \text{ M}$$

$$\log [H^+] = -7$$

$$\text{pH} = -\log [H^+] = 7$$

The pH scale ranges from 0 to 14 and is logarithmic, so each integer up or down the scale represents a 10-fold difference in $[H^+]$. This is exemplified by the following three strongly acidic pH values:

If $[H^+] = 0.1$ M  $\text{pH} = -\log 10^{-1} = 1.0$

If $[H^+] = 0.01$ M  $\text{pH} = -\log 10^{-2} = 2.0$

If $[H^+] = 0.001$ M  $\text{pH} = -\log 10^{-3} = 3.0$

The less concentrated the $H^+$, the higher the pH. pH values below 7.0 are considered acidic. Above 7.0, they are basic or alkaline. The following three values lie at the basic end of the pH scale:

If $[H^+] = 0.000000000001$ M  $\text{pH} = -\log 10^{-12} = 12.0$

If $[H^+] = 0.0000000000001$ M  $\text{pH} = -\log 10^{-13} = 13.0$

If $[H^+] = 0.00000000000001$ M  $\text{pH} = -\log 10^{-14} = 14.0$

# APPENDIX C

## PERIODIC TABLE OF THE ELEMENTS

Nineteenth-century chemists discovered that when they arranged the known elements by atomic weight, certain properties reappeared periodically. In 1869, Russian chemist Dmitri Mendeleev published the first modern periodic table of the elements, leaving gaps for those that had not yet been discovered. He accurately predicted properties of the missing elements, which helped other chemists discover and isolate them.

Each row in the table is a *period* and each column is a *group (family)*. Each period has one electron shell more than the period above it, and as we progress from left to right within a period, each element has one more proton and electron than the one before. The dark steplike line from boron (5) to astatine (85) separates the metals to the left of it (except hydrogen) from the nonmetals to the right. Each period begins with a soft, light, highly reactive *alkali metal,* with one valence electron, in family IA. Progressing from left to right, the metallic properties of the elements become less and less pronounced. Elements in family VIIA are highly reactive gases called *halogens,* with seven valence electrons. Elements in family VIIIA, called *noble (inert) gases,* have a full valence shell of eight electrons, which makes them chemically unreactive.

Ninety-one of the elements occur naturally on earth. Physicists have created elements up to atomic number 118 in the laboratory, but the International Union of Pure and Applied Chemistry has established formal names only through element 112 to date.

The 24 elements with normal roles in human physiology are color-coded according to their relative abundance in the body (see table 2.1). Others, however, may be present as contaminants with very destructive effects (such as arsenic, lead, and radiation poisoning).

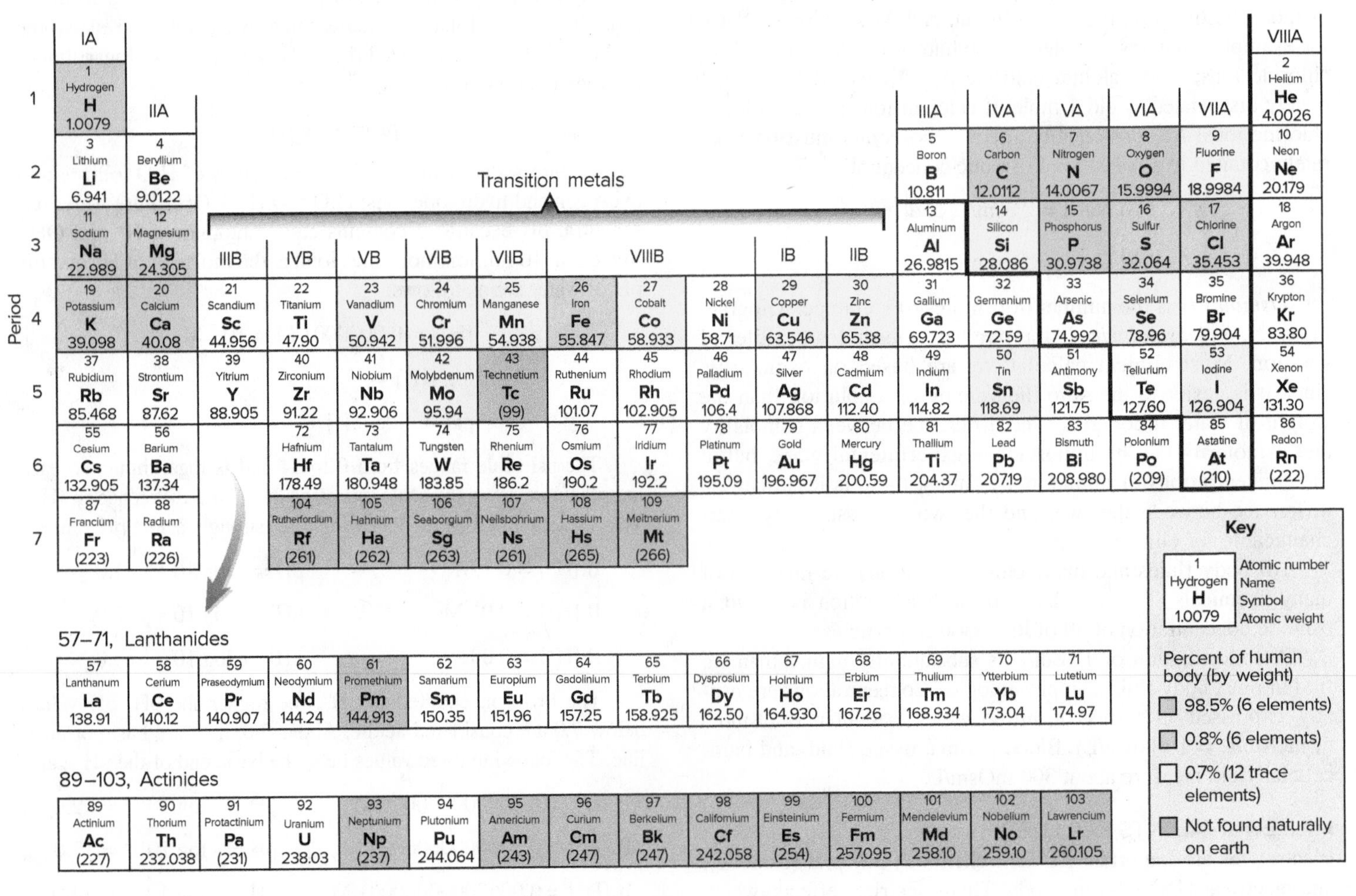

# APPENDIX D

## THE GENETIC CODE AND AMINO ACIDS

**Table D.1** lists the 20 amino acids involved in protein structure, with the three-letter and one-letter symbols used in writing out amino acid sequences (as in fig. 2.25, for example). **Table D.2** is the genetic code, relating mRNA codons to the amino acids. To determine what amino acid is encoded by a given mRNA codon, choose the first letter of the codon from the column on the left, the second letter from the row across the top, and the third letter from the column on the right. The amino acid symbol is at the intersection of these three. For example, codon GCU codes for alanine (Ala) and CAC codes for histidine (His). Codons UAA, UAG, and UGA are *stop codons,* which do not code for any amino acid but indicate the end of the message to be translated, like the period at the end of a sentence.

**TABLE D.1 The 20 Amino Acids and Their Symbols**

| | | | | | |
|---|---|---|---|---|---|
| Alanine | Ala | A | Leucine | Leu | L |
| Arginine | Arg | R | Lysine | Lys | K |
| Asparagine | Asn | N | Methionine | Met | M |
| Aspartate | Asp | D | Phenylalanine | Phe | F |
| Cysteine | Cys | C | Proline | Pro | P |
| Glutamate | Glu | E | Serine | Ser | S |
| Glutamine | Gln | Q | Threonine | Thr | T |
| Glycine | Gly | G | Tryptophan | Trp | W |
| Histidine | His | H | Tyrosine | Tyr | Y |
| Isoleucine | Ile | I | Valine | Val | V |

**TABLE D.2 The Genetic Code**

| First Position | Second Position | | | | Third Position |
|---|---|---|---|---|---|
| | A | G | C | U | |
| A | Lys | Arg | Thr | Ile | A |
| | Lys | Arg | Thr | Met | G |
| | Asn | Ser | Thr | Ile | C |
| | Asn | Ser | Thr | Ile | U |
| G | Glu | Gly | Ala | Val | A |
| | Glu | Gly | Ala | Val | G |
| | Asp | Gly | Ala | Val | C |
| | Asp | Gly | Ala | Val | U |
| C | Gln | Arg | Pro | Leu | A |
| | Gln | Arg | Pro | Leu | G |
| | His | Arg | Pro | Leu | C |
| | His | Arg | Pro | Leu | U |
| U | STOP | STOP | Ser | Leu | A |
| | STOP | Trp | Ser | Leu | G |
| | Tyr | Cys | Ser | Phe | C |
| | Tyr | Cys | Ser | Phe | U |

? *The following genetic code represents a well-known hormone, angiotensin II: UUU-CCC-CAC-AUA-UAU-GUA-AGG-GAC. The amino acid sequence represented by this code begins Phe-Pro. . . . Write the rest of the sequence. (Answer is found in appendix A.)*

| | | | |
|---|---|---|---|
| H<br>$H_2N$—C—COOH<br>$CH_3$<br>**Alanine** | H<br>$H_2N$—C—COOH<br>$(CH_2)_3$<br>NH<br>C=$N^+H_2$<br>$NH_2$<br>**Arginine** | H<br>$H_2N$—C—COOH<br>$CH_2$<br>$H_2N$—C=O<br>**Asparagine** | H<br>$H_2N$—C—COOH<br>$CH_2$<br>COOH<br>**Aspartic acid** |
| H<br>$H_2N$—C—COOH<br>$CH_2$<br>SH<br>**Cysteine** | H<br>$H_2N$—C—COOH<br>$CH_2$<br>$CH_2$<br>COOH<br>**Glutamic acid** | H<br>$H_2N$—C—COOH<br>$CH_2$<br>$CH_2$<br>$H_2N$—C=O<br>**Glutamine** | H<br>$H_2N$—C—COOH<br>H<br>**Glycine** |
| H<br>$H_2N$—C—COOH<br>$CH_2$<br>C—NH<br>CH<br>HC—N<br>**Histidine** | H<br>$H_2N$—C—COOH<br>H—C—$CH_2$<br>$CH_2$<br>$CH_3$<br>**Isoleucine** | H<br>$H_2N$—C—COOH<br>$CH_2$<br>CH<br>$H_3C$ $CH_3$<br>**Leucine** | H<br>$H_2N$—C—COOH<br>$(CH_2)_4$<br>$^+NH_3$<br>**Lysine** |
| H<br>$H_2N$—C—COOH<br>$CH_2$<br>$CH_2$<br>S<br>$CH_3$<br>**Methionine** | H<br>$H_2N$—C—COOH<br>$CH_2$<br>**Phenylalanine** | H<br>$H_2N^+$—C—COOH<br>$H_2C$ $CH_2$<br>C<br>$H_2$<br>**Proline** | H<br>$H_2N$—C—COOH<br>$CH_2$<br>OH<br>**Serine** |
| H<br>$H_2N$—C—COOH<br>H—C—OH<br>$CH_3$<br>**Threonine** | H<br>$H_2N$—C—COOH<br>$CH_2$<br>C=CH<br>NH<br>**Tryptophan** | H<br>$H_2N$—C—COOH<br>$CH_2$<br>OH<br>**Tyrosine** | H<br>$H_2N$—C—COOH<br>CH<br>$H_3C$ $CH_3$<br>**Valine** |

# APPENDIX E

## MEDICAL WORD ROOTS AND AFFIXES

**a-** no, not, without (atom, agranulocyte)
**ab-** away (abducens, abduction)
**acetabulo-** small cup (acetabulum)
**acro-** tip, extremity, peak (acromion, acromegaly)
**ad-** to, toward, near (adsorption, adrenal)
**adeno-** gland (lymphadenitis, adenohypophysis)
**aero-** air, oxygen (aerobic, anaerobic)
**af-** toward (afferent)
**ag-** together (agglutination)
**-al** pertaining to (parietal, pharyngeal, temporal)
**ala-** wing (ala nasi)
**albi-** white (albicans, linea alba, albino)
**algi-** pain (analgesic, myalgia)
**aliment-** nourishment (alimentary)
**allo-** other, different (allele, allograft)
**amphi-** both, either (amphiphilic, amphiarthrosis)
**an-** without (anaerobic, anemic)
**ana-** **1.** up, build up (anabolic, anaphylaxis)
**2.** apart (anaphase, anatomy)
**3.** back (anastomosis)
**andro-** male (androgen)
**angi-** vessel (angiogram, angioplasty, hemangioma)
**ante-** before, in front (antebrachium)
**antero-** forward (anterior, anterograde)
**anti-** against (antidiuretic, antibody, antagonist)
**apo-** from, off, away, above (apocrine, aponeurosis)
**arbor-** tree (arboreal, arborization)
**artic-** **1.** joint (articulation)
**2.** speech (articulate)
**-ary** pertaining to (axillary, coronary)
**-ase** enzyme (polymerase, kinase, amylase)
**ast-, astro-** star (aster, astrocyte)
**-ata, -ate** **1.** possessing (hamate, corniculate)
**2.** plural of -a (stomata, carcinomata)
**athero-** fat (atheroma, atherosclerosis)
**atrio-** entryway (atrium, atrioventricular)
**auri-** ear (auricle, binaural)
**auto-** self (autolysis, autoimmune)
**axi-** axis, straight line (axial, axoneme, axon)
**baro-** pressure (baroreceptor, hyperbaric)
**bene-** good, well (benign, beneficial)
**bi-** two (bipedal, biceps, bifid)
**bili-** bile (biliary, bilirubin)
**bio-** life, living (biology, biopsy, microbial)
**blasto-** precursor, bud, producer (fibroblast, osteoblast, blastomere)
**brachi-** arm (brachium, brachialis, antebrachium)
**brady-** slow (bradycardia, bradypnea)
**bucco-** cheek (buccal, buccinator)
**burso-** purse (bursa, bursitis)
**calc-** calcium, stone (calcaneus, hypocalcemia)
**callo-** thick (callus, callosum)
**calori-** heat (calorie, calorimetry, calorigenic)
**calv-, calvari-** bald, skull (calvaria)
**calyx** cup, vessel, chalice (glycocalyx, renal calyx)
**capito-** head (capitis, capitate, capitulum)
**capni-** smoke, carbon dioxide (hypocapnia)
**carcino-** cancer (carcinogen, carcinoma)
**cardi-** heart (cardiac, cardiology, pericardium)
**carot-** **1.** carrot (carotene)
**2.** stupor (carotid)
**carpo-** wrist (carpus, metacarpal)
**case-** cheese (caseosa, casein)
**cata-** down, break down (catabolism)
**cauda-** tail (cauda equina, caudate nucleus)
**-cel** little (pedicel)
**celi-** belly, abdomen (celiac)
**centri-** center, middle (centromere, centriole)
**cephalo-** head (cephalic, encephalitis)
**cervi-** neck, narrow part (cervix, cervical)
**chiasm-** cross, X (optic chiasm)
**choano-** funnel (choana)
**chole-** bile (cholecystokinin, cholelithotripsy)
**chondro-** **1.** grain (mitochondria)
**2.** cartilage, gristle (chondrocyte, perichondrium)
**chromo-** color (dichromat, chromatin, cytochrome)
**chrono-** time (chronotropic, chronic)
**cili-** eyelash (cilium, superciliary)
**circ-** about, around (circadian, circumduction)
**cis-** cut (incision, incisor)
**cistern, cisterna** reservoir (Golgi cistern, cisterna chyli)
**clast-** break down, destroy (osteoclast)
**clavi-** hammer, club, key (clavicle, supraclavicular)
**-cle** little (tubercle, corpuscle)
**cleido-** clavicle (sternocleidomastoid)
**cnemo-** lower leg (gastrocnemius)
**co-** together (coenzyme, cotransport)
**collo-** **1.** hill (colliculus)
**2.** glue (colloid, collagen)
**contra-** opposite (contralateral)
**corni-** horn (cornified, corniculate, cornu)
**corono-** crown (coronary, corona, coronal)
**corpo-** body (corpus luteum, corpora quadrigemina)
**corti-** bark, rind (cortex, cortical)
**costa-** rib (intercostal, subcostal)
**coxa-** hip (os coxae, coxal)
**crani-** helmet (cranium, epicranius)
**cribri-** sieve, strainer (cribriform, area cribrosa)
**crino-** separate, secrete (holocrine, endocrinology)
**crista-** crest (crista galli, mitochondrial crista)
**crito-** to separate (hematocrit)
**cruci-** cross (cruciate ligament)
**-cule, -culus** small (canaliculus, trabecula, auricular)
**cune-** wedge (cuneiform, cuneatus)
**cutane-, cuti-** skin (subcutaneous, cuticle)
**cysto-** bladder (cystitis, cholecystectomy)
**cyto-** cell (cytology, cytokinesis, monocyte)

**de-** down (defecate, deglutition, dehydration)
**demi-** half (demifacet, demilune)
**den-, denti-** tooth (dentition, dens, dental)
**dendro-** tree, branch (dendrite, oligodendrocyte)
**derma-, dermato-** skin (dermatology, hypodermic)
**desmo-** band, bond, ligament (desmosome, syndesmosis)
**dia- 1.** across, through, separate (diaphragm, dialysis)
**2.** day (circadian)
**dis- 1.** apart (dissect, dissociate)
**2.** opposite, absence (disinfect, disability)
**diure-** pass through, urinate (diuretic, diuresis)
**dorsi-** back (dorsal, dorsum, latissimus dorsi)
**duc-** to carry (duct, adduction, abducens)
**dys-** bad, abnormal, painful (dyspnea, dystrophy)
**e-** out (ejaculate, eversion)
**-eal** pertaining to (arboreal, pineal)
**ec-, ecto-** outside, out of, external (ectopic, ectoderm, splenectomy)
**ef-** out of (efferent, effusion)
**-elle** small (fontanelle, organelle, micelle)
**electro-** electricity (electrocardiogram, electrolyte)
**em-** in, within (embolism, embedded)
**emesi-, emeti-** vomiting (emetic, hyperemesis)
**-emia** blood condition (anemia, hypoxemia)
**en-** in, into (enzyme, parenchyma)
**encephalo-** brain (encephalitis, telencephalon)
**enchymo-** poured in (mesenchyme, parenchyma)
**endo-** within, into, internal (endocrine, endocytosis)
**entero-** gut, intestine (mesentery, myenteric)
**epi-** upon, above (epidermis, epiphysis, epididymis)
**ergo-** work, energy, action (allergy, adrenergic, synergist)
**eryth-, erythro-** red (erythema, erythrocyte)
**esthesio-** sensation, feeling (anesthesia, somesthetic)
**eu-** good, true, normal, easy (eupnea, aneuploidy)
**exo-** out (exopeptidase, exocytosis, exocrine)
**facili-** easy (facilitated)
**fasci-** band, bundle (fascia, fascicle)
**fenestr-** window (fenestrated)
**fer-** to carry (efferent, uriniferous)
**ferri-** iron (ferritin, transferrin)
**fibro-** fiber (fibroblast, fibrosis)
**fili-** thread (myofilament, filiform)
**flagello-** whip (flagellum)
**foli-** leaf (folic acid, folia)
**-form** shape (cuneiform, fusiform)
**fove-** pit, depression (fovea)
**funiculo-** little rope, cord (funiculus)
**fusi- 1.** spindle (fusiform)
**2.** pour out (perfusion)
**gamo-** marriage, union (monogamy, gamete)
**gastro-** belly, stomach (gastrointestinal, digastric)
**-gen, -genic, -genesis** producing, giving rise to (pathogen, carcinogenic, glycogenesis)
**genio-** chin (geniohyoid, genioglossus)
**germi- 1.** sprout, bud (germinal, germinativum)
**2.** microbe (germicide)
**gero-** old age (progeria, geriatrics, gerontology)
**gesto- 1.** to bear, carry (ingest).
**2.** pregnancy (gestation, progesterone)
**glia-** glue (neuroglia, microglia)
**globu-** ball, sphere (globulin, hemoglobin)
**glom-** ball (glomerulus)
**glosso-** tongue (glossopharyngeal, hypoglossal)
**glyco-** sugar (glycogen, glycolysis, hypoglycemia)
**gono- 1.** angle, corner (trigone)
**2.** seed, sex cell, generation (gonad, oogonium, gonorrhea)
**gradi-** walk, step (retrograde, gradient)
**-gram** recording of (electrocardiogram, sonogram)
**-graph** recording instrument (sonograph, electrocardiograph)
**-graphy** recording process (sonography, radiography)
**gravi-** severe, heavy (gravid, myasthenia gravis)
**gyro-** turn, twist (gyrus)
**hallu-** great toe (hallucis)
**hemato-** blood (hematology, hematopoiesis)
**hemi-** half (hemidesmosome, hemisphere)
**-hemia** blood condition (polycythemia)
**hemo-** blood (hemophilia, hemoglobin)
**hetero-** different, other, various (heterozygous)
**histo-** tissue, web (histology, histone)
**holo-** whole, entire (holistic, holocrine)
**homeo-** constant, unchanging, uniform (homeostasis, homeothermic)
**homo-** same, alike (homologous, homozygous)
**hyalo-** clear, glassy (hyaline, hyaluronic acid)
**hydro-** water (dehydration, hydrolysis, hydrophobic)
**hyper-** above, above normal, excessive (hyperkalemia, hypertonic)
**hypo-** below, below normal, deficient (hypogastric, hyponatremia, hypophysis)
**-ia** condition (anemia, hypocalcemia, osteomalacia)
**-ial** pertaining to (hypophysial, epiphysial)
**-ic** pertaining to (isotonic, hemolytic, antigenic)
**-icle, -icul** small (ossicle, canaliculus, reticular)
**ilia-** flank, loin (ilium, iliac)
**-illa, -illus** little (papilla)
**-in** protein, substance (trypsin, fibrin, melanin)
**infra-** below (infraspinous, infrared)
**ino-** fiber (inotropic, inositol)
**insulo-** island (insula, insulin)
**inter-** between (intercellular, intervertebral)
**intra-** within (intracellular, intraocular)
**iono-** ion (ionotropic, cationic)
**ischi-** to hold back (ischium, ischemia)
**-ism 1.** process, state, condition (metabolism, rheumatism)
**2.** doctrine, belief, theory (holism, reductionism, naturalism)
**iso-** same, equal (isometric, isotonic, isomer)
**-issimus** most, greatest (latissimus, longissimus)
**-ite** little (dendrite, somite)
**-itis** inflammation (dermatitis, gingivitis)
**jug-** to join (conjugated, jugular)
**juxta-** next to (juxtamedullary, juxtaglomerular)
**kali-** potassium (hypokalemia)
**karyo-** seed, nucleus (megakaryocyte, karyotype)
**kerato-** horn (keratin, keratinocyte)
**kine-** motion, action (kinetic, kinase, cytokinesis)
**labi-** lip (labium, levator labii)
**lacera-** torn, cut (foramen lacerum, laceration)
**lacrimo-** tear, cry (lacrimal gland, nasolacrimal)
**lacto-** milk (lactose, lactation, prolactin)
**lamina-** layer (lamina propria, laminar flow)
**latero-** side (bilateral, ipsilateral)
**lati-** broad (fascia lata, latissimus dorsi)
**-lemma** husk (sarcolemma, neurilemma)
**lenti-** lens (lentiform)
**-let** small (platelet)

**leuko-** white (leukocyte, leukemia)
**levato-** to raise (levator labii, elevation)
**ligo-** to bind (ligand, ligament)
**line-** line (linea alba, linea nigra)
**litho-** stone (otolith, lithotripsy)
**-logy** study of (histology, physiology, hematology)
**lucid-** light, clear (stratum lucidum, zona pellucida)
**lun-** moon, crescent (lunate, lunule, semilunar)
**lute-** yellow (macula lutea, corpus luteum)
**lyso-, lyto-** split apart, break down (lysosome, hydrolysis, electrolyte, hemolytic)
**macro-** large (macromolecule, macrophage)
**macula-** spot (macula lutea, macula densa)
**mali-** bad (malignant, malocclusion, malformed)
**malle-** hammer (malleus, malleolus)
**mammo-** breast (mammary, mammillary)
**mano-** hand (manus, manipulate)
**manubri-** handle (manubrium)
**masto-** breast (mastoid, gynecomastia)
**medi-** middle (medial, mediastinum, intermediate)
**medullo-** marrow, pith (medulla)
**mega-** large (megakaryocyte, hepatomegaly)
**melano-** black (melanin, melanocyte, melancholy)
**meno-** month (menstruation, menopause)
**mento-** chin (mental, mentalis)
**mero-** part, segment (isomer, centromere, merocrine)
**meso-** in the middle (mesoderm, mesentery)
**meta-** beyond, next in a series (metaphase, metacarpal)
**metabol-** change (metabolism, metabolite)
**-meter** measuring device (calorimeter, spirometer)
**metri-** **1.** length, measure (isometric, emmetropic).
**2.** uterus (endometrium)
**micro-** small (microscopic, microcytic, microglia)
**mito-** thread, filament (mitochondria, mitosis)
**mono-** one (monocyte, monogamy, mononucleosis)
**morpho-** form, shape, structure (morphology, amorphous)
**muta-** change (mutagen, mutation)
**myelo-** **1.** spinal cord (poliomyelitis, myelin)
**2.** bone marrow (myeloid, myelocytic)
**myo-, mysi-** muscle (myoglobin, myosin, epimysium)
**natri-** sodium (hyponatremia, natriuretic)
**neo-** new (neonatal, gluconeogenesis)
**nephro-** kidney (nephron, hydronephrosis)
**neuro-** nerve (aponeurosis, neurosoma, neurology)
**nucleo-** nucleus, kernel (nucleolus, nucleic acid)
**oo-** egg (oogenesis, oocyte)
**ob-** **1.** life (aerobic, microbe)
**2.** against, toward, before (obstetrics, obturator, obstruction)
**oculo-** eye (oculi, oculomotor)
**odonto-** tooth (odontoblast, periodontal)
**-oid** like, resembling (colloid, sigmoid, ameboid)
**-ole** small (arteriole, bronchiole, nucleolus)
**oligo-** few, a little, scanty (oligopeptide, oliguria)
**-oma** tumor, mass (carcinoma, hematoma)
**omo-** shoulder (omohyoid, acromion)
**onycho-** nail, claw (hyponychium, onychomycosis)
**op-** vision (optics, myopia, photopic)
**-opsy** viewing, to see (biopsy, rhodopsin)
**or-** mouth (oral, orbicularis oris)
**orbi-** circle (orbicularis, orbit)
**organo-** tool, instrument (organ, organelle)
**ortho-** straight (orthopnea, orthodontics, orthopedics)
**-ose** **1.** full of (adipose)
**2.** sugar (sucrose, glucose)
**-osis** **1.** process (osmosis, exocytosis)
**2.** condition, disease (cyanosis, thrombosis).
**3.** increase (leukocytosis)
**osmo-** push (osmosis, chemiosmotic)
**osse-, oste-** bone (osseous, osteoporosis)
**oto-** ear (otolith, otitis, parotid)
**-ous** **1.** full of (nitrogenous, edematous)
**2.** pertaining to (mucous, nervous)
**3.** like, characterized by (squamous, filamentous)
**ovo-** egg (ovum, ovary, ovulation)
**oxy-** **1.** oxygen (hypoxia, oxyhemoglobin)
**2.** sharp, quick (oxytocin)
**palli-** pale (pallor, globus pallidus)
**palpebro-** eyelid (palpebrae)
**pan-** all (panhypopituitarism, pancreas)
**panni-** cloth, rag (pannus, panniculus)
**papillo-** nipple (papilla, papillary)
**par-** birth (postpartum, parturition, multiparous)
**para-** next to (parathyroid, parotid)
**parieto-** wall (parietal)
**patho-** **1.** disease (pathology, pathogen)
**2.** feeling (sympathetic)
**pecto-** **1.** chest (pectoralis)
**2.** comblike (pectineus)
**pedi-** **1.** foot (bipedal, pedicle)
**2.** child (pediatrics)
**pelvi-** basin (pelvis, pelvic)
**-penia** deficiency (leukopenia, thrombocytopenia)
**penna-** feather (unipennate, bipennate)
**peri-** around (periosteum, peritoneum, periodontal)
**perone-** fibula (peroneus tertius, peroneal nerve)
**phago-** eat (phagocytosis, macrophage)
**philo-** loving, attracted to (hydrophilic, amphiphilic)
**phobo-** fearing, repelled by (hydrophobic)
**phor-** to carry, bear (diaphoresis, electrophoresis)
**phragm-** partition (diaphragm)
**phreno-** diaphragm (phrenic nerve)
**physio-** nature, natural cause (physiology, physician)
**-physis** growth (diaphysis, hypophysis)
**pilo-** hair (piloerection)
**pino-** drink, imbibe (pinocytosis)
**planto-** sole of foot (plantaris, plantar wart)
**plasi-** growth (hyperplasia, neoplasia)
**plasm-** shaped, molded (cytoplasm, endoplasmic)
**plasti-** form (thromboplastin)
**platy-** flat (platysma)
**pnea-** breath, breathing (eupnea, dyspnea)
**pneumo-** air, breath, lung (pneumonia, pneumothorax)
**podo-** foot (pseudopod, podocyte)
**poies-** forming (hematopoiesis, erythropoietin)
**poly-** many, much, excessive (polypeptide, polyuria)
**primi-** first (primary, primipara, primitive)
**pro-** **1.** before, in front, first (prokaryote, prophase, prostate)
**2.** promote, favor (progesterone, prolactin)
**pseudo-** false (pseudopod)
**psycho-** mind (psychosis, psychosomatic)
**ptero-, pterygo-** wing (pterygoid)
**-ptosis** dropping, falling, sagging (apoptosis, nephroptosis)

**puncto-** point (puncta)
**pyro-** fire (pyrogen, antipyretic)
**quadri-** four (quadriceps, quadratus)
**quater-** fourth (quaternary)
**radiat-** radiating (corona radiata)
**rami-** branch (ramus)
**recto-** straight (rectus abdominis, rectum)
**reno-** kidney (renal, renin)
**reti-** network (reticular, rete testis)
**retinac-** retainer, bracelet (retinaculum)
**retro-** behind, backward (retroperitoneal, retrovirus)
**rhombo-** rhombus (rhomboideus, rhombencephalon)
**rubo-, rubro-** red (bilirubin, rubrospinal)
**rugo-** fold, wrinkle (ruga, corrugator)
**sacculo-** little sac (saccule)
**sarco-** flesh, muscle (sarcoplasm, sarcomere)
**scala-** staircase (scala tympani)
**sclero-** hard, tough (sclera, sclerosis)
**scopo-** see (microscope, endoscopy)
**secto-** cut (section, dissection)
**semi-** half (semilunar, semimembranosus)
**sepsi-** infection (asepsis, septicemia)
**-sis** process (diapedesis, amniocentesis)
**sole-** sandal, sole of foot, flatfish (sole, soleus)
**soma-, somato-** body (somatic, somatotropin)
**spheno-** wedge (sphenoid)
**spiro-** breathing (inspiration, spirometry)
**splanchno-** viscera (splanchnic)
**spleno- 1.** bandage (splenius capitis)
**2.** spleen (splenic artery)
**squamo-** scale, flat (squamous, desquamation)
**stasi-, stati-** put, remain, stay the same (hemostasis, homeostatic)
**steno-** narrow (stenosis)
**ster-, stereo-** solid, three-dimensional (steroid, stereoscopic)
**sterno-** breast, chest (sternum, sternocleidomastoid)
**stria-** stripe (striated, corpus striatum)
**sub-** below (subcutaneous, subclavicular)
**sulc-** furrow, groove (sulcus)
**supra-** above (supraspinous, supraclavicular)
**sura-** calf of leg (triceps surae)
**sym-** together (sympathetic, symphysis)
**syn-** together (synostosis, syncytium)
**tachy-** fast (tachycardia, tachypnea)
**tarsi-** ankle (tarsus, metatarsal)
**tecto-** roof, cover (tectorial membrane, tectum)
**telo-** last, end (telophase, telencephalon)
**tempo-** time (temporal)
**terti-** third (tertiary)
**theli-** nipple, female, tender (epithelium, polythelia)
**thermo-** heat (thermogenesis, thermoregulation)
**thrombo-** blood clot (thrombosis, thrombin)
**thyro-** shield (thyroid, thyrohyoid)
**-tion** process (circulation, pronation)
**toci-** birth (oxytocin)
**tomo- 1.** cut (tomography, atom, anatomy)
**2.** segment (dermatome, myotome, sclerotome)
**tono-** force, tension (isotonic, tonus, myotonia)
**topo-** place, position (isotope, ectopic)
**trabo-** plate (trabecula)
**trans-** across (transpiration, transdermal)
**trapezi- 1.** table, grinding surface (trapezium)
**2.** trapezoidal (trapezius)
**tri-** three (triceps, triglyceride)
**tricho-** hair (trichosiderin, peritrichial)
**trocho-** wheel, pulley (trochlea)
**troph- 1.** food, nourishment (trophic, trophoblast)
**2.** growth (dystrophy, hypertrophy)
**tropo-** to turn, change (metabotropic, gonadotropin)
**tunica-** coat (tunica intima, tunica vaginalis)
**tympano-** drum, eardrum (tympanic, tensor tympani)
**-ul** small (trabecula, tubule, capitulum, glomerulus)
**-uncle, -unculus** small (homunculus, caruncle)
**uni-** one (unipennate, unipolar)
**uri-** urine (glycosuria, urinalysis, diuretic)
**utriculo-** little bag (utriculus)
**vagino-** sheath (invaginate, tunica vaginalis)
**vago-** wander (vagus)
**vaso-** vessel (vascular, vas deferens, vasa recta)
**ventro-** belly, lower part (ventral, ventricle)
**vermi-** worm (vermis, vermiform appendix)
**vertebro-** spine (vertebrae, intervertebral)
**vesico-** bladder, blister (vesical, vesicular)
**villo-** hair, hairy (microvillus)
**vitre-** glass (in vitro, vitreous humor)
**vivi-** life, alive (in vivo, revive)
**zygo-** union, join, mate (zygomatic, zygote, azygos)

# GLOSSARY

## A

**abdominal cavity** The body cavity between the diaphragm and pelvic brim. fig. A.5

**abduction** (ab-DUC-shun) Movement of a body part away from the median plane, as in raising an arm away from the side of the body. fig. 9.13

**absorption** **1.** Process in which a chemical passes through a membrane or tissue surface and becomes incorporated into a body fluid or tissue. **2.** Any process in which one substance passes into another and becomes a part of it. *Compare* adsorption.

**acetylcholine (ACh)** (ASS-eh-till-CO-leen) A neurotransmitter released by somatic motor fibers, parasympathetic fibers, and some other neurons, composed of choline and an acetyl group. fig. 12.22

**acetylcholinesterase (AChE)** (ASS-eh-till-CO-lin-ESS-ter-ase) An enzyme that hydrolyzes acetylcholine, thus halting signal transmission at a cholinergic synapse.

**acid** A proton ($H^+$) donor; a chemical that releases protons into solution.

**acidosis** An acid–base imbalance in which the blood pH is lower than 7.35.

**acinus** (ASS-ih-nus) A sac of secretory cells at the inner end of a gland duct. fig. 5.30

**actin** A filamentous intracellular protein that provides cytoskeletal support and interacts with other proteins, especially myosin, to cause cellular movement; important in muscle contraction and membrane actions such as phagocytosis, ameboid movement, and cytokinesis. fig. 11.3

**action** The movement produced by contraction of a particular muscle, or its role in preventing an unwanted movement; the function of a muscle.

**action potential** A rapid voltage change in which a plasma membrane briefly reverses electrical polarity; has a self-propagating effect that produces a traveling wave of excitation in nerve and muscle cells.

**active site** The region of a protein that binds to a ligand, such as the substrate-binding site of an enzyme or the hormone-binding site of a receptor.

**active transport** Transport of particles through a selectively permeable membrane, up their concentration gradient, with the aid of a carrier that consumes ATP.

**acute** Pertaining to a disease with abrupt onset, intense symptoms, and short duration. *Compare* chronic.

**adaptation** **1.** An evolutionary process leading to the establishment of species characteristics that favor survival and reproduction. **2.** Any characteristic of anatomy, physiology, or behavior that promotes survival and reproduction. **3.** A sensory process in which a receptor adjusts its sensitivity or response to the prevailing level of stimulation, such as dark adaptation of the eye.

**adaptive immunity** A system of pathogen-specific defenses, developed upon initial exposure to an antigen and entailing cellular memory and accelerated responses to the pathogen on later reexposure, thereby preventing or minimizing disease. Includes various T and B lymphocytes, plasma cells, and antibodies. *Compare* innate immunity.

**adduction** (ad-DUC-shun) Movement of a body part toward the median plane, such as bringing the feet together from a spread-legged position. fig. 9.13

**adenosine triphosphate (ATP)** (ah-DEN-oh-seen tri-FOSS-fate) A molecule composed of adenine, ribose, and three phosphate groups that functions as a universal energy-transfer molecule; yields adenosine diphosphate (ADP) and an inorganic phosphate group (Pi) upon hydrolysis. fig. 2.29a

**adenylate cyclase** (ah-DEN-ih-late SY-clase) An enzyme of the plasma membrane that makes cyclic adenosine monophosphate (cAMP) by removing two phosphate groups from ATP; important in the activation of the cAMP second-messenger system.

**adipocyte** (AD-ih-po-site) A fat cell.

**adipose tissue** A connective tissue composed predominantly of adipocytes; fat.

**adrenergic** (AD-ren-UR-jic) Pertaining to norepinephrine (NE) and epinephrine, as in adrenergic nerve fibers that secrete NE, adrenergic receptors that bind it, and adrenergic effects on a target organ.

**adrenocorticotropic hormone (ACTH)** A hormone secreted by the anterior pituitary gland that stimulates the adrenal cortex to secrete cortisol and other glucocorticoids; one of the stress hormones.

**adsorption** The binding of one substance to the surface of another without becoming a part of the latter. *Compare* absorption.

**aerobic exercise** (air-OH-bic) Exercise in which oxygen is used to produce ATP; endurance exercise.

**aerobic respiration** Oxidation of organic compounds in a reaction series that requires oxygen and produces ATP.

**afferent** (AFF-ur-ent) Carrying toward, as in a blood vessel that carries blood toward a tissue or a nerve fiber that conducts signals toward the central nervous system.

**agglutination** (ah-GLUE-tih-NAY-shun) Clumping of cells by antibodies.

**albumin** (al-BYU-min) A class of small proteins constituting about 60% of the protein fraction of the blood plasma; plays roles in blood viscosity, colloid osmotic pressure, and solute transport.

**aldosterone** (AL-doe-steh-RONE, al-DOSS-teh-rone) A steroid hormone secreted by the adrenal cortex that acts on the kidneys to promote sodium retention and potassium excretion.

**alkalosis** An acid–base imbalance in which the blood pH is higher than 7.45.

**allele** (ah-LEEL) Any of the alternative forms that one gene can take, such as dominant and recessive alleles.

**alveolus** (AL-vee-OH-lus) **1.** A microscopic air sac of the lung. **2.** A gland acinus. **3.** A tooth socket. **4.** Any small anatomical space.

**amino acid** A small organic molecule with an amino group and a carboxyl group; amino acids are the monomers of which proteins are composed, and function also as neurotransmitters and in other roles.

**amnion** A transparent sac that encloses the fetus and amniotic fluid.

**amphipathic** (AM-fih-PATH-ic) Pertaining to a molecule that has both hydrophilic and hydrophobic regions, such as phospholipids, bile acids, and some proteins.

**ampulla** (am-PULL-uh) A wide or saclike portion of a tubular organ such as a semicircular duct or uterine tube.

**anabolism** (ah-NAB-oh-lizm) Any metabolic reactions that consume energy and construct more complex molecules with higher free energy from less complex molecules with lower free energy; for example, the synthesis of proteins from amino acids. *Compare* catabolism.

**anaerobic fermentation** (AN-err-OH-bic) A reduction reaction independent of oxygen that converts pyruvate to lactate and enables glycolysis to continue under anaerobic conditions.

**anastomosis** (ah-NASS-tih-MO-sis) An anatomical convergence, the opposite of a branch; a point where two blood vessels merge and combine their bloodstreams or where two nerves or ducts converge. fig. 20.10

**anatomical position** A reference posture that allows for standardized anatomical terminology. A subject in anatomical position is standing with the feet flat on the floor, arms down to the sides, and the palms and eyes directed forward. fig. A.1

**androgen** (AN-dro-jen) Testosterone or a related steroid hormone. Stimulates bodily changes at puberty in both sexes, adult libido in both sexes, development of male anatomy in the fetus and adolescent, and spermatogenesis.

**aneurysm** (AN-you-rizm) A weak, bulging point in the wall of a heart chamber or blood vessel that presents a threat of hemorrhage.

**angiogenesis** (AN-jee-oh-GEN-eh-sis) The growth of new blood vessels.

**angiotensin II** (AN-jee-oh-TEN-sin) A hormone produced from angiotensinogen (a plasma protein) by the kidneys and lungs; raises blood pressure by stimulating vasoconstriction and stimulating the adrenal cortex to secrete aldosterone.

**anion** (AN-eye-on) An ion with more electrons than protons and consequently a net negative charge.

**antagonist** **1.** A muscle that opposes the agonist at a joint. **2.** Any agent, such as a hormone or drug, that opposes another.

**antagonistic effect** **1.** An effect in which two hormones, neurotransmitters, or divisions of the nervous system oppose each other and produce opposite effects on a target cell or organ. **2.** An effect in which a drug blocks or otherwise opposes the action of one of the body's own signaling mechanisms.

**antebrachium** (AN-teh-BRAY-kee-um) The region from elbow to wrist; the forearm.

**anterior** Pertaining to the front (facial-abdominal aspect) of the body; ventral.

**anterior root** The branch of a spinal nerve that emerges from the anterior side of the spinal cord and carries efferent (motor) nerve fibers; often called *ventral root.* fig. 13.2b

**antibody** A protein of the gamma globulin class that reacts with an antigen and aids in protecting the body from its harmful effects; found in the blood plasma, in other body fluids, and on the surfaces of certain leukocytes and their derivatives.

**antidiuretic hormone (ADH)** (AN-tee-DYE-you-RET-ic) A hormone released by the posterior lobe of the pituitary gland in response to low blood pressure; promotes water retention by the kidneys. Also known as *arginine vasopressin.*

**antigen** (AN-tih-jen) Any large molecule capable of binding to an antibody or immune cells and triggering an immune response; usually a protein, glycoprotein, or glycolipid.

**antigen-presenting cell (APC)** A cell that phagocytizes an antigen and displays fragments of it on its surface for recognition by other cells of the immune system; chiefly macrophages and B lymphocytes.

**antiport** A cotransport protein that moves two or more solutes in opposite directions through a cellular membrane, such as the $Na^+$–$K^+$ pump.

**apical surface** The uppermost surface of an epithelial cell, usually exposed to the lumen of an organ. fig. 3.4

**apocrine** Pertaining to certain sweat glands with large lumens and relatively thick, aromatic secretions and to similar glands such as the mammary gland; named for a mistaken belief that they form secretions by pinching off bits of apical cytoplasm.

**apoptosis** (AP-op-TOE-sis) Programmed cell death; the normal death of cells that have completed their function. *Compare* necrosis.

**appendicular** (AP-en-DIC-you-lur) Pertaining to the limbs and their supporting skeletal girdles. fig. 8.1

**areolar tissue** (AIR-ee-OH-lur) A fibrous connective tissue with loosely organized, widely spaced fibers and cells and an abundance of fluid-filled space; found under nearly every epithelium, among other places. fig. 5.14

**arrector** A smooth muscle associated with each hair follicle that serves to erect the hair. fig. 6.7

**arteriole** (ar-TEER-ee-ole) A small artery that empties into a metarteriole or capillary.

**arteriosclerosis** (ar-TEER-ee-o-sclair-O-sis) Stiffening of the arteries correlated with age or disease processes, caused primarily by cumulative free radical damage and tissue deterioration. *Compare* atherosclerosis.

**articular cartilage** A thin layer of hyaline cartilage covering the articular surface of a bone at a synovial joint, serving to reduce friction and ease joint movement. fig. 9.5

**articulation** A skeletal joint; any point at which two bones meet; may or may not be movable.

**aspect** A particular view of the body or one of its structures, or a part that faces in a particular direction, such as the anterior aspect.

**atherosclerosis** (ATH-ur-oh-skleh-ROE-sis) A degenerative disease of the blood vessels characterized by the presence of lipid deposits; often leading to calcification of the vessel wall and obstruction of coronary, cerebral, or other vital arteries. *Compare* arteriosclerosis.

**atrioventricular (AV) node** (AY-tree-oh-ven-TRIC-you-lur) A group of autorhythmic cells in the interatrial septum of the heart that relays excitation from the atria to the ventricles.

**atrioventricular (AV) valves** The mitral (left) and tricuspid (right) valves between the atria and ventricles of the heart; the left AV valve was formerly known as the *bicuspid valve.*

**atrophy** (AT-ro-fee) Shrinkage of a tissue due to age, disuse, or disease.

**autoantibody** An antibody that fails to distinguish the body's own molecules from foreign molecules and thus attacks host tissues, causing autoimmune diseases.

**autoimmune disease** Any disease in which antibodies fail to distinguish between foreign and self-antigens and attack the body's own tissues; for example, systemic lupus erythematosus and rheumatic fever.

**autolysis** (aw-TOLL-ih-sis) Digestion of cells by their own internal enzymes.

**autonomic nervous system (ANS)** (AW-toe-NOM-ic) A motor division of the nervous system that innervates glands, smooth muscle, and cardiac muscle; consists of sympathetic and parasympathetic divisions and functions largely without voluntary control. *Compare* somatic nervous system.

**autoregulation** The ability of a tissue to adjust its own blood supply through vasomotion or angiogenesis.

**autosome** (AW-toe-some) Any chromosome except the sex chromosomes. Genes on the autosomes are inherited without regard to the sex of the individual.

**avascular** Devoid of blood vessels, as in epithelia and cartilage.

**axial** (AC-see-ul) Pertaining to the head, neck, and trunk; the part of the body excluding the appendicular portion. fig. 8.1

**axillary** (ACK-sih-LERR-ee) Pertaining to the armpit.

**axon terminal** The swollen tip at the distal end of an axon; the site of synaptic vesicles and neurotransmitter release. fig. 12.21

**axoneme** The central core of a cilium or flagellum, composed of microtubules; these are arranged in a circular array of nine microtubule pairs, and in flagella and mobile cilia, another microtubule pair at the center of the circle.

# B

**baroreceptor** (BER-oh-re-SEP-tur) A cardiovascular pressure sensor that triggers autonomic reflexes in response to fluctuations in blood pressure; baroreceptors are located in the heart, aortic arch, and carotid sinuses.

**basal surface** The lowermost surface of an epithelial cell, attached to either a basement membrane or an underlying epithelial cell. fig. 3.4

**base** **1.** A chemical that binds protons from solution; a proton acceptor. **2.** Any of the purines or pyrimidines of a nucleic acid (adenine, thymine, guanine, cytosine, or uracil) serving in part to code for protein structure. **3.** The broadest part of a tapered organ such as the uterus or heart or the inferior aspect of an organ such as the brain.

**basement membrane** A thin layer of glycoproteins, collagen, and glycosaminoglycans beneath the deepest cells of an epithelium, serving to bind the epithelium to the underlying tissue. fig. 5.33

**basophil** (BAY-so-fill) A granulocyte with coarse cytoplasmic granules that produces heparin, histamine, and other chemicals involved in inflammation. table 18.6

**belly** The thick part of a skeletal muscle between its origin and insertion. fig. 10.4

**bicarbonate buffer system** An equilibrium mixture of carbonic acid, bicarbonate ions, and hydrogen ions ($H_2CO_3 \rightleftharpoons HCO_3^- + H^+$) that stabilizes the pH of the body fluids.

**bicarbonate ion** An anion, $HCO_3^-$, that functions as a base in the buffering of body fluids.

**biogenic amines** A class of chemical messengers with neurotransmitter and hormonal functions, synthesized from amino acids and retaining an amino group; also called *monoamines*. Examples include epinephrine and thyroxine.

**bipedalism** The habit of walking on two legs; a defining characteristic of the family Hominidae that underlies many skeletal and other characteristics of humans.

**blood–brain barrier (BBB)** A barrier between the bloodstream and nervous tissue of the CNS that is impermeable to many blood solutes and thus prevents them from affecting the brain tissue; formed by the tight junctions between capillary endothelial cells, the basement membrane of the endothelium, and the perivascular feet of astrocytes.

**B lymphocyte** A lymphocyte that functions as an antigen-presenting cell and, in humoral immunity, differentiates into an antibody-producing plasma cell; also called a *B cell.*

**body** **1.** The entire organism. **2.** Part of a cell, such as a neuron, containing the nucleus and most other organelles. **3.** The largest or principal part of an organ such as the stomach or uterus; also called the *corpus*.

**brachial** (BRAY-kee-ul) Pertaining to the arm proper, the region from shoulder to elbow.

**bradykinin** (BRAD-ee-KY-nin) An oligopeptide produced in inflammation that stimulates vasodilation, increases capillary permeability, and stimulates pain receptors.

**brainstem** The stalklike lower portion of the brain, composed of the medulla oblongata, pons, and midbrain. fig. 14.8

**bronchiole** (BRON-kee-ole) A pulmonary air passage that is usually 1 mm or less in diameter and lacks cartilage but has relatively abundant smooth muscle, elastic tissue, and a simple cuboidal, usually ciliated epithelium.

**bronchus** (BRONK-us) A relatively large pulmonary air passage with supportive cartilage in the wall; any passage beginning with the main bronchus at the fork in the trachea and ending with segmental bronchi, from which air continues into the bronchioles.

**brush border** A fringe of microvilli on the apical surface of an epithelial cell, serving to enhance surface area and promote absorption. fig. 5.6

**bursa** A sac filled with synovial fluid at a synovial joint, serving to facilitate muscle or joint action. fig. 9.6

## C

**calcification** The hardening of a tissue due to the deposition of calcium salts.

**calorie** The amount of thermal energy that will raise the temperature of 1 g of water by 1°C. Also called a *small calorie* to distinguish it from a dietary Calorie (capital *C*), or kilocalorie.

**Calorie** *See* kilocalorie.

**canaliculus** (CAN-uh-LIC-you-lus) A microscopic canal, as in osseous tissue. fig. 7.4

**capillary** (CAP-ih-LERR-ee) The narrowest type of vessel in the cardiovascular and lymphatic systems; engages in fluid exchanges with surrounding tissues.

**capillary exchange** The process of fluid transfer between the bloodstream and tissue fluid through the walls of the blood capillaries.

**capsule** The fibrous covering of a structure such as the spleen or a synovial joint.

**carbohydrate** A hydrophilic organic compound composed of carbon and a 2:1 ratio of hydrogen to oxygen; includes sugars, starches, glycogen, and cellulose.

**carbonic anhydrase** An enzyme found in erythrocytes and kidney tubule cells that catalyzes the decomposition of carbonic acid into carbon dioxide and water or the reverse reaction ($H_2CO_3 \rightleftharpoons CO_2 + H_2O$).

**carcinogen** (car-SIN-oh-jen) An agent capable of causing cancer, including certain chemicals, viruses, and ionizing radiation.

**cardiac output *(CO)*** The amount of blood pumped by each ventricle of the heart in 1 minute.

**cardiomyocyte** A cardiac muscle cell.

**cardiovascular system** An organ system consisting of the heart and blood vessels, serving for the transport of blood. *Compare* circulatory system.

**carpal** Pertaining to the wrist (carpus).

**carrier** **1.** A protein in a cellular membrane that performs carrier-mediated transport. **2.** A person who is heterozygous for a recessive allele and does not exhibit the associated phenotype, but may transmit this allele to his or her children; for example, a carrier for sickle-cell disease.

**carrier-mediated transport** Any process of transporting materials through a cellular membrane that involves reversible binding to a transport protein.

**catabolism** (ca-TAB-oh-lizm) Any metabolic reactions that release energy and break relatively complex molecules with high free energy into less complex molecules with lower free energy; for example, digestion and glycolysis. *Compare* anabolism.

**catecholamine** (CAT-eh-COAL-uh-meen) A subclass of biogenic amines that includes epinephrine, norepinephrine, and dopamine. fig. 12.22

**cation** (CAT-eye-on) An ion with more protons than electrons and consequently a net positive charge.

**caudal** (CAW-dul) **1.** Pertaining to a tail or narrow tail-like part of an organ. **2.** Pertaining to the inferior part of the trunk of the body, where the tail of other animals arises. *Compare* cranial. **3.** Relatively distant from the forehead, especially in reference to structures of the brain and spinal cord; for example, the medulla oblongata is caudal to the pons. *Compare* rostral.

**celiac** (SEEL-ee-ac) Pertaining to the abdomen.

**central nervous system (CNS)** The brain and spinal cord.

**centriole** (SEN-tree-ole) An organelle composed of a short cylinder of nine triplets of microtubules, usually paired with another centriole perpendicular to it; origin of the mitotic spindle; identical to the basal body of a cilium or flagellum. fig. 3.33

**cephalic** (seh-FAL-ic) Pertaining to the head.

**cerebellum** (SER-eh-BELL-um) A large portion of the brain posterior to the brainstem and inferior to the cerebrum, responsible for equilibrium, motor coordination, and memory of learned motor skills. fig. 14.11

**cerebrospinal fluid (CSF)** (SERR-eh-bro-SPY-nul, seh-REE-bro-SPY-nul) A liquid that fills the ventricles of the brain, the central canal of the spinal cord, and the space between the CNS and dura mater.

**cerebrum** (seh-REE-brum, SERR-eh-brum) The largest and most superior part of the brain, divided into two convoluted cerebral hemispheres separated by a deep longitudinal fissure.

**cervical** (SUR-vih-cul) Pertaining to the neck or a narrow part (cervix) of certain organs.

**cervix** (SUR-vix) **1.** The neck. **2.** A narrow or necklike part of an organ such as the uterus and gallbladder. fig. 28.3

**channel protein** A transmembrane protein that has a pore through it for the passage of materials between the cytoplasm and extracellular fluid. fig. 3.7

**chemical bond** A force that attracts one atom to another, such as their opposite charges or the sharing of electrons.

**chemical synapse** A meeting of a nerve fiber and another cell with which the neuron communicates by releasing neurotransmitters. fig. 12.21

**chemoreceptor** An organ or cell specialized to detect chemicals, as in the carotid bodies and taste buds.

**chief cells** The majority type of cell in an organ or tissue such as the parathyroid glands or gastric glands.

**cholecystokinin (CCK)** (CO-leh-SIS-toe-KY-nin) A polypeptide employed as a hormone and neurotransmitter, secreted by some brain neurons and cells of the digestive tract. fig. 12.22

**cholesterol** (co-LESS-tur-ol) A steroid that functions as part of the plasma membrane and as a precursor for all other steroids in the body.

**cholinergic** (CO-lin-UR-jic) Pertaining to acetylcholine (ACh), as in cholinergic nerve fibers that secrete ACh, cholinergic receptors that bind it, or cholinergic effects on a target organ.

**chondrocyte** (CON-dro-site) A cartilage cell; a former chondroblast that has become enclosed in a lacuna in the cartilage matrix. figs. 5.19 to 5.21

**chorion** (CO-ree-on) An embryonic membrane external to the amnion; forms part of the placenta and has diverse functions including fetal nutrition, waste removal, and hormone secretion. fig. 29.7f

**chromatin** (CRO-muh-tin) Filamentous material in the interphase nucleus, composed of DNA and associated proteins.

**chromosome** A complex of DNA and protein carrying the genetic material of a cell's nucleus. Normally there are 46 chromosomes in the nucleus of each cell except germ cells. fig. 4.5

**chronic** **1.** Long-lasting. **2.** Pertaining to a disease that progresses slowly and has a long duration. *Compare* acute.

**chronic bronchitis** A chronic obstructive pulmonary disease characterized by damaged and immobilized respiratory cilia, excessive mucus secretion, infection of the lower respiratory tract, and bronchial inflammation; caused especially by cigarette smoking. *See also* chronic obstructive pulmonary disease.

**chronic obstructive pulmonary disease (COPD)** Certain lung diseases (chronic bronchitis and emphysema) that result in long-term obstruction of airflow and substantially reduced pulmonary ventilation; one of the leading causes of death in old age.

**cilium** (SILL-ee-um) A hairlike process, with an axoneme, projecting from the apical surface of an epithelial cell; often motile and serving to propel matter across the surface of an epithelium, but sometimes nonmotile and serving sensory roles. fig. 3.10

**circulatory shock** A state of cardiac output inadequate to meet the metabolic needs of the body.

**circulatory system** An organ system consisting of the heart, blood vessels, and blood. *Compare* cardiovascular system.

**circumduction** A joint movement in which one end of an appendage remains relatively stationary and the other end is moved in a circle. fig. 9.16

**cirrhosis** (sih-RO-sis) A degenerative liver disease characterized by replacement of functional parenchyma with fibrous and adipose tissue; causes include alcohol, other poisons, and viral and bacterial inflammation.

**cistern** (SIS-turn) A fluid-filled space or sac, such as the cisterna chyli of the lymphatic system and cisterns of the endoplasmic reticulum and Golgi complex. fig. 3.28

**climacteric** A period in the lives of men and women, usually in the early 50s, marked by changes in the level of reproductive hormones; a variety of somatic and psychological effects; and, in women, cessation of ovulation and menstruation (menopause).

**clone** A population of cells that are mitotically descended from the same parent cell and are identical to each other genetically or in other respects, such as a B- or T-cell clone.

**coagulation** (co-AG-you-LAY-shun) The clotting of blood, lymph, tissue fluid, or semen.

**coenzyme** (co-EN-zime) A small organic molecule, usually derived from a vitamin, that is needed to make an enzyme catalytically active; acts by accepting electrons from an enzymatic reaction and transferring them to a different reaction chain.

**cofactor** A nonprotein such as a metal ion or coenzyme needed for an enzyme to function.

**cohesion** The clinging of identical molecules such as water to each other.

**collagen** (COLL-uh-jen) The most abundant protein in the body, forming the fibers of many connective tissues in places such as the dermis, tendons, and bones.

**colloid** An aqueous mixture of particles that are too large to pass through most selectively permeable membranes but small enough to remain evenly dispersed through the solvent by the thermal motion of solvent particles; for example, the proteins in blood plasma.

**colloid osmotic pressure *(COP)*** A portion of the osmotic pressure of a body fluid that is due to its protein. *Compare* oncotic pressure.

**column** *See* funiculus.

**columnar** A cellular shape that is significantly taller than it is wide. fig. 5.6

**commissure** (COM-ih-shur) **1.** A bundle of nerve fibers that crosses from one side of the brain or spinal cord to the other. fig. 14.2 **2.** A corner or angle at which the eyelids, lips, or genital labia meet; in the eye, also called the *canthus*. fig. 16.23

**complement** **1.** To complete or enhance the structure or function of something else, as in the coordinated action of two hormones. **2.** A system of plasma proteins involved in defense against pathogens.

**computerized tomography (CT)** A method of medical imaging that uses X-rays and a computer to create an image of a thin section of the body; also called a *CT scan*.

**concentration gradient** A difference in chemical concentration from one point to another, as on two sides of a plasma membrane.

**conception** The fertilization of an egg, producing a zygote.

**conceptus** All products of conception, ranging from a fertilized egg to the full-term fetus with its embryonic membranes, placenta, and umbilical cord. *Compare* embryo, fetus, preembryo.

**condyle** (CON-dile) A rounded knob on a bone serving to smooth the movement of a joint. fig. 8.2

**conformation** The three-dimensional structure of a protein that results from interaction among its amino acid side groups, its interactions with water, and the formation of disulfide bonds.

**congenital** Present at birth; for example, an anatomical defect, a syphilis infection, or a hereditary disease.

**conjugated** A state in which one organic compound is bound to another compound of a different class, such as a protein conjugated with a carbohydrate to form a glycoprotein.

**connective tissue** A tissue usually composed of more extracellular than cellular volume and usually with a substantial amount of extracellular fiber; forms supportive frameworks and capsules for organs, binds structures together, holds them in place, stores energy (as in adipose tissue), or transports materials (as in blood).

**contractility** **1.** The ability to shorten. **2.** The amount of force that a contracting muscle fiber generates for a given stimulus; may be increased by epinephrine, for example, while stimulus strength remains constant. **3.** The amount of force that a contracting heart chamber generates for a given preload.

**contralateral** On opposite sides of the body, as in reflex arcs in which the stimulus comes from one side of the body and a response is given by muscles on the other side. *Compare* ipsilateral.

**cooperative effect** Effect in which two hormones, or both divisions of the autonomic nervous system, work together to produce a single overall result.

**corona** A halo- or crownlike structure, as in the corona radiata of the brain and ovaries, coronary circulation of the heart, and coronal suture of the skull.

**corona radiata** **1.** An array of nerve tracts in the brain that arise mainly from the thalamus and fan out to different regions of the cerebral cortex. **2.** The first layer of cuboidal cells immediately external to the zona pellucida around an egg cell.

**coronal plane** *See* frontal plane.

**coronary circulation** A system of blood vessels that serve the wall of the heart. fig. 19.10

**corpus** **1.** Body or mass, such as the corpus callosum and corpus luteum. **2.** The main part of an organ such as the stomach or uterus, as opposed to such regions as the head, tail, or cervix.

**corrosion cast** *See* vascular corrosion cast.

**cortex** The outer layer of some organs such as the adrenal glands, kidneys, cerebrum, lymph nodes, ovaries, and hairs; usually covers or encloses tissue called the *medulla.*

**corticosteroid** (COR-tih-co-STERR-oyd) Any steroid hormone secreted by the adrenal cortex, such as aldosterone, cortisol, and sex steroids.

**costal** (COSS-tul) Pertaining to the ribs.

**cotransport** A form of carrier-mediated transport in which a membrane protein transports two solutes simultaneously or within the same cycle of action by either facilitated diffusion or active transport; for example, the sodium–glucose transporter and the $Na^+$–$K^+$ pump.

**countercurrent** A situation in which two fluids flow side by side in opposite directions, as in the countercurrent multiplier of the kidney and the countercurrent heat exchanger of the scrotum.

**cranial** (CRAY-nee-ul) **1.** Pertaining to the cranium of the skull. **2.** In a position relatively close to the head or a direction toward the head. *Compare* caudal.

**cranial nerve** Any of 12 pairs of nerves connected to the base of the brain and passing through foramina of the cranium.

**crista** (plural, *cristae*) An anatomical crest, such as the crista galli of the ethmoid bone or the crista of a mitochondrion.

**cross section** A cut perpendicular to the long axis of the body or an organ.

**crural** (CROO-rul) Pertaining to the leg proper or to the crus (leg) of a organ.

**crus** (pronounced cruss; plural, *crura*) **1.** A leglike extension of an organ such as the penis or clitoris. figs. 27.10b, 28.8 **2.** The leg proper (crural region, from knee to ankle) of the lower limb.

**cuboidal** (cue-BOY-dul) A cellular shape that is roughly like a cube or in which the height and width are about equal; typically looks squarish in tissue sections. fig. 5.5

**current** A moving stream of charged particles such as ions or electrons.

**cusp** **1.** One of the flaps of a valve of the heart, veins, and lymphatic vessels. **2.** A conical projection on the occlusal surface of a premolar or molar tooth.

**cutaneous** (cue-TAY-nee-us) Pertaining to the skin.

**cyanosis** (SY-uh-NO-sis) A bluish color of the skin and mucous membranes due to ischemia or hypoxemia.

**cyclic adenosine monophosphate (cAMP)** A cyclic molecule produced from ATP by the enzymatic removal of two phosphate groups; serves as a second messenger in many hormone and neurotransmitter actions. fig. 2.29b

**cytolysis** (sy-TOL-ih-sis) The rupture and destruction of a cell by such agents as complement proteins and hypotonic solutions.

**cytoplasm** The contents of a cell between its plasma membrane and its nuclear envelope, consisting of cytosol, organelles, inclusions, and the cytoskeleton.

**cytoskeleton** A system of protein microfilaments, intermediate filaments, and microtubules in a cell, serving in physical support, cellular movement, and the routing of molecules and organelles to their destinations within the cell. fig. 3.24

**cytosol** A clear, featureless, gelatinous colloid in which the organelles and other internal structures of a cell are embedded.

**cytotoxic T cell** A T lymphocyte that directly attacks and destroys infected body cells, cancerous cells, and the cells of transplanted tissues.

# D

**daughter cells** Cells that arise from a parent cell by mitosis or meiosis.

**deamination** (dee-AM-ih-NAY-shun) Removal of an amino group from an organic molecule; a step in the catabolism of amino acids.

**decomposition reaction** A chemical reaction in which a larger molecule is broken down into smaller ones. *Compare* synthesis reaction.

**decussation** (DEE-cuh-SAY-shun) The crossing of nerve fibers from the right side of the central nervous system to the left or vice versa, especially in the spinal cord, medulla oblongata, and optic chiasma.

**deep** Relatively far from the body surface; opposite of *superficial.* For example, most bones are deep to the skeletal muscles.

**degranulation** Exocytosis and disappearance of cytoplasmic granules, especially in platelets and granulocytes.

**denaturation** A change in the three-dimensional conformation of a protein that destroys its enzymatic or other functional properties, usually caused by extremes of temperature or pH.

**dendrite** Extension of a neuron that receives information from other cells or from environmental stimuli and conducts signals to the soma. Dendrites are usually shorter, more branched, and more numerous than the axon and are incapable of producing action potentials. fig. 12.4

**dendritic cell** An antigen-presenting cell of the epidermis and mucous membranes. fig. 6.3

**denervation atrophy** The shrinkage of skeletal muscle that occurs when the motor neuron dies or is severed from the muscle.

**dense connective tissue** A connective tissue with a high density of fiber, relatively little ground substance, and scanty cells; seen in tendons and the dermis, for example.

**depolarization** A shift in the electrical potential across a plasma membrane to a value less negative than the resting membrane potential; associated with excitation of a nerve or muscle cell. *Compare* hyperpolarization.

**dermal papilla** A bump or ridge of dermis that extends upward to interdigitate with the epidermis and create a wavy boundary that resists stress and slippage of the epidermis.

**dermis** The deeper of the two layers of the skin, underlying the epidermis and composed of fibrous connective tissue.

**desmosome** (DEZ-mo-some) A patchlike intercellular junction that mechanically links two cells together. fig. 5.28

**diabetes** (DY-uh-BEE-teez) Any disease characterized by chronic polyuria of metabolic origin; diabetes mellitus unless otherwise specified.

**diabetes insipidus** (in-SIP-ih-dus) A form of diabetes that results from hyposecretion of antidiuretic hormone; unlike other forms, it is not characterized by hyperglycemia or glycosuria.

**diabetes mellitus (DM)** (mel-EYE-tus) A form of diabetes that results from hyposecretion of insulin or from a deficient target-cell response to it; signs include hyperglycemia and glycosuria.

**diaphysis** (dy-AF-ih-sis) The shaft of a long bone. fig. 7.1

**diarthrosis** (DY-ar-THRO-sis) *See* synovial joint.

**diastole** (dy-ASS-toe-lee) A period in which a heart chamber relaxes and fills with blood; especially ventricular relaxation.

**diastolic pressure** (DY-ah-STAHL-ic) The minimum arterial blood pressure measured during the interval between heartbeats

**diencephalon** (DY-en-SEFF-uh-lon) A portion of the brain between the midbrain and corpus callosum; composed of the thalamus, epithalamus, and hypothalamus. fig. 14.12

**differentiation** Development of a relatively unspecialized cell or tissue into one with a more specific structure and function.

**diffusion** Spontaneous net movement of particles from a place of high concentration to a place of low concentration (down a concentration gradient).

**diploid (2*n*)** In humans, having 46 chromosomes in 23 homologous pairs, with one member of each chromosome pair coming from each parent.

**disaccharide** (dy-SAC-uh-ride) A carbohydrate composed of two simple sugars (monosaccharides) joined by a glycosidic bond; for example, lactose, sucrose, and maltose. fig. 2.16

**disseminated intravascular coagulation (DIC)** Widespread clotting of the blood within unbroken vessels, leading to hemorrhaging, congestion of the vessels with clotted blood, and ischemia and necrosis of organs.

**distal** Relatively distant from a point of origin or attachment; for example, the wrist is distal to the elbow. *Compare* proximal.

**disulfide bond** A covalent bond that links two cysteine residues through their sulfur atoms, serving to join one peptide chain to another or to hold a single chain in its three-dimensional conformation.

**diuretic** (DY-you-RET-ic) A chemical that increases urine output.

**dominant** **1.** Pertaining to a genetic allele that is phenotypically expressed in the presence of any other allele. **2.** Pertaining to a trait that results from a dominant allele.

**dopamine** (DOE-puh-meen) An inhibitory catecholamine neurotransmitter of the central nervous system, especially of the basal nuclei, where it acts to suppress unwanted motor activity. fig. 12.22

**dorsal** Toward the back (spinal) side of the body; in humans, usually synonymous with *posterior*.

**dorsal root** *See* posterior root.

**dorsiflexion** (DOR-sih-FLEC-shun) A movement of the ankle that reduces the joint angle and raises the toes. fig. 9.22

**duodenum** (DEW-oh-DEE-num, dew-ODD-eh-num) The first portion of the small intestine extending for about 25 cm from the pyloric valve of the stomach to a sharp bend called the *duodenojejunal flexure;* receives chyme from the stomach and secretions from the liver and pancreas. fig. 25.25

**dynein** (DINE-een) A motor protein involved in the beating of cilia and flagella and in the movement of molecules and organelles within cells, as in retrograde transport in a nerve fiber.

# E

**eccrine** (ECK-rin) Pertaining to gland cells that release their product by exocytosis; also called *merocrine*.

**ectoderm** The outermost of the three primary germ layers of an embryo; gives rise to the epidermis and nervous system.

**ectopic** (ec-TOP-ic) In an abnormal location; for example, ectopic pregnancy and ectopic pacemakers of the heart.

**edema** (eh-DEE-muh) Abnormal accumulation of tissue fluid resulting in swelling of the tissue.

**effector** A molecule, cell, or organ that carries out a response to a stimulus.

**efferent** (EFF-ur-ent) Carrying away or out, as in a blood vessel that carries blood away from a tissue or a nerve fiber that conducts signals away from the central nervous system.

**elastic fiber** A connective tissue fiber, composed of the protein elastin, that stretches under tension and returns to its original length when released; responsible for the resilience of organs such as the skin and lungs.

**elasticity** The tendency of a stretched structure to return to its original dimensions when tension is released.

**electrical synapse** A gap junction that enables one cell to stimulate another directly, without the intermediary action of a neurotransmitter; such synapses connect the cells of cardiac muscle and single-unit smooth muscle.

**electrolyte** A salt that ionizes in water and produces a solution that conducts electricity; loosely speaking, any ion that results from the dissociation of such salts, such as sodium, potassium, calcium, chloride, and bicarbonate ions.

**elevation** A joint movement that raises a body part, as in hunching the shoulders or closing the mouth.

**embolism** (EM-bo-lizm) The obstruction of a blood vessel by an embolus.

**embolus** (EM-bo-lus) Any abnormal traveling object in the bloodstream, such as agglutinated bacteria or blood cells, a blood clot, or an air bubble.

**embryo** A developing individual from the sixteenth day of gestation when the three primary germ layers have formed, through the end of the eighth week when all of the organ systems are present. *Compare* conceptus, fetus, preembryo.

**emphysema** (EM-fih-SEE-muh) A degenerative lung disease characterized by a breakdown of alveoli and diminishing surface area available for gas exchange; occurs with aging of the lungs but is greatly accelerated by smoking or air pollution.

**endocrine gland** (EN-doe-crin) A ductless gland that secretes hormones into the bloodstream; for example, the thyroid and adrenal glands. *Compare* exocrine gland.

**endocytosis** (EN-doe-sy-TOE-sis) Any process in which a cell forms vesicles from its plasma membrane and takes in large particles, molecules, or droplets of extracellular fluid; for example, phagocytosis and pinocytosis.

**endoderm** The innermost of the three primary germ layers of an embryo; gives rise to the mucosae of the digestive and respiratory tracts and to their associated glands.

**endogenous** (en-DODJ-eh-nus) Originating internally, such as the endogenous cholesterol synthesized in the body in contrast to the exogenous cholesterol coming from the diet. *Compare* exogenous.

**endometrium** (EN-doe-MEE-tree-um) The mucosa of the uterus; the site of implantation and source of menstrual discharge.

**endoplasmic reticulum (ER)** (EN-doe-PLAZ-mic reh-TIC-you-lum) An extensive system of interconnected cytoplasmic tubules or channels; classified as rough ER or smooth ER depending on the presence or absence of ribosomes on its membrane. fig. 3.28

**endothelium** (EN-doe-THEEL-ee-um) A simple squamous epithelium that lines the lumens of the blood vessels, heart, and lymphatic vessels.

**enteric** (en-TERR-ic) Pertaining to the small intestine, as in enteric hormones and enteric nervous system.

**eosinophil** (EE-oh-SIN-oh-fill) A granulocyte with a large, often bilobed nucleus and coarse cytoplasmic granules that stain with eosin; phagocytizes antigen–antibody complexes, allergens, and inflammatory chemicals and secretes enzymes that combat parasitic infections. table 18.6

**epidermis** A stratified squamous epithelium that constitutes the superficial layer of the skin, overlying the dermis. fig. 6.3

**epinephrine** (EP-ih-NEFF-rin) A catecholamine that functions as a neurotransmitter in the sympathetic nervous system and as a hormone secreted by the adrenal medulla; also called *adrenaline.* fig. 12.22

**epiphysial plate** (EP-ih-FIZ-ee-ul) A plate of hyaline cartilage between the epiphysis and diaphysis of a long bone in a child or adolescent, serving as a growth zone for bone elongation. figs. 7.9, 7.11

**epiphysis** (eh-PIF-ih-sis) **1.** The head of a long bone. fig. 7.1 **2.** The pineal gland (epiphysis cerebri).

**epithelium** A type of tissue consisting of one or more layers of closely adhering cells with little intercellular material and no blood vessels; forms the coverings and linings of many organs and the parenchyma of the glands. Also known as *epithelial tissue.*

**erectile tissue** A tissue that functions by swelling with blood, as in the penis and clitoris and inferior concha of the nasal cavity.

**erythrocyte** (eh-RITH-ro-site) A red blood cell.

**erythropoiesis** (eh-RITH-ro-poy-EE-sis) The production of erythrocytes.

**erythropoietin** (eh-RITH-ro-POY-eh-tin) A hormone that is secreted by the kidneys and liver in response to hypoxemia and stimulates erythropoiesis.

**estrogens** (ESS-tro-jenz) A family of steroid hormones known especially for producing female secondary sex characteristics and regulating various aspects of the menstrual cycle and pregnancy; major forms are estradiol, estriol, and estrone.

**evolution** A change in the relative frequencies of alleles in a population over a period of time; the mechanism that produces adaptations in human form and function. *See also* adaptation.

**excitability** The ability of a cell to respond to a stimulus, especially the ability of nerve and muscle cells to produce membrane voltage changes in response to stimuli.

**excitation–contraction coupling** Events that link the synaptic stimulation of a muscle cell to the onset of contraction.

**excitatory postsynaptic potential (EPSP)** A partial depolarization of a postsynaptic neuron or muscle cell in response to a neurotransmitter, making it more likely to reach threshold and produce an action potential.

**excretion** The process of eliminating metabolic waste products from a cell or from the body. *Compare* secretion.

**exocrine gland** (EC-so-crin) A gland that secretes its products into another organ or onto the body surface, usually by way of a duct; for example, salivary and gastric glands. *Compare* endocrine gland.

**exocytosis** (EC-so-sy-TOE-sis) A process in which a vesicle in the cytoplasm of a cell fuses with the plasma membrane and releases its contents from the cell; used in the elimination of cellular wastes, in the release of gland products and neurotransmitters, and for the replacement of membrane removed by endocytosis.

**exogenous** (ec-SODJ-eh-nus) Originating externally, such as exogenous (dietary) cholesterol; extrinsic. *Compare* endogenous.

**expiration** **1.** Exhaling. **2.** Dying.

**extension** Movement of a joint that increases the angle between articulating bones (straightens the joint). fig. 9.12 *Compare* flexion.

**extracellular fluid (ECF)** Any body fluid that is not contained in the cells; for example, blood, lymph, and tissue fluid.

**extrinsic** (ec-STRIN-sic) **1.** Originating externally, such as extrinsic blood-clotting factors; exogenous. **2.** Not fully contained within a specified organ or region but acting on it, such as the extrinsic muscles of the hand and eye. *Compare* intrinsic.

## F

**facilitated diffusion** The process of transporting a chemical through a cellular membrane, down its concentration gradient, with the aid of a carrier that does not consume ATP; enables substances to diffuse through the membrane that would do so poorly, or not at all, without a carrier.

**facilitation** Making a process more likely to occur, such as the firing of a neuron, or making it occur more easily or rapidly, as in facilitated diffusion.

**fascia** (FASH-ee-uh) A layer of connective tissue between the muscles or separating the muscles from the skin. fig. 10.1

**fascicle** (FASS-ih-cul) A bundle of muscle or nerve fibers ensheathed in connective tissue; multiple fascicles bound together constitute a muscle or nerve as a whole. figs. 10.1, 13.9

**fat** **1.** A triglyceride molecule. **2.** Adipose tissue.

**fatty acid** An organic molecule composed of a chain of an even number of carbon atoms with a carboxyl group at one end and a methyl group at the other; one of the structural subunits of triglycerides and phospholipids.

**fenestrated** (FEN-eh-stray-ted) Perforated with holes or slits, as in fenestrated blood capillaries and the elastic sheets of large arteries. fig. 20.5

**fetus** In human development, an individual from the beginning of the ninth week when all of the organ systems are present, through the time of birth. *Compare* conceptus, embryo, preembryo.

**fibrin** (FY-brin) A sticky fibrous protein formed from fibrinogen in blood, tissue fluid, and lymph; forms the matrix of a blood clot.

**fibroblast** A connective tissue cell that produces collagen fibers and ground substance; the only type of cell in tendons and ligaments.

**fibrosis** Replacement of damaged tissue with fibrous scar tissue rather than by the original tissue type; scarring. *Compare* regeneration.

**fibrous connective tissue** Any connective tissue with a preponderance of fiber, such as areolar, reticular, dense regular, and dense irregular connective tissues.

**filtration** A process in which hydrostatic pressure forces a fluid through a selectively permeable membrane (especially a capillary wall).

**fire** To produce an action potential, as in nerve and muscle cells.

**fix** **1.** To hold a structure in place; for example, by fixator muscles that prevent unwanted joint movements. **2.** To preserve a tissue by means of a fixative such as formalin.

**flexion** A joint movement that, in most cases, decreases the angle between two bones. fig. 9.12 *Compare* extension.

**fluid balance** A state in which average daily water gains (by intake and synthesis) equal water losses, and water is properly distributed among the body's fluid compartments. *Also called* water balance.

**fluid compartment** Any of the major categories of fluid in the body, separated by selectively permeable membranes and differing from each other in chemical composition. Primary examples are the intracellular fluid, tissue fluid, blood, and lymph.

**follicle** (FOLL-ih-cul) **1.** A small space, such as a hair follicle, thyroid follicle, or ovarian follicle. **2.** An aggregation of lymphocytes in a lymphatic organ or mucous membrane.

**follicle-stimulating hormone (FSH)** A hormone secreted by the anterior pituitary gland that stimulates development of the ovarian follicles and egg cells in females and sperm production in males.

**foramen** (fo-RAY-men) (plural, *foramina*) A hole through a bone or other organ, in many cases providing passage for blood vessels and nerves.

**formed element** An erythrocyte, leukocyte, or platelet; any cellular component of blood or lymph as opposed to the extracellular fluid component.

**fossa** (FOSS-uh) A depression in an organ or tissue, such as the fossa ovalis of the heart, cranial fossa of the skull, or olecranon fossa of the elbow.

**fovea** (FO-vee-uh) A small pit, such as the fovea capitis of the femur or fovea centralis of the retina.

**free energy** The potential energy in a chemical that is available to do work.

**free radical** A particle derived from an atom or molecule, having an unpaired electron that makes it highly reactive and destructive to cells; produced by intrinsic processes such as aerobic respiration and by extrinsic agents such as chemicals and ionizing radiation.

**frenulum** (FREN-you-lum) A fold of tissue that attaches a movable structure to a relatively immovable one, such as the lip to the gum or the tongue to the floor of the mouth. fig. 25.4

**frontal plane** An anatomical plane that passes through the body or an organ from right to left and superior to inferior, dividing the body or organ into anterior and posterior portions; also called a *coronal plane.* fig. A.1

**fundus** The base, the broadest part, or the part farthest from the opening of certain viscera such as the stomach and uterus.

**funiculus** (few-NICK-you-lus) A bundle of nerve fibers in the spinal cord, arranged in three pairs constituting the spinal white matter; subdivided into tracts (fasciculi). fig. 13.3

**fusiform** (FEW-zih-form) Shaped like the spindle of a spinning wheel; elongated, thick in the middle, and tapered at both ends, such as the shape of a smooth muscle cell or a muscle spindle.

## G

**gamete** (GAM-eet) An egg or sperm cell.

**gametogenesis** (geh-ME-to-JEN-eh-sis) The production of eggs or sperm.

**ganglion** (GANG-glee-un) A cluster of nerve cell bodies in the peripheral nervous system, often resembling a knot in a string.

**gangrene** Tissue necrosis resulting from ischemia.

**gap junction** A junction between two cells consisting of a pore surrounded by a ring of proteins in the plasma membrane of each cell; allows solutes to diffuse from the cytoplasm of one cell to the next; functions include cell-to-cell nutrient transfer in the developing embryo and electrical communication between cells of cardiac and smooth muscle. *See also* electrical synapse. fig. 5.28

**gastric** Pertaining to the stomach.

**gate** A protein channel in a cellular membrane that can open or close in response to chemical, electrical, or mechanical stimuli, thus controlling when substances are allowed to pass through the membrane. May occur in the plasma membrane as well as the membranes of cytoplasmic organelles.

**gene** An information-containing segment of DNA that codes for the production of a molecule of RNA, which in most cases goes on to play a role in the synthesis of one or more proteins.

**gene locus** The site on a chromosome where a given gene is located.

**genome** (JEE-nome) All the genes of one individual, estimated at about 20,000 genes in humans.

**genotype** (JEE-no-type) The pair of alleles possessed by an individual at one gene locus on a pair of homologous chromosomes; strongly influences the individual's phenotype for a given trait.

**germ cell** A gamete (sperm or egg) or any precursor cell destined to become a gamete, such as a primary oocyte or spermatogonium.

**germ layer** Any of the first three tissue layers of an embryo: ectoderm, mesoderm, or endoderm.

**gestation** (jess-TAY-shun) Pregnancy.

**globulin** (GLOB-you-lin) A globular protein such as an enzyme, antibody, or albumin; especially a family of proteins in the blood plasma that includes albumin, antibodies, fibrinogen, and prothrombin.

**glomerular capsule** (glo-MERR-you-lur) A double-walled capsule around each glomerulus of the kidney; receives glomerular filtrate and empties into the proximal convoluted tubule. fig. 23.7

**glomerulus** (glo-MERR-you-lus) **1.** A spheroidal mass of blood capillaries in the kidney that filters plasma and produces glomerular filtrate, which is further processed to form the urine. fig. 23.7 **2.** A spheroidal mass of nerve endings in the olfactory bulb where olfactory neurons from the nose synapse with mitral and dendritic cells of the bulb. fig. 16.7

**glucagon** (GLUE-ca-gon) A hormone secreted by alpha cells of the pancreatic islets in response to hypoglycemia; promotes glycogenolysis and other effects that raise blood glucose concentration.

**glucocorticoid** (GLUE-co-COR-tih-coyd) Any hormone of the adrenal cortex that affects carbohydrate, fat, and protein metabolism; chiefly cortisol and corticosterone.

**gluconeogenesis** (GLUE-co-NEE-oh-JEN-eh-sis) The synthesis of glucose from noncarbohydrates such as fats and amino acids.

**glucose** A monosaccharide ($C_6H_{12}O_6$) also known as blood sugar; glycogen, starch, cellulose, and maltose are made entirely of glucose, and glucose constitutes half of a sucrose or lactose molecule. The isomer involved in human physiology is also called *dextrose.*

**glucose-sparing effect** An effect of fats or other energy substrates in which they are used as fuel by most cells, so that those cells do not consume glucose; this makes more glucose available to cells such as neurons that cannot use alternative energy substrates.

**glycocalyx** (GLY-co-CAY-licks) A layer of carbohydrate molecules covalently bonded to the phospholipids and proteins of a plasma membrane; forms a surface coat on all human cells.

**glycogen** (GLY-co-jen) A glucose polymer synthesized by liver, muscle, uterine, and vaginal cells that serves as an energy-storage polysaccharide.

**glycogenesis** (GLY-co-JEN-eh-sis) The synthesis of glycogen.

**glycogenolysis** (GLY-co-jeh-NOLL-ih-sis) The hydrolysis of glycogen, releasing glucose.

**glycolipid** (GLY-co-LIP-id) A phospholipid molecule with a carbohydrate covalently bonded to it, found in the plasma membranes of cells.

**glycolysis** (gly-COLL-ih-sis) A series of anaerobic oxidation reactions that break a glucose molecule into two molecules of pyruvate and produce a small amount of ATP.

**glycoprotein** (GLY-co-PRO-teen) A protein molecule with a smaller carbohydrate covalently bonded to it; found in mucus and the glycocalyx of cells, for example.

**glycosaminoglycan (GAG)** (GLY-co-seh-ME-no-GLY-can) A polysaccharide composed of modified sugars with amino groups; the major component of a proteoglycan. GAGs are largely responsible for the viscous consistency of tissue gel and the stiffness of cartilage.

**glycosuria** (GLY-co-SOOR-ee-uh) The presence of glucose in the urine, typically indicative of a kidney disease, diabetes mellitus, or other endocrine disorder.

**goblet cell** A mucus-secreting gland cell, shaped somewhat like a wineglass, found in the epithelia of many mucous membranes. fig. 5.33a

**Golgi complex** (GOAL-jee) An organelle composed of several parallel cisterns, somewhat like a stack of saucers, that modifies and packages newly synthesized proteins and synthesizes carbohydrates. fig. 3.29

**Golgi vesicle** A membrane-bounded vesicle pinched from the Golgi complex, containing its chemical product; may be retained in the cell as a lysosome or become a secretory vesicle that releases the product by exocytosis.

**gonad** The ovary or testis.

**gonadotropin** (go-NAD-oh-TRO-pin) A pituitary hormone that stimulates the gonads; specifically FSH and LH.

**G protein** A protein of the plasma membrane that is activated by a membrane receptor and, in turn, opens an ion channel or activates an intracellular physiological response; important in linking ligand–receptor binding to second-messenger systems.

**gradient** A difference or change in any variable, such as pressure or chemical concentration, from one point in space to another; provides a basis for molecular movements such as gas exchange, osmosis, and facilitated diffusion, and for bulk movements such as the flow of blood, air, and heat.

**gray matter** A zone or layer of tissue in the central nervous system where the neuron cell bodies, dendrites, and synapses are found; forms the cerebral cortex and basal nuclei; cerebellar cortex and deep nuclei; nuclei of the brainstem; and core of the spinal cord. fig. 14.6c

**gross anatomy** Bodily structure that can be observed without magnification.

**growth factor** A chemical messenger that stimulates mitosis and differentiation of target cells that have receptors for it; important in such processes as fetal development, tissue maintenance and repair, and hematopoiesis; sometimes a contributing factor in cancer.

**growth hormone (GH)** A hormone of the anterior pituitary gland with multiple effects on many tissues, generally promoting tissue growth.

**gustation** (gus-TAY-shun) The sense of taste.

**gyrus** (JY-rus) A wrinkle or fold in the cortex of the cerebrum or cerebellum.

## H

**hair cell** Sensory cell of the cochlea, semicircular ducts, utricle, and saccule, with a fringe of surface microvilli that respond to the relative motion of a gelatinous membrane at their tips; responsible for the senses of hearing, body position, and motion.

**hair follicle** An epidermal pit that contains a hair and extends into the dermis or hypodermis.

**half-life ($T_{1/2}$)** **1.** The time required for one-half of a quantity of a radioactive element to decay to a stable isotope *(physical half-life)* or to be cleared from the body through a combination of radioactive decay and physiological excretion *(biological half-life)*. **2.** The time required for one-half of a quantity of hormone to be cleared from the bloodstream.

**haploid *(n)*** In humans, having 23 unpaired chromosomes instead of the usual 46 chromosomes in homologous pairs; in any organism or cell, having half the normal diploid number of chromosomes for that species.

**helper T cell** A type of lymphocyte that performs a central coordinating role in humoral and cellular immunity; target of the human immunodeficiency virus (HIV).

**hematocrit** (he-MAT-oh-crit) The percentage of blood volume that is composed of erythrocytes; also called *packed cell volume.*

**hematoma** (HE-muh-TOE-muh) A mass of clotted blood in the tissues; forms a bruise when visible through the skin.

**hematopoiesis** (he-MAT-o-poy-EE-sis) Production of any of the formed elements of blood.

**hematopoietic stem cell (HSC)** A cell of the red bone marrow that can give rise, through a series of intermediate cells, to erythrocytes, platelets, various kinds of macrophages, and any type of leukocyte.

**heme** (pronounced "heem") The nonprotein, iron-containing prosthetic group of hemoglobin or myoglobin; oxygen binds to its iron atom. fig. 18.5

**hemoglobin** (HE-mo-GLO-bin) The red gas transport pigment of an erythrocyte.

**heparin** (HEP-uh-rin) A polysaccharide secreted by basophils and mast cells that inhibits blood clotting.

**hepatic** (heh-PAT-ic) Pertaining to the liver.

**hepatic portal system** A network of blood vessels that connect capillaries of the intestines to capillaries (sinusoids) of the liver, thus delivering newly absorbed nutrients directly to the liver.

**heterozygous** (HET-er-oh-ZY-gus) Having nonidentical alleles at the same gene locus of two homologous chromosomes.

**high-density lipoprotein (HDL)** A lipoprotein of the blood plasma that is about 50% lipid and 50% protein; functions to transport phospholipids and cholesterol from other organs to the liver for disposal. A high proportion of HDL to low-density lipoprotein (LDL) is desirable for cardiovascular health.

**hilum** (HY-lum) A point on the surface of an organ where blood vessels, lymphatic vessels, or nerves enter and leave, usually marked by a depression and slit; the midpoint of the concave surface of any organ that is roughly bean-shaped, such as the lymph nodes, kidneys, and lungs. Also called the *hilus.* fig. 22.9b

**histamine** An amino acid derivative secreted by basophils, mast cells, and some neurons; functions as a paracrine secretion and neurotransmitter to stimulate effects such as gastric secretion, bronchoconstriction, and vasodilation. fig. 12.22

**histology** **1.** The microscopic structure of tissues and organs. **2.** The study of such structure.

**homeostasis** (HO-me-oh-STAY-sis) The tendency of a living body to maintain relatively stable internal conditions in spite of greater changes in its external environment.

**homologous** (ho-MOLL-uh-gus) **1.** Having the same embryonic or evolutionary origin but not necessarily the same function, such as the scrotum and labia majora. **2.** Pertaining to two chromosomes with identical structures and gene loci but not necessarily identical alleles; each member of the pair is inherited from a different parent.

**homozygous** (HO-mo-ZY-gus) Having identical alleles at the same gene locus of two homologous chromosomes.

**hormone** A chemical messenger that is secreted by an endocrine gland or isolated gland cell, travels in the bloodstream, and triggers a physiological response in distant cells with receptors for it.

**host cell** Any cell belonging to the human body, as opposed to foreign cells introduced to it by such causes as infections and tissue transplants.

**human chorionic gonadotropin (HCG)** A hormone of pregnancy secreted by the chorion that stimulates continued growth of the corpus luteum and secretion of its hormones. HCG in urine is the basis for pregnancy testing.

**human immunodeficiency virus (HIV)** A virus that infects human helper T cells and other cells, suppresses immunity, and causes AIDS.

**hyaline cartilage** (HY-uh-lin) A form of cartilage with a relatively clear matrix and fine collagen fibers but no conspicuous elastic fibers or coarse collagen bundles as in other types of cartilage.

**hyaluronic acid** (HI-ul-yur-ON-ic) A glycosaminoglycan that is particularly abundant in connective tissues, where it becomes hydrated and forms the tissue gel.

**hydrogen bond** A weak attraction between a slightly positive hydrogen atom on one molecule and a slightly negative oxygen or nitrogen atom on another molecule, or between such atoms on different parts of the same molecule; responsible for the cohesion of water and the coiling of protein and DNA molecules, for example.

**hydrolysis** (hy-DROL-ih-sis) A chemical reaction that breaks a covalent bond in a molecule by adding an —OH group to one side of the bond and —H to the other side, thus consuming a water molecule.

**hydrophilic** (HY-dro-FILL-ic) Pertaining to molecules that attract water or dissolve in it because of their polar nature.

**hydrophobic** (HY-dro-FOE-bic) Pertaining to molecules that do not attract water or dissolve in it because of their nonpolar nature; such molecules tend to dissolve in lipids and other nonpolar solvents.

**hydrostatic pressure** The physical force exerted against a surface by a liquid such as blood or tissue fluid, as opposed to osmotic and atmospheric pressures.

**hypercalcemia** (HY-per-cal-SEE-me-uh) An excess of calcium ions in the blood.

**hypercapnia** (HY-pur-CAP-nee-uh) An excess of carbon dioxide in the blood.

**hyperextension** A joint movement that increases the angle between two bones beyond 180°. fig. 9.12

**hyperglycemia** (HY-pur-gly-SEE-me-uh) An excess of glucose in the blood.

**hyperkalemia** (HY-pur-ka-LEE-me-uh) An excess of potassium ions in the blood.

**hypernatremia** (HY-pur-na-TREE-me-uh) An excess of sodium ions in the blood.

**hyperplasia** (HY-pur-PLAY-zhuh) The growth of a tissue through cellular multiplication, not cellular enlargement. *Compare* hypertrophy.

**hyperpolarization** A shift in the electrical potential across a plasma membrane to a value more negative than the resting membrane potential, tending to inhibit a nerve or muscle cell. *Compare* depolarization.

**hypersecretion** Excessive secretion of a hormone or other gland product; can lead to endocrine disorders such as Addison disease or gigantism, for example.

**hypertension** Excessively high blood pressure; criteria vary but it is often considered to be a condition in which systolic pressure exceeds 140 mm Hg or diastolic pressure exceeds 90 mm Hg at rest.

**hypertonic** Having a higher osmotic pressure than human cells or some other reference solution and tending to cause osmotic shrinkage of cells.

**hypertrophy** (hy-PUR-truh-fee) The growth of a tissue through cellular enlargement, not cellular multiplication; for example, the growth of muscle under the influence of exercise. *Compare* hyperplasia.

**hypocalcemia** (HY-po-cal-SEE-me-uh) A deficiency of calcium ions in the blood.

**hypocapnia** (HY-po-CAP-nee-uh) A deficiency of carbon dioxide in the blood.

**hypodermis** (HY-po-DUR-miss) A layer of connective tissue deep to the skin; also called *superficial fascia, subcutaneous tissue,* or when it is predominantly adipose, *subcutaneous fat.*

**hypoglycemia** (HY-po-gly-SEE-me-uh) A deficiency of glucose in the blood.

**hypokalemia** (HY-po-ka-LEE-me-uh) A deficiency of potassium ions in the blood.

**hyponatremia** (HY-po-na-TREE-me-uh) A deficiency of sodium ions in the blood.

**hyposecretion** Inadequate secretion of a hormone or other gland product; can lead to endocrine disorders such as diabetes mellitus or pituitary dwarfism, for example.

**hypothalamic thermostat** A nucleus in the hypothalamus that monitors body temperature and sends afferent signals to hypothalamic heat-promoting or heat-losing centers to maintain thermal homeostasis.

**hypothalamus** (HY-po-THAL-uh-muss) The inferior portion of the diencephalon of the brain, forming the walls and floor of the third ventricle and giving rise to the posterior pituitary gland; controls many fundamental physiological functions such as appetite, thirst, and body temperature and exerts many of its effects through the endocrine and autonomic nervous systems. fig. 14.12b

**hypothesis** An informed conjecture that is capable of being tested and potentially falsified by experimentation or data collection. *See also* theory.

**hypotonic** Having a lower osmotic pressure than human cells or some other reference solution and tending to cause osmotic swelling and lysis of cells.

**hypoxemia** (HY-pock-SEE-me-uh) A deficiency of oxygen in the bloodstream.

**hypoxia** (hy-POCK-see-uh) A deficiency of oxygen in any tissue.

## I

**immune system** A system of diverse defenses against disease, including leukocytes and other immune cells, defensive chemicals such as antibodies, physiological processes such as fever and inflammation, and physical barriers to infection such as the skin and mucous membranes; not an organ system in itself but an inclusive term for defensive components of multiple organ systems. *See also* adaptive immunity; innate immunity.

**immunity** The ability to ward off a specific infection or disease by means of any of the body's innate or adaptive immune mechanisms.

**immunoglobulin** (IM-you-no-GLOB-you-lin) *See* antibody.

**implantation** The attachment of a conceptus to the endometrium of the uterus.

**inclusion** Any visible object in the cytoplasm of a cell other than an organelle or cytoskeletal element; usually a foreign body or a stored cell product, such as a virus, dust particle, lipid droplet, glycogen granule, or pigment.

**infarction** (in-FARK-shun) **1.** The sudden death of tissue from a lack of blood perfusion. **2.** An area of necrotic tissue produced by this process; also called an *infarct.*

**inferior** Lower than another structure or point of reference from the perspective of anatomical position; for example, the stomach is inferior to the diaphragm.

**inflammation** A complex of tissue responses to trauma or infection serving to ward off a pathogen and promote tissue repair; recognized by the cardinal signs of redness, heat, swelling, and pain.

**inguinal** (IN-gwih-nul) Pertaining to the groin.

**inhibitory postsynaptic potential (IPSP)** Hyperpolarization of a postsynaptic neuron in response to a neurotransmitter, making it less likely to reach threshold and fire.

**innate immunity** Nonspecific defenses against infection or disease that are present and functional from birth, work equally against multiple disease agents, do not require prior exposure, and do not possess immune memory. Includes epithelial barriers, natural killer cells, other leukocytes, macrophages, antimicrobial proteins, and the processes of inflammation and fever. *See also* adaptive immunity.

**innervation** (IN-ur-VAY-shun) The nerve supply to an organ.

**insertion** Traditionally, the attachment of a skeletal muscle to a bone or other structure that moves when the muscle contracts. This term is now being abandoned by authorities in human anatomy. *Compare* origin.

**inspiration** **1.** Inhaling. **2.** The stimulus that resulted in this book.

**integral protein** A protein of the plasma membrane that penetrates into or all the way through the phospholipid bilayer. fig. 3.6

**integration** A process in which a neuron receives input from multiple sources and their combined effects determine its output; the cellular basis of information processing by the nervous system.

**intercalated disc** (in-TUR-ka-LAY-ted) A complex of fascia adherens, gap junctions, and desmosomes that join two cardiac muscle cells end to end, microscopically visible as a dark line that helps to histologically distinguish this muscle type; functions as a mechanical and electrical link between cells. fig. 19.11

**intercellular** Between cells.

**intercostal** (IN-tur-COSS-tul) Between the ribs, as in the intercostal muscles, arteries, veins, and nerves.

**interdigitate** (IN-tur-DIDJ-ih-tate) To fit together like the fingers of two folded hands; for example, at the dermal–epidermal boundary, intercalated discs of the heart, and foot processes of the podocytes in the kidney. fig. 23.10b

**interleukin** (IN-tur-LOO-kin) A hormonelike chemical messenger from one leukocyte to another, serving as a means of communication and coordination during immune responses.

**interneuron** (IN-tur-NEW-ron) A neuron that is contained entirely in the central nervous system and, in the path of signal conduction, lies anywhere between an afferent pathway and an efferent pathway.

**interosseous membrane** (IN-tur-OSS-ee-us) A fibrous membrane that connects the radius to the ulna and the tibia to the fibula along most of the shaft of each bone. fig. 8.34

**interphase** That part of the cell cycle between one mitotic phase and the next, from the end of cytokinesis to the beginning of the next prophase.

**interstitial** (IN-tur-STISH-ul) **1.** Pertaining to the extracellular spaces in a tissue. **2.** Located between other structures, as in the interstitial cells of the testis and interstitial (extracellular) fluid of the tissues.

**intervertebral disc** A cartilaginous pad between the bodies of two adjacent vertebrae.

**intracellular** Within a cell.

**intracellular fluid (ICF)** The fluid contained in the cells; one of the body's major fluid compartments.

**intravenous (I.V.)** **1.** Present or occurring within a vein, such as an intravenous blood clot. **2.** Introduced directly into a vein, such as an intravenous injection or I.V. drip.

**intrinsic** (in-TRIN-sic) **1.** Arising from within, such as intrinsic blood-clotting factors; endogenous. **2.** Fully contained within a specified organ or region, such as the intrinsic muscles of the hand and eye. *Compare* extrinsic.

**involuntary** Not under conscious control, including tissues such as smooth and cardiac muscle and events such as reflexes.

**involution** (IN-vo-LOO-shun) Shrinkage of a tissue or organ by autolysis, such as involution of the thymus after childhood and of the uterus after pregnancy.

**ion** A chemical particle with unequal numbers of electrons or protons and consequently a net negative or positive charge; it may have a single atomic nucleus as in a sodium ion or a few atoms as in a bicarbonate ion, or it may be a large molecule such as a protein.

**ionic bond** The force that binds a cation to an anion.

**ionizing radiation** High-energy electromagnetic rays that eject electrons from atoms or molecules and convert them to ions, frequently causing cellular damage; for example, X-rays and gamma rays.

**ipsilateral** (IP-sih-LAT-ur-ul) On the same side of the body, as in reflex arcs in which a muscular response occurs on the same side of the body as the stimulus. *Compare* contralateral.

**ischemia** (iss-KEE-me-uh) Insufficient blood flow to a tissue, typically resulting in metabolite accumulation and sometimes tissue death.

**isometric** Pertaining to a form of muscle contraction in which internal tension increases but the muscle does not change length or move a resisting object.

**isotonic** **1.** Having the same osmotic pressure as human cells or some other reference solution. **2.** Pertaining to a form of muscle contraction in which a muscle changes length but maintains a constant amount of tension.

## J

**jaundice** (JAWN-diss) A yellowish color of the skin, corneas, mucous membranes, and body fluids due to an excessive concentration of bilirubin; usually indicative of a liver disease, obstructed bile secretion, or hemolytic disease.

## K

**ketone** (KEE-tone) Any organic compound with a carbonyl (C=O) group covalently bonded to a two-carbon backbone.

**ketone bodies** Certain ketones (acetone, acetoacetic acid, and β-hydroxybutyric acid) produced by the incomplete oxidation of fats, especially when fats are being rapidly catabolized. *See also* ketosis.

**ketonuria** (KEE-toe-NEW-ree-uh) The abnormal presence of ketones in the urine; a sign of diabetes mellitus but also occurring in other conditions that entail rapid fat oxidation.

**ketosis** (kee-TOE-sis) An abnormally high concentration of ketone bodies in the blood, occurring in pregnancy, starvation, diabetes mellitus, and other conditions; tends to cause acidosis and to depress the nervous system.

**kilocalorie** The amount of heat energy needed to raise the temperature of 1 kg of water by 1°C; 1,000 calories. Also called a *Calorie* or *large calorie*. *See also* calorie.

**kinase** Any enzyme that adds an inorganic phosphate ($P_i$) group to another organic molecule. Also called a *phosphokinase.*

## L

**labium** (LAY-bee-um) A lip, such as those of the mouth and the labia majora and minora of the vulva.

**lactate** A small organic acid produced as an end product of the anaerobic fermentation of pyruvate; called *lactic acid* in its nonionized form.

**lacuna** (la-CUE-nuh) (plural, *lacunae*) A small cavity or depression in a tissue such as bone or cartilage; called a *cavernous space* in erectile tissues of the penis and clitoris.

**lamella** (la-MELL-uh) A little plate, such as a lamella of bone. fig. 7.4

**lamina** (LAM-ih-nuh) A thin layer, such as the lamina of a vertebra or the lamina propria of a mucous membrane. fig. 8.22

**lamina propria** (LAM-ih-nuh PRO-pree-uh) A thin layer of areolar tissue immediately deep to the epithelium of a mucous membrane. fig. 5.33a

**larynx** (LAIR-inks) A cartilaginous chamber in the neck containing the vocal cords; colloquially called the voicebox.

**latent period** The interval between a stimulus and response, especially in the action of nerve and muscle cells.

**lateral** Away from the midline of an organ or median plane of the body; toward the side. *Compare* medial.

**law** A verbal or mathematical description of a predictable natural phenomenon or of the relationship between variables; for example, Boyle's law of gases and the law of complementary base pairing in DNA.

**lesion** A circumscribed zone of tissue injury, such as a skin abrasion or myocardial infarction.

**leukocyte** (LOO-co-site) A white blood cell.

**leukotriene** (LOO-co-TRY-een) An eicosanoid that promotes allergic and inflammatory responses such as vasodilation and neutrophil chemotaxis; secreted by basophils, mast cells, and damaged tissues.

**libido** (lih-BEE-do) Sex drive; psychological motivation to engage in sex.

**ligament** A collagenous band or cord that binds one organ to another, especially one bone to another, and serves to hold organs in place; for example, the cruciate ligaments of the knee, broad ligament of the uterus, and falciform ligament of the liver.

**ligand** (LIG-and, LY-gand) A chemical that binds reversibly to a receptor site on a protein, such as a neurotransmitter that binds to a membrane receptor or a substrate that binds to an enzyme.

**ligand-gated channel** A channel protein in a plasma membrane that opens or closes when another chemical (ligand) binds to it, enabling the ligand to determine when substances can enter or leave the cell.

**light microscope (LM)** A microscope that produces images with visible light.

**linea** (LIN-ee-uh) An anatomical line, such as the linea alba of the abdomen or linea aspera of the femur.

**lingual** (LING-gwul) Pertaining to the tongue, as in lingual papillae.

**lipase** (LY-pace) An enzyme that hydrolyzes a triglyceride into fatty acids and glycerol.

**lipid** A hydrophobic organic compound composed mainly of carbon and a high ratio of hydrogen to oxygen; includes fatty acids, fats, phospholipids, steroids, and prostaglandins.

**lipoprotein** (LIP-oh-PRO-teen) A protein-coated lipid droplet in the blood plasma or lymph, serving as a means of lipid transport; for example, chylomicrons and high- and low-density lipoproteins.

**load** **1.** To pick up a gas for transport in the bloodstream. **2.** The resistance acted upon by a muscle.

**lobule** (LOB-yool) A small subdivision of an organ or of a lobe of an organ, especially of a gland.

**locus** The site on a chromosome where a given gene is located.

**long bone** A bone such as the femur or humerus that is markedly longer than wide and that generally serves as a lever.

**longitudinal** Oriented along the longest dimension of the body or of an organ.

**loose connective tissue** *See* areolar tissue.

**low-density lipoprotein (LDL)** A lipoprotein of the blood plasma that is about 80% lipid (mainly cholesterol) and 20% protein; functions to transport cholesterol to target cells. A high proportion of LDL to high-density lipoprotein (HDL) is a risk factor for cardiovascular disease.

**lumbar** Pertaining to the lower back and sides, between the thoracic cage and pelvis.

**lumen** (LOO-men) The internal space of a hollow organ such as a blood vessel or the esophagus, or a space surrounded by secretory cells as in a gland acinus.

**luteinizing hormone (LH)** (LOO-tee-in-ize-ing) A hormone secreted by the anterior pituitary gland that stimulates ovulation in females and testosterone secretion production in males.

**lymph** The fluid contained in lymphatic vessels and lymph nodes, produced by the absorption of tissue fluid.

**lymphatic system** (lim-FAT-ic) An organ system consisting of lymphatic vessels, lymph nodes, the tonsils, spleen, and thymus; functions include tissue fluid recovery and immunity.

**lymph node** A small organ found along the course of a lymphatic vessel that filters the lymph and contains lymphocytes and macrophages, which respond to antigens in the lymph. fig. 21.11

**lymphocyte** (LIM-fo-site) A relatively small agranulocyte with numerous types and roles in innate, humoral, and cellular immunity. table 18.6

**lysosome** (LY-so-some) A membrane-bounded organelle containing a mixture of enzymes with a variety of intracellular and extracellular roles in digesting foreign matter, pathogens, and expired organelles.

**lysozyme** (LY-so-zime) An enzyme found in tears, milk, saliva, mucus, and other body fluids that destroys bacteria by digesting their cell walls. Also called *muramidase*.

## M

**macromolecule** Any molecule of large size and high molecular weight, such as a protein, nucleic acid, polysaccharide, or triglyceride.

**macrophage** (MAC-ro-faje) Any cell of the body, other than a leukocyte, that is specialized for phagocytosis; usually derived from a blood monocyte and often functioning as an antigen-presenting cell.

**macula** (MAC-you-luh) A patch or spot, such as the macula lutea of the retina and macula sacculi of the inner ear.

**malignant** (muh-LIG-nent) Pertaining to a cell or tumor that is cancerous; capable of metastasis.

**mast cell** A connective tissue cell, similar to a basophil, that secretes histamine, heparin, and other chemicals involved in inflammation; often concentrated along the course of blood capillaries.

**matrix** **1.** The extracellular material of a tissue. **2.** The fluid within a mitochondrion containing enzymes of the citric acid cycle. **3.** The substance or framework within which other structures are embedded, such as the fibrous matrix of a blood clot. **4.** A mass of epidermal cells from which a hair root or nail root develops.

**mechanoreceptor** A sensory nerve ending or organ specialized to detect mechanical stimuli such as touch, pressure, stretch, or vibration.

**medial** Toward the midline of an organ or median plane of the body. *Compare* lateral.

**median plane** The sagittal plane that divides the body or an organ into equal right and left halves; also called *midsagittal plane*. fig. A.1

**mediastinum** (MEE-dee-ah-STY-num) The thick median partition of the thoracic cavity that separates one pleural cavity from the other and contains the heart, great blood vessels, esophagus, trachea, and thymus. fig. A.5

**medulla** (meh-DULE-uh, meh-DULL-uh) Tissue deep to the cortex of certain two-layered organs such as the lymph nodes, adrenal glands, hairs, and kidneys.

**medulla oblongata** (meh-DULL-uh OB-long-GAH-ta) The most caudal part of the brainstem, immediately superior to the foramen magnum of the skull, connecting the spinal cord to the rest of the brain. figs. 14.2, 14.8

**meiosis** (my-OH-sis) A form of cell division in which a diploid cell divides twice and produces four haploid daughter cells; occurs only in gametogenesis.

**melanocyte** A cell of the stratum basale of the epidermis that synthesizes melanin and transfers it to the keratinocytes.

**meninges** (meh-NIN-jeez) (singular, *meninx*) Three fibrous membranes between the central nervous system and surrounding bone: the dura mater, arachnoid mater, and pia mater. fig. 14.5

**merocrine** (MERR-oh-crin) *See* eccrine.

**mesenchyme** (MES-en-kime) A gelatinous embryonic connective tissue derived from the mesoderm; differentiates into all permanent connective tissues and cardiac and smooth muscle.

**mesentery** (MESS-en-tare-ee) A serous membrane that binds the intestines together and suspends them from the abdominal wall; the visceral continuation of the peritoneum. fig. 25.3

**mesoderm** (MES-oh-durm) The middle layer of the three primary germ layers of an embryo; gives rise to muscle and connective tissue.

**metabolism** (meh-TAB-oh-lizm) Chemical reactions within a living organism.

**metabolite** (meh-TAB-oh-lite) Any chemical produced by metabolism.

**metaplasia** Transformation of one mature tissue type into another; for example, a change from pseudostratified to stratified squamous epithelium in an overventilated nasal cavity.

**metastasis** (meh-TASS-tuh-sis) The spread of cancer cells from the original tumor to a new location, where they seed the development of a new tumor.

**microtubule** An intracellular cylinder composed of the protein tubulin, forming centrioles, the axonemes of cilia and flagella, and part of the cytoskeleton.

**microvillus** An outgrowth of the plasma membrane that increases the surface area of a cell and functions in absorption and some sensory processes; distinguished from cilia and flagella by its smaller size and lack of an axoneme.

**milliequivalent** One-thousandth of an equivalent, which is the amount of an electrolyte that would neutralize 1 mole of $H^+$ or $OH^-$. Electrolyte concentrations are commonly expressed in milliequivalents per liter (mEq/L).

**mitochondrion** (MY-toe-CON-dree-un) An organelle specialized to synthesize ATP, enclosed in a double unit membrane with infoldings of the inner membrane called cristae.

**mitosis** (my-TOE-sis) A form of cell division in which a cell divides once and produces two genetically identical daughter cells; sometimes used to refer only to the division of the genetic material or nucleus and not to include cytokinesis, the subsequent division of the cytoplasm.

**moiety** (MOY-eh-tee) A chemically distinct subunit of a macromolecule, such as the heme and globin moieties of hemoglobin or the lipid and carbohydrate moieties of a glycolipid.

**molarity** A measure of chemical concentration expressed as moles of solute per liter of solution.

**mole** The mass of a chemical equal to its molecular weight in grams, containing $6.023 \times 10^{23}$ molecules.

**monocyte** (MON-oh-site) An agranulocyte specialized to migrate into the tissues and transform into a macrophage. table 18.6

**monomer** (MON-oh-mur) **1.** One of the identical or similar subunits of a larger molecule in the dimer to polymer range; for example, the glucose monomers of starch, the amino acids of a protein, or the nucleotides of DNA. **2.** One subunit of an antibody molecule, composed of four polypeptides.

**monosaccharide** (MON-oh-SAC-uh-ride) A simple sugar, or sugar monomer; chiefly glucose, fructose, and galactose.

**motor neuron** A neuron that transmits signals from the central nervous system to any effector (muscle or gland cell); its axon is an efferent nerve fiber.

**motor protein** Any protein that produces movements of a cell or its components owing to its ability to undergo quick repetitive changes in conformation and to bind reversibly to other molecules; for example, myosin, dynein, and kinesin.

**motor unit** One motor neuron and all the skeletal muscle fibers innervated by it.

**mucosa** (mew-CO-suh) A tissue layer that forms the inner lining of an anatomical tract that is open to the exterior (the respiratory, digestive, urinary, and reproductive tracts). Composed of epithelium, connective tissue (lamina propria), and often smooth muscle (muscularis mucosae). fig. 5.33a

**mucous membrane** See *mucosa.*

**multipotent** Pertaining to a stem cell that has the potential to develop into two or more types of fully differentiated, functional cells, but not into an unlimited variety of cell types.

**muscle fiber** One skeletal muscle cell; a myofiber.

**muscle tone** A state of continual, partial contraction of resting skeletal or smooth muscle.

**muscular system** An organ system composed of the skeletal muscles, specialized mainly for maintaining postural support and producing movements of the bones.

**muscularis externa** The external muscular wall of certain viscera such as the esophagus and small intestine. fig. 25.2

**muscularis mucosae** (MUSK-you-LERR-iss mew-CO-see) A layer of smooth muscle immediately deep to the lamina propria of a mucosa. fig. 5.33a

**mutagen** (MEW-tuh-jen) Any agent that causes a mutation, including viruses, chemicals, and ionizing radiation.

**mutation** Any change in the structure of a chromosome or a DNA molecule, often resulting in a change of organismal structure or function.

**myelin** (MY-eh-lin) A lipid sheath around a nerve fiber, formed from closely spaced spiral layers of the plasma membrane of a Schwann cell or oligodendrocyte. fig. 12.8

**myelin sheath gap** A short unmyelinated segment between Schwann cells of a myelinated nerve fiber; site of action potential generation during saltatory conduction; also called *node of Ranvier.* fig. 12.4

**myocardium** (MY-oh-CAR-dee-um) The middle, muscular layer of the heart.

**myoepithelial cell** An epithelial cell that has become specialized to contract like a muscle cell; important in dilation of the pupil and ejection of secretions from gland acini.

**myofilament** A protein microfilament responsible for the contraction of a muscle cell, composed mainly of myosin or actin. fig. 11.2

**myoglobin** (MY-oh-GLO-bin) A red oxygen-storage pigment of muscle; supplements hemoglobin in providing oxygen for aerobic muscle metabolism.

**myosin** A motor protein that constitutes the thick myofilaments of muscle and has globular, mobile heads of ATPase that bind to actin molecules; also serves contractile functions in other cell types. fig. 11.3

## N

**necrosis** (neh-CRO-sis) Pathological tissue death due to such causes as infection, trauma, or hypoxia. *Compare* apoptosis.

**negative feedback** A self-corrective mechanism that underlies most homeostasis, in which a bodily change is detected and responses are activated that reverse the change and restore stability and preserve normal body function.

**negative feedback inhibition** A mechanism for limiting the secretion of a pituitary tropic hormone. The tropic hormone stimulates another endocrine gland to secrete its own hormone, and that hormone inhibits further release of the tropic hormone.

**neonate** (NEE-oh-nate) A newborn infant up to 4 weeks old.

**neoplasia** (NEE-oh-PLAY-zhuh) Abnormal growth of new tissue, such as a tumor, with no useful function.

**nephron** (NEF-ron) One of approximately 1 million blood-filtering, urine-producing units in each kidney; consists of a glomerulus, glomerular capsule, proximal convoluted tubule, nephron loop, and distal convoluted tubule. fig. 23.8

**nerve** A cordlike organ of the peripheral nervous system composed of multiple nerve fibers ensheathed in connective tissue.

**nerve fiber** The axon of a single neuron.

**nerve impulse** A wave of self-propagating action potentials traveling along a nerve fiber.

**nervous tissue** A tissue composed of neurons and neuroglia.

**net filtration pressure** A net force favoring filtration of fluid from a capillary or venule when all the hydrostatic and osmotic pressures of the blood and tissue fluids are taken into account.

**neural pool** A group of interconnected neurons of the central nervous system that perform a single collective function; for example, the vasomotor center of the brainstem and speech centers of the cerebral cortex.

**neural tube** A dorsal hollow tube in the embryo that develops into the central nervous system. fig. 14.3

**neuroglia** (noo-ROG-lee-uh) All cells of nervous tissue except neurons; cells that perform various supportive and protective roles for the neurons.

**neuromuscular junction** A synapse between a nerve fiber and a muscle fiber; also called a *motor end plate*. fig. 11.7

**neuron** (NOOR-on) A nerve cell; an electrically excitable cell specialized for producing and conducting action potentials and secreting chemicals that stimulate adjacent cells.

**neuropeptide** A peptide secreted by a neuron, often serving to modify the action of a neurotransmitter; for example, endorphins, enkephalin, and cholecystokinin. fig. 12.22

**neurotransmitter** A chemical released at the distal end of an axon that stimulates an adjacent cell; for example, acetylcholine, norepinephrine, or serotonin.

**neutrophil** (NEW-tro-fill) A granulocyte, usually with a multilobed nucleus, that serves especially to destroy bacteria by means of phagocytosis, intracellular digestion, and secretion of bactericidal chemicals. table 18.6

**nitrogenous base** (ny-TRODJ-eh-nus) An organic molecule with a single or double carbon–nitrogen ring that forms one of the building blocks of ATP, other nucleotides, and nucleic acids; the basis of the genetic code. fig. 4.1

**nitrogenous waste** Any nitrogen-containing substance produced as a metabolic waste and excreted in the urine; chiefly ammonia, urea, uric acid, and creatinine.

**nociceptor** (NO-sih-SEP-tur) A nerve ending specialized to detect tissue damage and produce a sensation of pain; pain receptor.

**norepinephrine (NE)** (nor-EP-ih-NEF-rin) A catecholamine that functions as a neurotransmitter and adrenal hormone, especially in the sympathetic nervous system. fig. 12.22

**nuclear envelope** A pair of membranes enclosing the nucleus of a cell, with prominent pores allowing traffic of molecules between the nucleoplasm and cytoplasm. fig. 3.27

**nucleic acid** (new-CLAY-ic) An acidic polymer of nucleotides found or produced in the nucleus, functioning in heredity and protein synthesis; of two types, DNA and RNA.

**nucleotide** (NEW-clee-oh-tide) An organic molecule composed of a nitrogenous base, a monosaccharide, and a phosphate group; the monomer of a nucleic acid.

**nucleus** (NEW-clee-us) **1.** A cell organelle containing DNA and surrounded by a double membrane. **2.** A mass of neurons (gray matter) surrounded by white matter of the brain, including the basal nuclei and brainstem nuclei. **3.** The positively charged core of an atom, consisting of protons and neutrons. **4.** A central structure, such as the nucleus pulposus of an intervertebral disc.

**nurse cell** A supporting cell in the seminiferous tubules of the testes, acting to enfold and protect developing germ cells and promote the production of sperm; also called *Sertoli cell; sustentacular cell.*

## O

**olfaction** (ole-FAC-shun) The sense of smell.

**oncotic pressure** (on-COT-ic) The difference between the colloid osmotic pressure of the blood and that of the tissue fluid, usually favoring fluid absorption by the blood capillaries. *Compare* colloid osmotic pressure.

**oocyte** (OH-oh-site) In the development of an egg cell, any haploid stage between meiosis I and fertilization.

**oogenesis** (OH-oh-JEN-eh-sis) The production of a fertilizable egg cell through a series of mitotic and meiotic cell divisions; female gametogenesis.

**opposition** A movement of the thumb in which it approaches or touches any fingertip of the same hand.

**orbit** The eye socket of the skull.

**organ** Any anatomical structure that is composed of at least two different tissue types, has recognizable structural boundaries, and has a discrete function different from the structures around it. Many organs are microscopic and many organs contain smaller organs, such as the skin containing numerous microscopic sense organs.

**organelle** Any structure within a cell that carries out one of its metabolic roles, such as mitochondria, centrioles, endoplasmic reticulum, and the nucleus; an intracellular structure other than the cytoskeleton and inclusions.

**origin** Traditionally, the relatively stationary attachment of a skeletal muscle to a bone or other structure. This term is now being abandoned by authorities in human anatomy. *Compare* insertion.

**osmolality** (OZ-mo-LAL-ih-tee) The molar concentration of dissolved particles in 1 kg of water.

**osmolarity** (OZ-mo-LERR-ih-tee) The molar concentration of dissolved particles in 1 L of solution.

**osmoreceptor** (OZ-mo-re-SEP-tur) A neuron of the hypothalamus that responds to changes in the osmolarity of the extracellular fluid.

**osmosis** (oz-MO-sis) The net flow of water through a selectively permeable membrane, resulting from either a chemical concentration difference or a mechanical force across the membrane.

**osmotic pressure** The amount of pressure that would have to be applied to one side of a selectively permeable membrane to stop osmosis; proportional to the concentration of nonpermeating solutes on that side and therefore serving as an indicator of solute concentration.

**osseous** (OSS-ee-us) Pertaining to bone.

**ossification** (OSS-ih-fih-CAY-shun) Bone formation.

**osteoblast** Bone-forming cell that arises from an osteogenic cell, deposits bone matrix, and eventually becomes an osteocyte.

**osteoclast** Macrophage of the bone surface that dissolves the matrix and returns minerals to the extracellular fluid.

**osteocyte** A mature bone cell formed when an osteoblast becomes surrounded by its own matrix and entrapped in a lacuna.

**osteon** A structural unit of compact bone consisting of a central canal surrounded by concentric cylindrical lamellae of matrix. fig. 7.4

**osteoporosis** (OSS-tee-oh-pore-OH-sis) A degenerative bone disease characterized by a loss of bone mass, increasing susceptibility to spontaneous fractures, and sometimes deformity of the vertebral column; causes include aging, estrogen hyposecretion, and insufficient resistance exercise.

**ovulation** (OV-you-LAY-shun) The release of a mature oocyte by the bursting of an ovarian follicle.

**ovum** Any stage of the female gamete from primary oocyte until fertilization; a primary or secondary oocyte; an egg.

**oxidation** A chemical reaction in which one or more electrons are removed from a molecule, lowering its free energy content; opposite of reduction and always linked to a reduction reaction.

## P

**pancreatic islet** (PAN-cree-AT-ic EYE-let) A small cluster of endocrine cells in the pancreas that secretes insulin, glucagon, somatostatin, and other intercellular messengers; also called *islet of Langerhans.* fig. 17.12

**papilla** (pa-PILL-uh) A conical or nipplelike structure, such as a lingual papilla of the tongue or the papilla of a hair bulb.

**papillary** (PAP-ih-lerr-ee) **1.** Pertaining to or shaped like a nipple, such as the papillary muscles of the heart. **2.** Having papillae, such as the papillary layer of the dermis.

**paracrine** (PAIR-uh-crin) **1.** A chemical messenger similar to a hormone whose effects are restricted to the immediate vicinity of the cells that secrete it; sometimes called a *local hormone.* **2.** Pertaining to such a secretion, as opposed to *endocrine.*

**parasympathetic nervous system** (PERR-uh-SIM-pa-THET-ic) A division of the autonomic nervous system that issues efferent fibers through the cranial and sacral nerves and exerts cholinergic effects on its target organs.

**parathyroid hormone (PTH)** A hormone secreted by the parathyroid glands that raises blood calcium concentration by stimulating bone resorption by osteoclasts, promoting intestinal absorption of calcium, and inhibiting urinary excretion of calcium.

**parenchyma** (pa-REN-kih-muh) The tissue that performs the main physiological functions of an organ, especially a gland, as opposed to the tissues (stroma) that mainly provide structural support.

**parietal** (pa-RY-eh-tul) **1.** Pertaining to a wall, as in the parietal cells of the stomach and parietal bone of the skull. **2.** Pertaining to the outer or more superficial layer of a two-layered membrane such as the pleura, pericardium, or glomerular capsule. *Compare* visceral. fig. A.6

**pathogen** Any disease-causing microorganism.

**pedicle** (PED-ih-cul) A small footlike process, as in the vertebrae and renal podocytes; also called a *pedicel.*

**pelvic cavity** The space enclosed by the true (lesser) pelvis, containing the urinary bladder, rectum, and internal reproductive organs.

**pelvis** A basinlike structure such as the pelvic girdle of the skeleton or the urine-collecting space near the hilum of the kidney. figs. 8.36, 23.4

**peptide** Any chain of two or more amino acids. *See also* polypeptide, protein.

**peptide bond** A group of four covalently bonded atoms (a —C=O group bonded to an —NH group) that links two amino acids in a protein or other peptide. fig. 2.23b

**perfusion** The amount of blood supplied to a given mass of tissue in a given period of time (such as mL/g/min.).

**perichondrium** (PERR-ih-CON-dree-um) A layer of fibrous connective tissue covering the surface of hyaline or elastic cartilage.

**perineum** (PERR-ih-NEE-um) The region between the thighs bordered by the coccyx, pubic symphysis, and ischial tuberosities; contains the orifices of the urinary, reproductive, and digestive systems. figs. 27.6, 28.8

**periosteum** (PERR-ee-OSS-tee-um) A layer of fibrous connective tissue covering the surface of a bone. fig. 7.1

**peripheral nervous system (PNS)** A subdivision of the nervous system composed of all nerves and ganglia; all of the nervous system except the central nervous system.

**peripheral protein** A protein of the plasma membrane that clings to its intracellular or extracellular surface but does not penetrate into the phospholipid bilayer.

**peristalsis** (PERR-ih-STAL-sis) A wave of constriction traveling along a tubular organ such as the esophagus or ureter, serving to propel its contents.

**peritoneum** (PERR-ih-toe-NEE-um) A serous membrane that lines the peritoneal cavity of the abdomen and covers the mesenteries and viscera.

**perivascular** (PERR-ih-VASS-cue-lur) Pertaining to the region surrounding a blood vessel.

**phagocytosis** (FAG-oh-sy-TOE-sis) A form of endocytosis in which a cell surrounds a foreign particle with pseudopods and engulfs it, enclosing it in a cytoplasmic vesicle called a *phagosome.*

**phalanx** (FAY-lanks) (plural, *phalanges*) Any of the bones in the fingers or toes; there are two in the thumb and great toe and three in each of the other digits.

**pharynx** (FAIR-inks, FAR-inks) A muscular passage in the throat at which the respiratory and digestive tracts cross.

**phospholipid** An amphipathic molecule composed of two fatty acids and a phosphate-containing group bonded to the three carbons of a glycerol molecule; composes most of the molecules of the plasma membrane and other cellular membranes.

**phosphorylation** Addition of an inorganic phosphate ($P_i$) group to an organic molecule.

**piloerector** *See* arrector.

**pinocytosis** (PIN-oh-sy-TOE-sis) A form of endocytosis in which the plasma membrane sinks inward and imbibes droplets of extracellular fluid.

**plantar** (PLAN-tur) Pertaining to the sole of the foot.

**plaque** A small scale or plate of matter, such as dental plaque, the fatty plaques of atherosclerosis, and the amyloid plaques of Alzheimer disease.

**plasma** The noncellular portion of the blood; its liquid matrix, usually constituting slightly over one-half of its volume.

**plasma membrane** The membrane that encloses a cell and controls the traffic of molecules in and out of the cell. fig. 3.5

**platelet** A formed element of the blood derived from a megakaryocyte, known especially for its role in stopping bleeding, but with additional roles in dissolving blood clots, stimulating inflammation, promoting tissue growth and blood vessel maintenance, and destroying bacteria.

**pleura** (PLOOR-uh) A double-walled serous membrane that encloses each lung.

**plexus** A network of blood vessels, lymphatic vessels, or nerves, such as a choroid plexus of the brain or brachial plexus of nerves.

**pluripotent** Pertaining to a stem cell of the inner cell mass of a blastocyst that is capable of developing into any type of embryonic cell, but not into cells of the accessory organs of pregnancy.

**polymer** A molecule that consists of a long chain of identical or similar subunits, such as protein, DNA, and starch.

**polypeptide** Any chain of more than 10 or 15 amino acids. *See also* protein.

**polysaccharide** (POL-ee-SAC-uh-ride) A polymer of simple sugars; for example, glycogen, starch, and cellulose. fig. 2.17

**polyuria** (POL-ee-YOU-ree-uh) Excessive output of urine.

**popliteal** (pop-LIT-ee-ul) Pertaining to the posterior aspect of the knee.

**positron emission tomography (PET)** A method of producing a computerized image of the physiological state of a tissue using injected radioisotopes that emit positrons.

**posterior** Near or pertaining to the back or spinal side of the body; dorsal.

**posterior root** The branch of a spinal nerve that enters the posterior side of the spinal cord and carries afferent (sensory) nerve fibers; often called *dorsal root.* fig. 13.2b

**postganglionic** (POST-gang-glee-ON-ic) Pertaining to a neuron that conducts signals from a ganglion to a more distal target organ.

**postsynaptic** (POST-sih-NAP-tic) Pertaining to a neuron or other cell that receives signals from the presynaptic neuron at a synapse. fig. 12.19

**potential** A difference in electrical charge from one point to another, especially on opposite sides of a plasma membrane; usually measured in millivolts.

**preembryo** A developing individual from the time of fertilization to the time, at 16 days, when the three primary germ layers have formed. *Compare* conceptus, embryo, fetus.

**preganglionic** (PRE-gang-glee-ON-ic) Pertaining to a neuron that conducts signals from the central nervous system to a ganglion.

**presynaptic** (PRE-sih-NAP-tic) Pertaining to a neuron that conducts signals to a synapse. fig. 12.19

**primary germ layers** The ectoderm, mesoderm, and endoderm; the three tissue layers of an early embryo from which all later tissues and organs arise.

**prime mover** The muscle that produces the most force in a given joint action; agonist.

**programmed cell death** *See* apoptosis.

**prolactin (PRL)** A hormone secreted by the anterior pituitary gland that stimulates the mammary glands to secrete milk.

**pronation** (pro-NAY-shun) A rotational movement of the forearm that turns the palm downward or posteriorly. fig. 9.18

**proprioception** (PRO-pree-oh-SEP-shun) The nonvisual perception, usually subconscious, of the position and movements of the body, resulting from input from proprioceptors and the vestibular apparatus of the inner ear.

**proprioceptor** (PRO-pree-oh-SEP-tur) A sensory receptor of the muscles, tendons, and joint capsules that detects muscle contractions and joint movements.

**prostaglandin** (PROSS-ta-GLAN-din) An eicosanoid with a five-sided carbon ring in the middle of a hydrocarbon chain, playing a variety of roles in inflammation, neurotransmission, vasomotion, reproduction, and metabolism. fig. 2.21

**prostate** (PROSS-tate) A male reproductive gland that encircles the urethra immediately inferior to the bladder and contributes to the semen. (Avoid the mispronunciation "prostrate.") fig. 27.10

**protein** A large polypeptide; while criteria for a protein are somewhat subjective and variable, polypeptides over 50 amino acids long are generally classified as proteins.

**proteoglycan** (PRO-tee-oh-GLY-can) A large molecule composed of a bristlelike arrangement of glycosaminoglycans surrounding a protein core in a shape resembling a bottle brush. Binds cells to extracellular materials and gives the tissue fluid a gelatinous consistency.

**proximal** Relatively near a point of origin or attachment; for example, the shoulder is proximal to the elbow. *Compare* distal.

**pseudopod** (SOO-doe-pod) A temporary cytoplasmic extension of a cell used for locomotion (ameboid movement) and phagocytosis.

**pseudostratified columnar epithelium** A type of epithelium with tall columnar cells reaching the free surface and shorter basal cells that do not reach the surface, but with all cells resting on the basement membrane; creates a false appearance of stratification. fig. 5.7

**pulmonary circuit** A route of blood flow that supplies blood to the pulmonary alveoli for gas exchange and then returns it to the heart; all blood vessels between the right ventricle and the left atrium of the heart.

**pyrogen** (PY-ro-jen) A fever-producing agent.

## R

**ramus** (RAY-mus) An anatomical branch, as in a nerve or in the pubis.

**receptor** **1.** A cell or organ specialized to detect a stimulus, such as a taste cell or the eye. **2.** A protein molecule that binds and responds to a chemical such as a hormone, neurotransmitter, or odor molecule.

**receptor-mediated endocytosis** A process in which certain molecules in the extracellular fluid bind to receptors in the plasma membrane, these receptors gather together, the membrane sinks inward at that point, and the molecules are incorporated into vesicles in the cytoplasm. fig. 3.21

**receptor potential** A variable, local change in membrane voltage produced by a stimulus acting on a receptor cell; generates an action potential if it reaches threshold.

**recessive** **1.** Pertaining to a genetic allele that is not phenotypically expressed in the presence of a dominant allele. **2.** Pertaining to a trait that results from a recessive allele.

**reduction** **1.** A chemical reaction in which one or more electrons are added to a molecule, raising its free energy content; opposite of *oxidation* and always linked to an oxidation reaction. **2.** Treatment of a fracture by restoring the broken parts of a bone to their proper alignment.

**reflex** A stereotyped, automatic, involuntary response to a stimulus; includes somatic reflexes, in which the effectors are skeletal muscles, and visceral (autonomic) reflexes, in which the effectors are usually visceral muscle, cardiac muscle, or glands.

**reflex arc** A simple neural pathway that mediates a reflex; involves a receptor, an afferent nerve fiber, often one or more interneurons, an efferent nerve fiber, and an effector.

**refractory period** **1.** A period of time after a nerve or muscle cell has responded to a stimulus in which it cannot be reexcited by a threshold stimulus. **2.** A period of time after male orgasm when it is not possible to reattain erection or ejaculation.

**regeneration** Replacement of damaged tissue with new tissue of the original type. *Compare* fibrosis.

**renin** (REE-nin) An enzyme secreted by the kidneys in response to hypotension; converts the plasma protein angiotensinogen to angiotensin I, leading indirectly to a rise in blood pressure.

**repolarization** Reattainment of the resting membrane potential after a nerve or muscle cell has depolarized.

**residue** Any one of the amino acids in a protein or other peptide.

**resistance** **1.** A force that opposes the flow of a fluid such as air or blood. **2.** A force, or load, that opposes the action of a muscle or lever.

**resting membrane potential (RMP)** A stable voltage across the plasma membrane of an unstimulated nerve or muscle cell.

**reticular cell** (reh-TIC-you-lur) A delicate, branching phagocytic cell found in the reticular connective tissue of the lymphatic organs.

**reticular fiber** A fine, branching collagen fiber coated with glycoprotein, found in the stroma of lymphatic organs and some other tissues and organs.

**reticular tissue** A connective tissue composed of reticular cells and reticular fibers, found in bone marrow, lymphatic organs, and in lesser amounts elsewhere.

**ribosome** A granule found free in the cytoplasm or attached to the rough endoplasmic reticulum or nuclear envelope composed of ribosomal RNA and enzymes; specialized to read the nucleotide sequence of messenger RNA and assemble a corresponding sequence of amino acids to make a protein.

**risk factor** Any environmental factor or characteristic of an individual that increases one's chance of developing a particular disease; includes such intrinsic factors as age, sex, and race and such extrinsic factors as diet, smoking, and occupation.

**rostral** Relatively close to the forehead, especially in reference to structures of the brain and spinal cord; for example, the frontal lobe is rostral to the parietal lobe. *Compare* caudal.

**ruga** (ROO-ga) (plural *rugae,* ROO-jee) **1.** An internal fold or wrinkle in the mucosa of a hollow organ such as the stomach and urinary bladder; typically present when the organ is empty and relaxed but not when the organ is full and stretched. **2.** Tissue ridges in such locations as the hard palate and vagina. fig. 25.12

## S

**saccule** (SAC-yule) A saclike receptor in the inner ear with a vertical patch of hair cells, the macula sacculi; senses the orientation of the head and responds to vertical acceleration, as when riding in an elevator or standing up. fig. 16.20

**sagittal plane** (SADJ-ih-tul) Any plane that extends from anterior to posterior and cephalic to caudal and that divides the body into right and left portions. *Compare* median plane.

**sarcomere** (SAR-co-meer) In skeletal and cardiac muscle, the portion of a myofibril from one Z disc to the next, constituting one contractile unit. fig. 11.5

**sarcoplasmic reticulum (SR)** The smooth endoplasmic reticulum of a muscle cell, serving as a calcium reservoir. fig. 11.2

**scanning electron microscope (SEM)** A microscope that uses an electron beam in place of light to form high-resolution, three-dimensional images of the surfaces of objects; capable of much higher magnifications than a light microscope.

**sclerosis** (scleh-RO-sis) Hardening or stiffening of a tissue, as in multiple sclerosis of the central nervous system or atherosclerosis of the blood vessels.

**sebum** (SEE-bum) An oily secretion of the sebaceous glands that keeps the skin and hair pliable.

**secondary active transport** A mechanism in which solutes are moved through a plasma membrane by a carrier that does not itself use ATP but depends on a concentration gradient established by an active transport pump elsewhere in the cell.

**second messenger** A chemical that is produced within a cell (such as cAMP) or that enters a cell (such as calcium ions) in response to the binding of a messenger to a membrane receptor, and that triggers a metabolic reaction in the cell.

**secretion** **1.** A chemical released by a cell to serve a physiological function, such as a hormone or digestive enzyme. **2.** The process of releasing such a chemical, often by exocytosis. *Compare* excretion.

**selectively permeable membrane** A membrane that allows some substances to pass through while excluding others; for example, the plasma membrane and dialysis membranes.

**semicircular ducts** Three ring-shaped, fluid-filled tubes of the inner ear that detect angular accelerations of the head; each is enclosed in a bony passage called the semicircular canal. fig. 16.21

**semilunar valve** A valve that consists of crescent-shaped cusps, including the aortic and pulmonary valves of the heart and valves of the veins and lymphatic vessels. fig. 19.8

**semipermeable membrane** *See* selectively permeable membrane.

**senescence** (seh-NESS-ense) Degenerative changes that occur with age.

**sensation** Conscious perception of a stimulus; pain, taste, and color, for example, are not stimuli but sensations resulting from stimuli.

**sensory nerve fiber** An axon that conducts information from a receptor to the central nervous system; an afferent nerve fiber.

**serosa** (seer-OH-sa) A thin epithelial membrane composed of a simple squamous epithelium overlying a thin layer of areolar tissue; covers the external surfaces of viscera such as the lungs, stomach, and intestines, and forms membranes such as the peritoneum, pleura, and pericardium, or a portion of such membranes. Also called *serous membrane.*

**serous fluid** (SEER-us) A watery, low-protein fluid similar to blood serum, formed as a filtrate of the blood or tissue fluid or as a secretion of serous gland cells; moistens the serous membranes.

**serous membrane** A membrane such as the peritoneum, pleura, or pericardium that lines a body cavity or covers the external surfaces of the viscera; composed of a simple squamous mesothelium and a thin layer of areolar connective tissue. Also called *serosa.* fig. 5.33b

**sex chromosomes** The X and Y chromosomes, which determine the sex of an individual.

**shock** **1.** Circulatory shock, a state of cardiac output that is insufficient to meet the body's physiological needs, with consequences ranging from fainting to death. **2.** Insulin shock, a state of severe hypoglycemia caused by administration of insulin. **3.** Spinal shock, a state of depressed or lost reflex activity inferior to a point of spinal cord injury. **4.** Electrical shock, the effect of a current of electricity passing through the body, often causing muscular spasm and cardiac arrhythmia or arrest.

**sign** An objective manifestation of illness that any observer can see, such as cyanosis or edema. *Compare* symptom.

**simple epithelium** An epithelium in which all cells rest directly on the basement membrane; includes simple squamous, cuboidal, and columnar types, and pseudostratified columnar. fig. 5.3

**sinuatrial node** The pacemaker of the heart; a patch of autorhythmic cells in the right atrium that initiates each heartbeat.

**sinus** **1.** An air-filled space in the cranium. **2.** A modified, relatively dilated vein that lacks smooth muscle and is incapable of vasomotion, such as the dural sinuses of the cerebral circulation and coronary sinus of the heart. **3.** A small fluid-filled space in an organ such as the spleen and lymph nodes. **4.** Pertaining to the sinuatrial node of the heart, as in *sinus rhythm.*

**sodium–glucose transporter (SGLT)** A symport that simultaneously transports $Na^+$ and glucose into a cell.

**sodium–potassium ($Na^+$–$K^+$) pump** An active transport mechanism in the plasma membrane that uses energy from ATP to expel three sodium ions from the cell and import two potassium ions into the cell for each cycle of the pump; used to drive secondary active transport processes, regulate cell volume, maintain an electrical charge gradient across the plasma membrane, and generate body heat.

**somatic** **1.** Pertaining to the body as a whole. **2.** Pertaining to the skin, bones, and skeletal muscles as opposed to the viscera. **3.** Pertaining to cells other than germ cells.

**somatic nervous system** A division of the nervous system that includes efferent fibers mainly from the skin, muscles, and skeleton and afferent fibers to the skeletal muscles. *Compare* autonomic nervous system.

**somatosensory** **1.** Pertaining to widely distributed *general senses* in the skin, muscles, tendons, joint capsules, and viscera, as opposed to the *special senses* found in the head only; also called *somesthetic.* **2.** Pertaining to the cerebral cortex of the postcentral gyrus, which receives input from such receptors.

**somite** One segment in a linear series of mesodermal masses that form on each side of the neural tube and give rise to trunk muscles, vertebrae, and dermis. fig. 29.7

**spermatogenesis** (SPUR-ma-toe-JEN-eh-sis) The production of sperm cells through a series of mitotic and meiotic cell divisions; male gametogenesis.

**spermatozoon** (spur-MAT-oh-ZO-on) A sperm cell.

**sphincter** (SFINK-tur) A ring of muscle that opens or closes an opening or passageway; found, for example, in the eyelids, around the urinary orifice, and at the beginning of a blood capillary.

**spinal nerve** Any of the 31 pairs of nerves that arise from the spinal cord and pass through the intervertebral foramina or through the gap between the spine and cranium.

**spindle** **1.** An elongated structure that is thick in the middle and tapered at the ends (fusiform). **2.** A football-shaped complex of microtubules that guide the movement of chromosomes in mitosis and meiosis. fig. 4.15 **3.** A stretch receptor in the skeletal muscles. fig. 13.24

**spine** **1.** The vertebral column. **2.** A pointed process or sharp ridge on a bone, such as the styloid process of the cranium and spine of the scapula.

**splanchnic** (SPLANK-nic) Pertaining to the digestive tract.

**squamous** (SKWAY-mus) **1.** Thin and flat. **2.** A cellular shape that is flat or scaly; pertains especially to a class of epithelial cells. figs. 5.4, 5.12

**stem cell** Any undifferentiated cell that can divide and differentiate into more functionally specific cell types such as blood cells and germ cells.

**stenosis** (steh-NO-sis) The narrowing of a passageway such as a heart valve or uterine tube; a permanent, pathological constriction as opposed to physiological constriction of a passageway.

**steroid** (STERR-oyd, STEER-oyd) A lipid molecule that consists of four interconnected carbon rings; cholesterol and several of its derivatives.

**stimulus** A chemical or physical agent in a cell's surroundings that is capable of creating a physiological response in the cell; especially agents detected by sensory cells, such as chemicals, light, and pressure.

**strain** The extent to which a body, such as a bone, is deformed when subjected to stress. *Compare* stress.

**stratified epithelium** A type of epithelium in which some cells rest on top of others instead of on the basement membrane; includes stratified squamous, cuboidal, and columnar types, and urothelium. fig. 5.3

**stress** **1.** A mechanical force applied to any part of the body; important in stimulating bone growth, for example. *Compare* strain. **2.** A condition in which any environmental influence disturbs the homeostatic equilibrium of the body and stimulates a physiological response, especially involving the increased secretion of certain adrenal hormones.

**stroke volume** The volume of blood ejected by one ventricle of the heart in one contraction.

**stroma** The connective tissue framework of a gland, lymphatic organ, or certain other viscera, as opposed to the tissue (parenchyma) that performs the physiological functions of the organ.

**subcutaneous** (SUB-cue-TAY-nee-us) Beneath the skin.

**substrate** **1.** A chemical that is acted upon and changed by an enzyme. **2.** A chemical used as a source of energy, such as glucose and fatty acids.

**substrate specificity** The ability of an enzyme to bind only one substrate or a limited range of related substrates.

**sulcus** (SUL-cuss) A groove in the surface of an organ, as in the cerebrum or heart.

**summation** **1.** A phenomenon in which multiple stimuli combine their effects on a cell to produce a response; seen especially in nerve and muscle cells. **2.** A phenomenon in which multiple muscle twitches occur so closely together that a muscle fiber cannot fully relax between twitches but develops more tension than a single twitch produces. fig. 11.15

**superficial** Relatively close to the surface; opposite of deep. For example, the ribs are superficial to the lungs.

**superior** Higher than another structure or point of reference from the perspective of anatomical position; for example, the lungs are superior to the diaphragm.

**supination** (SOO-pih-NAY-shun) A rotational movement of the forearm that turns the palm so that it faces upward or forward. fig. 9.18

**surfactant** (sur-FAC-tent) A chemical that reduces the surface tension of water and enables it to penetrate other substances more effectively. Examples include pulmonary surfactant and bile acids.

**sympathetic nervous system** A division of the autonomic nervous system that issues efferent fibers through the thoracic and lumbar nerves and usually exerts adrenergic effects on its target organs; includes a chain of paravertebral ganglia adjacent to the vertebral column, and the adrenal medulla.

**symphysis** (SIM-fih-sis) A joint in which two bones are held together by fibrocartilage; for example, between bodies of the vertebrae and between the right and left pubic bones.

**symport** A cotransport protein that moves two solutes simultaneously through a plasma membrane in the same direction, such as the sodium–glucose transporter.

**symptom** A subjective manifestation of illness that only the ill person can sense, such as dizziness or nausea. *Compare* sign.

**synapse** (SIN-aps) **1.** A junction at the end of an axon where it stimulates another cell. **2.** A gap junction between two cardiac or smooth muscle cells at which one cell electrically stimulates the other; called an *electrical synapse.*

**synaptic cleft** (sih-NAP-tic) A narrow space between an axon terminal and the membrane of the postsynaptic cell, across which a neuro-transmitter diffuses. fig. 12.21

**synaptic vesicle** A spheroidal organelle in an axon terminal containing neurotransmitter. fig. 12.21

**syndrome** A suite of related signs and symptoms stemming from a specific pathological cause.

**synergist** (SIN-ur-jist) A muscle that works with the prime mover (agonist) to contribute to the same overall action at a joint.

**synergistic effect** An effect in which two agents working together (such as two hormones) exert an effect that is greater than the sum of their separate effects. For example, neither follicle-stimulating hormone nor testosterone alone stimulates significant sperm production, but the two of them together stimulate production of vast numbers of sperm.

**synovial fluid** A lubricating fluid similar to egg white in consistency, found in the synovial joint cavities and bursae.

**synovial joint** A point where two bones are separated by a narrow, encapsulated space filled with lubricating synovial fluid; most such joints are relatively mobile. Also called *diarthrosis.*

**synthesis reaction** A chemical reaction in which relatively small molecules are combined to form a larger one. *Compare* decomposition reaction.

**systemic** (sis-TEM-ic) Widespread or pertaining to the body as a whole, as in the systemic circulation.

**systemic circuit** All blood vessels that convey blood from the left ventricle to all organs of the body and back to the right atrium of the heart; all of the cardiovascular system except the heart and pulmonary circuit.

**systole** (SIS-toe-lee) The contraction of any heart chamber; ventricular contraction unless otherwise specified.

**systolic pressure** (sis-TOLL-ic) The peak arterial blood pressure measured during ventricular systole.

## T

**target cell** A cell acted upon by a nerve fiber, hormone, or other chemical messenger.

**tarsal** Pertaining to the ankle (tarsus).

**T cell** A type of lymphocyte involved in innate immunity, humoral immunity, and cellular immunity; occurs in several forms including helper, cytotoxic, and suppressor T cells and natural killer cells.

**tendon** A collagenous band or cord associated with a muscle, usually attaching it to a bone and transferring muscular tension to it.

**tetanus** **1.** A state of sustained muscle contraction produced by temporal summation as a normal part of contraction; also called *tetany.* **2.** Spastic muscle paralysis produced by the toxin of the bacterium *Clostridium tetani* or other causes.

**thalamus** (THAL-uh-muss) The largest part of the diencephalon, located immediately inferior to the corpus callosum and bulging into each lateral ventricle; a point of synaptic relay of nearly all signals passing from lower levels of the CNS to the cerebrum. figs. 14.8, 14.12a

**theory** An explanatory statement, or set of statements, that concisely summarizes the state of knowledge on a phenomenon and provides direction for further study; for example, the fluid-mosaic theory of the plasma membrane and the sliding filament theory of muscle contraction. *See also* hypothesis.

**thermogenesis** The production of heat, for example, by shivering or by the action of thyroid hormones.

**thermoreceptor** A neuron specialized to respond to heat or cold, found in the skin and mucous membranes, for example.

**thermoregulation** Homeostatic regulation of the body temperature within a narrow range by adjustments of heat-promoting and heat-losing mechanisms.

**thorax** A region of the trunk between the neck and the diaphragm; the chest.

**threshold** **1.** The minimum voltage to which the plasma membrane of a nerve or muscle cell must be depolarized before it produces an action potential. **2.** The minimum combination of stimulus intensity and duration needed to generate an afferent signal from a sensory receptor.

**thrombosis** (throm-BO-sis) The formation or presence of a thrombus.

**thrombus** A clot that forms in a blood vessel or heart chamber; may break free and travel in the bloodstream as a thromboembolus. *Compare* embolus.

**thyroid hormone** Either of two similar hormones, thyroxine and triiodothyronine, synthesized from iodine and tyrosine.

**thyroid-stimulating hormone (TSH)** A hormone of the anterior pituitary gland that stimulates the thyroid gland; also called *thyrotropin.*

**thyroxine** (thy-ROCK-seen) The thyroid hormone secreted in greatest quantity, with four iodine atoms; also called *tetraiodothyronine.* fig. 17.17

**tight junction** A region in which adjacent cells are bound together by fusion of the outer phospholipid layer of their plasma membranes; forms a zone that encircles each cell near its apical pole and reduces or prevents flow of material between cells. fig. 5.28

**tissue** An aggregation of cells and extracellular materials, usually forming part of an organ and serving some discrete aspect of that organ's function; all tissues belong to one of the four primary classes—epithelial, connective, muscular, and nervous tissue.

**totipotent** Pertaining to a stem cell of the early preembryo, prior to development of a blastocyst, that has the potential to develop into any type of embryonic, extraembryonic, or adult cell.

**trabecula** (tra-BEC-you-la) A thin plate or layer of tissue, such as the calcified trabeculae of spongy bone or the fibrous trabeculae that subdivide a gland. fig. 7.4

**trachea** (TRAY-kee-uh) A cartilage-supported tube from the inferior end of the larynx to the origin of the main bronchi; conveys air to and from the lungs; colloquially called the *windpipe.*

**translation** The process in which a ribosome reads an mRNA molecule and synthesizes the protein specified by its genetic code.

**transmembrane protein** An integral protein that extends through a plasma membrane and contacts both the extracellular and intracellular fluid. fig. 3.6

**transmission electron microscope (TEM)** A microscope that uses an electron beam in place of light to form high-resolution, two-dimensional images of ultrathin slices of cells or tissues; capable of extremely high magnification.

**triglyceride** (try-GLISS-ur-ide) A lipid composed of three fatty acids joined to a glycerol; also called a *triacylglycerol* or *neutral fat.* fig. 2.18

**trunk** **1.** That part of the body excluding the head, neck, and appendages. **2.** A major blood vessel, lymphatic vessel, or nerve that gives rise to smaller branches; for example, the pulmonary trunk and spinal nerve trunks.

**T tubule** Transverse tubule; a tubular extension of the plasma membrane of a muscle cell that conducts action potentials into the sarcoplasm and excites the sarcoplasmic reticulum. fig. 11.2

**tunic** (TOO-nic) A layer that encircles or encloses an organ, such as the tunics of a blood vessel or eyeball.

**tympanic membrane** The eardrum.

## U

**ultrastructure** Fine details of tissue and cell structure, as far down as the molecular level, revealed by the electron microscope.

**ultraviolet radiation** Invisible, ionizing, electromagnetic radiation with shorter wavelength and higher energy than violet light; causes skin cancer and photoaging of the skin but is required in moderate amounts for the synthesis of vitamin D.

**unipotent** Pertaining to a stem cell that has the potential to develop into only one type of fully differentiated, functional cell, such as an epidermal stem cell that can become only a keratinocyte.

**unmyelinated** (un-MY-eh-lih-NAY-ted) Lacking a myelin sheath. fig. 12.9

**urea** (you-REE-uh) A nitrogenous waste produced from two ammonia molecules and carbon dioxide; the most abundant nitrogenous waste in the blood and urine. fig. 23.2

**urothelium** A type of stratified epithelium that lines much of the urinary tract, characterized by domed *umbrella cells* at the surface, protecting underlying cells from the acidity and hypertonicity of urine. Also called *transitional epithelium.* fig. 5.11

**uterine tube** A duct that extends from the ovary to the uterus and conveys an egg or conceptus to the uterus; also called *fallopian tube* or *oviduct.*

**utricle** (YOU-tri-cul) A saclike receptor in the inner ear with a nearly horizontal patch of hair cells, the macula utriculi; senses the orientation of the head and responds to horizontal acceleration, as when accelerating or decelerating in a car. fig. 16.20

## V

**van der Waals force** A weak attraction between two atoms occurring when a brief fluctuation in the electron cloud density of one atom induces polarization of an adjacent atom; important in association of lipids with each other, protein folding, and protein–ligand binding.

**varicose vein** A vein that has become permanently distended and convoluted due to a loss of competence of the venous valves; especially common in the lower limb, esophagus, and anal canal (where they are called hemorrhoids).

**vas** (vass) (plural, *vasa*) A vessel or duct.

**vascular** Pertaining to blood vessels.

**vascular corrosion cast** A technique for visualizing the blood vessels of organs and tissues, especially the microvasculature, by flushing blood from the vessels, injecting a resin and letting it solidify, then digesting the actual tissue away with a corrosive agent, leaving only the resin cast; this is then viewed with a scanning electron microscope. figs. 20.1b, 23.10a

**vasoconstriction** (VAY-zo-con-STRIC-shun) The narrowing of a blood vessel due to muscular contraction of its tunica media.

**vasodilation** (VAY-zo-dy-LAY-shun) The widening of a blood vessel due to relaxation of the muscle of its tunica media and the outward pressure of the blood exerted against the wall.

**vasomotion** Collective term for vasoconstriction and vasodilation; any change in the diameter of a blood vessel.

**vasomotor center** A nucleus in the medulla oblongata that transmits signals to the blood vessels and regulates vessel diameter.

**ventral** Pertaining to the front of the body, the regions of the chest and abdomen; anterior.

**ventral root** *See* anterior root.

**ventricle** (VEN-trih-cul) A fluid-filled chamber of the brain or heart.

**venule** (VEN-yule) The smallest type of vein, receiving drainage from capillaries.

**vertebra** (VUR-teh-bra) One of the bones of the vertebral column.

**vertebral column** (VUR-teh-brul) A posterior series of usually 33 vertebrae; encloses the spinal cord, supports the skull and thoracic cage, and provides attachment for the limbs and postural muscles. Also called *spine* or *spinal column.*

**vesicle** A fluid-filled tissue sac or an organelle such as a synaptic or secretory vesicle.

**vesicular transport** The movement of particles or fluid droplets through the plasma membrane by the process of endocytosis or exocytosis.

**viscera** (VISS-er-uh) (singular, *viscus*) The organs contained in the body cavities, such as the brain, heart, lungs, stomach, intestines, and kidneys.

**visceral** (VISS-er-ul) **1.** Pertaining to the viscera. **2.** The inner or deeper layer of a two-layered membrane such as the pleura, pericardium, or glomerular capsule. *Compare* parietal. fig. A.6

**visceral muscle** Unitary smooth muscle found in the walls of blood vessels and the digestive, respiratory, urinary, and reproductive tracts.

**viscosity** The resistance of a fluid to flow; the thickness or stickiness of a fluid.

**voluntary muscle** Muscle that is usually under conscious control; skeletal muscle.

**vulva** The female external genitalia; the mons, labia majora, and all superficial structures between the labia majora.

## W

**water balance** An equilibrium between fluid intake and output or between the amounts of fluid contained in the body's different fluid compartments.

**white matter** White myelinated nervous tissue deep to the cortex of the cerebrum and cerebellum and superficial to the gray matter of the spinal cord. fig. 14.6

## X

**X chromosome** The larger of the two sex chromosomes; males have one X chromosome and females have two in each somatic cell.

**X-ray** **1.** A high-energy, penetrating electromagnetic ray with wavelengths in the range of 0.1 to 10 nm; used in diagnosis and therapy. **2.** A photograph made with X-rays; radiograph.

## Y

**Y chromosome** Smaller of the two sex chromosomes, found only in males and having little if any genetic function except development of the testis.

**yolk sac** An embryonic membrane that encloses the yolk in vertebrates that lay eggs and serves in humans as the origin of the first blood and germ cells.

## Z

**zygomatic arch** An arch of bone anterior to the ear, formed by the zygomatic processes of the temporal, frontal, and zygomatic bones; origin of the masseter muscle.

**zygote** A single-celled, fertilized egg.

# INDEX

*Note:* Page numbers in *italics* indicate illustrations and their captions; page numbers followed by *t* indicate material in tables.

## A

## B

# C

## D

## H

## J

## K



## L

# M

## N

# O

## Q



## R

## S

# T

## U